The *Official* Great British Factory Shop Guide®

by Gill Cutress
& Rolf Stricker

ISBN 0 948965 72 X
ISSN 1369-7269

The *Official* Great British Factory Shop Guide®

✓ ***Where they are***
✓ ***When they open***
✓ ***What they sell***
✓ ***How to get there***

WINNER IN 1998
CORPORATE PUBLISHING AWARD

Personally researched, written & published by

Gill Cutress & Rolf Stricker

1 Rosebery Mews, Rosebery Road
London SW2 4DQ
Phone 0181-678 0593 *Fax* 0181-674 1594
E-mail: factshop@macline.co.uk
Web site: www.factoryshopguide.co.uk

1993 The Official *Great British Factory Shop Guide: 1994–1995*
Updated and reprinted three times
1995 The Official *Great British Factory Shop Guide: 1996–1997*
Updated and reprinted three times
1998 The Official *Great British Factory Shop Guide: 1998–1999*
3rd update & reprint

This is the 74th edition published in this series

Please do not have a wasted journey!

The vast majority of the entries in this guide were checked by the companies just before we went to press
But – especially so in the current economic climate – organisations change, shops open at new times, holidays alter, shops decide to close for stocktaking and, from time to time, a shop ceases to trade altogether.
We deeply regret any inconveniences such changes cause, but it is a fact of life that these things do happen.

Therefore we cannot recommend strongly enough that you phone the shop first if you are going a long way or making a special journey.

Changes and mistakes

We have done our best to ensure that all the information in this guide is correct. However, as we deal with thousands of details, it is possible that an error has occasionally slipped in. Do please let us know of any error you notice. As every reasonable care has been taken in the preparation of this book, we can accept no responsibility for errors, omissions, or damage, however caused.

Welcome

to the third edition of *The Official Great British Factory Shop Guide*, the largest yet with over 1000 entries, almost 800 pages, and a new format.

The previous edition had to be re-printed three times and, each time, we incorporated changes to ensure that the book was kept up-to-date.

This book should save you a great deal of money, whether you are looking for designer and brand name fashions, clothing for the whole family or almost anything to equip your home.

The Official Great British Factory Shop Guide® is part of the only series of publications in Great Britain (there are ten regional guides too) which lead you to each factory shop by means of carefully prepared directions and specially drawn maps. You need not fear losing your way in unfamiliar parts of the country or, indeed, in your local seemingly impenetrable industrial areas.

Our guides were the first to list and describe such shops, and we are proud of our role in bringing this highly rewarding way of shopping to the notice of value-conscious shoppers over the last 12 years.

We know you'll save money ... and that you'll have fun into the bargain too.

Gill and Rolf

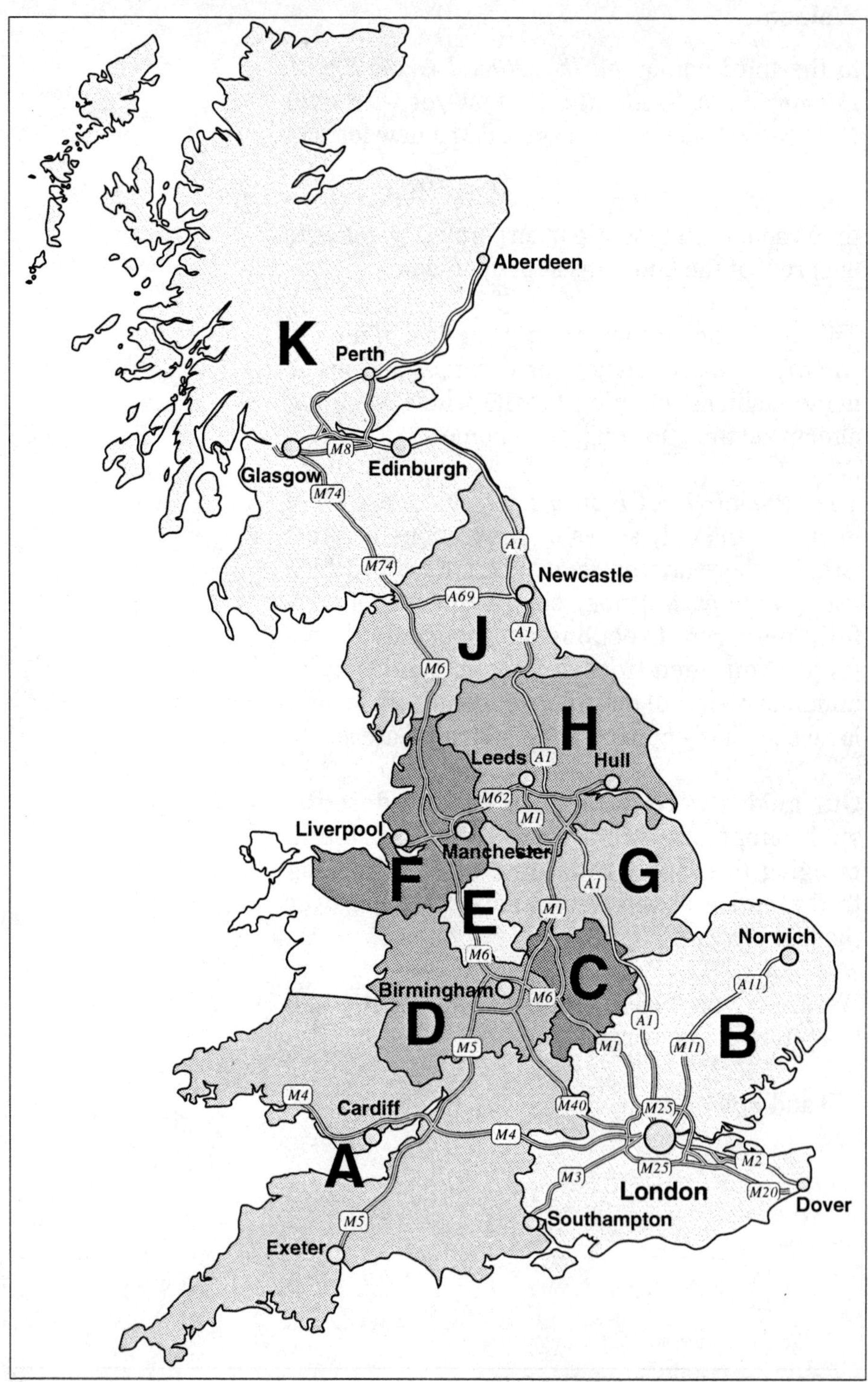
Aberdeen
K
Perth
M8
Glasgow
Edinburgh
M74
M74
A1
Newcastle
A69
A1
J
M6
H
Leeds
A1
Hull
M62
M1
Liverpool
Manchester
F
G
A1
E
M1
M6
Norwich
A11
Birmingham
M6
C
D
A1
B
M5
M1
M11
M4
Cardiff
M40
M25
M4
A
M2
M25
M3
London
M20
Dover
M5
Southampton
Exeter

Contents

What are factory shops?

Twelve years ago, when we began our quest, factory shops were unknown to the majority of the British public. Even now many people in Britain do not realise that this economical way of shopping is available within easy driving distance of their own homes.

The media like to promote factory shops as a 'new concept' in shopping. A good story – but not strictly true: many have existed throughout this century, and the oldest we know has been trading for 200 years. The 'newness', in fact, consists of the increasing awareness of these places by the public, coupled with companies' recognition of factory shops as a vital part of their revenue.

Traditionally, factory shops began as 'staff shops'. Companies needed to dispose of stock which, for various reasons, they could not sell through high street retailers. So they made such goods available to their staff at favourable prices. Gradually staff were allowed to invite their families too. These 'families' grew surprisingly large: eventually other local people were allowed to drop in without having to produce birth certificates! What started off as rummage boxes in a factory corner evolved into organised selling spaces.

The recession in recent years has had a huge influence. Forced to cut costs (and in need of ready cash), manufacturers became keen to avoid costly storage of unwanted stock. They increasingly took advantage of on-site shops to sell direct to the public – much to the benefit of shoppers who recognised factory shopping as a means of buying luxury goods (and even humble everyday necessities) which they could not afford at normal high street prices.

The term 'factory shop' has become somewhat diffused. In years past, manufacturers only sold goods which they themselves had produced. Gradually they began to buy in stock to supplement their ranges. It has become common for factory shops to trade with one another, with the result that their ranges are ever more comprehensive (although this can have the effect of making shops appear less distinctive). Some manufacturers sell their surplus and faulty goods to independent retailers. Some shops sell ex-catalogue bargains, which are returns, seconds or last season's stock. Another category comprises manufacturers who do not work through retailers but always sell direct to the public; from them you buy perfect products at excellent prices because there is no middle man.

It is worth noting that our great chainstores are not manufacturers, but have goods made for them by dozens of factories which themselves sell the seconds and surplus stock from their own factory shops. Chainstores impose stringent rules about what their manufacturers may sell in their factory shops, and how soon items may be sold after they first appeared in the high street. Chainstore quality control is notoriously tough; they reject even the slightest flaws (many invisible to the untrained eye). A chainstore's reject may be a shopper's good fortune! Chainstores are reluctant to have such goods sold under their own name, and demand that their labels be removed. We too respect their wishes – knowing that our readers will be aware of what they are buying (especially when they see the tell-tale logos on large lorries waiting at the factory despatch bays).

Inevitably some less scrupulous shops masquerade as 'factory shops', cashing in on what has become a cult expression when, in reality, they sell shoddy goods, often imported, and sporting smart-sounding labels. We do our best to avoid listing a business which, in our opinion, does not offer the kind of value that has given genuine factory shopping such an appealing reputation.

As factory shops have grown in size, sophistication and number, so companies have realised that, when shopping in a pleasant environment, customers are likely to linger longer, spend money, and come back for more. Small factory shops have grown in size and grown up: they offer ever better facilities. Pram and wheelchair access is improving. Some companies offer cups of tea or coffee; others have opened visitor centres, demonstration areas and museums. If you have time to take part in the many tours on offer, you will see the best of British industry at work – and we promise it will be an enlightening experience.

Finally, there are the proliferating factory outlet villages. For a brief description of this 'new concept' in factory shopping, see the next page.

Far from being secretive about their existence, factory shops now flaunt themselves, and the value-conscious public is delighted.

Alan Paine Knitwear

Factory outlet villages

American style 'factory shop villages' are increasing in number and size throughout Europe. The first such 'village' opened, in Britain, about five years ago. They already form part of the landscape and have clocked up literally millions of visitors in a short period.

About 15 shopping villages operate in the UK and more are on the drawing board. As the definition of 'factory shop' becomes harder to specify, so too the definition of 'factory shop village'. In addition to manufacturers operating shops on these sites, famous retailers are taking premises too. In other words, increasing emphasis is being attached to brand names. For example, you will find famous French, Danish and American labels alongside the British ones, as overseas companies take advantage of this unique opportunity to reach the British public.

British factory outlet villages comprise between 10 and 120 units. Most are planned with future expansion in mind. The tenants adhere to strict rules about pricing, most being contractually bound to sell at prices at least 30% below those in the high street.

Factory shop villages have great appeal in that they offer a selection of shops on one site, together with excellent parking, a range of eating places and good facilities for all members of the family, including the disabled. (We would put in a plea, however, for more villages to offer free electric self-driven buggies, as at The Galleria in Hatfield. Readers who have shared our experience of taking less-than-agile relatives shopping will know the joy for all concerned when the non-mobile person suddenly experiences the freedom to go shopping independently.)

In addition to the official 'factory outlet villages', an increasing number of independent factory shop complexes are opening in converted mills, or factories or even former harbour sheds. They carry a wide variety of brand names and have in-store concessions. They too offer catering, parking and access.

How many factory outlet centres can thrive in the UK is debatable; only once the British public's zest for this type of shopping is known (and the effects of tighter out-of-town shopping regulations come into play) can the number be quantified. The latest estimate from an authority in the field was 'about 20'; other experts predict fewer, or considerably more. Will we – one day – emulate the USA where there are factory outlets that specialise in selling items which failed to sell in the original factory outlets ...?

In our unique position as factory shop specialists of 12 years' standing, we conducted a detailed survey of factory shoppers' likes and dislikes. No comprehensive surveys on this kind of shopping in the UK have been carried out before.

We wanted to know what 'experienced' factory shoppers (ie, only those already in the habit of visiting factory shops) think of on-site shops and of the new factory outlet villages.

Over 2000 of our readers gave us the benefit of their considerable experience. More than 76% have been keen factory shoppers for over five years; a quarter go factory shopping at least once a month. Nearly 70% had already visited a factory outlet village.

These are some of the questions we asked:

How did you first hear about factory shops?
What attracts you to the original on-site factory shops?
Which, if any, of the new villages have you visited?
What attracts you to the new 'villages'?
How do you react to each type?
Do new villages attract you away from individual shops?
How can on-site shops be improved?
How can villages be improved?
How far do you travel?
How much do you spend?

Much interesting information comes to light. For example, the outstanding attraction of on-site factory shops is 'value for money' (83%), followed by 'sense of anticipation' (42%) and the 'lack of pressure from staff' (38%). The reasons given most frequently for visits to factory outlet villages are 'curiosity' (60%), 'value for money' (53%) and 'mix of well known brands' (47%). This presents an interesting contrast with the great appeal (58%) of those on-site shops which only sell their own production rather than bought-in or specially made items.

'Easy parking' is the favourite feature of factory outlet villages (68%); 'lack of facilities' (26%) is a prime moan about on-site shops. We have received more letters about refreshment and toilet facilities over the last 12 years than on any other topic – and this survey also highlights the fact that shoppers like to be able to sit down and have a cup of coffee. (Several respondents claim they no longer go to factory shops where a hot drink is not available!)

With sincere thanks to the thousands of our readers who took the time to respond to our questionnaire.

What do factory shoppers like? Results of our own special survey

We sometimes wondered if factory shops were always aware of what their customers were looking for …

So we decided to find out!

If you would like further details about our report 'British factory shoppers: their likes and dislikes' please contact us.

Who are the authors?

No two people could have been more surprised than we were to find our lives taken over by factory shopping. One of us had trained as an entomologist specialising in Australian ants; the other expected to spend life flying small planes in the remoter regions of the earth.

As the result of a series of accidents (including redundancy), coupled with an insatiable curiosity about new places to be discovered in this country and a determination to find best value for money, we became the first people in Britain to track down factory shops on an organised basis. We were certainly the first people to write about them.

Since our small beginnings, we have received hundreds of appreciative letters from other shoppers who had heard that these places existed – but did not know where to look. We, in turn, are grateful for our readers' marvellous support, hints and information. We have made many friends (both readers and factory shop managers) and have derived a lot of fun during our never-ending quest for factory shops. Needless to say, we have also seen a great deal of money slip through our fingers ... always satisfied that it was well spent!

We have each passed at least six months of every year on the road. In contrast to other people now writing about factory shops, we know the shops personally and have visited most several times. A conservative estimate of our visits is 8000.

Add to those our exploration of each new British factory outlet village, and visits to hundreds of outlets in the USA, Australia, Hong Kong, South Africa and much of Europe. Sometimes we feel 'factory shopped-out'. But then we find something special, yet again, and the adrenalin flows anew.

Also keen factory shoppers are the other members of our small team who have spent many months working on this book. Yanka and Emma have done an amazing task in compiling and checking information (the number of phone calls made and faxes sent is in the thousands); Debbie has spent weeks drawing new, and re-fashioning earlier, maps (we wish her fun and success in her new life overseas); Lee does an invaluable job keeping the accounts and paper-work straight; and Paula ensures that books get sent out promptly. Very sincere thanks to them all.

We take credit for raising the profile of factory shopping in Britain. We are delighted that our efforts have helped people buy 'more for less' – both luxury items that they could not normally afford; and necessities which seem more pleasurable when acquired for a smaller outlay.

We need your help

We are a very small and personal venture.
Precisely because we are small, we need your help.
Mainline publishers organise expensive and impressive publicity campaigns.
We rely on personal contact. This is especially important when it comes to shops in this book: they need to know that it brings them customers.

PLEASE TELL THE SHOP MANAGER THAT YOU USE THE FACTORY SHOP GUIDE
(or carry the book!)

Thank you very much.

Changes to roads make our job of writing precise directions exceptionally complicated. If shops are in one-way streets or accessed from dual-carriageways, it can take an hour or more to prepare directions to each. Multiply that by 2500 shops over the years and you will understand why our research is so labour-intensive.

We have come to the conclusion that if local councils desisted from inventing one-way systems, erecting endless signposts, constructing new road islands and raising humps, traffic flow would be just as effective – and there would be fewer enraged drivers. And fewer anguished direction-writers.

One-way streets have recently blossomed into an art-form. We are amazed how often road schemes change. In Leeds, for example, the new road scheme caused us a 40-minute delay in reaching a car-park which we knew well – and could see! The city centre in Sheffield is now such a mass of one-way streets and 'no entry' signs that locals pray that they will not have cause to go there. Tamworth has the brand new A5 cutting straight across town. Stoke-on-Trent is in the throes of a five-year major road building scheme. Bradford city centre has altered significantly each year over the last ten. Eastern suburbs of Manchester are being ravaged by major road-works prior to the opening of the new motorway link.

All shops are asked to confirm the directions; in many cases they do. Other shops tell us to print 'ask somebody' – which would nullify our aim to tell readers how to *find* the shop. (It is not always easy, anyway, to find a pedestrian – especially one who is au fait with the local area. Our favourite answer from a passer-by was 'Go right twice, pass over the railway, then go left in front of the doodah'. Somebody else instructed us to look for the Co-op 'that was pulled down 15 years ago'.)

We hope that you will have patience if you find errors in our guide – and that you will take the trouble to let us know, in order to save problems for factory shoppers in future.

We work on the assumption that readers possess maps and atlases and can find the numbered roads which we use as starting points. From there, we aim to give useful details such as pubs and petrol stations. Our researches suggest that while some people prefer to navigate from maps, others find verbal directions easier to use. We therefore include maps if several shops are near one another and if visual aids would appear to be helpful.

Finding your way there

Areas in this book

The chapters in this book correspond to our ten regional editions. While county names are useful, their shape or geography do not always lend themselves to logical division. On occasion, we include a shop in two areas – in its own county and in the neighbouring area where there is obvious overlap. We hope this helps.

Accommodation

Reflections on our travels ...

While researching factory shops all over Britain, we have experienced a wonderful selection of Bed and Breakfast (B&B) establishments. We congratulate the network of Tourist Information Centres (TICs) around Britain for their patience and unsurpassed service in arranging accommodation, often at short notice. Some offices don't even ask for a fee; most take a 10% deposit which is then deducted from the payment you make at the place where you stay.

Of course we have had some memorably bad experiences (funny in retrospect) – such as booking into what turned out to be a ghostly and very damp hotel, in January, which hadn't been heated for weeks because it was going up for auction that afternoon; being handed dirty old floor cloths which we were informed were bath towels.

On the plus side, staying in so many places, we have met super people and experienced delightful and unexpectedly interesting houses, converted cowsheds, cottages, barns, mill owners' mansions, a 14th century stately home with *two* priests' holes, and farms. Farms are our favourite, and the annual Farm Holiday Bureau publication *Stay on a Farm* is well thumbed by the end of each year.

Tea shops

In our next lives, we are going to establish a chain of attractive cafés where factory shoppers can relax, and buy delectable food at a modest price. Many factory shops are located in industrial areas; but shoppers still need welcoming places in which to eat and relax. Over the years, an increasing number of shops have set up their own refreshment corners with hot and cold drinks machines, and some, especially larger ones and those with well planned visitor centres, have dedicated space to coffee shops. Some are extremely successful ('we feel as if we have become restaurateurs who also run a factory shop'), others less so. We believe that if factory shop cafés were to offer more imaginative food they would attract more customers. It is not good enough for a world-famous pottery, for example, to promote a tearoom where customers are welcome only once the staff have been accommodated. We appreciate that catering demands financial and staff resources, and compliance with health and safety regulations. But why not dream?

As shopping is a hungry and thirsty occupation, we do our best to include details of local places where factory shoppers can find refreshment at the right time of day (experience shows, however, that few cafés in England serve food at about 5pm – when we usually finish shopping).

Scotland scores high on our list. Other favourite coffee shops are in Macclesfield, Newcastle-under-Lyme, Tutbury, Whitefield (Manchester) and Wirksworth.

Car-parks

We must have parked in nearly every multi-storey car-park across Britain at some time. They often seem to have been designed by architects and approved by planners with their aesthetic senses numbed. It cannot be denied that many modern building developments torture rather than enhance British towns. One of the booby prizes for attrocious design and siting is still held by Gloucester. Nor can the public car-park in Nelson be held up as a public joy. Things are looking up in North-West England, however, where towns such as Wigan and Bolton have built attractive car-parks which merge into the townscape.

Petrol stations

When writing directions, our favourite landmarks are pubs and petrol stations. However, petrol brands change so frequently (believe it or not) that we have become quite nervous about using specific names. *Shell* and *BP* have been known to exchange outlets; two nationwide brands are being phased out; and small names are being taken over by newly named multi-nationals. We hope that not too many such changes occur during the life of this book.

Toilets

An increasing number of factory shops now offer toilet facilities; others are not equipped to do so (or are not insured to allow visitors into the factory) but are usually sympathetic in dire circumstances. Where none is available we direct readers to the nearest public lavatories. Regrettably, some public toilets in Britain defy civilised standards of hygiene. Why are such basic facilities allotted so low a priority in this country? But we are delighted to give special praise to the public toilets in Hinckley. They are a pleasure to visit ... clean, well equipped, and easily accessible. Our congratulations to Hinckley come with a strong recommendation to officials who are responsible for public toilets elsewhere to travel to this part of Leicestershire to see what can be achieved and, moreover, maintained.

Tips on factory shopping

1. **Allow yourself to be surprised!** Go with an open mind about what you might like to buy. Stock can be very variable – according to what is being made that week in some factories – and you can rarely predict what will be on sale.

2. **But don't get carried away.** (Our best ever buy was 80 yds of elegant lampshade fringing at only £1.25 for the entire length – we just know that it will come in useful ...).

3. **Electrical goods**. Some readers have expressed doubts whether it is wise to buy electrical items from factory shops. Let us dispel all such doubts at once! Both manufacturers and sellers of electrical goods are bound to ensure that everything reaches the high safety standards laid down by the law. Whatever you buy will be covered by guarantee. 'Catalogue surplus' items will have been tested twice: once when sent out initially and again before they are put on sale in the factory shop. The main reasons why electrical goods appear in factory shops are that they are perfect previous seasons' designs, or they have tiny cosmetic flaws, or the boxes are damaged or missing. Or, in the case of nightlights or Christmas tree lamps, for example, the company does not want to sit on stock for several months until the seasonal demand comes round again. While you are visiting these shops, don't forget that good value can be found in accessories as well as appliances: one of our best buys was four dozen perfect (British made) plugs for £4. Light bulbs can also offer surprising savings.

4. **Household textiles, furnishings & accessories.** Be sure to carry fabric and wallpaper swatches and paint samples with you all the time. Often you go into a factory shop which specialises in other products only to discover that they have bought in, for example, a pile of delightful cushions.

5. **Curtains or curtaining**. Don't forget to bring accurate window dimensions. This is a heartfelt plea from the manageress of a fabric shop who says that she cannot believe how many customers turn up without this vital information, so missing out on unrepeatable bargains.

6. **Clothing.** Carry a tape measure. Sometimes garments are reduced in price because they are mis-sized.

7. **The more you spend, the more you save**. If you anticipate spending hundreds of pounds on large items such as carpets or curtains you can *save* hundreds of pounds too.

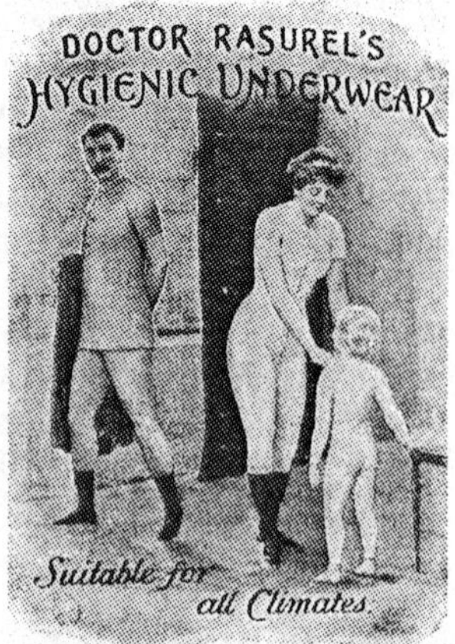

'Serious factory shoppers are prepared for all weathers'

Foreign visitors can get tax breaks on items bought in factory shops (just as they can in places like top Knightsbridge department stores). Provided you spend a minimum sum, usually £50, in a shop which is set up to organise refund documents, you can reclaim the Value Added Tax (VAT) (17.5%) when you leave this country. Factory shops offering this service tend to be top pottery and crystal companies.

Before you come to Britain, check what you may import back home and what the financial limits are. There are myriads of international regulations.

Credit cards are now accepted by many on-site factory shops. Of the shops in our database, 21 accept JCB; 61 take Diners; 186 welcome Amex; 1100 take MasterCard and Visa. 325 do not accept any cards. All shops in factory outlet village accept credit cards. A large shop in Dover has tills for French francs. Some large pottery shops accept a few foreign currencies. According to our records, just one shop, selling knitwear in Scotland, accepts any currency.

Some shops will ship; others will not. There is no pattern to this service, and it is a matter of ask and see.

British factory shops are rarely set up to gift wrap.

Hints for overseas visitors

We often come across foreign visitors in British factory shops. We also send books all over the world to travellers coming to Britain who want to plan their shopping before they arrive.

International clothing sizes

MEN

Suits and coats

British	36	38	40	42	44	46
USA	36	38	40	42	44	46
Europe	46	48	50	52	54	56

Shirts

British	14	14½	15	15½	16	16½
USA	14	14½	15	15½	16	16½
Europe	36	37	38	39/40	41	42

Shoes

British	7	7½	8½	9½	10½	11
USA	8	8½	9½	10½	11½	12
Europe	41	42	43	44	45	46

LADIES

Dresses and suits

British	8	10	12	14	16	18
USA	6	8	10	12	14	16
Europe	34	36	38	40	42	44

Shoes

British	4½	5	5½	6	6½	7
USA	6	6½	7	7½	8	8½
Europe	38	38	39	39	40	41

An outstanding institution of Great Britain is the chain of tourist information offices which straddle the country. The staff are invariably helpful and friendly and over the years they have given us enormous support. If you need somewhere to stay, they will go out of their way to find the type of accommodation you are looking for, and they operate an excellent 'book ahead' service to find accommodation further afield. We would suggest, however, that they stay open later (some close at 4.30 pm, just when you begin thinking about where to stay).

Make the most of the excellent Tourist Information Centres (TICs)

We would also suggest that, beautifully produced as they are, brochures published by town and county authorities could include more information about the present day. Personally, we are just as interested in the 1990s as we are in who is buried where. We like to know something about modern developments but, reading through tourist brochures, you might think that Britain is one huge theme park. And we have yet to find a brochure which does not extol the fine shopping, the modern leisure facilities, the beautiful gardens, the welcoming atmosphere and the friendliness of the residents.

Tongue in cheek (because we really do admire the tourist services) we interpret some of the brochures:

'This famous film star lived in and loved this town for over 30 years. He donated a bench in a favourite spot overlooking the sea.' *Just how much can you love a place?*

'Spend a day, a week or longer in this fascinating river town and you'll never be at a loss for things to do.'
A town holding most tourists' interest for two hours if they dawdle.

'An unspoilt corner of the British Isles where you have the freedom to please yourself.'
One of the most densely populated counties of England.

'A true garden town.'
A small town utterly dominated by heavy industry.

'The world's ultimate medieval experience ... giving you the greatest adventure of your life.'
Ultimate praise for the ultimate theme park?

'A new concept in pedestrianised areas.' *Not another one!*

'One of our most famous sons was the man who is purported to have conducted on the ill-fated Titanic.'
Presumably no one was left alive to confirm whether he did or not.

Dear All at the Factory Shop Guide

We cannot resist printing this ecstatic letter from a factory shopaholic in Kent

You have changed my way of life and my holidays.

Last year my husband suggested a cruise to the fjords of Norway as he thought it was the only place where I wouldn't find a factory shop! The cruise was wonderful but I did have to have a few days away later to shop or I might have had withdrawal symptoms.

You ask how many shops we have done in one day. I can tell you, if you plan from home beforehand and set off to take advantage of traffic etc, you can get masses in.

On one memorable day we started off from Kent, up the motoway to Burton-on-Trent. A call into Webb Ivory buying all the Christmas cards, wrapping paper, crackers etc for the next few years to the tune of £60, all at half price or well under, set us up nicely for the rest of the day. At Arthur Price in Lichfield I picked up silver plated knives for £1.99 instead of over £10 quoted in other shops. And ever onward:

The Potteries ... too many to count and so much fun, and then, as our 21-year old daughter was with us, the undie shops.

Talk about 'shop till you drop'. We almost had total burn-out.

We now make sure we hire a cottage for the week. On one holiday, when I had promised myself the Denby pottery I had wanted for years, we filled the cottage in Derbyshire. We thought our daughter would have to be sent home by train as we couldn't fit her in the car for the return journey.

Honestly, I had got so carried away. The Denby dinner service with EVERYTHING came to a third of the normal shop price. Where I had thought to collect just three of everything, I went the whole hog and collected six instead (with a couple of extras in case of breakage).

I make christening gowns for a living and have found the most wonderful lace in David Nieper at a fraction of the cost and bought lots of fabric at the Fabric Factory. We also ended up with a good year's supply of soap of terrific quality.

Shopping, now, is never just 'go out and get'. We always look in your books to see where we can get it cheaper. And, boy oh boy, we have found some things well worth going a distance to get.

Thanks again for your wonderful books and my new 'hobby' – even if it has ruined my husband's holidays. He has suggested another cruise this year. I wonder why.

SIZE CHART

Now you have no excuse for not remembering the sizes of your family or your home!

Ring size									
Shoes									
Socks									
Tights Stockings									
Pants									
Bra									
Shirt collar									
Jacket									
Trouser leg									
Trouser waist									
Trousers									
Sweater									
Skirt									
Dress Blouse									
Bust Waist Hip									
NAME									

Bed size						
Yds fabric upholstery						
Rolls wallpaper						
Yds fabric needed 2						
Curtain length 2						
Window 2 dimensions						
Yds fabric needed 1						
Curtain length 1						
Window 1 dimensions						
Room size						
ROOM						

South-West England & South Wales

A

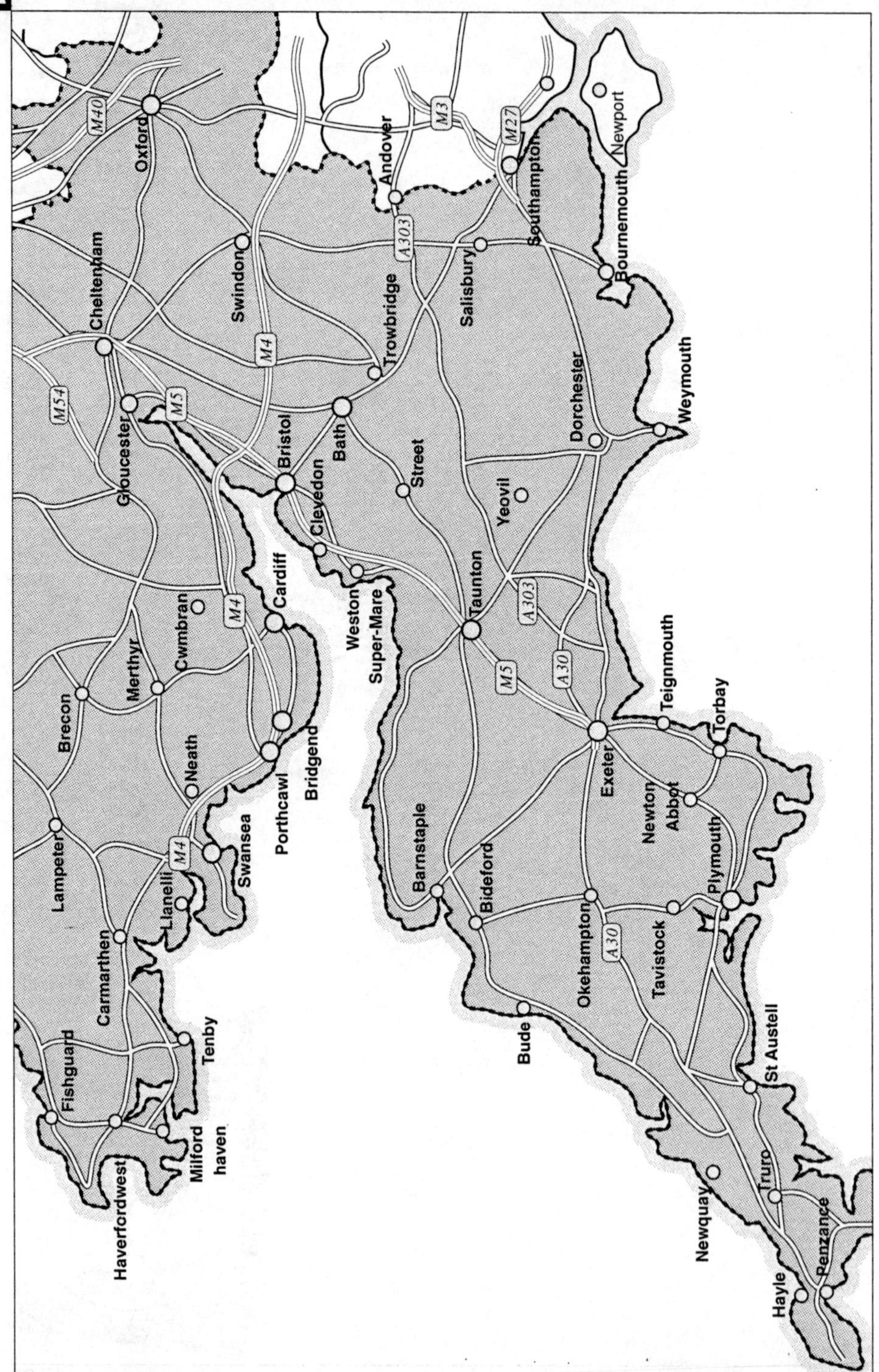

Oxford
M40
Cheltenham
Swindon
Andover
M3
M27
Southampton
Newport
Bournemouth
A303
Salisbury
Trowbridge
M4
M54
M5
Gloucester
Bristol
Bath
Street
Dorchester
Weymouth
Yeovil
Clevedon
Cardiff
Weston Super-Mare
Taunton
A303
Cwmbran
Merthyr
Brecon
Neath
Bridgend
Porthcawl
Swansea
Teignmouth
Torbay
Exeter
A30
Newton Abbot
Barnstaple
Bideford
Okehampton
A30
Plymouth
Tavistock
Lampeter
Llanelli
Carmarthen
Tenby
Fishguard
Haverfordwest
Milford haven
Bude
St Austell
Truro
Newquay
Penzance
Hayle

South-West England & South Wales

This large area – from Oxfordshire westwards to Cornwall, including South Wales, and also the Channel Islands – offers a huge variety of products: clothing for the entire family, traditional woollen fabrics and knitwear, superb cashmere, all kinds of items for the home, including high quality carpets and tiles, household textiles, glassware, chocolate for diabetics – the list seems endless.

We are particularly happy to have found so many new and interesting shops. In St Nicholas, in Dyfed, you will find unique and stylish ranges of rugs and blankets. A company in Wiltshire is one of the largest makers of church candles in Britain; a pottery in Oxford hand-crafts English delftware using 17th century techniques; another shop in the same county specialises in natural slate products. In Swindon is the only factory shop we know which sells house plants and plant arrangements. And if you like unusual settings (both in the countryside and on your dining table!), you will feel at peace in an abbey in Gloucestershire which sells fine ceramic tableware made by the monks.

Swindon is home to one of the newest and largest factory outlet villages in Britain. In fact, South-West England is well served by such villages: with other excellent developments in Street, the original purpose-built factory outlet village in Europe, and Bicester. The first factory outlet villages have recently opened in South Wales too.

This chapter is divided into three sections:

South Wales
The Channel Islands
South-West England.

Tregwynt

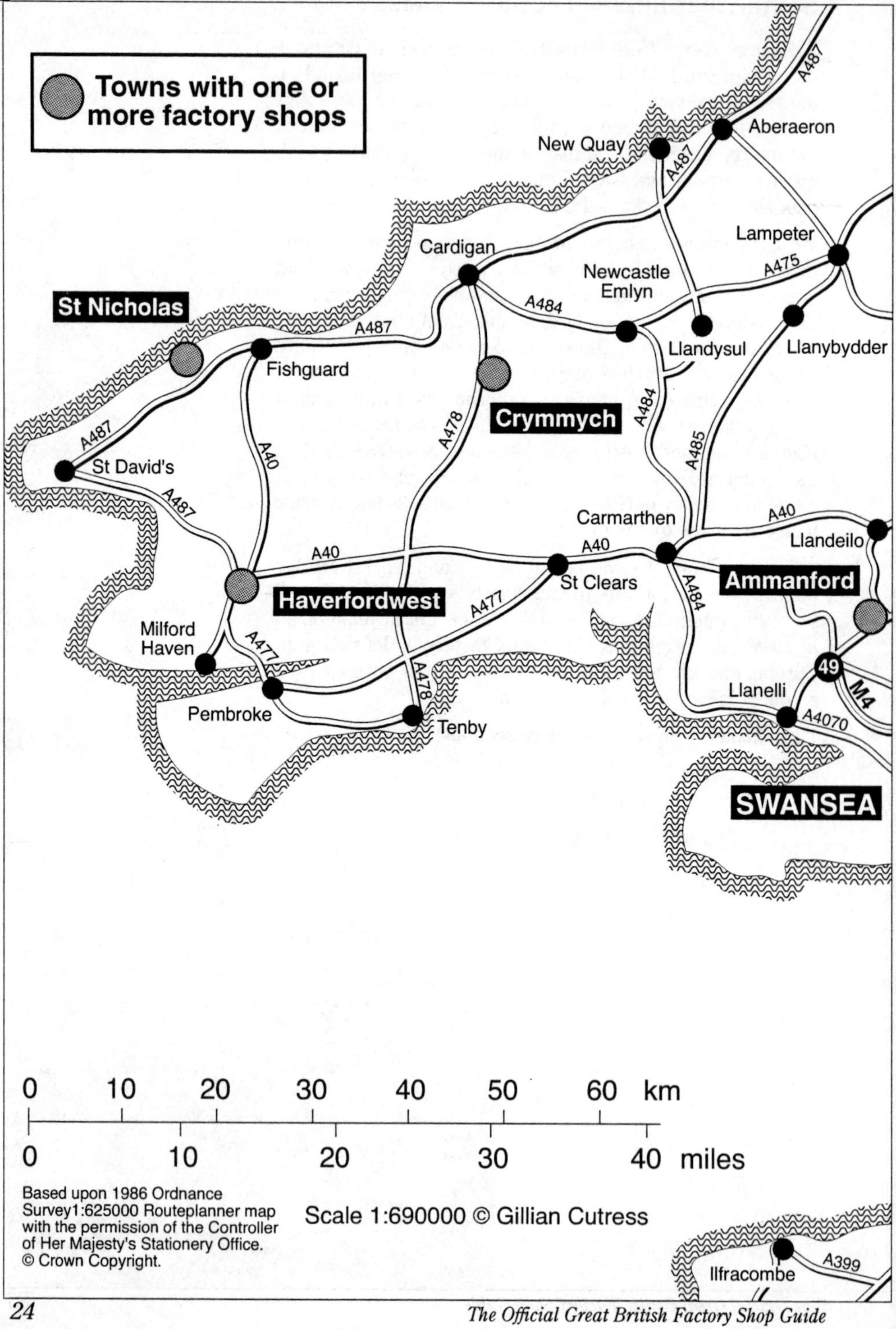

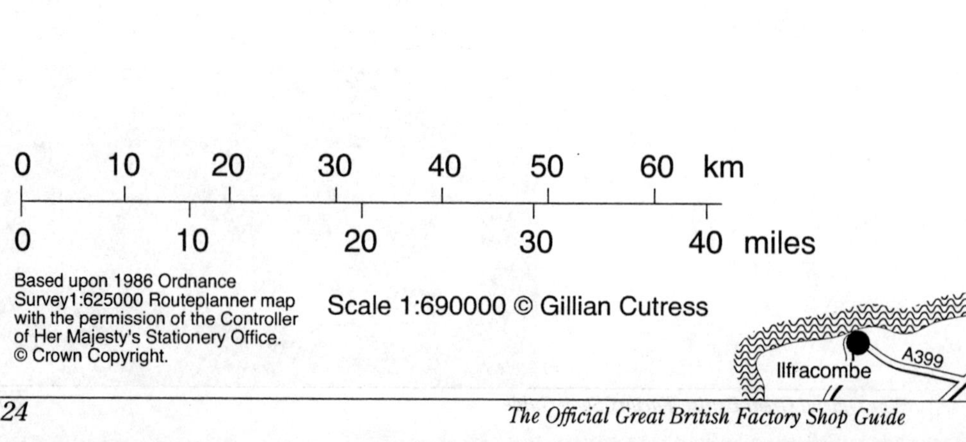

Based upon 1986 Ordnance Survey1:625000 Routeplanner map with the permission of the Controller of Her Majesty's Stationery Office. © Crown Copyright.

Scale 1:690000 © Gillian Cutress

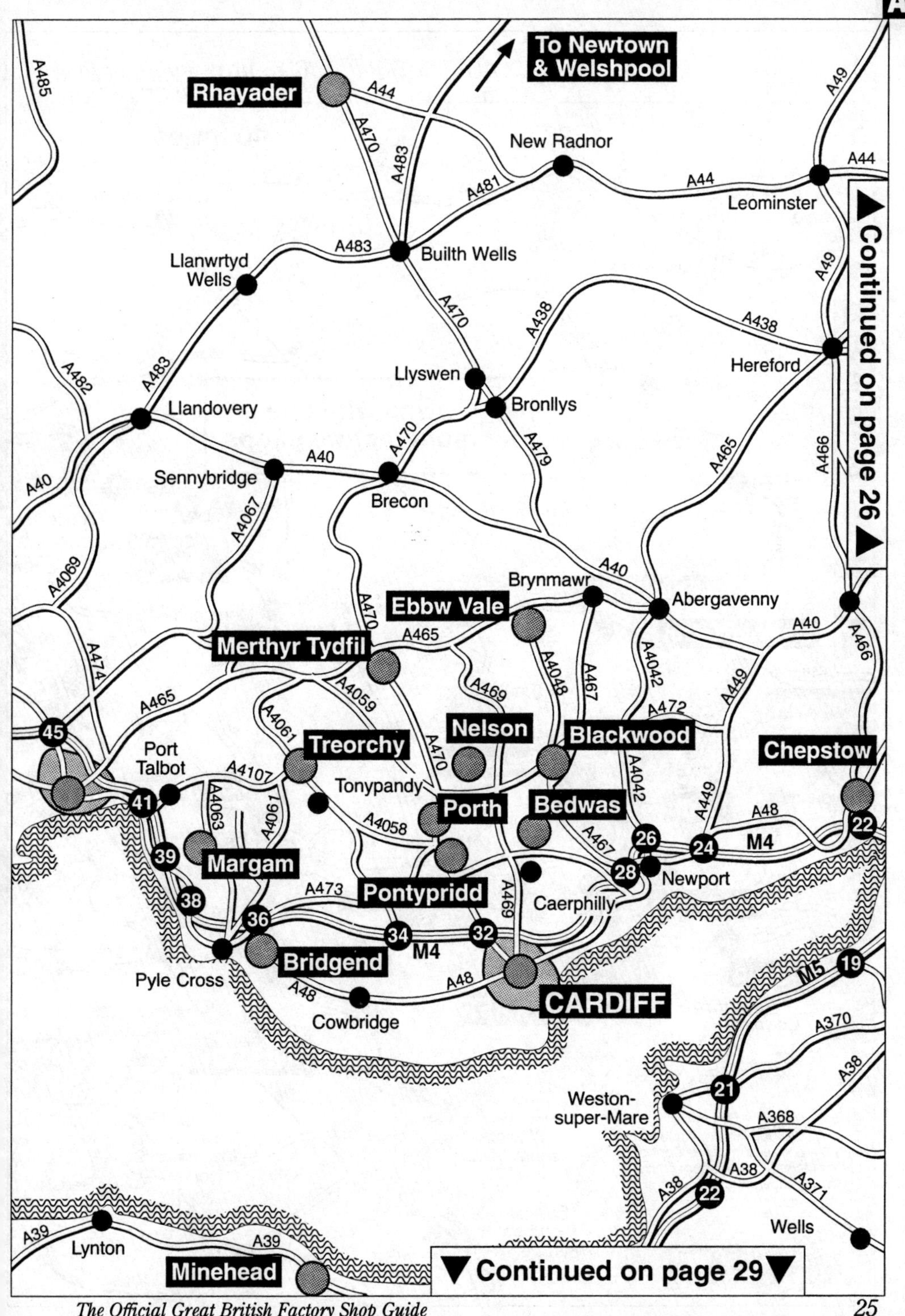

▲Continued on page 26▲

▼Continued on page 29▼

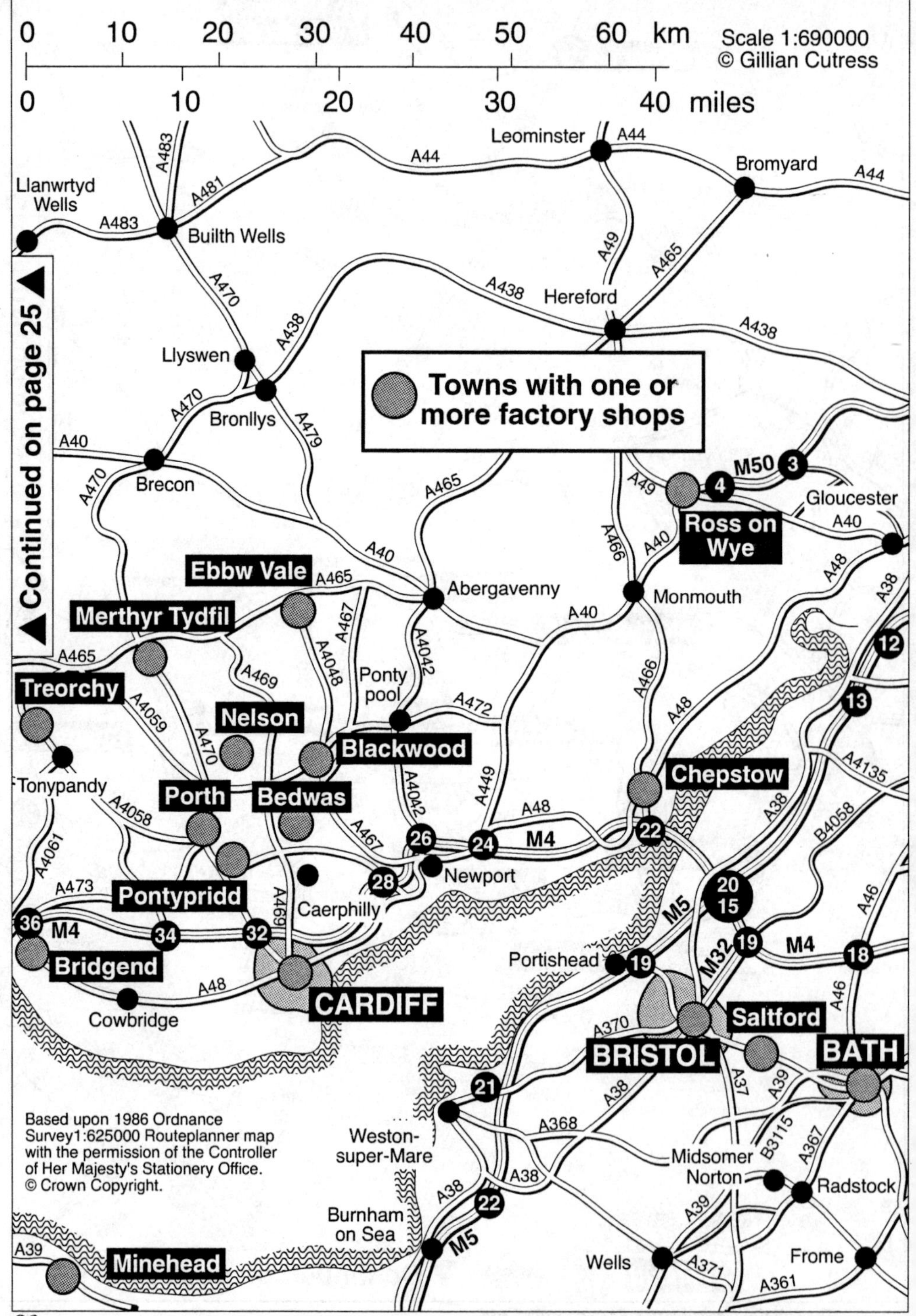
0 10 20 30 40 50 60 km
0 10 20 30 40 miles
Scale 1:690000
© Gillian Cutress
▲ Continued on page 25 ▲
Towns with one or more factory shops
Leominster
Bromyard
Llanwrtyd Wells
Builth Wells
Hereford
Llyswen
Bronllys
Brecon
Abergavenny
Monmouth
Gloucester
Ross on Wye
Ebbw Vale
Merthyr Tydfil
Treorchy
Tonypandy
Nelson
Blackwood
Ponty pool
Porth
Bedwas
Chepstow
Newport
Caerphilly
Pontypridd
Bridgend
Cowbridge
CARDIFF
Portishead
BRISTOL
Saltford
BATH
Weston-super-Mare
Midsomer Norton
Radstock
Burnham on Sea
Wells
Frome
Minehead
M4
M5
M32
M50
A44
A483
A481
A470
A438
A49
A465
A479
A40
A466
A48
A38
A4042
A4048
A467
A469
A472
A449
A4059
A4058
A4061
A473
A4135
B4058
A46
A370
A368
A37
A39
B3115
A367
A371
A361
Based upon 1986 Ordnance Survey1:625000 Routeplanner map with the permission of the Controller of Her Majesty's Stationery Office. © Crown Copyright.

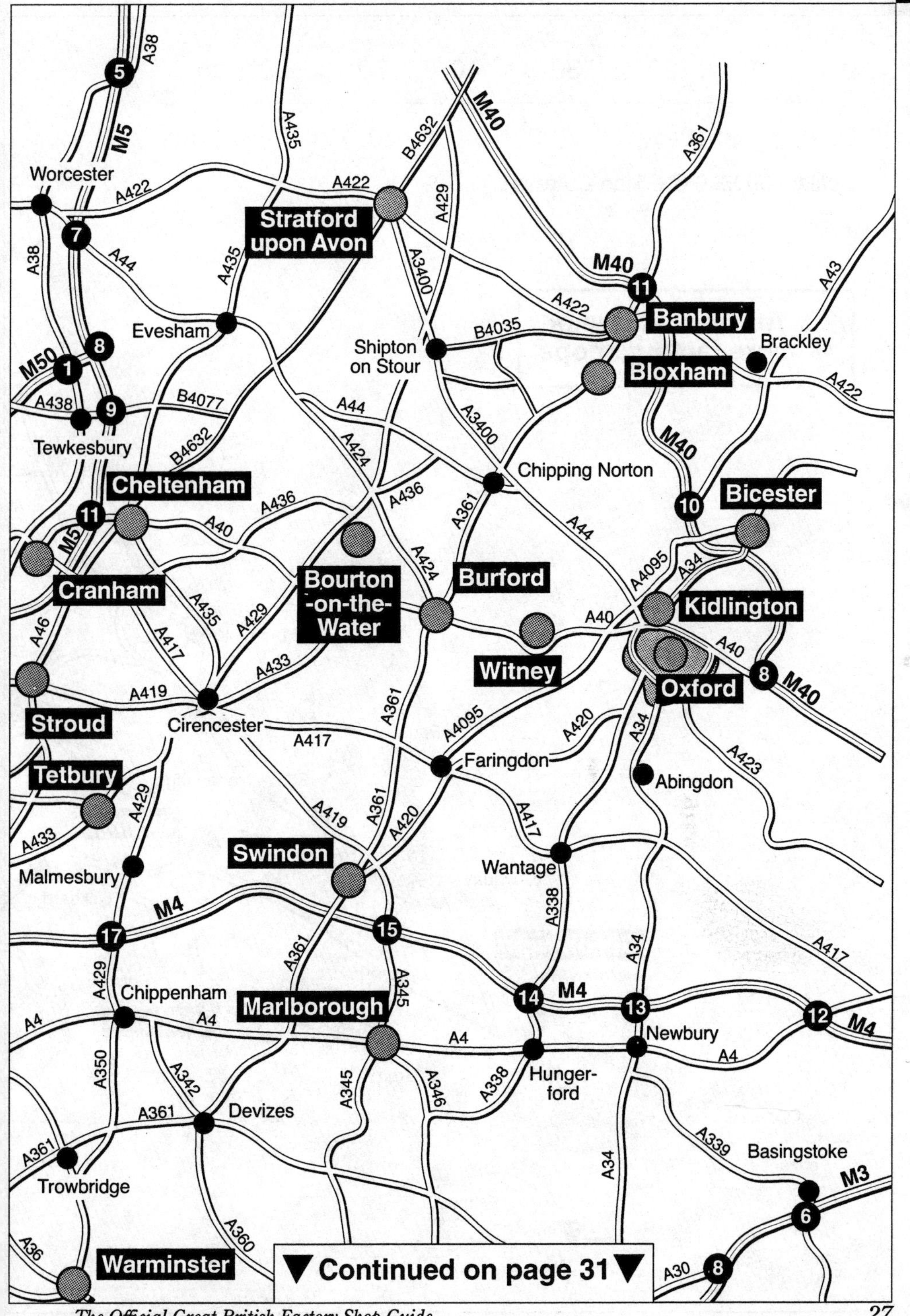

▼ Continued on page 31 ▼

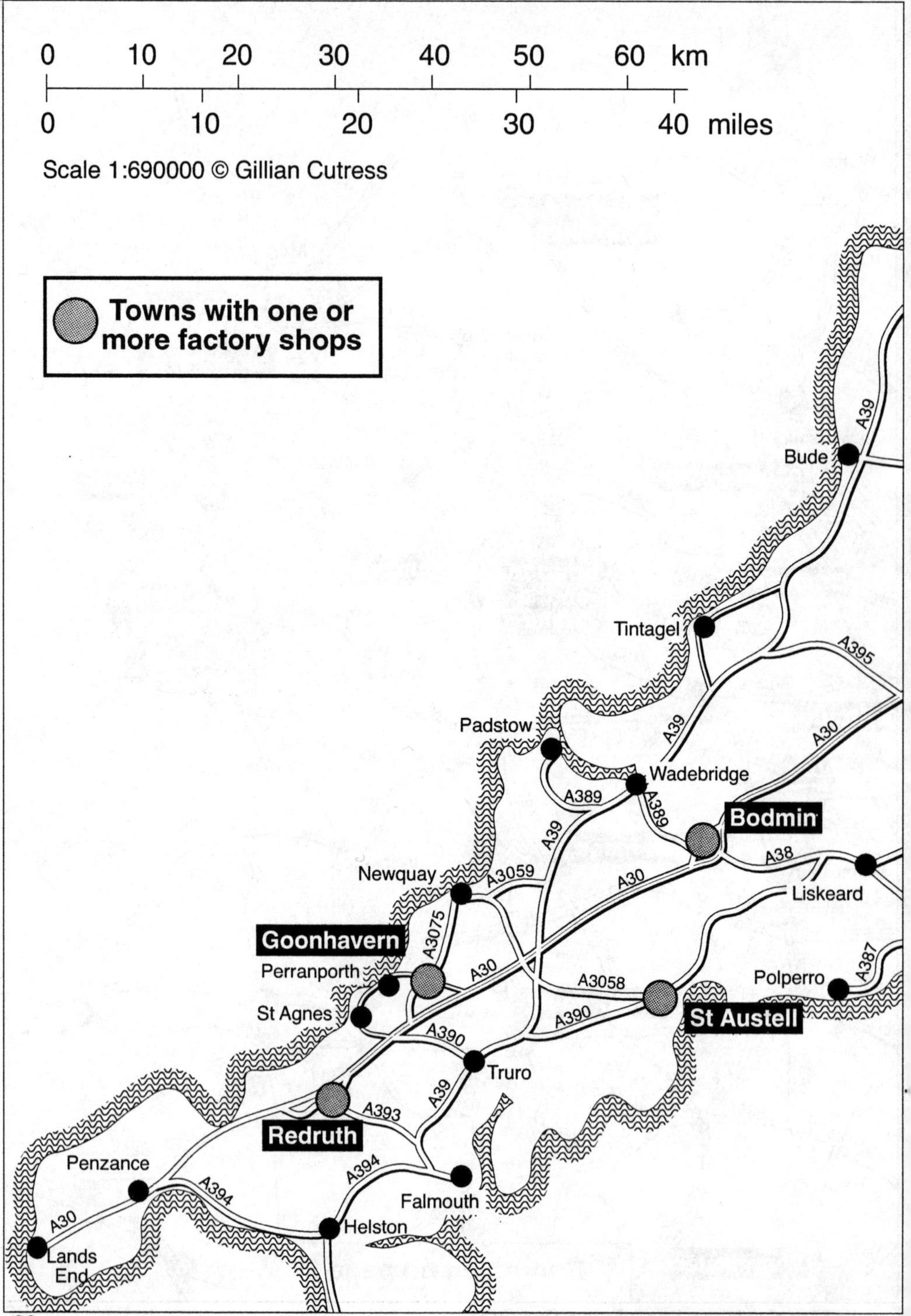

0 10 20 30 40 50 60 km
0 10 20 30 40 miles
Scale 1:690000 © Gillian Cutress
Towns with one or more factory shops
Bude
A39
Tintagel
A395
Padstow
A39
A30
Wadebridge
A389
A389
Bodmin
A39
A38
Newquay
A3059
A30
Liskeard
Goonhavern
A3075
A30
Perranporth
A3058
Polperro
A387
St Agnes
A390
St Austell
A390
Truro
A39
Redruth
A393
Penzance
A394
Falmouth
A394
A30
Helston
Lands End

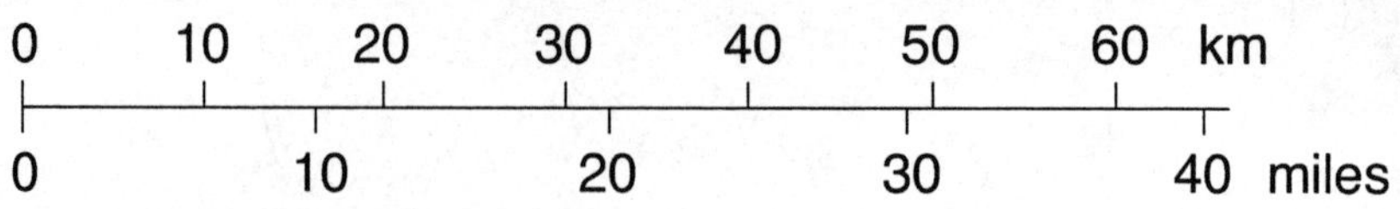

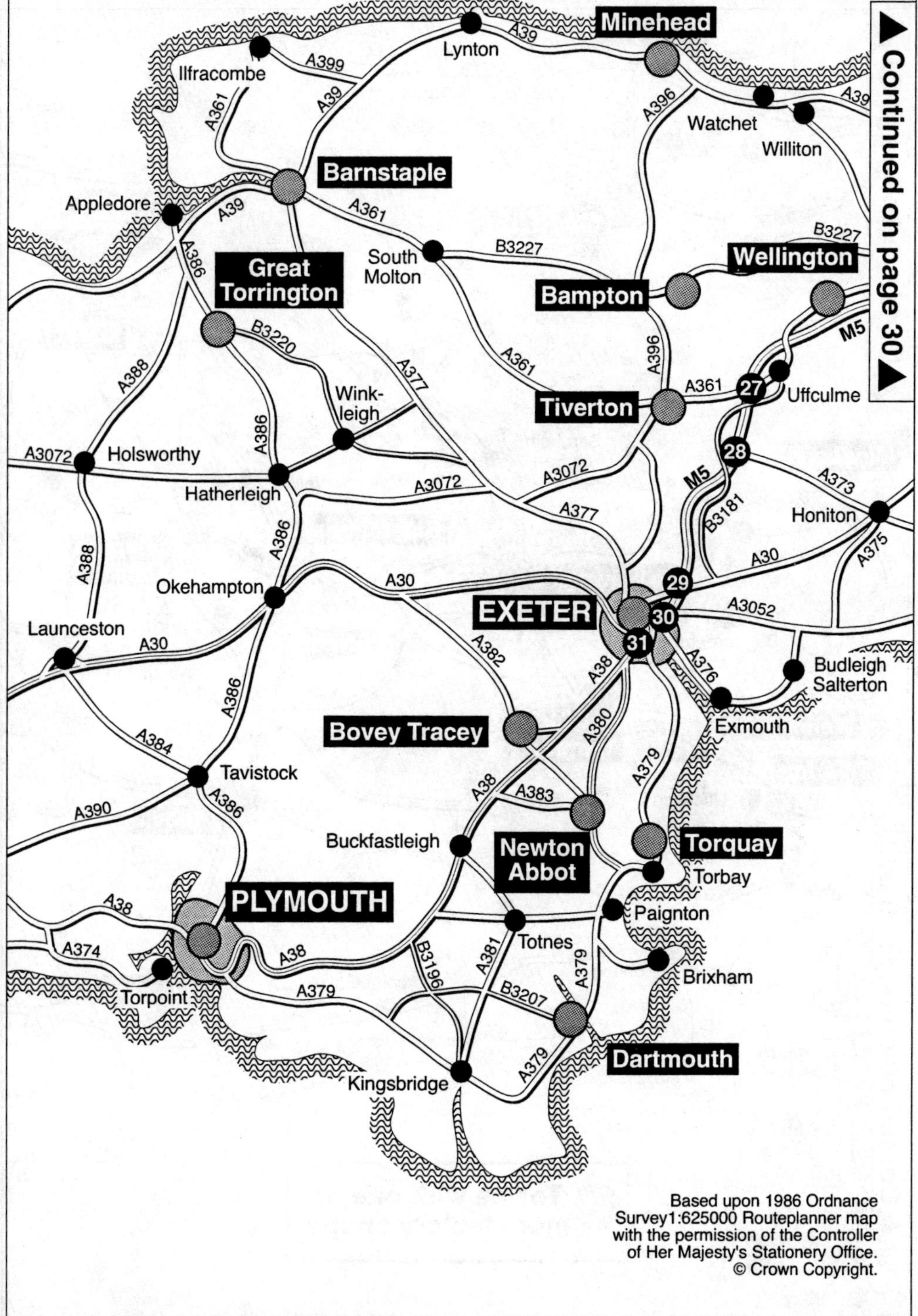

▶ Continued on page 30 ▶

Based upon 1986 Ordnance Survey1:625000 Routeplanner map with the permission of the Controller of Her Majesty's Stationery Office.

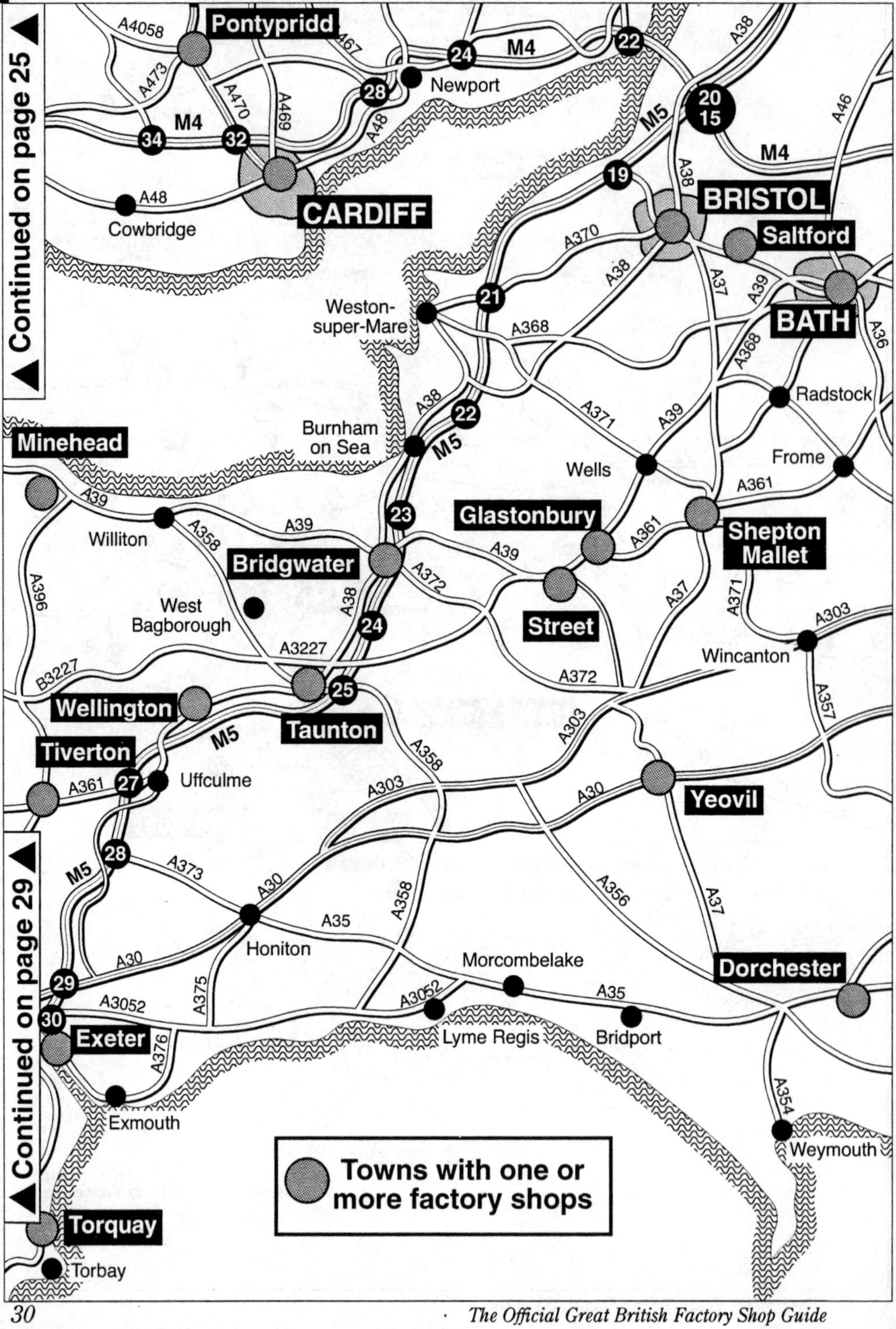

A

▲ Continued on page 25 ▲

Pontypridd
A4058
A467
A473
A470
A469
M4
24
22
28
Newport
34
32
A48
20
15
M5
A46
A38
CARDIFF
A48
Cowbridge
19
A38
BRISTOL
Saltford
A370
A38
A37
A39
BATH
21
Weston-super-Mare
A368
A368
A36
Radstock
A38
22
A371
A39
Minehead
Burnham on Sea
M5
Wells
Frome
A39
A361
23
Glastonbury
A361
Shepton Mallet
Williton
A358
A39
Bridgwater
A39
A372
A396
West Bagborough
A38
Street
A37
A371
A303
24
A3227
Wincanton
B3227
A372
Wellington
25
Taunton
A303
M5
A357
Tiverton
A358
A361
27
Uffculme
Yeovil
A303
A30
M5
28
A373
A30
A358
A356
A37
A35
Honiton
A30
Morcombelake
Dorchester
29
A375
A3052
A35
A3052
30
Exeter
A376
Lyme Regis
Bridport
A354
Exmouth
Weymouth

Towns with one or more factory shops

▲ Continued on page 29 ▲

Torquay
Torbay

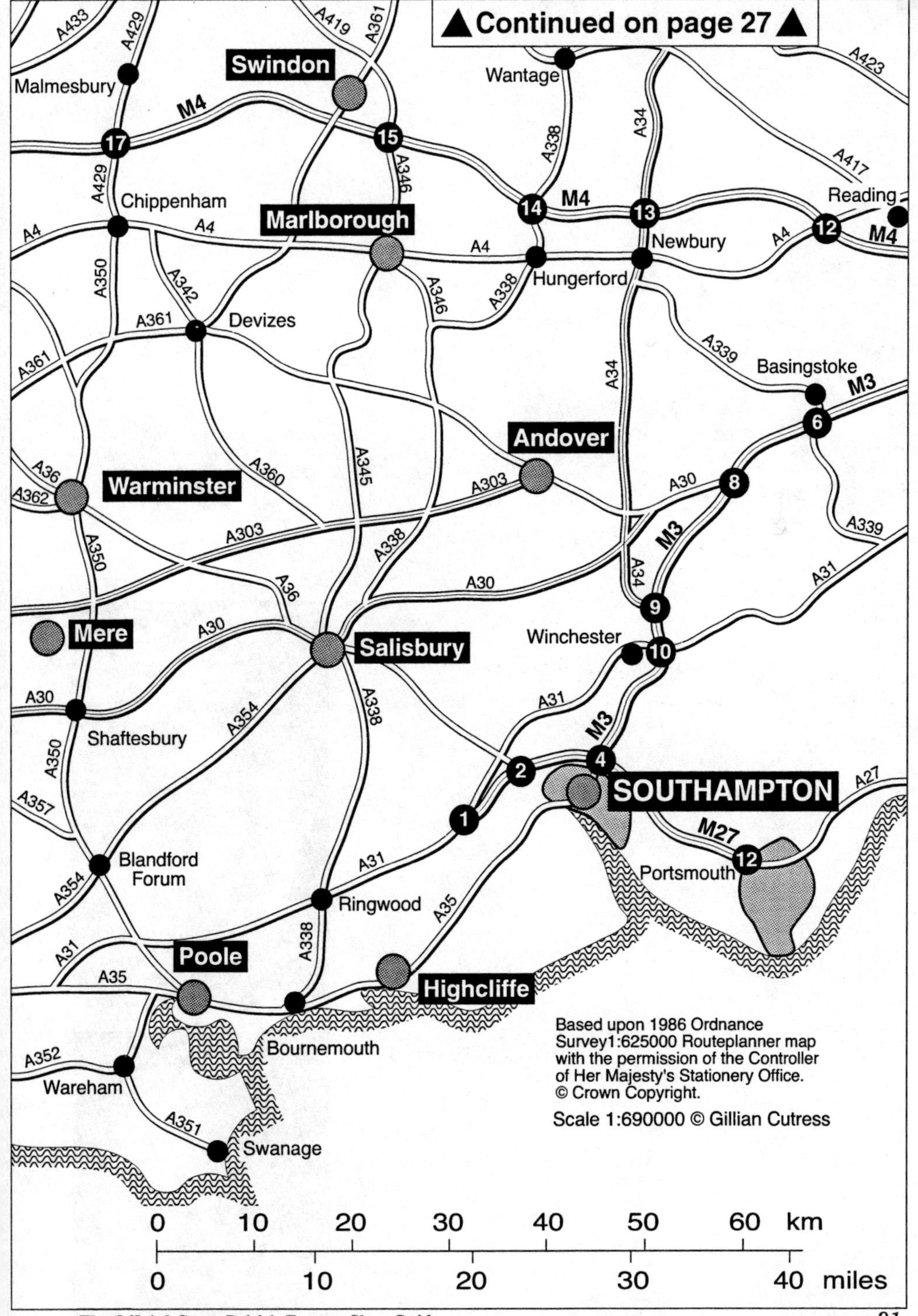
▲Continued on page 27▲
Swindon
Malmesbury
Wantage
M4
17
15
14
13
12
A433
A429
A419
A361
A423
A338
A34
A417
A346
Chippenham
Reading
Marlborough
A4
Newbury
Hungerford
A350
A342
A361
Devizes
A339
Basingstoke
M3
6
Andover
A345
A360
A36
A362
Warminster
A303
A30
8
A339
A31
9
Mere
Salisbury
Winchester
10
A354
A338
A357
Shaftesbury
2
4
1
SOUTHAMPTON
A27
M27
12
Portsmouth
Blandford
Forum
Ringwood
A35
A31
Poole
Highcliffe
A352
Bournemouth
Wareham
A351
Swanage
Based upon 1986 Ordnance Survey1:625000 Routeplanner map with the permission of the Controller of Her Majesty's Stationery Office. © Crown Copyright.
Scale 1:690000 © Gillian Cutress
0 10 20 30 40 50 60 km
0 10 20 30 40 miles

Gallery Home Fashion

Wilton Carpet Factory

Make the most of Welsh variety!

A most enjoyable aspect of factory shopping in South Wales is the unexpectedly wide range of items on sale. We do not know any other area in Britain where you can buy, for example, wedding decorations, world famous bone china, Christmas garlands, fine hand woven cloth, cashmere fit for a prince, family clothing, wallpaper and diabetic chocolate within a few miles of each other ...

If you are a newcomer to the area, you will find comfortable bed and breakfast accommodation – in one memorable farmhouse we were fed a delicious breakfast based on traditional Welsh recipes – but we must point out that finding somewhere to stay at the last minute in Cardiff and Swansea has proved difficult several times. Make the most of the excellent booking services offered by tourist offices.

With the decline of traditional heavy industries, such as coal mining, steel and copper processing, South Wales has been forced to rethink its economic strategy. (It is easy to assume the devastation of the coal mining industry to be a very recent phenomenon, but in the decade following 1921 a quarter of million people left South Wales to find employment elsewhere.) International engineering and electronics companies have established their European bases here. As industries have closed down, so the Welsh heritage has been given greater prominence. You can experience the 'Big Pit' mine and mining museum in Blaenafon (01495 790311) and Rhondda Heritage Park (01443 682036) on the site of Lewis Merthyr colliery, with its audio-visual record of life in the valleys during the coal boom. (It is difficult now to appreciate that Merthyr was the largest town in Wales throughout the first half of last century!) The new Techniquest (01222 475475), a purpose built science discovery centre, with planetarium, in the renovated Cardiff docks appeals to children, but many an adult will enjoy playing with the hands-on interactive exhibits.

Shoppers with a literary leaning could aim for Laugharne, the waterside village where Dylan Thomas and his family stayed for a few years. The Boat House, on stilts and half way up a cliff, has been turned into a museum (01994 427420). While there, visit the ruins of the castle which is re-opening to the public after extensive restoration and excavation. A Victorian garden, using exclusively Victorian plants and flowers, is recreated on the site.

Tregwynt Woollen Mill

Cardiff Tourist Office,
Cardiff Central Station,
Cardiff CF1 1QY.
phone (01222) 227281

Cardiff Marketing offers a free accommodation finding service:
phone (01222) 395173,
fax (01222) 377653.
Oliver House, 16 High Street, Cardiff CF1 2AX.

Swansea Tourist Information Centre,
Singleton Street, Swansea SA1 3QG
phone (01792) 468321
fax (01792) 464602

Other Tourist Information Centres are at :

Abergavenny (01873) 857588
Carmarthen (01267) 231557
Llandarcy (Neath) (01792) 813030
Merthyr (01685) 379884
Newport (01633) 842962
Pembroke (01646) 622388
St Davids (01437) 720392

1 Ammanford Carmarthenshire

Alan Paine Knitwear

New Road SA18 3ET
(01269) 592316

Luxury knitwear in natural fibres including cashmere, camelhair, lambswool and cotton (sweaters, cardigans, slipovers).

'Knitwear made here for sale worldwide. All stock at factory shop prices, mostly perfects, some seconds. Stock approximately half price. Lambswool from £17.50, cashmere from £60. Special offers from time to time. Genuine factory shop!'

Easy to find, about ½ mile south-west of traffic lights in town centre.

From these traffic lights, take A483 south (for Swansea/M4). After ½ mile, take left fork to 'New Road Industrial Estate/ Pantyffynon 1'. The factory is 400 yds on left, after Corgi.

From M4 going north via A483: go right, about ⅓ mile after 'Ammanford' town sign, at sign to New Road Industrial Estate/Pantyffynnon. Factory is 400 yds on left.

Open: Please phone first. Mon–Sat 9–4.
Closed: Bank Holidays; Easter Tuesday; Christmas, Boxing and New Year's Days.
Cards: MasterCard, Switch, Visa.
Cars: Outside shop, within factory complex.
Toilets: No.
Wheelchairs: Three steps.
Changing rooms: No.
Teas: In Ammanford.
Groups: Shopping groups welcome provided they phone first. No factory tours.
Transport: ½ mile walk from Pantyffynnon station.
Mail order: No.

2 Ammanford Carmarthenshire

Corgi Hosiery

New Road SA18 3DR
(01269) 592104/593147

Superb hand-framed knitwear and hosiery in cashmere, wool and other natural fibres. Top quality products in original designs. Most items perfects at factory prices.

'The only Welsh company to hold a Royal Warrant for HRH The Prince of Wales for knitwear and hosiery.'

Easy to find, about ½ mile south-west of traffic lights in town centre.

From these traffic lights, take A483 south (for Swansea/M4). After ½ mile, take left fork to 'New Road Industrial Estate/ Pantyffynon 1'. The factory is 300 yds on left.

From M4 going north via A483: go right, about ⅓ mile after Ammanford town sign, at sign to New Road Industrial Estate/Pantyffynnon. Factory is 300 yds on left.

BY APPOINTMENT TO
H.R.H. THE PRINCE OF WALES
KNITWEAR AND HOSIERY
MANUFACTURERS

Open: Mon–Thur 9–4.30; Fri 9–1.
Closed: Bank Holidays; last week July/first week Aug; Christmas–New Year.
Cards: MasterCard, Visa.
Cars: Own car-park.
Toilets: Yes.
Wheelchairs: Easy access, small ground floor display area.
Changing rooms: You are welcome to try on sweaters.
Teas: In Ammanford.
Tours: You can see knitters in action as you go through to sales area. Interesting factory – hosiery machines are over 100 years old and all garments individually made on hand-operated intarsia knitting machines.
Transport: A ½ mile walk from Pantyffynnon station.
Mail order: No.

See our entries no. 8 and below

3 Nelson Mid Glamorgan

Stuart Crystal (moved from Bargoed)

Llancaiach Fawr, Living History Museum CF46 6ER
(01443) 413438

Wide selection of lead crystal – wine suites, whisky glasses, tumblers, vases, rose bowls, jugs, decanters. Other items include trays, tantaluses (lockable display cases for decanters) and souvenirs.

'Perfects and seconds on sale. Chip repair service available.'

See our display advertisement above

NB Shop has moved from Aberbargoed to Nelson (7 miles west).

Now within the Living History Museum on B4254 north of Nelson and east of Treharris (see brown 'museum' signs on local roads).

From A470 Cardiff/Merthyr Tydfill road: turn east on to A472 for Ystrach Mynach. In Nelson go north on B4255. Follow brown signs, going right on to B4254 for Gelligaer. Museum is shortly on right; go in main entrance: shop on right.

Open: Seven days a week: 10–5. Please phone first.
Closed: Christmas and Boxing Days.
Cards: Amex, MasterCard, Switch, Visa.
Cars: Own car-park.
Toilets: Yes.
Wheelchairs: No steps, large showroom.
Teas: On-site coffee shop.
Tours: Groups to museum welcome to visit shop too.
Transport: None.
Mail order: Yes (firsts and seconds).
Catalogue: Free stemware catalogue.

4 Bedwas Caerphilly

Gallery Home Fashion

Pantglas Industrial Estate NP1 8DR
(01222) 868311

Wide range of wallpapers (including vinyl and blown vinyl, ie embossed) and co-ordinating borders. Paste and scissors.

'Prices reduced by 50% on perfects and current ranges (even more on clearance lines).'

Bedwas is a short distance north-east of Caerphilly and this industrial estate is south of the A468.

From M4 exit 28: take A467 north-west. At roundabout, fork left on to A468 for Caerphilly. Go through Trethomas, pass the Bedwas town sign; take first left to Pantglas Industrial Estate.*

From Caerphilly: take the A468 east. Do not turn left into Bedwas, but bypass it, then turn right into Pantglas Industrial Estate.*

****At the bottom of the slope, turn left: the shop is about 650 yds on left.***

Open: Mon–Fri 9.30–5; Sat 9.30–3.30.
Closed: Some Bank Holidays, please phone to check.
Cards: None.
Cars: In car-park.
Toilets: No.
Wheelchairs: One step to medium sized shop.
Teas: Local pubs and cafés.
Groups: Small groups welcome to shop.
Transport: Caerphilly and Newport rail stations. Bus no. 50 from both stations to Bedwas.
Mail order: No.

5 Blackwood Caerphilly

Gossard

Penmaen Road, Pontllanfraith NP2 2DK
(01495) 221103

Gossard and *Berlei* ranges of bras and co-ordinates.

'Discontinued items and slight seconds. 25–70% off high street prices.'

On the south-east side of Blackwood, on the B4251 (Oakdale–Ystrad Mynach road). On the east side of the River Sirhorwy.

From traffic lights, where Penmaen Road (B4251) crosses Commercial Road/Newbridge Road (A472): go north for Oakdale. After ½ mile go left into small industrial estate marked 'Penmaen Industrial Estate'. Gossard, clearly marked, is first factory on right.

From the new bypass A472: at roundabout, take B4251 for Newbridge/Pentwynmawr. At next roundabout, go left for Pontllanfraith, staying on B4251. At traffic lights, go right for Oakdale (B4251). Continue to signposted industrial estate.

The shop, clearly signed, is behind the Gossard factory.

Open: Mon–Sat 9.30–5.30.
Closed: Bank Holidays. Christmas–New Year.
Cards: No.
Cars: Own car-park.
Toilets: In Blackwood.
Wheelchairs: No steps, easy access.
Changing rooms: Yes.
Teas: In Blackwood.
Groups: Larger groups please phone first.
Transport: Local buses, two minutes' walk.
Mail order: Yes.
Catalogue: No.

6 Cardiff

Avana Bakeries

Pendyris Street CF1 7YI
(01222) 225521

Large range of fruit, slab and madeira cakes, birthday and celebration cakes. Christmas puddings and cakes.

'The "factory reject shop" where you can buy items that are slightly damaged.'

In the city centre.

About ¼ mile from Cardiff Central Bus and Rail Station: walk west over Taff river bridge, turn left under bridge and follow footpath to factory on right.

Open: Mon–Fri 9.30–4.30.
Closed: Bank Holidays.
Cards: No.
Cars: Outside shop.
Toilets: In town.
Wheelchairs: Easy access to small shop.
Teas: Great variety in Cardiff.
Tours: Unfortunately no factory tours.
Transport: Easy walking from all transport.

Stop press
Recently opened: Bridgend Designer Outlet Wales
Factory outlet village with 46 shops (01656 665702), at M4 exit 36

'The finest porcelain in the world'

Nantgarw Pottery stands on the same site, a couple of miles south-west of Caerphilly, where Nantgarw porcelain was made in the early 1800s. That porcelain is still considered to be amongst the finest ever produced because of its whiteness and translucency. It was the dream of one William Billingsley.

Billingsley, born in 1758, worked for 20 years at Derby China Works. He was principal flower painter and is still recognised as an outstanding artist. He portrayed blooms with great delicacy, and was famous for his roses. His designs were so highly prized that more work has been attributed to him than he could have possibly executed!

Billingsley arrived at Nantgarw with his daughters and son-in-law Samuel Walker in 1813. Between them they had £250, which they used to erect factory buildings, and production of porcelain began at Nantgarw using Billingsley's own secret formula.

Unfortunately, many pieces became distorted in the first ('biscuit') firing. The family was quickly in financial difficulties, and in 1814 Billingsley and Walker were invited to work in Swansea, using the Nantgarw recipe. In 1817 the pair returned to Nantgarw with financial assistance. But wastage was still high. Although the porcelain was in huge demand by London decorators and designers, the money soon dried up. In 1820 they left for Coalport.

The pottery subsequently made clay tobacco pipes and production continued until 1920. Nantgarw Pottery today has revived the tradition of pottery making here, in the same style as the early 1800s.

Calico

71–73 City Road CF2 3BM
(01222) 493020

Huge range of printed and plain furnishing fabrics by the yard. Upholstery fabrics. Polycottons for duvets and bed covers.

'First and second qualities. Many fabrics at 50% discount. Specialise in fabric from rolls. Many items bought in from major store clearances.'

City Road (B4261), on the north-east side of city centre, leads north towards A48/M4.

From the east side of city centre: at traffic lights in Newport Road, go north for ¼ mile, pass Andrews Garage: shop is on the left.

Coming south from M4 on A470: turn off for A48 at large roundabout, go over A48 and take next left, Whitchurch Road (A469) which eventually leads to City Road. Shop is ¾ mile along on right (opposite Exchange pub).

Open: Mon–Sat 9.30–5.
Closed: Bank Holidays; Christmas–New Year.
Cards: Delta, MasterCard, Switch, Visa.
Cars: Parking in street (2-hour zone).
Toilets: Nearby.
Wheelchairs: One step to large shop.
Teas: Next door.
Groups: Shopping groups welcome – please book first.
Transport: Local buses from city centre.

Crossing the River Severn

The impressive new Severn Bridge, constructed by an Anglo-French enterprise, is more than 5000 m long. It took over four years to build and cost £330 million. The main pylons stand 148 m above high water level. The volume of concrete needed was 450,000 cu m, and 50,000 tons of reinforcing steel were used.

On a more practical note for shoppers, we should add that a toll, about £4 per car, is charged on the way into Wales (but not on the way back). The toll for the original, more northerly, bridge is the same.

8 Chepstow Monmouthshire

Stuart Crystal

Bridge Street NP6 5EZ
(01291) 620135

Lead crystal such as wine suites, wine glasses, tumblers, vases, rose bowls, jugs, decanters. Other items include trays, tantaluses (lockable display cases for decanters) and souvenirs.

'Perfects and seconds. Engraving and chip-repair service.'

See our display advertisement on p. 35

At bottom end of Chepstow town, opposite the castle and 100 yds from Chepstow Museum.

Coming south towards Chepstow on the A48: turn right at sign to Chepstow Castle.*

From the south via M4/A48: follow signs to Chepstow, then go left at second 'Town Centre' sign.*

****Keep following signs to Chepstow Castle. The shop, in a one-way street, is directly opposite the castle car-park in an old converted school.***

Open: Seven days, 9–5; Bank Holidays.
Closed: Christmas, Boxing Days.
Cards: Access, Amex, Switch, Visa.
Cars: Large car-park opposite; Chepstow Castle car-park.
Toilets: Yes, for the disabled too. Also in town.
Wheelchairs: Easy access: ramp, wide door, ground floor shop.
Teas: Own coffee shop.
Tours: You get a feel for how glass is made from the video and museum exhibits. Free entry.
Transport: Train and bus stations within 5 minutes' walk of shop.
Mail order: Yes (firsts and seconds).
Catalogue: Free stemware catalogue.

9 Crymmych Pembrokeshire

Frenni Furniture

Tenby Road SA4 3QG
(01239) 831557

Solid mahogany furniture, such as tables, cabinets, bookcases, chairs, bureaux, desks, bedside cabinets etc all made on the premises.

'All products are seconds, and are sold at around 30–40% less than high street prices. Special commissions undertaken. Delivery can be arranged, £10 anywhere within the UK.'

Crymych is on the A478 about eight miles south of Cardigan.

Coming south from Cardigan: stay on this road into the village; the shop is on the right, opposite the pharmacy.

Coming north towards Cardigan: go into village, pass petrol station, then butcher on left, then this shop is shortly on the left.

Open: Mon–Thur 8–5; Fri 8–2.
Closed: Some Bank Holidays, please phone to check; Christmas–New Year.
Cards: Eurocard, MasterCard, Visa.
Cars: Large car-park at rear.
Toilets: Across the road.
Wheelchairs: One step.
Teas: Café and pub meals within 50 yds.
Tours: Guided tours of factory, for small groups only, must be booked in advance.
Transport: Daily bus service from Cardigan.
Mail order: No.
Catalogue: Yes.

10 Ebbw Vale Gwent

Start-rite Shoes

Festival Park, Victoria Road, Victoria NP3 6UF
(01495) 305700

Huge stock of all kinds of footwear for children of all ages.

'We specialise in selling ends of ranges, discounted lines and slight seconds from previous seasons' merchandise. Savings vary but could be from 30–50%.'

On B4046 south of Ebbw Vale.

From Ebbw Vale: leave town, pass steel works on left. At large roundabout, go right for Festival Park.*

From the south via A467: turn on to A4046 for Ebbw Vale. Go through Cwm, then over river; at roundabout, go left for Festival Park.*

****Follow signs to Factory Shopping Village.***

Open: Mon–Sat 10–6; Sun 10–4. For Bank Holidays, please phone.
Closed: Easter Sunday; Christmas Day.
Cards: Amex, MasterCard, Switch, Visa.
Cars: Huge car-park.
Toilets: On-site, including for the disabled.
Wheelchairs: Easy access: no steps to medium sized shop.
Teas: Cafeteria on site.
Groups: Shopping groups always welcome but please phone first.
Transport: None to date.
Mail order: No.

This shop is in the new factory shopping village at Ebbw Vale for which final details are not available as we go to press (phone 01495 350010).

11 Haverfordwest Pembrokeshire

Thistle Trading Co.

Withybush Industrial Estate SA62 4BV
(01437) 763080

Wide range of clothing with something for all the family. Famous chainstore items at very reasonable prices, especially men's and boys' underwear; polo, rugby and sweatshirts.

'Genuine factory shop with many goods made by this company. The range is expanded by buying in from other manufacturers and clearance outlets.'

Just off the A40 on the north side of town.

From Fishguard coming south on A40: as you reach town, pass Ridgeway service station on right; at first roundabout, go left into the industrial estate, with CEM Day's Ford garage on left.*

From town centre: aim north on A40 for Fishguard. At large roundabout, exit for Withybush industrial estate.*

From Carmarthen on A40: do not go into town centre, but at two roundabouts stay on A40 around town. At third roundabout, exit for industrial estate. Follow signs for Sunday market for about ½ mile.*

****Go right in front of Bookers: the well signed shop is behind it.***

Open: Wed–Sat 9–5; Sun 10–4. Phone for Bank Holiday opening hours.
Closed: Monday, Tuesday; Christmas–New Year; factory holidays (phone to check).
Cards: No.
Cars: Own car-park.
Toilets: In showground across the road.
Wheelchairs: Ramp to spacious shop.
Changing rooms: Yes.
Teas: Café in garden centre ½ mile away.
Groups: Shopping groups welcome. Please phone Mrs Gillian Richards to arrange.
Transport: Haverfordwest rail station then taxi (about £3).
Mail order: No.

12 Margam Neath Port Talbot

ISE International Furniture

Kenfig Industrial Estate SA13 2PG
(01656) 742003/746586

A wide range of pine furniture including tables, chairs, coffee tables, nests of tables, occasional tables, bedroom furniture, television and video units.

'Firsts and seconds available here. Seconds are reduced by approximately 50%. Delivery can be arranged.'

On the B4283 west of Pyle.

From M4 exit 37: take A4229 towards Porthcawl. At first roundabout turn right on to B4283. Go under motorway, through the village of North Cornelly, then under the railway. Kenfig Industrial Estate is about 300 yds on the left. Go under the motorway; take first right. After 300 yds go right for well signed company, which is at far end.

Open: Fri and Sat 9–5.
Closed: Christmas–New Year.
Cards: MasterCard, Visa.
Cars: Large car-park.
Toilets: Yes.
Wheelchairs: Unfortunately no access, metal staircase to shop.
Teas: In Margam, Cornelly and Porthcawl.
Groups: Groups are welcome; please telephone Steve Jones beforehand.

13 Merthyr Tydfil

The Factory Toy Shop

Dragon Parc A, Abercanaid CF48 1PQ
(01685) 377011

Large range of brand name toys and gifts.

'Massive reductions on a large range of brand name end of line and trade seconds.'

On the south side of Merthyr, just off the old A470.

Going north towards Merthyr centre on the old A470 (disregard bypass): pass Hoover on the left then go left at next roundabout for Dragon Parc.*

Coming south from Merthyr centre for Cardiff: pass Ford garage on left; at roundabout take third exit (for Dragon Parc).*

****Go over bridge; at next roundabout go left for Dragon Parc A. Clearly marked company is 100 yds on left: shop is at the entrance to the UK Can factory building just inside barrier on right. Follow signs.***

Open: Tues–Sat 10–5; Sun 2–5.
Closed: Monday; Christmas–New Year.
Cards: No.
Cars: Own large car-park clearly signed.
Toilets: If necessary.
Wheelchairs: 4 steps to shop.
Teas: In Merthyr.
Groups: Groups welcome, please phone in advance.
Transport: Stagecoach bus nos. 70, 78, X78, 80, 81, 82 every 10 minutes from Merthyr bus station.

14 Merthyr Tydfil

O P Chocolate

Dowlais CF48 3TC
(01685) 723291

Selection of biscuits and confectionery, such as cream filled wafers, chocolate covered wafers and mallow products, eg *Snowballs*. Diabetic chocolate bars and wafers. Other food and drink items from time to time, eg Easter eggs and Christmas novelties.

'Stock changes frequently and is subject to availability. Some goods are misshapen.'

On the A4102 on north-eastern edge of Merthyr Tydfil.

Via Heads of the Valleys road (A465): at roundabout (Asda, large BP garage) take exit to Merthyr, Dowlais (A4102) downhill for about 1 mile. Go left just before next roundabout.

From town centre: take A4102 for Abergavenny. Go uphill for a mile: look for conspicuous OP Chocolate on right above roundabout.

From south: stay on A470 dual carriageway to Merthyr to far end. Take third turning at roundabout (A4060 to Abergavenny). Go uphill for 1 mile, go left at roundabout into Goatmill Road. After ½ mile take third exit off roundabout. OP Chocolate is on the right.

Use visitors' car-park: entrance to well signposted shop at rear.

Open: Mon–Fri 9–4.30.
Closed: Bank Holidays; Spring Bank Holiday week; Christmas–New Year.
Cards: None.
Cars: Factory car-park.
Toilets: In town.
Wheelchairs: Not really suitable – shop is small. One step.
Teas: In Merthyr.
Groups: Unfortunately you cannot see chocolate being made. Coach parties welcome to shop but please book first, mentioning this guide.
Transport: Local buses stop outside factory.
Mail order: No.

15 Merthyr Tydfil

Pendor (Clothing)

Mayphil Buildings, Goat Mill Road, Dowlais Industrial Estate CF48 3TF (01685) 722681 Fax (01685) 388013

Wide range of quality chainstore clothing for all the family: outerwear; ladies' lingerie, men's underwear; full range of children's wear 0–12 yrs. Specialists in sports brands eg *Adidas, Puma, Reebok, Nike, Umbro, Mizuno*. Full range of shoes.

'Very popular family owned business. Kiddies corner. Most goods are perfects at half normal retail price or less. If you can find same product cheaper anywhere in UK, we'll beat that price on the spot!'

Just off the A4102 on north-eastern edge of town.

Via Heads of the Valleys road (A465): at roundabout (with Asda/ large BP garage) turn off downhill (A4102) for Merthyr/Dowlais. Go through Dowlais and left at roundabout into Goat Mill Road.*

From town centre: take A4102 for Abergavenny. Go uphill for about a mile then go right at unmarked roundabout (OP Chocolate high up above far right side) into Goat Mill Road.*

***Mayphil Buildings are few hundred yards on right.**

From the south: stay on A470 dual carriageway to Merthyr to the end. At roundabout take third exit A4102 (A4060) to Abergavenny. Go uphill; at T-junction go left for Dowlais Industrial Estate. Follow road round; shop is on left.

Open: Mon–Fri 9.30–7; Sat 9.30–6; Sun 11–5. Bank Holidays.
Closed: Christmas, Boxing and New Year's Days.
Cards: MasterCard, Switch, Visa.
Cars: Large car-park.
Toilets: Yes.
Wheelchairs: Easy access, huge, spacious ground floor shop.
Changing rooms: Yes.
Teas: Vending machines in seating area.
Groups: Day, evening and weekend visits to shop arranged for groups. Coaches welcome any time: a phone call in advance is helpful. Discounts can be arranged for larger groups.
Transport: Local buses stop outside.
Mail order: No.

Choosing upholstered furniture

Glossy home magazines always advise readers to buy well made furniture but they never tell you how to *identify* it. Buying an upholstered three piece suite is somewhat akin to having your teeth fixed or roof mended. You never know how good your craftsman was until it is too late. Nor can you know, unless you ask the correct questions, what life-span your chairs are likely to have. The beautiful surface appearance can belie a poor interior construction.

We asked PF Collections of Long Eaton, a manufacturer of upholstered suites in Nottinghamshire, for a list of questions to ask before you buy.

1. Is the frame made of particle board or more substantial hard wood?

2. Is the frame stapled together of does it have a stronger construction with glue and dowels?

3. Is there a protective layer between the frame and covering fabric? *Without this protective layer, your upholstery fabric will wear out more quickly. You can tell if there is a protective layer by feeling the frame.*

4. Which springing system is used? *A no-sag springing system gives a firmer seat (not for use with feathers). Mesh-topped coil springs give a softer overall feel. Remember that the springing system and cushion have to work together to give the feel you want.*

5. Is there a choice of cushion filling? *Comfort is subjective and only you can choose from feathers, foam, fibre or feather/fibre mix.*

6. Is the upholstery fabric cut by hand to ensure a high degree of pattern matching? *A sign of quality is that the fabric matches all the way over the piece, ie bottom border, platform, inside and outside back, and cushions.*

7. What is the wearability of the upholstery fabric? *Choose from careful domestic through to heavy contract quality.*

In addition to upholstered furniture (and re-upholstery services), this book leads you to a wide range of pine, mahogany, yew and walnut furniture, fine period style pieces, farmhouse tables, kitchen and bathroom fittings, office and computer desks, beds, conservatory chairs and even luxurious swing hammocks.

You also have the opportunity to have a item made to fit your room, stained to match your other furniture or covered in your own fabric. And the shops arrange very reasonably priced delivery around the country.

16 Newtown Powys

Laura Ashley Sale Shop

Bear Lanes SY16 2QZ
(01686) 626549

Ladies' and children's clothing. Hats. Dress and furnishing fabrics and remnants. Cushions and cushion covers. Wallpapers. Some lamps, furniture such as sofas, and china.

Easy to find in the pedestrianised Bear Lane shopping precinct in the centre of town.

Open: Mon–Sat 9.30–5.30.
Closed: Check Bank Holidays and Christmas.
Cards: MasterCard, Visa.
Cars: Nearby car-park.
Toilets: In town.
Wheelchairs: Easy access.
Changing rooms: Yes.
Teas: In town.
Transport: Trains and buses to town.

17 Pontypridd Rhondda Cynon Taff

Alexon

Cardiff Road, Hawthorn CF35 7AA
(01443) 402615 (480673 after 4.30 & all day Sat)

Large range of clothing. *Alexon* ladies' wear. Co-ordinated outfits, separates, blouses, skirts, coats and leisurewear. *'Significant reductions in prices.'*

Two miles south-east of Pontypridd, on minor road which runs parallel to and immediately south of A470(T).

Coming south from Pontypridd on A470: turn off at first sign to Treforest Industrial Estate. From next roundabout, take 4th exit (sign to Hawthorn). Continue to building on left with sign 'Mead'.

Open: Mon–Sat 10–5.
Closed: Phone about Bank Holidays.
Cards: MasterCard, Visa.
Cars: Own large car-park.
Wheelchairs: Ramp to huge, spacious shop.
Changing rooms: Yes.
Teas: Teas in Pontypridd. Pub on this estate.
Transport: Pontypridd–Cardiff buses stop outside.

18 Pontypridd Rhondda Cynon Taff

Fabric World

Factory E6, Treforest Industrial Estate CF37 5YR
(01443) 843091

Large range of fabrics: dress and bridal fabrics, sheeting, furnishing prints, dralons, cotton, velvets and tapestries etc.

'Much reduced prices, including remnants. Curtain-making.'

Six miles north-west of M4 exit 32, 3 miles south of Pontypridd.

From Cardiff/M4: take A470(T) north for Pontypridd. At large roundabout, follows signs to Treforest Estate. Go along major road through estate to pub on left. Go left: huge shop 80 yds on left.

Open: Mon–Sat 9–5. (Thur until 7).
Closed: Phone for holidays.
Cards: MasterCard, Visa.
Cars: Own large car-park.
Toilets: Yes.
Wheelchairs: Easy access to huge shop on ground floor.
Teas: Hot drinks machine. Pub and restaurant close by.
Transport: Regular buses from Cardiff..

19 Porth Rhondda Cynon Taff

Royal Worcester & Spode

Unit D, Dinas Enterprise Centre, Cymmer Road CF39 9BS
(01443) 688120

Porcelain and fine bone china tableware, figurines and giftware. Also *Spode, Dartington Crystal, Cloverleaf* mats, *Pimpernel* mats, *Worcester Ornamental Studios, Lakeland Plaques*, and *Paw Prints*.

'Seconds sold at 25% off high street price.'

Just outside (west of) Porth, on the road to Tonypandy.

From Porth (Pioneer Superstore, which is on the one-way system): with the superstore on your left, aim for Tonypandy. Stay in the left lane then fork left. At mini-roundabout go right for Tonypandy B4278. After about 350 yds go right into the service road. Pass Integrasol and Remploy on right; Royal Worcester is in the next building, past the carpet shop.

From Tonypandy: go east to Porth, follow signs to Pontypridd. Go along Dinas Road (B4278) which becomes Cymmer Road. Look for tyre company on left: Royal Worcester is just past it.

Open: Mon–Sat 10–5. Some Bank Holidays – please phone to check.
Closed: Christmas and Boxing Days.
Cards: Amex, Diners, MasterCard, Visa.
Cars: In access road leading to shop.
Toilets: Pioneer superstore.
Wheelchairs: No steps, spacious shop.
Teas: Cafés in town.
Groups: Shopping groups and coaches welcome. Please book beforehand with shop manager.
Transport: Porth rail station or buses to Porth then short taxi ride.
Mail order: Yes. Any package, large or small, can be mailed world-wide.

20 Rhayader Powys

Welsh Royal Crystal

5 Brynberth Industrial Estate LD6 5EM
(01597) 811005

Manufacturers of hand-blown, hand-cut lead crystal. Wine glasses, tumblers, decanters, vases, bowls, jugs, perfume bottles.

'Company specialises in corporate trophies and special commissions. Shop sells factory seconds, other quality gifts and discontinued merchandise.'

From main cross-roads in centre of Rhayader: take A44 towards Leominster, passing clocktower in middle of road. Continue on this road out of town, following brown tourist signs, and go right to the Visitor Centre.

Open: Seven days: *April–Oct* 9.30–5; *Nov–March* 9.30–4.30.
Closed: Christmas and Boxing Days.
Cards: Amex, JCB, MasterCard, Visa.
Cars: Cars outside shop; also coach park.
Toilets: Yes, and for disabled.
Wheelchairs: Easy access via ramp.
Teas: Tea room for cakes, sandwiches, tea, coffee.
Tours: Daily guided tours when glass blowing (please check times): adults £2, OAPs, children £1; if not blowing (mainly weekends and Bank Holidays) £1 and 50p. Coaches welcome – phone first, mentioning this guide.
Transport: Post Bus from Llandrindod Wells (3 times/day).
Mail order: Yes, but no seconds sent; delivery charge.
Catalogue: Free.

Industrial Roots of Swansea

The Swansea city and dock areas are currently being rebuilt, landscaped and developed. The electronics and the motor industries have gained significance as major employers, during the steady decline of heavy industry. During the late 1800s, Swansea was the world centre of the non-ferrous metals refining industry; it was even known as 'Copperopolis'. Copper was initially imported from Cornwall but later a regular trade developed with South America; in the heyday of the copper works, ships brought copper from Chile, Cuba and the USA and carried Welsh coal on their return journey. The docks, railway and town all expanded. The coal industry increased in importance, as did tin-plating. The Mumbles Railway – opened in 1807 but closed in 1960 – was the first established passenger carrying (horse drawn) railway in the world.

Until recently the docks were derelict. The general purpose warehouse, built in 1904 for the Coast Lines Shipping Co., which now houses the Maritime & Industrial Museum was one of only two buildings left standing. However, this area has now been given new life with thriving residential and recreational developments and is proving increasingly attractive for locals and visitors.

This waterfront museum has floating maritime exhibits such as a lightship, tug, trawler and a 1906 lifeboat; old motorbikes and cars; a tramshed annexe with Swansea trams. It shows the history of the copper industry and has, as its major exhibit, the rebuilt and working equipment of a Welsh woollen mill.

Phone (01792) 650351 (fax 01792 654200) for opening dates/times of the different sections.

21 St Nicholas Pembrokeshire

Tregwynt Woollen Mill

SA62 5UX
(01348) 891644

Unique range of stylish bright blankets, rugs and double-weave bedspreads all woven here. Designer knitwear and a range of blanket/polar fleece garments for men and women made from fabrics woven here.

'This mill has been in the same family since 1912. It is in very attractive countryside and makes an interesting outing. Orders taken for weaving to customers' own colour preferences (minimum order 150 m). Knitwear from £30–£150; baby blankets from £20; king size blankets from £130.'

About 6 miles south-west of Fishguard.

Travelling south from Fishguard: turn right off the A487 (Fishguard–St David's road) after about 4½ miles, towards 'Abermawr'. There is also a sign to 'Tregwynt Woollen Mill'. Keep following the signs to this mill.

Open: Mon–Sat 9–5.
Closed: Christmas and New Year, mill closed but shop open, phone to check exact dates.
Cards: Amex, Delta, MasterCard, Switch, Visa.
Cars: Large car-park.
Toilets: Yes.
Wheelchairs: Easy access to shop and weaving shed.
Changing rooms: Yes.
Teas: Own cafe. (Easter–October).
Tours: You can walk round the weaving shed and also see the water wheel. Tregwynt Mill can be seen working Mon–Fri 9–4. Free entry.
Mail order: Yes.
Catalogue:. Free. Will make bespoke blankets in special sizes. Post anywhere in the world. No seconds by post.

22 Swansea

Abbey Woollen Mill

Swansea Maritime & Industrial Museum, Museum Square, Maritime Quarter SA1 1SM
(01792) 650351

Pure wool blankets, rugs, turnovers, shawls, scarves and knitting wools. All made in the mill from Welsh wools.

'Very competitive prices, good value. The mill was originally located in Port Talbot, then Neath. In 1974 all equipment was rebuilt in this museum and continues to produce traditional patterns.'

This museum is on the fascinating redeveloped quayside, close to the town centre.

From town centre: follow signs to Maritime Quarter. The Woollen Mill is inside the Maritime & Industrial Museum.

Open: Tues–Sun 10–5. Bank Holiday Mondays.
Closed: Monday; Christmas, Boxing and New Year's Days.
Cards: MasterCard, Visa.
Cars: Nearby car-parks.
Toilets: Yes.
Wheelchairs: Full access for disabled.
Teas: Lots of cafés and restaurants in Swansea.
Tours: See the processes of dyeing, carding, spinning and weaving on original machinery. Ensure you allow sufficient time to enjoy the whole of this museum.
Transport: Easy walking from city centre, bus and train stations.
Mail order: Goods can be posted on to customer.

23 Swansea

Clothing Factory Shop

Ystrad Road, Fforestfach
(01792) 584564

Huge selection of ladies' clothing: blouses, trousers, knitwear, jeans, jackets, coats, suits.

'Firsts, seconds and ends of lines.'

See our display advertisement opposite

From Swansea: take road to Carmarthen (A483), follow signs to Fforestfach. These die out, so then follow sign to 'Swansea Industrial Park' – go left when you see this sign. You will be in Kingsway.*

From M4 exit 47: follow signs to Swansea Industrial Park. Go right at traffic lights after Shell petrol station to Kingsway.*

****Go to bottom of hill; go left: this building, with big sign 'Kingsway Apparel', is several hundred yards on left, opposite Bookers on right, and just before Greyhound Stadium on right.***

Open: Mon–Sat 9–4.30. Bank Holidays.
Closed: Christmas and Boxing Days.
Cards: MasterCard, Visa.
Cars: Outside shop.
Toilets: No.
Wheelchairs: Eight steps.
Changing rooms: Yes.
Teas: Local cafés.
Groups: Shopping groups please phone in advance.

24 Treorchy Rhondda Cynon Taff

Burberrys

Ynyswen Road CF42 6EE
(01443) 772020

Wide range of men's and ladies' clothing including suits, jackets, trousers, blazers etc.

Easy to find in centre of Treorchy.

Coming along main road from south: pass Cardiff Arms Hotel on right, then Wynnes Garage. After three bungalows on right and post office on left, turn left into factory car-park.

Coming from the north: enter Ynyswen and just before off licence and post office on right, go right into factory car-park.

Open: Mon–Thur 9–4; Fri 9–2; Sat 9–1.30.
Closed: Please phone to check.
Cards: Amex, Diners, Mastercard, Visa.
Cars: Outside shop.
Toilets: Yes.
Wheelchairs: Easy access.
Changing rooms: Yes.
Teas: Locally.
Transport: Any bus to Treorchy.

See our entry opposite

25 Treorchy Rhondda Cynon Taff

Porth Innovations

Caemawr Industrial Estate
(01443) 441736 Fax (01443) 422617

Huge selection of Christmas decorations: artificial trees, garlands, baubles, wreaths etc. Floral displays & arrangements. Wedding decorations. Craft products. Wicker furniture.

In the industrial estate off the A4058 between Treorchy and Pentre.

From south: pass Elf petrol on right then take first left into Caemawr Industrial Estate (signed).*

From town centre/north: follow signs to Porth A4058. Cross pedestrian lights; go right for industrial estate just after right bend.*

****After bridge, go straight through gate and in front of factory go left following signs around one-way system to far end of factory.***

Open: Mon, Tues, Fri 10–4.30; Wed, Thur 10–5.30; Sat, Sun 10–4.
Closed: Christmas–New Year.
Cards: Access, Visa.
Cars: Large car-park.
Toilets: Yes.
Wheelchairs: No steps to huge shop.
Teas: Vending machines in seating area. Café on site.
Transport: Treorchy rail station 10 minutes. Local buses.
Mail order: No.

26 Welshpool Powys

Silver Scenes

Berriew SY21 8QA
(01686) 640695

Silver-plated photo frames, pill boxes, clocks, jewellery, thimbles, spoons and decorated perfume bottles. Gold-plated jewellery.

'Perfects sold at normal retail price, seconds at half price, sometimes larger reductions for discontinued items. Frames £5.50–£47; pill boxes £10.50–£20; clocks £30–£40; perfume bottles £5.25–£11.25; jewellery £5–£14.'

Berriew is 5 miles south-west of Welshpool and 10 miles north-east of Newtown, just west of the A483.

From the A483: follow signs into Berriew. Company is on left, clearly marked, as you reach the outskirts of the village.

Open: Mon–Fri 9–5.
Closed: Bank Holidays; three weeks at Christmas, please phone to check.
Cards: All major cards.
Cars: Outside shop or 5 minutes' away in village.
Toilets: Yes.
Wheelchairs: Please phone in advance to make arrangements.
Teas: Tea, coffee, cold drinks and biscuits all provided free of charge. Two pubs in Berriew.
Tours: Free tours around the factory for groups of 20–30: please book in advance with Michela Bath.
Transport: Bus or taxi from Welshpool station, 5 miles.
Mail order: Yes.
Catalogue:. Free catalogue for perfect items only. Items will be posted upon receipt of remittance (p&p extra).

Market days in South Wales

Ammanford	Fri outdoor general
Bargoed	Thur outdoor general
Blackwood	Tues Fri, Sat outdoor general
Caerphilly	Thur outdoor general
Cardiff	Sun outdoor/indoor general
Crymmych	Indoor general
Ebbw Vale	Fri outdoor general
Haverfordwest	Mon–Sat indoor general
Merthyr Tydfil	Mon–Sat indoor general. Tues, Sat outdoor general
Newtown	Tues, Sat indoor/outdoor general
Pontypridd	Tues, Wed, Fri, Sat indoor general. Wed, Sat outdoor
Port Talbot	Tues, Sat outdoor general
Swansea	Wed indoor general
Tonypandy	Fri outdoor general
Treorchy	Thur outdoor general

With thanks to World's Fair Ltd for allowing us to use information from their 'Markets Yearbook'.

Gallery Home Fashion

Welsh Royal Crystal

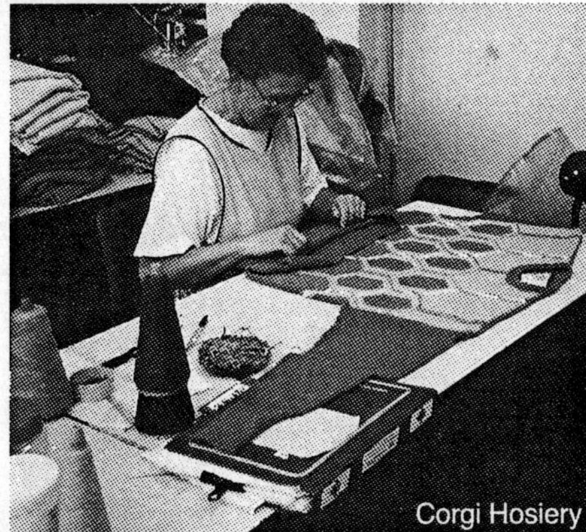
Corgi Hosiery

Tregwynt

Go island shopping and skip VAT!

The Channel Islands, which are located only 14 miles off the Normandy coast, are a mecca for shoppers – not least because VAT is not levied in these islands. (Valued Added Tax, currently at 17.5%, is added to just about everything in mainland Britain except children's clothes, books, newspapers and transport. Although the islands form part of the customs territory of the EC, they are not full member states and not part of the single market for VAT purposes.) That means that the factory shops located here offer even *better* value! You just have to remember that on your return to the mainland, you may import up to a value of £145 (apart from wines and spirits) before paying VAT on entry.

Some years ago we needed a complete break from the daily grind and from factory shopping ... so we eliminated all the places we associated with factory shops, and decided to fly to Jersey for a long winter weekend. But, as soon as we walked into the arrivals lounge, we came face to face with leaflets about companies selling woollens direct to the public. So, it proved a money-saving stay after all, and we came home wearing *genuine* guernseys.

Jersey Tourist Office,
St Helier
phone (01534) 878000

Guernsey Tourist Office
St Peter Port
phone (01481) 723552

States of Jersey Customs & Excise, 12 Caledonia Place, St Helier, Jersey JE2 3NG
phone (01534) 873561
fax (01534) 37060

HM Customs, Southampton
phone (01703) 330330

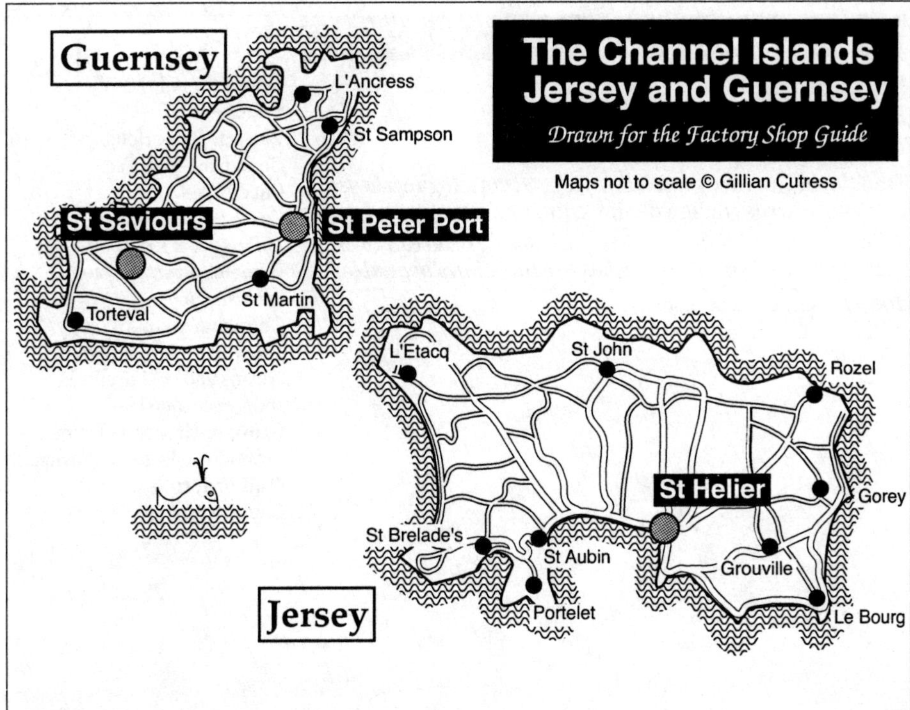

27 Guernsey : St Peter Port

Guernsey Woollens

Pitronnerie Road GY1 2RH
(01481) 727176

Guernseys in wool and cotton in various designs and colours; cardigans, jackets and gilets. Own design sweatshirts.

'Seconds as well as firsts sold here.'

North-east of St Peter Port, 20 minutes' walk from town.

Coming from Town Church: go left and walk east towards St Sampson along sea front for 10 minutes, then go left (by supermarket) into road called Bouet, go over traffic lights, then right into Pitronnerie Road Industrial Estate. Turn left again, and shop is at end on left.

Open: Mon–Fri 9–5.
Closed: Bank Holidays; 9 May; Christmas–New Year.
Cards: MasterCard, Visa.
Cars: Outside factory.
Toilets: Yes.
Wheelchairs: One step, medium-sized shop.
Changing rooms: No.
Teas: In St Peter Port.
Groups: Yes; please book in advance with Philip Walker.
Transport: By bus to Bouet and then 100 yds walk.

28 Guernsey : St Saviours

Le Tricoteur

Perelle Bay GY7 9QE
(01481) 64040

Traditional Guernsey sweaters; jackets; cotton guernseys; hats and scarves. Indigo denim, cotton knitwear.

'Discontinued styles and colours available at reduced prices. Most items are perfect but seconds are sometimes available.'

200 yds off the coast road.

Open: Mon–Fri 8–5. Sat 8.30–3.
Closed: Bank Holidays; Christmas–New Year.
Cards: Yes.
Cars: Large car-park.
Toilets: Ask if desperate.
Wheelchairs: One step to small shop.
Changing rooms: Yes.
Teas: In St Saviours. Ice creams and cold drinks in shop; seats outside.
Groups: Groups welcome.
Transport: Bus to St Saviours.
Mail order: Yes.
Catalogue: Free.

See our entry below

29 Jersey : St Helier

Summerland

Rouge Bouillon JE2 3ZA
(01534) 33511

Men's suits, shirts, ties, underwear, socks, trousers, knitwear, jackets, coats and shoes; ladies' skirts, blouses, knitwear, trousers, underwear, hosiery, coats and shoes.

'VAT free shopping at half the UK price. One stop shopping for men's and ladies' wear.'

See our display advertisement above

On the northern side of St Helier.

Travelling west along the Esplanade: turn right at traffic lights outside The Grand Hotel. Follow road and turn right at pedestrian lights at Cheapside. Take first major left turn into Rouge Bouillon. Go straight at lights; factory shop is on left, next door to ambulance station.

From town centre (on foot): walk past General Hospital, through Parade Gardens on to Rouge Bouillon.

Open: Mon–Fri 9–6; Sat 9–4.30.
Closed: Good Friday; Christmas, Boxing and New Year's Days.
Cards: MasterCard, Switch, Visa.
Cars: Ample car-parking.
Toilets: Yes.
Wheelchairs: Ramp to large shop.
Changing rooms: Yes.
Teas: Tea-room inside shop.
Groups: Groups welcome to shop. Tours of factory can be arranged, please phone.
Transport: Bus nos. 5 and 19 from Weighbridge bus station.
Mail order: No.

Jersey and Guernsey knitwear

The knitting industry in the Channel Islands dates back centuries. Queen Elizabeth I is reputed to have had her stockings knitted here. With the abundance of sheep on the islands, used for meat and wool, spinning and knitting were time-consuming occupations for men, women and children. So important were these activities, that as long ago as 1603 an act was passed ordering local people to cease knitting at the time of harvest and during the season of seaweed gathering (for fertiliser).

The popularity of jerseys and guernseys has flourished, now with the advantage of modern machinery. Traditional designs are still produced and all items are made in 100% pure wool (albeit bought from Bradford now that the sheep population in the islands has declined). Nine operations go into the making of the garments, all of which are finished by hand by skilled local women.

Sturdy knitwear was originally produced to combat the freezing temperatures of the Newfoundland cod fishing grounds. Jerseys and guernseys are recognised throughout the world as warm and serviceable. Guernseys have individual and distinctive patterns on the shoulders depicting rope ladders and ripples on the sand. The story goes that if a seaman drowned, it was possible to identify the island or particular parish in that island he came from.

Although we hope that this function will not be needed, we strongly recommend that you stock up with this attractive knitwear while you have the chance!

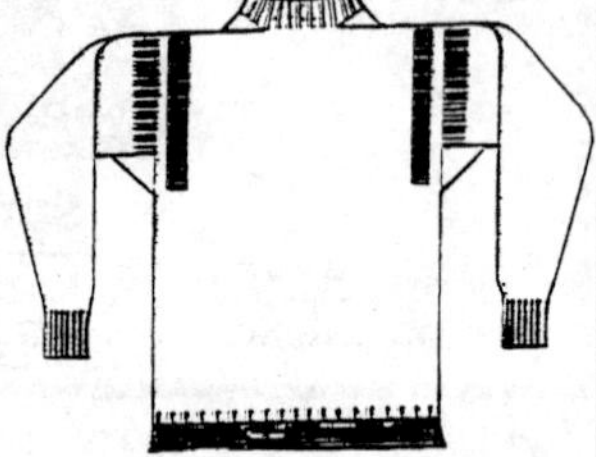

With thanks to Guernsey Woollens

Go south-west & save a fortune

South-West England, in the context of this book, covers the large and attractive area of Cornwall, Devon, Somerset, (former) Avon, Gloucestershire and Wiltshire, and continues into Oxfordshire too. If you are a stranger to these counties, you will find very worthwhile shops. If you live here, you have a host of exciting shops on your doorstep in which to save money. New shops include those selling exquisite tableware, fine silk ties and ladies' silk fashions as well as bathroom accessories, curtains, candles and many other items. With a total of nearly 70 shops in the area, plus a couple of large factory outlet centres, it will take some time for even the most devoted shoppers to make their way around!

Almost every town has a Tourist Information Office. In our experience, they are extremely helpful.
Here are a few numbers:
Bath (01225) 477101
Bournemouth (01202) 451700
Bristol (0117) 9260767
Cheltenham (01242) 522878
Exeter (01392) 265700
Minehead (01643) 702624
Poole (01202) 253253
Salisbury (01722) 334956
Taunton (01823) 336344
Truro (01872) 274555
Warminster (01985) 218548
Wells (01749) 672552

Much has happened to retailing in the last 100 years. Now, as regular factory shoppers may have noticed, even factory shops have given up their customary reticence, and are beginning to advertise on radio and television. In the early nineteenth century, brand awareness hardly existed. A shop keeper received deliveries from the manufacturer in bulk, and goods were stored in wooden chests and sacks, to be repacked when needed.

Towards the end of the 1800s, however, manufacturers became more inventive. They began to distribute *pre-packaged* goods to the retailer, which enabled manufacturers to promote products with logos, slogans and artwork, and gave them more freedom in naming them. This new product awareness led to a huge increase in advertising campaigns. Products were sold to consumers who recognised the packaging as they walked into shops.

To learn about this history, visit the fascinating Museum of Advertising & Packaging in Gloucester docks. Many childhood memories will come flooding back with the displays of bygone packs, tins and bottles (01452) 302309.

Museum of Advertising & Packaging

While in the Gloucester and Hereford area, extend your shopping to some truly local products: cider and perry. Fifteen producers, ranging from those large enough to supply supermarkets down to hobby operators who can only make their drinks by taking their fruit to colleagues for processing, have formed an association to promote their products – which you can usually buy direct from them. Some show visitors around. Pick up a leaflet showing the cider trail from local tourist offices.

Hereford Museum of Cider

30 Andover Hants

Croydex

Unit 27, Chantry Centre SP10 1LS
(01264) 336018

Large range of bathroom and household accessories including bath panels, cabinets, mirrors, toilet seats, towel rings and rails, soap dishes, bath mats, shower and window curtains, Austrian blinds, trays, chopping boards, place mats and coasters, wine coolers, ice buckets, pillows etc.

'Goods made for well known chainstores: at least 40% off normal retail prices. Firsts, seconds, samples and ends of ranges.'

From all directions aim for town centre.

The Chantry Centre is a pedestrianised shopping precinct in the town centre. The shop is close to the multi-storey car-park, opposite Le Café and by Boots.

Open: Mon–Sat 9–5.30.
Closed: Most Bank Holidays; Christmas, Boxing and New Year's Days.
Cards: MasterCard, Visa.
Cars: Multi-storey car-park.
Toilets: Outside shopping mall.
Wheelchairs: No steps.
Teas: Café opposite shop.
Groups: Groups welcome.
Transport: Any bus or train to Andover.
Mail order: No.

31 Bampton Devon

Origin

Station Road Trading Estate EX16 9NF
(01398) 331704

Large selection of ladies' dresses, soft suits and separates in *Liberty of London, Truella, Rose & Hubble* and other select fabrics. Garments in denim and silk.

'First quality garments only in predominantly natural fibres (sizes 10–20). Extremely well priced.'

See our display advertisement opposite

West of the town centre, near the public car-park.

From town centre crossroads: take B3277 towards South Molton. Go left at sign to trading estate, take first left and first right. Factory is to the right.

Open: Mon–Fri 9–5; Sat 9–1.
Closed: Christmas–New Year.
Cards: Delta, MasterCard, Switch, Visa.
Cars: Outside factory and public car-park.
Toilets: Yes.
Wheelchairs: No steps.
Changing rooms: Yes, seven.
Teas: In town.
Groups: Coaches welcome.
Transport: None.
Mail order: No.

See our entry opposite

32 Banbury Oxon

A & J Fabrics

5 Malthouse Walk OX16 8PW
(01295) 275550

Large range of upholstery and furnishing fabrics: cottons, linens, damasks, velvets etc. Nets, voiles, calico, interlinings, waddings, linings. Haberdashery, fringing. Curtain rails/ poles and accessories. Cushion covers and fillers. Foam to order.

'About 2000 rolls in stock. Fabrics from £4.99 per metre. Curtain-making service with free measuring, advice & design.'

See our display advertisement on p. 195

This shop is in the town centre opposite Littlewoods' side entrance (in the Cherwell Centre).

Open: Mon–Sat 9–5; Sun & Bank Holidays 10–4.
Closed: Easter Sunday; Christmas & Boxing Days.
Cards: All major debit and credit cards.
Cars: NCP car-park 15 yds from shop.
Toilets: Within 60 yds.
Wheelchairs: One step, sizeable shop.
Teas: Various places in town.
Groups: Shopping groups welcome, no need to phone. Can arrange evening visits.
Transport: Any bus or train to Banbury. Bus and train stations 5 minutes' walk.
Mail order: No.

Banbury Oxon

Late Entry

där lighting

Wildmere Industrial Estate OX16 7JZ
(01295) 259391

Wide range of traditional and contemporary light fittings: flush lights, wall washers and brackets; ceiling fittings; low voltage halogen products; table lamps and shades; outdoor lighting. Selection of complementary decorative pieces, eg photo frames and book ends.

'We are one of UK's foremost lighting manufacturers, supplying most major high street retailers and 700 independent shops. 800+ items in current range displayed here. Always cut price samples and variety of specials. Current ranges at discounted prices.'

Wildmere Industrial Estate is beside M40 exit 11.

From M40 exit 11: follow signs to Banbury; at first roundabout go right, signposted Wildmere Industrial Estate.*

From Banbury: follow signs to M40; turn left at last roundabout before motorway.*

****Wildmere Industrial Estate is a loop road; follow it around until you see factory.***

Open: Mon–Sat 9.30–5.30. For Bank Holidays please phone.
Closed: Christmas and Boxing Days. Some Bank Holidays.
Cards: MasterCard, Visa.
Cars: In factory car-park.
Toilets: Yes.
Wheelchairs: Easy access to ground floor.
Teas: Cafés in town.
Groups: No factory tours, but shopping groups welcome.
Transport: Unfortunately none.
Mail order: Yes.
Catalogue: £5, refundable if returned in good order. Phone for details.

33 Barnstaple Devon

C H Brannam

Roundswell Industrial Estate EX31 3NK
(01271) 343035

Huge range of terracotta pottery for the home (kitchen and table) and garden in all sizes. Glazed and decorated stoneware.

'North Devon's oldest tourist attraction. Factory seconds shop with highly competitive prices.'

South of town and the river Taw, off B3232 and new bypass.

From town centre, Braunton via A361 and Lynton via A39: follow signs to Bideford/Torrington. Pass large Sainsbury's, go left at next roundabout, follow brown signs to Brannam's Pottery.

From the east on A361 and south on A377: follow brown signs to pottery as you reach bypass.

From Bideford on A39: go left at roundabout with brown signs to pottery.

Once in estate go right to pottery.

Open: Mon–Sat 9–5; *also May–Sept:* Sun 10–4; Bank Holidays.
Closed: Christmas–New Year.
Cards: MasterCard, Visa.
Cars: Own large car-park.
Toilets: Yes, and baby changing room.
Wheelchairs: Easy access including to restaurant.
Teas: Own restaurant.
Tours: Pottery tours Mon–Fri and Bank Holidays 9–4.15. £3.50 adults, £2.90 OAPs, £2.25 children. Throw your own pot to take away! Tour also includes museum visit.
Transport: Free bus service from Barnstaple town centre to Sainsbury's then short walk; or bus no. 12 either to Sainsbury's or Roundwell Estate. Barnstaple train station.
Mail order: No.

34 Barnstaple Devon

Croydex

RGB Building, Riverside Road, Pottington Industrial Estate EX31 1QN
(01271) 378555

Wide range of kitchen and bathroom accessories in natural, antique pine and mahogany finish, including bath panels, cabinets, mirrors, towel rings and rails. Shower and window curtains, Austrian blinds, chopping boards, place mats and coasters, wine coolers, ice buckets, bath mats and pillows.

'Goods made here for well known chainstores: at least 40% off normal retail prices. Firsts, seconds, samples, ends of ranges etc.'

NB This shop has moved locally.

From town centre (bus station): take road to Braunton, keeping left at Mermaid Cross roundabout and over Rolle Quay bridge. Continue along Rolle Quay into Braunton Road. Pottington industrial estate is on left behind Superbowl.

Open: Mon–Sat 9–5.
Closed: Bank Holidays; Christmas, Boxing and New Year's Days.
Cards: MasterCard, Visa.
Cars: Ample parking outside.
Toilets: No.
Wheelchairs: Access difficult, but assistance gladly given. Medium sized shop.
Teas: Cafés, restaurants and pubs in town.
Groups: Groups welcome but no factory tours.
Transport: Bus nos. 3 and 308 from Barnstaple bus station stop at Pottington Industrial Estate 5 minutes' walk.
Mail order: No.

35 Barnstaple Devon

Factory Fabric Warehouse

Units 4–5 Roundswell Industrial Estate EX32 9DD
(01271) 327755

Upholstery and furnishing fabrics: cottons, linens, damasks, velvets etc. Nets, voiles, calico, interlinings, waddings, linings. Haberdashery, fringing. Curtain rails/poles, accessories. Cushion covers and fillers. Ready-made curtains. Foam cut to shape.

'Curtain-making service, free quotations in local customers' homes. About 2000 rolls in stock. Fabrics from £2.99 per metre.'

See our display advertisement on p. 195

South of town and the river Taw, off the B3232 and near the bypass.

From town centre and places north: go south over river; follow signs to Bideford/Torrington. Take B3232 for Torrington. Keep straight till you see large Sainbury's complex on left. Drive into Sainsbury's car-park. Go past Boots and this shop is in next unit.

From directions south and the bypass: get on to B3232 towards Barnstaple. At the roundabout by Sainsbury's, go right into shopping complex. Go past Boots and this shop is in next unit.

Open: Mon–Sat 9.30–5; Sun 10–4. Bank Holidays 10–4.
Closed: Phone for Christmas and New Year dates.
Cards: Access, Connect, Delta, Switch, Visa.
Cars: Large car-park.
Toilets: Nearby.
Wheelchairs: No steps, ground floor shop.
Teas: In Sainsbury's.
Groups: Shopping groups welcome, no need to phone.
Transport: Buses from various towns stop outside.

36 Barnstaple Devon

LS & J Sussman (Shirt Manufacturers)

Riverside Road, Pottington Industrial Estate
(01271) 379305

Shirts, men's wear, ladies' wear, children's wear, bedding, towels, etc.

'Ends of ranges and good seconds all at factory prices.'

On the west side of Barnstaple.

From the town centre: take the A361 heading west towards Ilfracombe, following signs to Pottington Industrial Estate. Beyond the Barnstaple Hotel turn left; and at the end of the road turn right into Riverside Road. Sussmans can be found approximately 200 yds on the left. Use the second turning marked 'entrance' and the factory shop is on the left.

Open: Tues–Thur 9–4.45; Fri–Sat 9–2.
Closed: Monday; Bank Holidays; Christmas–New Year. Please phone if in doubt over holiday periods.
Cards: MasterCard, Switch, Visa.
Cars: Own car-park at rear of factory.
Toilets: Facilities not always available.
Wheelchairs: No access.
Changing rooms: Yes.
Teas: In town.
Groups: No factory tours. Groups of shoppers welcome – no need to phone.
Transport: Barnstaple–Braunton/Ilfracombe buses stop at industrial estate entrance.
Mail order: No.

37 Bath Somerset

Roper Rhodes

Unit 5, Brassmill Trading Estate BA1 3JF (01225) 481815

Wide range of bathroom accessories: wooden toilet seats, bath panels, wall cabinets, toilet roll holders, towel rails & free-standing towel stands, wood linen bins, mug & toothbrush holders, soap dishes, loo brush holders, mirrors, shelves etc.

'An Aladdin's cave! Low prices on slight imperfects and ends of ranges. Solid wood toilet seats from £7.50. Solid oak bath panels from £79.95, solid wood panels from £24.95, MDF panels from £19.95, vanity units from £49.95 (with basin £89.95). Shower shelves from £5.95; bath racks from £9.95; brass, chrome or gold plate and wood accessories from 99p.'

West of Bath on industrial estate near the river Avon.

Coming from Bristol on A4 and Wells on A39: at first traffic lights follow signs to Bath (A4). Go over river bridge and take first right immediately after Murco petrol on right.

From Bath, the east, M4 and south-east: take A36 for Bristol. Continue until you pass Mitsubishi and BMW garages on right: take next right at lights (Windsor Bridge Road). Pass gas works on right; go left at T-junction. Continue for a mile, forking left at lights, passing Citroën and Rover on left; go left in front of Murco.*

****Pass Bath Marina on right and take next right for Brassmill Lane Trading Estate. Shop is about 120 yds on left.***

Open: Mon–Fri 9–5; Sat 9–4.
Closed: Bank Holidays; Christmas–New Year.
Cards: MasterCard, Visa.
Cars: Ample free parking.
Toilets: Ask if desperate.
Wheelchairs: Shop is upstairs on first floor.
Teas: Terrific selection of refreshments in Bath.
Groups: Groups welcome to shop (please book in advance if coming on Saturday). No factory tours.
Transport: Train to Bath; park-&-ride stop 10 minutes' walk.
Mail order: No.

38 Bicester Oxon

Bicester Village

OX6 7WD
(01869) 323200

End-of-season designer fashions, men's and children's wear, tableware, shoes and more.

'Over 50 shops owned by famous British and international brands, bringing Bond Street style to Bicester Village. Discounts of 25–60% off retail prices. For a list of shops, see p. 122.'

Easy to find on the outskirts of Bicester.

From M40 exit 9: take A41 two miles towards Bicester. At the first roundabout follow signs to Village Retail Park, clearly visible past the superstore.

Open: Mon–Sun (including Bank Holidays) 10–6.
Closed: Christmas Day.
Cards: All shops accept major credit cards.
Cars: Free parking for 675 cars and 12 coaches.
Toilets: Yes, and for the disabled.
Wheelchairs: Easy access to all shops.
Changing rooms: Where applicable.
Teas: Facilities on site.
Groups: Coach parties always welcome.
Transport: Bicester North rail station 15 minutes' walk.

39 Bloxham Oxon

The Weavers Shop

Barford Road OX15 4HB
(01295) 721225

Wide range of Wilton, broadloom and tufted carpets. New range of natural floor coverings, including sisal, seagrass and coir. Wools for weaving, knitting and tapestry work. Rugs, canvas, carpet-fitting accessories.

'Expert advice willingly given, together with accessories and delivery service. List of recommended fitters. Perfects, seconds and ends of ranges.'

Bloxham is on the A361 (Chipping Norton–Banbury road).

Coming north on A361 from Chipping Norton: as you reach Bloxham, pass Esso station on right then take next right (Barford Road) towards Adderbury.*

From Banbury: take A361 south-west. Keep straight through Bloxham, passing church and Old School House Hotel on left, then go left for Adderbury.*

****Keep going straight till you see Steele's Carpets on left. The shop, clearly marked, is at back.***

From the Barfords: as you reach village outskirts, Steele's are on right.

Open: Mon–Sat 9–5.
Closed: Bank Holidays; Christmas–New Year.
Cards: MasterCard, Visa.
Cars: Large car-park.
Toilets: Yes.
Wheelchairs: Easy access; large shop.
Teas: Pubs in the village and locally.
Tours: Factory tours by appointment. Groups of shoppers welcome but preferably book first.
Transport: Local buses from Banbury.
Mail order: No.

40 Bodmin Cornwall

Silken Ladder Factory Shops

Victoria Square, Roche PL26 8LY
(01726) 891092

Huge range of ladies' blouses and tops. Also co-ordinates, skirts, nightwear. Cotton, polyester, polycotton, silk etc. Hand embroidery, fine cutwork and plain everyday designs in wide price range. Accessories. Men's jackets, blazers, trousers; ties by *Kinloch Anderson*, *Frank Theak* and *Roskilly*; shirts by *Monckton* and *Don Smith*. Remnants. Extended shop with more *Silken Ladder* and *La Scala Di Seta* goods, *Kinloch Anderson* and *Westerlind* skirts, *Hourihan* and *Acorn* jackets, *Arabella* lingerie. *Balmoral* knitwear and sweatshirts. Enlarged section for large sizes up to 30.

'Line ends, samples, seconds and "experiments" at good reductions. Blouses from £2.99. Current range at full price from £14–£120. Many lines at bargain prices. Up to size 30. Supply groups including choirs, restaurants, hotels and tour guides.'

On A30, 6 miles west of Bodmin and 6 miles north of St Austell.
The shop is next to the BP petrol station, on the north side of the road opposite the Victoria Inn.

Open: Mon–Sat (including Bank Holidays) 9.30–5.30; Sun 10–5.
Closed: Good Friday; Easter; Christmas and Boxing Days.
Cards: Diners, JCB, MasterCard, Switch, Visa.
Cars: Plenty of parking in front and behind. Please don't block filling station access.
Toilets: No, but nearby.
Wheelchairs: Easy access.
Changing rooms: Yes.
Teas: Little Chef 400 yds; Victoria Inn for food opposite.
Groups: Shopping groups welcome; please book an evening appointment with Hilary or Brian Spong.
Mail order: No.

Clarks

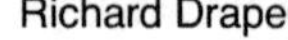
Richard Draper

Great Western Village

41 Bourton-on-the-Water Gloucs

Warwick Fabrics Clearance Shop

Hackling House, Industrial Park GL54 2EN
(01451) 820772

Own-label furnishing fabrics: cotton satins, co-ordinating linen unions in patterns and plains plus woven jacquards. Linings, chintz, cushions, laptrays, muslins, moirés; heading tapes, fringes, cords, threads, tracks and poles.

'Perfect discontinued designs and some seconds. Discontinued designs from £1.99 per metre for cottons (originally about £17.60). Ends of rolls from £1.50 per metre. Current ranges also available. Most fabrics at 50–75% less than high street prices. Can recommend local seamstresses for curtain-making.'

On the northern side of the village, off the A429.

Coming south from Stow: just before you reach Bourton, follow sign left into Bourton Industrial Park.*

Coming north on A429: keep straight for Stow (don't go right into Bourton village); pass Coach and Horses Inn on right then take first right (for Bourton Industrial Park).*

****At first mini-roundabout go right; go over two speed humps. Shop is clearly visible on left.***

Open: Mon–Fri 10–5; Sat 10–2.
Closed: Bank Holidays; Christmas–New Year.
Cards: Eurocard, MasterCard, Switch, Visa.
Cars: Car-park next to shop.
Toilets: In village.
Wheelchairs: One step to large ground floor shop.
Teas: Croft Cottage Restaurant in centre of village.
Groups: Groups always welcome to shop (larger groups please phone first).
Mail order: Yes. Samples of fabrics gladly sent.

42 Bovey Tracey Devon

House of Marbles and Teign Valley Glass

The Old Pottery, Pottery Road TQ13 9DR
(01626) 835358

Decorative glass gifts, vases, glasses, scent bottles etc. Traditional games and toys; the largest collection of marbles in the world. Also men's gifts, kitchen ideas, hundreds of toys and games, many from local craftsmen and others from all over world.

'Firsts and seconds in glass, including one-off practice pieces, at discounted prices.'

At the southern end of Bovey Tracey.

From A38: turn on to A382 towards Bovey Tracey. After about 2 miles fork left at roundabout with sign to Pottery Road. Shop about 100 yds on right.

From town centre: follow signs to Newton Abbot; at roundabout at southern end of town, follow signs to Pottery Road.

Open: Seven days a week 9–5.
Closed: Christmas and Boxing Days. First week of January.
Cards: MasterCard, Visa.
Cars: Own large car-park.
Toilets: Yes.
Wheelchairs: Easy access, no steps.
Teas: Own coffee shop/ restaurant.
Groups: Self guided tours with free leaflets.
Transport: Bovey Tracey –Newton Abbot buses pass by.
Mail order: Yes.
Catalogue: Free catalogue sent upon receipt of written request. No marbles sent out.

43 Bridgwater Somerset

Sedgemoor Shoes

River Lane, Dunwear TA7 OAB
(01278) 427662

Made-to-measure shoes in wide range of leathers, colours, styles and fittings. Free measuring and quotations. Some ready-made shoes.

'Small business specialising in problem feet. Personal service. Occasional seconds.'

East of Bridgwater off A372 (Bridgwater–Weston Zoyland road).

From Bridgwater on A372: pass signs to college on left; as open country begins follow sign to Dunwear on right. Travel by the river under motorway; after you round a corner with phone kiosk on right, industrial estate is on left.

From Weston Zoyland going north-west for Bridgwater: after 1½ miles go left to Dunwear; after 1 mile, company is on right.

Open: Mon–Fri 9–5.
Closed: Bank Holidays; Spring Bank Holiday week; last week July/first week August; 2 weeks at Christmas.
Cards: No.
Cars: In front of shop.
Toilets: Yes.
Wheelchairs: Easy access, small ground floor shop.
Teas: In Bridgwater.
Groups: Offer personal service so not really suitable for groups. Individuals may be able to see shoes being made.
Transport: Taxi from Bridgwater.
Mail order: Yes.
Catalogue: Brochure available.

Poole Pottery

Early's of Witney

House of Marbles

Bristol Carpets

44 Bristol : Clifton *see map next page*

Factory Fabric House

40–42 Regent Street, Clifton BS8 2XP
(0117) 970 6512

Large stock of upholstery and furnishing fabrics: cottons, linens, damasks, velvets etc. Voiles, calico, interlinings, waddings, linings. Haberdashery, fringing. Curtain rails/ poles, accessories. Cushion covers and fillers. Ready-made curtains.

'1000 plus rolls in stock. Curtain making service. Prices from £1.99 per metre.'

See our display advertisement on p. 195

Clifton is a suburb on the west side of Bristol.

From the east end of Clifton suspension bridge: go along Suspension Bridge Road B2139, then follow the main road right (Clifton Down Road). Just after zebra crossing, shop is on left (facing Princess Victoria Street and the Quandrant pub).

From the centre of Bristol: go up Park Street; turn left at top of Park Street. Once in the small one-way system, turn right then left towards Clifton and fork left again towards Clifton. Go along Queen's Road; at T-junction turn right. Shop is on right (facing Princess Victoria Street and the Quandrant pub).

Open: Seven days a week: Mon–Sat 9.30–5; Sun & Bank Holidays 10–4.
Closed: Please phone for Christmas closures.
Cards: Access, Connect, Delta, Switch, Visa.
Cars: Local streets.
Toilets: Yes.
Wheelchairs: Three steps to medium sized shop. Help gladly given to customers with prams or wheelchairs.
Teas: Lots of tea shops and wine bars in Clifton.
Groups: Shopping groups welcome; please phone first.
Transport: Bus no. 8 from city centre.

45 Bristol : Bedminster *see map next page*

Calico

78–82 Bedminster Parade BS3 4HK
(0117) 953 3663

Huge range of printed and plain furnishing and upholstery fabrics. Polycottons for duvets and bed covers. Many items bought in from major store clearances.

'Many fabrics at 50% discount. Specialise in sale of fabric from rolls. First and second qualities.'

Bedminster Parade is part of A38 just south of River Avon.

From all directions (except A38 from Taunton): follow signs to City Centre; join Inner City Circuit Road. Follow signs to south/ Taunton A38. At large roundabout over river follow signs to Bedminster: shop is 250 yds on left in an ordinary row of shops opposite huge Asda.

From Taunton on A38: as you come into the city centre, look for huge Asda on left: shop is on right, opposite end of Asda building.

Open: Mon–Sat 9.30–5.
Closed: Bank Holidays; Christmas–New Year.
Cards: Delta, MasterCard, Switch, Visa.
Cars: Limited parking in street. Large car-parks nearby.
Toilets: Opposite.
Wheelchairs: Easy access to large shop.
Teas: Local cafés and pubs.
Groups: Shopping groups welcome – please book first.
Transport: Local buses.

46 Bristol : St George

see map below

Bristol Carpets

Weavers Mill, Crew's Hole Road BS5 8AV
(0117) 954 1011

Ends of rolls, remnants and sub-standard stock and a wide range of Axminster, Wilton and tufted carpets.

'All carpets at big savings on shop prices. Free quotations for fitting throughout UK. £5 delivery charge in 10-mile radius.'

On the east side of Bristol, halfway towards Kingswood.

From centre of Bristol: take A420 east for Chippenham.*

From M4 exit 19: take M32 for Bristol. At large roundabout (M32 exit 3), turn south, Easton Way. At next roundabout go left on to A420 for Chippenham.*

****At St George's Park traffic lights, go right into Blackswarth Road, pass the Three Crowns on right then turn left into Crew's Hole Road. Company entrance is visible shortly on left.***

Coming west into Bristol on A420: go through Kingswood, then downhill into St George. Pass Action petrol on right. At traffic lights, go left (Blackswarth Road) for St Annes/Brislington. Pass the Three Crowns on right ; go left into Crew's Hole Road. Company entrance is visible shortly on left.

Open: Mon–Sat 9–5. Most Bank Holidays 10–4, please phone to check.
Closed: Christmas and Boxing Days.
Cards: Amex, MasterCard, Visa.
Cars: Own large car-park.
Toilets: Yes.
Wheelchairs: Easy access to huge showroom.
Teas: Vending machines for hot and cold drinks and snacks in seating area.
Transport: Local buses stop in St George's Park then 5 minutes' walk.
Mail order: Yes.

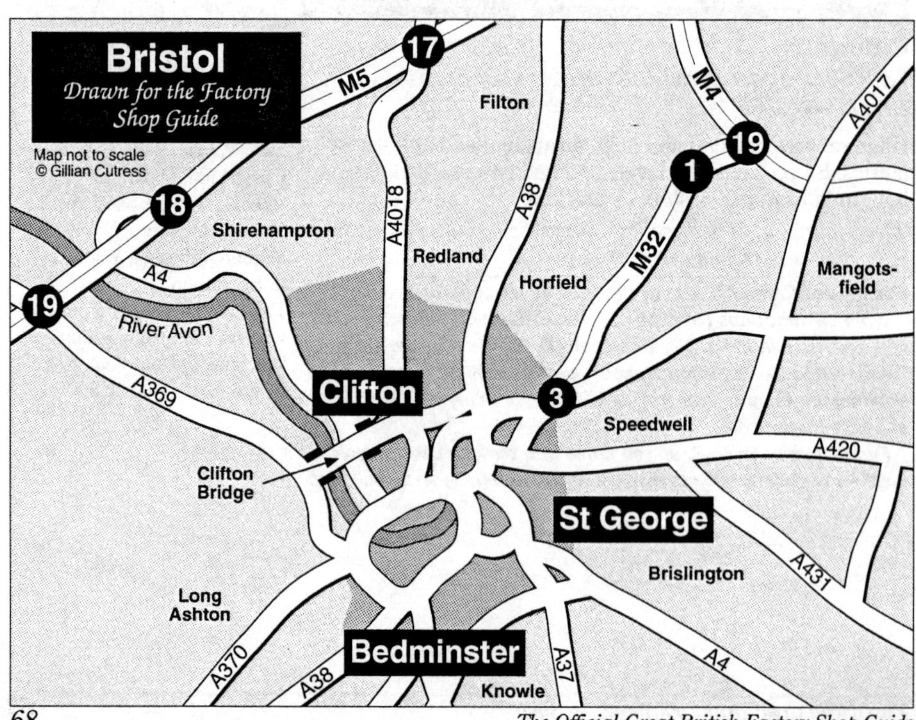

47 Burford Oxon

Just Fabrics

Burford Antiques Centre, Cheltenham Road OX18 4JA
(01993) 823391

Wide range of furnishing fabrics: own range of linen unions, weaves, checks and stripes. Florals and chintzes, chenilles, damasks, tapestries, jaquards, silks, moirés. Some designer clearance and seconds.

'Designer fabric clearance shop. Large stocks, all great value. Fabrics from £3–£25 per metre.'

Clearly visible on the A40, south of Burford and 50 yds west of the major roundabout where A361 (Burford–Lechlade road) crosses the A40.

Shop is on the south-west side of junction, diagonally opposite the Cotswold Gateway Hotel and beside Burford Antiques.

Open: Mon–Sat 9.30–5.30; Sun 2–5. Bank Holidays.
Closed: Christmas–New Year.
Cards: MasterCard, Visa.
Cars: In forecourt.
Toilets: In Burford.
Wheelchairs: No steps to new large showroom.
Teas: Lots of hotels, old pubs and tea shops in Burford.
Groups: Shopping groups welcome if they phone first.
Transport: Buses from Oxford.
Mail order: Yes.
Catalogue: No. Please ring for our mail order and swatch enquiry service.

48 Cheltenham Gloucs

Cotswold Fabric Warehouse

5 Tewkesbury Road GL51 9AH
(01242) 255959

Upholstery and furnishing fabrics: cottons, linens, damasks, velvets etc. Nets, voiles, calico, interlinings, waddings, linings. Haberdashery, fringing. Curtain rails/poles and accessories. Cushion covers and fillers. Ready-made curtains. Foam cut to shape. Dress fabrics.

'Measuring, fitting and curtain making services. About 4000 rolls in stock.'

See our display advertisement on p. 195

Tewkesbury Road (A4019) leads north-west from Cheltenham town centre.

From town: take the A4019 for about a mile. Pass the church on the left, then this shop is next (before Kwik-Fit and B&Q).

Going towards Cheltenham on A4019: go over railway, pass B&Q then Kwik-Fit on right. This shop is next.

Open: Mon–Sat 9–5; Sun and Bank Holidays 10–4.
Closed: Christmas, Boxing and New Year's Days.
Cards: Access, Connect, Delta, Switch, Visa.
Cars: Own car-park.
Toilets: Nearby supermarket.
Wheelchairs: No steps.
Teas: Lots of tea shops in Cheltenham.
Groups: Shopping groups welcome (larger groups please phone first).
Transport: Buses from town centre, or taxi.

49 Cheltenham Gloucs

Marlborough Tiles

14 Montpellier Street GL50 1SX *(01242) 224870*

Wall tiles made by *Marlborough Tiles*; floor tiles imported from elsewhere.

'In the Montpellier area where individual boutiques mix happily with antique and craft shops. Prices from £3.24 per sq yd for seconds. Wall tiles are seconds and discontinued lines (may be perfect); floor tiles mostly perfects at reduced prices.'

In town centre. You can park in any town centre car-park.

From Gloucester on A40: follow signs to town centre. Pass Gulf petrol on right, go up tree-lined road to island, The Rotunda; take second left, follow signs to Montpellier Street (first on right). Shop is about 100 yds on left.

Coming from east on A40, and from Cirencester on A435: go straight at traffic lights: follow signs to town centre/Town Hall.*

From Stroud on A46: pass Cheltenham College on right. Follow signs to town centre and Town Hall.*

****From Town Hall on your left in one-way street, follow signs to Gloucester A40 and M5 (do not stay on inner ring road). This takes you past Queen's Hotel on left. Go to roundabout, pass Midland Bank on left, double back at this island, and follow signs to Montpellier Street (The Courtyard). Shop is 100 yds on left.***

Open: Mon–Sat 9.30–5.
Closed: Bank Holidays; please phone for Christmas times.
Cards: MasterCard, Visa.
Cars: 90 minutes' free parking outside.
Toilets: In Montpellier Gardens on Montpellier Walk (2 minutes).
Wheelchairs: Factory shop is on lower ground floor; access by stairs.
Teas: Many restaurants and street cafés nearby.
Groups: No tours (factory at different site). Groups welcome to shop.
Transport: Bus nos. 46, 46B, 50. Bus station nearby. Easy walk from town centre.
Mail order: Yes.

Cheltenham Gloucs

Penny Plain

Late Entry

2 Queen's Circus, Montpellier
(01242) 571901

Ladies' separates and knitwear in smart and casual, summer and winter styles. Garments are made in colourful luxurious fabrics, especially natural fibres: pure cotton, linen, silk, wool, velvet and cupro. Sizes 8–22.

'Overstocks and ends of lines from Penny Plain mail order collections; also designer samples and slight seconds. High quality, well made clothes. Superb savings on original prices.'

In a small area of interesting shops close to the town centre. Follow signs for Montpellier and look for the large Queen's Hotel. This shop is beside the hotel.

Open: Mon–Sat 9–5.
Closed: Bank Holidays; Christmas, Boxing and New Year's Days.
Cards: Connect, Delta, MasterCard, Solo, Switch, Visa.
Cars: Limited free parking near.
Toilets: Yes.
Wheelchairs: Access to current range on ground floor but not to reduced price items on lower floor.
Changing rooms: Yes.
Teas: Many pubs, restaurants and cafés in town.
Groups: Shopping groups welcome. Please phone for organiser/driver incentives.
Transport: From station 15 minutes' walk or taxi £3. Short walk (or free road train) from town centre.
Mail order: Yes.
Catalogue: Free. Full price catalogue only.

50 Cranham Gloucs

Prinknash Pottery

Prinknash Abbey GL4 8EX
(01452) 812066

Large selection of ceramics, complete ranges of pottery tableware, coffee sets, giftware, vases and bowls. Pictures, books, toys, jewellery. Religious items, eg ceramic figurines.

'Famous for unique pewter pottery, and black and gold pottery. Wide range of prices for firsts and seconds. Personalised goblets for special occasions.'

Prinknash Pottery is set in the grounds of Prinknash Abbey. It is on the A46, half way between Cheltenham and Stroud.

Follow brown signs to Prinknash Abbey as you approach Cranham.

Open: Seven days 9.30–5.30.
Closed: Good Friday; Christmas and Boxing Days.
Cards: MasterCard, Switch, Visa.
Cars: Large car-park.
Toilets: Yes, including facilities for the disabled.
Wheelchairs: Wheelchairs welcome.
Teas: Own self service restaurant: light lunches, hot and cold snacks and cream teas. Also picnic and play area.
Tours: Viewing gallery in pottery, no charge. Conducted pottery tours *(April–Oct)*. Adults £1; children 50p.
Mail order: Yes, including overseas service. Only pottery sent.
Catalogue: Free.

51 Dartmouth Devon

Dartmouth Pottery Seconds Shop

Warfleet TQ6 9BY
(01803) 832258

Ceramic bathroom, gift and floral accessories including wide selection of vases. Exclusive hand-painted tableware designed by *Maryse Boxer*. Solid brass home furnishing accessories.

'The range of vases is of special interest to florists and flower arrangers. Extremely reasonably priced seconds.'

Warfleet is a short distance south of Dartmouth.

From Dartmouth: take B3205 coast road due south, follow signs to castle through Warfleet. Pottery is well marked on left, just after turning to castle.

From Kingsbridge: follow A379 to Stoke Fleming. Go right along B3205, signposted to castle and Warfleet. Pottery is in very attractive old 19th century mill on right.

Open: *April–Dec:* Mon–Sun 10–5. *Jan–March:* Mon–Fri 10–5.
Closed: Christmas Eve–2 Jan.
Cards: No.
Cars: Limited parking outside.
Toilets: Yes.
Wheelchairs: Four steep steps, medium-sized shop.
Teas: At the castle – *Easter–October*.
Groups: No pottery tours. Groups welcome to shop; please give advance notice.
Transport: 10-minute walk from Dartmouth.
Mail order: No.

52 Dorchester Dorset

The National Trust Gift Shop

65 High West Street DT1 1XB
(01305) 267535

Exclusive *National Trust* ranges of glassware, china, glass-cloths, PVC aprons and bags, place mats, coasters, trays and picture frames etc. Books, stationery, greetings cards and wrapping papers. Some seasonal items, eg Christmas decorations and Easter products.

'Ends of season ranges and clearance lines at at least a third less than original prices in National Trust shops.'

See our display advertisement opposite

Easy to find in the centre of town, next to Peter's Church (which is next to the town hall). Park in any car-park then short walk.

Open: Mon–Sat 9.15–5.15. Bank Holiday Mondays 10–4.
Closed: Phone to check Christmas–New Year period.
Cards: Amex, MasterCard, Visa.
Cars: In town car-parks.
Toilets: No.
Wheelchairs: Two steps in shop: help always available.
Teas: In town centre.
Groups: Welcome; must phone first.
Transport: Bus stop by shop. Bus nos. 10 from Weymouth, 184 from Salisbury, 187 from Bournemouth.
Mail order: No.

53 Exeter Devon

Factory Fabric Warehouse

1 Bridford Road, off Trusham Road, Marsh Barton Trading Estate EX2 8QX
(01392) 422881

Large stock of upholstery and furnishing fabrics: cottons, linens, damasks, velvets etc. Nets, voiles, calico, interlinings, waddings, linings. Haberdashery, fringing. Curtain rails/poles and accessories. Cushion covers and fillers. Ready-made curtains. Foam cut to shape. Dress fabrics.

'At least 5000 rolls of fabric in stock. Curtain-making service. Free quotations in local customers' homes.'

See our display advertisement on p. 195

South of the city centre, on the west side of the river Exe. Follow signs to Marsh Barton Trading Estate.

From city centre: aim south on A377. Go along Alphington Street. After ½ mile go left into well marked estate (Marsh Barton Road). After 300 yds go right into Trusham Road, then shop is 150 yds on left (well signed).

From M5: take exit 30 and aim for city centre.

Open: Mon–Sat 9–5.30; Sun & Bank Hols 10–4. New Year's Day.
Closed: Christmas Eve, Day & Boxing Day.
Cards: Access, Connect, Delta, Switch, Visa.
Cars: Free parking in local roads.
Toilets: Yes.
Wheelchairs: No steps, sizeable shop.
Teas: Free cups of coffee for customers. Café across road.
Groups: Shopping groups welcome, no need to phone.
Transport: City centre bus stops outside.

See our entry opposite

Glastonbury & Street

Drawn for the Factory Shop Guide

Map not to scale © Gillian Cutress

55	Morlands
56	Richard Draper
81	Clarks Village
124	Griffin Products

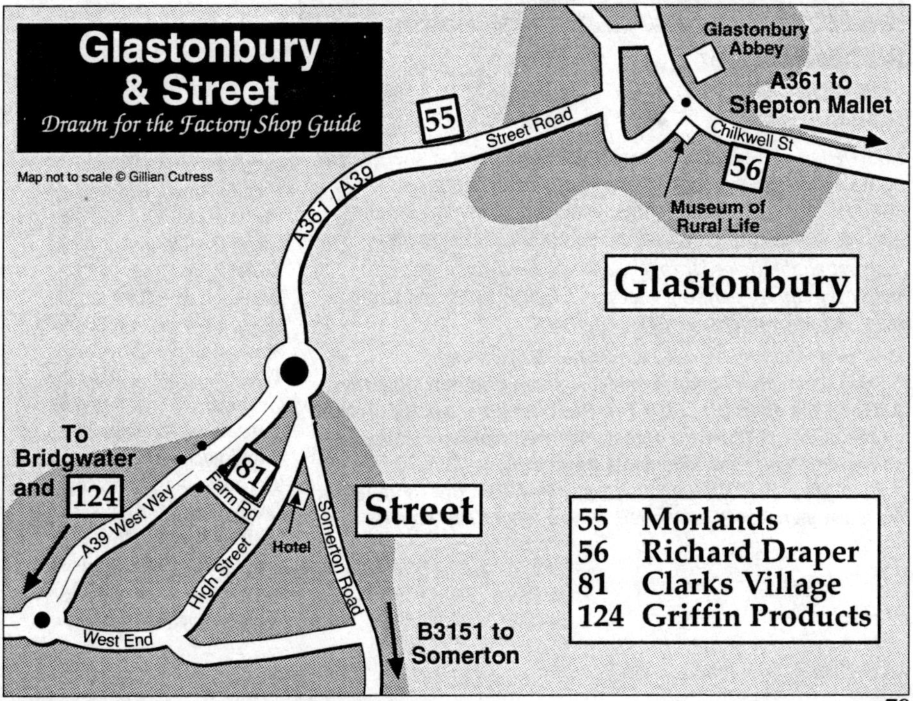

54 Glastonbury Somerset *See map earlier page*

Morlands

Northover BA6 9YB
(01458) 835042

Traditional designs in quality men's and women's sheepskin garments. Rugs, mittens, hats, renowned sheepskin slippers and boots; small leather goods.

'Largest supplier of Morlands' products, all at factory prices. Perfects and seconds. Sheepskin coats from £199–£500, rugs from £33, gloves from £18, mittens £10; hats from £12; slippers from £14, moccassins from £10, toys from £4 and leather handbags from £14.'

Northover is on the A39 between Glastonbury and Street.

From Glastonbury: take A39 for Street; continue past roundabout by B&Q. Factory is clearly signed on right after ½ mile.

From M5 exit 23: follow signs to Glastonbury on A39. In Street, at roundabout where B3151 comes in, continue left on A39 – factory is short distance on left.

Open: Mon–Sat 9.30–5; Bank Holidays 10–4.
Closed: Christmas and Boxing Days; Good Friday.
Cards: Amex, Diners, MasterCard, Visa.
Cars: Visitors' car park.
Toilets: Street or Glastonbury.
Wheelchairs: Three flights of stairs to large, spacious shop.
Changing rooms: No.
Teas: Teashops in Street and Glastonbury.
Groups: Coach parties welcome; please book first if possible.
Mail order: No.

55 Glastonbury Somerset *See map earlier page*

Richard Draper

Chilkwell Street BA6 8YA
(01458) 831118

Footwear manufacturers, making *Draper* brand sheepskin boots and slippers. Traditional shoes and sandals. Also sheepskin rugs, mittens, hats, scarves, knitwear, small leather goods, gifts, etc. Large selection of products on sale.

'Largest suppliers of Draper products. Quality footwear including ladies' walking shoes in width fittings and large sizes. All at competitive factory prices.'

Easy to find, on the south-east side of Glastonbury.

From Glastonbury centre: follow signs to Shepton Mallet on A361, in the direction of the Tor. Pass the Museum of Rural Life on the corner of Chilkwell Street; this well marked company is on the right, past the Rifleman's Arms pub.

From Shepton Mallet, coming west on A361: this large factory is clearly signposted on the left as you reach Glastonbury.

Open: Mon–Sat 9.30–5.30; some Bank Holidays – please phone to check.
Closed: Christmas, Boxing and New Year's Days.
Cards: Amex, Diners, MasterCard, Visa.
Cars: Own large car-park.
Toilets: Yes.
Wheelchairs: Two small steps, large ground floor shop. Stairs to upper showroom.
Teas: Tea rooms by Abbey.
Groups: Groups welcome to shop; please book in advance with Frances Draper, mentioning this book. No factory tours.
Transport: Local buses.
Mail order: Yes. Free mailing list. No seconds sent.
Catalogue: Free catalogues twice a year. Write or phone.

56 Goonhavern near Perranporth Cornwall

Kernewek Pottery Shop

(01872) 573505

Glazed storage jars, bread crocks, tableware, vases and a variety of other items.

'Very competitive prices. Visit our other shop at 6a Cliff Road, Newquay (01637) 875353.'

Goonhavern is near the north coast of Cornwall, a couple of miles inland from Perranporth and 6 miles south of Newquay.

This shop is at the roundabout in village opposite the New Inn.

Open: *April–May:* Mon–Fri 9–5; Sat 9.30–1; *June-Sept:* Mon–Fri 9–late; Sat & Sun 10–5; *Oct:* 10–5; Sat & Sun 11–5; *Nov–Mar:* Mon–Fri 10–4.
Closed: *November–March:* Saturday and Sunday; *April–May:* Sunday; Christmas Eve for two weeks.
Cards: MasterCard, Switch, Visa.
Cars: Own car-park adjacent to shop.
Toilets: Yes.
Wheelchairs: One small step.
Teas: Café opposite shop.
Groups: Groups welcome.
Transport: Difficult.
Mail order: Yes. Item price plus p&p. Goods sent upon receipt of cheque.

57 Great Torrington Devon

Dartington Crystal

Linden Close EX38 7AN
(01805) 626262

Wide choice of slightly imperfect *Dartington Crystal*: clear crystal wine glasses, decanters, tumblers, bowls, vases etc. Wide selection of china, kitchenware, cards and gifts. Also Tarka Mill Shop (Edinburgh Woollen Mill) for family knitwear and clothing.

'Items slightly below normal first quality; good discounts.'

Six miles south-east of Bideford.

From Bideford (A386): enter Great Torrington along New Street, look for church on right and go left into School Lane.*

From Barnstaple (B3232) and South Molton (B3227): look for hospital at a roundabout. Go west along New Street, go right into School Lane opposite church.*

****Linden Close is second turning on left. Factory clearly marked.***

Open: Mon–Sat 9.30–5; Sun 10.30–4.30. Bank Holidays.
Closed: Easter Sunday; Christmas and Boxing Days.
Cards: MasterCard, Visa.
Cars: Large car-park.
Toilets: Yes.
Wheelchairs: Easy access to huge shop. Please arrange in advance for tours.
Teas: Licensed restaurant.
Tours: Tours (including Visitor Centre) to see glass blown & crafted from overhead galleries: Mon–Fri 9.30–3.30 (not Bank Holidays). £2.75 adults, children free when accompanied by full-paying adult. Groups of 15+ must book in advance (£1.95 pp). School parties £1 pp.
Transport: Local bus service to New Street.
Mail order: Yes. Please phone for details.
Catalogue: Free.

58 Highcliffe Dorset

The Catalogue Shop

401 Lymington Road BH23 5HE
(01425) 271202 Fax (01425) 278478

Huge selection of ex-catalogue stock ranging from ladies' wear, men's wear, leather and suede shoes, top brand trainers, bed linen, curtains, personal stereos and cameras.

'Firsts and seconds from all leading mail order catalogues. All items are at least half catalogue price, many are as little as 10% of original value. Stock changes daily. Large sizes available. Franchise available – phone (01425) 616121.'

On A337 near eastern end of Highcliffe.

From Lymington going west on A337: as you reach Highcliffe, this shop is in the first parade of shops on your left shortly after you enter town (about 25 yds before the traffic lights).

From Bournemouth and Christchurch: take the A337 east for Lymington. Continue through Highcliffe, passing the Rover garage on the left; go over the traffic lights: the shop is on the right after about 25 yds.

Open: Mon–Sat 9–5; Sun 10–5.
Closed: Christmas and New Year's Days.
Cards: Amex, MasterCard, Visa.
Cars: Behind shop; or large car-park in town centre.
Toilets: 10 yds from shop.
Wheelchairs: One step into medium sized shop.
Changing rooms: Yes.
Teas: Several places in town.
Groups: Shopping groups welcome, please phone first.
Transport: Hinton Admiral rail station 15 minutes' walk.
Mail order: No.

59 Kidlington Oxon

Freelance Fabrics

Shop 4, The Kidlington Centre, High Street OX5 2DL
(01865) 841088

Upholstery and furnishing fabrics: cottons, linens, damasks etc. Nets, voiles, calico, interlinings, waddings, linings. Fringing. Curtain rails/poles and accessories. Cushions and fillers. Ready-made curtains. Foam can be cut to shape.

'About 800 rolls. Curtain making service.'

See our display advertisement on p. 195

Kidlington is north of Oxford, a couple of miles outside Oxford outer ring road (A34).

From all directions: follow signs into village centre. At traffic lights (Exeter Community Hall on corner) turn into Sterling Road Approach. Follow road round into Kidlington Centre; shop at rear.

Open: Mon–Sat 9.30–5; Sun & Bank Holidays 10.30–4.
Closed: Christmas, Boxing and New Year's Days.
Cards: Access, Connect, Delta, Switch, Visa.
Cars: Plenty of free parking.
Toilets: In car-park.
Wheelchairs: No steps, ground floor shop.
Teas: Local cafés.
Groups: Shopping groups welcome, no need to phone.
Transport: Buses from Oxford.
Mail order: No.

60 Marlborough Wilts

Marlborough Tiles

16 High Street SN8 1AA
(01672) 515287

Wall tiles (seconds and discontinued lines) made by *Marlborough Tiles*. Imported floor tiles.

'Prices from £3.24 per sq yd for seconds. Wall tiles are seconds and discontinued lines (may be perfect). Floor tiles mostly perfects at reduced prices.'

In town centre, on south side of High Street, next to Waitrose and opposite Lloyds Bank (large black & white building).

From east or west: enter town via the A4 and you come along the High Street.

From M4 exit 15: take A345 south. Keep going downhill into town; at roundabout go right into New Road (town hall on right after 100 yds) then go straight into High Street – shop is on left.

Open: Mon–Sat 9.30–5.
Closed: Bank Holidays. Please phone for Christmas times.
Cards: MasterCard, Visa.
Cars: In High Street or behind Waitrose.
Toilets: Behind Town Hall in High Street.
Wheelchairs: Not possible; shop on lower ground floor.
Teas: Several super tea shops; local hotels and pubs.
Groups: No tours, small shop on different site from factory.
Transport: Bus no. 48 Swindon–Marlborough via Hungerford. Bus stop in High Street.
Mail order: Yes. Payment, including cost of mailing, to be received before goods sent.

61 Mere Wilts

Ethos Candles

Quarry Fields Industrial Estate BA12 6LB
(01747) 860960

A wide range of candles in varying sizes, colours and perfumes: for dining, decoration, church, garden etc. Also large variety of china, glass and metal candle holders.

'One of the leading makers of church candles in the UK. Most items slight seconds with prices from 10p. Almost all candles made on site. Discounts around 50% – more on certain items. Firsts and seconds sold. Any colour matched.'

Mere is just south of A303, about 7 miles east of Wincanton. This company is on the west side of the village.

From the east on A303: turn left on to B3095 for Mere. Go through town following signs to Quarry Industrial Estate. This estate is on the right just as you leave town. Shop is at the end of the first drive on the left.

From the west: turn off the A303 on to B3092 for Mere. After the right turn-off to Gillingham (B3095), go left into Quarry Industrial Estate. Take next left: shop is at the end, facing you.

Open: Mon–Fri 9–5.
Closed: Bank Holidays; Christmas–New Year.
Cards: MasterCard, Visa.
Cars: Own forecourt by shop.
Toilets: Main car-park in Mere.
Wheelchairs: No steps to small shop.
Teas: Several pubs and teashops locally. Don't forget to visit the famous wine shipper in same village!
Groups: Small shopping groups welcome. No factory tours.
Transport: Nearest rail station in Gillingham (Dorset).
Mail order: No.

62 Minehead Somerset

The Factory Shop Ltd

Mart Road TA24 5BJ
(01643) 705911

Large selection of men's, ladies' and children's clothing and footwear. Luggage, toiletries, hardware, household textiles, bedding, lighting and new fashion concessions department with famous brand names. Books and greetings cards. Leather jackets for men and women. *Cape Country* pine furniture exclusively produced for The Factory Shop.

'Large stock of branded and chainstore items, all at greatly reduced prices. Deliveries of new stock every week to give an ever changing selection.'

A short walk off the seafront, at the back of the station.

From all directions: probably easiest to follow signs to station. With station on your left, go along Warren Street which becomes The Avenue.*

From the seafront: go into The Avenue.*

****After a few yards go left into Glenmore Road; take third left (Mart Road): shop is on right, opposite Jewsons.***

Open: Mon–Sat 9.30–5.30; Sun 11–5.
Closed: Easter Sunday; Christmas, Boxing and New Year's Days.
Cards: Delta, MasterCard, Switch, Visa.
Cars: Own large car-park.
Toilets: Yes.
Wheelchairs: No steps to large shop. Wide aisles.
Changing rooms: Yes.
Teas: In town.
Groups: Shopping groups welcome. For organiser/driver incentives please phone.
Transport: Any bus to town; West Somerset Railway along coast from Watchet and inland towards Taunton.
Mail order: Home delivery service for pine furniture. Please phone for free catalogue and price list.

63 Newton Abbot : Heathfield Devon

Candy & Co.

Great Western Potteries TQ12 6RF
(01626) 832641 x 244

Wall and floor tiles, including Victorian designs; adhesives, bathroom accessories, tiling tools, fireplaces and surrounds.

'Firsts, slight seconds and clearance lines at reduced prices.'

About 4 miles north-west of Newton Abbot, on the A38 (north side of dual-carriageway) near exit for A382/Newton Abbot.

From Plymouth going north on A38: pass roundabout/exit to Newton Abbot A383; go under next large roundabout (A382 junction): go slowly for ½ mile. Entrance on left, 400 yds after slipway.

From Exeter going south on A38: at large roundabout, exit for A382 to Newton Abbot but continue round and backtrack about 400 yds on other side of dual-carriageway to factory entrance.

Open: Mon–Sat 8.30–5. Bank Holidays 10–4.
Closed: Christmas–New Year please phone for opening times.
Cards: Access, Eurocard, Mastercard, Switch, Visa.
Cars: Own car-park.
Toilets: Yes.
Wheelchairs: Small step.
Teas: Canteen and hot drinks machine.
Transport: Newton Abbot–Bovey Tracey buses stop 100 yds away in Battle Road.
Mail order: No.
Catalogue: Free brochure.

Isis Ceramics

The Old Toffee Factory, 120a Marlborough Road
(01865) 722729

Hand-crafted and hand-painted English delftware using 17th century techniques. Tableware, ornamental giftware and lamps in traditional blue and white, green and white and plum and white.

'Seconds at 50% less than normal retail price. Special commissions accepted.'

On south side of city centre. From all directions, you need to get on St Aldgates, the main A4144 leading south out of city.

Going south out of city along St Aldgates (A4144): cross river Thames at Folley Bridge. Take first right, Western Road. At the end, go left into Marlborough Road. Company on right, opposite St Matthew's church.

Coming north towards city centre on Abingdon Road A4144: shortly before Folley Bridge, go left into White House Road. At end, go right into Marlborough Road. Company on left, opposite St Matthew's church.

Open: Mon–Sat 10–4.
Closed: Bank Holidays, Christmas–New Year period.
Cards: Amex, MasterCard, Visa.
Cars: Park-&-ride on Abingdon Road; public car-parks.
Toilets: Yes.
Wheelchairs: Shop in old factory building on first floor (15 steps to showroom).
Teas: In town.
Groups: Small groups welcome. Tours of factory (maximum 10 people) can be arranged, depending on workload; please phone Virginia Staples.
Transport: Local buses and rail station; bus no. 400 from park-&-ride in Abingdon Road. Alight at Folley Bridge Inn.
Mail order: Please phone for price list with sketches of patterns, shapes and ranges.

Isis Ceramics

Ethos Candles

Marlborough Tiles

Cloverleaf

Brannams Pottery

65 Plymouth Devon

Factory Fabric Warehouse

Unit 7–9, Faraday Mill Business Park, Cattwater Road, Prince Rock PL4 0ST
(01752) 253351

Large range of upholstery and furnishing fabrics: cottons, linens, damasks, velvets etc. Nets, voiles, calico, interlinings, waddings, linings. Haberdashery, fringing. Curtain rails/ poles and accessories. Cushion covers and fillers. Ready-made curtains. Foam cut to shape. Dress fabrics.

'About 5000 rolls in stock. Curtain-making service (free quotation in customer's home). Always bargains.'

See our display advertisement on p. 195

On the east side of the city centre.

From city centre: take A374 Exeter Street for Cattdown/ Prince Rock. At roundabout, go right for Cattdown/Prince Rock. After 100 yds go left for Cattdown/Prince Rock. At end of road, go right then first left (Cattwater Road). Shop in first unit on right.

Open: Mon–Sat 9–5; Sun & Bank Holidays 10–4. New Year's Day.
Closed: Christmas & Boxing Days.
Cards: Access, Connect, Delta, Switch, Visa.
Cars: Own large car-park.
Toilets: No.
Wheelchairs: No steps, ground floor shop.
Teas: Cafés nearby.
Groups: Shopping groups welcome, no need to phone.
Transport: Bus no. 31 from city centre.

66 Plymouth Devon

Jaeger

Now closed

Union Street PL1 3HG
(01752) 613523

Large range of ladies' wear including knitwear, blouses, skirts, trousers, jackets, suits. Men's knitwear, shirts, ties and socks.

'Ladies' and men's wear at bargain prices.'

On the west side of the city centre.

From A38: take A374 Embankment Road to city centre. This leads into Exeter Street. At Charles Cross roundabout and St Andrew's Cross roundabout go straight into Royal Parade, then straight over Derry's Cross roundabout into Union Street. Factory is on left: access to factory shop, situated at end of main factory, is via staff car-park.

Open: Tues–Fri 9.30–4; Sat 9–11.45.
Closed: Monday; Bank Holidays and factory holidays; Christmas and New Year. Please phone to check.
Cards: Access, Connect, Switch, Visa.
Cars: Side streets nearby.
Toilets: In city centre.
Wheelchairs: Seven steps to sizeable shop.
Changing rooms: Yes.
Teas: In city centre.
Groups: Please phone Sara or Sue.
Transport: Any bus to city centre.
Mail order: No.

67 Poole Dorset

Catalogue

80 High Street BH15 1DB
(01202) 677977

Wide cross section of ex-catalogue goods from major mail order houses. Clothing and footwear for all the family, sportswear, curtains, bedding and general household items.

'Perfects sold at 40–45% of original mail order price. Any item with a fault is marked as imperfect.'

In the High Street, near the old quayside (clearly signposted).

From Blandford on A350 or Dorchester on A35: follow signs to Upton and Hamworthy. Cross over Poole Bridge: take first possible right, Bay Hog Lane. Go left, West Street. At traffic lights, go right into New Orchard. Use one of the car-parks and walk along the pedestrianised High Street.

From Bournemouth on A35, or from Wimborne Minster on A349: follow signs to Old Town. Park where possible (Hill Street car-park best); walk along the High Street.

Open: Mon–Fri 9.30–5; Sat 9.30–5.30; Sun 11–4.
Closed: Christmas and Boxing Days; also Sundays from *New Year–Easter.*
Cards: Amex, Delta, JCB, MasterCard, Switch, Visa.
Cars: Public car-park in Hill Street directly behind shop.
Toilets: No.
Wheelchairs: No steps to large shop.
Changing rooms: Yes.
Teas: Numerous cafés and pubs in town.
Groups: Groups welcome.
Transport: Poole station 5 minutes' walk. Wilts & Dorset Buses to Poole bus station (10 minutes' walk through Dolphin shopping centre).
Mail order: No.

68 Poole Dorset

Poole Pottery Factory Shopping and Visitor Attraction

The Quay BH15 1RE
(01202) 666200 or 668681

Popular ranges of *Poole Pottery* including *Dorset Fruit* in four variations (apple, orange, pear and plum); the *Vineyard* range and *Vincent*, the sunflower range, all with matching textiles; the famous blue dolphins, bread crocks, butter boxes and large storage jars. *Le Creuset, Dartington Crystal, Stuart Crystal, Colony Candles* and *Henry Watson* terracotta.

'Seconds and some perfects at discounts of around 30%.'

On the old quayside, clearly signposted.

From Blandford on A350 or Dorchester on A35: follow signs to Upton and Hamworthy. Cross over Poole Bridge: the Quay is first turning on right (but no entry from here, so take first possible right and make your way around). Pottery about 500 yds on left.

From Bournemouth on A35, or from Wimborne Minster on A349: follow signs to Old Town and go on to the Quay.

From town centre: follow signs to the Quay.

Open: Mon–Sun 9–5.30. *Also* some evenings in summer, please phone.
Closed: Christmas and Boxing Days.
Cards: MasterCard, Visa.
Cars: Quayside and car-park in Castle Street.
Toilets: Yes, and for the disabled.
Wheelchairs: Easy access to all areas.
Teas: Own tea room 10–4.30; Delphis Brasserie Bar open until late.
Tours: Self-guided tours round museum, cinema, factory and glass blowing workshop. Children's pottery and painting area. Groups welcome, no need to book.
Transport: 10 minutes' walk from railway and bus stations.

69 Redruth Cornwall

The Fabric Shop

52 Fore Street TR15 2AF
(01209) 314439

Large range of upholstery and furnishing fabrics: cottons, linens, damasks, velvets etc. Nets, voiles, calico, interlinings, waddings, linings. Haberdashery, fringing. Curtain rails/ poles and accessories. Cushion covers and fillers. Ready-made curtains. Foam cut to shape.

'About 2000 rolls of fabric in stock. Curtain-making service. Prices from £2.99 per metre.'

See our display advertisement on p. 195

Fore Street is the main street (partly pedestrianised, partly one-way) in town.

This shop is around the corner from the station on the same side as the post office, which is about 100 yds away.

Open: Mon–Sat 9–5. Bank Holidays 10–4.
Closed: Christmas–New Year.
Cards: Access, Connect, Delta, Switch, Visa.
Cars: Car-park across road.
Toilets: At station.
Wheelchairs: Ramp to front door.
Teas: Local cafés.
Groups: Shopping groups welcome, no need to phone.
Transport: Any bus or train to town centre.

70 Redruth Cornwall

The Factory Shop Ltd

Mount Ambrose, Scorrier
(01209) 219116

Men's, ladies' and children's clothing, footwear, luggage, toiletries, kitchenware, electricals, bedding, lighting, glass, china, books, tapes and compact discs. *Cape Country* pine furniture exclusively produced for The Factory Shop.

'Large stock of branded and chainstore items, all at greatly reduced prices. Deliveries of new stock every week to give an ever changing selection.'

Scorrier is a short distance north-east of Redruth.

From the A30: follow signs for Scorrier then head for Redruth on A3047. Shop is on left, at the mini-roundabout where Redruth by-pass goes right (and Mount Ambrose leads into town).

From Redruth town centre: aim north-east. Shop is on the right at mini-roundabout.

Open: Mon–Fri 10–5.30; Sat 9–5.30; Sun and Bank Holidays 11–5.
Closed: Easter Sunday and Christmas Day.
Cards: MasterCard, Switch, Visa.
Cars: Own car-park.
Toilets: In town.
Wheelchairs: Access through 'exit' doors.
Changing rooms: Yes.
Teas: Tea room within store.
Groups: Shopping groups welcome. For organiser/driver incentives please phone.
Transport: Trains to Redruth. Redruth–Truro buses.
Mail order: Home delivery service available for pine furniture. Please telephone for free catalogue and price list.

71 Ross-on-Wye Hereford

Barker Shoes Factory Shop at Herrings

17 Gloucester Road HR9 5BV
(01989) 562431

Imperfect and discontinued ranges of high quality men's and ladies' shoes. Brands include *Barkers, Church's, Camel, Cheaney, Ecco, Loakes, Rohde, Van-Dal*. Ladies' widths AA–E and larger sizes.

'Under new management with more quality brands at factory prices. Our Rohde department offers 25% discount on rrp. Many oddments at half price or less to clear, so now is the time to stock up on your fashion, business, walking & casual shoes.'

In the centre of Ross-on-Wye.

From M50 exit 4: turn left at the second roundabout for the town centre. Turn left in the Market Place into Gloucester Road: the shop is 150 yds on the left, opposite Midland Bank.

Open: Mon–Sat 9–5.30. Some Bank Holidays – please phone first.
Closed: Christmas–New Year.
Cards: MasterCard, Switch, Visa.
Cars: Limited street parking and local car-parks.
Toilets: Yes.
Wheelchairs: Easy access, wide doors.
Teas: Café opposite.
Tours: No factory tours.
Transport: Any bus to town centre.
Mail order: No.

72 Ross-on-Wye Hereford

Ross Labels

Overross House, Overross HR9 7QJ
(01989) 769000

Ladies' lingerie, hosiery, footwear, hats, mix and match separates, leisure wear, jeans, 18+ section, coats and jackets, handbags, jewellery. Men's underwear, wax and leather hats, wax jackets, golfing/leisure/casual wear, suits, shirts, ties, dinner jackets; also 'king size'. Huge selection of clothing for children of all ages (babies to early teens). Candles, gifts, confectionery, biscuits and jams.

'Famous-label fashions at affordable prices.'

North of town on a roundabout near M50 exit 4.

Coming via the M50 from the east: go to the end of M50, pass petrol station on left then shop is on right by the next roundabout.

From Wales on A40: bypass Ross-on-Wye, and the shop is on the left by roundabout where the A40 goes right to Gloucester.

From town centre: go north towards M50. At large roundabout with A40, go straight. The shop is on the far right corner.

From Gloucester: stay on the A40. The shop is by the roundabout, on the far right corner where the M50 spur joins the A40.

Open: Mon–Fri 9–5.30; Sat 9–6; Sun and Bank Holidays 10–5.
Closed: Christmas, Boxing and New Year Days.
Cards: All major credit and debit cards.
Cars: Large free car-park.
Toilets: Yes, including for the disabled.
Wheelchairs: Huge ground floor shop on one level.
Changing rooms: Yes.
Teas: Licensed coffee shop for hot and cold dishes, cakes and beverages. Cater for up to 80. Refreshments gladly taken downstairs for the disabled.
Groups: Pleased to accept coach parties by appointment.
Transport: Difficult.
Mail order: No.

73 Salisbury Wilts

Marlborough Tiles

13 Milford Street SP1 2AJ
(01722) 328010

Wall tiles made by *Marlborough Tiles*: seconds and discontinued lines. Imported floor tiles.

'Prices from £3.24 sq yd for seconds. Wall tiles are seconds and discontinued lines (may be perfect); floor tiles mostly perfects at reduced prices.'

In the centre of Salisbury, opposite the Red Lion Hotel in Milford Street, just off the Market Place.

Open: Mon–Sat 9.30–5.00.
Closed: Bank Holidays; please phone for Christmas times.
Cards: MasterCard, Visa.
Cars: Limited parking outside; car-parks nearby.
Toilets: In Market Square.
Wheelchairs: No; factory shop is on first floor (ground floor is first quality shop).
Teas: Numerous tea shops.
Groups: No tours, factory at different site. Groups welcome to shop.
Transport: Railway station is 10/15 minutes' walk.
Mail order: Yes. Payment, including cost of mailing, to be received before goods sent.

74 Salisbury Wilts

The Wilton Carpet Factory

The Original Weaving Works, King Street, Wilton SP2 0AV
(01722) 742733/744919

Huge range of first grade Axminster woven patterns and tufted carpets in twist and velvet, sold by the metre or by the roll. Large quantity of 80/20% wool/nylon from medium domestic to heavy contract. Discontinued ranges, remnants and seconds. Hand woven Chinese and Persian rugs.

'Delivery anywhere in the UK and fitting can be arranged. Make exceptional savings by purchasing direct from factory.'

See our display advertisement opposite

Wilton is about 3 miles west of Salisbury.

From Salisbury going west on A36: go over roundabout as you enter Wilton; after 100 yds, company is clearly marked on left.

From Bath/Warminster coming east on A36: factory is clearly marked on right. Slow down on bend into Wilton (The Wheatsheaf on right): turn right into concealed entrance.

Now new shopping village with other shops too.

Open: Mon–Sat 9–5; Sun 11–5.
Closed: Easter Sunday; ten days over Christmas/New Year: please phone to check.
Cards: MasterCard, Switch, Visa.
Cars: Large car-park.
Toilets: Yes.
Wheelchairs: Huge ground floor shop.
Teas: Restaurant for snacks and full meals.
Tours: Four tours a day: Mon–Sat: 10.15, 11.45, 2 and 3.30; Sun 11.30, 2 and 3.30. Please phone in advance.
Transport: Bus nos. 60, 61 from Salisbury (at new canal) every 10 minutes. From Salisbury train station: go left under bridge to bus stop for Wilton buses.
Mail order: Please phone for details of rug-making yarns and canvasses (01722) 744183.

See our entry opposite

75 Saltford Wilts

Factory Pine

501 Bath Road BS18 3HO
(01225) 874355

Over 400 items of hand-made, hand-waxed quality pine furniture.

'Good old fashioned value! No sales, special offers, or middle men. Pay around 30–40% less than in the high street. We also have shops at Westbury (01373) 825424 and Southampton (01703) 772222, both with wheelchair access.'

Saltford is on A4, south-east of Bristol and north-west of Bath.

Bath Road (A4) is the main road going through Saltford and the shop is in the middle of Saltford.

If you come from Bath, shop is on right, just after the Co-Op.

From Bristol: shop is on left, just past Vauxhall garage.

Open: Mon–Fri 10–5; Sat–Sun 10–6. Bank Holidays.
Closed: Christmas Day.
Cards: No.
Cars: Ample free parking.
Toilets: Yes.
Wheelchairs: One small step to shop.
Teas: In Saltford.
Groups: Groups welcome to shop.
Transport: Buses to Saltford from Bath and Bristol.
Mail order: No.

76 Shepton Mallet Somerset

Mulberry

The Old School House, Kilver Street BA4 5NF
(01749) 340583

Men's and women's outer garments and stylish casual wear; straw hats; wide range of leather bags, rucksacks, belts, organisers, wallets, travel collection etc. Some dressmaking and upholstery fabrics. Household items, eg furniture (settees, tables etc), china and glass.

'Last season's goods, some seconds.'

On the north-east side of Shepton Mallet on the A37.

From London (M4 exit 18): follow signs to Exeter, and then Shepton Mallet.

Coming south on A37: pass the Downside Inn on right then the right turn-off to Shepton town centre. Shop is a short distance on left, clearly visible, opposite Showerings.

From traffic lights at junction of A361 (Frome–Wells road) and A37: take A37 north for Bristol. Clearly visible shop is a few hundred yards on right (opposite Showerings on left).

Open: Mon–Sat 10–6; Sun 11–4.
Closed: Christmas, Boxing and New Year's Days.
Cards: Amex, Connect, Diners, Eurocard, JCB, MasterCard, Switch, Visa.
Cars: Clearly marked free car-park adjacent to shop.
Toilets: Yes, and for disabled. Baby changing facilities.
Wheelchairs: Side entrance; no steps. Huge shop.
Changing rooms: Yes.
Teas: Tea room in shop.
Groups: By prior appointment only with manageress.
Transport: Castle Cary rail station then taxi (about 6 miles).
Mail order: No.

77 Southampton Hants

Factory Pine

370-372 Shirley Road SO15 3HV
(01703) 772222

Over 600 items of hand-made, hand-waxed quality pine furniture.

'Good old fashioned value! No sales, special offers, or middle men. Pay around 30–40% less than in the high street. We also have shops at Westbury (01373) 825424 and Saltford (01225) 874355.'

Shirley is a western suburb of Southampton.

From southern end of M271: take A35 east. Continue straight on to A3024, going over overpass. Go straight at traffic lights, under footbridge. At traffic lights go left for Shirley A3057 then over railway.*

From other directions: get on to A3024 (major dual-carriageway which runs east–west parallel to the docks/river Test). At traffic lights go right for Shirley A3057 then over railway.*

****At roundabout go left for Romsey/Shirley. Keep straight for about a mile. Pass Ford on left then Total petrol. Shop is immediately on left.***

Open: Seven days a week 10–6. Bank Holidays.
Closed: Christmas Day.
Cards: No.
Cars: Ample free parking.
Toilets: Yes.
Wheelchairs: Easy access.
Teas: Local pubs and cafés.
Groups: Groups welcome.
Transport: Local buses.
Mail order: No.

78 Southampton Hants

Freelance Fabrics (Southampton)

West Quay Road SO15 1GZ
(01703) 336410 Fax (01703) 336403

Large range of upholstery and furnishing fabrics: cottons, linens, damasks, velvets etc. Nets, voiles, calico, interlinings, waddings, linings. Haberdashery, fringing. Curtain rails/ poles and accessories. Cushion covers and fillers. Ready-made curtains. Foam cut to shape. Dress fabrics.

'Curtain making service.'

See our display advertisement on p. 195

On south-west side of the city centre, near docks 4–8.

From southern end of M271: take A35 east. Continue straight on to A3024; go over overpass. Go straight at traffic lights, under footbridge. At traffic lights, go right (south) for Dock Gates 1–10.*

From other directions: get on to A3024 (major dual-carriageway which runs east–west parallel to the docks/river Test). At traffic lights go south for Dock Gates 1–10.*

****Pass Novotel on left. At traffic lights, go left for Dock Gates 4–8. Pass McDonald's on left. Go over traffic lights. In front of Honda turn right: shop is 50 yds on right.***

Open: Mon–Sat 9.30–5; Sun and Bank Holidays 10–4.
Closed: Christmas and Boxing Days.
Cards: Access, Connect, Delta, Switch, Visa.
Cars: In forecourt.
Toilets: Yes.
Wheelchairs: Easy access to vast shop.
Teas: Restaurants in nearby retail park.
Groups: Shopping groups welcome, no need to phone.
Transport: Unfortunately none.

79 St Austell Cornwall

LS & J Sussman (Shirt Manufacturers)

Daniels Lane, Holmbush Industrial Estate PL25 3HP
(01726) 70030

Wide range of men's, ladies' and children's clothing; bedding and towels.

'We sell both end-of-range stock and good seconds.'

To the east of St Austell, off A390 (St Austell–Liskeard road).

From town centre on A390: go over roundabout near Asda, go straight over next roundabout, heading for Liskeard; go under a railway bridge, go left at first traffic lights into Daniel's Lane.*

From Liskeard on A390: cross the first two traffic lights, and go right at the next set into Daniel's Lane.*

****Take second right into Stennack Road; shop is through first entrance on left.***

Open: Mon, Thur 9–1 & 2–4.45; Tues, Fri 9–1 & 1.30–4.45; Wed 9–12.30 & 1–4.45; Sat 9–12.
Closed: Bank Holidays; Christmas–New Year.
Cards: MasterCard, Visa.
Cars: Yes.
Toilets: In Asda on the bypass.
Wheelchairs: Yes.
Changing rooms: Yes.
Teas: In Asda.
Groups: No factory tours. Shopping groups by appointment with the shop manageress please.
Transport: Hopper bus from bus station to Holmbush Industrial Estate. Plymouth–Lostwithiel buses along A390.
Mail order: No.

80 Stratford-upon-Avon Oxon

Stratford Tile Warehouse

Unit 1 Avenue Farm Industrial Estate, off Birmingham Road
(01789) 299445

Importers of many varieties of natural slate. Hand-made terracotta wall and floor tiles.

'We decorate a wide range of kitchen and bathroom ceramic tiles, and cut and decorate border tiles in a wide range of designs. Slight seconds and discontinued lines available: reductions up to 50%.

Birmingham Road A3400 (was A34) is main road leading north out of Stratford. This company is about two miles north of town.

From Stratford: aim north for Henley-in-Arden and Birmingham. Go over roundabout (Tesco on right). Keep straight for a few hundred yards. Go left after large John Yarnold 4x4 garage on left into Avenue Farm.*

Coming south on A3400 (was A34): pass Range Rover garage then turn right into Avenue Farm.*

****At far end, company is on right (behind bedding company).***

Open: Mon–Fri 8–5.30 (Thur late till 8); Sat 9–5.30.
Closed: Most Bank Holidays, please phone to check.
Cards: MasterCard, Visa.
Cars: In adjoining car-park.
Toilets: Yes.
Wheelchairs: Unfortunately not suitable for wheelchairs.
Teas: In town.
Transport: 15 minutes' walk from town centre.
Mail order: Yes. Payment by credit card accepted over phone.

See our entry below

81 Street Somerset

See map on p. 73

Clarks Village

Farm Road BA16 0BB
(01458) 840064

40 manufacturers' shops selling quality branded merchandise, including shoes, tableware, clothing, home furnishings etc. at factory prices.

'On Clarks Shoes' original manufacturing site, a shopping and leisure development in an attractive landscaped setting.'

See our display advertisement above

See next two pages for full details of the shops

Easy to find and clearly marked off the Street by-pass, A39.

Open: *Summer:* Mon–Sat 9–6; Sun 11–5; Bank Holidays 9–6. *Winter:* Mon–Sat 9–5.30; Sun 11–5; Bank Holidays 9–5.30; Boxing Day 11–5.
Closed: Christmas Day.
Cards: Access, Delta, Switch, Visa.
Cars: Large car and coach park adjoining town centre car-park.
Toilets: Yes, & baby changing and facilities for disabled.
Wheelchairs: Easy access plus wheelchairs available on request.
Changing rooms: Yes.
Teas: *Food Factory Restaurant, Upper Crust Sandwiches, Jacket Potatoes, Donut Hut* and *Burger King* takeaway, plus picnic area.
Groups: Groups welcome. Please phone for details of special events. Free entry to Shoe Museum.
Transport: Any bus to Street.

82 Alexon/Eastex
(01458) 841831
Classic, formal and casual wear for women.

83 The Baggage Factory
(01458) 843163
Luggage, designer handbags, briefcases and leather goods.

84 Benetton
(01458) 840826
Full range of *Benetton* merchandise for children & adults.

85 Black & Decker
(01458) 840205
Reconditioned tools and accessories from this famous range.

86 Blazer
(01458) 448682
Men's formal and casual wear.

87 Clarks Factory Shop
(01458) 843156
Family footwear: quality shoes, boots, trainers. Sports equipment.

88 The Clarks Shop
(01458) 843150
Huge selection of latest *Clarks* top quality products. Full price.

89 Crabtree & Evelyn
(01458) 841440
Luxury foods, toiletries, fragrances, gifts. Gift baskets.

90 Dartington Crystal
(01458) 841618
Clear crystal wine glasses, decanters, bowls, vases. Family clothing.

91 Denby Pottery
(01458) 840940
Earthenware tableware, dishes, bowls, jugs, mugs, cookware.

92 Esprit
(01458) 446627
Men's & women's quality designer clothing, shoes, accessories.

93 Farah Menswear
(01458) 841744
Men's wear: trousers, knitwear, shirts and T-shirts.

94 Fred Perry
(01458) 841730
Men's, women's and children's casual and sportswear.

95 Hallmark Cards
(01458) 447005
Greeting cards, stationery, soft toys and gifts.

96 Jaeger/Jaeger Man
(01458) 447215
Top name in men's and women's stylish fashion clothing.

97 James Barry
(01458) 840478
Quality men's suits, jackets, trousers and accessories.

98 Jeffrey Rogers
(01458) 448123
Women's fashion clothing: skirts, T-shirts, blouses, dresses.

99 JoKids
(01458) 841909
Baby & children's wear (0–10) including casual and party clothes.

100 Jumper
(01458) 840320
Knitwear and casual clothing for men & women.

101 Laura Ashley
(01458) 840405
Ladies' fashions, casual and formal. Home furnishings.

102 The Linen Cupboard
(01458) 447447
Bedding, towels, duvets, pillows, blankets, sleeping bags etc.

103 Michael Cooper's Studio
(01458) 445742
Rural watercolours; prints and cards from artist's own studio.

104 Monsoon/Accessorize
(01458) 840890
Women's fashion clothing & accessories, scarves to jewellery.

105 Poole Pottery
(01458) 840039
Broad range of clearance stock from well known brand.

106 Remington
(01458) 840209
Small electricals, cutlery, scissors, kitchen knives & gadgets.

107 Rohan
(01458) 841849
Clothing for travellers, adventurers and everyday use.

108 Royal Brierley
(01458) 840039
Hand-made crystal bowls, vases, glasses etc. *Poole Pottery.*

109 Royal Worcester
(01458) 840554
Fine china & earthenware, from small gifts to dinner services.

110 The Sock Shop
(01458) 840320
Socks and underwear.

111 The Sports Factory
(01458) 843164
Branded sporting equipment and clothing.

112 The Suit Company
(01458) 448681
Men's formal and casual wear.

113 Thorntons Chocolates
(01458) 841553
Quality confectionery: toffees, chocolates, seasonal lines.

114 Tridias
(01458) 448080
Extensive range of toys from leading manufacturers.

115 Triumph/Hom
(01458) 840700
Ladies' and men's underwear, nightwear and swimwear.

116 Van Heusen
(01458) 447233
Van Heusen shirts and silk ties.

117 The Village Gift Shop
(01458) 842436
Gifts, postcards and souvenirs from local area.

118 Village Pottery
(01458) 443889
Rebecca Landrock's unique range of pottery and 'have a go yourself'.

119 Viyella
(01458) 448533
Ladies' clothing in classic styles and fashions.

120 Whittard of Chelsea
(01458) 841323
Everthing to do with tea and coffee.

121 Windsmoor/Centaur
(01458) 840888
Well known clothing labels for men and women.

122 Woolea/Aquascutum
(01458) 841378
Suede, leather, lambskin and wool for men, women & children.

123 Wrangler
(01458) 841799
Jeans, shirts, jackets and T-shirts for the family.

Clarks Village

Griffin Products

124 Street Somerset See map on p. 73

Griffin Products

Pipers' Farm, Ashcott TA7 9QN
(01458) 210324

Top quality unique country-style coats and jackets (designed and made on premises and sold only directly from *Griffin*) in tweed, melton, ventile etc. Top of the range equestrian items: numnahs, girth sleeves, wither pads etc. Leisure items under the *Griffin* label – cross-country shirts, sweatshirts etc.

'Sample garments and clearance lines always available with jackets and coats at up to 50% off. All regular and equestrian stock sells at normal retail price. Made-to-measure service: please phone for details.'

Near the junction of A361 and A39, about 3 miles west of Street.

From M5 exit 23 and Bridgwater on A39: go through Ashcott. After about ½ mile, turn right (not sharp right), immediately before the Pipers' pub.*

From Street on A39: watch for A361 Taunton turn-off and Pipers' pub. Turn sharp left immediately after pub.*

****After 80 yds, turn right into drive to Pipers' Farm.***

Open: Mon–Fri 10–5.
Closed: Bank Holidays.
Cards: MasterCard, Switch, Visa.
Cars: Outside shop.
Toilets: Yes.
Wheelchairs: One small step to medium-sized shop.
Changing rooms: Yes.
Teas: Pipers' pub 80 yds from shop; pubs and cafés in Street.
Tours: Groups welcome, please book in advance. Free tours of factory arranged (maximum six people at a time).
Transport: No immediate access by public transport.
Mail order: Yes.
Catalogue: Free.

125 Stroud Gloucs

Carpet Shop (Carpets of Worth)

Ham Mills, Thrupp GL5 2BE
(01453) 882421

Wide range of woven Axminster carpets in good variety of colours and patterns and in different widths; few Axminster rugs; picture rugs; tufted carpets. Mainly wool/nylon.

'Seconds, imperfects, overmakes or discontinued lines. Don't forget to take room measurements! Free delivery if company's carpet fitter used.'

On the A419 (Stroud–Cirencester road), 1½ miles east of Stroud.

From Cirencester direction: pass Thrupp post office on right then after 200 yds look for factory shop sign on left; take next left turning into mill.

From Stroud: look for this clearly marked mill on right with the large sign 'Carpet bargains'. Keep going on main road – take next entrance into mill yard.

Open: Mon–Fri 9–4.30; Sat 9–1.
Closed: Bank Holidays; Easter; Spring Bank Holiday week; last week July/first week Aug (please check for exact dates); two days mid-Sept; Christmas–New Year.
Cards: None.
Cars: Outside shop.
Toilets: In Stroud.
Wheelchairs: Easy access, large display area.
Teas: In Stroud; lots of attractive local pubs.
Groups: Groups welcome to shop; please book in advance with Pauline Goddard.
Transport: Buses from Stroud to Thrupp every half hour.
Mail order: No.

126 Stroud Gloucs

The Factory Shop Ltd.

Westward Road, Cainscross GL5 4JF
(01453) 756655

Clothing and footwear for all the family. Good range of branded bedding, towels, kitchenware, toiletries and fancy goods; pottery; toys; wicker. *Cape Country* pine furniture exclusively produced for The Factory Shop.

'Large stock of branded and chainstore items, all at greatly reduced prices. Deliveries of new stock every week to give an ever changing selection.'

On A419 (Stroud–Bristol road) on western outskirts of Stroud.

From the town centre: follow signs to Bristol (A419), go over the large roundabout in Cainscross.*

From Nailsworth/Bath: turn left off A46 south of Stroud into Dudbridge Road for Cheltenham, Gloucester, M5; go to roundabout with A419; turn left for Bristol.*

****Go right after 100 yds in front of the White Horse Inn, turn first left and the shop is at the back left.***

Coming into Stroud on A419 from Bristol: turn left for 'Cashe's Green & Randwick' 100 yds before large roundabout on outskirts of town.

Open: Mon–Sat 9–5; Sun 10–4. Bank Holidays.
Closed: Christmas, Boxing and New Year's Days.
Cards: MasterCard, Switch, Visa.
Cars: Own free large car-park.
Toilets: Locally.
Wheelchairs: Easy entry to large ground floor shop.
Changing rooms: Yes.
Teas: Pubs locally.
Groups: Shopping groups welcome. For organiser/driver incentives please phone.
Transport: Local buses; 30 minutes' walk from town centre.
Mail order: Home delivery service for pine furniture. Please phone for free catalogue and price list.

127 Swindon Wilts

Blackwell Bros. (International Plants)

Stephenson Road, Groundwell Industrial Estate SN2 5AY
(01793) 706275

Company supplies major high street and DIY stores with house plants, patio plants, imported ceramics, house plant arrangements, terracotta patio pots, compost, basketware and a range of garden sundries.

'Britain's only houseplant factory shop! Most items, including house plant arrangements, are ends of lines at discounted prices (often about 30% off).'

On northern side of Swindon, off the A419 (M4–Cricklade Road).

From M4 exit 15: go north on Swindon bypass (A419) for 6+ miles; go left on to A4311 for Swindon centre. At first mini-roundabout, go left into Arkwright Road, then left into Stephenson Road.*

From town: with railway station on your left, go along Station Road; go left under low railway bridge. At next roundabout (Cockleberry), go right on to Great Western Way B4289. At next roundabout (Transfer Bridges), go straight, following signs to Cirencester. Continue north on A4311 for about a mile. At double mini-roundabout (Moonrakers pub on left) go straight. Continue for about a mile. At roundabout, go right for Groundwell Industrial Estate into Arkwright Road. Take first left, Stephenson Road. Blackwells are at end on right.

Open: Mon–Sat 10–4. Bank Holidays.
Closed: Christmas Eve–New Year's Eve.
Cards: Delta, MasterCard, Switch, Visa.
Cars: Own car-park.
Toilets: No.
Wheelchairs: One step to shop – assistance available.
Teas: Happy Eater nearby.
Groups: Small shopping groups welcome, but no coaches. No tours of the works.
Transport: Bus no. 16 to Penhill estate, 1/2 mile away.
Mail order: No.

128 Swindon Wilts

Cloverleaf Giftware

Arkwright Road, Groundwell SN2 5BA
(01793) 724556

Large selection of table mats, trays, coasters, moulded melamine goods, kitchen accessories, oven-to-tableware, pottery etc. Many co-ordinated lines. Large selection of bathroom cabinets plus wooden bathroom and kitchen accessories.

'Perfects, seconds and many ends of lines at reduced prices.'

On northern side of Swindon, off A419 (M4–Cricklade road).

From M4 exit 15: go north on Swindon bypass (A419) for 6+ miles. Go left on to A4311 for Swindon centre. At first mini-roundabout go left into Arkwright Road. Entrance on right.

From town: with railway station on your left, go along Station Road; go left under low railway bridge. At next roundabout (Cockleberry), go right on to Great Western Way B4289. At next roundabout (Transfer Bridges), go straight, following signs to Cirencester. Continue north on A4311 for about a mile. At double mini-roundabout (Moonrakers pub on left) go straight. Continue for about a mile. At roundabout, go right for Groundwell Industrial Estate into Arkwright Road. Keep straight to company on right.

Open: Mon–Sat 9.30–4.30; Sun and Bank Holidays 10–4.
Closed: Easter Sunday; please phone to check Christmas dates.
Cards: MasterCard, Switch, Visa.
Cars: Own car-park.
Toilets: Yes.
Wheelchairs: Four shallow steps, large shop. Ask for special access.
Teas: Tea and coffee from vending machine.
Tours: Free ¾ hour tours by appointment only, Tuesday evenings. Coach parties welcome. Shop is open – and cup of tea!
Transport: Bus no. 16 to Penhill Estate ½ mile away.
Mail order: Yes. No seconds.
Catalogue: £1.

129 Swindon Wilts

Great Western Designer Outlet Village

Kemble Drive
(01793) 507600

Over 100 designer and brand name shops, like *Aquascutum, Austin Reed, Jaeger, Christian Lacroix, Jigsaw, Nike, Laura Ashley, Le Creuset, Windsmoor,* selling a huge range of goods from women's, men's and children's fashion and footwear to accessories, books, music and home furnishings. Discounts of 30% or more off retail prices.

'Crèche, indoor and outdoor children's play area.'

See our display advertisement inside back cover

In the old railway works, near the station. Three miles from M4 exit 16.

From all directions: follow signs to 'Great Western'.

Open: Mon–Sat 9–6 (late night Thur to 8); Sun & Bank Holidays 11–5.
Closed: Christmas Day.
Cards: Yes.
Cars: 2000 car spaces (50p all day Sun & Bank Holidays) and 22 for coaches.
Toilets: Yes, and for disabled.
Wheelchairs: Easy access to entire shopping area; free wheelchairs.
Teas: Themed food court including *Harry Ramsden's, McDonald's, Singapore Sam, Villa Pizza, Fat Jackets, Nana Massarella's* and *Seattle Coffee Co.*
Groups: Coach parties always welcome. Please phone for group bookings.
Transport: 10-minute walk from railway station via covered walkway. Shuttle-bus between station, town centre and village Mon–Sat every 10 minutes.

130 Taunton Somerset

Frederick Theak

South Street TA1 3AD
(01823) 354317

Men's shirts for day and evening wear, also tunic shirts. Wedding accessories, waistcoats, cravats, bows, silk ties. Cufflinks and studs etc. Fabrics: silks, cottons, velvet (all fabrics used in production).

'A genuine factory shop selling first quality and seconds.'

About ½ mile east of town centre.

From the east and M5 exit 25: follow A358 (Wellington Road) along Toneway, crossing one traffic light. At the roundabout turn left into Victoria Parkway, travel in right lane. Turn into left lane past a garage; at traffic lights turn left into Victoria Street.*

From Taunton town centre: follow A38 towards M5 along East Street. Pass old hospital on right; take first right at traffic lights into Victoria Street.*

From the west: follow A358 towards M5, looking out for old hospital on right. At traffic lights go right into Victoria Street.*

****Take first right (Queen Street) then at T-junction go right into South Street. Factory is on right.***

Open: Fri 9.30–3; Sat 9.30–12.30.
Closed: Good Friday, Easter Saturday, Christmas–New Year.
Cards: All major cards accepted.
Cars: Limited parking available.
Toilets: Ask if desperate.
Wheelchairs: One step to front entrance, no steps to rear (please ask).
Changing rooms: No.
Teas: Locally.
Transport: Southern National bus nos. 22–31 to old hospital.
Mail order: No.

131 Taunton Somerset

Sewing Paradise

142 East Reach TA6 4SL
(01823) 276861

Misprints, seconds and remnants of dress and upholstery fabrics from major British factories. Clearance haberdashery. Upholstery foam at factory prices. Curtaining, sheeting and craft fabrics.

'Perfects and seconds available. Fabrics from £1 per metre; lace edging from 10p per metre. Thread from £1 per 1000 m.'

East Reach is a major street in the town centre, leading into town from locations east.

Coming into town along East Reach: shop is on the left, after Victoria Street on left and just before South Street.

From the town centre (pedestrianised area): walk along East Reach. Pass the pizza takeaway on the right, cross South Street and this shop is on the right.

Open: Mon–Sat 9.15–5.15.
Closed: Bank Holidays.
Cards: MasterCard, Visa.
Cars: Time-limited parking almost in front of shop.
Toilets: 150 m from shop.
Wheelchairs: Easy access.
Teas: Co-op store 200 m. Lots of places in town.
Groups: Groups welcome, no need to book.
Transport: ½ mile to Taunton train and coach stations.
Mail order: Yes. Non-bulky items only.

132 Tetbury Gloucs

Top Cat Designs

Units 5 & 6, Silk Mill Studios, Charlton Road GL8 8DY
(01666) 505890

Large range of ladies' hats in assorted fabrics such as velvets, cottons, tartans, wools etc. Special occasion hats in straw, sinamay (natural plant fibre), coloured palm fibres and silk.

'We specialise in weather-proofed wax hats. Reductions on retail price for perfect stock, some seconds and end-of-line bargain hats. Special sale of spring/summer products in week after August Bank Holiday. Commissions gladly accepted, including hats for weddings etc customised to your own style/requirements.'

About 100 yds from the old Market Hall (at the cross-road in the centre of Tetbury). On the south-west side of the village..

From Cirencester: turn right at crossroads (police station on near left corner) on to A4135 to Dursley.*

From village centre: take A4135 for Dursley.*

****Pass fire station on left, then village green. Silk Mill Studios courtyard is 25 yds on left.***

Open: Mon–Fri 9–5; Sat & Sun by arrangement. Most Bank Holidays, please phone to check.
Closed: Christmas–New Year.
Cards: Amex, Eurocard, MasterCard, Visa.
Cars: Own car-park.
Toilets: Yes.
Wheelchairs: Ramp up to wide doors with access to factory. Showroom on first floor.
Changing rooms: Yes.
Teas: Free tea or coffee offered. Several tea shops, pubs and restaurants in town.
Groups: Free tours of factory for groups of up to 10 people; please book in advance with Jacqui Morris.
Transport: Bus nos. 92 & 93 every hour from Gloucester and Stroud. Alight in town centre, then 3 minutes' walk.
Mail order: Yes.
Catalogue: Please phone for free catalogue.

133 Tiverton Devon

John Heathcoat & Co. (Sales)

West Exe EX16 5LL *(01884) 252816/254949*

Extensive range of furnishing and fashion fabrics (many made here) – cottons, polycottons, polyester, satin, silk, crèpe-de-chine, bridal fabrics, embroidered lace, wools, suiting, cords, fishermen's and garden nets, ripstop for kites and hot air balloons. All you require for dressmaking – haberdashery, patterns etc. Craft and toy-making fabrics.

'Home furnishing studio with curtain-making service. Perfects and seconds at factory shop prices.'

See our display advertisement opposite

Close to town centre.

From A361 dual carriage bypass go to roundabout where the A396 crosses. Then follow 'town centre' signs on A396. Pass East Devon Technical College on right; go right at next mini-roundabout, pass Safeways on left; go over bridge, go left past Heathcoats. Stay in left lane of one-way system; pass stone wall on left which becomes metal fence. Here make sharp left turn into factory entrance. Shop on right.

NB Some road atlases show show the A361 as A373.

From the south on A395 enter one-way system and keep going right until you see large sign to Heathcoat on left. Shop is on right as you drive into factory.

Open: Mon–Fri 9–4.30; Sat 9–1. Bank Holidays 9–4.30.
Closed: Christmas–New Year.
Cards: MasterCard, Switch, Visa.
Cars: Own car-park.
Toilets: Yes.
Wheelchairs: Ramp to huge three-roomed shop.
Teas: Machine in canteen; lots of places in town.
Groups: Shopping groups welcome, please phone in advance.
Transport: Bus station in town – no buses pass mill.
Mail order: Yes.
Catalogue: No.

See our entry opposite

134 Tiverton Devon

Sheridan

Unit 10, Kennedy Way Industrial Estate, Mountbatten Road
EX16 6SW
(01884) 255997

Printed and fashion-dyed bed linen, full range of accessories including curtains, lampshades, borders and towels. Co-ordinating furnishing fabrics.

'Ends of line and slightly imperfect Sheridan branded bedlinen and accessories at up to 50% off normal retail prices.'

Close to town centre.

Coming south on the A396: pass East Devon Technical College on right; go right at next mini-roundabout; go left towards Safeway.*

Coming north on the A396: pass John Heathcoat on right, go over bridge and take first right towards Safeway.*

****Pass Safeway on left; take first turning on right after garage and follow road veering left to T-junction. Shop on far end on left.***

Open: Mon–Sat 10–5.
Closed: Bank Holidays; Christmas–New Year.
Cards: Amex, MasterCard, Switch, Visa.
Cars: Own car-park outside shop.
Toilets: Ask if desperate.
Wheelchairs: No access, unfortunately. Shop is upstairs.
Teas: In Safeway.
Groups: Groups welcome, please phone in advance.
Mail order: Yes.
Catalogue: Free.

135 Torquay Devon

Factory Fabric Warehouse

12–14 Market Street TQ1 3AQ
(01803) 211444

Large range of upholstery and furnishing fabrics: cottons, linens, damasks, velvets etc. Nets, voiles, calico, interlinings, waddings, linings. Haberdashery, fringing. Curtain rails/poles and accessories. Cushion covers and fillers. Ready-made curtains. Foam cut to shape. Some dress fabrics.

'About 2500 rolls in stock. Curtain-making service. Interior design service.'

See our display advertisement on p. 195

In the centre of town. Market Street leads north off Union Street (a major shopping street).

Best to aim for town centre. Turn out of Union Street at the traffic lights into Market Street. The shop is 200 yds on the right, opposite the entrance of the old covered market.

Open: Mon–Sat 9–5.
Bank Holidays 10–4.
Closed: Phone for Christmas closures.
Cards: Access, Connect, Delta, Switch, Visa.
Cars: Own car-park at rear.
Toilets: Yes (on first floor).
Wheelchairs: No steps to ground floor; stairs to first floor (staff happy to bring down items). Large shop.
Teas: Lots of cafés nearby.
Groups: Shopping groups welcome, no need to phone.
Transport: Any bus to Torquay centre.

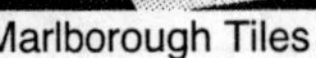

Marlborough Tiles

Dent's

Croydex

136 Warminster Wilts

Dent's

Fairfield Road BA12 9DL
(01985) 212291

Gloves in many styles and colours in leather, suede and wool for ladies and men. Sports gloves (eg, shooting, equestrian). Extensive range of handbags. Leather briefcases, wallets, belts, purses, gifts, umbrellas etc.

'Discontinued and imperfect ranges, many at less than half retail price.'

Near the town centre: aim for main car-park, library, station and tourist information.

From Trowbridge: on reaching town centre, turn left at mini-roundabout; go over lights (where A350 goes off to Shaftesbury) and continue along main road through town (A36); turn left at mini-roundabout (in front of post office).*

From Shaftesbury: at lights in town centre turn right on to A36, continue along main road through town then go left at mini-roundabout (in front of post office).*

***Follow sign for station, library, tourist information. Fairfield Road is first turning on right (just after Warminster police station on left). Company is clearly visible, shortly on right.**

Open: *1 Sept–end July:* Tues–Sat 10–4.
Closed: Monday; August; Christmas and Boxing Days.
Cards: Delta, MasterCard, Switch, Visa.
Cars: Own car-park.
Toilets: No.
Wheelchairs: Easy access.
Teas: In Warminster.
Groups: Shopping groups welcome. Visit Dent's Museum, by prior appointment only.
Transport: Local buses. 400 yds from Warminster rail station.
Mail order: No.

137 Wellington Somerset

Fox's Mill Shop

Tonedale Mills TA21 0AW
(01823) 661860

Range of suiting, worsted and woollen cloths; remnants. Skirt lengths. Most fabrics made on premises. Men's bespoke tailoring and men's second-hand jackets.

'Both perfects and seconds on sale. Prices range from £4–£15 per metre x 60 ins wide. Interesting varied range of cloth weights in plain greys, navy blue, tweeds and designed cloths. Bespoke tailoring on premises, please ask for details.'

North-east of town, not far from M5 exit 26.

From M5 exit 26: follow signs to Wellington. In town centre turn right into North Street B3187 for Milverton at traffic lights.*

From the south on A38: turn off at roundabout signposted to Wellington. In town centre turn left at lights for B3187 to Milverton. Pub called Kings Arms on corner.*

***Continue for ¾ mile, pass a garage on the left then cross a railway bridge. Take first left (Mill Stream Gardens); after 200 yds turn left into large courtyard. Shop at back up five steps.**

Open: Fri 10–4; Sat 10–1.
Closed: Bank Holidays; Christmas–New Year.
Cards: No.
Cars: Outside.
Toilets: In Wellington.
Wheelchairs: No access, five steps to shop.
Changing rooms: Yes.
Teas: In Wellington.
Groups: Groups welcome to shop.
Transport: Shuttle bus half hourly from post office in High Street to Tonedale.
Mail order: Yes. No seconds.

138 Witney Oxon

Early's of Witney

Burford Road OX8 5EA
(01993) 703131

Wool, cotton and acrylic blankets and throws; branded bed linens, towels, kitchen textiles, quilts and pillows. Offcuts of fabrics and woollens.

'First quality goods and slight imperfects at very competitive prices. Discontinued and clearance lines.'

From town centre (old covered market cross with stone columns and clock): go north (Tourist office on right) along High Street. At second mini-roundabout, go left into Mill Street (to Faringdon A4095/4047) which becomes Burford Road. Mill is on right – after tall brick chimney go right through Gate 5.

From places west via A40: turn off to 'Witney, Abingdon A415'. At bottom of slip road, go left to 'Witney'.*

From Oxford on A40: don't take first exit to 'Witney East' but next exit to 'South & West Witney'. Go right at roundabout to 'Witney A415'.*

****At next roundabout go left to 'Bampton' & 'Industrial Estates'. Keep going round towards Minster Lovell (B4047); at T-junction traffic lights go right for Bicester (A4095). Continue to Early's chimney on left.***

Open: Mon–Sat 10–5.
Closed: Public holidays; Christmas–New Year.
Cars: Free parking outside shop.
Cards: MasterCard, Switch, Visa.
Toilets: In Witney.
Wheelchairs: Special ramp with hand-rail, to large shop on ground floor.
Teas: In Witney.
Tours: Shopping groups always welcome. Factory tours arranged (minimum 6 people) – please telephone to organise.
Transport: Local buses pass the mill.
Mail order: Yes. Please phone during shop trading hours to discuss requirements and product availability.

139 Yeovil Somerset

West of England Reproduction Furniture

8 Bardel Court, Houndstone Business Park BA22 8RU
(01935) 706331

Wide range of reproduction furniture in mahogany, oak, yew and cherry. Dining-tables, chairs, bookcases, corner cabinets, desks, captain chairs etc.

'4ft x 2ft desks from £295, 7ft mahogany dining-table with four chairs and two carvers from £645.'

West of Yeovil and north of A3088.

From north via A37: go right at 2nd roundabout into Preston Rd.*

From east on A30: go right on to A37 for Bristol (at roundabout with hospital on right). At next roundabout, go left (Preston Rd).*

****Continue straight for about 1 mile; at the roundabout with Pioneer supermarket on left, go straight.*****

From south via A37: go left at T-junction for Crewkerne. At next roundabout, go right for Taunton and M5.***

From west on A30: turn left at roundabout for Bristol.***

******At next roundabout, go left (pass airfield on right); go straight at following roundabout; pass crematorium on left; at roundabout with Pioneer supermarket on right turn left.*****

From Ilminster: turn off A303 on to A3088. At first roundabout at beginning of town go left for crematorium; at roundabout with Pioneer supermarket, go left.**

*****Pass Toyota on right then turn right in front of Volkswagen. Take next right and right again. Shop is straight ahead.***

Open: Mon–Fri 9–5; Sat 10–4.
Closed: Phone to check hours for Bank Holidays and during Christmas–New Year period.
Cards: Delta, JCB, MasterCard, Switch, Visa.
Cars: Car-park next to factory.
Toilets: Yes.
Wheelchairs: One step to ground floor showroom.
Teas: In Yeovil.
Groups: Groups welcome, please phone in advance.
Mail order: Yes, with money back guarantee.
Catalogue: Catalogue and price list on request.

Market days in South-West England

Andover	Thur, Sat outdoor general
Banbury	Thur, Sat outdoor general
Barnstaple	Tues, Fri, Sat pannier market; Wed antiques & books; Mon, Thur craft market
Bath	Mon–Sat indoor general; Thur outdoor general
Bicester	Fri outdoor general; Sat outdoor general
Bridgwater	Sat outdoor general
Bristol	Mon–Sat indoor general; Sun outdoor general (largest market in West of England).
Cheltenham	Fri, Sat outdoor general; Sun outdoor general
Chippenham	Fri indoor/outdoor general
Cirencester	Mon, Fri outdoor general (one of Britain's oldest)
Dorchester	Wed indoor/outdoor general
Exeter	Mon–Fri indoor general; Mon–Fri outdoor general
Exmouth	Mon–Sat indoor general
Frome	Wed, Sat outdoor general
Glastonbury	Tues outdoor general
Gloucester	Mon–Sat indoor general; Sat outdoor general
Marlborough	Wed, Sat outdoor general
Minehead	Tues, Thur (Easter to October) outdoor general
Newton Abbot	Wed, Sat outdoor general; Mon to Sat indoor general
Oxford	Wed outdoor general; Mon–Sat indoor general
Plymouth	Sat outdoor general; Tues, Fri, Sat indoor general
Poole	Wed, Sat; outdoor general
Ross-on-Wye	Thur, Sat outdoor general
Salisbury	Tues, Sat outdoor general
Shepton Mallett	Fri outdoor general
Southampton	Thur, Fri, Sat indoor general; Tues antiques
St Austell	Sat, Sun indoor/outdoor (largest all-weather complex in the South-West)
Stroud	Sat outdoor general
Swindon	Thur outdoor general; Wed, Sat, Sun indoor/outdoor general
Taunton	Sat indoor/outdoor
Tiverton	Tues, Fri, Sat indoor/outdoor general
Torquay	Mon outdoor general
Truro	Mon outdoor general
Warminster	Fri outdoor general
Wellington	Tues, Thur, Fri, Sat indoor/outdoor general
Witney	Thur, Sat outdoor general
Yeovil	Fri outdoor general

With thanks to World's Fair Ltd for allowing us to use information from their 'Markets Yearbook'.

Towns with factory shops

Ammanford	1	Alan Paine Knitwear
Ammanford	2	Corgi Hosiery
Bedwas	4	Gallery Home Fashion
Blackwood	5	Gossard
Cardiff	6	Avana Bakeries
Cardiff	7	Calico
Chepstow	8	Stuart Crystal
Crymmych	9	Frenni Furniture
Ebbw Vale	10	Start-rite Shoes
Haverfordwest	11	Thistle Trading
Margam	12	ISE International Furniture
Merthyr Tydfil	13	The Factory Toy Shop
Merthyr Tydfil	14	O P Chocolate
Merthyr Tydfil	15	Pendor (Clothing)
Nelson	3	Stuart Crystal
Newtown	16	Laura Ashley Sale Shop
Pontypridd	17	Alexon
Pontypridd	18	Fabric World
Porth	19	Royal Worcester & Spode
Rhayader	20	Welsh Royal Crystal
St Nicholas	21	Tregwynt Woollen Mill
Swansea	22	Abbey Woollen Mill
Swansea	23	Clothing Factory Shop
Treorchy	24	Burberry's
Treorchy	25	Porth Innovations
Welshpool	26	Silver Scenes
Guernsey : St Peter Port	27	Guernsey Woollens
Guernsey : St Saviours	28	Le Tricoteur
Jersey : St Helier	29	Summerland
Andover	30	Croydex
Bampton	31	Origin
Banbury	32	A & J Fabrics
Banbury	p60	där lighting
Barnstaple	33	C H Brannam
Barnstaple	34	Croydex
Barnstaple	35	Factory Fabric Warehouse
Barnstaple	36	LS & J Sussman
Bath	37	Roper Rhodes
Bicester	38	Bicester Village
Bloxham	39	Weavers Shop, The
Bodmin	40	Silken Ladder
Bourton-on-the-Water	41	Warwick Fabrics
Bovey Tracey	42	House of Marbles and Teign Valley Glass
Bridgwater	43	Sedgemoor Shoes
Bristol	44	Factory Fabric House
Bristol : Bedminster	45	Calico
Bristol : St George	46	Bristol Carpets
Burford	47	Just Fabrics
Cheltenham	48	Cotswold Fabric Warehouse

Towns with factory shops

Town	No.	Shop
Cheltenham	49	Marlborough Tiles
Cheltenham	p70	Penny Plain
Cranham	50	Prinknash Pottery
Dartmouth	51	Dartmouth Pottery
Dorchester	52	The National Trust
Exeter	53	Factory Fabric Warehouse
Glastonbury	54	Morlands
Glastonbury	55	Richard Draper
Goonhavern near Perranporth	56	Kernewek Pottery
Great Torrington	57	Dartington Crystal
Highcliffe	58	The Catalogue Shop
Kidlington	59	Freelance Fabrics
Marlborough	60	Marlborough Tiles
Mere	61	Ethos Candles
Minehead	62	The Factory Shop Ltd.
Newton Abbot	63	Candy
Oxford	64	Isis Ceramics
Plymouth	65	Factory Fabric Warehouse
Plymouth	66	Jaeger
Poole	67	Catalogue
Poole	68	Poole Pottery
Redruth	69	The Fabric Shop
Redruth	70	The Factory Shop Ltd.
Ross-on-Wye	71	Barker Shoes Factory Shop at Herrings
Ross-on-Wye	72	Ross Labels
Salisbury	73	Marlborough Tiles
Salisbury	74	Wilton Carpet Factory
Saltford	75	Factory Pine
Shepton Mallet	76	Mulberry
Southampton	77	Factory Pine
Southampton	78	Freelance Fabrics (Southampton)
St Austell	79	LS & J Sussman
Stratford-upon-Avon	80	Stratford Tile Warehouse
Street	81–123	Clarks Village
Street	124	Griffin Products
Stroud	125	Carpet Shop (Carpets of Worth)
Stroud	126	The Factory Shop Ltd.
Swindon	127	Blackwell Bros. (International Plants)
Swindon	128	Cloverleaf Giftware
Swindon	129	Great Western Designer Outlet Village
Taunton	130	Frederick Theak
Taunton	131	Sewing Paradise
Tetbury	132	Top Cat Designs
Tiverton	133	John Heathcoat
Tiverton	134	Sheridan
Torquay	135	Factory Fabric Warehouse
Warminster	136	Dent's
Wellington	137	Fox's
Witney	138	Early's of Witney
Yeovil	139	West of England Reproduction Furniture

B

South-East England
London &
East Anglia

B

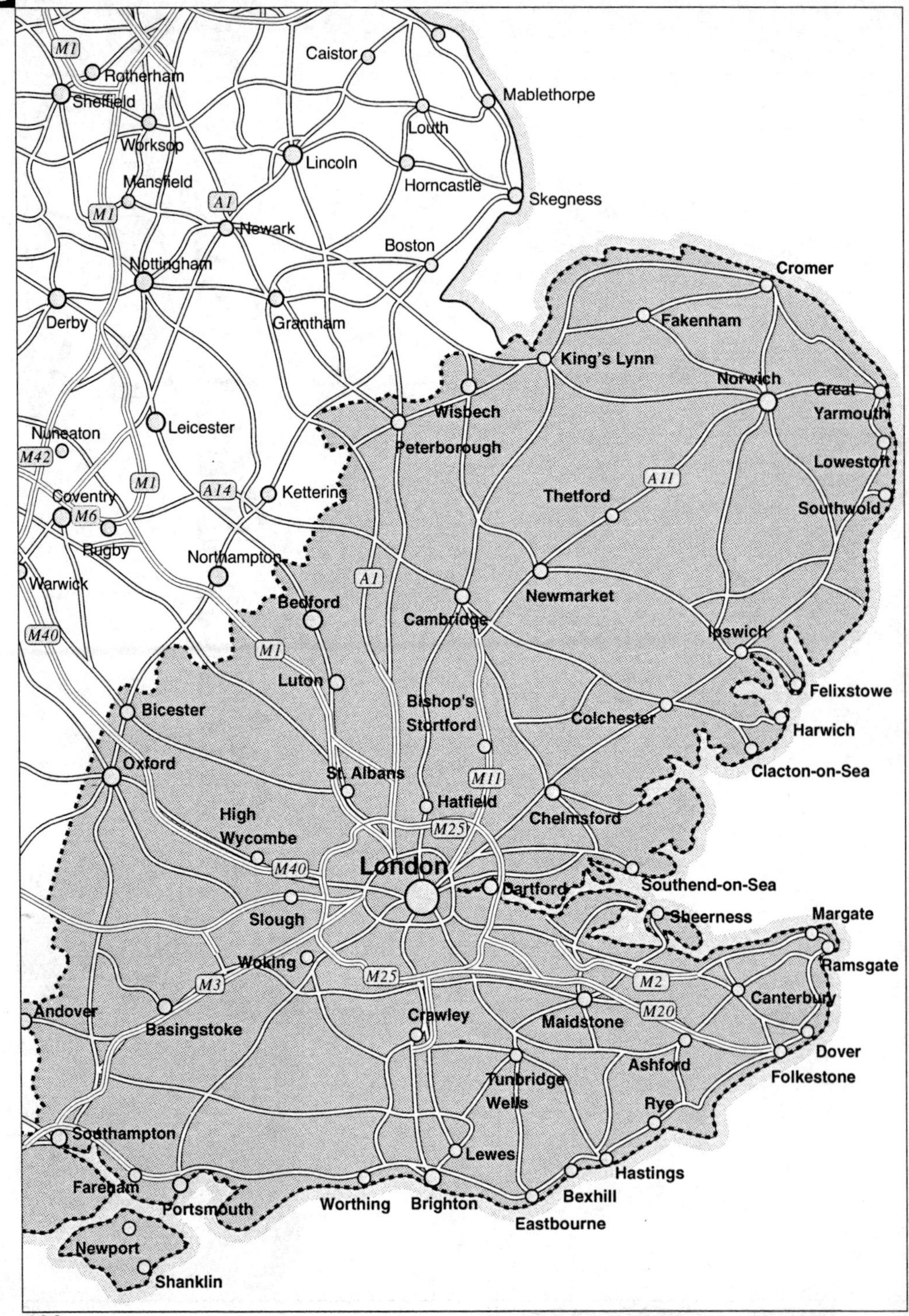
M1
Rotherham
Sheffield
Caistor
Mablethorpe
Louth
Worksop
Lincoln
Horncastle
Mansfield
Skegness
A1
M1
Newark
Boston
Nottingham
Derby
Grantham
Cromer
Fakenham
King's Lynn
Norwich
Great Yarmouth
Wisbech
Leicester
Peterborough
Nuneaton
M42
Lowestoft
A11
Thetford
M1
A14
Kettering
Coventry
M6
Southwold
Rugby
Northampton
Warwick
A1
Newmarket
Bedford
Cambridge
M40
Ipswich
M1
Luton
Felixstowe
Bishop's Stortford
Bicester
Colchester
Harwich
Oxford
St. Albans
M11
Clacton-on-Sea
Hatfield
High Wycombe
Chelmsford
M25
London
M40
Southend-on-Sea
Dartford
Slough
Sheerness
Margate
Woking
Ramsgate
M25
M2
M3
Canterbury
Andover
Crawley
Maidstone
M20
Basingstoke
Dover
Ashford
Tunbridge Wells
Folkestone
Rye
Southampton
Lewes
Hastings
Fareham
Worthing
Brighton
Bexhill
Portsmouth
Eastbourne
Newport
Shanklin

South-East England, London & East Anglia

After a slow start, South-East England and East Anglia have advanced by leaps and bounds ... from a factory shop point of view. The range of reduced price goods on offer has exploded, and shoppers have quickly latched on to the concept.

It is one of the few regions where large kitchen appliances such as vacuum cleaners, microwaves, videos and televisions are available at discounted prices. The companies featured here have exclusive contracts with specific manufacturers and catalogue companies to take their ex-display models, returned items and surplus stock (on the same principle as factory shops). One company began as the distributor for a nationwide chainstore – then had the chance to sell the ends of ranges and ex-display models. This has worked out an excellent arrangement all round, benefiting the chainstore, the warehouse and the public – who can save several hundred pounds on one or two pieces of furniture.

Economies on large items can be remarkable. If you are furnishing a room from scratch, savings of a couple of thousands of pounds are perfectly feasible.

Carpets and furnishing fabrics are well worth travelling for in the south-east. You can even indulge yourself in the luxury of having a carpet made to the shade of your choice – while still spending considerably less than you would for equivalent quality in the high street.

East Anglia is brilliant for terracotta pots for both kitchen and garden, for footwear (Norwich has long been one of the traditional centres of shoemaking) including made-to-measure shoes at a very reasonable price (what luxury!), for crystal and for brand name clothes and silks. The home counties come into their own for stylish hats, trendy head-gear and leisurewear, designer jeans, fashion jewellery, furnishing fabrics and furniture. London offers a diverse range such as chainstore furniture, electrical items, upmarket clothing, glass and candles. Go further south for occasion wear, chainstore clothing, jewellery, ladies' quality knitwear, lampshades, superb quality cotton and lace bedding and nightdresses.

Take the opportunity to visit the factory shop centres in Bicester, Brighton, Clacton and Hatfield, and the new complex in Dover – they make interesting outings for the whole family and you are most unlikely to leave without some special bargain.

The Fabric Factory

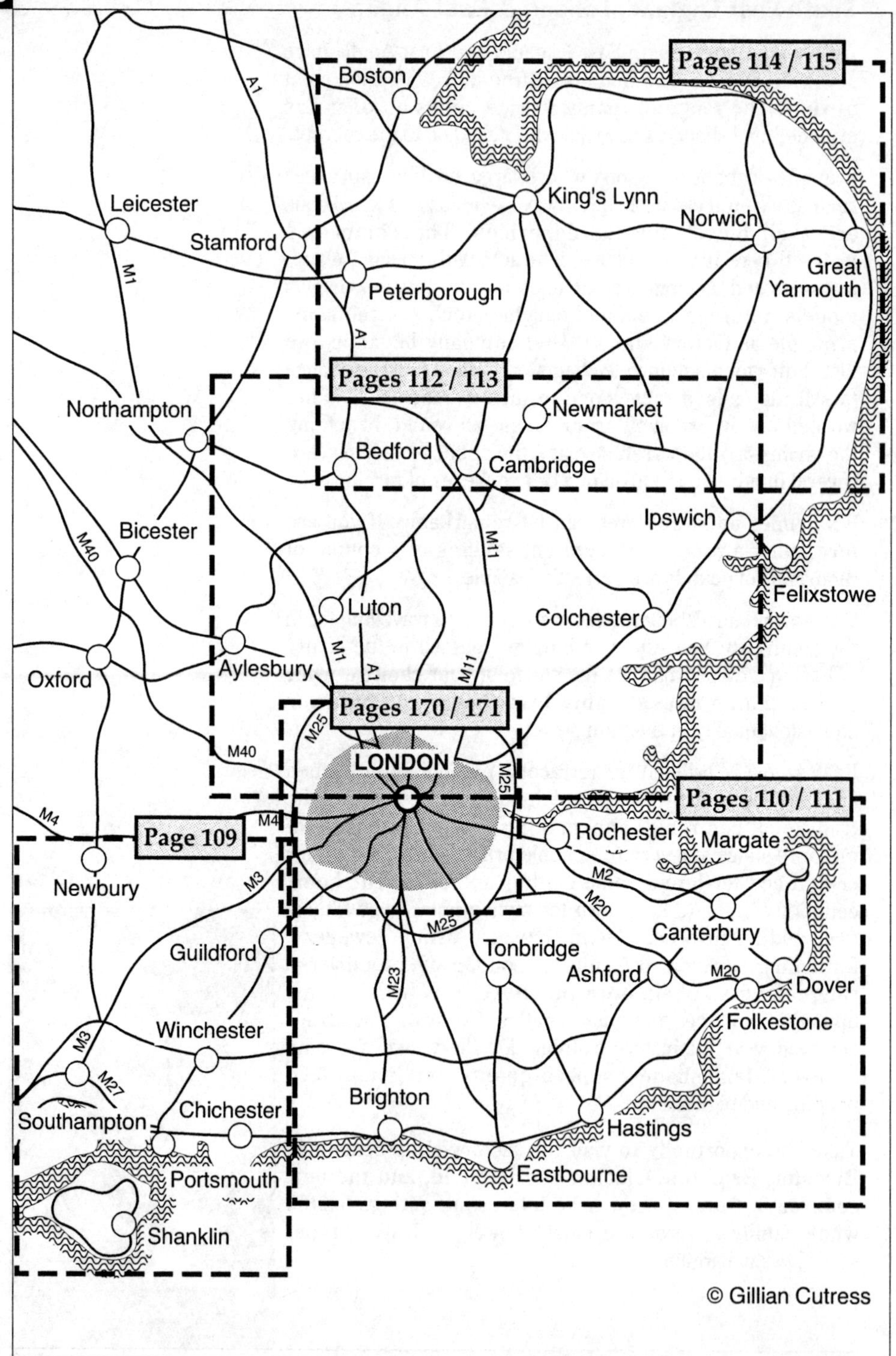
Pages 114 / 115
Boston
A1
Leicester
King's Lynn
Norwich
Stamford
Great Yarmouth
M1
Peterborough
A1
Pages 112 / 113
Northampton
Newmarket
Bedford
Cambridge
Bicester
Ipswich
M40
M11
Felixstowe
Luton
Colchester
Oxford
Aylesbury
M1
A1
M11
Pages 170 / 171
M25
LONDON
M40
M25
Pages 110 / 111
M4
M4
Page 109
Rochester
Margate
Newbury
M3
M2
M20
Canterbury
M25
Guildford
Tonbridge
Ashford
M20
Dover
M23
Folkestone
Winchester
M3
M27
Brighton
Chichester
Southampton
Hastings
Portsmouth
Eastbourne
Shanklin
© Gillian Cutress

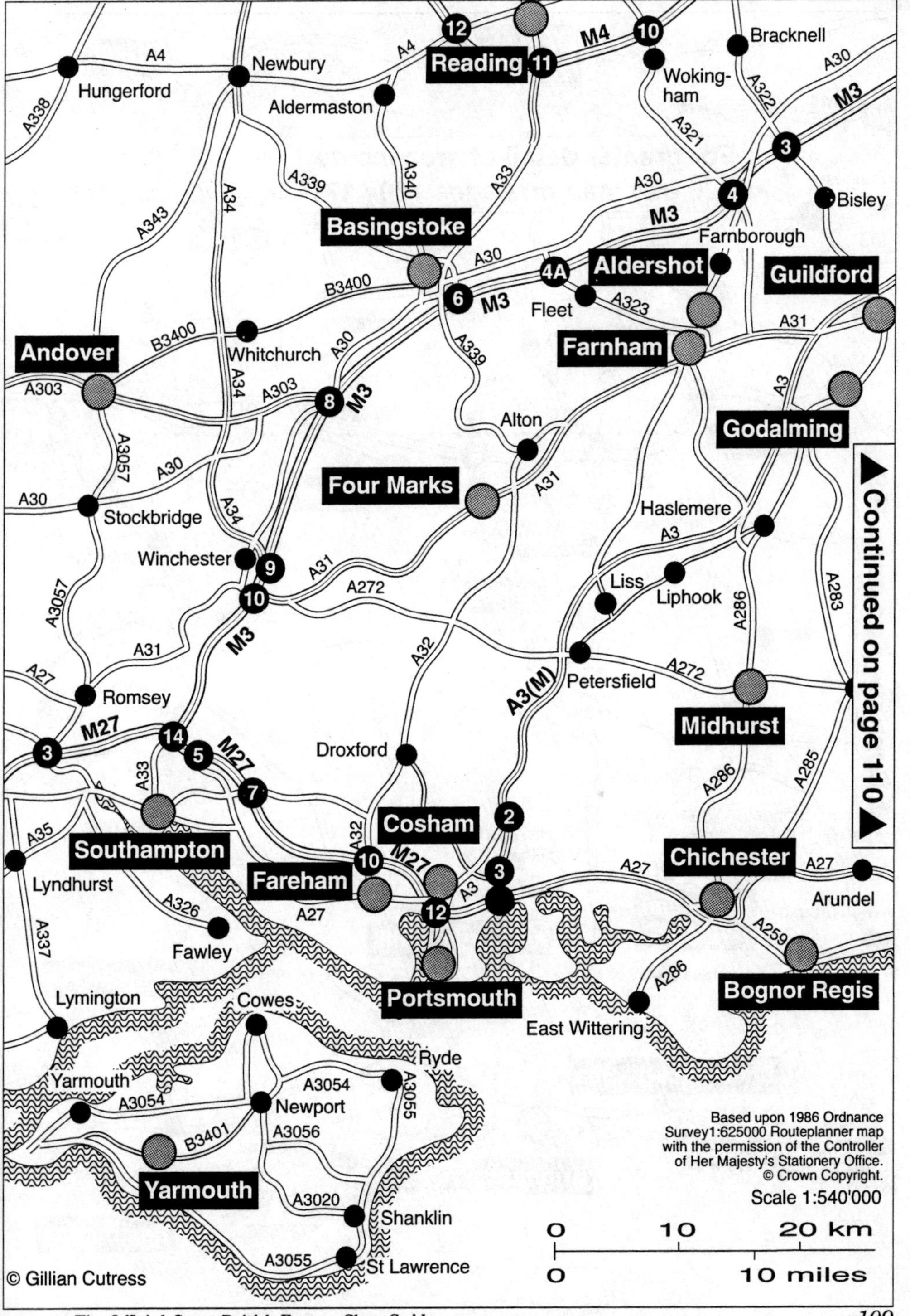

▲ Continued on page 110 ▲

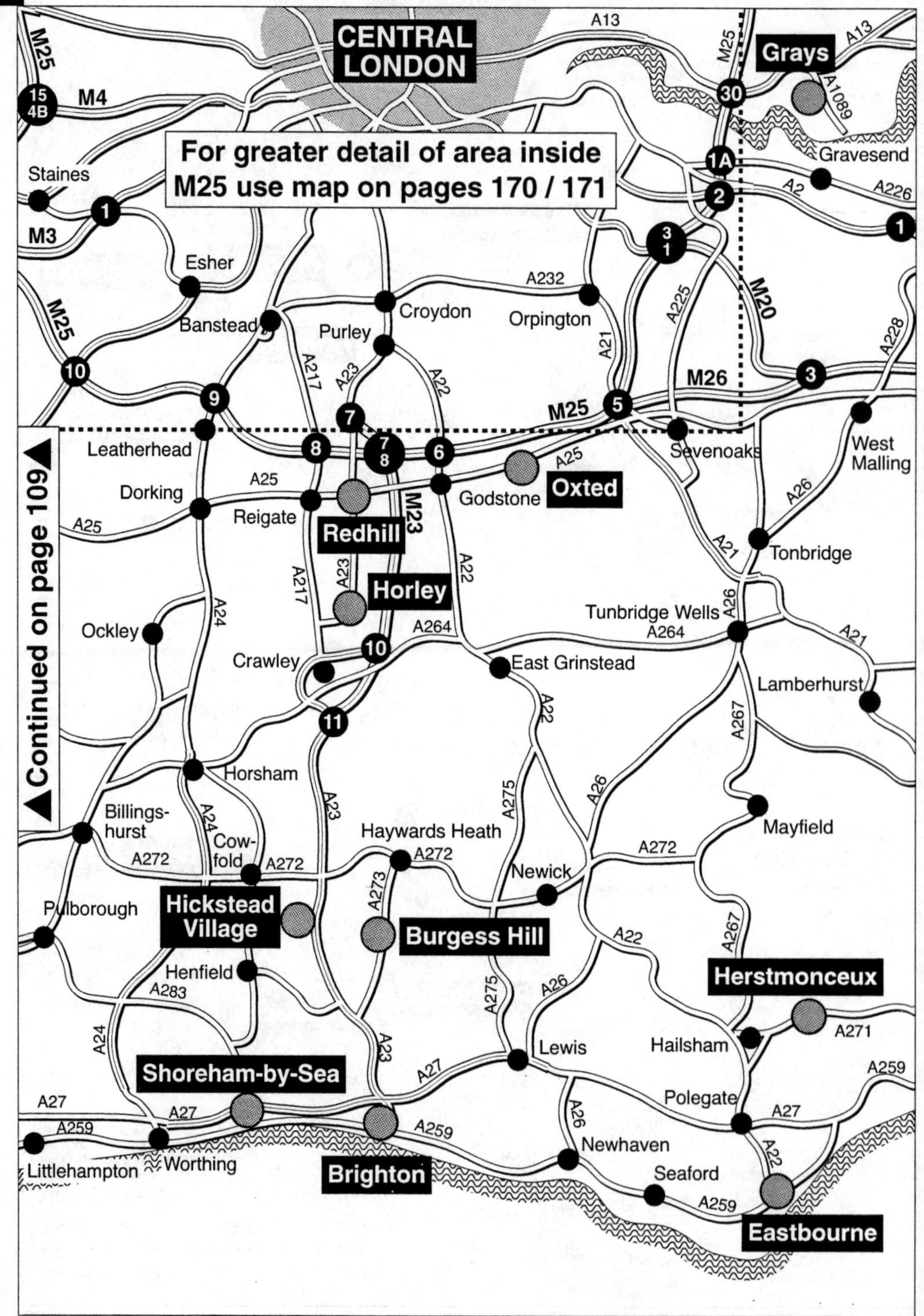
CENTRAL LONDON
For greater detail of area inside M25 use map on pages 170 / 171
Continued on page 109
Grays
Oxted
Redhill
Horley
Hickstead Village
Burgess Hill
Herstmonceux
Shoreham-by-Sea
Brighton
Eastbourne
Staines
Esher
Banstead
Croydon
Purley
Orpington
Gravesend
Leatherhead
Dorking
Reigate
Godstone
Sevenoaks
West Malling
Tonbridge
Tunbridge Wells
Ockley
Crawley
East Grinstead
Lamberhurst
Horsham
Billings-hurst
Cow-fold
Haywards Heath
Newick
Mayfield
Pulborough
Henfield
Lewis
Hailsham
Polegate
Newhaven
Seaford
Littlehampton
Worthing
M25
M4
M3
M26
M20
M23
A13
A1089
A2
A226
A232
A225
A21
A228
A217
A23
A22
A25
A26
A24
A264
A267
A275
A272
A273
A283
A271
A27
A259

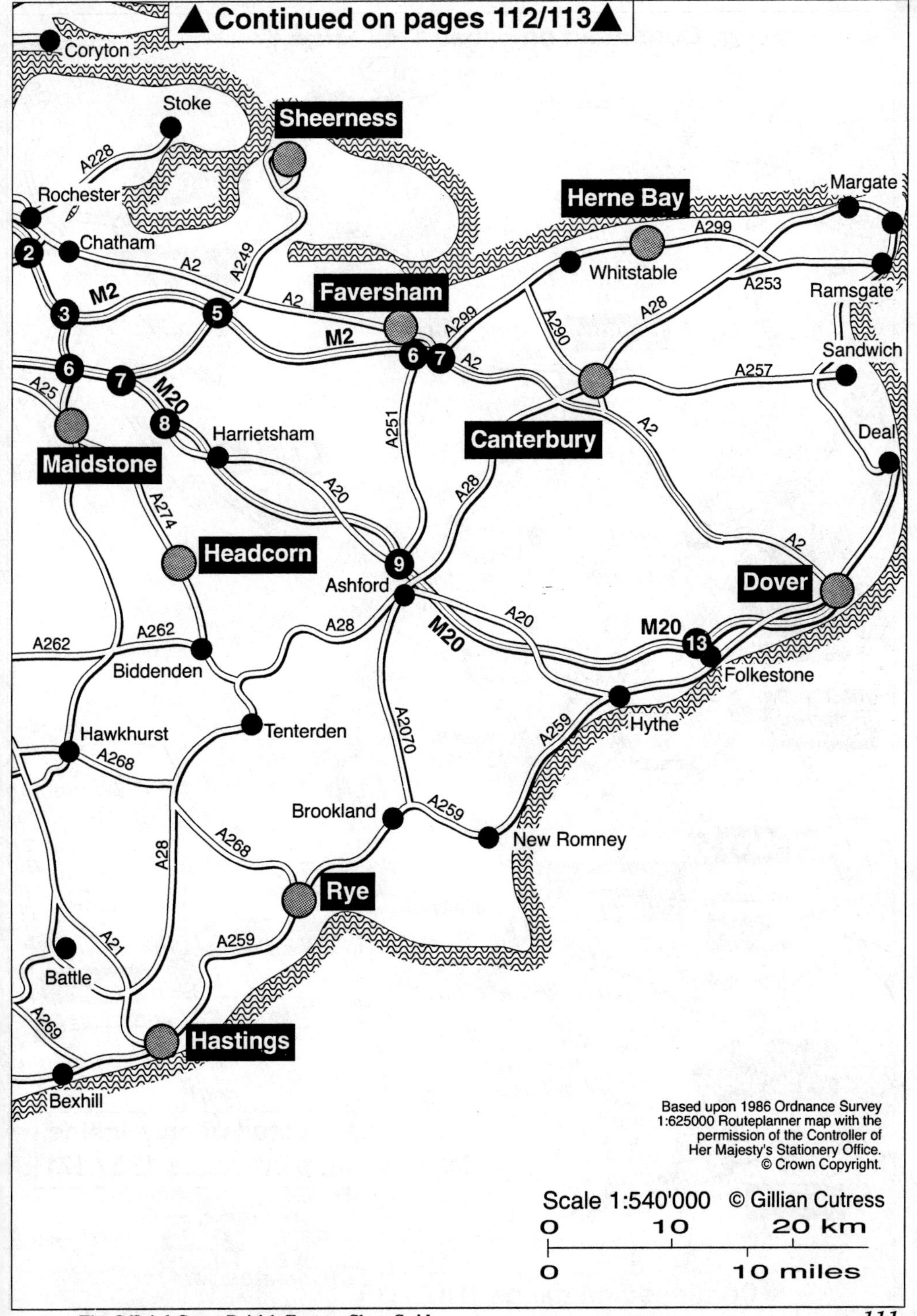
▲Continued on pages 112/113▲
Coryton
Stoke
Sheerness
A228
Rochester
Chatham
2
A2
A249
3
M2
5
A2
Faversham
M2
6
7
A2
A299
Herne Bay
Whitstable
A299
Margate
A253
Ramsgate
A28
A290
Sandwich
A257
6
7
A25
M20
8
Maidstone
Harrietsham
A251
Canterbury
A2
Deal
A20
A28
A274
Headcorn
9
Ashford
A2
Dover
A262
A262
A28
A20
M20
M20
13
Folkestone
Biddenden
Hythe
Tenterden
Hawkhurst
A268
A2070
A259
Brookland
A259
New Romney
A268
A28
Rye
A21
A259
Battle
A269
Hastings
Bexhill
Based upon 1986 Ordnance Survey 1:625000 Routeplanner map with the permission of the Controller of Her Majesty's Stationery Office. © Crown Copyright.
Scale 1:540'000 © Gillian Cutress
0 10 20 km
0 10 miles

▲ Continued on pages 114 / 115▲

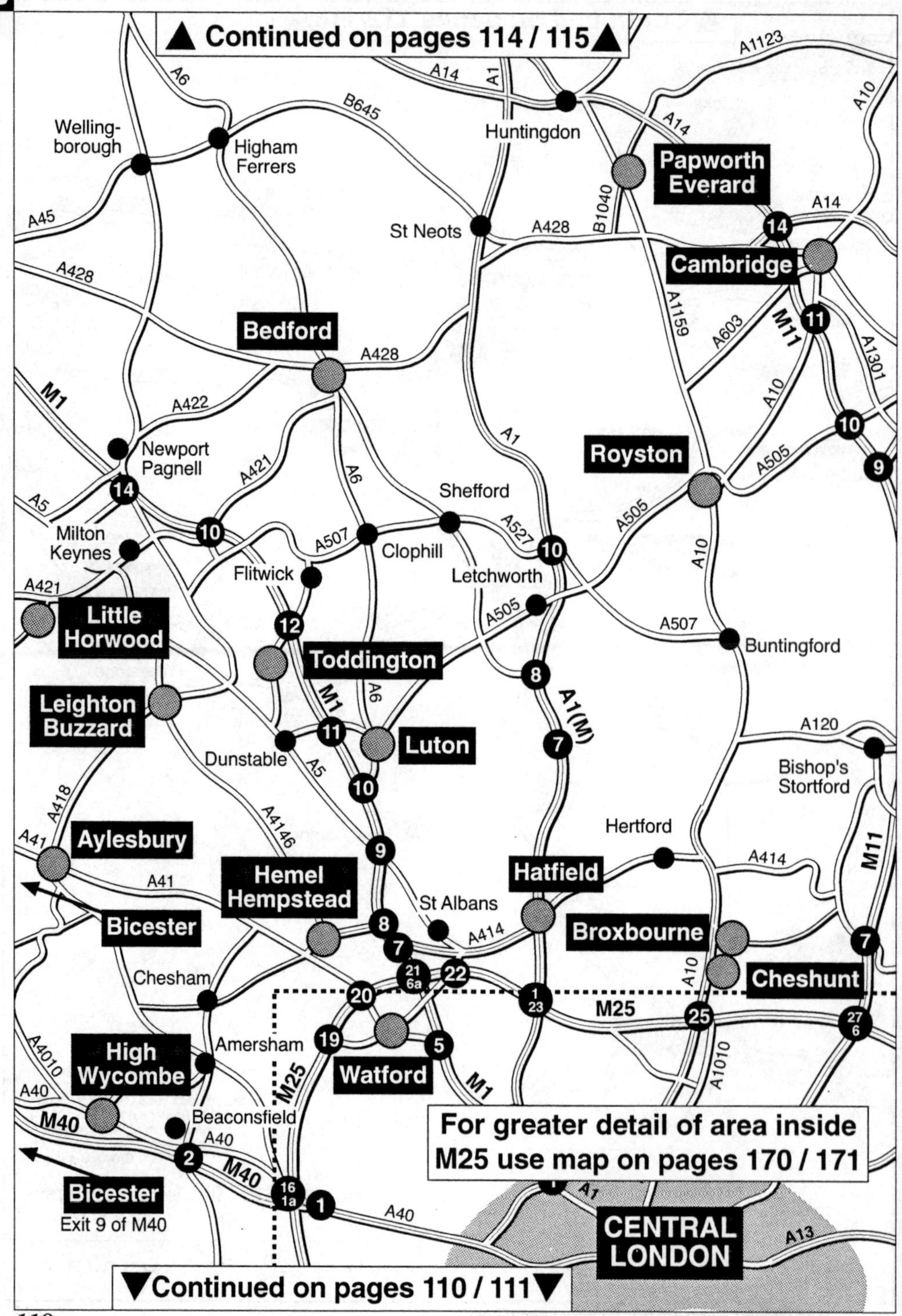

For greater detail of area inside
M25 use map on pages 170 / 171

▼Continued on pages 110 / 111▼

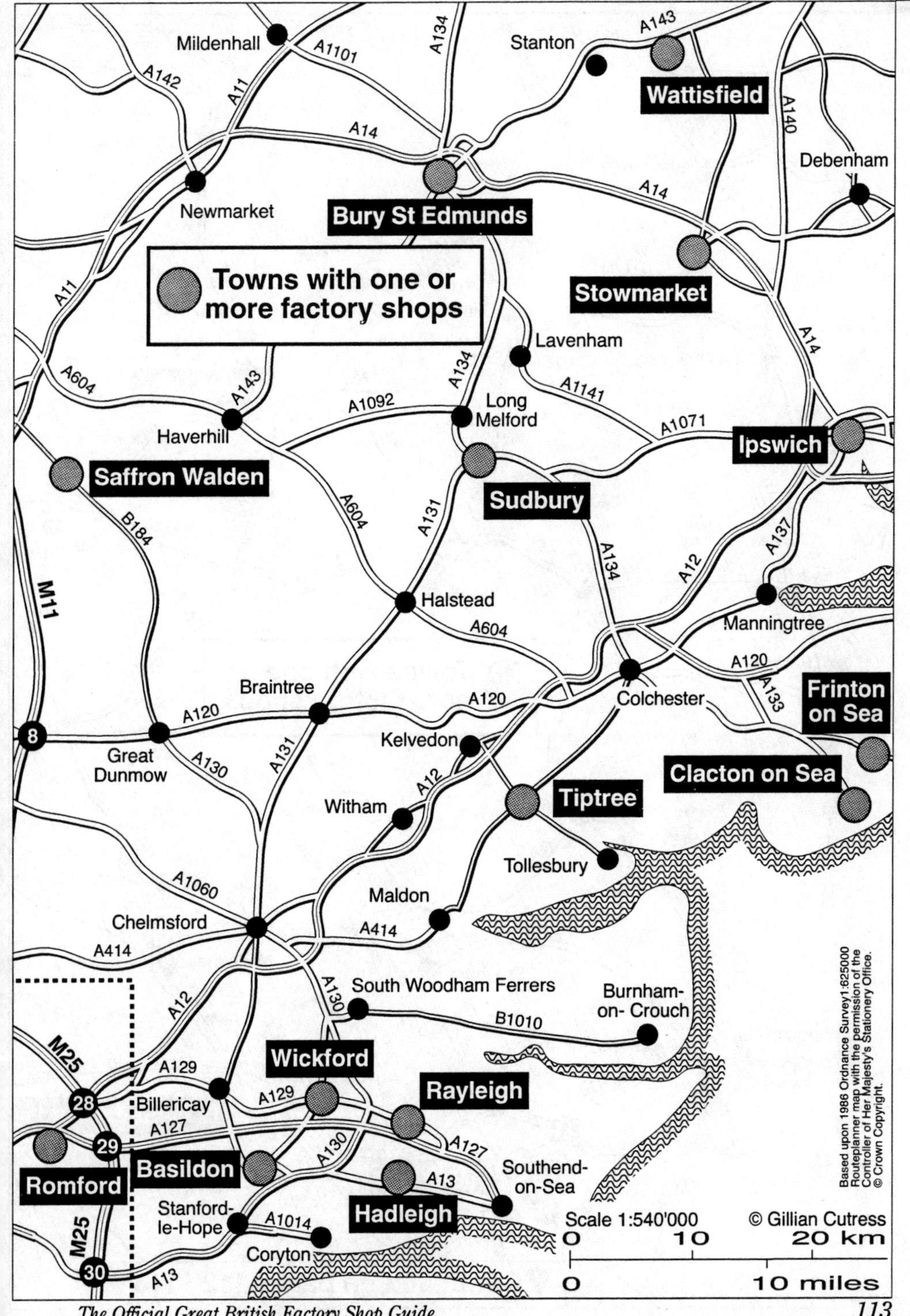
Mildenhall
A1101
A134
Stanton
A143
Wattisfield
A142
A11
A14
A140
Debenham
Newmarket
Bury St Edmunds
A14
Towns with one or more factory shops
Stowmarket
A11
Lavenham
A14
A604
A143
A134
A1141
Long Melford
A1092
Haverhill
A1071
Ipswich
Saffron Walden
Sudbury
A604
A131
B184
A134
A137
A12
M11
Halstead
Manningtree
A604
A120
Braintree
A120
Colchester
A133
Frinton on Sea
8
A120
Great Dunmow
A130
A131
Kelvedon
Clacton on Sea
A12
Witham
Tiptree
Tollesbury
A1060
Maldon
Chelmsford
A414
A414
A130
South Woodham Ferrers
Burnham-on- Crouch
B1010
A12
M25
A129
Wickford
Rayleigh
28
Billericay
A129
A127
29
A127
A130
Romford
Basildon
Southend-on-Sea
A13
Stanford-le-Hope
A1014
Hadleigh
M25
Coryton
30
A13
Scale 1:540'000
© Gillian Cutress
0 10 20 km
0 10 miles
Based upon 1986 Ordnance Survey 1:625000 Routeplanner map with the permission of the Controller of Her Majesty's Stationery Office. © Crown Copyright.

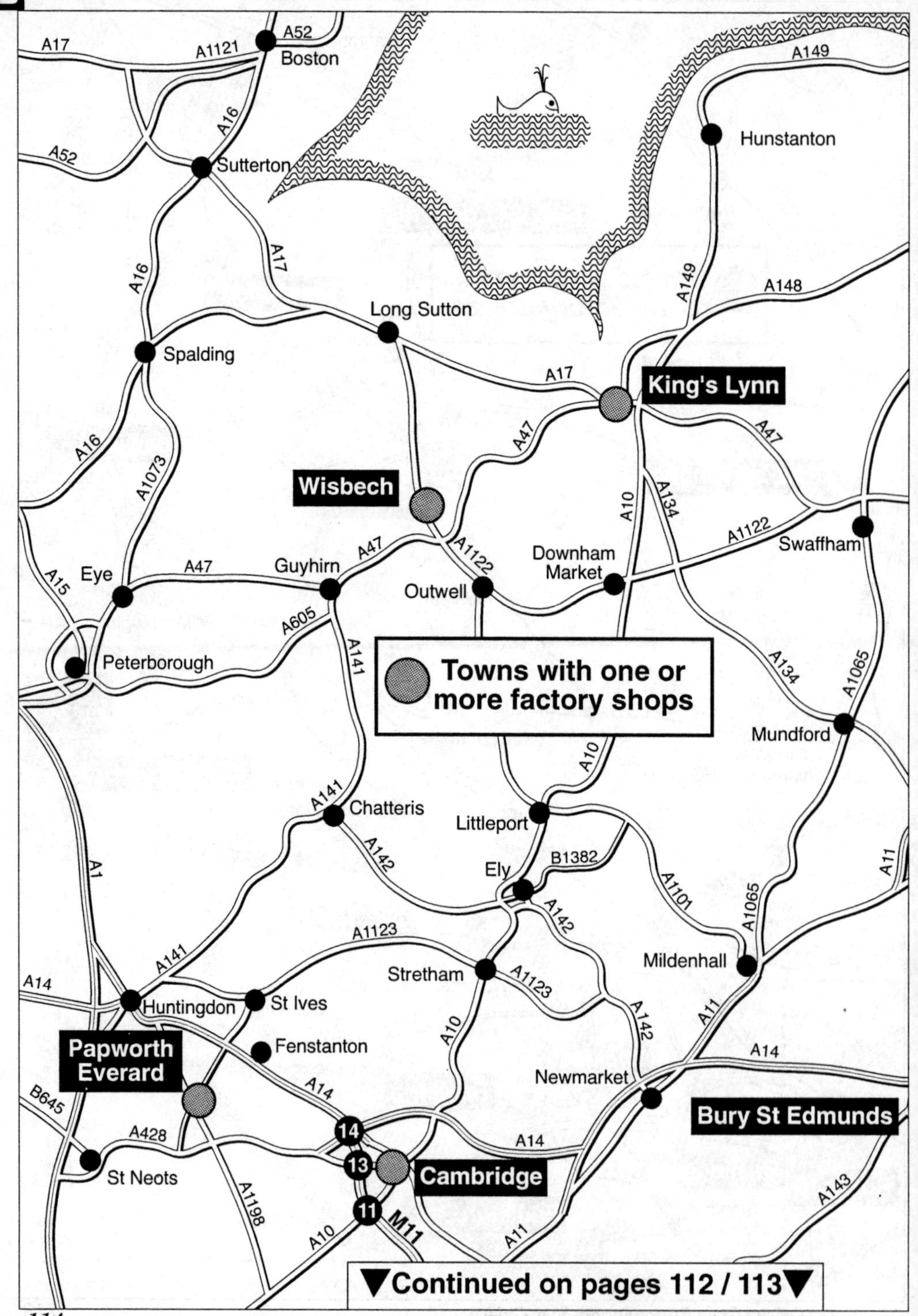

▼Continued on pages 112 / 113▼

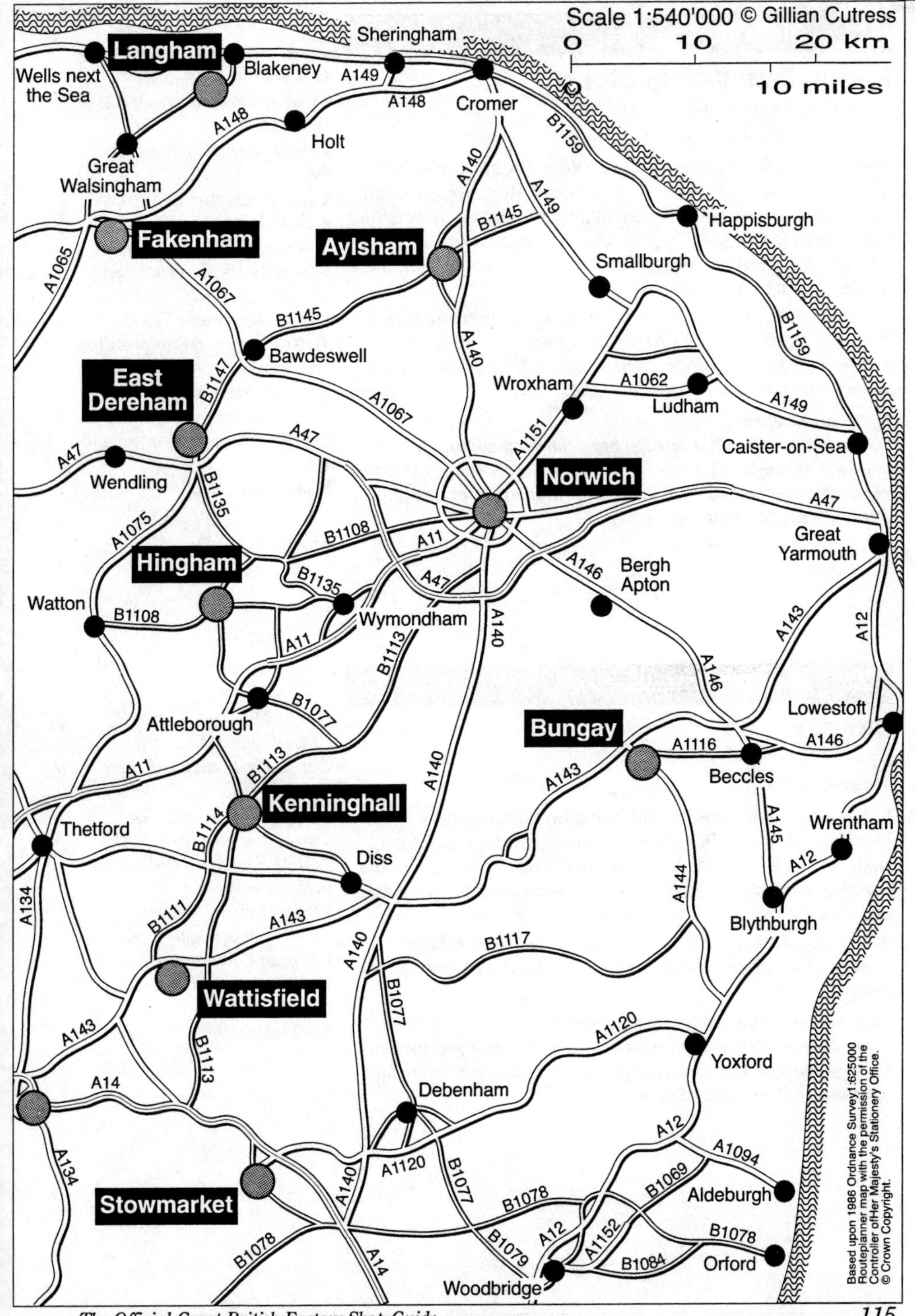
Scale 1:540'000 © Gillian Cutress
0 10 20 km
0 10 miles
Langham
Wells next the Sea
Blakeney
Sheringham
A149
A148
Cromer
Holt
Great Walsingham
B1159
A140
A149
Happisburgh
Fakenham
Aylsham
B1145
A1065
A1067
Smallburgh
B1145
Bawdeswell
East Dereham
B1147
A140
Wroxham
A1062
Ludham
A1067
A149
A47
A1151
Caister-on-Sea
A47
Wendling
Norwich
B1135
A47
A1075
B1108
A11
Great Yarmouth
Hingham
B1135
A47
A146
Bergh Apton
Watton
B1108
Wymondham
A140
A143
A12
A11
B1113
A146
B1077
Attleborough
Bungay
Lowestoft
B1113
A140
A1116
A146
A11
A143
Beccles
Kenninghall
Thetford
B1114
A145
Wrentham
Diss
A12
A134
A144
Blythburgh
B1111
A143
B1117
A140
Wattisfield
B1077
A143
B1113
A1120
Yoxford
A14
Debenham
A12
A1094
A134
A140
A1120
B1077
B1069
Aldeburgh
Stowmarket
B1078
A12
A1152
B1078
B1078
B1079
A14
B1084
Orford
Woodbridge
Based upon 1986 Ordnance Survey1:625000 Routeplanner map with the permission of the Controller ofHer Majesty's Stationery Office. © Crown Copyright.

1 Aldershot Hants

FactoryGate Variety Stores

16 Wellington Street GU11 1DB
(01252) 338530

Wide range of consumer products sold direct by over 100 manufacturers in one shop. Housewares (textiles, pots and pans, kitchen utensils); electrical goods (toasters to washing machines); family clothing; sports and outdoor leisure items; DIY items for home and garden; CDs, videos and equipment to play them; books; toys and games.

'Genuine 'factory direct' bargains from many manufacturers who rent space here. Significant discounts on all products. Constantly changing stock, something for all the family. New shops opening frequently, phone (01243) 555561 for latest news.'

In the town centre.

From either M3 exit 4 or A31: head for town centre. Park in multi-storey car-park for Wellington Centre. This shop is in the pedestrianised part of Wellington Street, opposite double doors to the Wellington shopping centre.

Open: Mon–Sat 9–5.30.
Closed: Phone to check Bank Holidays.
Cards: Major credit cards, Switch.
Cars: Wellington Centre car-park. Collection facilities at rear.
Toilets: In Wellington Centre.
Wheelchairs: Easy access to ground floor shop.
Changing rooms: Yes.
Teas: Wellington Centre atrium.
Groups: Shopping groups welcome – just drop in, no need to phone.
Transport: Any bus or train to Cosham.
Mail order: No.

2 Andover Hants

Croydex

Unit 27, Chantry Centre SP10 1LS
(01264) 336018

Large range of bathroom and household accessories including bath panels, cabinets, mirrors, toilet seats, towel rings and rails, soap dishes, bath mats, shower and window curtains, Austrian blinds, trays, chopping boards, place mats and coasters, wine coolers, ice buckets, pillows etc.

'Goods made for well known chainstores: at least 40% off normal retail prices. Firsts, seconds, samples and ends of ranges.'

From all directions aim for town centre.

The Chantry Centre is a pedestrianised shopping precinct in the town centre. The shop is close to the multi-storey car-park, opposite Le Café and by Boots.

Open: Mon–Sat 9–5.30.
Closed: Most Bank Holidays; Christmas, Boxing and New Year's Days.
Cards: MasterCard, Visa.
Cars: Multi-storey car-park.
Toilets: Outside the shopping mall.
Wheelchairs: No steps.
Teas: Café opposite shop.
Groups: Groups welcome.
Transport: Any bus or train to Andover.
Mail order: No.

3 Aylesbury Bucks

Aylesbury Fabric Warehouse

Unit 5 Cambridge Close, Cambridge Retail Park HP20 1DF
(01296) 337717

Large range of upholstery and furnishing fabrics: cottons, linens, damasks, velvets etc. Nets, voiles, calico, interlinings, waddings, linings. Haberdashery, fringing. Curtain rails/poles and accessories. Cushion covers and fillers. Ready-made curtains. Foam cut to shape.

'Over 3000 rolls. Interior design and curtain-making services.'

See our display advertisement on p. 195

Close to the town centre, on the north-east side. Cambridge Close leads off Cambridge Road, the A418 leading north-east .

From town centre: take A418 for Leighton Buzzard. After a few hundred yards, pass fire station on left. Take next left, Cambridge Close, into this large retail estate.*

Coming south on A418 into Aylesbury: pass the prison then hospital on left then shortly go right into this large retail estate.*

****Pass Argos and other stores: this shop is on left.***

Open: Mon–Sat 9.30–5.30; Sun 10–4. Bank Holidays.
Closed: For Christmas please phone.
Cards: Access, Connect, Delta, Switch, Visa.
Cars: Ample free car-park.
Toilets: Yes.
Wheelchairs: Ramp.
Teas: On retail park.
Groups: Groups welcome, please phone in advance.
Transport: Local buses along Cambridge Road.
Mail order: No.

4 Aylesbury Bucks

The Chiltern Brewery

Nash Lee Road, Terrick HP17 0TQ
(01296) 613647

Beer – including de-luxe Old Ale and new harvest ale brewed by the Earl of Buckinghamshire (pint bottles) and barley wine (½ pints). Unique range of beer-related items – beer and mustard cheeses, beer mustards, beer bread, Old Ale chutney, malt marmalade, barley wine cake, onions pickled in hop vinegar, pickled eggs and some pickled customers! New range of beer, malt and hop-based toiletries, eg shampoo, hop cologne. Hampers, fruit wines and speciality ciders.

'Most people regard the brewery as an experience, not just a shopping excursion. Ask for leaflet, mentioning this book. You may bring your own bottles to be filled.'

Tiny village 4 miles south of Aylesbury, 2½ miles west of Wendover.

From A413 (Aylesbury–Wendover road): go west on to B4009 for Princes Risborough/High Wycombe. Keep going for nearly a mile; well signposted brewery is on left, in farm building.

From Princes Risborough: take A4010 north for Aylesbury. After Great Kimble go right at next roundabout, following signs to Wendover (B4009). Keep straight; brewery short distance on right.

Open: Mon–Sat 9–5; Bank Holidays.
Closed: Christmas, Boxing and New Year's Days.
Cards: Delta, MasterCard, Switch, Visa.
Cars: Own yard.
Toilets: Yes.
Wheelchairs: No steps.
Teas: In Aylesbury and Wendover.
Groups: For 12–50 people by arrangement: Tippler's tour, £5.50, includes free drink, as does the Drayman's at £11.95 (with substantial buffet). Saturday tours at noon, £3, conducted by Head Brewer; England's first small brewery museum included in tours.
Transport: Aylesbury–High Wycombe buses stop ¼ mile .
Mail order: Yes. Please phone for details.

5 Aylsham Norfolk

Black Sheep

9 Penfold Street NR11 6ES
(01263) 733142

Knitwear and classic country wear for men, women and children in pure oiled wool of Black Welsh sheep; gifts and accessories.

'Undyed wool comes from local flock of sheep which you may see in Ingworth, further north. Most items perfect but always some seconds.'

Located 100 yds from the Market Place in Aylsham, and near the post office.

Leave Market Place with Black Boys Inn on your right (going towards Reepham and Blickling (B1354/B1145); pass post office on left – shop is 100 yds on left, clearly visible.

From Cawston (B1145) or Blickling (B1354): look for old pump, with columns and thatched roof, where these two roads meet at start of town. Shop is opposite this pump, on right corner as you go into village.

Open: Mon–Sat 9–5.30.
Closed: Bank Holidays; Christmas and Boxing Days.
Cards: Amex, MasterCard, Visa.
Cars: Limited parking beside shop; local streets.
Toilets: In village.
Wheelchairs: Easy access, medium-sized shop (2 steps to rear area).
Changing rooms: Yes.
Teas: Pubs in village.
Groups: You can see knitwear being made in next building but no demonstrations. Shopping groups with prior notice.
Transport: Any bus to Aylsham.
Mail order: Yes.
Catalogue: Free. Please mention this book with your request.

6 Barkingside Essex

Choice Discount Stores

26–28 High Street IG6 2DO
(0181) 551 2125

Surplus stocks including men's, women's and children's fashions and footwear from *Next plc, Next Directory* and other high street fashions. Household items from *Next Interiors.*

'Save up to 50% of normal Next first quality prices; seconds sold from ⅓ of normal retail price. Special sales January and September.'

In modern dark brown building in the High Street.

From the south on A123 from Gants Hill roundabout: pass the Barkingside police station and McDonald's on left and Chequers pub on right. The shop is about 100 yds on right in the only brown building.

From the north and Fullwell Cross on A123: pass the Fullwell Cross swimming pool and recreation centre on left, go across pedestrian lights and the shop is 100 yds on left after the next street traffic lights.

Open: Mon–Sat 9–5.30; Sun 10–4.
Closed: Easter Sunday; Christmas and Boxing Days.
Cards: Amex, MasterCard, Switch, Visa.
Cars: In street or in Sainsbury's large car-park.
Toilets: No.
Wheelchairs: No steps to large shop.
Changing rooms: No, but refund if returned in perfect condition within 28 days.
Teas: In town centre.
Groups: Shopping groups welcome! Book with store manager.
Transport: Gants Hill tube station, then bus nos. 129, 150 or 167. Barkingside tube station, then a short walk.

7 Basildon Essex

Choice Discount Stores

Unit 6a, Mayflower Retail Park, Gardiners Link SS14 3AR
(01268) 288331

Surplus stocks including men's, women's and children's fashions and footwear from *Next plc, Next Directory* and other high street fashions. Household items from *Next Interiors*.

'Save up to 50% of normal Next first quality prices; seconds sold from ⅓ off normal retail price. Special sales January and September.'

North-east of Basildon, next to huge Tesco and Pizza Hut.

From London on A127: don't turn off on to A176 but take next exit for A132 and turn back on yourself towards London on A127.*

From the east on A127: pass over the exit for A132, continuing straight.*

From Basildon centre: follow signs to Wickford A132. Pass the huge Watermill pub on right, then GEC Marconi Avionics on left and then turn on to A127 towards London.*

***After 800 yds take slip road signposted to Mayflower Retail Park. Pass McDonald's on left and shop is near the end, next to Pizza Hut.**

Open: Mon–Wed 9–6; Thur, Fri 9–7; Sat 9–5.30; Sun 11–5.
Closed: Easter Sunday; Christmas and Boxing Days.
Cards: Amex, MasterCard, Switch, Visa.
Cars: Large free car-park in front of store.
Toilets: At Tesco, on same site.
Wheelchairs: Easy access. No steps.
Changing rooms: No, but refund if returned in perfect condition within 28 days.
Teas: On-site Tesco, McDonald's, Kentucky.
Groups: Shopping groups welcome! Book with store manager.
Transport: Wickford or Basildon stations.
Mail order: No.

8 Basildon Essex

Essex Fabric Warehouse

Unit 2, Sainbury's Homebase, London Road, Vange SS16 4PR
(01268) 552224

Large range of upholstery and furnishing fabrics: cottons, linens, damasks, velvets etc. Nets, voiles, calico, interlinings, waddings, linings. Haberdashery, fringing. Curtain rails/poles and accessories. Cushion covers and fillers. Ready-made curtains. Foam cut to shape. Dress fabrics.

'About 10,000 rolls of fabric in stock. Curtain-making service.'

See our display advertisement on p.195

On the A13 on the south side of Basildon, on the Five Bells roundabout next to Sainsbury's Homebase.

From all directions: aim for the A13. The shop is on the corner facing the Beefeater pub. Entrance is from London Road B1464.

Open: Seven days a week: Mon–Sat 9–5 (Fri till 7); Sun, Bank Holidays and New Year's Day 10–4.
Closed: Christmas & Boxing Days.
Cards: Access, Connect, Delta, Switch, Visa.
Cars: Own free car-park.
Toilets: Yes.
Wheelchairs: No steps, large ground floor shop.
Teas: Beefeater pub serves tea and coffee all day, and meals.
Groups: Shopping groups welcome, no need to phone.
Transport: Local buses.
Mail order: No.

9 Basildon Essex

The Factory Shop

4c The Gloucesters, Luckyn Lane, Pipps Hill Industrial Estate SS14 3AY *(01268) 520446*

Large selection of melamine, household lines, china, glass, linens, fancy goods, toys, garden furniture and accessories, seasonal lines and novelties, greetings and Christmas cards, paper, stationery. Underwear, clothes, tracksuits, trainers and some food.

'Specialise in ends of ranges: brand name stock clearances, seconds, rejects, ends of line etc.'

On industrial estate north-east of Basildon.

From town centre: take A176 for Billericay. At large roundabout, go right for Pipps Hill; at next roundabout go left; take first left, Luckyn Lane; shop 200 yds on left.

From M25 exit 29: take A127 for Southend. Look for A176 Basildon/Billericay exit – at end of slip road go left; take first left, Miles Gray Road. At traffic lights go right; take first left, Luckyn Lane.*

Going towards London on A127: take A176 (Basildon/Billericay exit). At end of slip road, go straight across on to Miles Gray Road. At traffic lights, go right. Take first left (Luckyn Lane).*

****Shop clearly signed on right.***

Open: Mon–Sat 9–5.30; Sun and Bank Holidays 10–5.
Closed: Christmas and Boxing Days.
Cards: Amex, MasterCard, Switch, Visa.
Cars: Outside shop.
Toilets: Ask if desperate.
Wheelchairs: Easy access, no steps to huge shop.
Changing rooms: Yes.
Teas: Cold drinks, prepacked sandwiches, crisps and sweets.
Groups: Groups welcome to shop, but please phone Mr Cantor first.
Mail order: No.

10 Basingstoke Hants

Western House

Armstrong Road, Daneshill Estate RG24 8QE
(01256) 462341

Large selection of glassware, cookware, oven-to-table ware and ceramics; silverware; giftware.

'Well established distributor of glassware, gifts, ceramics at factory prices. Arrange glass engraving. First and second class qualities available.'

On east side of Basingstoke two miles from town centre.

From M3 exit 6: follow sign for A33 towards Reading/Daneshill Industrial Estate.*

From town centre, follow signs to Reading.*

****At Reading Road roundabout (second roundabout off M3) follow signs to Daneshill Industrial Estate; go left into Faraday Road. Follow this road round to Daneshill roundabout; go straight over into Swing Swang Lane. Armstrong Road is first road on right; company clearly visible along on left.***

Open: Tues–Fri 10–4; Sat 9–2.
Closed: Monday; Bank Holidays; Christmas, Boxing & New Year's Days.
Cards: MasterCard, Visa.
Cars: Car-park in front of shop.
Toilets: Yes.
Wheelchairs: No steps to very large ground floor shop on one level.
Teas: Basingstoke.
Tours: No.
Transport: Local buses along Swing Swang Lane.
Mail order: Yes.
Catalogue: No.

11 Bedford Beds

Grumbridge

14 The Manton Centre, Manton Lane MK41 7PX
(01234) 273232

Tins for biscuits, decorative tins, waste bins, tin household jars, cake tins, pencil tins, mugs, stationery items, lots of gifts.

'Perfects and seconds, all below high street prices.'

North-west of Bedford off the A6.

From town centre and all other directions (except the A6 from Rushden): follow the A6 for Kettering through Bedford. At large roundabout with sign to Brickhill, go right for Brickhill.*

From the north/Rushden on the A6: turn left at the first roundabout towards Brickhill.*

****At first lights turn left, then take second left: shop is 150 yds on right.***

Open: Mon–Fri 9–5.
Closed: Bank Holidays; Christmas–New Year.
Cards: No.
Cars: Own car-park.
Toilets: Yes.
Wheelchairs: Easy access to very small shop.
Teas: Many cafés within 2 minutes' drive.
Groups: No tours; shopping groups welcome anytime, but large groups please phone.
Transport: Unfortunately none.

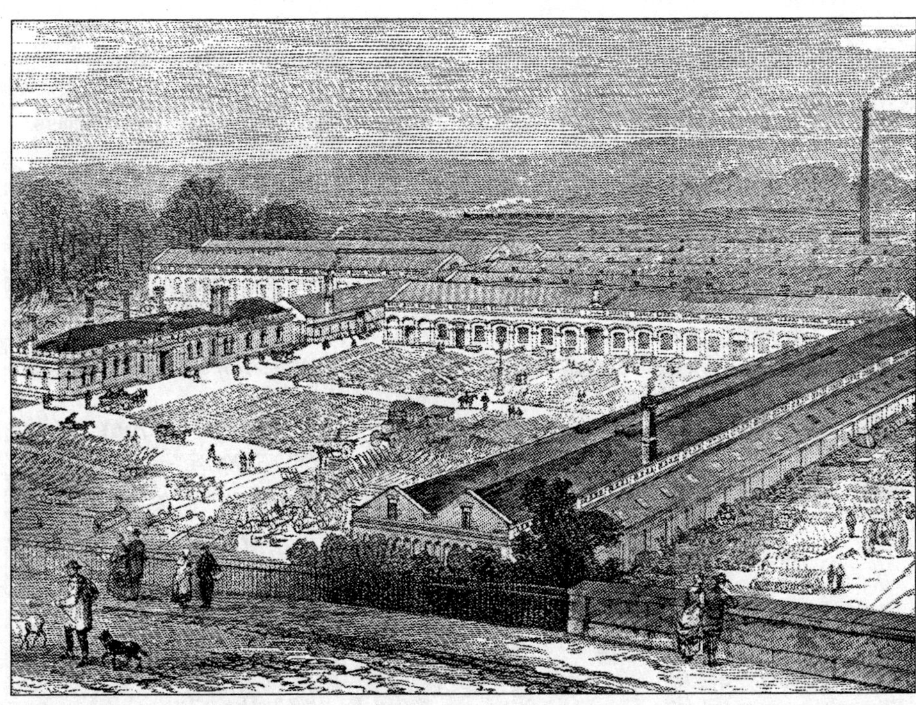

Britannia Ironworks & Agricultural Implement Manufactory in Bedford *The Illustrated London News 11 July 1874*

12 Bicester Oxon

Bicester Village

OX6 7WD
(01869) 323200

End-of-season designer fashions, men's and children's wear, tableware, shoes and more.

'Over 50 shops owned by famous British and international brands, bringing Bond Street style to Bicester Village. Discounts of 25–60% off retail prices.'

Easy to find on the outskirts of Bicester.

From M40 exit 9: take A41 two miles towards Bicester. At the first roundabout follow signs to Village Retail Park, clearly visible past the superstore.

Open: Mon–Sun (including Bank Holidays) 10–6.
Closed: Christmas Day.
Cards: All shops accept major credit cards.
Cars: Free parking for 675 cars and 12 coaches.
Toilets: Yes, and for the disabled.
Wheelchairs: Easy access to all shops.
Changing rooms: Where applicable.
Teas: Facilities on site.
Groups: Coach parties always welcome.
Transport: Bicester North rail station 15 minutes' walk.

13 Aquascutum
(01869) 325943
Men's & women's top brand ready-to-wear. Stylish accessories.

14 Benetton
(01869) 320030
Full range of *Benetton* merchandise for children & adults.

15 Big Dog
(01869) 323280
Californian casual wear and sleepwear for children and adults.

16 Blazer
(01869) 323200
Men's classic and casual suits.

17 Cerruti 1881 Femme
(01869) 325519
Women's ready-to-wear designer collection. Accessories.

18 Christian Lacroix
(01869) 321318
Women's designer collection.

19 Clarks Factory Shop
(01869) 325646
Family footwear: quality shoes, boots, trainers. Sports equipment.

20 Converse
(01869) 325070
Sports shoes and wear. Unisex leisurewear. Lycra performance wear.

21 Descamps
(01869) 323636
Fine linens, bed linen, towelling, bathrobes, nightwear. Babywear.

22 The Designer Room
(01869) 320052
Women's top designer wear, eg *Christian Lacroix, Louis Feraud, Escada.*

23 Donna Karan
(01869) 253001
Women's and men's designer fashions including DKNY.

24 Edinburgh Crystal
(01869) 324209
Cut crystal tumblers, decanters, wine glasses, giftware etc.

25 Episode
(01869) 369370
Ladies' silk and other classic suits and separates. Accessories.

26 Fred Perry
(01869) 325504
Men's, women's and children's casual and sportswear.

27 French Connection/Nicole Farhi
(01869) 369582
Women's and men's designer fashion and casual wear.

28 Helly Hansen
(01869) 325944
Men's and women's outdoor sports clothing, waterproofs and fleeces.

29 Hico
(01869) 325650
Duvets, sheets, pillow cases, cushions, curtains, tablecloths.

30 Hobbs
(01869) 325660
Women's upmarket shoes and contemporary ready-to-wear.

31 InWear/Matinique
(01869) 369415
Men's and women's Danish fashion and casual clothes.

32 Jaeger
(01869) 369220
Top name in men's and women's stylish fashion clothing.

33 Jane Shilton
(01869) 325387
Handbags, luggage, belts, scarves, small leather goods, women's shoes.

34 Jeffrey Rogers
(01869) 323567
Women's fashion clothing: skirts, T-shirts, blouses, dresses.

35 Jigsaw
(01869) 325621
Women's contemporary ready-to-wear.

36 Joan & David
(01869) 323387
Stylish Italian-made shoes, ready-to-wear and accessories.

37 John Jenkins
(01869) 324300
Crystal glasses, porcelain tableware, vases, decorative items.

38 John Partridge
(01869) 325332
Country clothing, mainly men's: waxed jackets, *Gore-tex* coats etc.

39 JoKids
(01869) 324477
Baby & children's wear (0–10) including casual and party clothes.

40 Karen Millen
(01869) 325932
Women's contemporary ready-to-wear: suits, dresses, tops etc.

41 Kids Play Factory
(01869) 323434
Indoor and outdoor toys and games for children of all ages.

42 Kurt Geiger
(01869) 325410
Women's and men's shoes from wide range of top brands.

43 Lands' End
(01869) 369624
Casual and knitwear, polo shirts, jackets, jeans. Accessories.

44 Monsoon/Accessorize
(01869) 323286
Ladies' fashion clothing, accessories, summer shoes, evening wear.

45 Oneida
(01869) 324789
Silver and stainless steel cutlery. Silver trays, rose bowls etc.

46 OshKosh B'Gosh
(01869) 322855
American & European children's wear (3 months–12 years).

47 OuiSet
(01869) 242402
Contemporary women's fashions.

48 Paul Smith
(01869) 323200
Men's, women's and children's contemporary fashions.

49 Pepe Jeans
(01869) 325378
High fashion jeans and casual wear for adults and children.

50 Petit Bateau
(01869) 244336
Famous French children's wear.

51 Polo Ralph Lauren
(01869) 325200
Designer classic, casual and formal wear. Household textiles.

52 Price's Candles
(01869) 325520
Candles, holders and accessories suitable for every occasion.

53 Principles
(01869) 325300
Women's, men's, and children's fashion and casual wear.

54 Racing Green
(01869) 325484
Classic casual wear (not high fashionwear) for men and women.

55 Red/Green
(01869) 323324
Men's and women's Danish sports and outerwear for sailing, golf etc.

56 Reebok
(01869) 247222
Athletic shoes, sportswear and accessories.

57 Sapphire Books
(01869) 325417
Remainders, overstocks and end-of-line books.

58 The Scotch House
(01869) 323522
Men's and women's classic fashions, especially fine knitwear.

59 The Suit Company
(01869) 324321
Own brand and other top name men's wear.

60 Tog 24
(01869) 323278
Weatherproof golf, outdoor and leisure wear. Waterproofs and fleeces.

61 Travel Accessory Outlet
(01869) 240444
Luggage and leather goods by *Samsonite* and other brands.

62 Triumph/Hom
(01869) 329930
Ladies' lingerie and nightwear; men's underwear. Swimwear.

63 TSE Cashmere
(01869) 244030
Designer fashions and classic styles for women and men.

64 Versace
(01869) 252511
Men's and women's designer fashions.

65 Villeroy & Boch
(01869) 324646
Plain and highly decorated china tableware. Glassware, cutlery.

66 Warner's
(01869) 324401
Lingerie: bras, teddies, briefs etc. *Hathaway* men's shirts.

67 Whistles
(01869) 320755
Women's contemporary fashions.

68 Woods of Windsor
(01869) 325307
Traditional English fragrances, soaps, sprays, pot pourri, oils etc.

69 Wrangler
(01869) 325225
Jeans, shirts, jackets and T-shirts for all the family.

Heirlooms

2 Arun Business Park PO22 9SX
(01243) 820252

Top of the market pure cotton and lace items made by this company: bed and table linen, picture frames, christening robes, duvets and pillows, towels, dressing gowns, pure white cotton nightdresses, pyjamas. Egyptian cotton sheets and duvet covers. Cushions. Picnic rugs, handkerchiefs, scarves, covered coathangers, teddy bears.

'Exceptionally fine linens, exceptionally fine prices. Most items very slight seconds and ends of ranges.'

About a mile north of Bognor, on the A29 opposite Tesco.

Coming north on A29 from Bognor: follow signs for Shripney. On the dual-carriageway, look for Tesco on the left. Continue to next roundabout and double back.*

Coming souuth on A29 towards Bognor: follow signs for Arun Industrial Estate. Go along dual-carriageway.*

****After National Tyres on left and before Nissan, go left into the estate. The clearly marked blue building is directly ahead. Shop entrance at front.***

Open: Almost every Friday and some Saturdays 10–4; please check in advance.
Closed: Mon–Thur; some Saturdays; Bank Holidays.
Cards: MasterCard, Visa.
Cars: In front of shop and on estate.
Toilets: Yes.
Wheelchairs: One tiny step to sizeable ground floor shop.
Changing rooms: Yes.
Teas: At Tesco and in Bognor.
Groups: Groups welcome to shop.
Transport: Take bus to Tesco, then 1 minute walk.
Mail order: Yes.
Catalogue: £5. A service for readers living too far from an *Heirlooms* stockist.

Heirlooms

Sofa to Bed

Suffolk Carpet Weavers

Rococo Frames

Flower Smiths

Ellis Furniture

71 Borehamwood Herts

Rubert of London

Unit 7, Stirling Industrial Centre, Stirling Way WD6 2BS
(0181) 207 2620

Vast range of quality ladies' fashions. Coats and jackets in wool and cashmere, blazers, suits, skirts and blouses, rainwear and much more. Complete summer wardrobe.

'At least 20–40% off retail prices. No seconds. We offer a friendly personal service to our customers. Sundays very busy, so advise first visit on a weekday. Clearance sales in January and July/August.'

A few yards off the A1.

Going north or south on A1: at Stirling Corner (roundabout, with Shell garage and Bennigans restaurant, where the A411 crosses the A1) take small slip road in front of Curry's into industrial estate.*

From M25 exit 23: take A1 south for 3 miles; at first roundabout (Stirling Corner, with Shell garage on near left and Bennigans restaurant on far left corner) take small slip road in front of Curry's into industrial estate.*

***Pass BonusPrint on the left, then Stirling Industrial Centre on left and immediately go left into alley. Rubert is 50 yds on left.**

Open: Mon–Fri 10–4; Sun 10–2.
Closed: Saturday; Bank Holiday Sundays & Mondays; 2 weeks at Christmas–New Year; Sundays from May–August.
Cards: Delta, MasterCard, Switch, Visa.
Cars: Outside shop or nearby car-park.
Toilets: Yes.
Wheelchairs: Main showroom upstairs but items gladly brought down.
Changing rooms: Yes.
Teas: At Stirling Corner; also Borehamwood.
Groups: Shopping groups always welcome: please phone first.
Transport: Edgware tube station then taxi.

72 Brighton E Sussex

Kemptown Terracotta

Unit 8, 5 Arundel Road BN2 5TF
(01273) 676603

Terracotta pots (up to 20" high), urns, 'chimney pots', tubs – some with green glazed rims – and saucers. 'Long toms', ideal for lilies. Unusual ridge tiles with large flying dragons. Guaranteed frost-proof.

'Perfects and seconds at reduced prices – price depends on extent of flaw but often half price. Small personal business so please phone first if you are making special journey.'

One and a half miles east of Brighton central pier.

From Brighton: go east on cliff road (Marine Parade) almost to marina. Pass large Georgian crescent set back from road with overgrown private park in front; look for railings in middle of road (start of dual carriageway): go left here into Arundel Road.*

From Newhaven via Marine Drive: go left to 'Brighton Marina Village & Kemptown'; after underpass go right to Kemptown; after gasometer go left at lights; go left at next crossing into Arundel Road.*

***Park near The Bush pub. To right of pub, go through archway to workshop and showroom on right of mews.**

Open: Mon–Sat 9–6; *also April–end August* Sun 10–5; Bank Holidays. Always best to check.
Closed: Christmas–New Year.
Cards: No.
Cars: In Arundel Road.
Toilets: Locally.
Wheelchairs: Access to ground floor pottery and showroom.
Teas: Pub and café nearby. Lots of places in Brighton.
Groups: Demonstrations gladly given to groups of up to 12 people; but must be arranged in advance.
Transport: Buses to Kemptown, nos. 1 and 38C. Volksrailway on seafront.
Mail order: Yes.
Catalogue: Free illustrated price list. No seconds posted.

73 Brighton E Sussex

Merchants Quay

Brighton Marina Village BN2 5UE
(01273) 818504

Over 30 brand names in clothing, shoes, bedding, toiletries, cosmetics, ceramics, housewares, lighting, crystal and luggage.

'The relaxed atmosphere of a marina is combined with discount retail shopping. Facilities include pubs and restaurants, superstore and eight-screen cinema. Many products are at heavily discounted prices. Further retail development planned.'

Brighton Marina is on the east side of town, below the high chalk cliffs.

From Brighton town centre: go east on cliff road (Marine Parade), following signs to Marina.

From Newhaven via Marine Drive: go left at sign to 'Brighton Marina Village'.

Open: Seven days a week. Shops may vary but most open 10–5 at least.
Closed: Christmas and Boxing Days.
Cards: All major credit cards.
Cars: Free multi-storey car-park for 2000 cars.
Toilets: Yes.
Wheelchairs: Easy access within the complex.
Changing rooms: Yes, in clothing shops.
Teas: Three pubs and three restaurants.
Groups: Shopping groups very welcome.
Transport: Regular bus services from Brighton station.

74 Edinburgh Crystal

(01273) 818702

Cut crystal tumblers, decanters, wine glasses, giftware etc.

75 The Factory Shop Ltd./ Options

(01273) 818590

Family clothing, toiletries, footwear, luggage, housewares *(see next page for full details)*.

76 Giovanna

(01273) 818918

Ladies' designer fashion clothing and distinctive jewellery.

77 Honey Fashions

(01273) 818835

Ladies' fashion wear from high fashion to classics. Up to size 22.

78 Hornsea Pottery

(01273) 818444

Earthenware tableware, mugs, oven-to-table ware, kitchen storage.

79 Leave it to Jeeves

(01273) 818585

Photographs, old sepia prints and framing service.

80 Not Just Books

(01273) 818719

Discounted books, stationery, jigsaws, posters, CDs, videos.

81 Pulse

(01273) 572098

Rollerblades and accessories.

82 Sanctuary Cove

(01273) 818898

Candles, candle holders, cushions, rugs, glassware etc.

83 Tog 24

(01273) 818759

Weatherproof outdoor wear, fleeces, walking and casual wear.

84 Tom Sayers

(01273) 818705

Designer men's wear: suits, trousers, knitwear, shirts.

85 Toorak

(01273) 818964

Jeans and casual wear for men and women.

86 Brighton E Sussex

The Factory Shop Ltd.

Brighton Marina Village
(01273) 818590

Men's, ladies' and children's clothing, footwear, luggage, toiletries, hardware, household textiles, lighting and electrical goods. Fashion concessions department with famous brand names. *Cape Country* pine furniture exclusively produced for The Factory Shop.

'Large stock of branded and chainstore items, all at greatly reduced prices. Deliveries of new stock every week to give an ever changing selection.'

Within Brighton Marina, on the east side of town, below the high chalk cliffs.

From Brighton town centre: go east on cliff road (Marine Parade), following signs to Marina.

From Newhaven via Marine Drive: go left at sign to 'Brighton Marina Village'.

Open: Mon–Fri 10–5.30; Sat 10–6; Sun 10.30–4.30.
Closed: Easter Sunday and Christmas Day.
Cards: MasterCard, Switch, Visa.
Cars: Ample car-parking space within Marina Village.
Toilets: In Marina Village.
Wheelchairs: No steps.
Changing rooms: Yes.
Teas: Restaurants and cafés in Marina Village.
Groups: Shopping groups welcome.
Transport: Bus nos. 14, 44 and 46 to Marina Village.
Mail order: Home delivery service for pine furniture. Please phone for free catalogue and price list.

87 Broxbourne Herts

Nazeing Glassworks

New Nazeing Road EN10 6SU
(01992) 464485

Hand-made hand-cut lead crystal glasses, vases, glass ashtrays, candle-holders, decanters etc. Unusual items: wine carafes with own ice coolers; zodiac paperweights, apple-shaped apple sauce boats; melon, avocado, corn cob dishes. Range of items in black and coloured glass, especially Bristol Blue glass.

'Huge range of perfects and seconds, 50p–£70, usually 30% less than normal retail price. Welcome special commissions, including engraving and ceramic decoration. Specialise in Ladies' Nights presents.'

See our display advertisement opposite

Just outside M25 (exit 25) between Cheshunt and Hoddesdon.

From A10 (Great Cambridge Road): turn east for Broxbourne and get on to A1170 (NB If you are going north on A10, don't turn left for New River Trading Estate but take next left). At traffic lights go east on to B194 for Nazeing/Lee Valley Park Lido. After Broxbourne station continue for ½ mile to small industrial estate on left; follow signs.

From Nazeing on B194: go under pylons then over canal; after ¼ mile follow clear signs into estate on right.

Open: Mon–Fri 9.30–4.30; Sat 9.30–3.
Closed: Bank Holidays; Christmas–New Year.
Cards: Delta, Electron, Eurocard, JCB, MasterCard, Switch, Visa.
Cars: Own car-park.
Toilets: Yes.
Wheelchairs: Easy access.
Teas: In Cheshunt.
Groups: Party groups only: (10–15 people) per 30-minute tour. Thur & Fri at 11. Bookable in advance. Adults £1; children (5+ yrs) & pensioners 75p; local school parties (within 5-mile radius) free. £2 refundable deposit for safety goggles.
Transport: Broxbourne station ½ mile. Broxbourne–Harlow buses stop outside.
Mail order: Yes, for selected range.
Catalogue: Free: send large sae.

See our entry opposite

88 Bungay Suffolk

Nursey & Son (Est. 1790)

Upper Olland Street NR35 1BQ
(01986) 892821

Leather, suede and sheepskin coats, slippers, mittens, hats, handbags, gloves etc. for all the family. Leather trousers and gift items.

'Genuine factory shop with reasonable prices. Some seconds. Company supplies worldwide.'

15 miles south of Norwich, 15 miles west of Lowestoft, 6 miles west of Beccles.

Coming into Bungay from the north side on A144: go through town, ie along Broad Street into Market Place. Continue on A144 towards Halesworth, along St Mary's Street, passing church on left. After 150 yds take right fork into Upper Olland Street for Flixton/Homersfield. Clearly marked shop 100 yds on right.

Open: Mon–Fri 10–1 & 2–5; *Nov–Jan: also* Sat 9–5.
Closed: Bank Holidays; probably last week July & first week August (phone to check); Christmas–New Year.
Cards: MasterCard, Visa.
Cars: Further down the road; small car-park opposite.
Toilets: In Bungay.
Wheelchairs: Ramp to shop.
Changing rooms: No.
Teas: In Bungay.
Groups: No factory tours; groups of shoppers welcome if they arrange in advance.
Transport: Eastern Counties bus no. 871.
Mail order: Yes.
Catalogue: Free. No seconds.

B

89 Burgess Hill W Sussex

Jaeger Factory Sale Shop

Unit B, 208–216 London Road RH15 9RD
(01444) 333100

Ladies' blouses, skirts, jackets and knitwear etc. Men's jackets, trousers, ties, socks and knitwear. *Van Heusen* shirts.

'Perfect ends of lines etc.'

NB This shop has moved locally.

On London Road B2036 (a main north–south road west of town centre).

From A23/M23/Hickstead: take A2300 towards town. At large roundabout, go right for Victoria Industrial Estate on A273. Follow signs to town centre. At roundabout, go left into London Road B2036. Go over two roundabouts. Pass Do-It-All on left: Jaeger is on right, before Halfords.

Open: Mon–Fri 10–6; Sat 9–6; Sun 11–5.
Closed: Christmas and Boxing Days.
Cards: Amex, Diners, MasterCard, Switch, Visa.
Cars: Large car-park in front of shop.
Toilets: Yes.
Wheelchairs: Easy access.
Changing rooms: Yes.
Teas: Coffee shop on site.
Groups: Pre-booked shopping groups welcome.
Transport: 10 minutes' walk from town centre.

90 Bury St Edmunds Suffolk

The Factory Shop Ltd.

Barton Business Centre, Barton Road IP32 7BO
(01284) 701578

Men's, ladies' and children's clothing, footwear, luggage, toiletries, hardware, household textiles, gifts, bedding, lighting, and new fashion concessions department with famous brand names. *Cape Country* pine furniture exclusively produced for The Factory Shop.

'Large stock of branded and chainstore items, all at greatly reduced prices. Deliveries of new stock every week to give an ever changing selection.'

On the east side of Bury St Edmunds.

From A14 (the old A45T): exit at signs to Bury St Edmunds East and turn towards Moreton Hall Estate. Go straight at first roundabout (Sainsbury's on your right).*

From town centre: follow signs to Ipswich (A14) via A1302 ring road. Go underneath A14 (old A45) and straight at first roundabout with Sainsbury's on right.*

****Go left at second roundabout, then straight at the third and fourth roundabouts. Go downhill and turn left just before the railway bridge. Shop is in second building on right.***

Open: Mon–Fri 9.30–5.30; Sat 9–5.30; Sun 10–4.
Closed: Easter Sunday; Christmas, Boxing and New Year's Days.
Cards: MasterCard, Switch, Visa.
Cars: Own large car-park.
Toilets: In town.
Wheelchairs: No steps to large shop.
Changing rooms: Yes.
Teas: Cafés and pubs in town.
Groups: Shopping groups welcome. For organiser/driver incentives please phone.
Transport: 20 minutes' walk from station; 15 minutes from town centre.
Mail order: Home delivery service for pine furniture. Please phone for free catalogue and price list.

91 Cambridge Cambs

The Factory Shoe Shop

48 Woollards Lane, Great Shelford
(01223) 846723

Ladies' and men's quality footwear from own Norwich factories and associated continental factories. Slim to wide fittings usually in stock. Brands include *Van-Dal, Holmes* and *Jenny*. Also stock quality handbags.

'Over 2,000 pairs of slight seconds and ends of ranges at reduced prices.'

Great Shelford is four miles south-east of Cambridge, on the A1301.

From M11 exit 10: take A505 towards Newmarket. At first roundabout turn left on to A1301 to Great Shelford. Turn left at traffic lights in village.*

From Cambridge: take A1301 to Great Shelford. Turn right at traffic lights in village.*

****Shop is about 300 yds on right.***

Open: Mon–Fri 9.30–5.30; Sat 9.30–5.
Closed: Bank Holidays; Christmas, Boxing and New Year's Days.
Cards: Delta, MasterCard, Switch, Visa.
Cars: Two free car-parks within easy reach of shop.
Toilets: No.
Wheelchairs: No steps, easy access.
Teas: Local pub and tea room.
Transport: Bus no. 103 from Drummer Street, Cambridge, every half hour. Trains from Cambridge every 30 minutes and from Liverpool Street every hour. Shop is ¼ mile from station.

92 Cambridge Cambs

Langham Glass

Quayside, Thompson's Lane CB5 8AQ *Now closed*
(01223) 329144

Wide range of hand-made crystal glass – plain, decorated and highly coloured. Tableware such as wine glasses, tumblers and jugs. Range of paperweights. Wide selection of coloured glass animals. Unusual coloured bowls, vases, candlesticks and stemmed drinking glasses.

'Glass at factory shop prices – always special offers. Also first quality. Corporate and commission work welcomed. Facilities for engraving and sandblasting.'

On the north-west of city centre, on the bank of the river Cam, opposite Magdalene College. Park where you can and walk.

From the city centre: walk along the main thoroughfare (Sydney Street which becomes Bridge Street then Magdalene Street). Just before the bridge go right into the courtyard with restaurants.*

If you come south over Magdalene Bridge: at the end of the bridge, go left into the large courtyard.*

****Walk along the river for 100 yds. At the Langham Glass sign, turn inland along the alleyway to clearly marked shop on right.***

Open: Mon–Sat 9.30–5; Sun 11–5. Bank Holidays.
Closed: Christmas, Boxing and New Year's Days.
Cards: MasterCard, Switch, Visa.
Cars: Any town car-park.
Toilets: Yes, including for the disabled.
Wheelchairs: No steps, large, spacious ground floor shop.
Teas: Nearby cafés and restaurants.
Groups: Shopping groups welcome. Large screen video of Cambridge and glassmaking (free).
Transport: Any bus or train to Cambridge.
Mail order: Yes.
Catalogue: £1.50.

93 Canterbury Kent

Essentially Hops

Chalkpit Farm, School Lane, Bekesbourne CT4 5ER
(01227) 830666

Wide variety of home grown dried flowers. Arrangements ready-made and made to order. Dried hop bines (traditional Kentish garland 8–10 ft long) for sale all year; fresh bines in August/September if ordered in advance (always ring to check harvest dates).

Two miles east of Canterbury, near Howletts Zoo.

From London on A2: after Canterbury exit, take slip road to Howletts Zoo/Bekesbourne.*

From Canterbury: head for Dover/A2. Follow signs to Howletts Zoo/Bekesbourne.*

From Dover via A2: take slip road to Bekesbourne/Bridge and Howletts Zoo. Keep following signs to Bridge village. Go through Bridge, then right to Bekesbourne. Go to mini-roundabout then to Howletts Zoo/Bekesbourne.*

****In Bekesbourne, before railway bridge, go right into School Lane, following brown 'Hop Farm' signs – farm entrance ½ mile on right. (If you get to Howletts Zoo, you've gone too far!)***

Open: Mon–Fri 12.30–5; Sat 9–5; Sun 12.30–4.30. Always phone first to check. Bank Holidays.
Closed: For two weeks following Christmas Day.
Cards: Delta, MasterCard, Switch, Visa.
Cars: Ample parking.
Toilets: Yes.
Wheelchairs: Gravelled car-park, one small step to shop, please ask for assistance.
Teas: Local pubs.
Transport: Trains from Victoria to Bekesbourne.
Mail order: Yes.
Catalogue: Free. Mail order hops available – fresh hop orders by 31 August. Dried flowers & mixed dried flower boxes available.

94 Chertsey Surrey

The Fabric Factory

Church Walk, Windsor Road, KT16 8AP
(01932) 570028

Famous brand furnishing and dress fabric seconds and ends of rolls by the metre. Includes top designer furnishing fabrics – most at least 50% less than retail.

'Complete curtain-making service for both trade and individual customers, including soft blinds and cushions.'

Chertsey is just inside the M25, just south of the M3.

From M3 exit 2: aim for Chertsey. You come on to M25.*

****From M25 exit 11: exit for Chertsey A320. Follow signs for town centre. Church Walk is in town centre next to St Peter's Church.***

Open: Mon–Sat 9.15–5.30; Sun 10–4.
Closed: Bank Holidays.
Cards: MasterCard, Visa.
Cars: Ample parking on site.
Toilets: Ask if desperate.
Wheelchairs: No steps, easy access, large shop.
Teas: In Chertsey.
Groups: Small shopping groups welcome; please phone in advance if possible.
Transport: Chertsey train station 5 minutes' walk.
Mail order: No.

Finding good value in earlier centuries

A sure-fire method of finding good value was rife in Kent in the eighteenth and nineteenth centuries: smuggling. Highly skilled in the complex and frequently violent practice of landing and disposing of vast quantities of contraband, these smugglers' modern-day equivalent is probably the mafia. They smuggled in all manner of goods from macabre grave shrouds to cannon, and from currency to wheat. Favourite hide-out of the smugglers was Romney Marsh, just 20 miles from France.

The origins of smuggling were closely connected with the wool trade. By 1200, England was prime producer of high quality wool. In 1203 King John placed a tax on the export of wool, which was greatly sought after by continental weavers. Taxes were also imposed on the import of wine, cloth and leather. Plenty of people were willing and well placed to make money by importing these items tax-free. Profits were always substantial. By the seventeenth century, brandy brought in at a cost of £1 a barrel was sold for £4; tea for 3d a pound sold in England for 2/-.

After the Napoleonic wars, the government was none too keen on the ill-gained wealth of Kent. In 1817 they formed the blockade with orders to attack smugglers wherever they were found. At first the blockade was based at sea but then a shore service was established. It was loathed by the local people – who faced penury once their illicit trade was eliminated. So they banded together and terrorised the blockade so successfully that they were able to carry on much as before.

With thanks to Kent CC Planning Department for their leaflet.

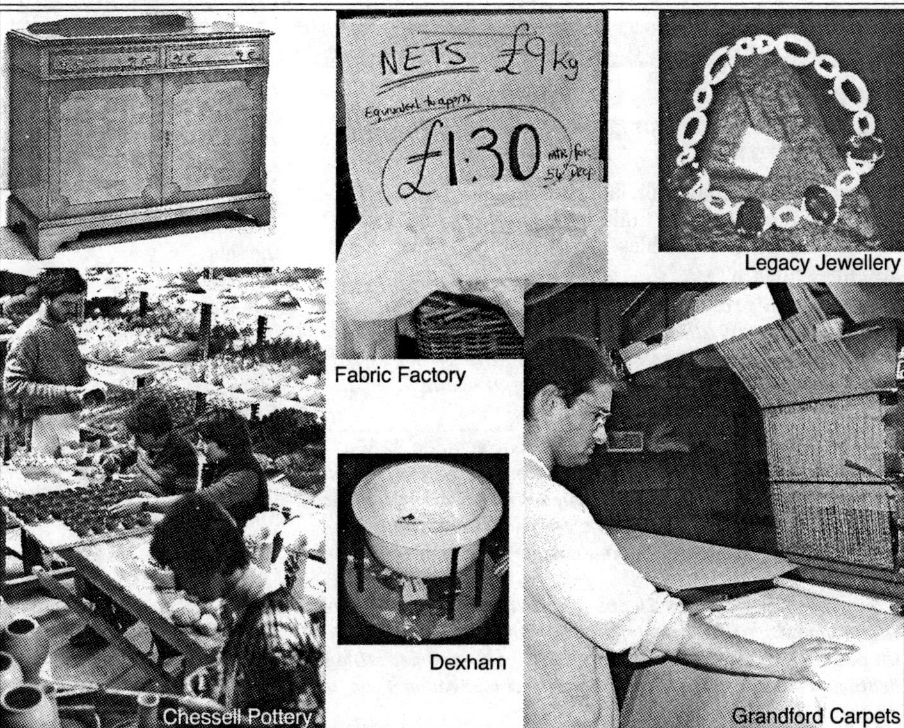

Legacy Jewellery

Fabric Factory

Dexham

Chessell Pottery

Grandford Carpets

95 Chichester W Sussex

Body Sense

26a The Hornet PO19 4JG *(01243) 774792*

Unique range of face & body products: cleansers, toners, etc, conditioners, bath soaks, shower gels and massage oils. Astrological shampoos.

'A small family business making toiletries & herbal remedies to our own high quality recipes. Lotions at half usual prices. Ladies' health studio for relaxing body treatments, massages, facials, reflexology etc. Allergy testing & acupuncture.'

Located 400 yds east of city centre (The Hornet runs on from East Street at traffic lights).

From the north: follow easterly ring road to cattle market car-park.**

From Portsmouth via A27: turn left at second roundabout (footbridge over road) on to southern Chichester bypass.*

From Worthing/Arundel via A27: turn right at fourth roundabout (footbridge over road) on southern Chichester bypass.*

****Go over level-crossing, pass station on left; follow main road for ¾ mile. Park in cattle market car-park on right.*****

*****On foot: turn right out of car-park to The Hornet (one-way street), walk 200 yds to shop on right.***

Open: Mon–Fri 9–7; Sat 8.30–5. Some Sundays and Bank Holidays – phone for details.
Closed: Christmas and Boxing Days.
Cards: MasterCard, Visa.
Cars: 900-place Cattle Market car-park 200 yds walk.
Toilets: No.
Wheelchairs: No steps, small shop.
Changing rooms: Yes.
Teas: Local tea rooms, wine bars and restaurants.
Groups: Groups welcome, please phone for details.
Transport: Buses to Cattle Market car-park; ¾ mile from Chichester train station.
Mail order: Yes.
Catalogue: Phone for free leaflet. All health products supplied. Horoscopes and biorhythm charts at special price.

96 Chichester W Sussex

Chelton Lighting

St James Works, St Pancras PO19 4NM *Now closed*
(01243) 530031

Top quality hand-made silk lampshades, also hand-made to individual requirements. Full range of central and wall light fittings. Curtain poles, tables, chairs, beds and firebaskets also made to order.

'Full lampshade recovering service. We will also make frames to your own specification, including continental and American fittings. Bespoke service in wrought iron fittings. Good quality products at keen prices (wholesale prices at around 50% less than retail).'

About ¾ of a mile north-east of the city centre on the A285.

From Chichester centre: go along St Pancras A285 towards Worthing (A27). Go over mini-roundabout where road goes left for Midhurst. Immediately go right (before pedestrian lights) into yard to rear of this clearly marked company in single storey building.

Coming south-west into Chichester on A285 from A27: go over large roundabout with Sainsbury's and aim for town centre. Pass UK petrol on the left. Go over mini-roundabout then pedestrian lights and immediately go left (before next mini-roundabout) into drive to rear of this company.

Open: Mon 9–1; Tues–Fri 8–4.45; Sat 10–4.
Closed: Monday afternoons; Bank Holidays.
Cards: MasterCard, Visa.
Cars: In courtyard outside the shop.
Toilets: Yes.
Wheelchairs: One deep step into small showroom.
Teas: Lots of places in Chichester.
Groups: Showroom not really suitable for groups.
Transport: Chichester bus and train stations within ½ a mile.
Mail order: Yes.

Market days

Aylesbury	Wed, Fri, Sat outdoor general
Basildon	Tues, Fri, Sat outdoor general
Basingstoke	Wed, Sat outdoor general
Battle	Tues, Fri outdoor general; Sat antiques
Bedford	Wed, Sat outdoor general
Brighton	Daily outdoor general
Burgess Hill	Wed, Sat outdoor and indoor general
Bury St Edmunds	Wed, Sat outdoor general
Cambridge	Mon to Sat outdoor general
Canterbury	Wed outdoor general
Chelmsford	Tues, Fri, Sat general; Thur flea market
Chichester	Wed, Sat outdoor general
Clacton	Tues, Sat outdoor general
Dover	Daily except Sun indoor general
Eastbourne	Tues, Fri, Sat outdoor general
Ely	Thur, Sat outdoor general
Fakenham	Thur outdoor general market and flea
Fareham	Mon outdoor general
Farnham	Wed outdoor general
Faversham	Tues, Fri, Sat outdoor general
Folkestone	Thur, Sun outdoor general
Godalming	Fri outdoor general
Guildford	Tues, Wed, Thur outdoor general
Hailsham	Fri outdoor general
Hastings	Daily except Sun outdoor general
Hemel Hempstead	Thur, Fri, Sat outdoor general
Herne Bay	Sat outdoor general
Hertford	Sat outdoor general
High Wycombe	Fri, Sat outdoor general
Hove	Thur, Sat, Sun outdoor general; indoor auction
Ipswich	Tues, Fri, Sat outdoor general
King's Lynn	Tues, Fri, Sat outdoor general
Leighton Buzzard	Tues, Sat outdoor general
Luton	Mon to Sat outdoor/indoor general
Maidenhead	Daily outdoor general
Milton Keynes	Tues, Sat outdoor general
Norwich	Mon to Sat outdoor general
Peterborough	Tues to Sat outdoor general
Romford	Wed, Fri, Sat outdoor general
Rye	Thur outdoor general
Saffron Walden	Tues, Sat outdoor general
Sevenoaks	Wed outdoor general
Sheerness	Tues, Sat outdoor general
St Albans	Wed to Sat outdoor general
Stowmarket	Thur, Sat outdoor general
Sudbury	Thur, Sat outdoor general
Tonbridge	Sat, Sun outdoor general; Tues, Fri indoor general
Tunbridge Wells	Wed, Sat outdoor general
Watford	Tues, Fri, Sat outdoor general
Whitstable	Thur outdoor general

97 Clacton-on-Sea Essex

Clacton Common Factory Shopping Village

Stephenson Road West
(0131) 220 6535

43 stores selling everything from fashion and footwear to china, glass and much more.

'Save at least 30% on high street prices.'

See our display advertisement opposite

Nearly three miles inland from the pier, on the north-east side of town (between the Bursville Park and Cooks Green areas of Clacton).

From Colchester: take A133 for Clacton. At Weeley roundabout, go on to Little Clacton and Weeley bypass (towards Clacton). At next roundabout, take B1442 for Oakwood industrial estate. Go over two roundabouts, passing Safeway on right. The village is past the office blocks.

From the pier: aim for A133 for Colchester. In Great Clacton, go right; follow signs to this new centre.

Open: Shopping village under construction as we go to press. Expected hours: Mon–Sat 10–6; Sun 11–5. Please phone for further information.
Closed: Christmas, Boxing & New Year's Days.
Cards: All major cards.
Cars: 1030 car spaces.
Toilets: Yes.
Wheelchairs: Full access for disabled.
Changing rooms: Yes.
Teas: Full restaurant and café facilities.
Groups: Groups welcome.
Transport: Trains to Clacton, Hopper bus to site.

98 Clacton-on-Sea Essex

Mascot Clothing

401 Old Road CO15 3RK
(01255) 432773

Ends of ranges and seconds of quality waxed cotton; breathable waterproof clothing for men, ladies and children. Tweed shooting jackets; quilted garments and hats, caps. Materials.

'Savings of up to 40%.'

North of Clacton.

From Colchester on A133: turn left on to B1027 to Frinton/Walton at roundabout with fire station on far right. Pass Queen's Head Hotel then turn sharp right 20 yds after pedestrian lights: shop is first on right.

From Clacton town centre: follow signs to A133 Colchester. At crossing with Esso on far left, follow signs to B1369 Great Clacton. You are now in Old Road. Shop is on left in last building by T-junction.

Open: Wed & Fri 12–4; first Sat in every month 10–1.
Closed: Bank Holidays; Christmas; New Year's Day.
Cards: MasterCard, Visa.
Cars: Large car-park.
Toilets: Public toilets across the road.
Wheelchairs: Easy access to large shop.
Changing rooms: No.
Teas: Several tea shops and pubs in village.
Groups: Coach parties welcome by prior arrangement. Please phone.
Transport: Local bus 50 yds; station 10 minutes' walk.

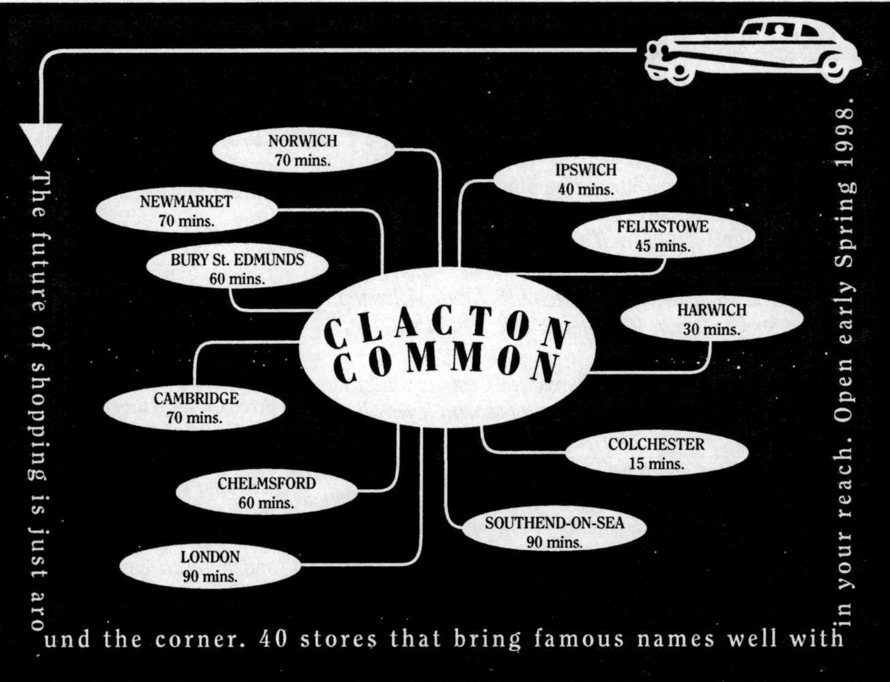

See our entry opposite

99 Cosham Hants

FactoryGate Variety Stores

77–79 High Street PO6 3AZ
(01705) 210067

Wide range of consumer products sold direct by over 100 manufacturers in one shop. Housewares (textiles, pots and pans, kitchen utensils); electrical goods (toasters to washing machines); family clothing; sports and outdoor leisure items; DIY items for home and garden; CDs, videos and equipment to play them; books; toys and games.

'Genuine 'factory direct' bargains from many manufacturers who rent space here. Significant discounts on all products. Constantly changing stock, something for all the family. New shops opening frequently, phone (01243) 555561 for latest news.'

In Cosham centre (just north of M27, north of Portsmouth).

Follow signs into town or to railway station. This shop is in main non-pedestrianised street, almost opposite Boots and between NatWest and Abbey National.

If you walk along the High Street from the railway station, it is 200 yds on right.

Open: Mon–Sat 9–5.30.
Closed: Phone to check Bank Holidays.
Cards: Major credit cards, Switch.
Cars: Nearby town car-parks and 1-hr parking across road.
Toilets: In town.
Wheelchairs: Easy access, huge ground floor shop.
Changing rooms: Yes.
Teas: Good cake shop and café next door.
Groups: Shopping groups welcome – just drop in, no need to phone.
Transport: Any bus or train to Cosham.
Mail order: No.

100 Crayford Kent

David Evans and Co.

Bourne Road DA1 4BR
(01322) 529198

Silk fabric by the metre; wide range of articles in silk, woven or printed by the company. Ties, handkerchiefs, scarves, shawls. Ladies' and gentlemen's exclusive range of gifts, eg boxer shorts, handbags, purses, wallets.

'Lots of bargains in famous name seconds. All at mill shop prices. Ring for Christmas late nights and special sales, mentioning this book.

STOP PRESS: Top fashion designer Paul Costello outlet now open – current stock, samples and end of season lines all at discount prices.'

A short distance east of the A2.

From M25 exit 2: take A2 for London. Turn off at Black Prince Interchange for Bexley/Bexleyheath; following brown tourist signs, take first exit at first roundabout and third exit at next roundabout.*

From London via A2: exit at Black Prince Interchange on to A223 (for Crayford, Bexley, Erith), take second exit at roundabout, following brown tourist signs.*

****Pass Hall Place on right; shortly after car showroom on right (and 50 yds before T-junction) go right into Bourne Industrial Park.***

Open: Mon–Fri 9.30–5; Sat 9.30–4.30.
Closed: Bank Holidays; please check for Christmas–New Year.
Cards: MasterCard, Switch, Visa.
Cars: Own car-park.
Toilets: Yes.
Wheelchairs: No steps, large shop, coffee shop, craft centre.
Teas: Own Mulberry Tree coffee shop for home baked produce, light lunches, cream teas etc. (01322) 529198 for catering manageress.
Groups: Pre-booked guided tours Mon–Fri to see hand-screen printing and finishing, and museum. Including video tour lasts 1¼ hours. Adults £2.50, OAPs and students £2.
Transport: Crayford station. Buses: London Transport no. 96; Greenline nos. 725, 726.

101 Dover Kent

De Bradelei Wharf

Cambridge Road CT17 9BV
(01304) 226616

Women's clothing from: *Windsmoor, Planet, Précis Petite, Country Casuals, Elvi*, top German & American designer labels, *Dutch Casuals, French Connection, Jake, Jaeger Knitwear Shop*. Men's wear from: *Wolsey, Farah, Tog 24, Countrywear, Pierre Cardin, French Connection*. Sports and leisurewear. Rober Leonard's Menswear sells *Grieff, Pierre Cardin, Gabicci, Gurteen, Oakman, Savile Row, John Slim etc.* Massive shoe department for all the family. Huge home furnishings department including *Waterford Wedgwood, Royal Doulton, Cloverleaf, Hornsea Pottery, Ponden Mill, Arthur Price.*

'Vastly enlarged outlet in superb maritime setting, just off Dover seafront. Up to 70% discount on top brand fashions and furnishings. Easy parking, excellent service.'

See our display advertisement opposite

In single storey harbour buildings facing yacht basin near hoverport.

From all directions: go into Dover. Follow signs to hoverport. Go over swing bridge towards hoverport; go left towards beach (50 yds before the hoverport entrance on right). Take first road (Cambridge Road) left then continue round right. Well marked shop is on left: car-park beyond shop on left.

Open: Mon–Fri (including Bank Holidays) 9.30–5.30; Sat 9.30–6; Sun 11–5.
Closed: Easter Sunday; Christmas & New Year's Days.
Cards: MasterCard, Switch, Visa.
Cars: Own large car-park.
Toilets: Yes.
Wheelchairs: Easy access to large shops.
Changing rooms: Yes.
Teas: On-site Waves coffee shop serving home-made lunch, morning coffee and afternoon tea.
Groups: Shopping groups welcome, but if over 50 people please phone in advance.
Transport: Priory train station nearby. Five minutes' walk from bus station.
Mail order: No.

See our entry opposite

102 East Dereham Norfolk

The Factory Shop Ltd.

Norwich Street NR19 1AD
(01362) 691868

Men's, ladies' and children's clothing, footwear, luggage, toiletries, hardware, household textiles, gifts, bedding, lighting and new fashion concessions department with famous brand names for ladies and men. *Cape Country* pine furniture exclusively produced for The Factory Shop.

'Large stock of chainstore items, all at greatly reduced prices. Deliveries of new stock every week to give an ever changing selection.'

Close to the town centre, this shop is housed in the former leisure centre. It is by traffic lights (junction with Station Road) and near large Somerfields (five minutes' walk from town centre).

Open: Mon–Sat 9–5.30; Sun 10–4.
Closed: Bank Holidays (but phone to check). Christmas, Boxing and New Year's Days.
Cards: Delta, MasterCard, Switch, Visa.
Cars: Own large car-park.
Toilets: Yes.
Wheelchairs: Easy access.
Changing rooms: Yes.
Teas: Tea room with home-made hot and cold food.
Groups: Shopping groups welcome. For organiser/driver incentives please phone.
Transport: Bus no. 794 to town centre, then 5 minutes' walk.
Mail order: Home delivery service for pine furniture. Please phone for free catalogue and price list.

103 Eastbourne E Sussex

Napier

3 Courtlands Road BN22 8SV
(01323) 644511 Fax (01323) 639420

Quality end-of-line and limited edition designer fashion jewellery in classic and contemporary designs direct from USA manufacturers. Classic chains, necklaces, brooches, hundreds of earrings, rings, chokers, bracelets.

'Quality merchandise at bargain prices. Items (all perfects) up to 75% off usual retail price, from £2.50–£500. Sale after Christmas. Ask to join customer list.'

On north-east side of town.

Going south on A22/from A27: at roundabout go left for Sea Front & Town Centre (East). Stay on A2021. Pass Travis Perkins on right.*

From Brighton on A259: follow signs for Hastings (A259)/A2040. Pass Travis Perkins on right.*

****At second lights, go left (Waterworks Road).*****

From town: with station on left, follow 1-way system. Don't go right to ring road (for Samaritans) but keep straight on Ashford Road. At T-junction with lights, go right; at next lights, go left (Waterworks Rd).**

From Hastings on A259: stay on this road, pass fire station on left: after 50 yds go right (Waterworks Road).**

*****Pass Unigate on left, follow road round and go left (Courtlands Road). Shop is on left.***

Open: Mon–Sat 10–6; Sun 10–4; some Bank Holidays – please phone to check.
Closed: Christmas, Boxing and New Year's Days.
Cards: MasterCard, Visa.
Cars: Own car-park.
Toilets: In town.
Wheelchairs: Ramp.
Teas: Lots of cafés in town.
Groups: Shopping groups welcome; please book first with Janet Wake.
Transport: 10 minutes' walk from nearest bus stop.
Mail order: No.

104 Fakenham Norfolk

Gilchris Confectionery

1–2 Oxborough Lane NR21 8AE
(01328) 862632

Wide range of high-quality confectionery made here – chocolates, marzipan, biscuits, seasonal novelties etc, depending on what is being made that week.

'All items rejects, eg slightly scuffed and occasional misshapes.'

Very close to the town centre, on the south side.

From Market Place: walk along to post office then turn down White Horse Street. At end go left into Oxborough Lane.*

From Norwich via A1067: turn left at Fakenham Town Centre sign into Norwich Road, continue towards town centre. Go left at junction (White Horse Street) then left again (Oxborough Lane).*

Coming north from Dereham (B1146): go over bridge into Bridge Street, look for Limes Hotel on left and turn right opposite it. Continue along Cattle Market Street. As road bears left, take right turn (Oxborough Lane).*

****Company well marked on right.***

Open: *Sept–June*: Mon–Wed 8.30–4.30; Thur 7.30–4.30; Fri 8.30–4; Sat 9–12. *July–Aug*: Mon–Wed: 8.30–2; Thur 8.30–3; Fri 8.30–2.
Closed: Bank Holidays; Christmas–New Year.
Cards: No.
Cars: Own car-park and also at rear of site; paid parking at Budgens.
Toilets: In Fakenham.
Wheelchairs: No access (tiny sales area).
Teas: In town.
Groups: No tours.
Transport: Any bus to Fakenham then 5 minutes' walk.
Mail order: No.

See our entry below

105 Fareham Hants

Grandford Carpet Mills

Unit 11, Bridge Industries, Broadcut, PO16 8ST
Freephone (0500) 717124

Carpets tufted here: 4-m wide heavy duty domestic range in various qualities from 100% synthetic fibre to 80/20% wool/nylon. Specialise in 80/20% heather mixtures. Also rubber underlay and accessories.

'Small family business also offering dye-to-order service (minimum 50 sq yds). Seconds sometimes available. Prices from £7.95–£15.95 per square yard, about half usual retail prices.'

See our display advertisement above

On north-eastern side of Fareham, about 1 mile from town centre.

From M27 exit 11: go towards Fareham; follow signs to Fareham Industrial Park at two roundabouts, passing Sainsbury's on the left. You come into Broadcut.**

From Portchester: take A27 and follow signs for Fareham.*

From town centre: go towards A32.*

****At huge roundabout with railway and motorway over the top, take dual-carriageway A32 (second turn-off before the large Roundabout hotel); at next roundabout (with Sainsbury's) go right into Broadcut.*****

*****Unit 11 is in one of the industrial buildings 400 yds on right.***

Open: Mon–Fri 9–5; Sat 10–4. Some Bank Holidays, please phone to check.
Closed: Christmas–New Year; Easter.
Cards: MasterCard, Visa.
Cars: In own forecourt.
Toilets: Ask if you are desperate.
Wheelchairs: Easy access, ramp to shop.
Teas: In Fareham.
Tours: Free tours for groups of up to 12; please phone Mr Copplestone first.
Transport: None.
Mail order: No.

106 Farnham Surrey

Freelance Fabrics

Unit 12, Lion and Lamb Yard GU9 7LL
(01252) 737428

Large stock of upholstery and furnishing fabrics: cottons, linens, damasks, velvets etc. Nets, voiles, calico, interlinings, waddings, linings. Haberdashery, fringing. Curtain rails/poles and accessories. Cushion covers and fillers. Ready-made curtains. Foam cut to shape. Dress fabrics.

'We will pay up to one hour's parking if you spend £5 or more. Friendly reliable service.'

See our display advertisement on p. 195

Close to the centre of Farnham, on the west side.

From the west/Petersfield: take A325 into Farnham. In town, pass the post office on the left. After 50 yds, go left (pedestrians only) through archway in half-timbered/brick building. Shop is at top right of yard.

From all other directions: go into town then round the one-way system. Follow sign left into two-way road for Petersfield A325. After 100 yds, go right (pedestrians only) through archway in half-timbered/brick building. Shop is at top right of yard.

Open: Mon–Sat 9.30–5; Sun and Bank Holidays 10–4.
Closed: Christmas and Boxing Days, please phone to check.
Cards: Access, Connect, Delta, Switch, Visa.
Cars: Town car-parks.
Toilets: In car-park 100 yds from shop.
Wheelchairs: Easy access, large ground floor shop.
Teas: Three appealing cafés nearby.
Groups: Shopping groups welcome, no need to phone.
Transport: Any bus or train to Farnham.
Mail order: No.

107 Faversham Kent

Catalogue Bargain Shop

19A Preston Street ME13 8NY
(01795) 591203

Huge range of mail order surplus items: clothing, fashions, household, footwear, hardware, furniture, electrical, toys and gifts.

'Large savings from original catalogue prices. Firsts & seconds.'

In the town centre opposite Safeways.

From M2 exit 6: take A251 (Ashford Road) for Faversham; pass fire station on left. At T-junction go left on to A2 then first right (The Mall). Follow road round under railway bridge, go left by Alldays store to shoppers' car-park. With The Railway Hotel on your right, walk into Preston Street. Shop is on right, opposite Safeways.

On foot from the station: turn left out of station, take first right (Preston Street): shop is about 100 yds on right.

Open: Mon–Sat 9–5.30; Sun 10–4. Bank Holidays.
Closed: Christmas and Boxing Days.
Cards: Access, Delta, Switch, Visa.
Cars: Several car-parks within a few minutes; disabled parking outside shop.
Toilets: Near Safeways.
Wheelchairs: No steps into large shop, but stairs to first floor area.
Changing rooms: Yes.
Teas: Cartons, Preston Street; Shelly's, High Street; several others.
Transport: Faversham station 200 yds; bus stop 3 minutes' walk.
Mail order: No.

108 Faversham Kent

Nova Garden Furniture

Graveney Road ME13 8UM *(01795) 535321*

Wide range of garden furniture made in different materials: luxurious swing hammocks, tubular folding frames, resin patio sets, reclining chairs and sunbeds, cast aluminium chairs, armchairs, benches and tables, timber benches, chairs and tables. A huge selection of cushions to fit most frames. Parasols and other accessories.

'One of Britain's leading manufacturers of attractive luxury upholstered garden furniture. Seconds, discontinued lines; many items half price or less.'

East of Faversham, two minutes from M2 exit 7.

From M2 exit 7 and A299 (Thanet Way, main Faversham–Whitstable road): take B2040 for Faversham. As you come into town go right for Graveney.*

From Faversham town centre: with station on right, follow road round to left. At traffic lights go right (B2040 for Whitstable). Cross railway; take first left, for Graveney.*

From Sittingbourne via A2: stay on A2 to Shell petrol on left – go left for Graveney. Go right for Graveney Industrial Estate.*

****Pass Nova factory on left: shop 150 yds on left.***

From east via A2: take first turn-off to Faversham; keep going towards Faversham – company is on right.

Open: *March–September* only; Mon, Wed, Fri 10.30–2; Sat 9.30–3; Bank Holidays except Good Friday.
Closed: Tuesday, Thursday; *October–February*; Good Friday.
Cards: No.
Cars: Outside shop.
Toilets: In Faversham (1½ miles)
Wheelchairs: Wide double doors, huge shop, no steps.
Teas: In Faversham.
Groups: Groups welcome to shop, please phone first, mentioning this guide.
Transport: No.

109 Feltham Middlesex

Legacy Jewellery

Hanworth Trading Estate, Hampton Road West TW13 6DH (0181) 755 2638

About 5000 designs of high fashion & designer jewellery: including *Florsheim of London* & Victorian antique collection by *English Eras. The Earth Collection* of hand-made jewellery in natural metals (brass & copper) & semi-precious stones. Austrian crystal rings. Necklaces, bracelets, earrings, brooches, chokers, rings etc plated in gold, silver & pewter. Components, findings and beads for craft hobby trade.

'Jewellery (limited editions) at 50–75% off normal retail, from 99p–£100. New lines constantly introduced so drop in often!'

Two miles north of Hampton Court Palace, 3 miles south of Heathrow.

Easy to find off Hampton Road, A312 (at the south, A316 end).

From A316: at huge roundabout (McDonald's on one side, Currys and Wickes on the other side), exit north for Feltham A312. After ¼ mile (cross first traffic lights) go left into Hanworth Trading Estate.*

Coming south on A312: go over traffic lights (Horse & Groom pub on far left; Hanworth public library on far right). Pass Texaco on right. After 250 yds, go right into Hanworth Trading Estate.*

****After 100 yds bear right: company is 50 yds on left.***

Open: Mon–Fri 9–4.
Closed: Bank Holidays; Christmas–New Year.
Cards: MasterCard, Switch, Visa.
Cars: On the estate.
Toilets: Yes.
Wheelchairs: Tricky at present: one step, ground floor shop but narrow corridor. Alterations in progress.
Teas: Own coffee shop for English cream teas and light refreshments.
Groups: Groups welcome by advance arrangement.
Transport: From Feltham train station: 15 minutes' walk or bus nos. 90, 285 (alight at The Mount). From Richmond train/tube station, bus no. 90 or 10 minutes by taxi.
Mail order: No.

110 Four Marks near Alton Hants

The Village Furniture Factory

Unit 4, Hazel Road GU34 5EV
(01420) 562111

Quality reproduction furniture in mahogany and yew: dining and bedroom furniture; TV and hi-fi cabinets; book cases; desks etc.

'Try us for lowest possible prices eg, mahogany dining tables £249; regency chairs from £69, also bargain monthly offers. Delivery arranged. New factory outlet at Farnborough, Hampshire (off M3) opposite B&Q. (01252) 520913.'

On A31 between Winchester and Alton.

From Winchester: take A31 north-east to Four Marks; pass Total petrol on right, go over pedestrian lights and take next right, Hazel Road, almost opposite Windmill pub. Turn right into car-park behind Hinson Hire: showroom is to the left of it.

From Alton: take A31 south-west. Pass petrol station on right and the Windmill pub on the right, and after 30 yds turn left into Hazel Road. Go right into car-park behind Hinson Hire: showroom is to the left of it.

Open: Seven days 10–5.30 (Thur late night to 8).
Closed: Christmas Day.
Cards: MasterCard, Visa.
Cars: Outside showroom.
Toilets: Yes.
Wheelchairs: One step to big ground floor showroom, but no access to upper showroom.
Teas: Little Chef about 1 mile direction Winchester.
Transport: Mon–Sat: bus nos. 64, X64 (Southampton–Guildford). Sun and Bank Holidays: bus no. 65 (Guildford–Winchester).
Mail order: No.
Catalogue: Yes. Free.

111 Frinton-on-Sea Essex

Park Fruit Farm

Pork Lane, Great Holland CO13 0ER
(01255) 674621

37 varieties of apples, sold loose, bagged and in boxes. Plums, pears and cane fruit also grown here. Range of fresh pressed, natural (unpasteurised) apple juices suitable for freezing – free tasting before you buy. Cider made here. Also some local vegetables, eg potatoes, and genuine free range eggs. PYO plums and cane fruit.

'Quality fruit supplied in peak condition from the growers. You are welcome to wander round the plum orchards in season to see the blossom. Bring your own bottles for re-filling with apple juice.'

Great Holland is about 1½ miles inland from Frinton.

Travelling south-east towards Frinton on B1033: at mini-roundabout, go right for Great Holland. At the start of Great Holland village (where the road bends left) go right into Pork Lane.*

From Clacton on B1032: go through Great Holland and past Methodist church on right. Where road bends right, turn left into Pork Lane.*

****Continue ½ of a mile to clearly marked farm on right.***

Open: *Aug–April*: Mon–Sat 9–5; also *Aug–Dec*: Sun 10–4.
Closed: May–July inclusive; Christmas–New Year inclusive; Sundays after Christmas until end July.
Cards: No.
Cars: Own car-park by shop.
Toilets: Ask if desperate.
Wheelchairs: Easy access, no steps.
Teas: In Frinton-on-Sea or Clacton.
Tours: If pressing is in progress, it is possible to see the apple juicing operation. Please ask. Phone for details of Apple Day in October.
Transport: None.
Mail order: No.

112 Godalming Surrey

Alan Paine Knitwear

Scats Country Store, Brighton Road GU7 1NS
(01483) 419962

Luxury knitwear in natural fibres including cashmere, camelhair, lambswool and cotton (sweaters, cardigans, slipovers).

'Stock about half price; always some seconds. Lambswool from £20, cashmere from £85. Knitwear made here for sale worldwide. Mostly perfects, some seconds. Special offers from time to time. Genuine factory shop!'

In Scats Country Store complex on B2130 on eastern side of town.

From A3100, main road through town: turn on to B2130 to Cranleigh at traffic lights. After 50 yds go left into the Scats Country Store yard. Shop is on left as you go into complex.

Open: Mon–Fri 9–5; Sat 8.30–4.30.
Closed: Bank Holidays; Christmas, Boxing and New Year's Days.
Cards: MasterCard, Switch, Visa.
Cars: Outside shop.
Toilets: In town centre.
Wheelchairs: Easy access to shop.
Changing rooms: Yes.
Teas: In Godalming.
Groups: Shopping groups welcome provided they phone first. No factory tours.
Transport: 10 minutes' walk from railway station.
Mail order: No.

Apples

An apple-growing nation, we still seem remarkably unimaginative when it comes to buying apples. Flavour and texture of apples are enormously varied and depend – like grapes – on variety, maturity, climate, soil, weather and time of picking etc. Picking can take place any time between August and December. Storage can be successful for as little as three days after picking to as long as six months, depending on the variety. Buying directly from the grower, as at the farm featured in this book, enables you to sample many more varieties than ever found in even the best greengrocer (let alone a supermarket). You can also enjoy the fruit when it is at its peak. Apples should be stored cool, ideally at the bottom of the fridge. Plums freeze very well. Pears bought when hard should be stored in the fridge then softened for a few days in a warm room (but don't let them go 'sleepy').

In addition to the old adage about an apple a day, new wisdom suggests that 'two apples a day reduce and stabilise cholesterol; reduce and stabilise blood pressure; reduce the risk of intestinal cancer; help the digestion, are a slimming aid, and clean teeth'.

Support British fruit growers and keep well too!

With thanks to Park Fruit Farm

113 Godalming Surrey

Kent & Curwen

8a Farncombe Street, Farncombe GU7 3AY
(01483) 426917

Top quality men's wear – suits, jackets, shirts, ties, trousers, knitwear and sportswear including cricket sweaters. Large selection of top quality golf wear. Silk ties made to order for colleges, clubs etc.

'Many perfect items at full price. Ends of line, samples and seconds at reduced prices in this genuine factory shop.'

Farncombe is a village a short distance north-east of Godalming.

From Godalming: take A3100 north towards Guildford. Look for the conservatory company on left then The Three Lions pub on left. Turn left into Hare Lane.*

Coming south from Guildford on A3100: pass Burmah petrol on right, then take third right (Hare Lane) in front of The Three Lions.*

****Keep going uphill to the T-junction; turn left. Shop is on right, just before the level crossing.***

Open: Fri–Sat 10–5.
Closed: Mon–Thur; Bank Holidays; Christmas–New Year.
Cards: Amex, MasterCard, Visa.
Cars: Far side of the railway.
Toilets: Across the railway.
Wheelchairs: One very small step to medium sized shop.
Changing rooms: Yes.
Teas: Local pubs in Godalming.
Groups: Shopping groups welcome but only by prior arrangement.
Transport: Next to Farncombe station (direct service from London, Waterloo).
Mail order: Yes. Please ring, Mon–Fri 9–4.30, for free brochure. Normal price merchandise only, no samples, seconds or ends of ranges available by mail order.

114 Grays Essex

Choice Discount Stores

14–16 High Street RM17 6LV
(01375) 385780

Surplus stocks including men's, women's and children's fashions and footwear from *Next plc, Next Directory* and other high street fashions.

'Save up to 50% of normal Next first quality prices; seconds sold from ⅓ of normal retail price. Special sales January and September.'

In the pedestrianised High Street in the centre of town.

From all directions aim for town centre. This gets you to the ring road around the centre. Park in any car-park and then walk. The shop is near the war memorial at the northern end of the pedestrian area, on the left as you go north.

Open: Mon–Sat 9–5.30.
Closed: Christmas and Boxing Days.
Cards: Amex, MasterCard, Switch, Visa.
Cars: Town centre car-park.
Toilets: No.
Wheelchairs: No steps to large shop.
Changing rooms: No, but refund if returned in perfect condition within 28 days.
Teas: In town centre.
Groups: Shopping groups welcome! Book with store manager.
Transport: Grays station.
Mail order: No.

Susan Walker Classics

12 High Street, Bramley GU5 0HF
(01483) 893602

Now closed

Top quality perfect Scottish knitwear in cotton, silk, lambswool, merino and cashmere (*N. Peal & Co.* and *Lyle & Scott* labels) for men and women.

'Perfect quality at about a third of London prices – ladies' cashmere from £65, with occasional seconds.'

Bramley is about 3 miles south of Guildford on the A281.

If you come south from Guildford, go into the high street. This shop is at the far end on the left, just before the traffic lights.

Coming north into Bramley: this shop is on the right, past the library and traffic lights.

Open: Mon–Fri 9.30–1 & 2–5; Sat 10–4.
Closed: Bank Holidays; please check Christmas–New Year opening.
Cards: Amex, MasterCard, Switch, Visa.
Cars: Free car-park by library; free car-parking spaces beside and behind shop.
Toilets: Nearby side street.
Wheelchairs: Easy access into medium sized shop.
Changing rooms: Yes.
Teas: Local pubs.
Groups: Larger groups please phone first.
Transport: Any bus to Bramley.
Mail order: Happy to send specific items on request. Please phone for details.

Rational Dress in Surrey

The area of Surrey around Guildford (good shopping for people needing a taste of full-price shopping along with their factory shopping) has had a mixed industrial history. Cloth-making was once an important trade. So too were the extraction of clunch (hard chalk building stone, also carved into ornamental fireplaces) and the burning of chalk into lime for mortar. Lime was also needed for paper-making and tanning – important in the Guildford and Godalming areas and which continued until 1988 in Gomshall.

Ferrari have a base in Surrey; Tyrrells are located in Ockham. Car and motor-cycle manufacture have featured strongly in the history of this area. Cycling and tricycling have been particularly popular sports: iron-tyred two-wheel 'velocipedes' were sold in Guildford High Street as early as 1870. Early bicycles needed good surfaced roads without too many hills and the Guildford road, largely deserted after the railway reached Portsmouth in 1847, proved ideal. The Surrey Bicycle Club organised a race from Kingston to Guildford then Ripley in 1876 The 24 miles were averaged at 16 mph – shortly after it was written that 'when the Queen comes from Windsor to Claremont she drives at a great pace, 12 miles an hour'.

The invention of the pneumatic tyre by Dunlop in 1888 made cycling more appealing to women. Ground length skirts and petticoats presented a problem, however, until The Rational Dress Association sought to make baggy knickerbockers acceptable. A court case against one Mrs Sprague of Ockham established that women travellers, wearing rational dress, could not be refused refreshments by innkeepers who took exception to this new-fangled garb!

This interesting information was taken from 'A Guide to the Industrial History of Guildford' by F. Haveron (published by the Surrey Industrial History Group).

116 Hackbridge, Wallington Surrey

South London Fabric Warehouse

Unit F2, Felnex Trading Estate, 190 London Road SM6 7EL
(0181) 647 3313

Large stock of upholstery and furnishing fabrics: plain and printed cottons, damasks, velvets etc. Nets, voiles, calico, interlinings, waddings, linings. Haberdashery, fringing. Curtain rails/poles and accessories. Cushion covers and fillers. Ready-made curtains. Foam cut to shape. Dress fabrics.

'Over 7000 rolls in stock. Full curtain making service. Re-upholstery and loose cover services. High quality fabrics at the lowest prices.'

See our display advertisement on p. 195

Hackbridge is west of Croydon. It is north of Wallington and south of Mitcham (just off the A237 which links them).

Coming south from Mitcham on A327: pass the Hungry Horse pub on right, continue for ½ mile, go right for Carshalton B277 (Hackbridge Road).*

From Croydon: take A232 west for Carshalton. At traffic lights in Wallington (war memorial in park on far left corner), go right on to A327 north. Go over railway bridge, pass Hackbridge station on right. Go over zebra; take next left (B277, Hackbridge Road).*

****Shop is clearly visible 400 yds on left.***

Open: Mon–Sat 10–5; Sun and Bank Holidays 10–4.
Closed: Christmas and Boxing Days.
Cards: Access, Connect, Delta, Switch, Visa.
Cars: Own large car-park.
Toilets: Yes.
Wheelchairs: Easy access, huge shop.
Teas: Local pubs in Carshalton and Sutton.
Groups: Shopping groups welcome, no need to phone.
Transport: 150 yds from train station.
Mail order: No.

117 Hadleigh Essex

Choice Discount Stores

14–20 Rectory Road SS7 2ND
(01702) 555245

Surplus stock including men's, women's and children's fashions and footwear from *Next plc, Next Directory* and other high street fashions. Household items from *Next Interiors.*

'Save up to 50% off normal Next first quality prices; seconds from ½ of normal retail price. Special sales January and September.'

In town centre near Iceland.

From the west on A13: as you pass Safeway and Elf petrol on left, enter one-way system.*

From the east on A13: enter one way system with church on right. Take next right, following one way system, and pass Safeway and Elf petrol on left.*

****At next traffic lights go left (Bradford & Bingley on left): shop is 50 yds on right.***

Open: Mon–Sat 9–5.30.
Closed: Christmas, Boxing and New Year's Days.
Cards: Amex, MasterCard, Switch, Visa.
Cars: Car-park opposite shop.
Toilets: Public toilet facing store.
Wheelchairs: Easy access. No steps.
Changing rooms: No, but refund if returned in perfect condition within 28 days.
Teas: Tea shops in Hadleigh town.
Groups: Shopping groups welcome! Book with store manager.
Transport: Hadleigh bus stop on A13; Rayleigh train station.
Mail order: No.

118 Hastings E Sussex

Collins and Hayes

Menzies Road, Ponswood Industrial Estate TN34 1XE
(01424) 443834

Upholstered furniture: sofas, chairs and some sofa beds. Upholstery/furnishing fabrics by the metre.

'All top quality upholstered furniture made in our factories on site. Most items perfect ends of lines and cancelled orders at about half high street price or less. Furniture delivered free within the UK.'

On the north-west side of Hastings.

From Hastings: go along seafront towards Bexhill. Pass the pier on left and White Rock Theatre on right. At traffic lights go right (London Road) and keep straight for ⅔ mile. At next traffic lights, in Silverhill, go straight for Battle. A short way down the hill (fish & chip shop on far left corner), take first left (for Ponswood Industrial Estate, Menzies Road). Company is 300 yds on left.

From Battle: take A2100 south-east for Hastings. Pass Beauport Park Hotel on left. At mini-roundabout follow sign to Hastings/Ponswood. Go under bridge, downhill, over lights then zebra. Pass the Tivoli Tavern on right. Take first right (Menzies Road) signed Ponswood. Company is 300 yds on left.

Open: Mon–Sat 9–5.
Closed: Bank Holidays; Christmas–New Year period.
Cards: MasterCard, Visa.
Cars: In factory car-park.
Toilets: Yes.
Wheelchairs: Not suitable.
Teas: Local cafés and pubs in St Leonards and Hastings.
Groups: No factory tours, but groups welcome to shop.
Transport: St Leonards Warrior Square train station, then taxi.
Mail order: No.

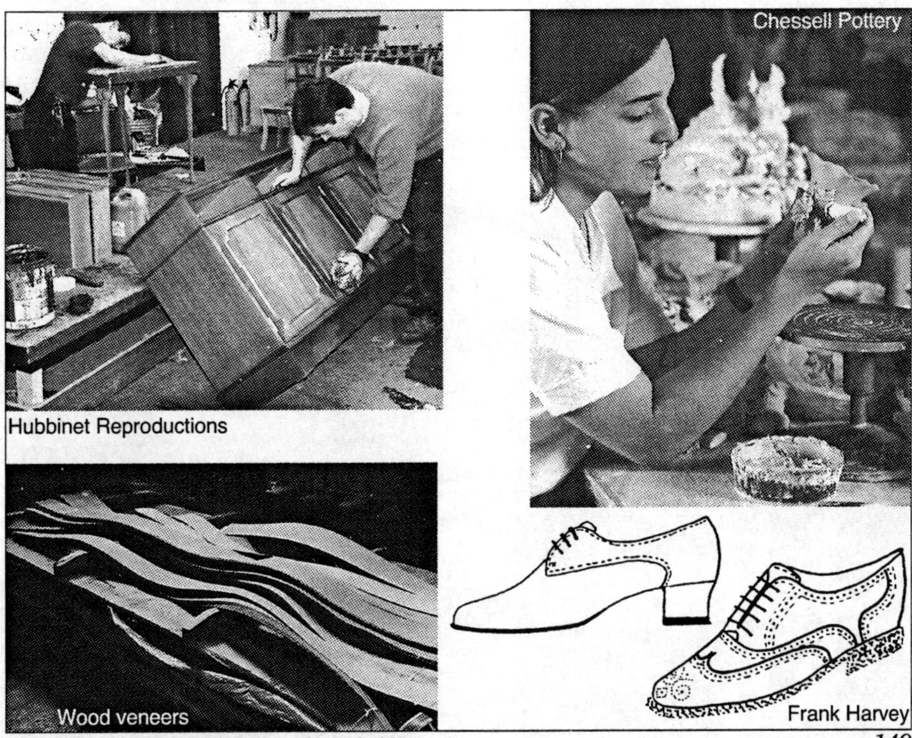

Chessell Pottery

Hubbinet Reproductions

Wood veneers

Frank Harvey

119 Hatfield Herts

Choice Discount Stores

The Galleria, Unit 45, Comet Way AL10 0XR
(01707) 258545

Surplus stock including men's, women's and children's fashions and footwear from *Next plc, Next Directory* and other high street brands.

'Save up to 50% of normal next first quality prices; seconds sold from ⅛ of normal retail price. Special sales January and September.'

Easy to see, in this conspicuous purpose built shopping centre which spans the A1 at Hatfield, between junctions 3 & 4.

Driving north or south on A1: turn off at signs to Hatfield then follow signs to The Galleria.

Open: Mon–Fri 10–8; Sat 10–6; Sun and Bank Holidays 11–5.
Closed: Christmas, Boxing, New Year's Day and Easter Sunday.
Cards: Amex, MasterCard, Switch, Visa.
Cars: Free surface and multi-storey car-park.
Toilets: Yes, and for disabled. Parent & baby facilities.
Wheelchairs: Easy access.
Changing rooms: No, but refund if returned in perfect condition within 28 days.
Teas: McDonald's, Mama Amalfi, Deep Pan Pizza, self-service café.
Groups: Coach parties welcome. Please book in advance with store manager.
Transport: Trains (King's Cross to Hatfield). Local buses from Hatfield town centre.
Mail order: No.

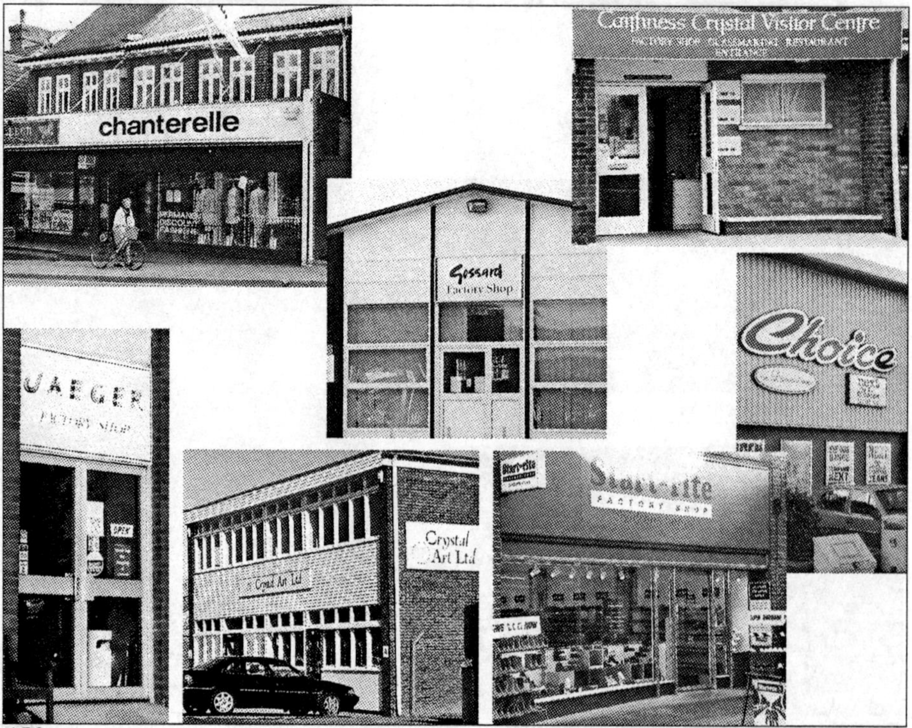

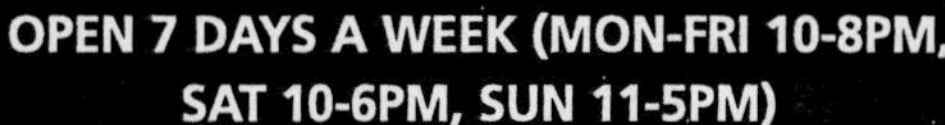

FANTASTIC SAVINGS OF 20% TO 60% OFF QUALITY BRAND RETAIL PRICES AT OVER 45 EXCITING OUTLET STORES

•

OPEN 7 DAYS A WEEK (MON-FRI 10-8PM, SAT 10-6PM, SUN 11-5PM)

•

FREE AND AMPLE PARKING

•

INDOOR CHILDREN'S PLAY AREA, DRY ICE SKATING AND CRAZY GOLF

•

RESTAURANTS, CAFÉS AND 9 SCREEN CINEMA

•

SITUATED OVER A1M HATFIELD (EASY ACCESS BY ROAD), BETWEEN JUNCTIONS 3 & 4 AND 6 MILES NORTH OF M25 JUNCTION

•

WHEELCHAIR AND PUSHCHAIR FRIENDLY

Comet Way, Hatfield, Herts AL10 0XR.
Tel: 01707 278301

Internet: www.factory-outlets.co.uk

See our entry overleaf

120 Hatfield Herts

The Galleria Outlet Centre

Comet Way AL10 0XR
(01707) 278301

Ladies', mens' and childrens' fashions, footwear, jewellery, china and glass, housewares, linens, furnishings, luggage, leathers and more.

'The factory outlet centre for London and the south-east. Major savings of 20–60% on quality brand names at about 50 outlet stores, all year round. Restaurants, cafés, 9-screen cinema, toddlers' play area, dry ice skating and crazy golf.'

See our display advertisement on previous page

Easy to see, in this conspicuous purpose built shopping centre which spans the A1 at Hatfield between junctions 3 and 4.

Driving north or south on A1(M): turn off at signs to Hatfield then follow signs to The Galleria.

Open: Mon–Fri 10–8; Sat 10–6; Sun 11–5; Bank Holidays 11–6.
Closed: Easter Sunday, Christmas and Boxing Days.
Cards: Most shops accept credit cards.
Cars: Free surface and multi-storey car-park for 1,800 cars.
Toilets: Yes, including for disabled. Parent & baby facilities.
Wheelchairs: Easy access, and lifts, to all areas. Wheelchairs (from Shopmobility) on loan.
Changing rooms: Yes.
Teas: Eight restaurants and cafés.
Groups: Coach parties welcome. Please phone in advance.
Transport: Trains (King's Cross to Hatfield station). Local buses from station and Hatfield town centre.
Mail order: No.

121 Alphamarque
(01707) 266262
Recreational and mobility equipment for the elderly and disabled.

122 B52
(01707) 257508
Jeans and leisure clothing.

123 The Baggage Factory
(01707) 257779
Luggage, travel accessories and handbags.

124 Bed & Bath Works
(01707) 259202
Branded bedlinen, towels, small home decorative accessories.

125 Bella Ricco Shoes
(01707) 266662
Shoes for all the family, handbags and belts.

126 The Big Picture
(01707) 260260
Modern and classical prints and originals. *Disney* framed prints.

127 Burton Menswear
(01707) 251688
Men's suits, shirts, sweaters, ties, trousers and jackets.

128 Buster Brown
(01707) 259850
America's leading manufacturer of children's clothes (0–8 years).

129 Carlton Cards
(01707) 251810
Cards, stationery, gifts and toys for the whole family.

130 CBS
(01707) 267067
Catalogue clothing and goods from GUS home shopping.

131 Chamberlaine's
(01707) 268433
Raleigh bikes and accessories for adults and children.

132 Choice Discount Store
(01707) 258545
Famous high street fashion *(see entry no.119)*.

133 Ciro Citterio
(01707) 259665
Men's wear.

134 City Menswear
(01707) 259846
Moss Bros men's wear.

135 County Books
(01707) 256860
Books and notelets.

New shop The Designer Room
(01707) 275014
Women's wear by Christian Lacroix, Armani, Dolce & Gabbana, Moschino, Gucci etc.

136 Discount Dressing
(01707) 259925
Women's continental labels including larger sizes.

137 Dorothy Perkins
(01707) 263640
Women's fashions.

138 Ecco Shoes
(01707) 258399
Footwear for the whole family.

139 Event
(01707) 261116
Women's fashions.

140 Feet Street
(01707) 258653
Footwear, belts and handbags.

142 Freetime Sports
(01707) 259768
Sportswear and equipment.

143 Gallagher
(01707) 260260
Men's fashion.

144 Hawkes Bay
(01707) 258662
Casual wear from Canada for the whole family.

145 Hobbyhorse
(01707) 261996
Children's wear.

146 Hornsea Pottery
(01707) 257877
China and ceramics.

147 Jeffrey Rogers
(01707) 258144
Women's fashion including larger sizes.

148 Kids Play Factory
(01707) 258720
Brand name toys, games and dolls.

149 Lands' End
(01707) 264161
Catalogue casual wear for the whole family.

New shop Lillywhites
(01707) 273270
One of the most prestigious sports shops in the world. Full range of last season's stock.

150 London China Shops
(01707) 275525
Well known names in china and glass.

151 The Main Event
(01707) 260028
Bridal wear and accessories.

152 Millano
(01707) 259199
Leather and sheepskin jackets and coats.

153 Moist
(01707) 267192
Women's and men's clubwear.

154 Music Store
(01707) 271800
Instruments from guitars to electric pianos.

155 Outdoor Trading Post
Freephone (0800) 413650
Skis and skiwear, specialist outdoor performance clothing and footwear.

156 Pilot
(01707) 258030
Women's fashions.

157 R S Shoes
(01707) 258021
Family footwear.

158 Suits You
(01707) 260009
Men's wear.

159 T K Maxx

(01707) 260066

Top label clothes for the whole family; gifts, luggage, china, ceramics and stationery.

160 Take Flight

(01707) 266288

Luggage and briefcases.

161 Tog 24

(01707) 258088

Outdoor clothing, rucksacks, hats and boots.

162 Tom Sayers

(01707) 257729

Men's sweaters, trousers and shirts.

163 Walker & Hall

(01707) 270121

Jewellery and watches.

164 Whittard

(01707) 273930

Famous name tea and coffee, china, cafetières and teapots.

Bicester Village

Merchants Quay

Galleria Outlet Centre

De Bradelei Wharf

165 Headcorn Kent

The Factory Shop Ltd.

The Foreman Centre, High Street TN27 9NE
(01622) 891651

Men's, ladies' and children's clothing, designer labels and country sporting clothes. Footwear, luggage, hardware, household textiles, bedding, rugs, gifts, ornaments, pictures, silk flowers, lighting, tapes, compact discs, videos and books. *Cape Country* pine furniture exclusively produced for The Factory Shop.

'Large stock of branded and chainstore items, all at greatly reduced prices. Deliveries of new stock every week to give an ever changing selection.'

In the centre of the village.

The Foreman Centre is identified by a series of small units in traditional weatherboard buildings fronting the High Street. The shop is at the rear of the units in the main car-park.

Coming south on A274 from Sutton Valence direction: go into High Street, pass the Foreman Centre then take first right, for car-park. The Factory Shop is signposted.

Open: Mon–Fri 10–5.30; Sat 9–5.30; Sun and Bank Holidays 10–4.
Closed: Easter Sunday; Christmas, Boxing and New Year's Days.
Cards: All major cards.
Cars: Own large car-park.
Toilets: In village.
Wheelchairs: No steps.
Changing rooms: Yes.
Teas: Tearoom opposite and George & Dragon pub in village.
Groups: Shopping groups welcome. For organiser/driver incentives please phone.
Transport: On Charing Cross/Ashford train line: station 5 minutes' walk. Hourly bus no. 12 from Maidstone.
Mail Order: Home delivery service for pine furniture. Please phone for free catalogue and price list.

166 Hemel Hempstead Herts

Aquascutum

Cleveland Road, Maylands Wood Estate HP2 7EV
(01442) 248333

Wide selection of men's and women's suits, jackets, coats, raincoats, trousers, knitwear, shirts, blouses, skirts.

'Last season's stock, returned items, rejects, factory clearance lines. Occasional sales.'

On the east side of town.

From M1 exit 8: take A414 for Hemel Hempstead; go over first roundabout, right at second (to 'Industrial Area') into Maylands Avenue (A4147).*

From town centre: take St Alban's Road (A414) for M1 exit 8. At large roundabout, go left into Maylands Avenue (A4147) for industrial area.*

****Go straight at traffic lights; take first road to left (Cleveland Road). Shop on a far right corner, clearly signed.***

Open: Mon–Sat 10–4. Please check times before visit.
Closed: Please check.
Cards: Most major cards.
Cars: Large car-park by shop.
Toilets: No.
Wheelchairs: One step to large shop.
Changing rooms: Yes.
Teas: In town.
Groups: Shopping groups should check beforehand.

167 Herne Bay Kent

Peter Newman

Eddington Park, Thanet Way (A299) CT6 5TS
(01227) 741112

10,000+ shoes for all the family on display: *Clarks, K, Rohde, Equity, Lotus*. Shoes, boots, trainers and slippers.

'Branded shoes at factory prices. This company does not manufacture but these shoes are ends of ranges etc from their other retail shops. Prices considerably reduced.
***An extra 5% discount given if you mention The Factory Shop Guide.**'*

Large conspicuous shop on the A299 (Thanet Way) on the south side of Herne Bay.

Shop is on the left, next to Homebase, if you are going east towards Ramsgate.

Open: Mon–Sat 9–5.30; Sun 10–4.
Closed: Easter Sunday, Christmas and Boxing Days.
Cards: Connect, MasterCard, Switch, Visa.
Cars: Car-park outside shop.
Toilets: Available on site.
Wheelchairs: No steps, huge shop.
Teas: Refreshment area with tea/coffee/soft drinks machines in store. Tea rooms in Herne Bay.
Groups: No factory tours. Shopping groups and coach parties welcome – prior phone call appreciated.
Transport: Herne Bay station close by: go out of station, turn right, through alleyway to rear of factory shop.
Mail order: No.

168 Herstmonceux E Sussex

Thomas Smith's Trug Shop (Herstmonceux)

BN27 4LI
(01323) 832137

Three ranges of trugs plus some wooden fruits and gifts etc. Trugs in many sizes, made here, from sweet chestnut (rims and handles) with cricket bat willow; also in plywood. 'Walking stick' trugs, fireside log trugs, square and oblong trugs.

'Trugs at £15–£40. Personalised with pokerwork dates, initials to order etc. Most perfects but small range of seconds.'

In village centre, on A271, easy to see near turn-off to Stunts Green and Cowbeech.

Coming west from Battle: go into village, round left bend, and company is 50 yds on left, with large sign 'Royal Sussex Trugs'.

From Hailsham: as you come into village you will see the company on the right, just before phone box on left.

Open: Mon–Fri 8–5; Sat 9–4.
Closed: Bank Holidays; Christmas–New Year.
Cards: None.
Cars: Car-park at rear of Woolpack pub.
Toilets: Across the road.
Wheelchairs: One step to small showroom. Wheelchairs can be assisted over step, door 30" wide.
Teas: Local pubs.
Tours: Gladly arrange an hour's tour for groups in working hours: please book with Robin Tuppen. Individuals welcome to walk round workshop to view craftsmen at work (Mon–Fri only). No charge if trug purchased.
Transport: Any bus to village.
Mail order: Yes. Only first quality trugs by mail order.
Catalogue: Free.

169 Hickstead Village W Sussex

M & G Designer Fashions

Old London Road (A23) RH17 5RK
(01444) 881511

Wide range of upmarket designer label clothing for men and women at least 30–70% less than normal retail prices. Sizes 10–26. Daywear, separates, cocktail wear, ballgowns, special occasion outfits, millinery, ladies' shoes.

'Look on our permanent "£30 or less" rails.'

On A23 (old London–Brighton road), on north-bound side of dual carriageway.

Going south on A23: shop is on far side of dual carriageway, so you must cross A23 and double back: take left slip-road for Hickstead Village/Twineham; cross A23 and go back north (following signs to Ricebridge) to warehouse ½ mile on left.

Going north on A23: take slip-road to Hickstead Village/ Twineham. Go up to roundabout then straight ahead (following signs to Ricebridge) to warehouse ½ mile on left.

Open: Mon–Sat 10–5.
Closed: Please phone for Christmas and Bank Holidays.
Cards: Amex, MasterCard, Switch, Visa.
Cars: Free large car-park outside warehouse.
Toilets: Yes.
Wheelchairs: One step; ramp available to warehouse.
Changing rooms: Yes.
Teas: Everyone offered free tea or coffee. Pub and café nearby.
Groups: Shopping groups welcome – please phone first. Coach parties can be accommodated.
Transport: None.
Mail order: No.

170 High Barnet Herts

Catalogue Bargain Shop

101–107 High Street EN5 5UZ
(0181) 364 9654

Huge range of mail order surplus items: clothing, fashions, household, footwear, hardware, toys and gifts.

'Large savings from original catalogue prices. Firsts & seconds.'

In the centre of High Barnet.

Going north from Whetstone/Finchley on A1000: go up Barnet Hill; at traffic lights in High Barnet fork right (church on left). Look for Halifax building society on a far left corner: this shop is immediately past it. [To park, pass the shop, bear left at traffic lights into St Albans Road (A1081), go left into Stapylton Road for open car-park on right or Spires Centre on left.]

Coming south into High Barnet: go over traffic lights then this shop is shortly on right, beside the Halifax. Multi-storey car-park (Spires Centre) is behind this shop in Stapylton Road.

Open: Mon–Sat 9–5.30; Sun 10–4. Bank Holidays.
Closed: Christmas and Boxing Days.
Cards: Access, Delta, Switch, Visa.
Cars: Spires Centre; meters in High Street.
Toilets: Spires Centre.
Wheelchairs: No steps, large ground floor shop.
Changing rooms: Yes.
Teas: McDonald's or Moon under Water pub.
Transport: High Barnet tube station; bus stop 100 yds away.
Mail order: No.

171 High Wycombe Bucks *see map next page*

GP & J Baker & Parkertex Fabrics

The Warehouse, Desborough Road HP11 2QE
(01494) 467467

Shop closed

Wide range of curtain and upholstery fabrics: prints, damasks, jacquards, selected range of naturals; also wallpapers and borders.

'Britain's leading suppliers of fine furnishing fabrics and wallpapers. Large selection of near perfect and discontinued lines at substantially reduced prices.'

Stop press: This shop has closed. For further details, dates and locations of possible sales, please phone company on (01494) 467467.

West of town centre.

From M40 exit 4: follows signs A404 into town centre. At triple roundabout at bottom of hill, follow signs for Aylesbury A40/Gt Missenden A4128.*

From London via A40: at triple roundabout in High Wycombe, follow signs for Aylesbury A40/Gt Missenden A4128.*

****With huge Buckinghamshire College on left and fire station on right, go on to dual carriageway. Go left just after college for Desborough Road Shopping Area. At T-junction go left. Pass Job Centre on left then Iceland on right. Shop is on left.***

From Oxford on A40: at traffic lights (Budget cars on near right), go right for Wycombe General Hospital. At double mini-roundabout, go left. After ¼ mile look for Rose & Crown on left: shop is on right.

172 High Wycombe Bucks *see map next page*

Furniture Direct

Riverside Business Centre, Victoria Street HP11 2LS
(01494) 462233

Quality upholstered furniture: sofas, upholstered chairs and sofa beds. Choose your own fabric from thousands available.

'All furniture made here to customers' own requirements at factory direct prices.'

See our display advertisement opposite

One mile west of High Wycombe centre, just off West Wycombe Road (A40, High Wycombe–Oxford road).

From High Wycombe: take A40; go over traffic lights with Budget cars on far left corner; after 100 yds go left into Victoria Street.*

From Oxford via A40: as you reach High Wycombe, pass BP on right then The White Horse then Bird in Hand on right; take next right, Victoria Street.*

****Riverside Business Centre is clearly visible on left with large off-road car-park in front.***

Open: Mon–Sat 9.30–5; Sun 10–4; Bank Holidays.
Closed: Easter Sunday, Christmas and Boxing Days.
Cards: Delta, Switch, MasterCard, Visa. Interest-free credit also available.
Cars: Own car-park.
Toilets: Yes.
Wheelchairs: One tiny step, large showroom.
Teas: In High and West Wycombe.
Groups: No tours.
Transport: Local buses go along the A40.
Mail order: No.

See our entry opposite

173 High Wycombe Bucks *see map below*

Highly Sprung

12 Oakridge Road HP11 2PF
(01494) 439596

Quality upholstered furniture in traditional and modern styles; all major fabrics available. Sofas, sofa beds and armchairs. Re-covering service.

'Visit our factory and see furniture being made, combining the best of traditional methods with modern materials. Special commissions undertaken. Delivery charged according to volume and distance.'

About ¾ mile north-west of High Wycombe centre, immediately south of A40 (High Wycombe–Oxford road).

From High Wycombe: take A40 north for Oxford. Turn left off the A40 immediately after 'The White Horse' into Oakridge Road.*

From Oxford coming south on A40: turn right in front of 'The White Horse'.*

****The clearly marked company, set back from the road, is 100 yds on the right.***

Open: Mon–Fri 9–5; Sat 10–4.
Closed: Bank Holidays, Christmas–New Year.
Cards: MasterCard, Switch, Visa.
Cars: Own forecourt.
Toilets: Yes.
Wheelchairs: One step to ground floor; first floor showroom difficult.
Teas: In town.
Groups: Welcome to see furniture being made. Groups by appointment only.
Transport: Train to High Wycombe station, then taxi.
Mail order: Yes.
Catalogue: Free.

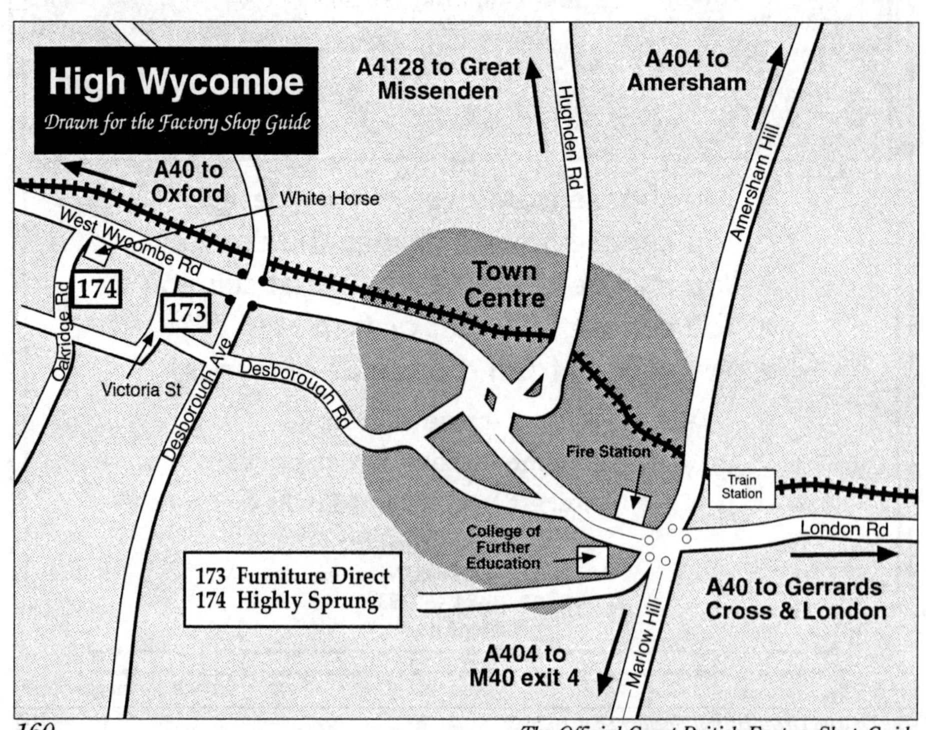

Chair-making capital of England

High Wycombe is synonymous with upholstered and wooden chairs, particularly the 'Windsor' style. An amazing one and a half million Windsor chairs a year were produced by the 100 furniture factories in this town during the middle of last century. High Wycombe is still home to nationally known manufacturers as well as smaller, family-owned businesses, and the 'Furniture Discovery Trail' leads to you to several companies where you can see showrooms and watch traditional caning and rush seating.

No one knows how the Windsor chair got its name (the first known reference was in 1742). Early models are known as 'comb-backs' – with backs looking like a large comb or hay rake. As with all country furniture, fashion gradually changed and some extremely ornate pieces were produced in exotic and expensive woods (normally the turned parts were in beech, the seats in elm and bent parts in ash, yew or fruitwood). The most significant change to design came in the 1780s, when the wheel-back motif was introduced. It was instantly successful and the town of High Wycombe alone produced over 5000 such chairs a day. The popularity has endured too: this design accounts for over 75% of Windsor chairs ever produced.

Visit the world famous collection of chairs at the Wycombe Chair Museum, Priory Avenue, High Wycombe HP13 6PX. (01494) 421895. Mon–Fri 10–5, Sat 10–1 & 2–5. Free admission.

With thanks to the museum for this information.

174 Hingham Norfolk

Rombah Wallace

14–17 Ironside Way NR9 4LF
(01953) 851106

Wide range of top-quality leather shoes for men & women; also some slippers, sandals, sports shoes, boots; handbags; some leather jackets.

'All items perfects at 25–35% less than high street prices, eg, ladies' shoes £35 (rrp £50).'

Hingham is about 15 miles west of Norwich, on the B1108 (Norwich–Watton) road.

Coming west from Norwich direction: turn right into this small industrial estate as soon as you reach the outskirts of Hingham.*

From the Watton direction: go through Hingham, passing church on right and village green on left. After ½ mile, at end of the village and after speed de-restriction sign, turn left into small industrial estate.*

***Company is in second turning on left, clearly marked on right.**

Open: Mon–Sat 9–5; Bank Holidays 10–5.
Closed: Christmas, Boxing and New Year's Days.
Cards: MasterCard, Visa.
Cars: Outside factory and shop.
Toilets: In Hingham.
Wheelchairs: Easy access to sizeable shop.
Teas: In Hingham.
Groups: No factory tours but groups welcome to shop.
Transport: Local buses may stop at request; otherwise 10/15 minutes' walk from Hingham bus stop.
Mail order: Yes.
Catalogue: £3.

175 Horley Surrey

The Factory Shop Ltd.

Old Engine Shed, Consort Way East RH6 7AV
(01293) 823883

Men's, ladies' and children's clothing, footwear, luggage, toiletries, hardware, electricals, household textiles, gifts, bedding, lighting and fashion concessions department with famous brand names for ladies and men. *Cape Country* pine furniture exclusively produced for The Factory Shop.

'Large stock of branded and chainstore items, all at greatly reduced prices. Deliveries of new stock every week to give an ever changing selection.'

Close to the town centre.

Find the station. With the station on your left: go over railway line into High Street; take first right, Consort Way East. The shop is 200 yds on the right (after Do-It-All) in a converted engine shed.

Open: Mon–Sat 9–5.30; Sun 10–4.
Closed: Christmas, Boxing and New Year's Days.
Cards: MasterCard, Switch, Visa.
Cars: Own car-park.
Toilets: In town centre.
Wheelchairs: Easy access – ramps and lifts to both floors of huge shop.
Changing rooms: Yes.
Teas: In town centre.
Groups: Shopping groups welcome. For organiser/driver incentives please phone.
Transport: Two minutes' walk from Horley town centre.
Mail order: No. Home delivery service for pine furniture. Please phone for free catalogue and price list.

176 Ipswich Suffolk

Ellis Furniture

Dormers, Main Road, Ashbocking IP6 9JX
(01473) 890309

Traditional hand-crafted oak furniture: corner cupboards, dressers, wall racks with plate grooves, foot stools, kitchen tables, drop-leaf tables etc. Full range of complete items in showroom; also made to order.

'Our craftsmen aim for impeccable quality. Designs and finishes can be adapted to your requirements, distressed and polished as requested. Very reasonable prices. We also exhibit our products at craft and country shows: please phone for places and dates.'

Ashbocking is 6 miles north of Ipswich. Company is on B1077.

From Ipswich: go north to Ashbocking on B1077. Cross the B1078. Pass Limes garage on right then this company is on left.

Open: By appointment at any time, please phone for details.
Cards: MasterCard, Visa.
Cars: Own car-park.
Toilets: Ask if desperate.
Wheelchairs: One step to small shop.
Teas: In Ipswich.
Groups: No.
Transport: No buses to Ashbocking.
Mail order: No.
Catalogue: Free brochure, please ring for details.

177 Ipswich Suffolk

Lambourne Clothing

15 Christchurch Street IP4 2DR
(01473) 250404

Skirts, blouses, trousers, jackets; men's jackets, trousers, suits; waistcoats; knitwear and shirts; small range of T-shirts and knitwear, depending on season; tights. Some towels, bedding.

'Overmakes, seconds, ends of ranges, some samples of own label and well known high street labels. 10% discount for senior citizens.'

Few hundred yards north-east of city centre.

From Colchester: follow signs to town centre. At roundabout with Civic Hall straight ahead, go left; go right at next roundabout on to A1156 eastbound.*

From south and east: follow 'Through Traffic' signs; at roundabout with Civic Hall on right, go straight; at next roundabout go right on to A1156 (Crown Street).*

****Pass bus station on right, swimming pool on left. Pass Odeon on right; after 50 yds turn left into car-park.***

From Norwich/Stowmarket: go left on to A1156 for Ipswich; stay on it to Odeon on right. After 50 yds go into Christchurch St.

Open: Tues–Fri 10–4. Please phone first.
Closed: Monday; Bank Holidays; last week July and first week August; Christmas; New Year's Day.
Cards: Diners, MasterCard, Visa.
Cars: One-hour parking 100 yds up road. Multi-storey car-park nearby.
Toilets: Yes.
Wheelchairs: No steps.
Changing rooms: Yes.
Teas: Local pubs, cafés.
Groups: No factory tours; shopping groups welcome with prior phone call.
Transport: Short walk from town centre and bus station.

178 Ipswich Suffolk

Suffolk Carpet Weavers

Unit D, Hill Farm Estate, Witnesham IP6 9EV
(01473) 785111

Fine carpets made here: tufted twist and velvet pile, woven Axminsters. Up to 5 metres in width, any weight of wool blends. Many shapes, styles and sizes in pure wool rugs, from one-off to small production runs, in traditional, contemporary, deco or ultra modern themes.

'Gladly make rugs and carpets to your own design or colourways and with borders. Both perfect and second qualities. Trade prices.'

See our display advertisement opposite

Witnesham is 5 miles north of Ipswich; the company is at the north end of the village.

From Ipswich: take B1077 north. Once in Witnesham, pass the Barley Mow pub on right. Continue for several hundred yards then follow signs on verge to company on right. Turn into the drive.

Open: Mon–Fri 9–5; Sat 9–1.
Closed: Bank Holidays; Christmas–New Year.
Cards: None.
Cars: Own car-park.
Toilets: Yes.
Wheelchairs: Ramp to shop, easy access through wide doorway.
Teas: Local pubs.
Tours: Visits to factory available in the evening (maximum 30 people): please book in advance with Mr J Masters. Groups welcome to shop.
Transport: Buses from Ipswich to Witnesham.

179 Ipswich

Suffolk Fabric Warehouse

Solar Superstore, Sproughton Road IP1 5AQ
(01473) 462229 Fax (01473) 241256

Large stock of upholstery and furnishing fabrics: cottons, linens, damasks, velvets etc. Nets, voiles, calico, interlinings, waddings, linings. Haberdashery, fringing. Curtain rails/poles and accessories. Cushion covers and fillers. Ready-made curtains. Foam cut to shape. Dress fabrics.

'About 8000 rolls in stock. Custom made curtain making service. High quality fabrics at the lowest prices.'

See our display advertisement on p. 195

About a mile out of the city on the north-west side of Ipswich, Sproughton Road leads south off Bramford Road B1067.

Open: Mon–Sat 8.30–5 (late night Fri to 7); Sun and Bank Holidays 10–4.
Closed: Easter Sunday; Christmas and Boxing Days.
Cards: Access, Connect, Delta, Switch, Visa.
Cars: Own free car-park.
Toilets: In shopping centre.
Wheelchairs: Easy access, no steps.
Teas: Café in shopping centre.
Groups: Shopping groups welcome.
Transport: None.
Mail order: No.

See our entry opposite

180 Isle of Wight : Yarmouth

Chessell Pottery (Chessell Enterprises)

Chessell, Yarmouth PO41 OUF
(01983) 531248
Internet: chessell-pottery@isle-of-wight.uk.com

Fine decorative, ornamental porcelain; vases, animals, fountains, dishes etc.

'Seconds available. Collectors' Club with members' discounts.'

On the western end of the island.

From Freshwater: take B3399 for Brighstone and Newport. After 3½ miles fork left on to B3401 for Newport. Go right after 150 yds.*

From Newport: take B3401 for Freshwater and the Needles. After 6 miles pass Calbourne Mill on right; after 1 mile go left.*

****Follow brown signs to pottery.***

Open: Mon–Sat 9–5.30; *also April–Dec*: Sun 10–5.
Closed: Christmas–New Year for 2 weeks.
Cards: Diners, MasterCard, Switch, Visa.
Cars: Free car-park.
Toilets: Yes.
Wheelchairs: Full facilities for the disabled.
Teas: Own coffee shop: drinks and snacks.
Groups: Porcelain made and decorated Mon–Sat 9–5. Admission to studios: adults 40p, children (5–15) 20p.
Transport: No. 7 bus.
Mail order: Yes.
Catalogue: Free to readers of this guide. No seconds sent.

181 Kenninghall Norfolk

Suffolk Potteries

Lopham Road NR16 2DT
(01379) 687424

Wide range of terracotta storage jars, wine coolers, bread and flour crocks, plant and parsley pots, insect-repellent garden candles, *Suffolk Smellies* (pots impregnated with aromatic oil) etc.

'From £2–£65. Some seconds. All pots hand-made on potter's wheel in workshop. Viewing usually possible. Commissions undertaken.'

One mile south of Kenninghall village centre, 2 miles north of South Lopham, 10 miles east of Thetford, 6 miles west of Diss.

From South Lopham (A1066): take B1113 north for Kenninghall; Suffolk Potteries well signposted on left (2 miles).

From Kenninghall market place (post office on left, White Horse on right): go straight for ¼ mile then go south on to B1113 for N Lopham/Stowmarket; Suffolk Potteries well signposted on right (1 mile).

Open: Mon–Fri 9–5. Some weekends and Bank Holidays – phone to check.
Closed: Phone for Christmas.
Cards: No.
Cars: Own car-park.
Toilets: Yes, including for disabled.
Wheelchairs: Easy access to small showroom.
Teas: Quidenham Tea Gardens about 2 miles north of shop. Please ask at shop for details of other places.
Groups: Tours of pottery by arrangement – maximum 15 visitors. Contact Steve Harold. Groups welcome to shop if you phone first.
Transport: Sparse!
Mail order: Yes.
Catalogue: Free. Pots can be personalised and made to customers' specification.

182 King's Lynn Norfolk *see map opposite*

Caithness Crystal

11 Paxman Road, Hardwick Industrial Estate PE30 4NF
(01553) 765111 Internet: http://www.caithnessglass.co.uk

Glass and crystal giftware and tableware in assorted colours and designs; vases, bowls, paperweights, jewellery, glass animals and new line – *Royal Doulton* crystal. Pot pourri, gift wrap and glass nuggets.

'Super bargains in extensively stocked factory shop. Personalised engraving service. Factory seconds. Christmas sale in November/ December.'

Easy to find on southern outskirts of town.

From town centre: go south for A10 /Downham Market. Look for Campbell Soups on right; Caithness Crystal in industrial estate on left.

From south on A10 or Norwich on A47: get on King's Lynn southern bypass (A47/A149); exit for King's Lynn at large roundabout.*

From west: continue on southern bypass to major roundabout where A10 joins.*

From north: go left on to the southern bypass from wherever you hit the ring road. At major roundabout go to King's Lynn.*

****Go along Hardwick Road. Take second right (Hansa Road). Pass Comet on right; take second left (phone box far corner). Shop on left.***

Open: Mon–Sat 9–5; *also Easter–Xmas* Sun 10.30–4.30.
Closed: Christmas & New Year.
Cards: Amex, MasterCard, Visa.
Cars: Free for cars & coaches.
Toilets: Yes, also for disabled.
Wheelchairs: No steps to large complex.
Teas: Own restaurant for light lunches, homemade cakes. Shop hours.
Tours: Self-conducted glassmaking demonstrations Mon–Fri 9.15–4.15; *also mid-June* to *mid-Sept* Sun 11–4. No booking needed. See the skill of the glassmaker at close quarters. Free admission.
Transport: Swaffham and Downham Market buses.
Mail order: Yes.
Catalogue: Free. Only factory seconds sold by mail order.

183 King's Lynn Norfolk *see map below*

Jaeger

1 Hansa Road, Hardwick Industrial Estate PE30 4HY
(01553) 732132

Ladies' coats, dresses, blouses, skirts, knitwear. Men's suits, jackets, trousers, knitwear, shirts etc. Also household goods, hosiery, wool.

'Quality merchandise at reduced prices.'

Easy to find on southern outskirts of town.

From town centre: go south towards A10 and Downham Market. Look for Campbell Soups on right; Jaeger is on left.

From south on A10 or Norwich on A47: get on to King's Lynn southern bypass (A47/A149); exit for King's Lynn at large roundabout.*

From west: continue on southern bypass to major roundabout where A10 joins.*

From north: go left on to the southern bypass from wherever you hit the ring road. At major roundabout go to King's Lynn.*

****Go along Hardwick Road towards King's Lynn. Take second right (Hansa Road). Shop is on the left.***

Open: Mon–Sat 9–5.30; Sun 11–4.
Closed: Please phone for holiday closures.
Cards: Amex, Delta, Diners, MasterCard, Switch, Visa.
Cars: Outside shop.
Toilets: Nearby.
Wheelchairs: Easy access, ramp to large shop.
Changing rooms: Yes.
Teas: Plenty of places in town; Caithness Crystal; Little Chef nearby.
Groups: Shopping groups welcome with prior phone call.
Transport: Swaffham and Downham Market buses.
Mail order: No.

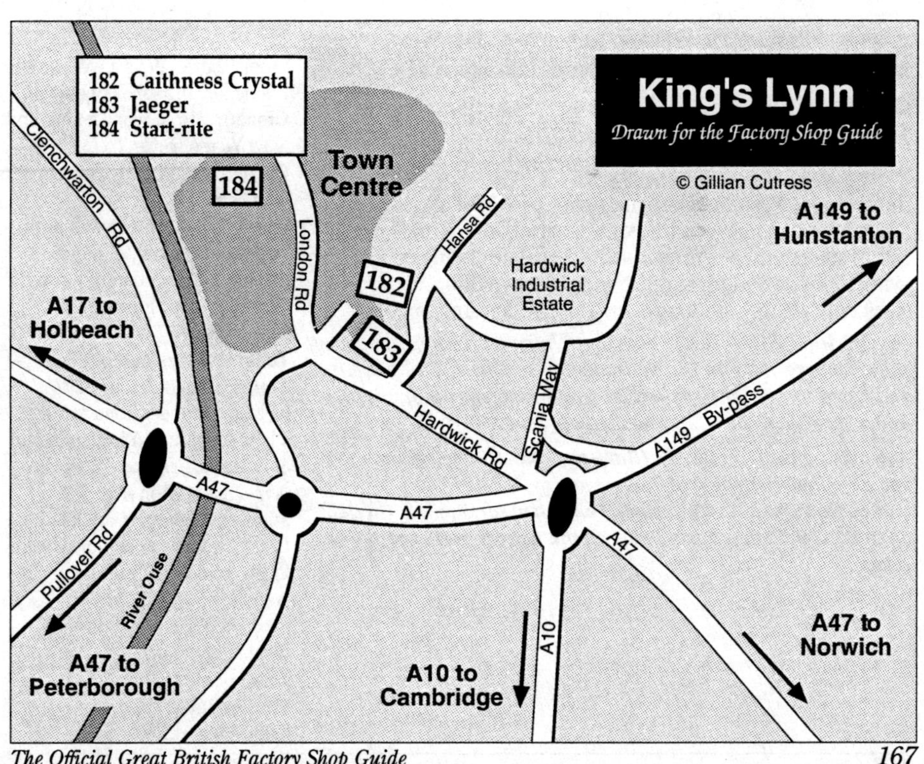

184 King's Lynn Norfolk *see map on previous page*

Start-rite Shoes

8 High Street PE30 1BX
(01553) 760786

Huge stock of footwear for children of all ages.

'Terrific bargain prices. Seconds and discontinued lines.'

The High Street is a pedestrianised street in centre of town, parallel to (and west of) Tower Street. No. 8 is closer to the Saturday Market Place end of High Street.

Park in any central car-park and walk to shop (next but one to Debenhams).

Open: Mon–Sat 9–5.30.
Closed: Bank Holidays; Christmas, Boxing, New Year's Days.
Cards: Amex, Delta, MasterCard, Switch, Visa.
Cars: Town car-park between Tower Street and High Street.
Toilets: In town.
Wheelchairs: Large ground floor shop.
Teas: Lots of places in town.
Groups: Not suitable for groups.
Transport: Any transport to King's Lynn then walk.
Mail order: No.

185 Langham near Holt Norfolk

Langham Glass

The Long Barn, North Street NR25 7DG
(01328) 830511 Fax (01328) 830787

Hand-made crystal glass: ornaments, bowls of all descriptions, paperweights, vases, variety of animals, candlesticks and perfume bottles. Local crafts including pyrography, wood-turning, stained glass-making, glass-engraving, salt dough and enamelling on copper.

'A collection of restored 18th century barn workshops. Viewing gallery where you can watch craftsmen sculpting molten glass and listen to master glass-maker's informative commentary. Adventure playground and walled gardens.'

Two miles inland, on B1388 (Blakeney–Great Walsingham road) and 12 miles north-east of Fakenham.

From Holt: take A148 towards Fakenham for 3 miles. Go right on to B1156. Follow signs to Langham: factory and shop are in village.

Open: Seven days a week 10–5. Phone for Christmas openings.
Closed: Christmas, Boxing and New Year's Days.
Cards: MasterCard, Switch, Visa.
Cars: Large car & coach park.
Toilets: Yes, including for disabled. Baby changing rooms.
Wheelchairs: Easy access throughout.
Teas: Own restaurant.
Tours: Coach & tour parties welcome, concessionary rates. Visits to glass-making, museum & video *Easter–Oct*, 7 days; *Nov–Easter*, Mon–Fri. Site admission charges: adults £2.50; children & senior citizens £1.50 (under 5s free); family £6; 2 adult season £7; family season £10; free for attendants with disabled persons.
Transport: No buses.
Mail order: Yes.
Catalogue: £1.50.

186 Leighton Buzzard Beds

Gossard

Grovebury Road LU7 8SM
(01525) 859749

Gossard and *Berlei* bras and coordinates.

'Gossard and Berlei bras and lingerie at ⅓ – ⅔ of original retail price. Discontinued items and slight seconds. Please phone this genuine factory shop for occasional Saturday sales with special prices, mentioning this book.'

South of the town centre.

From Leighton Buzzard: take A4146 south for Hemel Hempstead. Pass Tesco petrol on left, go over mini-roundabout then right into Grovebury Road.*

From Hemel Hempstead: go north on A4146 for Leighton Buzzard. Keep going straight to town outskirts. Go left immediately before mini-roundabout into Grovebury Road.*

****Look for Gossard 500 yds on left.***

Open: Mon–Sat 9.30–5.30.
Closed: Bank Holidays; Christmas–New Year.
Cards: No.
Cars: Car-park in front of building.
Toilets: In town.
Wheelchairs: Ramp to shop.
Changing rooms: Yes.
Teas: In town; farmhouse along road.
Groups: No factory tours but pre-booked shopping groups welcome.
Transport: 10 minutes' walk from town centre.
Mail order: Yes.
Catalogue: No.

187 Little Horwood Bucks

Phoenix Carpets

Units 15–17, Bacon House Farm MK17 0PS
(01908) 501019 (phone & fax)

Wool twist plain and heather tufted carpets in wide range of colours in 80/20% wool/nyion and 50/50% wool/nylon or polypropylene mix. From 40 oz (heavy domestic weight). Carpets can be made to colour requirements (minimum order of 30 sq yd (18 x 15 ft)).

'Can organise complete fitting service. Delivery £10 within 20-mile radius of Milton Keynes.'

Little Horwood is about 8 miles south-west of Milton Keynes. This company is north of Little Horwood, just off the A421.

From M1 exit 13: take A421 towards Buckingham. Go through Milton Keynes and Bletchley. Shortly after roundabout with sign to Mursley (left) and Whaddon (right) turn left (signposted Little Horwood). After about 400 yds turn left, between the first house and a white bungalow, then follow signs.

From Buckingham coming east on A421: turn right towards Little Horwood at crossroads. At T-junction turn left and after about ½ mile turn right immediately after the white bungalow. Then follow signs.

Open: Tues–Fri 9–5.30; Sat 10–4.
Closed: Monday; Bank Holidays; Christmas Eve–New Year.
Cars: Ample.
Toilets: Yes.
Wheelchairs: Easy access, no steps.
Teas: Can supply hot drinks on request.
Groups: Groups welcome by prior arrangement.
Transport: None.
Mail order: No.

B

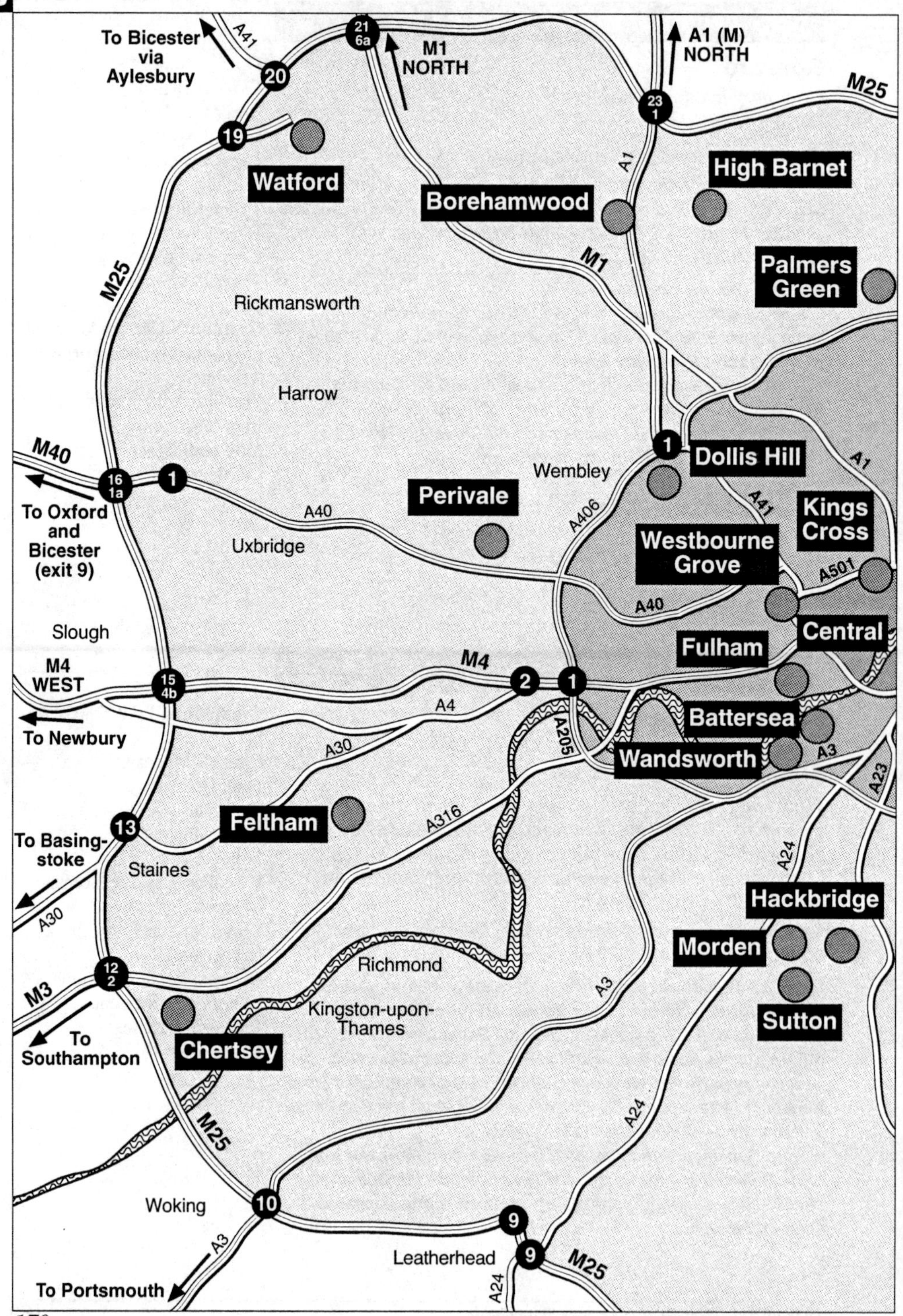

To Bicester
via
Aylesbury
A41
20
21
6a
M1
NORTH
A1 (M)
NORTH
M25
23
1
19
Watford
Borehamwood
A1
High Barnet
M1
Palmers
Green
M25
Rickmansworth
Harrow
M40
16
1a
1
To Oxford
and
Bicester
(exit 9)
1
Dollis Hill
A1
Wembley
Perivale
A40
A406
A41
Kings
Cross
Westbourne
Grove
Uxbridge
A501
A40
Slough
Central
Fulham
M4
WEST
M4
15
4b
2
1
To Newbury
A4
A205
Battersea
A30
Wandsworth
A3
A23
A316
13
Feltham
To Basing-
stoke
Staines
A24
A30
Hackbridge
Morden
12
2
Richmond
M3
Kingston-upon-
Thames
A3
Sutton
To
Southampton
Chertsey
A24
M25
Woking
10
9
9
A3
Leatherhead
M25
A24
To Portsmouth

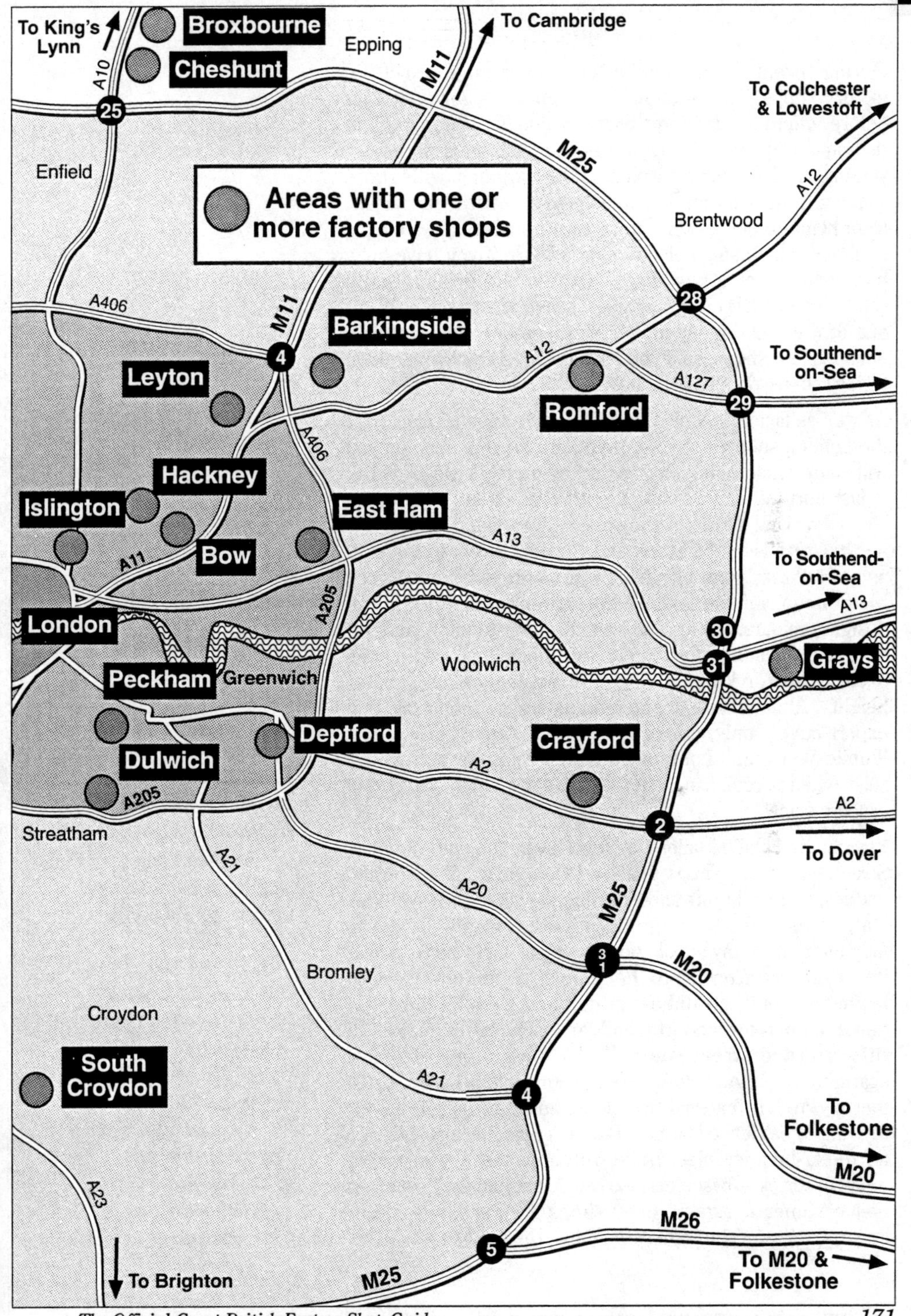

To King's Lynn
Broxbourne
Cheshunt
Epping
To Cambridge
M11
A10
25
To Colchester & Lowestoft
Enfield
M25
Areas with one or more factory shops
A12
Brentwood
28
A406
M11
Barkingside
4
To Southend-on-Sea
A12
Leyton
Romford
A127
29
A406
Hackney
Islington
East Ham
A13
Bow
A11
To Southend-on-Sea
A13
A205
London
30
Grays
31
Peckham
Greenwich
Woolwich
Deptford
Crayford
Dulwich
A2
A205
A2
2
Streatham
To Dover
A21
A20
M25
3 1
M20
Bromley
Croydon
South Croydon
A21
4
To Folkestone
M20
A23
M26
5
To M20 & Folkestone
To Brighton
M25

London

During recent years, London has seen a huge growth in factory shops. This section of the book, larger than ever before, offers a tempting variety of goods for shoppers in the capital. Readers living within the M25 need no longer venture far for their own pick of the bargains, with shops ranging from furniture warehouses to swimwear specialists; from piano to pot makers, to picture framers, and a couple of shops selling small electrical goods. So if you have been hankering after a new state of the art television set, a replacement VCR or simply need to update an old iron, try one of these shops. As always we keep our eyes and ears open for new shops, so if you have discovered other London factory shops, do please let us know.

As well as factory shops, there are other unusual places for the London shopper to visit. If you are keen on fashion you will enjoy window shopping in the rag-trade district of W1. It is just north of Oxford Street, within the area bordered by Great Portland Street to the west, Cavendish Street to the north, Great Tichfield Street and Berners Street to the east, and Great Marlborough Street just south of Oxford Street. Many famous-name fashion houses are based here. The designs, colours, fabrics and knitwear are stunning, and seldom seen in such profusion in retail shops. If you are a keen dressmaker or knitter they will inspire you to greater heights. Although some showrooms are for wholesale and export buyers only, others have hand-written signs saying 'Public Welcome'. Look out for their summer and winter sales when bargains are offered by shops which are glad of cash up front.

You can find skilled tailors in New Cavendish and Margaret Street. There are shops dealing in motor cyclists' outfits, textiles, fabrics, braids and trimmings, side-by-side with delicatessens and travel agents. Lively Carnaby Street is famous for its many small shops specialising in high-fashion items ranging from up-to-the-minute fashion jewellery to leather boots in a rainbow of colours. Berwick Street is home of the renowned fruit and vegetable street market. In this crowded street you will also find superb fabrics: sparkling sequinned cloth, velvet, satin, silk, brocade, shimmering stretch material, woollens, and novelty fabrics for toys and theatrical costumes. Berwick Street is also a centre for the fashion jewellery trade with an amazing assortment of accessories – bracelets, earrings, necklaces, brooches, hair ornaments. Again, many shops are for wholesale or export trade only, but others welcome the public.

Information on London

Detailed information packs can be obtained from the London Tourist Board, 26 Grosvenor Gardens, London SW1 0DU (0171) 932 2000 who offer a selection of recorded messages on Places to Visit, Shopping in London, *etc. Their* Hotel Bookings Hotline *is (0171) 932 2020. Other central London Tourist Information Centres can be found at the British Travel Centre, 1 Regent Street (south of Piccadilly Circus) and Victoria Station forecourt, both having an excellent range of guidebooks.*

Designer clothes in the centre of London

'Designer sale shops' continue to thrive in the capital. These include the Paul Smith Sale Shop (0171 493 1287) in Avery Row, Whistles Sale Shop in St Christopher Place and Browns 'Labels for Less' (0171 491 7833) in South Molton Street. You might also visit other shops in King's Road and off Oxford Street, especially around St Christopher Place. Warehouse style shops (eg, The Brand Centre in Enfield, 0181 805 8080) and discount clubs sell 'names' at reduced prices too.

Second hand dress agencies are also popular for hunting down bargains, especially in well-heeled areas like Knightsbridge (as in Cheval Place) where you can indeed buy designer clothes at much reduced prices.

But 'factory shop' and 'designer shop' have become cult expressions, and are sometimes misused. We feel justified in asking you to note the existence of certain down-market shops with poorly made (but expensive!) clothes, which claim to sell discounted designer outfits.

The East End

Another distinctive part of London for shopping is the East End – the Whitechapel, Bethnal Green and Hackney area. There are masses of small shops although they cannot be called factory shops. Many describe themselves as 'Cash & Carry', others welcome retail shoppers as well as wholesale traders. Opening hours vary: most close on Saturday, with the busiest period on Sunday morning when you can also visit Petticoat Lane market. But examine items carefully before you part with cash.

Here you find oriental fabrics, and in Kingsland Road look for luggage shops and importers of foreign shoes (but many sell to the trade). Leather goods are sold to the public in Brick Lane. In Hackney Road are shops selling specialised items such as amazing ranges of balustrades, stair spindles, ornate radiator covers and lamp posts.

For great gifts, enjoy the art and craft market in the original three-acre Spitalfields Market under a huge glass roof. Britain's largest organic fruit and vegetable market operates here on Sunday. Near Liverpool Street station, between Commercial Road and Bishopsgate. Mon–Fri & Sun (not Sat).

Excellent leaflets on the East End are available from Tower Hamlets Information Centre (0171 364 5000, ext. 4970). They include 'Shopping & markets', 'Food & drink', 'What to do and how to get there' and 'Great days out'.

Spitalfields

Spitalfields (*see previous page*) expanded rapidly in the 18th century. In recent years it had became run-down with buildings decayed and destroyed; but now it is a fashionable area once again with houses lovingly restored. It was the main area to where protestant Huguenot silk weavers fled in the 17th century, escaping from punishing Catholic regulations across the Channel. To get a feel for domestic life over the centuries, visit 18 Folgate Street (0171 247 4013 for times). This house has been furnished authentically in different periods to show how generations of one Huguenot family thrived then declined. The idiosyncratic American owner gives vivid three-hour personal tours.

Hackney

At the end of last century, Shoreditch was the centre of London's furniture industry. In 1889 Curtain Road alone had '66 furniture makers, including cabinet makers, carvers, upholsterers, mirror frame makers, chair makers and french polishers, as well as cabinet maker's porter, upholsterer's clerk, picture dealer and brass manufacturer'. In the last two decades, a new generation of furniture designers has moved back into the East End and Hackney now has one of the most active creative communities in Britain. Many modern designers in the area are delighted to make to commission. For the excellent free, illustrated 'Hackney Furniture Directory' – which leads you to makers of furniture, lighting, stained glass, mirrors, textiles and other specialist items – contact *Hackney 2000* (0181) 525 3252.

Hatton Garden

The street called Hatton Garden [Chancery Lane tube] offers a greater selection of jewellery than anywhere else. Just outside the walls of the City of London, qualified and skilled craftsmen congregated here when waves of immigrants arrived in this country from various European states.

Now a pleasant enough area in which to gaze at the amazing selection of jewellery displayed in the dozens of shop windows, Clerkenwell and Hatton Garden were desperately poor in Victorian times. The building of Holborn Viaduct, Farringdon Road and the underground cleared away the slums. Today lots of small roads criss-cross one another, with old buildings still occupied by hundreds of workshops.

If you wish to trade in the family heirlooms, Hatton Garden is one place where you can get cash on the spot. But bullion dealers are not sentimental! No matter how fine the craftsmanship, or how gripping the history, the value of the item depends entirely on the quality and weight of the silver, gold or platinum.

In Hatton Garden, whether you are looking for a specific item, or wish to have your own design made up, you have a tremendous choice. Some shops are well lit and upmarket; others less so. We are pleased to note that most shop windows display prices clearly. It is generally accepted that prices are on average about 20% lower than in high street shops.

Many services are on offer: insurance valuations (at 1% of value), bead & pearl stringing (from £11.75), jewellery and watch cleaning, engraving and repairs.

At the time of going to press, the international gold price (24 carat) was around £187 per troy ounce; and the trade-in price was just under £168.

Markets in the Capital

From antiques to modern hand-made crafts, jewellery to second-hand bikes, antiquarian books to designer boots, fruit and veg to an enormous selection of plants, there is a market for everyone. This is far from an exhaustive list of London markets but should give plenty of food for thought!

Many traditional street markets are still in the great outdoors, so dress accordingly. Bartering is generally expected, even encouraged, and cash is king. For the best selections in antique markets, arrive very early before the dealers have traded amongst themselves. If you can wait until plant, fruit and vegetable stalls are starting to pack up, you should be able to pick up good bargains.

Some of the more famous open-air markets include:

Bermondsey Market (also known as New Caledonian Market), SE1. Open 4.30 am–12 noon on Fridays, so set the alarm clock! Here you find an extensive range of good jewellery, fine glass and china, silver, brass, maps and prints.

Farringdon Road Market, EC1. (Farringdon tube.) Daily. Old bound periodicals and lots of second-hand books.

Portobello Road, W11. (Notting Hill Gate tube.) One of the longest street markets in Britain. During the week mainly fruit and veg, but on Sat (8–5) an enormous variety of traders descend on the street. Coins, jewellery, antiques, art deco lamps, cigarette cards, African and Caribbean crafts, fabrics, clothing and lace abound.

Columbia Road Market, E2. (Bethnal Green tube.) Sun (inc. Easter Day) 7–2. The market for plants. Gardeners and would-be gardeners will be sorely tempted by the huge variety of plants. Also a garden pot maker and several interesting one-off shops. Good bargains towards closing time.

Petticoat Lane. E1. (Liverpool Street or Aldgate East stations.) Sun, 9–2. This huge market is centred around Middlesex Street, E1, and spreads out into neighbouring streets. Many bargains to be found here, particularly clothes, shoes, handbags and jewellery. A lot of junk is also sold, so choose carefully.

Roman Road, E1. (Bethnal Green tube.) Mon–Fri 10–2; Sat 9–5. Saturday is the best day for this haven for fashion victims. Knock-off designer clothes alongside fruit and veg.

Camden Lock. (Camden Town or Chalk Farm stations.) Sat and Sun 9–6. A bohemian mix of crafts, bric-à-brac, health foods. jewellery, trendy clothes plus much more.

Leather Lane, EC1. (Chancery Lane tube.) Mon–Fri 10–2.30 (not Bank Holidays). Wonderful bulbs and plants in season, clothes, shoes, household goods, fruit, vegetables.

High Street, Walthamstow, E17. (Walthamstow Central tube.) Europe's longest street market, which stretches more than a mile down the High Street. Thur–Sat. A much smaller market, on some of the same site, Mon and Tues.

Brixton, SW2 (Brixton tube). A mixed market, some of it under the railway arches, especially noted for fish and Caribbean vegetable stalls.

For the colder, wetter days, there are numerous covered markets, the best-known of which include :

Greenwich Market, SE1. Sat (all year) and Sun from Easter–September 9–5. Housed under a Nash-style arched roof built in 1831, and a great place for Christmas shopping. Handknits, silk cushions and ties, clocks, earrings and ceramics are just some of the goods here.

Leadenhall Market, Gracechurch Street, EC3. (Monument tube.) Mon–Fri 9–5. In the heart of the city. Although technically a street market, a wooden arched roof protects the stalls from the elements. A huge variety of poultry, game and seafood are specialities here. Numerous pubs and restaurants refresh weary shoppers.

Apple Market and Jubilee Market Hall, Old Covent Garden, WC2. (Covent Garden tube.) Tues–Sat 10–7, Mon 7–7; Sun 9–7. A huge variety of crafts, including hand-painted silk cushions, toy clocks, ceramics and handknits. On Monday and the first Sunday of each month, antiques are the speciality.

Alfies Market, 13–25 Church Street, NW8. (Edgware Road tube.) Tues–Sat 10–6. Housed in a former department store, this market specialises in antiques.

Camden Passage, N1. (Angel tube.) Wed 6.45–4; Thur 7–4; Sat 8–5. Another market specialising in antiques. On Thursday, prints and drawings are also sold.

For a totally different experience, try one of the famous wholesale markets. Quantities are probably greater than you usually purchase so why not club together with some friends? These start very early in the morning.

Smithfield, EC1. (Farringdon tube.) For meat, poultry, game (and excellent local pubs open for breakfast!).

Billingsgate, E14, for fish.

New Covent Garden, SW8, and Borough, SE1, for fruit, vegetables and flowers.

Spitalfields Market, E10 (0181 518 7670). Mon–Fri 3am–11am and Sat 3am–9am. For fruit and vegetables.

188 London : Battersea

Price's Patent Candle Co.

100 York Road SW11 3RV
(0171) 801 2030

Candles, holders and accessories for every occasion.

'Bargains always available – discontinued lines, damaged stock and lots more.'

Immediately south of the Thames, between Wandsworth and Battersea bridges.

Open: Mon–Sat 9.30–5.30; Sun 11–5 in summer and Christmas sales, maybe all year. Phone to check.
Closed: Phone for Christmas.
Cards: Connect, MasterCard, Switch, Visa.
Cars: Own parking spaces.
Toilets: No.
Wheelchairs: Seven shallow steps to medium sized shop.
Teas: Locally.
Tours: No.
Transport: Local buses.

189 London : Bow

Nicole Farhi/French Connection

75–83 Fairfield Road E3 3QP
(0181) 980 2568

Nicole Farhi coats, jackets, skirts, trousers, blouses, knitwear; *French Connection* coats, knitwear, blouses, skirts, trousers etc. Men's and ladies' wear.

'Previous season's stock plus samples and some seconds.'

In Bow, just north of the A11/A12 (Bow Road).

From London going east along Bow Road: pass Bow Road tube station on right then go left at traffic lights immediately after white concrete old Poplar Town Hall (and in front of NatWest bank) into Fairfield Road. Go under railway bridge: shop on left.

Going west towards London on A12: from large roundabout/overpass on A12 where Blackwall Tunnel road goes south, go north on to A102 (ie, do NOT take overpass); take left slip road (A1030) for Old Ford; at top of slip road go left into Tredegar Road; after 150 yds go left into Fairfield Road. Company on right, 50 yds before railway bridge.

Open: Tues and Wed 10–3; Thur 11–6.30; Fri 10–5.30; Sat 10–3.
Closed: Monday; Bank Holidays; Christmas–New Year.
Cards: MasterCard, Visa.
Cars: In street outside.
Toilets: No.
Wheelchairs: No step, small shop.
Changing rooms: Yes.
Teas: Local pubs and cafés.
Groups: Shopping groups welcome if you phone first.
Transport: Local buses. Bow Road tube station. Bow Church station on Docklands Light Railway.
Mail order: No.

190 London : Deptford

Bucks Furniture Warehouse

125 Evelyn Street SE8 5RJ
(0181) 692 4447 Fax (0181) 469 3136

Huge range of upholstered and wooden furniture. Sofas, sofabeds, suites, armchairs, beds, mattresses, dressing tables, wardrobes, mirrors, bookcases, tables, chairs and tv/video cabinets. New bed showroom now open.

'Over 15,000 sq ft of top quality furniture. End-of-line fabrics, ends of lines, ex-display models and slight seconds from leading retailers at a fraction of the price. Delivery service available, within M25 about £30; further afield from £40.'

Evelyn Street (A200), is the main Rotherhithe–Greenwich road.

From south end of Tower Bridge: follow A200 through to Deptford (Tooley Street then Jamaica Road). Pass Southwark Park on left. At roundabout with signs to Rotherhithe Tunnel take third exit (A200, Lower Road) which becomes Evelyn Street. Go under footbridge, pass Shell petrol on left. Huge shop is 100 yds on left immediately before bridge.

From Greenwich going north on A200: go over pedestrian lights, pass fire station on left then Black Horse pub on right. Go over bridge: huge shop is on right.

Open: Wed 10–6; Thur, Fri 10–7; Sat 10–5; Sun 10–4.
Closed: Monday; Tuesday. Easter Sunday; Christmas, Boxing & New Year's Days.
Cards: Delta, MasterCard, Visa.
Cars: Own car-park.
Toilets: Yes.
Wheelchairs: Easy access to huge shop.
Teas: Local pubs.
Groups: Groups welcome, please phone in advance.
Transport: Surrey Docks and New Cross tube stations.

191 London : Dollis Hill

Tymbuktu

Units 8/9 The Edge Business Centre, Humber Road NW2 6EW
(0181) 450 9991

Wide range of swimwear and co-ordinating leisure wear including T-shirts, sarongs and shorts. Costume jewellery, hair accessories, scarves and bags.

'Firsts and seconds sold here.'

Half a mile south of M1 exit 1 (Staples Corner); and the junction of the north circular (A406) with Edgware Road (A5).

From the end of the M1: aim west for the north circular road (A406). Go under railway to next roundabout. Keep straight. As you go up slip road, pass UNO store on left. Go left, Coles Green Road. Pass Oxgate pub on left; keep straight. Take next left, Humber Road. Edge Business Centre (blue and grey building) is on left, just before Wing Yip. Unit 8/9 is in far corner of courtyard.

Coming north along Edgware Road (A5) from Cricklewood: pass ParcelForce on right. After Total then Jet petrol on left, take first left (in front of Peugeot) which is Humber Road. Edge Business Centre is 150 yds on right, past Wing Yip.

Open: Mon–Fri 1–5; Sat 10–2. Some Bank Holidays (please phone) or by prior arrangement.
Closed: Christmas Eve for two weeks.
Cards: Visa.
Cars: Behind unit and two spaces in front.
Toilets: Yes, including facilities for disabled.
Wheelchairs: Easy access.
Changing rooms: Yes.
Teas: Brent Cross shopping centre (15 minutes' walk).
Groups: Shopping groups welcome, please phone first.
Transport: Brent Cross tube 15 minutes' walk. Bus nos. 16a and 266 pass Humber Road.
Mail order: No.

192 London : Dulwich

The Pottery

12 Red Post Hill SE21 7BX
(0171) 978 8310

Huge selection of terracotta pots in all shapes, designs and sizes, including very large pots and urns. Plain, decorated and glazed, for inside and outdoor use.

'Most items perfects. Usually some slightly damaged pots at reduced prices. Delivery up to 100 miles. Prices usually less than other retailers; special offers at half price.'

Easy to find, beside North Dulwich Station.

From traffic lights in centre of Dulwich Village: with Dulwich Hamlet school on left and shops on right, continue for 400 yds to next traffic lights. Go straight. After 100 yds, pass station on right: path into pottery is almost next door.

Open: *March–Dec*: seven days a week, 9.30–4.30. Bank Holidays.
Closed: January, February.
Cards: MasterCard, Switch, Visa.
Cars: In front of pottery and local streets.
Toilets: Yes.
Wheelchairs: Concrete paths but not too difficult.
Teas: Several wine bars and restaurants in Dulwich Village.
Groups: Groups of gardeners welcome.
Transport: Trains to North Dulwich; bus nos. 37 and P4 through village.
Mail order: No.

193 London : East Ham

Tronage

Tronage House, 166 High Street North E6 2JA
(0181) 472 1373

Wide range of electrical equipment: 6"–40" televisions, videos, camcorders, hi-fi systems, hi-fi separates, microwaves, vacuum cleaners, radio cassettes and in-car entertainment.

'We specialise in firsts and seconds on top brands including Hitachi, Panasonic, Technics, Pioneer and Philips. All goods are guaranteed for 1 year, extended guarantees available. Always have "specials" – please phone for details.'

High Street North, partly pedestrianised, is main shopping street.

Coming east from Plaistow on A124 Barking Road: pass Nissan on right & Gala Bingo on left. Go left at lights (Ron Leighton Way) for town centre/parking, Manor Park & Wanstead (A117).*

Coming west from Barking on A124: turn right at lights (Ron Leighton Way) following signs to car parks and Manor Park (A117).*

****Keep straight at lights for Service Routes A, B & C. Pass Top Rank bingo on right. Go straight at mini-roundabout. At lights (Kentucky Fried Chicken on near right), swing left. Shop is 150 yds on right, just past Boots.***

Coming south from Manor Park: pass East Ham tube station on left. Go straight at lights (C & A on left-hand corner). Shop is 100 yds on left, just before Boots.

Open: Mon–Wed & Fri 9–6; Sat 10–6.
Closed: Thursday. Christmas and Boxing Days. Please phone to check Bank Holidays.
Cards: MasterCard, Visa.
Cars: Own car-park (access at rear of premises), local car-parks and on-street parking.
Toilets: Yes.
Wheelchairs: Easy access.
Teas: Cafés nearby.
Groups: Groups welcome, no need to book.
Transport: Fifty yards from East Ham underground station.
Mail order: No.

194 London : Fulham

The Curtain Fabric Factory Shop

236a North End Road W14 9NU
(0171) 381 1777

Designer and own brand curtain fabric and curtain accessories. Net curtains and upholstery fabrics. Quilted bedspreads, also bedspreads made to order from customers' own fabrics.

'Curtain-making service (about 2–3 weeks). Fabrics from £3 per metre. Overstocks, seconds and cancelled orders. Curtain tracks can be supplied and fitted. Prices normally about half shop/store prices.'

See our display advertisement opposite

Five minutes from Earls Court exhibition centre.

Turn off Lillie Road A3218 (continuation of Old Brompton Road) at roundabout with William Hill on corner. Go north into North End Road. This shop is just past the betting office, opposite mini-roundabout at junction.

Open: Mon–Fri 10–6; Sat 9.30–5.30.
Closed: Christmas–New Year.
Cards: Amex, MasterCard, Switch, Transax, Visa.
Cars: Pay-&-display car-park adjoining shop. Also facing side road.
Toilets: Ask if desperate.
Wheelchairs: Easy access to warehouse style shop.
Teas: Local pubs and cafés.
Groups: Groups welcome, please phone in advance.
Transport: Five minutes' walk from West Kensington, Fulham Broadway and West Brompton tube stations.
Mail order: No.

195 London : Fulham

Rococo Frames

19 Jerdan Place SW6 1BE
(0171) 386 0506

Ready-made picture and photo frames in huge variety of styles from simple to ornate. Large range of mirrors. Also sell interior accessories, cards, mounts, prints and pictures.

'Mainly firsts at factory prices: 25–35% lower than comparable goods in other stores. Also bargains at 40–50% less than normal prices. Huge clearance sales in January and August: many styles at 2, 3 or 4 for £10. Commissions for all types of frames and mirrors taken: allow one week for order.'

Virtually in Fulham Broadway, about 250 yds west of Fulham Broadway tube. (Jerdan Place does not appear on some London street maps!)

Coming west from central London: go along Fulham Broadway. Pass Fulham Broadway tube on right then Barclays Bank on right. This shop is immediately after the pedestrian lights, on right.

Coming east along Dawes Road or North End Road: at the mini-roundabout where these two roads meet, aim for central London. Pass the large pub on left (with huge lion on top): Rococo is facing you, 50 yds on left.

Open: Mon–Sat 9.30–6. Please phone to check Bank Holidays.
Closed: Christmas, Boxing and New Year's Days. Please check hours in holiday periods.
Cards: Delta, Switch, JCB, MasterCard, Visa.
Cars: In side streets (parking meters) or Safeway nearby.
Toilets: Ask if desperate.
Wheelchairs: Access limited.
Teas: Two cafés in Jerdan Place, many other local cafés.
Groups: Large groups of more than 10 people are asked to phone the manager on the morning of the visit.
Transport: Fulham Broadway tube 2 minutes' walk. Bus nos. 14, 28, 211, 295, 391 and C4. Ask for Jerdan Place.
Mail order: Yes.
Catalogue: Free. Limited range of styles & smaller sizes. Please phone (0171) 385 9929.

196 London : Fulham

Roger Lascelles Clocks

29 Carnwath Road SW6 3HR
(0171) 731 0072 Fax (0171) 384 1957

Highly distinctive award-winning range of traditionally inspired quartz clocks featuring dial designs taken from antique clocks of the last century. Available in all major department stores and leading gift shops.

'Seconds and previous year's lines at half price; regular lines at competitive retail prices. "The ideal gift." Family business.'

Immediately north of Wandsworth Bridge.

From Chelsea/Fulham/Central London: go along King's Road until it becomes New King's Road. Go left down Wandsworth Bridge Road. Carnwath Road is last right turn before bridge (with traffic lights).*

From south London: go over Wandsworth Bridge; take first left at traffic lights (Carnwath Road).*

****After 200 yds, pass Fulham Kitchen Centre on left; go in through gates. Company is at back right.***

Open: Mon–Fri 9–4.30.
Closed: Bank Holidays; Christmas Eve–New Year.
Cards: MasterCard, Visa.
Cars: Off-street directly outside factory.
Toilets: Yes.
Wheelchairs: Easy access, no steps to small shop.
Teas: Lots of places in locality. Easy walk to excellent riverside pub.
Tours: Phone Mrs Winship about free tours. Maximum 15 adults. Flexible times.
Transport: District Line tube to Fulham Broadway, then bus nos. 28 or 295 to Wandsworth Bridge.
Mail order: Yes.
Catalogue: Free. Mail order service to anywhere in the world – mention this guide when requesting catalogue.

197 London : Hackney

Burberrys

29–53 Chatham Place E9 6LR
(0181) 985 3344

Men's and women's raincoats, trenchcoats, knitwear, shirts, skirts; accessories including umbrellas, scarves, handbags. Golf shoes. Jams, sauces etc. Room sprays etc.

Just east of Mare Street (A107) in Hackney.

Going south along Mare Street: go under railway bridge, go left at traffic lights (Morning Lane) for Bow/Leyton.*

Coming north on Mare Street: pass Hackney Central Library (stone building with classical columns on right corner site); go right at traffic lights for Bow/Leyton (B113).*

****After 400 yds pass Duke of Wellington pub on right; go right (Chatham Place). Go in Burberrys' main door 150 yds on right.***

Open: Mon–Fri 11–6; Sat 9–4; Sun 11–5.
Closed: Check with shop.
Cards: Yes.
Cars: Local streets.
Toilets: No.
Wheelchairs: Ramps to and in huge shop.
Changing rooms: No.
Teas: Pubs and cafés locally.
Transport: Buses and trains to Mare Street.

198 London : Hackney

The Factory Shop (Sofa to Bed)

Unit 1, Bayford Street E8
(0181) 533 0915 Fax (0181) 985 2953

Sofas, sofa beds, lounge suites and divan sets. Matching curtains.

'All pieces made to order (some display models available at greatly reduced prices). Also re-upholstery and re-covering services.'

Coming south down Mare Street (A107) towards London: pass Cordwainer's College on left. Go over traffic lights and take first right, Bayford Street.*

From London along Mare Street (A107): after Texaco on right and BP on left (before traffic lights at major junction with Wells Street) go left into Bayford Street (letter box on corner) opposite old cinema.*

****After 30 yds go right, then left into complex with six units.***

Open: Mon–Fri 8–5.30; Sat 10–4.30; Sun and Bank Holidays 10–2.30.
Closed: Christmas and Boxing Days.
Cards: Amex, MasterCard, Switch, Visa. Finance also available subject to status.
Cars: On forecourt.
Toilets: Yes.
Wheelchairs: One step to large shop.
Teas: Cup of tea gladly made for customers; cafés nearby.
Groups: Welcome to walk round workshop adjacent to showroom.
Transport: Bethnal Green station; bus nos. 26, 48, 55, 106, 236, 253, 277, D6.

199 London : Islington

Hockley's China and Glass Factory Shop

100 East Road N1 6AA
(0171) 684 8280 Fax (0171) 251 0242
Internet: shop@Trauffler.com.

Huge range of high quality famous brand glassware, cut crystal, formal and casual porcelain tableware, oven-to-table ware, ceramics, giftware and barware.

'Perfects & seconds sold. Ends of design lines. Chainstore items.'

See our display advertisement above

On the corner of East Road and Bevenden Street.

East Road is the main A1200 which joins City Road near Moorfields Eye Hospital. East Road is partly one-way, so if you are going north you must go up Provost Street (opposite the hospital) then the shop is at far end almost facing you on right.

From Old Street roundabout: go north-west along City Road to first traffic lights (Moorfields Eye Hospital on left); turn right into Vestry Street. Shop visible on right at end of one-way system. Go right into Bevenden Street in front of shop (to park at rear).

From Highbury Corner and the north: follow New North Road (A1200) past Essex Road station on right. Keep straight for ¾ mile plus; shop is on left, just before start of one-way system. Go left into Bevenden Street after shop (to park at rear).

Open: Mon–Fri 9.30–4.30.
Closed: Bank Holidays; Christmas–New Year.
Cards: Delta, MasterCard, Switch, Visa.
Cars: Own car-park at rear of building.
Toilets: No.
Wheelchairs: No steps to shop.
Teas: Café opposite shop, restaurant 2 minutes' walk.
Groups: Groups welcome, please phone shop manager in advance.
Transport: Old Street tube 5 minutes' walk. Bus nos. 76, 141 and 271.
Mail order: Yes. Goods can be sent worldwide.

200 London : King's Cross

Futon Express

23–27 Pancras Road, NW1 2QB
(0171) 833 3945

Futons, cushions and covers. Iron furniture including beds, tables, chairs, sofas and screens. Orthopaedic matresses. Beanbags.

'First quality double futons from £125 (complete sets); double iron beds from £240.'

Easy to find, in the road which runs north between St Pancras and King's Cross stations.

From the west on Euston Road (A501): pass St Pancras station on left. At traffic lights, go left. Shop is 100 yds on left, beneath the station.

Coming from the east side of King's Cross: pass King's Cross station on right and get into right lane to go right at traffic lights. Shop is 100 yds on left, under St Pancras station.

Open: Mon–Sat 10–6; Sun 11.30–5. Bank Holidays.
Closed: Christmas Eve, Christmas Day and New Year's Day.
Cards: MasterCard, Visa.
Cars: Free car-park at rear of shop; meters to front of shop.
Toilets: In stations.
Wheelchairs: No steps to shop.
Teas: Lots of nearby cafés and restaurants.
Groups: Shopping groups welcome, please phone first.
Transport: St Pancras and King's Cross train stations, and King's Cross underground all within 3 minutes' walk.
Mail order: Please phone for details. Delivery can be arranged to anywhere in Britain.

201 London : Leyton

R P Ellen

46 Church Road E10 5JR
(0181) 539 6872

Top quality ladies' leather fashion shoes, boots and sandals.

'Company is a leading wholesaler selling shoes from Britain, Italy, Spain and Portugal. Most items perfect, some seconds and quite a few samples in sizes 3 and 4 at very reasonable prices. From £5–£30, most about £20.'

Opposite Leyton Parish Church, just off one-way system in Leyton High Road. Shop is ¾ mile south of Lea Bridge Road (A104) but take care – restricted turning off this road.

Going along Lea Bridge Road east for Walthamstow: pass Lea Bridge station on left, go over traffic lights with public toilets on island (this is Church Road but no right turn!); pass Shell petrol on left, take next right, Vicarage Road.*

Coming south on Lea Bridge Road towards Hackney Marshes: go over Bakers Arms junction, pass exhaust centre on right, go left, Vicarage Road.*

****At far end (opposite Jet petrol) go right; after 100 yds you are in one-way system. Keep clockwise, pass Total on right and Wilmot Street on left, take next left for African-Caribbean Centre (Church Road). Conspicuous shop 150 yds on left corner site.***

Open: Mon–Sat 10–4.
Closed: Bank Holidays; Christmas & New Year.
Cards: No.
Cars: Own yard in front of shop.
Toilets: At junction with Lea Bridge Road.
Wheelchairs: One step to medium sized shop.
Teas: Local pubs and cafés.
Groups: Pre-booked shopping groups welcome.
Transport: Local buses; 10 minutes' walk to Leyton tube station or Leyton Midland Road train station.
Mail order: No.

EX-MAIL ORDER

END OF LINES

ALL STOCK FULLY GUARANTEED

CENTRAX DIRECT SALES LTD

UNIT 17, 193 GARTH ROAD, MORDEN, SURREY SM4 4LZ

TEL: 0181 330 7766 (10 LINES)

FAX: 0181 330 7726

See our entry overleaf

202 London : Morden

Centrax Direct Sales

Unit 17, 193 Garth Road
(0181) 330 7766 Fax (0181) 330 7726

Household electricals: televisions, videos, camcorders and stereos. Microwaves, kettles, toasters etc. Christmas lights. Ends of lines from *Sanyo, Hitachi, Philips, Tefal.*

'All items are throroughly checked over on arrival and are sold with our guarantee (valid for a minimum of six months).'

See our display advertisement previous page

About 2 miles south of Morden, just off A24.

From Morden tube station: go round one-way system. Stay in left lane (A24). Pass Iceland on left and Civic Centre on right. Keep straight for Lower Morden/North Cheam. Pass Jet petrol on right, go under railway bridge. Pass Morden South train station on left and Merton College on right. Go straight at lights. Pass Harvester pub on right. Go straight at lights. Pass The Woodstock on left. Go slightly downhill. At bottom of hill, after Territorial Army building, and just before zebra crossing, go right into Garth Road (signposted Civic Amenity & Recycling Centre).*

Coming north on A24: at North Cheam pass Sainsbury's on right, then St. Raphael's Hospice on left. Go straight with Lord Nelson pub on left. Turn left after zebra crossing into Garth Road.*

****Turn left into industrial park after ½ mile.***

Open: Mon–Sat 8.30–5; Sun 10–4.
Closed: Christmas, Boxing and New Year's Days.
Cards: MasterCard, Visa.
Cars: In front of shop.
Toilets: Yes.
Wheelchairs: One tiny step to shop.
Teas: Local pubs.
Groups: Shopping groups welcome, please phone in advance.
Transport: Morden tube then bus nos. 193 or 293.
Mail order: Yes.

203 London : Palmers Green

Catalogue Bargain Shop

252 Green Lanes N13 5TU
(0181) 886 9532

Huge range of mail order surplus items: clothing, fashions, household, footwear, hardware, electrical, toys and gifts.

'Large savings from original catalogue prices. Firsts & seconds.'

Half mile north of the North Circular.

From the North Circular: at traffic lights go north into Green Lanes (A105) for Winchmore Hill. Cross traffic lights (Aldermans Hill leading to Palmers Green station to left); shop is opposite triangle island in road near Woolworths, Cyprus Bank and Superdrug on right.

Coming south from Winchmore Hill along Green Lanes (A105): cross traffic lights (Bourne Hill to right, Hedge Lane to left); pass post office on left. Shop is on left, immediately before Superdrug.

Open: Mon–Sat 9–5.30; Sun 10–4. Bank Holidays.
Closed: Christmas Day.
Cards: Access, Delta, Switch, Visa.
Cars: In supermarket opposite Palmers Green station.
Toilets: On the triangle (island in middle of road near traffic lights).
Wheelchairs: No steps; easy access to medium sized ground floor shop.
Changing rooms: Yes, two.
Teas: Ice cream shop; burger bar; Inn on the Green pub.
Transport: Bus nos. W2, W3, 221, 329; Southgate tube.
Mail order: No.

204 London : Peckham

Catalogue Bargain Shop

103–113 Rye Lane SE15 4ST
(0171) 358 1308

Huge range of mail order surplus items: clothing, fashions, household, footwear, hardware, furniture, electrical, toys and gifts.

'Large savings from original catalogue prices. Firsts & seconds.'

Rye Lane is a busy main road; shop is across the road from Peckham Rye station.

If you come out of the station, go left: the shop is across the road, opposite McDonald's.

Open: Mon–Sat 9–5.30; Sun 10.30–4.30.
Closed: Easter Sunday; Christmas Day.
Cards: Access, Delta, Switch, Visa.
Cars: Safeway car-park.
Toilets: No.
Wheelchairs: No steps to ground floor; stairs to upper floor.
Changing rooms: Yes.
Teas: McDonald's and cafés.
Transport: Peckham train station 50 yds; bus nos. 12, 36, 63, 78, 171, P3.
Mail order: No.

205 London : Perivale

Bluthners Pianos

18 Aintree Road UB6 7LA
(0181) 997 4785

Wide range of recently restored or refurbished pianos, both grands and uprights.

'We also offer restoration of grand pianos and skilled advice. Collection and delivery of pianos arranged by company. Please phone for details. Part-exchanges welcome.'

On north side of A40, close to new Tesco in old Hoover building.

Going towards London on A40: go left for A456 for Perivale. Continue straight (do not go left for Perivale station). Turn left for Tesco.*

From London on A40: pass huge old Hoover building on far side of dual carriageway. Take left slip road and go over dual carriageway, aiming for Tesco.*

****Keep straight. Go under railway bridge then continue through industrial estate to Bluthners on right.***

Open: Mon–Fri 8–4.30; Sat 10–4.
Closed: Bank Holidays; Christmas–New Year.
Cards: MasterCard, Visa.
Cars: Local roads.
Toilets: Tesco.
Wheelchairs: One step into workshop.
Teas: Tesco.
Tours: Workshop can be seen, but no tours as such.
Transport: Bus to Tesco then 10 minutes' walk.
Mail order: No. Phone for free leaflet.

206 London : Wandsworth

InWear / Matinique / Part Two

100 Garratt Lane SW18 4DI
(0181) 871 2155

Wide range of ladies' and men's fashion jackets, trousers, dresses, shirts, skirts, jeans etc., from the *InWear, Matinique* and *Part Two* collections.

'Samples, ends of lines and slightly imperfect merchandise.'

South of Wandsworth on A217, just off South Circular Road (A205).

From all directions: go to Wandsworth then go clockwise round one-way system. Pass town hall on right, staying in left lane. Go left at traffic lights (before Arndale Centre). Clearly marked company is 300 yds on right (beyond Sainsbury's on left). Go right into car-park.

Coming north into Wandsworth on A217: look for clearly marked building on left, after the Old Sergeant pub on left.

Open: Mon–Fri 10–5; Sat 10–4.
Closed: Bank Holidays; Christmas–New Year.
Cards: Amex, MasterCard, Switch, Transax, Visa.
Cars: Own car-park.
Toilets: Yes.
Wheelchairs: Easy access, no steps, large ground floor shop.
Changing rooms: Yes.
Teas: In the Arndale Centre.
Groups: Shopping groups welcome – please phone first.
Transport: Several buses, including nos. 35, 37, 44; 10 minutes' ride from Wandsworth Town train station.
Mail order: No.

207 London : Wandsworth

Villeroy & Boch

267 Merton Road SW18 5JS
(0181) 870 4168

Large range of *Villeroy & Boch* china tableware, cookware, crystal glassware, gifts, cutlery etc.

'Discontinued stock, seconds, samples, perfects at reduced prices.'

South of Wandsworth on A218, just off South Circular Road (A205).

From all directions: go to Wandsworth then go clockwise round the one-way system. Pass town hall on right. Look for tall block of flats (Arndale Centre) ahead. Stay in left lane, go left after Arndale Centre. Continue for some distance along main road. Cross mini-roundabout, go over traffic lights. Shop in second building on left: large sign.

Coming north into Wandsworth on Merton Road (A218) from South Wimbledon: look for this clearly signed building (set back from road) on the right, about 100 yds before traffic lights.

Open: Mon–Sat 10–5; Sun 11–5.
Closed: Phone about Bank Holidays and Christmas.
Cards: Amex, Diners, MasterCard, Switch, Visa.
Cars: Own car-park in front of building.
Toilets: No.
Wheelchairs: Ramp from car-park to large shop.
Teas: Locally.
Groups: No pottery tours. Shopping groups welcome; check with shop first.
Transport: Local buses; Southfields tube station ½ mile (District Line).
Mail order: No.

208 London : Westbourne Grove

Crucial Trading

79 Westbourne Park Road W2 5QH
(0171) 221 9000

Large selection of rugs.

'List available of larger pieces of floor coverings (4 x 4 m) held at factory which can be purchased at large discount through this shop. Free measuring service. Fitting can be arranged for most parts of mainland Britain.'

Near the junction of Westbourne Park Villas and Westbourne Park Road.

From Notting Hill Gate: (with WH Smith on left) go north along Pembridge Road A4206 (towards Portobello market) but stay on this main road. At traffic lights with Westbourne Grove, bear left in front of 7-Eleven (Chepstow Road). At T-junction go right into Westbourne Park Road. By The Westbourne pub on left, swing right: the shop is on right.

From Royal Oak tube station: turn left out of tube. Take first right, Westbourne Park Villas. At far end, go left: shop is facing you.

Open: Tues–Fri 10–2 & 3–6; Sat 10–4.
Closed: Monday. Bank Holidays; Christmas–New Year.
Cards: Amex, MasterCard, Switch, Visa.
Cars: Reasonably easy street parking.
Toilets: Yes.
Wheelchairs: Easy access.
Teas: Local pubs and cafés.
Groups: No tours; unsuitable for group visits.
Transport: Royal Oak tube 5 minutes' walk.
Mail order: No seconds or factory shop merchandise posted.
Catalogue: Free.

209 Luton Beds

Ash Kay

114 Midland Road LU2 0BM
(01582) 725558

Top quality leather jackets, trousers, blousons, waistcoats and motorcycling leathers etc. made by this company. Specialise in leatherwear with logos/emblems etc for companies, rock groups etc.

'All items perfects, in best available leathers, ready-made up to 50% off usual retail prices. Jackets from £95. Also made-to-measure service.'

Easy to find in the road parallel to the railway line, and behind (uphill of) the station.

From M1 exit 11 and Dunstable: go into Luton. Follow signs to Luton station. After the Mirage club on your left, go left into Old Bedford Road. Take first right, Midland Road. This clearly marked company is 200 yds on left, in the old five-storey hat factory.

From M1 exit 10 and directions east: aim for the station. If you find yourself by the no-entry exit road from the station, continue uphill and under the railway then go left into Midland Road. Pass the back entrance to the station on left. This clearly marked company is 100 yds on right.

Open: Mon–Thur 8.30–4.30; Fri 8.30–3. *1 Sept–end March:* Mon–Fri 8.30–4.30; Sat 9–4; Sun 10–1.
Closed: Bank Holidays; Christmas, Boxing and New Year's Days.
Cards: MasterCard, Visa.
Cars: Own car-park at rear of factory. Nearby streets. Long term railway car-park directly facing.
Toilets: In town.
Wheelchairs: Shop on second floor, but lift available.
Changing rooms: Welcome to try anything on.
Teas: In Luton town centre.
Groups: You are welcome to discuss how your garment will be made, but no factory tours.
Transport: Any train or bus to Luton then short walk.

210 Luton Beds

Crystal Art

320 Selbourne Road LU4 8NV
(01582) 494904

Wide range of collectable cut and polished crystal figures of animals and flowers in 30% full lead Austrian crystal and English hand-worked glass. Crystal trees and hanging window decorations; crystal drops, individual faceted crystals sold by the gram. Selection of own-make glass mirrored display cabinets, including small ones ideal for figurines.

'Firsts, seconds and discontinued lines. Many chainstore items made here. Special commissions accepted. Also many one-off prototype designs that are not available anywere else.'

On the north-west side of the town centre.

From M1 exit 11: aim for Luton town centre along Dunstable Road (A505). After ½ mile, go straight at roundabout; take next left (Waller Avenue) at traffic lights.*

From town centre and other directions: aim for Dunstable/M1 along Dunstable Road (A505). By Lex car showroom, go right at traffic lights into Waller Avenue.*

****Before the road goes over the railway, go right (Selbourne Road). Company is shortly on left.***

Open: Mon–Fri 9–5.
Closed: Bank Holidays; Christmas–New Year period.
Cards: MasterCard, Visa.
Cars: Own car-park.
Toilets: Yes.
Wheelchairs: One step.
Teas: Luton town centre (1 mile).
Groups: Shopping groups welcome – please book with sales department. Factory tours also arranged for groups – £2 per person (free crystal oyster given to each person).
Transport: Luton station and bus nos. 31, 37, 38, 61 and 238.
Mail order: Yes.
Catalogue: £3 for full colour catalogue.

211 Luton Beds

Freelance Fabrics (Luton)

1–3 Hancock Drive, Bushmead Road LU2 7SF
(01582) 411522

Large range of upholstery and furnishing fabrics: cottons, linens, damasks, velvets etc. Nets, voiles, calico, interlinings, waddings, linings. Haberdashery, fringing. Curtain rails/poles and accessories. Cushion covers and fillers. Ready-made curtains. Foam cut to shape. Dress fabrics.

'About 2500 rolls in stock. Fitting, measuring and curtain-making services.'

See our display advertisement on p. 195

About 1½ miles north of the town centre.

Coming south on A6: go over roundabout, pass Barnfield College on left. At traffic lights, go left into Kingsdown Avenue.*

Coming north from Luton on A6: at traffic lights, go right into Kingsdown Avenue.*

****At next lights, go straight into Bushmead Road. Follow this road round. Turn right into Hancock Drive: shop is in first three units on right.***

Open: Mon–Fri 9.30–5.30; Sat 9–5; Sun and Bank Holidays 10–4.
Closed: One week at Christmas.
Cards: Access, Connect, Delta, Switch, Visa.
Cars: Own car-park.
Toilets: Yes.
Wheelchairs: No steps, large ground floor shop.
Teas: In town centre.
Groups: Shopping groups welcome, but please phone first.
Transport: Bus no. 6 from blood donor centre/library in town.
Mail order: No.

See our entry below

212 Luton Beds

Kangol

46 Church Street LU1 3JC
(01582) 405000

Range of formal and casual hats for men and women for all occasions including weddings and Ascot. Caps, berets, peak caps. T-shirts; belts; some scarves, key-rings and golf accessories.

'All hats are ends of ranges and slight seconds. Prices from about £2–£30.'

See our display advertisement above

Facing the Arndale Shopping Centre in Luton centre.

Coming into Luton from M1 exit 10: keep following signs to town centre. After traffic lights in town centre (large church on near left; multi-storey car-park on far left corner) company is on right, across dual carriageway, just before Herald & Post office and opposite Thrifty Car Rental. Best to follow signs into Market car-park on left.

On foot from Arndale Centre: Church Street goes at right-angles around two sides of shopping precinct. Exit the Centre at sign for 'Church Street', look for large college opposite; go left down to traffic lights: shop facing you on far side of road.

Open: Mon–Fri 9–4.30; Sat 9.30–12.30.
Closed: Bank Holidays; Christmas, Boxing and New Year's Days.
Cards: MasterCard, Visa.
Cars: Town car-parks. Nearest is Arndale Centre Market multi-storey.
Toilets: In Arndale Centre.
Wheelchairs: Shop on first floor up stairs.
Teas: In Arndale Centre.
Groups: Shoppers welcome with prior phone call. No factory tours.
Transport: 200 yds from bus station.
Mail order: No.

213 Maidstone Kent

Maidstone Fabric Warehouse

Units G14–G15 Business Centre, St Peter's Street ME16 0ST
(01622) 763030

Large range of upholstery and furnishing fabrics: cottons, linens, damasks, velvets etc. Nets, voiles, calico, interlinings, waddings, linings. Haberdashery, fringing. Curtain rails/poles and accessories. Cushion covers and fillers. Ready-made curtains. Foam cut to shape. Dress fabrics.

'5000 plus rolls in stock. Curtain making service.'

See our display advertisement on p. 195

On the west side of town, across the river from the town centre.

On foot from Maidstone East Station: cross the high level bridge over river: you come into St Peter's Street and the bottom of Buckland Hill. Go left down St Peter's Street. Turn into first open area on left: shop is in this car-park.

From M20 exit 6: take A229 south into Maidstone. Keep straight to roundabout/bridge over river: follow St Peter's Street sign. Pass Homebase/Courts on right then Trebor Bassett factory on right: go right into car-park for shop.

Open: Mon–Sat 9–5; Sun & Bank Holidays 10–4.
Closed: Easter Sunday; Christmas & Boxing Days.
Cards: Access, Connect, Delta, Switch, Visa.
Cars: Own car-park.
Toilets: In town.
Wheelchairs: Easy access to ground floor shop, no steps.
Teas: In town.
Groups: Shopping groups welcome, no need to phone.
Transport: Maidstone East train station 10 minutes' walk; buses into town centre.
Mail order: No.

214 Midhurst W Sussex

Dexam International

Holmbush Way Industrial Estate GU29 9HX
(01730) 814188

Wide range of cookware, kitchenware, glass, china, porcelain, giftware, greetings cards etc.
'Seconds and ends of ranges. All at exceptional prices.'

On the south side of Midhurst.

From the centre of Midhurst: go south towards Chichester. Go straight over mini-roundabout, continue for about ¼ mile to Midhurst fire station on right; turn right into Holmbush Way.*

Coming north from Chichester (A286): before you reach Midhurst, look for fire station on left. Turn left just after it into Holmbush Way.*

****Follow road to mini-roundabout, go straight over and take second turning left. Warehouse car-park at end of road.***

Open: Mon–Fri 10–3; Sat 10–1.
Closed: Bank Holidays; Christmas–New Year.
Cards: Delta, MasterCard, Switch, Visa.
Cars: Plenty of space.
Toilets: Yes.
Wheelchairs: Easy access to ground floor shop.
Teas: Hot drinks machine. Pubs and cafés nearby.
Groups: Shopping groups welcome if pre-arranged. Please phone.
Transport: 20 minutes' walk from town; bus no. 260 stops at fire station.
Mail order: No.

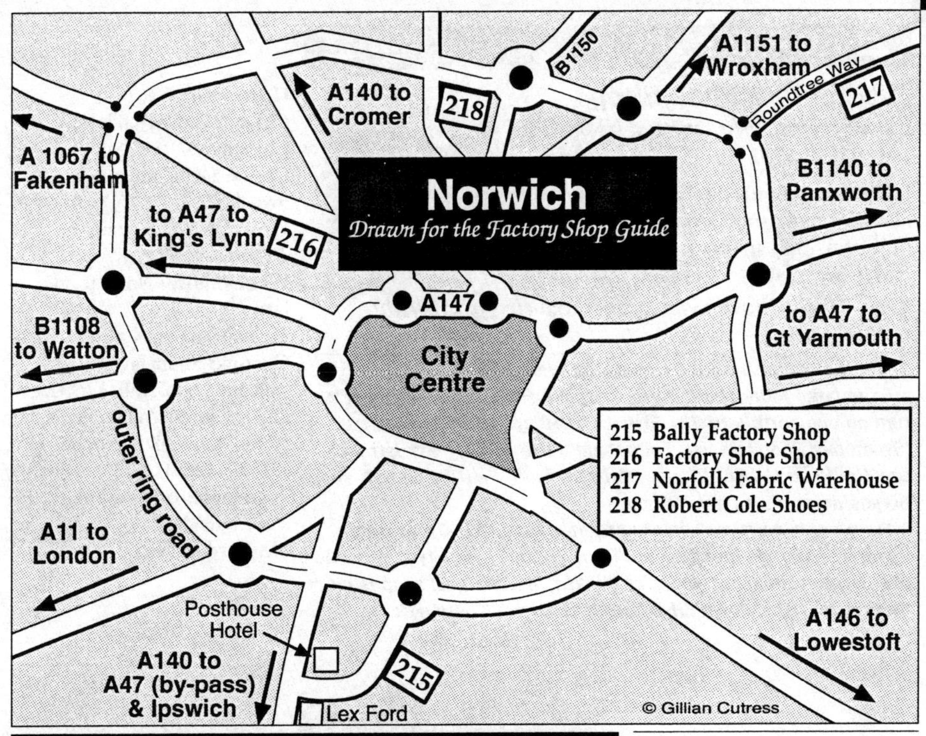

215 Norwich Norfolk *see map above*

The Bally Factory Shop

Hall Road NR4 6DP
(01603) 226040

Large range of ladies' and men's footwear. Handbags and accessories.

'Factory shop in factory complex.'

Near southern edge of town.

The A47 (King's Lynn–Great Yarmouth dual-carriageway) forms the southern bypass of Norwich.

From the A47 south of town, B1108, B1172, A11: stay on or turn on to A47 for Great Yarmouth. Turn north on to A140 for Norwich.*

From Great Yarmouth on A47 and Beccles on A146: stay on or turn on to A47 for King's Lynn. Then turn on to A140 for Norwich.*

From Ipswich on A140: go underneath A47 southern bypass.*

*****Turn right immediately after the Lex Ford garage on right.*****

From town centre and northerly directions: go to or around inner ring road and turn south on to A140 for Ipswich. About 2 miles from city centre go left after Forte Posthouse on left.**

******Pass Toyota, Nissan and Peugeot on right: after 200 yds go right in front of bollards into Bally car-park.****

Open: Mon–Fri 9.30–5.30; Sat 9–5.30; Sun 11–5. Most Bank Holidays – phone first to check.
Closed: Easter Sunday, Christmas, Boxing and New Year's Days.
Cards: Amex, Connect, Diners, MasterCard, Switch, Visa.
Cars: Ample free parking outside shop.
Toilets: Yes, and for disabled.
Wheelchairs: Ramp for easy access to huge shop.
Changing rooms: Yes.
Teas: Coffee shop for tea, cold drinks, light lunches, cream teas.
Groups: No factory tours but shopping groups and coaches always welcome by prior arrangement. Contact Sally Jackson or Shane Scott.
Transport: Cityline bus no. 11 stops virtually opposite.
Mail order: No.

216 Norwich Norfolk *see map previous page*

The Factory Shoe Shop

Esdelle Works, Drayton Road NR3 4RP
(01603) 425907

Ladies' and men's quality footwear from own Norwich factories and associated continental factories. Slim to wide fittings usually in stock. Brands include *Van-Dal, Holmes* and *Jenny*. Also stock quality handbags.

'Over 4,000 pairs of slight seconds and ends of ranges at reduced prices.'

About ¾ mile north-west of inner ring road (A147).

From large roundabout on St Crispin's Road (inner ring road): turn off due north into Pitt Street (A140 and A1067), for 'Swimming Pool, Cromer, Fakenham'; after ½ mile, fork left into Drayton Road (A1067); pass Wensum Park. Factory on left; shop 50 yds down drive past factory.

From north-west section of outer ring road (A140): at traffic lights by Asda, go into Drayton Road (A1067) for city centre. Go over large roundabout, look for Wickes DIY on right; shop is just beyond, on right, down drive before factory, well marked.

Open: Mon–Sat 10–4.
Closed: Bank Holidays; Christmas–New Year.
Cards: Delta, MasterCard, Switch, Visa.
Cars: Own large car-park.
Toilets: Nearby.
Wheelchairs: No steps to large shop.
Teas: Many places in Norwich.
Groups: Shopping groups welcome; book with Mrs Green and ask for discount details. For factory tour call Personnel on (01603) 426341.
Transport: Cityline bus no. 11 stops outside.
Mail order: No.

217 Norwich Norfolk *see map previous page*

Norfolk Fabric Warehouse

Roundtree Way NR7 8S2
(01603) 408454

Large range of upholstery and furnishing fabrics: cottons, linens, damasks, velvets etc. Nets, voiles, calico, interlinings, waddings, linings. Haberdashery, fringing. Curtain rails/ poles and accessories. Cushion covers and fillers. Ready-made curtains. Foam cut to shape. Small selection of dress fabrics.

'Curtain making service. 6–7000 rolls in stock. Curtain fabrics from £2.99 per metre.'

See our display advertisement opposite

North-east of the city centre, Roundtree Way leads north off the outer ring road (Mousehold Lane).

From city centre: take A1151 Sprowston Road north. At the roundabout at outer ring road, go right. After ⅔ mile, go left at traffic lights (Homebase on corner) into Roundtree Way.*

From other directions: aim for the outer ring road.

Going clockwise: cross roundabout with the A1151. After ⅔ mile, go left at traffic lights (Homebase on corner) into Roundtree Way.*

Going anti-clockwise: cross roundabout with B1140. After ⅔ mile, go right at traffic lights (Homebase on corner) into Roundtree Way.*

****Shop is at far end on right.***

Open: Mon–Sat 9–5;
Sun & Bank Holidays 10–4.
Closed: Easter Sunday; 3 days over Christmas.
Cards: Access, Connect, Delta, Switch, Visa.
Cars: Own car-park.
Toilets: Ask if required.
Wheelchairs: Easy access, large ground floor shop.
Teas: Lots of places in Norwich.
Groups: Shopping groups welcome, no need to phone.
Transport: Local buses about 5 minutes' walk.
Mail order: No.

See our entries nos. 3, 8, 106, 116, 179, 211, 213, 217, 223, 234 and in other chapters

218 Norwich Norfolk

see map on earlier page

Robert Cole Shoes

90 Catton Grove Road NR3 3AA
(01603) 487757

Shoes from local, UK and worldwide factories. Over 4,000 shoes on display in all makes, sizes, styles and colours. Major brands, chainstore seconds, discontinued lines, samples.

'The quality footwear discount shop of East Anglia. All stock sold at very competitive prices. Men's shoes from £16–£60; ladies' shoes from £10–£60; children's shoes from £6–£30.'

On the northern section of the main Norwich outer ring road between Cromer Road (A140) and North Walsham Road (B1150).

Shop is clearly visible at junction of Catton Grove Road and the ring road.

Open: Mon–Sat 9–5.30; Sun 10.30–4.30; Bank Holidays.
Closed: Christmas and Boxing Days.
Cards: Amex, MasterCard, Visa.
Cars: Own well signposted car-park.
Toilets: No.
Wheelchairs: One step.
Teas: In Norwich.
Groups: Shopping groups please book first with Robert Cole.
Transport: Several local buses stop outside door.
Mail order: Yes.

Shawl Manufacture in Norwich

As you read about the history of fabrics, you become conscious of how apparently small changes in fashion can stimulate, or kill off, entire manufacturing industries. The development of the bustle in the 1860s, for example, led to the demise of the shawl industry in Norwich. Although a fine accessory for the stylish lady wearing a crinoline, a shawl presented insuperable problems when attempting to make it drape gracefully over a bustle.

Norwich shawls were exquisite works of art. Made from fine cotton, with woollen hand embroidery, they were widely coveted. In the 1790s a single fine example could cost 50 guineas (the usual price being about 12 to 20 guineas). They won awards at international trade exhibitions and were prized by members of the royal family. The Norwich weaver Mr Knights – who invented a loom for weaving seamless shawls 12 ft wide – was official 'shawlman' to Queen Charlotte and would visit her at Kew.

In the 1790s, the French fashion for low cut dresses fashioned in fine thin fabrics had reached English shores. However, the climate did not improve … and a shawl provided an elegant and stylish answer to keeping warm. Developments in manufacture over the following 50 years added to the wonderful choice in shawls: they came in many sizes and shapes, were fashioned in silks and worsteds and were so soft and supple that they were a delight to wear. The less affluent indulged their whims with printed woollen shawls.

But, in 1869, the death of shawl manufacture in Norwich was recorded. 'We regret that these elegant articles of ladies' attire have recently gone almost entirely out of fashion.'

With thanks to Norfolk Central Library.

219 Oxted Surrey

Chanterelle

95–99 Station Road East RH8 OAY
(01883) 714389

Very large range of ladies' and men's fashions on two floors: jackets, suits, skirts, trousers, blouses, knitwear and dresses. Clothes for all occasions: casual wear, daytime, executive suits, special occasion and evening wear. Sizes 10–20.

'All current season stock at greatly reduced prices. Deliveries every week of new stock of clothes from all over Europe. All ranges are perfect. One of the largest fashion stores of its kind in the South East.'

In the centre of Oxted, 2 minutes from the station. Take care – the railway goes through the town centre and you need to get on the correct side of the line (with Boots etc), in Station Road East, not West. You can walk through or drive round if you come into town from the far side.

Follow signs to town centre and railway station. With the station on your right, continue down Station Road East: Chanterelle, clearly visible, is 100 yds on the right.

Open: Mon–Sat 9.30–5.30; Sun 10–4.
Closed: Christmas Day; please phone for Bank Holiday times.
Cards: Switch, MasterCard, Visa.
Cars: Town car-parks. 1-hour street parking across road.
Toilets: Ask if desperate.
Wheelchairs: Easy access to main floor. Stairs to first floor.
Changing rooms: Yes.
Teas: Local cafés and restaurants.
Groups: Coach trips welcome, please book in advance.
Transport: Two minutes' walk from Oxted station. Local buses.
Mail order: No.

220 Papworth Everard Cambs

Papworth Travel Goods

CB3 8RC
(01480) 831410

Moved, see below

Range of top quality leather travel goods, briefcases and suitcases.

'Seconds and discontinued lines only.'

Easy to find, on the A1198 (Huntingdon–Royston road) about 6 miles south of Huntingdon and 11 miles west of Cambridge.

There is only one road through this village. Shop is next to the park and beside the pedestrian lights. Follow signs to car-park. Shop entrance is through reception.

NB Relocated to Saffron Walden, please see entry No. 229 (Swaine Adeney Brigg)

Open: Mon–Thur 8.30–5; Fri 8.30–4. Some Saturdays 9.30–12.30: please phone to check.
Closed: Bank Holidays; Christmas–New Year.
Cards: Amex, MasterCard, Visa.
Cars: Outside reception.
Toilets: Yes.
Wheelchairs: No access to upstairs showroom.
Teas: Local pubs or Little Chef.
Groups: No factory tours. Groups of shoppers welcome.
Transport: Hourly buses from Cambridge and St Ives.
Mail order: Yes. Seconds and discontinued lines only.
Catalogue: Free.

221 Portsmouth Hants

Gieves & Hawkes

22 The Hard
(01705) 826648

Men's wear: suits, jackets, trousers, shirts, ties, hats etc. Ladies' suits, skirts, blouses, jackets, coat and dresses.

'Ends of ranges at very good value.'

Across the road from the Isle of Wight passenger ferry and Portsmouth Harbour railway station.

From all directions: follow brown tourist signs to Historic Ships. Pass the sign to the car-park for historic ships then follow signs to the Isle of Wight passenger ferry. Shop is opposite the entrance to Portsmouth Harbour railway station.

Open: Mon–Sat 9–5.30.
Closed: Phone about holidays.
Cards: MasterCard, Visa.
Cars: NCP car-park nearby.
Toilets: In town.
Wheelchairs: Small step.
Changing rooms: Yes.
Teas: Lots of cafés in Portsmouth.
Transport: Trains and buses to Portsmouth.

222 Rayleigh Essex

Falmer Jeans

24–26 Brook Road SS6 7XF
(01268) 749207

Wide range of men's and ladies' jeans and casual wear: shorts, T-shirts, blouses etc.

'All items are ends of lines, previous year's ranges or slightly substandard stock at reduced prices.'

On south side of Rayleigh, just off Southend Arterial Road (A127).

Going east on A127 to Southend: go left at Rayleigh Weir overpass/roundabout. At huge roundabout, take second left (The Weir pub on left) as if going back on to A127.*

From Southend on A127: go to major roundabout as above, then double back as if going back along dual carriageway.*

****Take first left, following signs to industrial estate; go right into Brook Road. Company clearly marked on right.***

Open: Mon–Sat 9–5.30. Phone for Bank Holidays. Some days between Christmas–New Year.
Closed: Some Bank Holidays.
Cards: MasterCard, Switch, Visa.
Cars: Outside shop.
Toilets: Ask if necessary.
Wheelchairs: Assistance into sizeable shop by prior arrangement.
Changing rooms: Yes.
Teas: In Rayleigh.
Groups: Shopping groups welcome if they phone first.
Transport: Buses to Rayleigh Weir then ¼ mile walk.
Mail order: No.

223 Reading Berks

Freelance Fabrics

130 Crockhamwell Road, Woodley Shopping Centre RG5 3JH
(0118) 969 7595

Large range of upholstery and furnishing fabrics: cottons, linens, damasks, velvets etc. Nets, voiles, calico, interlinings, waddings, linings. Haberdashery, fringing. Curtain rails/poles and accessories. Cushion covers and fillers. Ready-made curtains. Foam cut to shape. Dress fabrics.

'The original "Freelance", still the best. 5000 rolls. Prices from £2.99 per metre. Curtain-making, re-upholstery and interior design services.'

See our display advertisement on p. 195

Woodley is on the east side of Reading, south of Twyford.

From all directions: head for Woodley Centre. The shop is clearly visible in the pedestrianised shopping area (car-park is at side).

Open: Mon–Sat 9–5; Sun & Bank Holidays 10–4.
Closed: Easter Sunday; Christmas, Boxing and New Year's Days.
Cards: Access, Connect, Delta, Switch, Visa.
Cars: Pay-and-display car-park 50 yds from shop.
Toilets: In car-park.
Wheelchairs: Easy access, huge ground floor shop.
Teas: Café across precinct.
Groups: Shopping groups welcome, no need to phone.
Transport: Bus service from town centre.
Mail order: No.

224 Redhill Surrey

Choice Discount Stores

Unit 1, Warwick Quadrant, London Road RH1 1NN
(01737) 772777

Surplus stocks including men's, women's and children's fashions and footwear from *Next plc, Next Directory* and other high street fashions.

'Save up to 50% of normal Next first quality prices; seconds sold from 1/3 of normal retail price. Special sales January and September.'

In pedestrianised road in centre of town next to Sainsbury's.

From the north on A23: turn left at Lombard roundabout.*

From the west on A25: pass Sainsbury's on left and at Lombard roundabout turn right.*

****At next roundabout with train station on left double back and follow signs to Warwick Quadrant car-park.*****

From the east on A25 and from the south on A23: continue to roundabout by the train station. Then follow signs to Warwick Quadrant car-park.**

*****Once in car-park go up the sloping travelator: shop is first on left at the top.***

Open: Mon–Sat 9–5.30; Sun 10–4.
Closed: Christmas and Boxing Days.
Cards: Amex, MasterCard, Switch, Visa.
Cars: In town centre.
Toilets: No.
Wheelchairs: No steps to large shop.
Changing rooms: No, but refund if returned in perfect condition within 28 days.
Teas: In town centre.
Groups: Shopping groups welcome! Book with store manager.
Transport: Redhill station.
Mail order: No.

225 Romford Essex

Hubbinet Reproductions

Unit 7, Hubbinet Industrial Estate, Eastern Avenue West RM7 7NV
(01708) 762212

Maker of quality traditional and reproduction furniture in hand finished mahogany and yew wood veneer. Over 100 models of bookcases (from £80), library bookcases (from £500), dining sets (from £600), desks, bureaux, TV, hi-fi and video units (from £200), occasional tables.

'Factory seconds and export rejects at up to 50% off. Special sales January, April and November. Advice on furnishings; also modify and colour to customer's requirements.'

See our display advertisement opposite

Off the A12 north of Romford.

From London on A12: cross A1112 at traffic lights. After a mile cross another set of traffic lights, then take left turn after Mercedes garage.*

From M25 exit 28: aim for London on A12. At Gallows Corner (flyover/big roundabout) stay on A12. After 2 miles pass MFI and BAC on left then make U-turn at next traffic lights. After Mercedes garage take first left.*

****Pass Falconcraft on left then go into next industrial estate on left. Inside, turn left and follow signs.***

Open: Mon–Fri 9–5; Sat 10–4; Sun phone for information.
Closed: 24 Dec–10 Jan.
Cards: MasterCard, Visa.
Cars: Easy, outside shop.
Toilets: Yes.
Wheelchairs: No steps to shop.
Teas: Sandwiches and cold drinks at nearby garage.
Transport: Romford train station then bus to Eastern Avenue; Newbury Park tube station on Central Line. Then no. 66 or Eastern National bus to Parkside, Romford.

226 Royston Herts

Flower Smiths

Smith End Farm, Smith's End Lane, Barley SG8 8LL
(01763) 848545

Individually created Christmas decorations – pine garlands; swags and tails; wreaths and fir branches decorated with exotic seed heads, cones, pomegranates, oranges, nuts and cinnamon sticks and tied with ribbons. Table decorations, old handmade terracotta pots and church or beeswax candles. Dried flower arrangements plus everything needed to make your own decorations.

'We supply Christmas decorations to stores; sold here for at least 50% less.'

Barley is about 3 miles south-east of Royston where the B1039 crosses the B1368.

Smith's End is on the south side of Barley.

From Royston: take B1039 into Barley. Go right into High Street, follow road round sharp right hand bend, past Richmond's garage on right and Fox and Hounds pub on left. Go left into Smith's End Lane after 200 yds. Smith End Farm is 600 yds on left.

Open: *Oct–Christmas only:* Sat & Sun 10–5. By appointment throughout the year.
Closed: January–September.
Cards: No.
Cars: Outside shop.
Toilets: Yes.
Wheelchairs: Ten steps (goods can be brought down to view).
Teas: Gladly make tea or coffee while you browse. Local pubs: good food, children's play areas.
Groups: Small groups welcome, please phone Rosalind Wythe in advance. Visitors can be shown round workshop and demonstrations can also be arranged. Phone for details of flower arrangement courses. Commissions always accepted.
Mail order: Yes. All items are individually created – happy to discuss requirements and send photos, samples etc.

See our entry opposite

227 Rye E Sussex

Rye Pottery

Ferry Road TN31 7DJ
(01797) 223363

Wide range of decorated earthenware: some mugs, dishes, cake stands; selection of dogs, cats, owls, hares etc plus collector's range of figures from *Chaucer's Canterbury Tales* and *English Country House* figures.

'Perfects; and seconds reduced by 33%. Please mention this book when requesting catalogue. Special commissions accepted.'

On the west side of Rye.

By car: go round town till you see signs to 'Battle B2089' then follow them; go over level crossing; pottery is in large detached house 200 yds on right, just past The Ferry Boat Inn.

By train then foot: turn right outside station, go to end of road, turn right; go over level crossing; pottery is in large detached house 200 yds on right, just past The Ferry Boat Inn.

From Battle on B2089: go down Udimore Hill into Rye, pass the 'Cinque Ports' sign, then pottery is just over ½ mile on left, just before The Ferry Boat Inn.

Open: Mon–Fri 9–12 & 2–5; Sat 9.30–12.30 & 2.30–5.
Closed: Bank Holidays; Christmas–New Year.
Cards: MasterCard, Visa.
Cars: Two car spaces beside pottery; town car-parks and local streets.
Toilets: In town.
Wheelchairs: Five steps and cobbled path so not possible.
Teas: Lots of places in Rye.
Tours: No.
Transport: Five minutes' walk from train station.
Mail order: Yes, for firsts only.
Catalogue: Free.

228 Rye E Sussex

Rye Tiles

The Old Brewery, Wish Ward TN31 7DH
(01797) 223038

Wide selection of screen-printed tiles in about 150 colours and many designs. Hand-painted tiles, including murals. Also sell figures from other shop (see Rye Pottery).

'Make sure you take your exact measurements with you! Gladly match tile colours to your own furnishings. Seconds about half usual prices. Mail order for perfect tiles and figures.'

In the centre of town, facing bottom of Mermaid Street.

Coming into Rye from the north: go round lower road by the river; take first right, in front of large anchor set in pebbled area, then go left into Wish Ward. Company is 100 yds ahead.

By car in town centre (which is largely one-way): beside 'The Pipemaker's Arms' turn into Wish Ward; pottery is 50 yds on right.

Open: Mon–Fri 9–5; Sat 10–1 & 2.15–4.30.
Closed: Bank Holidays; Christmas–New Year.
Cards: MasterCard, Visa.
Cars: Town car-park or 1-hour parking in nearby streets.
Toilets: Few yards away.
Wheelchairs: Unfortunately not possible.
Teas: Lots of places in town.
Tours: No (but can probably see the screening if you ask).
Transport: Any bus or train to Rye.
Mail order: Yes. All tiles to order only, no seconds by mail.
Catalogue: Free.

229 Saffron Walden Essex

Swaine Adeney Brigg

Nursery Road, Great Chesterford CB10 1QV
(01799) 531522

Luxury country clothing: ladies' and men's tailored jackets, trousers, skirts, jumpers, blouses, shirts, scarves, gloves and wax and cotton outerwear; English bridle hide leather goods; gifts, toiletries and the famous *Brigg* umbrella. Now includes *Papworth Travel Goods.*

'Perfect ends of lines etc. Usually at least 30% off London retail prices.'

About four miles north-west of Saffron Walden and near M11 exit 9.

Going north on M11: take exit 9 (for A11 Norwich). At first roundabout (junction with A1301 for Sawston and Cambridge, and B184 for Saffron Walden) take exit for Saffron Walden.*

Going south on M11: take exit 10 then A505 towards Sawston. After 1½ miles go right on to A1301 for Saffron Walden. At roundabout with A11, take B184 for Saffron Walden.*

****At roundabout go right for Great Chesterford. Continue around sweeping left bend, pass glass house (nursery) on right and turn right immediately. Shop is at the end, straight ahead.***

Open: Mon–Sat 10.30–4.
Closed: Good Friday; Christmas–New Year.
Cards: Amex, MasterCard, Switch, Visa.
Cars: Factory car-park.
Toilets: Yes.
Wheelchairs: One step to small shop.
Changing rooms: Yes.
Teas: Gluttons Café in Saffron Walden.
Transport: Great Chesterford station behind factory.
Mail order: No.

230 Sheerness, Isle of Sheppey Kent

B & A Whelan

52 High Street, Blue Town ME12 1RV
(01795) 663879

Huge selection of concrete garden ornaments made here. Houses, wells, urns, troughs, pots, gnomes, cupids, wheelbarrows, bird baths, sundials, animals, pedestals, seats etc.

'Family run business, over 600 designs. Always some reduced prices. The UK's largest concrete ornament manufacturer.'

Go over bridge on to Isle of Sheppey. At first roundabout go left, then keep following signs to Sheerness Docks. Cross industrial railway crossing by steel mill then take third left.

Open: Seven days a week 9–6.
Closed: Christmas–New Year.
Cards: None.
Cars: Own car-park.
Toilets: Yes.
Wheelchairs: Easy access, huge outdoor show area.
Teas: Great variety of fish & chip shops, Chinese and Indian restaurants and pubs in Sheerness.
Groups: Shopping groups welcome. No guided tours.
Transport: Ten minutes' walk from railway and bus stations.
Mail order: No.

Whitstable Oysters

A food for the affluent in recent years (but now much more affordable), oysters used to be part of the staple diet rather than a luxury. The oyster beds of Kent have been worked for at least a thousand years (and probably even in Roman times). In their heyday, 100 boats dredged some 60 million oysters in a year. The fishing gradually went into decline this century: in part due to a virus, but largely because of drainage of the marshes, of pollution from the rapidly growing town of Whitstable and by agricultural chemicals. By the 1960s, most oyster fisheries had ceased production. Scientific research carried out by a biologist at that time resulted in new rearing techniques and the introduction of the pacific oyster – which matures in three years instead of the five years needed by the native oyster and which is more disease-resistant. These developments saved the Kent oyster industry: the unique hatchery, the first commercial hatchery in the world, now supplies many oyster growers throughout Europe. The hatchery has been moved to Reculver near Herne Bay; the small oysters are then taken back to the traditional Pollard ground at Whitstable to mature.

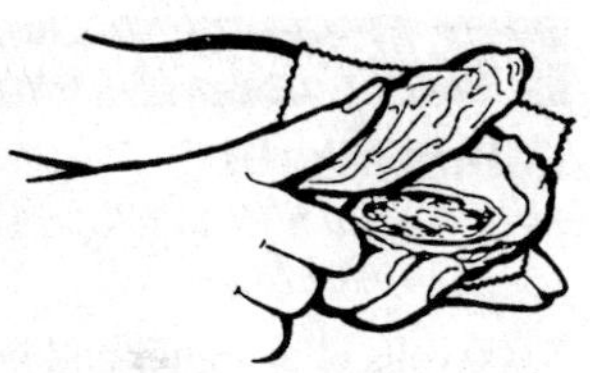

You can buy oysters – at reasonable prices – when you visit Whitstable (pacific oysters can be eaten any day that has a 'd' in its name, native oysters from September–April). Also visit the Whitstable Oyster & Fishery Exhibition in the original buildings of the Seasalter & Ham Oyster Fishery Company at the end of East Quay. April–October: phone (01227) 262003 for times and prices.

231 Shoreham-by-Sea W Sussex

Claremont Garments

26 Dolphin Road BN43 6PR
(01273) 463710

Ladies' and girls' underwear and nightwear; also ladies' and children's outerwear and leisurewear.

'Seconds and ends of lines, including chainstore items, sold here. Range of stock much wider now. Newly refurbished shop."

See our display advertisement on p. 539

Beside the railway line, a couple of hundred yards off the coast road, on the east side of the town centre.

From M23/Brighton: drive along seafront through Portslade and Southwick into Shoreham. Pass B&Q and Halfords on right; go right at traffic lights after Courts.*

From Worthing on coast road (A259): at roundabout go right for Shoreham town centre; drive through Shoreham. Pass large Esso petrol station on right then go left at traffic lights for Dolphin Industrial Estate.*

****Cross level crossing, go right into Dolphin Road (parallel to railway); well marked building on left. Go up drive on left.***

Open: Mon–Fri 9–4.30; Sat 9–3.
Closed: Phone for details.
Cards: Yes.
Cars: Own car-park.
Toilets: Ask if desperate!
Wheelchairs: Showroom on first floor (no lift).
Changing rooms: Yes.
Teas: Welcome to use factory canteen (8 am–2 pm).
Groups: Groups welcome to shop, but essential to phone first.
Transport: Ten minutes' walk from centre of Shoreham.
Mail order: No.

232 South Croydon Surrey

Fabric World

6–10 Brighton Road CR2 6AB
(0181) 688 6282

3,000 rolls of designer and branded curtain and upholstery fabrics sold by the metre.

'Most stock perfects (ends of ranges and repeatable designs), some seconds, at about 50% off normal high street prices. From £3.30–£20 per metre. Interior design service – we visit your home (free, without obligation). Also make-up service for all types of curtains.'

About ¼ mile south of Croydon on A235.

Going south from Croydon towards Purley: go straight at traffic lights (not left for Selsdon). Swan & Sugar Loaf pub is on left; Barclays Bank on far right corner. Shop is immediately after the bank. [To park, go right at these lights into Warham Road.]

Coming north from Purley: pass Whitgift School and sports field on left, then shop is shortly on left.

Open: Mon–Sat 9–5.30.
Closed: Most Bank Holidays. Christmas, Boxing and New Year's Days.
Cards: Connect, MasterCard, Visa, Switch.
Cars: Meters in Warham Road.
Toilets: Yes.
Wheelchairs: No steps, large shop.
Teas: Tea made for weary customers; or in Croydon.
Groups: Shopping groups welcome – please phone Debbie Shinerock first.
Transport: Lots of buses from near East Croydon station at Swan & Sugar Loaf opposite.
Mail order: No.

233 Southampton Hants

Factory Pine

370–372 Shirley Road SO15 3HV
(01703) 772222

Over 600 items of hand-made hand-waxed quality pine furniture.

'Good old fashioned value! No sales, special offers or middle men. Pay around 30–40% less than in the high street. We also have shops at Westbury (01373) 825424 and Saltford (01225) 874355.'

Shirley is a western suburb of Southampton.

From southern end of M271: take A35 east. Continue straight on to A3024, going over overpass. Go straight at traffic lights, under footbridge. At traffic lights go left for Shirley A3057 then over railway.*

From other directions: get on to A3024 (major dual-carriageway which runs east–west parallel to the docks/river Test). At traffic lights go right for Shirley A3057 then over railway.*

***At roundabout go for left for Romsey/Shirley. Keep straight for about a mile. Pass Ford on left then Total petrol. Shop is immediately on left.**

Open: Seven days 10–6. Bank Holidays.
Closed: Christmas Day.
Cards: No.
Cars: Ample free parking.
Toilets: Yes.
Wheelchairs: Easy access.
Teas: Local pubs and cafés.
Groups: Groups welcome to shop.
Transport: Local buses.
Mail order: No.

234 Southampton Hants

Freelance Fabrics (Southampton)

West Quay Road SO15 1GZ
(01703) 336410 Fax (01703) 336403

Large range of upholstery and furnishing fabrics: cottons, linens, damasks, velvets etc. Nets, voiles, calico, interlinings, waddings, linings. Haberdashery, fringing. Curtain rails/poles and accessories. Cushion covers and fillers. Ready-made curtains. Foam cut to shape. Dress fabrics.

'Curtain making service.'

See our display advertisement on p. 195

On south-west side of the city centre, near docks 4–8.

From southern end of M271: take A35 east. Continue straight on to A3024, going over overpass. Go straight at traffic lights, under footbridge. At traffic lights, go right (south) for Dock Gates 1–10.*

From other directions: get on to A3024 (major dual-carriageway which runs east–west parallel to the docks/river Test). At traffic lights go south for Dock Gates 1–10.*

***Pass Novotel on left. At traffic lights, go left for Dock Gates 4–8. Pass McDonald's on left. Go over traffic lights. In front of Honda turn right: shop is 50 yds on right.**

Open: Mon–Sat 9.30–5; Sun & Bank Holidays 10–4.
Closed: Christmas, and Boxing Days.
Cards: Access, Connect, Delta, Switch, Visa.
Cars: In forecourt.
Toilets: Yes.
Wheelchairs: Easy access to vast shop.
Teas: Restaurants on nearby retail park.
Groups: Shopping groups welcome, no need to phone.
Transport: Unfortunately none.
Mail order: No.

235 Stowmarket Suffolk

Frank Harvey Footwear

24 Tomo Business Park, Creeting Road (01449) 612646

Hand-crafted bespoke footwear: brogues, sandals, court shoes, golf shoes, boots etc. Orthopaedic footwear. Leather goods to order. Leather dyeing. Accessories – brushes, polishes, shoe and boot trees and a vast range of shoe laces.

'For bespoke footwear, please make an appointment (allow 1 hr for first appointment). Special commissions undertaken; can make to customers' own design. Also repair any make of shoe, leather goods and clothing. Shoe and handbag dyeing and shoe recovering. Complete restoration of riding boots. Bespoke footwear from £350–£400.'

Creeting Road is east of town centre, running beside station.

From town centre: follow signs to station. Go over level crossing, take first right (Creeting Road). Take second right into Tomo Industrial Estate.*

From south/Ipswich on A14 (formerly A45): turn off A14 at signs to A1120 for Stowmarket/Stowupland.**

From Bury St Edmunds coming south on A14 (formerly A45): take second slip road for Stowmarket/Stowupland A1120.**

*****At roundabout under A14, follow sign to Tomo Industrial Estate (couple of turnings: signs at each junction).****

****Once on estate, take first left, continue down hill. Shop is on right.***

Open: Mon–Fri 8–5.
Closed: Bank Holidays; two weeks at Christmas.
Cards: Eurocard, MasterCard, Visa.
Cars: By entrance or in car-park.
Toilets: Yes.
Wheelchairs: Easy access via ramp at front door (disabled may park by front door).
Teas: Freshly made coffee and tea on request. Plenty of cafés and pubs in town centre.
Tours: Customers can be shown factory, please ask.
Transport: Buses to town then free pick-up: please phone for details. Short walk from station.
Mail order: Yes. Handbag/shoe dyeing and re-covering plus repairs to footwear, leather goods and clothing. No bespoke footwear by mail order.
Catalogue: Small, free leaflet.

236 Sudbury Suffolk

Vanners Mill Shop

Gregory Street CO10 6BC
(01787) 313933

Silk fabric by the metre. Wide range of articles in silk, woven here or printed at company's Crayford mill – scarves, boxer shorts, ties, handkerchiefs, purses, wallets etc.

'Most items perfect but some fabric slightly substandard. All at mill shop prices. Many bargains in firsts and "famous name" seconds. From £2.50 per metre for pure silk. For special sale dates ring (01322) 559401, mentioning this book.'

Easy to find in middle of town (large one-way system).

From Market Square: go clockwise (Midland Bank on left).*

From other directions: follow road round for Bury St Edmunds (A134).*

****After junction where A131 goes left to Chelmsford, keep clockwise on A131 (A134) for Bury. Clearly marked mill 100 yds on right (before fire station on left).***

From Chelmsford on A131: you must go left on to one-way system as you reach town. Shop 100 yds on right.

From Bury St Edmunds on A134: go into town, take first turn for Chelmsford (A131) then A134 back towards Bury as above.

Open: Mon–Fri 9–5; Sat 9–12.
Closed: Bank Holidays; Christmas–New Year.
Cards: MasterCard, Visa.
Cars: Car-park opposite, beside fire station.
Toilets: In factory – ask if desperate!
Wheelchairs: No steps to expanded showroom.
Teas: Lots of places in town.
Groups: No mill tours. Shopping groups always welcome – prior phone call, please.
Transport: Any bus to town then short walk.
Mail order: No.

237 Sutton Surrey

Fabric World

287/9 High Street SM1 1LM
(0181) 643 5127

3,000 rolls of designer and branded curtain and upholstery fabrics sold by the metre.

'Most stock perfects (ends of ranges and repeatable designs), some seconds, at about 50% off normal high street price. From £3.30–£20 per metre. Interior design service – we visit your home (free, without obligation). Also make-up service for all types of curtains.'

In Sutton centre near Tesco and opposite The Crown pub.

From the huge roundabout in Rosehill: go south along Rose Hill into Sutton (B2230). Pass Magnet Kitchens on right then this shop is 150 yds on right just after huge Eagle Star building (immediately past car-park on right).

Coming north from Banstead/Epsom: because the High Street is partly pedestrianised, you have to bear left into one-way system. Pass Tesco and car-park on right. Fabric World is on left just before traffic lights at T-junction (next to huge Eagle Star building).

Open: Mon–Sat 9–5.30.
Closed: Most Bank Holidays. Christmas, Boxing and New Year's Days.
Cards: Connect, MasterCard, Visa, Switch.
Cars: Own car-park immediately before shop on left, or in supermarket car-park on right (on one-way system).
Toilets: Yes.
Wheelchairs: No steps into large shop.
Teas: Tea made for weary customers; or Sutton town centre.
Groups: Shopping groups welcome – please phone Debbie Shinerock first.
Transport: Any bus to Sutton. (Nearest tube Morden; nearest train Wimbledon.)
Mail order: No.

238 Tiptree Essex

The Factory Shop Ltd.

The Crossroads CO5 7VW
(01621) 817662

Large selection of men's, ladies' and children's clothing, footwear, luggage, toiletries, hardware, household textiles, gifts, bedding, lighting and new fashion concessions department with famous brand names. *Cape Country* pine furniture exclusively produced for The Factory Shop.

'Large stock of branded and chainstore items, all at greatly reduced prices. Deliveries of new stock every week to give an ever changing selection.'

In the middle of Tiptree by the crossing of the B1022 and the B1023.

From the north (on B1023): the shop is on the right just by the crossing with the B1022.

From the south: pass the windmill (no sails) and Burmah petrol on right; the shop is on far left corner of the crossing.

Open: Mon–Sat 9–5.30; Sun 10–4.
Closed: Easter Sunday; Christmas, Boxing and New Year's Days.
Cards: MasterCard, Switch, Visa.
Cars: Own large car-park.
Toilets: Public toilet facilities opposite.
Wheelchairs: No steps.
Changing rooms: Yes.
Teas: Cafés and pubs in town.
Groups: Shopping groups welcome. For organiser/driver incentives please phone.
Transport: Bus service from Clacton to Maldon. Bus stop outside.
Mail order: No. Home delivery service for pine furniture. Please phone for free catalogue and price list.

239 Toddington Beds

Royal Scot Crystal

Poplars Nursery, Harlington Road LU5 6HF
(01525) 875897

Hand-cut lead crystal glasses, decanters, vases etc. Specially engraved items. Crystal animals, paperweights and perfume bottles. Golf prizes.

'Most items made in own factory (not at this location). Sell first quality, some seconds and discontinued lines at substantially reduced prices.'

See our display advertisement opposite

Clearly visible on A5120.

From M1 exit 12: go north-east towards Flitwick (not Toddington) on the A5120. After ½ mile turn right into nursery. The shop is at the rear of the building next to the tearoom.

From Flitwick: go south towards M1. This nursery is on the left, ½ mile before the motorway.

Open: Mon–Sun 10–5.
Closed: Christmas, Boxing and New Year's Days.
Cards: MasterCard, Visa.
Cars: Garden centre car-park.
Toilets: Yes.
Wheelchairs: No steps.
Teas: Available in garden centre. Children's play area.
Groups: Small shopping groups welcome with prior phone call. Visit the garden centre at the same time!
Transport: None.
Mail order: No.
Catalogue: Free.

240 Watford Herts

Next 2 Choice

46 High Street WD1 2BR
(01923) 233255

Surplus stocks especially men's, women's and children's (up to 8 years) fashions and footwear from *Next plc* and *Next Directory*.

'Save up to 50% off normal Next first quality prices; seconds sold from ⅓ of normal retail price. Special sales January and September.'

Easy to find in the pedestrianised High Street, almost opposite WH Smith and next to The Moon Under The Water pub.

Driving clockwise round the inner ring road: take the right slip-road for Church multi-storey car-park. Go to High Street and turn left, then 300 yds walk and the shop is on left just after The Moon Under The Water pub.

Open: Mon–Sat 9–5.30.
Closed: Christmas and Boxing Days.
Cards: Amex, MasterCard, Switch, Visa.
Cars: Car-park in town centre.
Toilets: Church car-park.
Wheelchairs: No steps to large shop.
Changing rooms: No, but refund if returned in perfect condition within 28 days.
Teas: In town centre.
Groups: Shopping groups welcome! Book with store manager.
Transport: Watford station.
Mail order: No.

See our entry opposite

241 Wattisfield Suffolk

Henry Watson's Potteries

IP22 1NI
(01359) 251239

Good quality seconds of terracotta storage jars (including large square jars with 1600 ml capacity), wine coolers, bread crocks, lasagne dishes, bread bakers, herb and spice jars, flan dishes etc at about 25% off. New range of glazed terracotta tableware in two colours (plates, bowls, teapots, salad bowls etc, all dishwasher-safe.)

'Lots of bargains, wonderful seconds. Many products at greatly reduced prices – from £1.25–£25.'

Wattisfield is a small village on the A143, 14 miles north-east of Bury St Edmunds and 9 miles south-west of Diss. The pottery is well signposted on A143.

From Bury: as you reach Wattisfield, pass the right turn-off to Wattisfield church; after several hundred yards, go right into well marked lane.

From Diss: pass the Suffolk Barn restaurant on left; after hundred yards go sharp left into well marked lane to pottery.

Open: Mon–Sat 9.30–4.30; Bank Holidays (except Good Friday).
Closed: Good Friday; Christmas Day and following week.
Cards: MasterCard, Visa.
Cars: Large car-park.
Toilets: Yes, and for disabled.
Wheelchairs: No steps to shop, but no easy access for tours.
Teas: Own coffee shop.
Tours: Please phone to book 45-minute tour; see an original Roman kiln and the factory video. Groups welcome to shop.
Transport: None.
Mail order: No.

242 Wickford Essex

Next 2 Choice

10–11 Ladygate Centre, High Street SS12 9AK
(01268) 764893

Surplus stocks including men's, women's and children's fashions and footwear from *Next plc, Next Directory* and other high street fashions.

'Save up to 50% off normal Next first quality prices; seconds sold from ⅓ of normal retail price. Special sales January and September.'

Near southern end of Wickford High Street.

From A127: turn on to A132 towards Wickford. Stay on A132 to large roundabout where A129 goes left (Somerfield on far left). From this roundabout exit to Somerfield and Ladygate Centre. Shop is in this centre.

From the north on A132: stay on A132 as far as Somerfield on right (by roundabout where A129 turns right for Billericay). Exit this roundabout for Somerfield and Ladygate Centre.

Open: Mon–Thur 9–5.30; Fri 9–6; Sat 9–5.30.
Closed: Christmas and Boxing Days.
Cards: Amex, MasterCard, Switch, Visa.
Cars: In town centre car-park.
Toilets: No.
Wheelchairs: Easy access. No steps.
Changing rooms: No, but refund if returned in perfect condition within 28 days.
Teas: In town centre.
Groups: Shopping groups welcome! Book with store manager.
Transport: Wickford station.
Mail order: No.

243 Wisbech Cambs

Catalogue Bargain Shop

51 West Street PE13 2LV
(01945) 584327

Huge range of mail order surplus items: clothing, fashions, household, footwear, hardware, furniture, toys and gifts.

'Large savings from original catalogue prices. Firsts & seconds.'

Not far from town centre.

On foot from Market Square: exit into Church Terrace (Andrews china shop on right); take right fork (St Peter's car-park on right).*

Coming north on A47: follow signs into town. At roundabout, take first exit; keep straight, cross traffic lights (Maxey estate agents on right). At roundabout go right on to dual carriageway (petrol station on left); at next lights (Mervyn hairdresser on right), go right (right filter). Follow road round to left; go right into St Peter's car-park. Walk into West Street.*

****Pass Harlequin pub on right; shop (was Bevans/Bainbridges) is short distance further on, set back.***

Open: Mon–Sat 9–4.30; Sun 10.30–4.30. Bank Holidays.
Closed: Christmas and Boxing Days.
Cards: Access, Delta, Switch, Visa.
Cars: St Peter's car-park, 5 minutes.
Toilets: No.
Wheelchairs: No step to ground floor; stairs to first floor (ladies' and children's wear).
Changing rooms: Yes, two (but upstairs).
Teas: The Bread Bin or Honey Pot in Norfolk Street, or Westgate Restaurant.
Transport: Bus station 10 minutes.
Mail order: No.

Towns with factory shops

NUMBERS refer to the ENTRIES, NOT the PAGES

Town	Entry	Shop
Aldershot	1	FactoryGate Variety Stores
Andover	2	Croydex
Aylesbury	3	Aylesbury Fabric Warehouse
Aylesbury	4	The Chiltern Brewery
Aylsham	5	Black Sheep
Barkingside	6	Choice Discount Stores
Basildon	7	Choice Discount Stores
Basildon	8	Essex Fabric Warehouse
Basildon	9	The Factory Shop
Basingstoke	10	Western House
Bedford	11	Grumbridge
Bicester	12–69	Bicester Village
Bognor Regis	70	Heirlooms
Borehamwood	71	Rubert of London
Brighton	72	Kemptown Terracotta
Brighton	73–86	Merchants Quay
Broxbourne	87	Nazeing Glassworks
Bungay	88	Nursey & Son
Burgess Hill	89	Jaeger Factory Sale Shop
Bury St Edmunds	90	The Factory Shop Ltd.
Cambridge	91	The Factory Shoe Shop
Cambridge	92	Langham Glass
Canterbury	93	Essentially Hops
Chertsey	94	The Fabric Factory
Chichester	95	Body Sense
Chichester	96	Chelton Lighting
Clacton-on-Sea	97	Clacton Common Factory Shopping Village
Clacton-on-Sea	98	Mascot Clothing
Cosham	99	FactoryGate Variety Stores
Crayford	100	David Evans
Dover	101	De Bradelei Wharf
East Dereham	102	The Factory Shop Ltd.
Eastbourne	103	Napier
Fakenham	104	Gilchris Confectionery
Fareham	105	Grandford Carpet Mills
Farnham	106	Freelance Fabrics
Faversham	107	Catalogue Bargain Shop
Faversham	108	Nova Garden Furniture
Feltham	109	Legacy Jewellery
Four Marks near Alton	110	The Village Furniture Factory
Frinton-on-Sea	111	Park Fruit Farm
Godalming	112	Alan Paine Knitwear
Godalming	113	Kent & Curwen
Grays	114	Choice Discount Stores
Guildford	115	Susan Walker Classics
Hackbridge, Wallington	116	South London Fabric Warehouse
Hadleigh	117	Choice Discount Stores

Towns with factory shops

NUMBERS refer to the ENTRIES, NOT the PAGES

Town	Entry	Shop
Hastings	118	Collins and Hayes
Hatfield	119	Choice Discount Stores
Hatfield	120–164	The Galleria Outlet Centre
Headcorn	165	The Factory Shop Ltd.
Hemel Hempstead	166	Aquascutum
Herne Bay	167	Peter Newman
Herstmonceux	168	Thomas Smith's Trug Shop
Hickstead Village	169	M & G Designer Fashions
High Barnet	170	Catalogue Bargain Shop
High Wycombe	171	GP & J Baker & Parkertex Fabrics
High Wycombe	172	Furniture Direct
High Wycombe	173	Highly Sprung
Hingham	174	Rombah Wallace
Horley	175	The Factory Shop Ltd.
Ipswich	176	Ellis Furniture
Ipswich	177	Lambourne Clothing
Ipswich	178	Suffolk Carpet Weavers
Ipswich	179	Suffolk Fabric Warehouse
Isle of Wight : Yarmouth	180	Chessell Pottery
Kenninghall	181	Suffolk Potteries
King's Lynn	182	Caithness Crystal
King's Lynn	183	Jaeger
King's Lynn	184	Start-rite Shoes
Langham near Holt	185	Langham Glass
Leighton Buzzard	186	Gossard
Little Horwood	187	Phoenix Carpets
London : Battersea	188	Price's Patent Candle Co.
London : Bow	189	Nicole Farhi/French Connection
London : Deptford	190	Bucks Furniture Warehouse
London : Dollis Hill	191	Tymbuktu
London : Dulwich	192	The Pottery
London : East Ham	193	Tronage
London : Fulham	194	The Curtain Fabric Factory Shop
London : Fulham	195	Rococo Frames
London : Fulham	196	Roger Lascelles Clocks
London : Hackney	197	Burberrys
London : Hackney	198	The Factory Shop (Sofa to Bed)
London : Islington	199	Hockley's China and Glass
London : King's Cross	200	Futon Express
London : Leyton	201	R P Ellen
London : Morden	202	Centrax Direct Sales
London : Palmers Green	203	Catalogue Bargain Shop
London : Peckham	204	Catalogue Bargain Shop.
London : Perivale	205	Bluthners Pianos
London : Wandsworth	206	InWear / Matinique / Part Two
London : Wandsworth	207	Villeroy & Boch
London : Westbourne Grove	208	Crucial Trading

Towns with factory shops

NUMBERS refer to the ENTRIES, NOT the PAGES

Town	No.	Shop
Luton	209	Ash Kay
Luton	210	Crystal Art
Luton	211	Freelance Fabrics (Luton)
Luton	212	Kangol
Maidstone	213	Maidstone Fabric Warehouse
Midhurst	214	Dexam International
Norwich	215	The Bally Factory Shop
Norwich	216	The Factory Shoe Shop
Norwich	217	Norfolk Fabric Warehouse
Norwich	218	Robert Cole Shoes
Oxted	219	Chanterelle
Papworth Everard	220	Papworth Travel Goods
Portsmouth	221	Gieves & Hawkes
Rayleigh	222	Falmer Jeans
Reading	223	Freelance Fabrics
Redhill	224	Choice Discount Stores
Romford	225	Hubbinet Reproductions
Royston	226	Flower Smiths
Rye	227	Rye Pottery
Rye	228	Rye Tiles
Saffron Walden	229	Swaine Adeney Brigg
Sheerness	230	B & A Whelan
Shoreham-by-Sea	231	Claremont Garments
South Croydon	232	Fabric World
Southampton	233	Factory Pine
Southampton	234	Freelance Fabrics (Southampton)
Stowmarket	235	Frank Harvey Footwear
Sudbury	236	Vanners Mill Shop
Sutton	237	Fabric World
Tiptree	238	The Factory Shop Ltd.
Toddington	239	Royal Scot Crystal
Watford	240	Next 2 Choice
Wattisfield	241	Henry Watson's Potteries
Wickford	242	Next 2 Choice
Wisbech	243	Catalogue Bargain Shop

South London Fabric Warehouse

The Factory Shoe Shop

Essentially Hops

C

Leicestershire & Northamptonshire

C

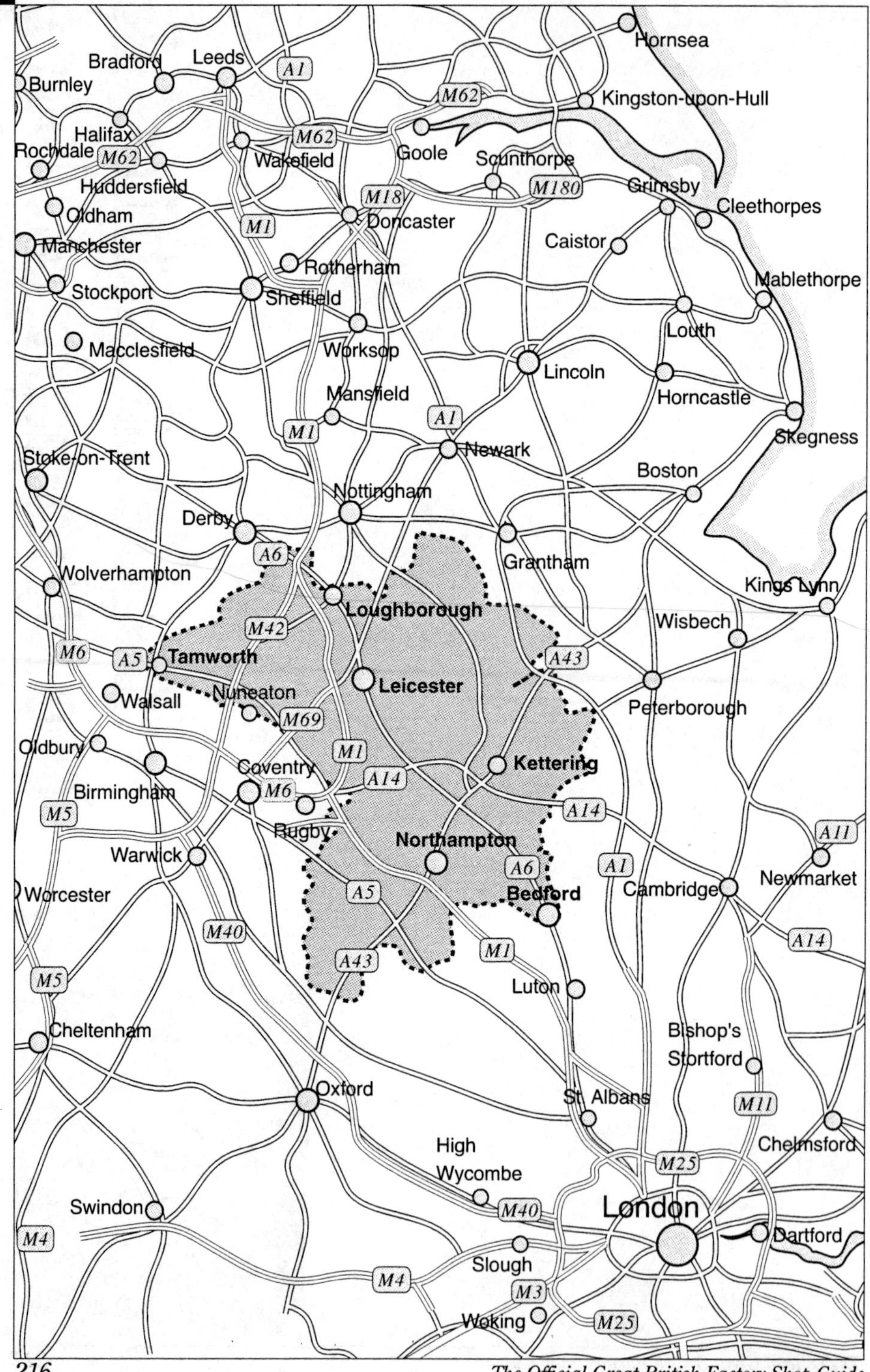
Hornsea
Bradford
Leeds
A1
Burnley
M62
Kingston-upon-Hull
Halifax
M62
Rochdale
M62
Wakefield
Goole
Scunthorpe
Huddersfield
M18
M180
Grimsby
Cleethorpes
Oldham
M1
Doncaster
Caistor
Manchester
Rotherham
Mablethorpe
Stockport
Sheffield
Louth
Macclesfield
Worksop
Lincoln
Mansfield
Horncastle
A1
M1
Skegness
Newark
Stoke-on-Trent
Boston
Nottingham
Derby
Grantham
A6
Wolverhampton
Kings Lynn
Loughborough
M42
Wisbech
M6
A5
Tamworth
A43
Leicester
Nuneaton
Walsall
Peterborough
M69
Oldbury
M1
Kettering
Coventry
Birmingham
A14
M6
A14
M5
Rugby
A11
Northampton
Warwick
A6
A1
Newmarket
Worcester
A5
Bedford
Cambridge
M40
M1
A14
A43
M5
Luton
Cheltenham
Bishop's
Stortford
Oxford
M11
St. Albans
Chelmsford
High
Wycombe
M25
Swindon
M40
London
M4
Dartford
Slough
M4
M3
Woking
M25

Leicestershire & Northamptonshire

Home of footwear, knitwear, hosiery, socks, pork pies and Stilton cheese, Leicestershire and Northamptonshire were traditionally sources of coal and steel before the decline of heavy industry in Britain. Although not the first counties to spring to mind as magnets for tourists, Rutland (famous for the TV gardening programme based in Barnsdale and for its beer) has delightful stone villages in rolling countryside; Leicestershire has the largest diving centre in Britain (50,000 people a year go diving in a single former granite quarry in this land-locked county); and Northamptonshire offers lovely deep yellow stone and thatch villages – and, like Leicestershire, a wonderful canal network.

One of the trendiest names in footwear in the world originates in Northamptonshire – which also produces one of the best loved brands of jeans and leisurewear. If you need a present with a difference for a teenager, you might consider a 'day return' to Northampton.

What a diverse selection of goods comes from this area – lampshades and light fittings, marvellous ranges of upholstery and curtain fabrics, luggage and briefcases, soaps and tablemats, garden ornaments, sewing machines, re-conditioned cookers, reduced price washing machines and family footwear. To say nothing of superb lingerie, family clothing, pure wool sweaters, jodhpur boots – and top quality hand-made men's leather shoes which are treasured here and in many countries overseas. One pair of leather shoes alone could more than save you the cost of the journey to Northamptonshire.

Many changes have taken place in the world of factory shopping over the last couple of years and, sadly, some old friends have closed down (usually because factory owners have been forced to realise the financial value of their sites, or, as in the case of footwear, production costs are so much lower in developing countries). We are, however, delighted to welcome some wonderful shops which appear in this book for the first time ... for lingerie, furniture, fabrics ... (even decorative tins across the border in Bedford).

Finally, we must congratulate the burghers of Hinckley for providing such outstanding public lavatories. They are a pleasure to visit ... clean, well equipped, easily accessible. We strongly recommend officials who are responsible for public toilets elsewhere to go and see what can be achieved.

"Unsurpassed for Style, Fit and Durability"
1884

c

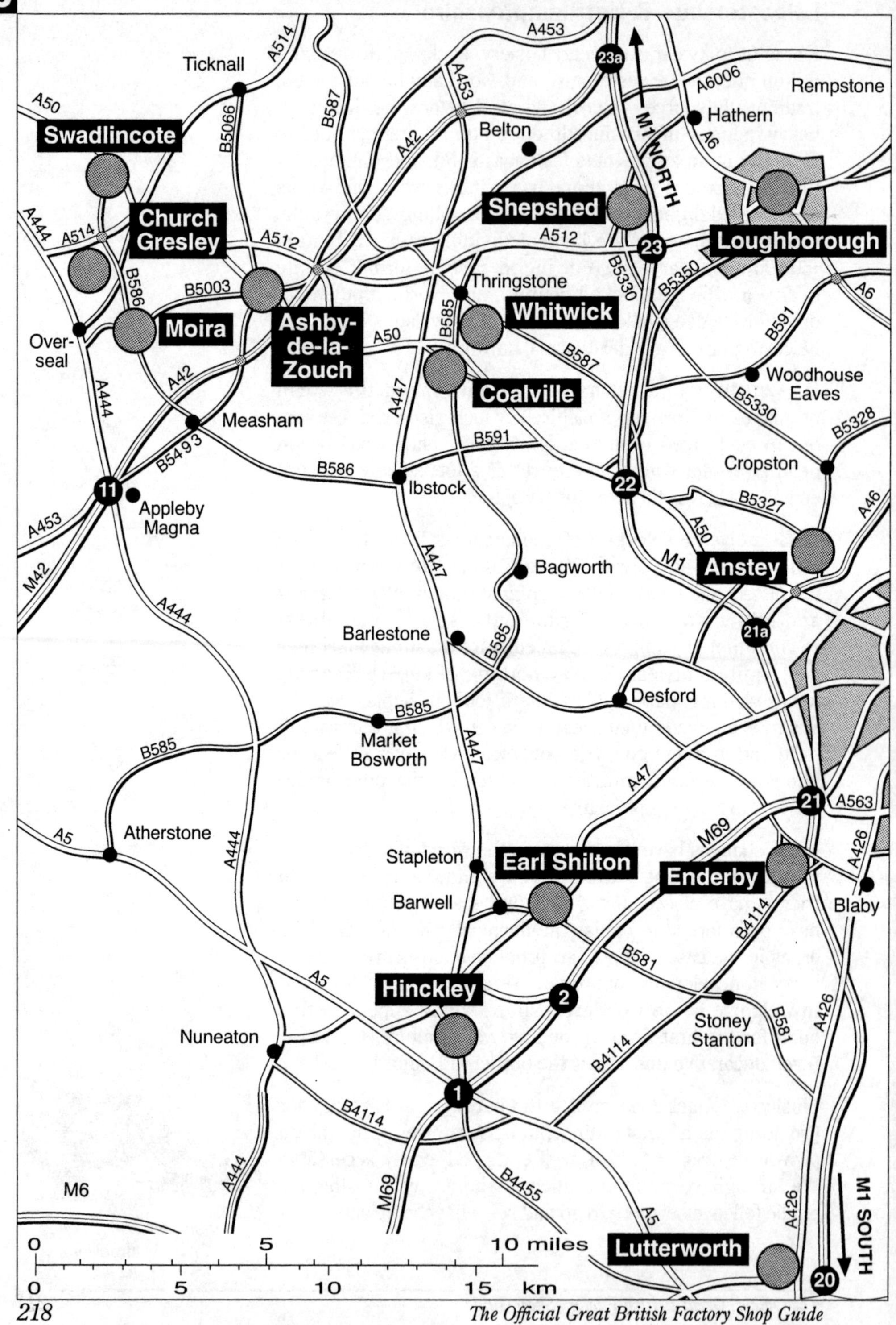

Swadlincote
Church Gresley
Moira
Ashby-de-la-Zouch
Shepshed
Whitwick
Coalville
Loughborough
Anstey
Earl Shilton
Enderby
Hinckley
Lutterworth
Ticknall
Belton
Hathern
Rempstone
Thringstone
Over-seal
Measham
Woodhouse Eaves
Cropston
Ibstock
Appleby Magna
Bagworth
Barlestone
Desford
Market Bosworth
Atherstone
Stapleton
Barwell
Blaby
Nuneaton
Stoney Stanton
M1 NORTH
M1 SOUTH
M6
M42
M69
M1
0 5 10 miles
0 5 10 15 km

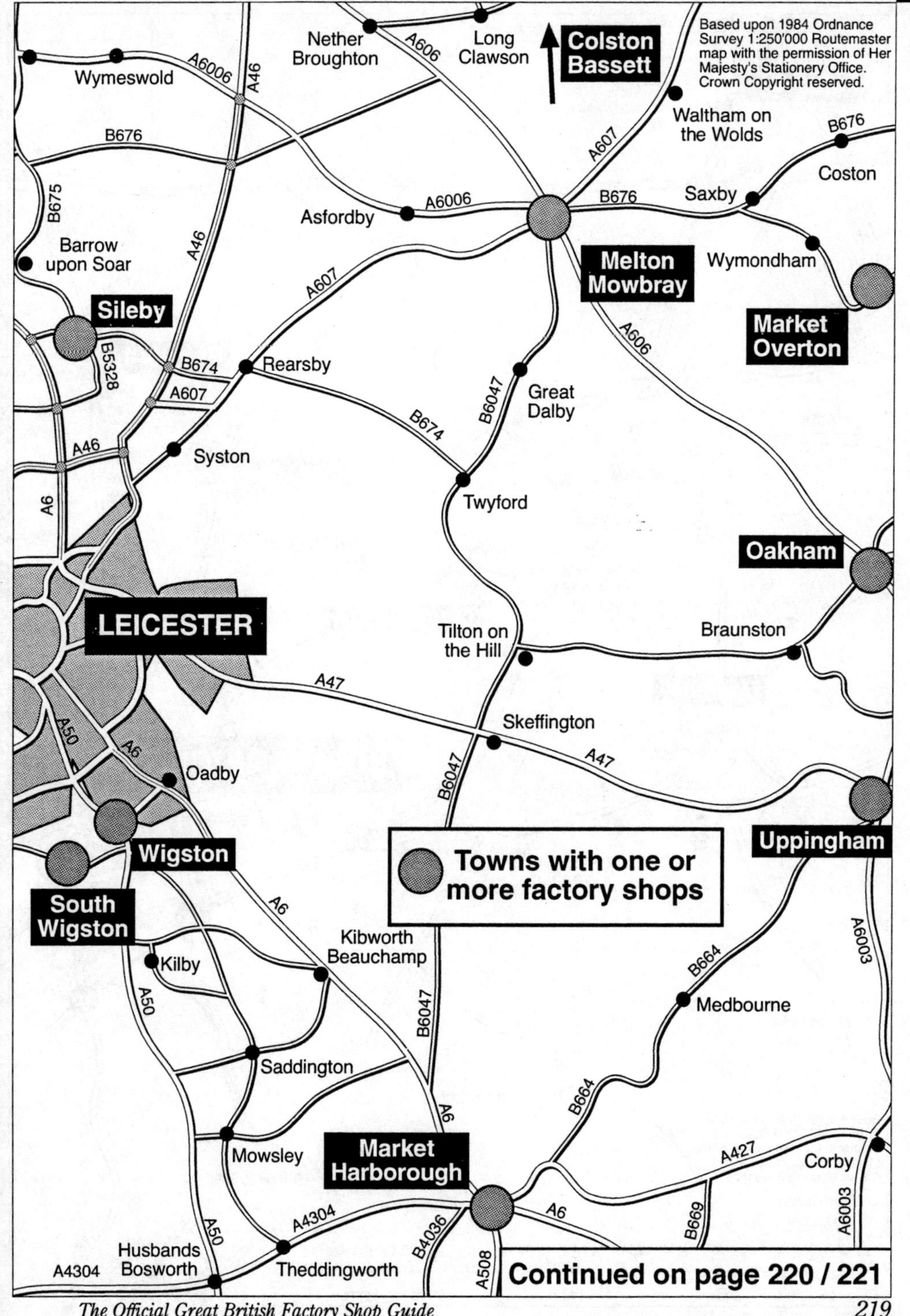

Continued on page 220 / 221

C

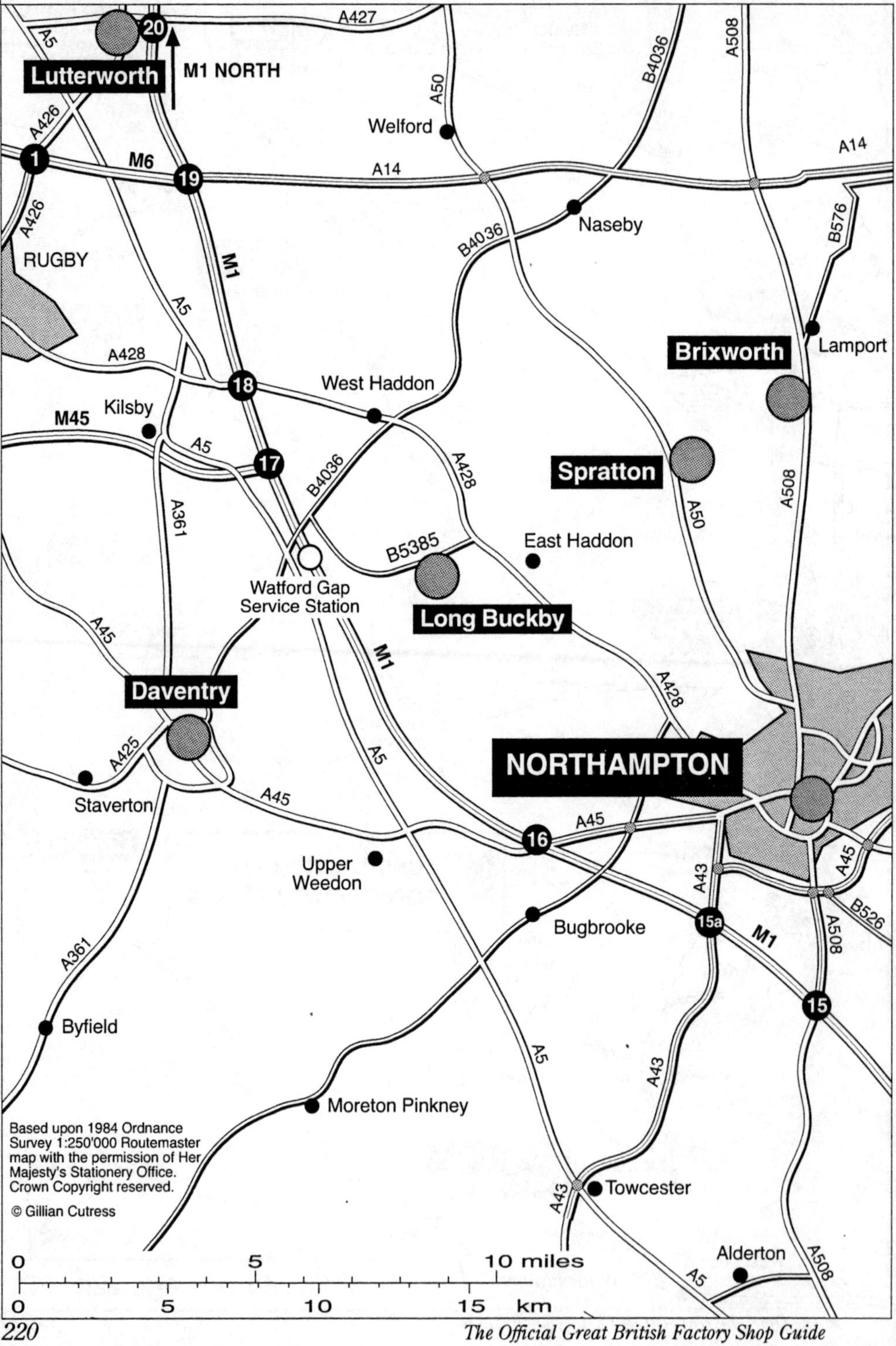

A427
A5
20
Lutterworth
M1 NORTH
A50
B4036
A508
A426
Welford
1
M6
19
A14
A14
A426
Naseby
B4036
B576
RUGBY
M1
A5
Lamport
Brixworth
A428
18
West Haddon
Kilsby
M45
A5
17
A428
Spratton
B4036
A361
A508
A50
B5385
East Haddon
Watford Gap
Service Station
Long Buckby
A45
M1
Daventry
A428
A425
A5
NORTHAMPTON
Staverton
A45
A45
16
Upper
Weedon
A43
A45
Bugbrooke
15a
M1
B526
A508
A361
15
Byfield
A5
A43
Moreton Pinkney
Towcester
A43
Alderton
A5
A508

Based upon 1984 Ordnance Survey 1:250'000 Routemaster map with the permission of Her Majesty's Stationery Office. Crown Copyright reserved.

© Gillian Cutress

0 5 10 miles

0 5 10 15 km

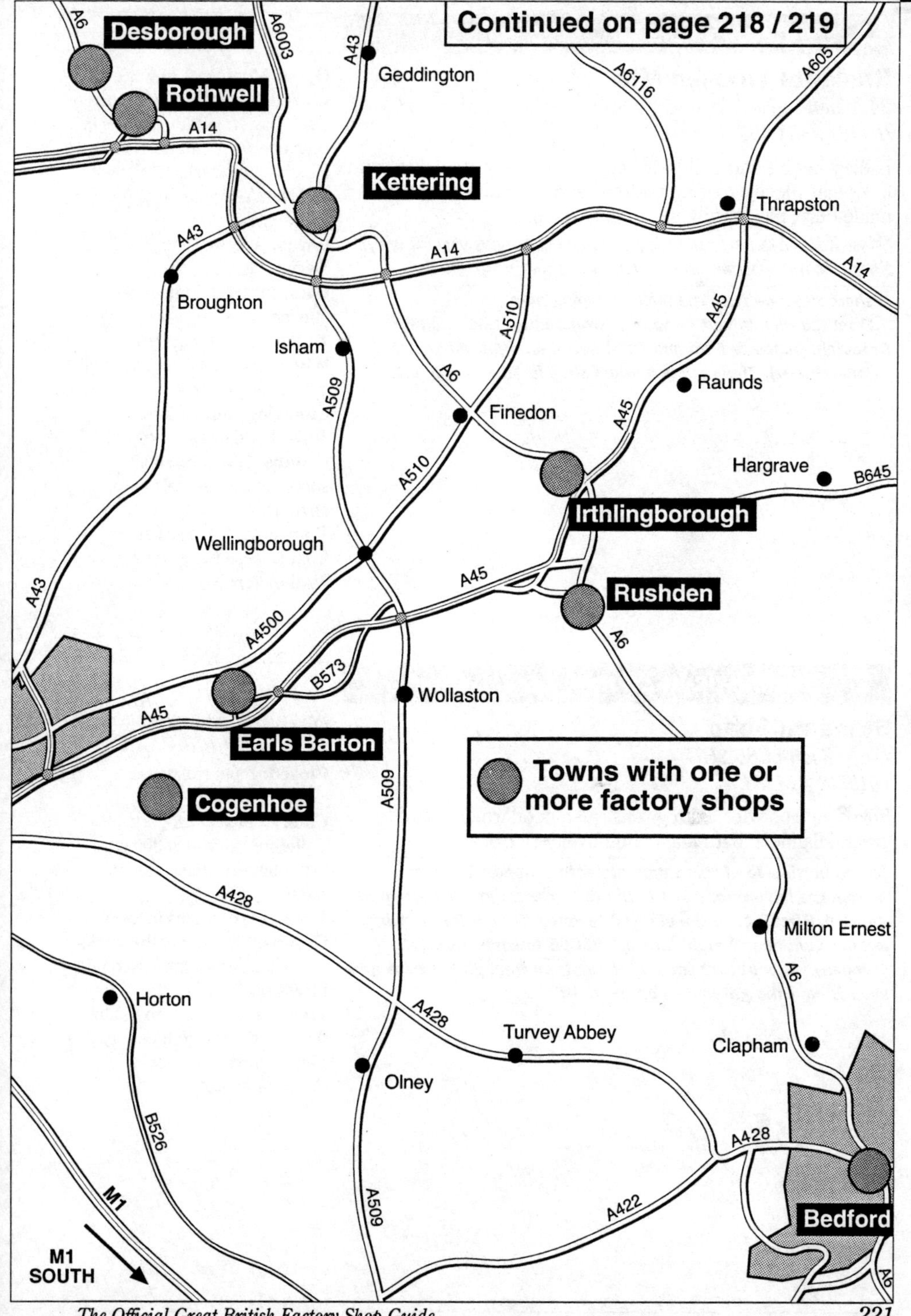
Continued on page 218 / 219
Desborough
Rothwell
Kettering
Geddington
Thrapston
Broughton
Isham
Raunds
Finedon
Hargrave
Irthlingborough
Wellingborough
Rushden
Wollaston
Earls Barton
Cogenhoe
Towns with one or more factory shops
Milton Ernest
Horton
Turvey Abbey
Clapham
Olney
Bedford
M1 SOUTH
A6
A6003
A43
A6116
A605
A14
A45
A510
A509
A4500
B573
B645
A428
A422
B526
M1

1 Anstey Leics

Bradgate Woollen Mill

24 Albion Street
(0116) 235 0455

Ladies', men's and children's fashion wear – casual wear and knitwear. Fleecy jogging bottoms and tops, and sweatshirts made here, plus cardigans, sweaters etc.

'Most items are perfects at factory prices. Always special offers. Special commissions such as club or school uniforms.'

A short distance from the main shopping area.

From the roundabout in Anstey town centre: take road for Cropston. Opposite Ford and Total petrol on right, go left (Albion Street). This clearly marked shop is 100 yds on left.

Open: Mon–Fri 9.30–5.30.
Closed: Bank Holidays. One week Easter; first two weeks in July; one week August Bank Holiday; two weeks Christmas and New Year; please phone for exact dates.
Cards: Access, Delta, Switch, Visa.
Cars: In street immediately outside shop.
Toilets: Yes, if required.
Wheelchairs: No step to small ground floor shop.
Changing rooms: Yes.
Teas: Local cafés.
Groups: No tours; small shopping groups welcome anytime.
Transport: Bus to Anstey from Leicester city centre.
Mail order: No.

2 Ashby-de-la-Zouch Leics

Standard Soap

Derby Road LE65 2HG
(01530) 414281

Soaps, talc powder, bath grains. Also deodorants, hand cream, flannels, bath foam and novelty soaps.

On the north side of this small, attractive market town.

From the mini-roundabout in the town centre at the bottom of the High Street: take the old A50 towards Burton. Don't swing left but continue straight into the B5006 towards Ticknall. Company is about 100 yds on the right: go through the gate and shop is past the gatehouse on the right.

Open: Mon–Thur 9.30–5; Fri 9.30–3.
Closed: Bank Holidays.
Cards: None.
Cars: Company car-park.
Toilets: No, nearest 300 yds.
Wheelchairs: Easy access; ramp.
Teas: Lots of places in town.
Groups: No tours of the works but coach parties are welcome. Please book if possible.
Transport: Any bus to Ashby then short walk from centre.
Mail order: No.
Catalogue: No.

Grumbridge

14 The Manton Centre, Manton Lane
(01234) 273232

Tins for biscuits, decorative tins, waste bins, tin household jars, cake tins, pencil tins, mugs, stationery items, lots of gifts.
'Perfects and seconds, all at below high street prices.'

North-west of Bedford off the A6.

From town centre and all other directions (except the A6 from Rushden): follow the A6 for Kettering through Bedford. At large roundabout with sign to Brickhill, go right for Brickhill.*

From the north/Rushden on the A6: turn left at the first roundabout towards Brickhill.*

****At first lights turn left, then take second left: shop is 150 yds on right.***

Open: Mon–Fri 9–5.
Closed: Bank Holidays; Christmas–New Year.
Cards: No.
Cars: Own car-park.
Toilets: Yes.
Wheelchairs: Easy access to very small shop.
Teas: Many cafés within 2 minutes' drive.
Groups: No tours; shopping groups welcome anytime, but large groups please phone.
Transport: Unfortunately none.

Ashby-de-la-Zouch

This must be one of the most unusual town names in Britain. It dates back to 1160 when Alain de Parrhoet la Zouch became Lord of the Manor of Ashby upon his marriage.

In the 1820s Ashby was famous as a health resort. Hence the Bath House which stood in a charming little park near the station. It was a Doric building with a 150ft long colonnade, and a pump room under the dome. The pump supplied hot and cold salt and freshwater. There was a swimming pool, kept at 83°F, shower baths, a dance d'eau (for applying water to any limb) and a vapour bath. With regard to disabled visitors, a suspended chair could lower invalids into the water (but bad cripples had to be lowered in a sheet held by two or three people), and there were no steps so bath chairs had easy access.

However, the saline water believed to be so efficacious against rheumatism did not originate at this spot. In fact it was pumped from the deep levels of the Bath Colliery at Moira, about three miles away. The plan had been to pump the water through pipes, but in practice it was brought to Ashby by rail in iron tanks – 'an ignominious method of supply'. The Royal Hotel, which still stands, was built to accommodate users of the spa. Travel organiser Thomas Cook (more about him a few pages on) was quick to see the potential of bringing visitors to Ashby after the opening of the railway in 1849, and the spa prospered for 40 years. Unfortunately the venture failed, and the baths were closed in 1884. The impressive building stood until the 1960s, when it was demolished as part of the wide spread architectural vandalism which took hold of this country during that decade.

Ashby Tourist Information Office (01530) 411767

4 Brixworth Northants

Haddonstone

NN6 9BY
(01604) 882300

Top quality stone garden urns, statues, troughs, seats, sundials, fountains, bird baths, copings, columns etc. Items on sale vary from day to day.

'Seconds and slightly faulty items sold at reduced prices.'

Brixworth is about nine miles north of Northampton.

The company is at the northern end of village, just off A508 (Market Harborough–Northampton road).

Going south on A508 from Market Harborough: at the first roundabout, go right for Brixworth.*

Going north on A508 from Northampton: do not go left at first roundabout for Brixworth but go left at next roundabout.*

****Take second right, pass UK petrol station on left, go to far end and turn right into company. Seconds area is straight ahead.***

Open: Mon–Fri 7.30–4.30. Please see local press for occasional weekend sales.
Closed: Bank Holidays; Christmas–New Year.
Cards: Mastercard, Switch, Visa.
Cars: Own car-park. Help with loading available.
Toilets: No.
Wheelchairs: Easy access to open air display area.
Teas: Local pubs.
Groups: No.
Transport: Difficult.
Mail order: Yes.
Catalogue: Colour brochures: £5 complete collection (128 pages); £3 garden ornaments. No seconds sent by mail order. Delivery by company's transport at extra cost.

5 Church Gresley Derbys

T G Green Pottery

John Street DE11 8EE
Mon–Fri: (01283) 217981; weekends: 226696

Large selection of decorated pottery; plain coloured cookware & tableware; Cornish kitchenware. Table mats, trays, coasters, melamine food preparations, co-ordinated linens & small gifts.

'Please ring for special sale dates.'

Five miles south-east of Burton upon Trent, just off the A50, on south side of Swadlincote.

From Burton: take A50 south-east for Ashby. In Woodville, go right on to A514 for Swadlincote; take first left to Church Gresley/ Nuneaton A514; go left at roundabout for Measham B586. After 100 yds go left into private road; pottery is 200 yds on right.

From Swadlincote: take B586 south for Measham. Go uphill, past artificial ski slope on left; go straight at roundabout. After 100 yds, go left through vehicle welder's yard into private road; pottery is 200 yds on right.

From Moira: go north on B586: pass Q8 petrol on left. After ⅓ mile go right into private road (100 yds before roundabout at A514).

From M42 exit 11: go north through Overseal to Castle Gresley. Take A514 east; go right on to B586; after 100 yds go left.

Open: Mon–Fri 9.30–5; Sat 9.30–4.30; Sun 10–4.
Closed: Easter Monday; please phone for Christmas opening.
Cards: Access, Switch, Visa.
Cars: Own car-park.
Toilets: Yes.
Wheelchairs: Access to fairly spacious shop.
Teas: In Swadlincote.
Groups: To shop only by prior arrangement. Arrangements can be made for parties of 15 people or more to tour factory at £2 each. Mon–Thur only. Must be pre-booked: please contact Brenda Maddock.
Transport: None.

Lady Clare

The Corsetry Factory

Furnishing fabrics

Haddonstone

Dr. Martens

6 Coalville Leics

Jaeger Factory Shop

Wolsey Road LE6 4ES
(01530) 835506

High quality *Jaeger* ladies' blouses, skirts, dresses and knitwear etc. *Viyella* ladies' wear.

In the town centre, 150 yds from the clocktower/war memorial.

From A50 (main road through town): take B585 for Whitwick. Pass clocktower.*

From Snibston Park: go into town; at traffic lights go left for Whitwick B585 then left again at the clocktower/war memorial.*

****Pass the first little road left then veer left, beside East Midlands Housing Association on your left, into Wolsey Road (do not go down the railway underpass!): shop is 40 yds on the left.***

Open: Mon–Sat 10–5.
Closed: Christmas Eve–New Year; and Bank Holidays.
Cards: Access, Switch, Visa.
Cars: In street.
Toilets: In town.
Wheelchairs: One large step to medium sized shop.
Changing rooms: Yes.
Teas: In town and at Snibston Park.
Groups: By prior arrangement with Mrs Coral Wells.
Transport: Short walk from town centre.
Mail order: No.

7 Colston Bassett Notts

Colston Bassett & District Dairy

Harby Lane NG12 3FN
(01949) 81322

Stilton cheese. Usually pre-cut cheese available from cheese sales shop to the right of the dairy.

'Traditionally-made Blue Stilton cheeses for sale.'

On the south side of this very small village about 10 miles north of Melton Mowbray.

From the south (Hose or Harby direction) you will see this dairy on your left as you reach the outskirts of village.

From Colston Bassett: follow signs to Hose and Harby. The dairy, easy to see, is on your right just as you leave the village.

Open: Mon–Fri 9.30–12.30 & 1.30–4; Sat 9.30–11.30.
Closed: Christmas, Boxing and New Year's Days; Bank Holidays.
Cards: None.
Cars: In yard frontage.
Toilets: No.
Wheelchairs: No steps; easy access to sales shop.
Teas: Excellent local pubs.
Tours: No.
Transport: None.
Mail order: Yes.

8 Daventry Northants

White and Co. (Earls Barton)

11 New Street NN11 4BO
(01327) 702291

Footwear: patented Tredair® Foam Injected, Gripfast™ Screw-on Soles, Dr Martens, safety steel capped, motor cycle, leather soled. All in unisex fashions.

'Won Queen's Award for Exports 1990.'

In the centre of town about 100 yds south of the cross in market square.

From M1 exit 16: follow A45 to Daventry. At the first roundabout with the hotel on left take second exit and go right at second roundabout. Pass Waitrose on left and shop is directly on right.

From all other directions: follow signs to Town Centre and you end up in New Street. Pass Waitrose on left and shop is directly on right.

Open: Tues, Fri, Sat 10–4. Some Bank Holidays: please phone to check.
Closed: Easter; Spring Bank Holiday week; last week in July; first week in Aug; third week Sept; Christmas–New Year.
Cards: No.
Cars: Free public car-park adjacent.
Toilets: In town.
Wheelchairs: Easy access.
Teas: Cafés in town.
Tours: Welcome to shop and to look round factory (max 20 people). Please book first with reception mentioning this book. No young children please.
Transport: Buses from station.
Mail order: No.

Desborough Northants

Cheaney

Rushton Road NN14 2RZ
(01536) 763760

Top quality *Goodyear* welted men's leather shoes.

'Shoes can be returns, ends of lines or slight seconds. Prices from £30 to £90.'

On north side of village.

From A6, coming south: as you reach Desborough, follow sign left to Pipewell. You come parallel to railway on left, with fire station on right.*

From A6, coming north: turn right by the Kings Arms, into Desborough, towards Pipewell & Rushton. Take first left, Station Road. Continue along then round right.*

****Immediately after left turning to Pipewell/Corby (which leads over railway bridge), well marked shop is on left (opposite factory) in a detached building set back from road.***

Late Entry

Open: Wed, Thur, Fri 10–5; Sat 10–4.
Closed: Monday, Tuesday. Bank Holidays. Second fortnight in July.
Cards: MasterCard, Switch, Visa.
Cars: Car-park in front of shop.
Toilets: No.
Wheelchairs: Easy access.
Teas: Attractive local pubs and pubs in nearby villages.
Groups: No factory tours or shopping groups.
Transport: Difficult.
Mail order: No.
Catalogue: Free. Catalogue for regular stock only.

9 Desborough Northants

The Corsetry Factory

Rothwell Road
(01536) 761252

Top quality designer lingerie: bras, bodies, briefs and basques; swimwear; knitted underwear such as vests and knickers; nightwear such as silk pyjamas and negligées.

'Most items are perfect, discontinued lines at around 50% off. Also a few seconds. Bras from £3. Always bargain rummage boxes. Gift vouchers available and gift wrapping service.'

On the main A6, on the Kettering (south) side of Desborough.

From the centre of Desborough: turn left (downhill) on to the A6. The clearly marked shop is several hundred yards on the right, at the bottom of the hill and just after pedestrian lights.

Coming north on the A6 from Rothwell/Kettering: as you reach Desborough, you go downhill into a sharp dip, with a pedestrian crossing. The shop is clearly marked on the left.

Open: Tues–Fri 10–4; Sat 9–1.
Closed: Monday; Bank Holidays. Please phone for Christmas closures.
Cards: No.
Cars: Limited parking in front of shop; unrestricted in side road; small car-park to rear of shop.
Toilets: No.
Wheelchairs: No steps to small shop.
Changing rooms: Yes.
Teas: In Kettering or Market Harborough.
Groups: Small groups welcome. Please book in advance with Mrs Anne Jennings.
Transport: Bus no. 19 from Kettering stops outside shop.
Mail order: No.

10 Desborough Northants

Littlestone & Goodwin

Elgee Works, Victoria Street NN14 2LW
(01536) 760084

Attractive range of ladies' handbags, in both leather and synthetic fabrics.

'Seconds and ends of ranges.'

In the centre of this small village.

From the main road through the village (A6): turn off towards Pipewell & Rushton by the Kings Arms, then take the second left into Victoria Street. Shop is in the first large building on the right through the first door of the factory.

Open: Fri 1.30–5 (including Good Friday) and second Saturday of every month 9–1.
Closed: Last two weeks in Dec.
Cards: None.
Cars: In road outside.
Toilets: Yes.
Wheelchairs: No access as shop on first floor.
Teas: Cafés and pubs in area.
Tours: No.
Transport: Buses from Kettering, then short walk.
Mail order: No.

11 Earl Shilton Leics

The Factory Shoe Company

Hill Top Works LE9 9DT
(01455) 823300 (office)

Ladies' leather fashion court shoes, sandals, fashion boots, ankle boots. Men's all-leather shoes. Leather jodhpur boots for ladies and children.

'Wide range of shoes with leather uppers including high fashion designer ranges and present catalogue shoes.'

This shop is on the A47 at the Leicester end of the village.

From Leicester: the shop is 100 yds on the right after the Thurlaston turn-off (to the left).

From Hinckley: go through Earl Shilton: pass petrol station on left; shop is 100 yds further also on left.

Open: Mon 12–4; Thur, Fri 12–5; Sat 10–1.
Closed: Tuesday & Wednesday; Christmas–New Year.
Cards: No.
Cars: Own car-park, and public car-park across the road.
Toilets: Ask if desperate.
Wheelchairs: No steps.
Teas: In village, and in Hinckley.
Groups: No.
Transport: Leicester–Hinckley buses pass the shop.
Mail order: No.

12 Earls Barton Northants

Barker Shoes

Station Road NN6 0NS
(01604) 810387 (811533 weekends)

Imperfect and discontinued ranges of high quality shoes for men and women. Also narrow (AA) ladies' shoes and larger sizes. Most shoes are made by the company on site.

'Excellent value quality footwear.'

From the A4500 or A45 (both going from Northampton to Wellingborough): go into the centre of Earls Barton. Turn off towards 'Village only' opposite the church: factory entrance is about 100 yds on right. The shop is clearly visible, straight ahead in the factory yard.

Open: Mon–Fri 10–5; Sat, Sun 10–4; some Bank Holidays 10–4 (please phone to check).
Closed: Good Friday, Easter Sunday, Monday & Tuesday; Christmas–New Year.
Cards: Access, Switch, Visa.
Cars: Ample car-park by shop.
Toilets: Yes, but not suitable for wheelchairs.
Wheelchairs: Very easy access to huge, spacious shop – no steps, wide doors and aisles.
Teas: Restaurant, pub and coffee shop on village green.
Tours: Factory tours by arrangement; groups/coaches welcome to shop on weekdays. Be sure to book.
Transport: Local buses from Northampton and Wellingborough; ask for Earls Barton Sq. Short walk to shop.
Mail order: No. Catalogue by request for full price goods only.

13 Enderby near Leicester *see map p. 233*

Creative Carpets

Unit 8, Mill Hill Industrial Estate, Quarry Lane LE9 5AV
(0116) 284 1455 Fax (0116) 275 2550

Quality heavy domestic carpets in 80/20% wool/nylon. Many colours, including plain dyed berbers and heather tweeds.

'A real factory shop; all carpets are made here. Genuine savings of about 50%. Unusual colours. First quality from about £8.75 per sq yd; seconds from £5.85.'

Enderby lies in the triangle south of where the M1 and M69 join. Company is north of village, just off B582 (Blaby–Desford road).

From Leicester go south (Narborough Road, A46): cross outer ring road, take next right (sign to Enderby). In village go right, take third left.*

From M1 exit 21: go towards Leicester; follow signs 'Outer ring road' and 'Narborough/Enderby'. Go towards Narborough; at roundabout with Foxhunter pub on left, go right to Enderby/ Desford. Go over motorway, through village and go left after the Plough into Quarry Lane.*

****Continue to back of estate; company on right.***

Open: Sat 9–3. Weekday visits gladly arranged if you phone.
Closed: Christmas–New Year.
Cards: No.
Cars: Plenty of space outside company.
Toilets: Yes.
Wheelchairs: Easy access via loading bay; large ground floor sales area.
Teas: Local pubs serve food.
Tours: You can see the tufting machines beyond the sales area but no tours as such.
Transport: Midland Fox bus no. 50 from Leicester.
Mail order: No.

14 Hinckley Leics

Richard Roberts

Station Yard, Southfield Road
(01455) 613634

Ladies' knitwear, dresses, skirts, blouses, trousers, T-shirts, men's knitwear.

'A large selection of perfect ladies' and men's knitwear, priced with huge reductions from high street retail prices.'

The railway station is south of Hinckley town centre, clearly marked from most directions, including the town centre.

Coming into Hinckley from Burbage or M69 exit 2 on A5070: go over the railway and shortly turn left into Southfield Road (B5402); keep going to the station on the left.*

From M69 exit 1 and A5 south of town: go along Rugby Road (A447), under the railway and turn right into Hawleys Road (B5402). Station is shortly on right.*

****Drive into the station forecourt; this medium sized shop is clearly visible on left.***

Open: Mon–Fri 10–5; Sat 10–4; May Day Bank Holiday 10–5.
Closed: Other Bank Holidays; Christmas, Boxing and New Year's Days.
Cards: Access, Visa.
Cars: Limited parking in station yard.
Toilets: In station.
Wheelchairs: No step, medium sized shop.
Changing rooms: Yes.
Teas: Coffee bars and cafés in town centre.
Groups: Shopping groups welcome but no factory tours. Please phone Mrs Taylor first.
Transport: Any bus or train to the station. Five minutes' walk from town centre.
Mail order: No.

See our entries below & no. 32

15 Irthlingborough Northants

Dr. Martens

Rushden & Diamonds Football Club, Nene Park,
Station Road NN9 5QF
(01933) 650345 x 2297

A huge range of *Doc Martens* boots and shoes for the entire family (including a large selection for children): most colours, sizes and designs in stock.

'Most items slightly substandard (such as slight scuff). Prices reduced by 30–50% off normal retail prices and all children's footwear £15.99. Probably the only factory shop in Britain located in a football stadium!'

See our display advertisement above

Easy to find on the (new) A6, a few hundred yards north of A45.

From the A45 (major road from Northampton): follow signs north for Irthlingborough. You are on the A6. Then follow signs to Nene Park – a football/leisure stadium clearly visible on the right.

From Kettering coming south on the A6: stay on this road, aiming for the A45 and Rushden. Do not turn off into Irthlingborough. Follow signs into Nene Park (on your left).

Open: Mon–Fri 9–5.30; Sat 9–5; Sun 10–4. Bank Holidays.
Closed: Christmas Day; for Boxing and New Year's Days please phone.
Cards: Connect, Electron, MasterCard, Solo, Switch, Visa.
Cars: Own huge car-park by shop.
Toilets: Yes.
Wheelchairs: Four steps to front entrance (but people in wheelchairs gladly admitted through other door).
Teas: Refreshments available in shop; lots of local pubs.
Groups: Groups of shoppers always welcome – please phone first. Factory is nearby, but no tours.
Transport: United Counties bus stops 1 mile away.
Mail order: Yes.

Kettering Northants

Late Entry

Countrywear

Albany House, Robinson Way, Telford Way Industrial Estate NN16 8PT
(01536) 481558

Tweed, waxed and fleece jackets, waterproofs, footwear, shirts, ties, socks, moleskin trousers, breeks, quilted jackets and waistcoats, hats and caps.

'Complete country clothing outfitters. Perfect goods at factory shop prices; occasional seconds. Waxed jackets from £20, fleece jackets from £15.'

On the north-west side of town centre.

From town centre: follow signs for Rothwell/Market Harborough/ A14. Go under railway, past General Hospital on left. At roundabout, go right into Telford Way.*

From Market Harborough/Rothwell coming east via A14: at roundabout where A43 comes in from left, exit for Kettering town centre. Pass crematorium on left. At roundabout, go left into Telford Way.*

****After ⅛ mile, go right into Robinson Way. Company is in first building on left (green building with factory shop sign on door).***

Open: *Early October to end February*: Mon–Sat 10–5.
Closed: *March–end Sept.* Christmas, Boxing and New Year's Days.
Cards: MasterCard, Visa.
Cars: Own good-sized car-park.
Toilets: Ask if desperate.
Wheelchairs: Unfortunately not, shop is on first floor.
Changing rooms: Yes.
Teas: Caféteria on industrial estate until 2 pm; also in town centre.
Groups: Shopping groups welcome; larger groups please phone in advance.
Transport: Bus from town centre to Kettering General Hospital, then 5 minutes' walk.
Mail order: Yes.
Catalogue: No.

16 Kettering Northants

Ian M Roberts

57–75 St Peters Avenue NN16 0EL
(01536) 518846

Men's good quality suits, sports jackets, overcoats (wool/cashmere), trousers, pure wool blazers, ladies' skirts. Jackets and suit sizes 36"–58"; trousers 30"–48" waist.

Near the cemetery south of the town centre.

Via A6 from the south: pass St Mary's Hospital on right. Go over next traffic lights, then take first right (St Peters Avenue).*

From the north: go through town centre. As you emerge from the one-way system go left after the church into St Peters Avenue.*

From the west (A43 and A6): stay on A6 for Bedford. Go right at traffic lights (George Hotel on left) then left at next lights (swimming pool on left). Take next right, St Peters Avenue.*

****Ignore the 'No Through Road' sign. Shop is behind long wooden fence 200 yds on left; go in 'IN' gate.***

Open: Tues–Fri 12.30–4.30; Sat 10–4.
Closed: Monday; Christmas–New Year. Phone for possible holiday closures.
Cards: Access, Visa.
Cars: Large car-park next to shop.
Toilets: Yes.
Wheelchairs: Very easy access; spacious shop.
Changing rooms: Yes.
Teas: In Kettering.
Groups: Groups welcome to visit shop – please phone to arrange time.
Transport: Short walk from town centre.
Mail order: No.

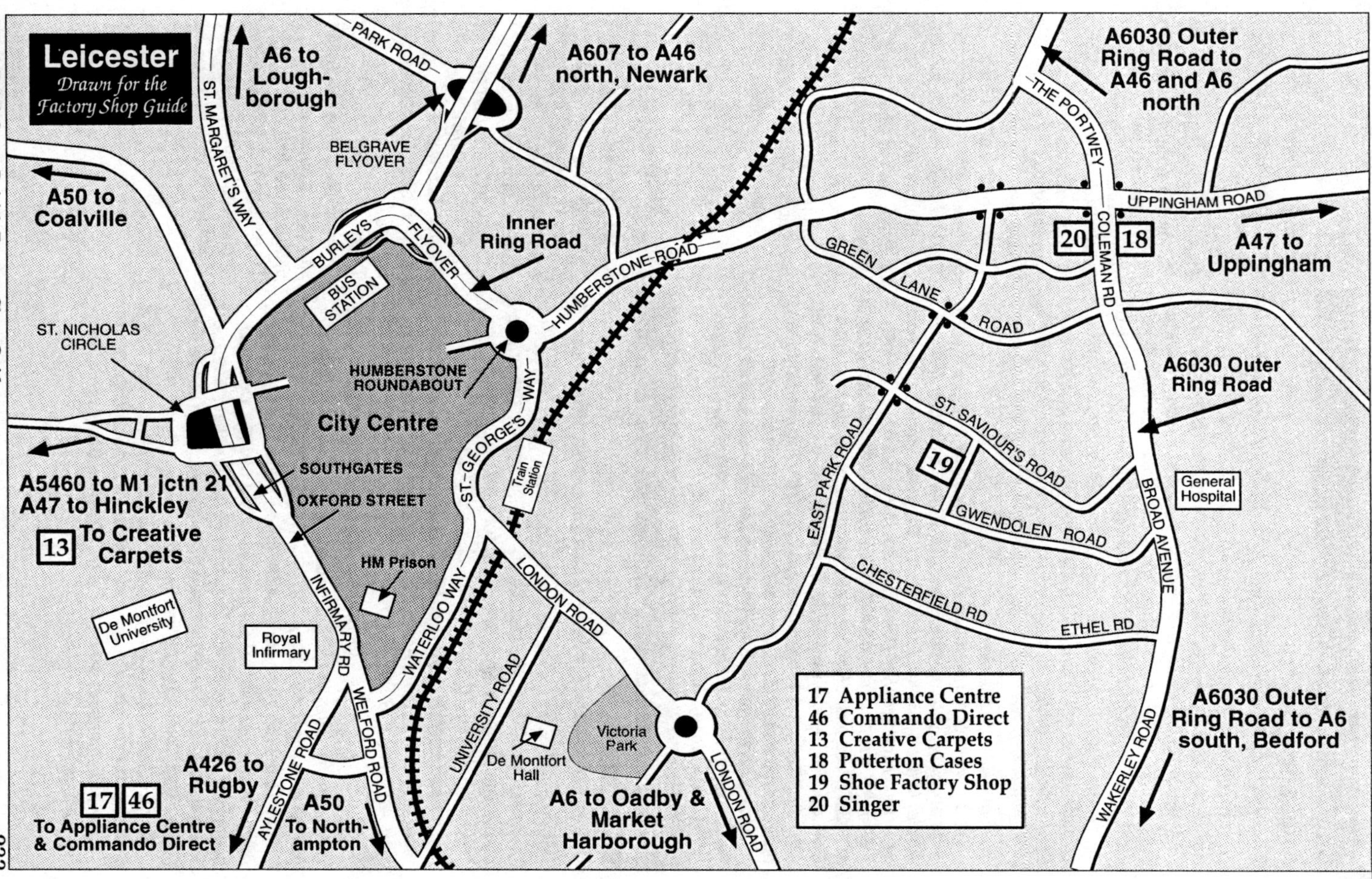
Leicester
Drawn for the Factory Shop Guide
A6 to Loughborough
PARK ROAD
A607 to A46 north, Newark
ST. MARGARET'S WAY
BELGRAVE FLYOVER
A50 to Coalville
BURLEYS
FLYOVER
Inner Ring Road
BUS STATION
ST. NICHOLAS CIRCLE
HUMBERSTONE ROUNDABOUT
City Centre
SOUTHGATES
OXFORD STREET
A5460 to M1 jctn 21
A47 to Hinckley
13 To Creative Carpets
HM Prison
De Montfort University
Royal Infirmary
INFIRMARY RD
WELFORD ROAD
AYLESTONE ROAD
A426 to Rugby
17 46 To Appliance Centre & Commando Direct
A50 To Northampton
HUMBERSTONE ROAD
ST. GEORGE'S WAY
Train Station
WATERLOO WAY
LONDON ROAD
UNIVERSITY ROAD
De Montfort Hall
Victoria Park
A6 to Oadby & Market Harborough
A6030 Outer Ring Road to A46 and A6 north
THE PORTWEY
UPPINGHAM ROAD
20
18
COLEMAN RD
A47 to Uppingham
GREEN LANE ROAD
A6030 Outer Ring Road
ST. SAVIOUR'S ROAD
19
EAST PARK ROAD
GWENDOLEN ROAD
CHESTERFIELD RD
ETHEL RD
BROAD AVENUE
General Hospital
WAKERLEY ROAD
A6030 Outer Ring Road to A6 south, Bedford
17 Appliance Centre
46 Commando Direct
13 Creative Carpets
18 Potterton Cases
19 Shoe Factory Shop
20 Singer

17 Leicester Leics *see map previous page*

Appliance Centre

87 Lothair Road, Aylestone Park LE2 7QE (0116) 244 0150

New perfect & slightly blemished appliances. Cookers, washing machines, dishwashers, fridges, freezers etc (freestanding & built-in). *AEG, Asko, Belling, Bosch, Cannon, Creda, Hotpoint, Leisure, New World, Parkinson-Cowan, Stoves, Tricity-Bendix* etc. Gas & electric cookers reconditioned to 'as new' standard.

'Huge discounts. New perfects/slightly blemished items with full manufacturers' guarantees. On-site reconditioning to high standard with 12 months' parts & labour guarantee (distance limitation on labour). Reconditioned cookers about half new prices.'

On south side of Leicester.

From Leicester: go south on A50; follow signs to A426 Rugby. After one-way system, take Aylestone Road (A426); in front of Toyota, fork left (B5366, Saffron Lane). Opposite sports centre before pedestrian lights, go right (Lothair Road). Shop is 150 yds on left.

From M1 exit 21: take A5460 for Leicester. After 1 mile, go right at lights (Posthouse Hotel on right) into B5418 Braunstone Lane East. Go over canal. At traffic lights go left (A426 Aylestone Road). After 1+ miles, after pedestrian lights, go right (Hughenden Drive), right again then left (Lothair Road). Shop is 50 yds on right.

Coming north from Oadby/Wigston: take B5366 Saffron Lane for Leicester. After 1¼ miles (after leisure centre on right), go left (Lothair Road). Shop is 150 yds on left.

Open: Mon–Fri 7.45–5.45.
Closed: Some Bank Holidays: please phone to check.
Cards: None.
Cars: Own car-park.
Toilets: In Knighton Lane East ⅓ mile from shop.
Wheelchairs: Easy access.
Teas: Two or three cafés within 5 minutes' walk.
Groups: No.
Transport: Bus no. 37 from Charles Street: alight on Aylestone Road at Lothair Road. Bus nos. 26 & 38 from Belvoir Street: alight on Saffron Lane at end of Lothair Road. Walk 200 yds.
Mail order: Yes. Phone for prompt quotation or free brochures. Delivery service. Can arrange installation.

Leicester Leics

Late Entry

Dr. Martens

Bruce Way, Cambridge Road Industrial Estate, Whetstone (0116) 286 5958

Huge range of Doc Martens boots and shoes for the entire family (including a large selection for children): most colours, sizes and designs in stock.

'Most items slightly substandard (such as slight scuff). Prices reduced by 30–50% off normal retail prices and children's footwear from £13.99.'

See our display advertisement on p. 231

Whetstone is south of Leicester. Company is beside (east of) the M1 but no access from here.

From Leicester: go south on A50; follow signs to A426 Rugby. After one-way system, take Aylestone Road (A426). Continue south on A426 (becomes Lutterworth Road) for about 5 miles. Go right off A426 (Blaby By-Pass) at roundabout into Grove Road (signposted Cambridge Rd Ind Est).*

From Lutterworth: go north on A426 for Leicester. Pass Dog & Gun pub. At roundabout on Blaby By-Pass, go left into Grove Road.*

At next roundabout take third exit. At T-junction go left. Shop is ¼ mile on right.

Open: Mon–Fri 9–5.30; Sat 9–5. Bank Holidays.
Closed: Christmas Day and New Year's Day.
Cards: Connect, Electron, MasterCard, Solo, Switch, Visa.
Cars: Own car-park.
Toilets: In town.
Wheelchairs: Easy access; one step.
Teas: In town.
Groups: No factory tours, but shopping groups welcome – please phone first.
Transport: Bus Midland Fox no. 184 stops outside shop.
Mail order: Yes.

18 Leicester Leics see map previous page

Potterton Cases

80 Coleman Road LE5 4LE
(0116) 276 7562

Executive briefcases (ABS, leather and vinyl), art portfolios, clipboards and presenters. Steamer trunks by *Mossman*. Luggage, suit carriers, overnight cases, travel bags by *Delsey, Carlton, Samsonite, Antler, Skyflite* and *Globetrotter*. Also *Potterton* tool cases and computer cases.

'Occasional special sales. Some seconds available. Too many other items to list here! Discounts always given.'

In North Evington, about 1½ miles east of the city centre.

From central Leicester: follow the A47 towards Uppingham. At crossing with A6030 (traffic lights, sign to General Hospital) go right for M1/M69. The clearly marked factory shop is 300 yds on left.

NB. The A6030 is not well marked; it is the outer ring road, not the inner ring road. Get on to the outer ring road from any direction coming into Leicester; keep going round until you find this factory shop, which will be on your left if you are going clockwise.

Open: Mon–Fri 9–5; Sat 9.30–12.30.
Closed: All Bank Holidays.
Cards: Access, Delta, Switch, Visa.
Cars: To sides and front of factory.
Toilets: Yes.
Wheelchairs: No steps to medium sized shop.
Teas: Lots of places in city centre.
Groups: No factory tours, but shopping groups welcome if they phone first.
Transport: Take bus no. 52 Fox Cub for Scraptoft Campus from outside Littlewoods and ask for Coleman Road.
Mail order: Yes.
Catalogue: Free.

19 Leicester Leics see map previous page

The Shoe Factory Shop

Constance Road, North Evington LE5 5EB
(0116) 249 0114

Huge selection (over 5,000 pairs) of ladies', men's and children's shoes at discount prices. Fashion shoes and boots from own factory.

'Rejects (only slightly imperfect), perfects, ends of lines, special purchases. Ladies' shoes from £5, boots from £10; children's from £4; men's shoes from £10.'

About 1½ miles east of the city centre.

From Leicester centre: take the A47 towards Uppingham. At huge Humberstone roundabout stay on A47 then turn right at fourth set of traffic lights into St Barnabas Road (which becomes East Park Road). Turn left at the second traffic lights into St Saviour's Road. Take the seventh right into Gedding Road, then first right into Linden Street and go right into Constance Road. Shop is 50 yds on the left within the factory premises (wide entrance to the car-park).

Open: Mon–Fri 10–5 (Thur 10–6); Sat 9–5. Some Bank Holidays.
Closed: Christmas, Boxing and New Year's Days.
Cards: Access, Visa, Switch.
Cars: Own car-park.
Toilets: No.
Wheelchairs: Small ramp to large, spacious shop on ground floor.
Teas: Plenty of places to eat in city centre.
Tours: No facilities for showing visitors around the factory, but shop always welcomes clubs, groups etc – contact manageress first, mentioning this book.
Transport: Leicester City bus nos. 31 and 33 from outside Woolworths in town centre (Humberstone Gate).
Mail order: No.

Gas in Leicester

The first gasworks in Leicester opened in 1821 in Gas Street, Belgrave (behind Thames Tower), and the first street lights – in Belgrave Gate – were also lit that year. The Leicester Chronicle recorded 'the brilliant display'. But reactions were variable. It was suggested that the use of gas would be 'hurtful to whale fishing *[a very important British industry at that time]* in reducing the consumption of whale oil'. Some critics expressed concern that gas lighting might be detrimental to the health of cattle in the area. In contrast, the penetrating smell from a gas works was thought, however, to help children suffering from whooping cough. 'Great numbers of children labouring under the disease now visit the gasworks to breathe the exhalations from the gas lime. It is said that the little sufferers feel considerably relieved and many are absolutely cured by this simple remedy.'

Gas had first been used to light a house in 1792. But for the next 100 years or so it was used (as naked flames) for little else apart from lighting factories, streets and theatres. People found it hard to imagine that gas could produce hot flames yet not get hot itself. When gas lighting was installed in the House of Commons, MPs touched the pipes with gloves because they expected their hands to get burnt.

The new electric lighting became available in 1884: for about 40 years the two facilities were in competition until electric lighting won the day. For a certain period houses were built with both gas pipes and electric wires so that the house owner could choose which supply to use. The shock of competition spurred the gas companies to start selling cookers – which had been available since 1826 – in earnest. Sales were boosted by the invention of coin-in-the-slot meters in 1890 which enabled people to rent or purchase the machine, as well as pay for the gas.

Leicester houses Britain's first specialist gas museum. It gives you a fascinating insight into the use of gas, especially in the East Midlands. Among the exhibits are a gas radio, a gas hairdryer and curling tongs.

With thanks to Mr Trevor Pickford, curator of The John Doran Gas Museum, Aylestone Road, Leicester. Tues–Fri 12.30–4.30 (closed Tues after Bank Holidays). Groups may visit at other times, please book in advance (0116) 250 3190.

'Leicester Corporation, with its well deserved Radical reputation, now owns the gas, water, electricity and tramways undertakings. Leicester is a large and busy place', wrote Mr Harper at the beginning of this century. 'It numbers 235,000 inhabitants, engaged chiefly in the making of boots, shoes and hosiery. They do things on a business footing here. In the public libraries ... the betting news in newspapers is discouraged. In other towns it is simply blacked out.... here in Leicester it is neatly pasted over with local advertisements – from which the library garners a modest income of between £20 and £30.'

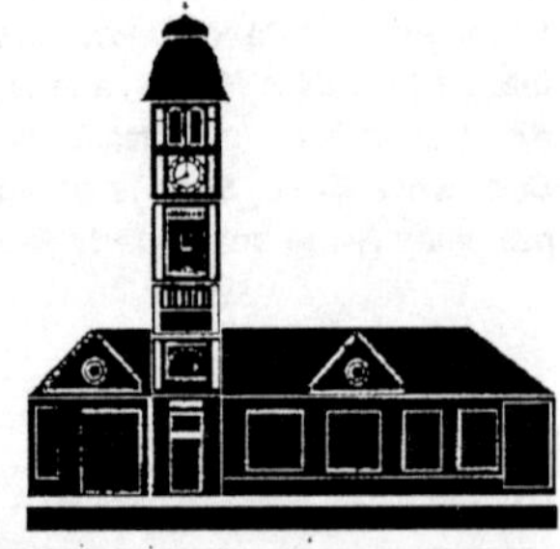

20 Leicester Leics

see map previous page

Singer Factory Services

77 Coleman Road
(0116) 274 2681/276 4969 Fax (0116) 246 0925

New and reconditioned (guaranteed) sewing machines (including industrial machines), presses, domestic overlockers. Spare parts, needles.

'Trade-in allowance. Reconditioned guaranteed sewing machines from £30; new slight imperfects at considerable savings. Delivery in UK £8.50.'

On the north-east side of Leicester.

From central Leicester: follow A47 for Uppingham. At the crossing with A6030 (traffic lights, sign to General Hospital) go right for M1/M69. Shop is shortly on right, just after Gulf petrol.

Via A6030 (outer ring road): you need to go round to where the ring road crosses A47 Uppingham Road, east of the city. Shop is short distance south of these traffic lights, near Gulf petrol.

NB. The A6030 is not well marked; it is the outer ring road, not the inner ring road. Get on to the outer ring road from any direction coming into Leicester; keep going round until you find this factory shop (on your right if you are going clockwise).

Open: Mon–Fri 10-4; Sat 10–2.
Closed: Christmas, Boxing and New Year's Days. Some Bank Holidays, please phone to check.
Cards: Access, Visa.
Cars: Free parking outside warehouse.
Toilets: Yes.
Wheelchairs: Two short flights, wide steps, handrail.
Teas: Local pubs and cafés.
Groups: No.
Transport: Yes. Phone shop to discuss best route.
Mail order: Yes.
Catalogue: No, but spare parts sent.

21 Long Buckby Northants

Regent Belt Co.

85 Station Road NN6 7QB
(01327) 842434

Wide selection of quality leather items: men's and ladies' belts; silk braces with leather attachments; wallets, organisers; travel bags, tie cases, garment bags, holdalls; handbags and shoulder bags; gift items.

'Leather belts at £5. Other items (all ends of lines or slightly substandard) about 30–50% off retail prices for perfect goods.'

On the south edge of this large village.

From A5: follow signs into Long Buckby. Pass railway station on right. Go uphill. Clearly marked factory is on the left, behind phone box. Shop entrance at far end, at side.

From small square in centre of Long Buckby: follow sign for Long Buckby castle. Keep straight. Pass Long Buckby Rugby Football Club on left. Factory is immediately on right. Shop entrance at near end of building.

Open: Thur, Fri 12.30–3.30; Sat 10–2.
Closed: Bank Holidays; Christmas–New Year.
Cards: Mastercard, Visa.
Cars: Car-park at rear.
Toilets: Public toilets in village square; or ask if desperate.
Wheelchairs: Unfortunately not suitable for wheelchairs.
Teas: Local pubs and tea rooms.
Groups: Shopping groups maximum 20 people welcome. No factory tours.
Transport: Train station in village, then ¼ mile walk to shop.
Mail order: No.

22 Long Buckby Northants

Shades

Unit 5, Old Station Yard NN6 7QA
(01327) 844464

Large range of vertical and roller blinds, venetians, wood slatted blinds and Austrian blinds for DIY and commercial applications. Shower curtains and towels.

'Blinds made to order to customers' exact measurements, also some ready-made products and slight seconds; fitting available. Prices about half normal retail.'

On the south edge of this large village.

From A5: follow signs into Long Buckby. Look for railway station on right; Station Yard is across the road.*

From small square in centre of Long Buckby: follow sign for Long Buckby castle. Keep straight. Pass Long Buckby Rugby Football Club on left and continue to station on left; Station Yard is across the road.*

****Shop is at far end of Station Yard on right.***

Open: Mon–Fri 10–5; Sat, Sun and Bank Holidays 10–4.
Closed: Christmas–New Year.
Cards: MasterCard, Switch, Visa.
Cars: Own car-park.
Toilets: Ask if required.
Wheelchairs: Easy access, no steps.
Teas: In village; good pubs in area.
Groups: Shopping groups welcome, no need to phone.
Transport: 50 yds from train station.

23 Loughborough Leics *see map opposite*

Selective Marketplace

Belton Road West LE11 5XL
(01509) 638616

Large selection of ladies' fashions and accessories – including ex-catalogue stock and rails of factory seconds. Sizes 12–24. Gifts such as crockery, cutlery, electrical and household wares.

'Bargain prices. Ladies' fashions from £2 to £50. Special offers, end of season clearance sales. Trade enquiries welcome if you mention this book.'

On a large industrial estate, ¾ of a mile north-west of town.

Lots of one-way streets, so from town aim for A6 north (Derby Road). Go right at traffic lights into Belton Road (B6004) then first left opposite Mercedes garage and beside B&Q to Industrial Estate. Keep going, over canal; company is on left.

Going south on A6 from Derby/Midlands Airport: turn off at large roundabout to Bishop Meadow/Derby Rd Estates.*

From M1 exit 23: take A512 for town. At first roundabout go left on to ring road (Epinal Way); turn off at large roundabout to Bishop Meadow/Derby Road Estates.*

****Take first right (Belton Road West) opposite Do-it-All; shop is ¼ mile on right.***

Open: Tues–Sat 9–4.
Closed: Monday; Bank Holidays.
Cards: Access, Visa.
Cars: Own large car-park beside shop.
Toilets: Please ask.
Wheelchairs: Large, spacious shop. One step to side door. Ramp to double doors at front gladly opened on request.
Changing rooms: Yes.
Teas: In town.
Groups: Coach parties welcome. No need to book but phone call appreciated.
Transport: Service 3 Kinchbus, from Swan Street, Loughborough.
Mail order: Yes.
Catalogue: Free.

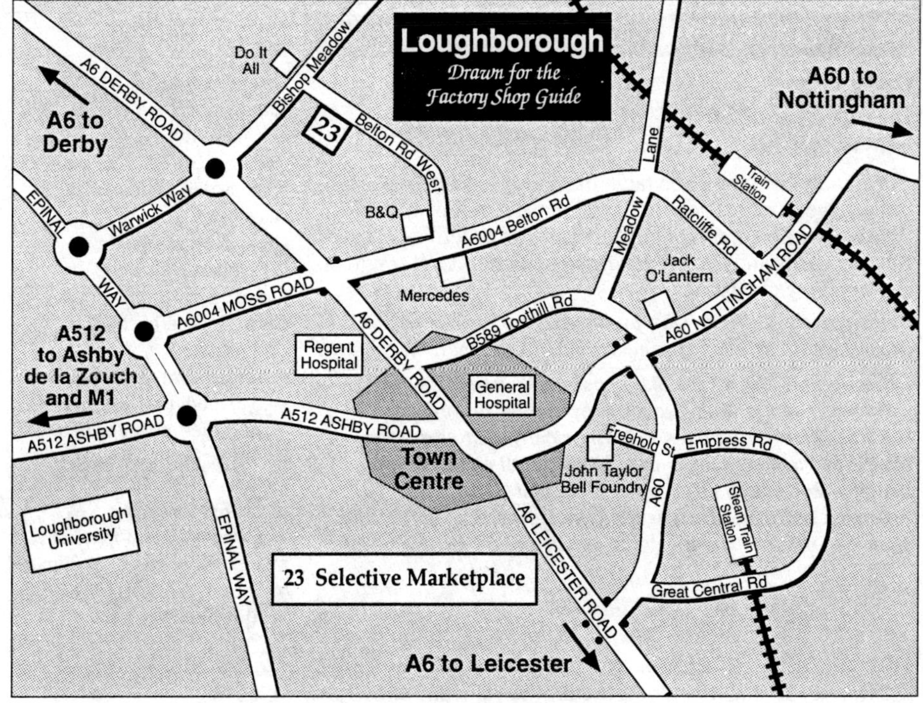

Linger in Loughborough

Among ecclesiologists Loughborough stands for bells. The bell-founding firm of John Taylor & Sons, established here in 1840, is the birthplace of 'many of these instruments of the barbarous practice of bell-ringing that has survived into an otherwise civilised age, and here in 1881 was cast the monster bell of St Paul's cathedral whose hoarse growl – like a bell with bronchitis – is heard daily at one o'clock in the city of London'. So wrote our favourite travel writer, Mr Charles Harper, in 1907. He went on to add, 'Great Paul is the largest bell in England, weighing 17½ tons, and is one of the most useless, being practically little else than the city man's luncheon bell'.

If your opinion on bells contradicts those of Mr Harper, or you are simply curious about bell founding, visit the firm of John Taylor, which still produces bells. Phone (01509) 233414.

Britain's only main line steam train puffs its way out of Loughborough station at weekends, on Bank Holidays, and on summer weekdays. It wends it way down the track eight miles to North Leicester. For 'the ultimate dining experience', book a traditional Sunday lunch or stately dinner served in the first class restaurant cars. The train and railway line have been restored by a large band of enthusiasts: you can see the working signal boxes and the museum at Loughborough. A coach adapted for disabled visitors can be booked. Maybe this stretch of the line will eventually link up again with the newly restored line south of Nottingham (*Nottingham Heritage Centre, Ruddington (0115) 940 5705)*.

Phone (01509) 230726 for timetable, to book meals, and to find out about special events .

25 Lutterworth Leics

Lady Clare

Leicester Road LE17 4HF
(01455) 552101

Top quality hand-finished table mats, trays, wastepaper bins, home accessories. Lacquer-finished or melamine mats. Also sell complementary giftware. *Medici* greetings cards; *Caspari* cards and *Alan Hutchinson* stationery; full range of *Factory Shop Guides.*

'Wide variety of prices. Can produce individual items. No chainstore items. Perfects and seconds (only small blemishes).'

Lutterworth is just off the M1, about a mile north-west of exit 20.

From the centre of this small, busy market town: go north towards Leicester on the A426. The clearly marked shop is almost at the end of town: pass Mobil petrol on right, then continue 250 yds to company also on right.

Coming south into Lutterworth from Leicester on A426: the shop is in the first factory on the left, after LCC garage on left.

Open: Mon–Thur 9–1 & 1.30–4.45; Fri 9–1 & 1.30–3.45; also in March, August, Nov sales: Sat 9.30–1 (These months could alter – phone to check sales dates.)
Closed: Bank Holidays; Christmas–New Year.
Cards: MasterCard, Visa.
Cars: In front of shop.
Toilets: Yes.
Wheelchairs: One shallow step to medium sized shop.
Teas: Cafés and pubs in town.
Groups: Groups welcome to shop if they phone first, but no factory tours.
Transport: Bus stop nearby but not many buses! 10 minutes' walk from centre of town.
Mail order: No.

Entry no. 24 has been deleted as the relevant shop is now closed

Market Harborough : Noseley Leics

Late Entry

Homebirds – The Fabric Trading Company

The Coach House, Noseley Hall LE7 9EH
(0116) 259 6588

Top makes in furnishing fabrics including small top designer names – from fine chintz to upholstery weights, Indian hand-loom checks, stripes and naturals. Complete make-up service, including curtains, cushions, loose covers, re-upholstery etc.

'Fabrics, some seconds and discontinued ranges, at bargain prices – from £3.95 per m. Perfect fabric and wallpaper to order (not discounted) including Osborne & Little, Hill & Knowles, Monkwell, Malabar Cotton Company, Nina Campbell, Liberty, Zoffany, Thomas Dare and Anna French.'

Noseley is a hamlet 9 miles north of Market Harborough.

From Market Harborough: take A6 north. At roundabout, go right on to B6047. Go under railway then up hill. Go straight at cross-roads (left turn goes to West Langton).*

From Leicester: take A6 south. After Kibworth Beauchamp, go left before railway bridge for The Langtons. Pass Langton Hall on left. At cross-roads go left.*

****Continue for 3½ miles, through Church Langton and Tur Langton. At Three Gates, go right for Noseley I mile. Go right through main gates into Noseley Hall. Follow Homebirds signs.***

From A47: go south on B6047 (Melton/Market Harboro' road). After 2 miles go left (past New Inn on right). After 1 mile go right into Noseley Hall. Follow Homebirds signs.

Open: Mon–Sat 9.30–5.
Closed: Bank Holidays; Christmas period.
Cards: Major credit and debit cards.
Cars: Own car-park.
Toilets: Yes.
Wheelchairs: Access limited: cobbled courtyard.
Teas: Local pubs; tea room in Kibworth Beauchamp.
Groups: Happy to accommodate pre-booked groups.
Transport: None.
Mail order: Can be arranged.
Catalogue: No.

26 Market Overton Rutland

Rutland Lighting

Thistleton Road Industrial Estate LE15 7PP
(01572) 767587

Full range of lampshades in many different styles and fabrics; table lamps, standard lamps, chandeliers, pendants; accessories.

'Many items about half retail price. Genuine factory shop with most goods made on the premises.'

Market Overton is between Oakham and the A1, 6 miles north-east of Oakham and 11 miles east of Melton Mowbray.

From Oakham: take B668 to Cottesmore, go left for Market Overton.*

From A1: turn off at Stretton on to B668 for Cottesmore; go right for Market Overton.*

***In the village, turn right at T-junction into Thistleton Road towards Thistleton. Take first left into industrial estate (sign-posted). Company is last building on the estate on right.**

Open: Mon–Sat 9–4.
Closed: Bank Holidays; Christmas–New Year.
Cards: Mastercard, Switch, Visa.
Cars: Own car-park.
Toilets: Yes.
Wheelchairs: One step.
Teas: Good pub in village.
Groups: Welcome to shop; please phone first, mentioning this book. Regret no factory tours.
Transport: None.
Mail order: No.
Catalogue: No.

Fabric Warehouse

27 Melton Mowbray Leics

Beck Mill Factory Shop

Kings Road LE13 1QE
(01664) 501105

Range of designer clothes from: *Feminella, Barry Sherrard, Jeffrey Brownleader, Silken Ladder, Elsie Whiteley, Astraka, Wolsey, Dannimac, Roman Originals, Double Two, James Barry, Lancers, Woodville, Blast, Tom Sayers* and many more. Also many famous chainstore surplus and seconds.

'Come and see our exciting selection of quality brands at up to 70% discount. Perfects and seconds at factory shop prices. Special clearance events on famous high street brands; please phone for details.'

See our display advertisement opposite

A short distance north of town centre off the A607.

From Leicester on A607: cross river, go towards Grantham. You come into Norman Way. Pass Rover garage on left; take second left.*

From Grantham on A607: pass Jet petrol station on left and go right at first traffic lights, then take first right.*

From Nottingham via A606: pass modern Council Offices on right and cattle market on left. At next lights go left for Grantham, Norman Way. Pass Raymond Mays' Rover Garage on left, take the second left.*

****In Kings Road go round S-bend; arched door to shop 50 yds on left.***

Open: Mon–Sat 10–5; Sun 10–4.
Closed: Easter Sunday; Christmas and New Year's Days.
Cards: MasterCard, Visa.
Cars: Own large car-park.
Toilets: Yes.
Wheelchairs: Easy access to large shop.
Changing rooms: Yes.
Teas: Drinks available in shop; cafés in Melton.
Groups: Coach parties and groups welcome to shop any time. Regular open evenings – please phone for details.
Transport: Local buses.
Mail order: No.

28 Moira Derbys

TDP Textiles

TDP House, Rawdon Road DE12 6DF
(01283) 550400

Fashions for ladies, men, teenage boys, girls, younger brothers and sisters, babies; character underwear, night-wear; T-shirts, denim jeans etc.

'The majority of our goods are manufactured under contract for major chainstores and mail order companies. This is a new look factory shop with a children's play area.'

See our display advertisement opposite

Moira is a small village; this shop is on the north side, on the former pottery site.

From the traffic lights at the main crossroad in the centre of Moira (where B5003 crosses B586): take B586 north for Swadlincote. Go under the railway: drive to shop is on the right after 100 yds.

From Swadlincote/Woodville: go south on the B586 towards Moira; go left into factory yard (100 yds before railway bridge).

Entrance to ground floor shop is clearly signed.

Open: Mon–Fri 10–6; Sat, Sun 10–4. Some Bank Holidays – please phone to check.
Closed: Christmas–New Year.
Cards: All major cards except Diners and Amex.
Cars: Own car-park by shop.
Toilets: Yes.
Wheelchairs: Easy access to large ground floor shop.
Changing rooms: Yes.
Teas: Available on premises.
Groups: Shopping groups welcome: please phone first. No factory tours.
Transport: Own transport necessary.
Mail order: No.

BECK MILL

33 Kings Road, Melton Mowbray, Leicestershire

SUPERB TOP LABEL FASHIONS WITH UP TO 70% DISCOUNT

Open 7 days a week

Roman Originals, Blast, Feminella, Astraka, Barry Sherrard, Jeffrey Brownleader, Silken Ladder, Elsie Whitely, Dannimac and many more

☎ 01664 480147

Wolsey, James Barry, Lancers, Woodville, Tom Sayers and many more

Special clearance events on famous high street brands. Phone for dates and details.

OPENING HOURS:
MON–SAT 10–5
SUN 10–4

See our entry opposite

Clothing for all the Family

TDP FACTORY SHOP, MOIRA

Cartoon Character T/shirts, Underwear, Pyjamas, Jeans, Sweatshirts, Dresses, Blouses, Shirts, Trousers, Shorts, Jackets and plenty more changing on a daily basis...

ALL AT RIDICULOUS PRICES !!

Childrens' Play Area & Disabled Facilities
Moira, Swadlincote, Derbyshire Tel:01283 550400

MON-FRI 10am-6pm
SAT-SUN 10am-4pm

See our entry opposite

Finding Shoes to Fit

As we travel the country, we come across specialised manufacturers who offer an excellent service or product but, for one reason or another, do not really fit into our guides. One such recent find is a small company of skilled shoemakers in Leicester who specialise in large high heeled shoes and long thigh boots for men – as worn by pantomime dames. They are happy to supply by mail order.

Readers often ask us where small/large/giant or odd sized shoes can be obtained. Over the years we have come to the conclusion that a shoe shop would find a good niche if it were to specialise, for example, in large sizes.

One typical cry for help from a reader runs: 'We don't know where to go, but we have just come across *The Factory Shop Guide* and hope that you can help us. I take shoes in size 8EE. My 14-year old daughter, who is 6ft 4ins tall, takes the same size but is, of course, looking for much younger styles. We are beginning to despair at having to buy footwear designed and made for men. What can we do?'

People in dire straits – footwise – will be pleased to hear that The British Footwear Association produces a booklet 'Footwear for Special Needs'. Send £2.50 (cheque to BFA) to 5 Portland Place, London W1N 3AA (but please don't contact them about your personal footwear problems).

Shoe-Making

The good news is that Britain still excels in the top end of the market of the footwear industry, and manufacture of high quality hand-made shoes is thriving. The explosion in popularity of 'Doc Martens', which are made in Northamptonshire, has also given great impetus to industry in this area.

Northamptonshire and Leicestershire have been major centres for footwear manufacture for centuries. In recent years, however, the British footwear industry has undergone huge changes and most manufacturing has ceased. Many of the impressive red-brick shoe factories have been pulled down because their sites have become more valuable than the businesses within. Eighty per cent of fashion footwear is now imported – as developing countries make shoes in their own right and British manufacturers transfer production to their own factories abroad. Cheap fashion footwear is almost always cheaper to import.

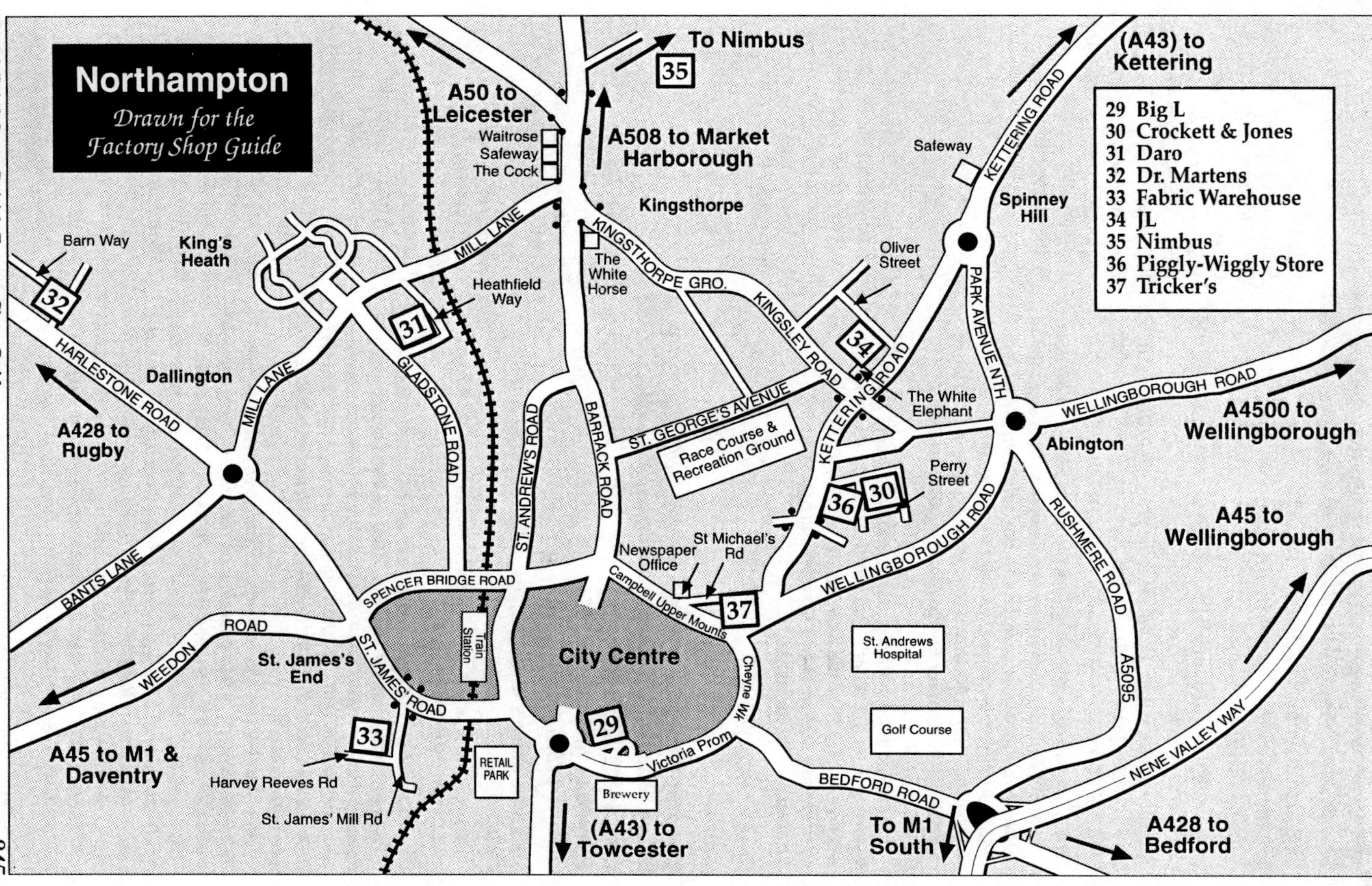

Northampton
Drawn for the Factory Shop Guide
29 Big L
30 Crockett & Jones
31 Daro
32 Dr. Martens
33 Fabric Warehouse
34 JL
35 Nimbus
36 Piggly-Wiggly Store
37 Tricker's
To Nimbus
35
(A43) to Kettering
A50 to Leicester
Waitrose
Safeway
The Cock
A508 to Market Harborough
Kingsthorpe
Safeway
KETTERING ROAD
Spinney Hill
Barn Way
King's Heath
32
MILL LANE
Heathfield Way
31
The White Horse
KINGSTHORPE GRO.
KINGSLEY ROAD
Oliver Street
34
PARK AVENUE NTH
HARLESTONE ROAD
Dallington
GLADSTONE ROAD
ST. ANDREW'S ROAD
BARRACK ROAD
ST. GEORGE'S AVENUE
Race Course & Recreation Ground
KETTERING ROAD
The White Elephant
WELLINGBOROUGH ROAD
A4500 to Wellingborough
A428 to Rugby
Abington
Perry Street
36
30
A45 to Wellingborough
St Michael's Rd
Newspaper Office
BANTS LANE
SPENCER BRIDGE ROAD
Campbell Upper Mounts
37
WELLINGBOROUGH ROAD
RUSHMERE ROAD
ROAD
WEEDON
Train Station
City Centre
St. Andrews Hospital
St. James's End
ST. JAMES' ROAD
Cheyne Wk
A5095
29
Golf Course
33
A45 to M1 & Daventry
RETAIL PARK
Victoria Prom
NENE VALLEY WAY
Harvey Reeves Rd
Brewery
BEDFORD ROAD
St. James' Mill Rd
(A43) to Towcester
To M1 South
A428 to Bedford

29 Northampton Northants *map previous page*

Big L Factory Outlet (Levi's)

Commercial Street NN1 1PK
(01604) 603022

Large range of jeans for all the family; T-shirts, sweatshirts, shirts and jackets.

'Most items slightly substandard with price reductions of about a third. Some perfect ends of lines. Jeans from £27, T-shirts from £10, sweatshirts from £18, jackets from £38.'

Off St Peter's Way roundabout, on the south side of town centre.

From M1 exit 15: go towards Northampton. Take slip road to roundabout, in order to go left on to ring road West [A45 for (A43)]. At next roundabout, go right for town centre (A508). Go downhill and over railway, passing retail park on left. At large roundabout, go right for Bedford A428. Take first left, Commercial Street.*

Coming south from Market Harborough and from town centre: follow signs for M1 South, going anti-clockwise round town. When you turn left at the roundabout, look for Carlsberg brewery on right then take next left, Commercial Street.*

***Shop is 100 yds ahead.**

Open: Mon, Tues 10–6; Wed, Thur, Fri 9.30–6; Sat 9–6. Bank Holidays 11–5.
Closed: Christmas, Boxing and New Year's Days.
Cards: Access, Electron, JCB, Visa.
Cars: Own car-park by shop; also huge public car-park opposite.
Toilets: Town centre.
Wheelchairs: Small ramp; wide doors; large ground floor shop.
Changing rooms: Yes, lots.
Teas: Lots of places in Northampton.
Groups: Shoppers very welcome. Prior phone call appreciated for coach parties.
Transport: Five minutes' walk from town centre.
Mail order: No.

30 Northampton Northants *map previous page*

Crockett & Jones

Perry Street NN1 4HN
(01604) 31515

Top quality men's leather shoes, ladies' walking and casual shoes.

'Factory seconds, ends of lines and samples from renowned quality shoe manufacturers.'

On north-east side of town centre just off A43 (Kettering Road).

From Kettering coming south on A43: go into Northampton. Pass Safeway on right. Keep straight where main road bears left. Go across traffic lights (White Elephant pub near right corner). Pass park on right. Take first left after pedestrian traffic lights into Derby Road.*

From town centre: aim towards Kettering on A43. Once on Kettering Road pass two churches on left then go right opposite post office shortly before pedestrian lights into Derby Road.*

From M1 exit 15: take A45 north. At a large roundabout, take A5095 (second exit) for Abington. At next roundabout, go left (Abington Avenue). Keep straight to T-junction facing park. Go left. Take first left after pedestrian traffic lights into Derby Road.*

***Take next right then second left around church into Perry Street. Factory is 20 yds on left after next crossing. Go in main door.**

Open: Fri 2–5.30; Sat 9.30–1.30.
Closed: For Easter and Christmas closures please phone.
Cards: No.
Cars: In street.
Toilets: Ask if you are desperate!
Wheelchairs: One easy step, assistance gladly given; wide aisles.
Teas: In town.
Groups: Shopping groups welcome, please phone first.
Transport: Buses from town centre to Kettering Road, then 5 minutes' walk.
Mail order: No.

31 Northampton Northants *map previous page*

Daro

Heathfield Way, King's Heath
(01604) 758989

Cane furniture such as upholstered two and three-seater sofas, armchairs, glass topped tables, side tables and stools.

'Most items perfect at about the same price as elsewhere but you have a much wider choice of fabrics (many designs, two grades of quality). Three week upholstery service. Always some seconds, clearouts and perfect samples at about 25% off, and scatter cushions. Delivery anywhere in the UK.'

King's Heath is about a mile north-west of Northampton centre.

From the town centre and ring road: get on to A428 for Rugby.*

From M1 exit 16: aim for Northampton. Go left on to A428 for Rugby.*

****Go right at the roundabout for King's Heath/Kingsthorpe (Waveney Way). At next roundabout, turn right (Gladstone Road), then first left (Heathfield Way): shop is 100 yds on left.***

Coming south on A50 or A508: after traffic lights, pass Waitrose then Asda on right. At Cock Hotel Junction traffic lights, go right (Mill Lane) for Kingsthorpe Village. Go over River Nene then railway. Take first left (Heathfield Way). Company is 300 yds on right.

Open: Mon–Sat 9.30–5.
Closed: Bank Holidays.
Cards: Yes.
Cars: Outside shop.
Toilets: No.
Wheelchairs: One step up, then ramp into large shop.
Teas: In town.
Transport: Buses from town centre stop a few minutes' walk away.
Mail order: No.

32 Northampton Northants *map earlier page*

Dr. Martens

Barn Way NN5 7UW
(01604) 591174

Huge range of *Doc Martens* boots and shoes for the entire family (including a large selection for children): most colours, sizes and designs in stock.

'Most items slightly substandard (such as slight scuff). Prices reduced by 30–50% off normal retail prices and all children's footwear £15.99.'

See our display advertisement on p. 231

North-west of Northampton, off the A428.

Coming south from Rugby on A428 towards Northampton: go through Harlestone. Pass The Rifle Butt on the right, then New Dunston Garage on the right. At traffic lights, go left for the industrial estate into Lodge Way.*

From other directions and M1 exit 16: follow signs for A428 to Rugby, or Lodge Farm (lorry route). Continue north-west through Dallington. After Mobil petrol on left, go right at traffic lights (filter lane) into Lodge Way.*

****Pass East Midlands Electricity on left; by Travis Perkins on right, go left (Barn Way). The clearly marked company is 300 yds on left: shop is at rear of building B.***

Open: Mon–Fri 9–5.30; Sat 9–5; Sun 10–4. Bank Holidays.
Closed: Christmas, Boxing and New Year's Days.
Cards: Connect, Electron, MasterCard, Solo, Switch, Visa.
Cars: In factory yard or street.
Toilets: Yes.
Wheelchairs: One tiny step to medium sized shop.
Teas: Local pubs; and in Northampton.
Groups: Groups of shoppers always welcome – please phone first. No factory tours.
Transport: United Counties bus stops 300 yds away.
Mail order: Yes.

33 Northampton Northants *map earlier page*

The Fabric Warehouse

Harvey Reeves Road, St James Mill Ind. Est. NN5 5JR
(01604) 759312 See display advertisement on p. 195

Huge stock of upholstery and furnishing fabrics: cottons, linens, damasks, velvets etc. Nets, voiles, calico, interlinings, waddings, linings. Haberdashery and fringing. Curtain rails/ poles and accessories. Cushion covers and fillers. Ready-made curtains. Curtain-making service. Any size foam cut to shape.

'Discontinued lines from £2 per metre. Many upholstery fabrics at £7.75. Muslin and voiles from £4 per metre.'

South-west of the town centre, just outside the ring road.

From town: aim for A45 Coventry. Follow signs for St James/ Station/Rugby then M1 north/Coventry.*

From M1 exit 16: go into Northampton. Aim for St James Mill Ind. Est./M1 South. Pass bus garage on right. At second lights, go right (St James Mill Road). Shop is 400 yds on right.

From M1 exit 15: aim for Northampton. Take slip road to roundabout, then go left on to ring road west (A45) for A43. At next roundabout, go right for town centre (A508). Go downhill, over railway, pass retail park on left. At large roundabout, go left for St James Mill Ind. Est./Station/Rugby then M1 north/Coventry.*

****Pass Esso petrol on left then Lex on right. At traffic lights, go left (St James Mill Road). Shop 400 yds on right.***

Open: Mon–Sat 9–5; Sun 10–4. Bank Holidays.
Closed: Easter Sunday; Christmas and Boxing Days.
Cards: Access, Connect, Switch, Visa.
Cars: Own forecourt.
Toilets: Yes.
Wheelchairs: Ramp into huge ground floor shop.
Teas: Own coffee bar.
Groups: No tours. Shopping groups welcome, no need to book.
Transport: Buses nearby
Mail order: No.

34 Northampton Northants *map earlier page*

J L & Co.

Westminster Works, Oliver Street NN2 7JL (01604) 715011

Makers of finest quality 'Goodyear' welted men's leather shoes for *John Lobb*. Brogues, loafers, lace-ups and ankle boots.

'A company owned by Hermès International and sister company to John Lobb, Paris. A wide range of seconds always in stock, at approximately half usual prices, from £175.'

North-east of town centre just off A43 (Kettering Road).

From Kettering coming south on A43: go into Northampton. Pass Safeway on right. Keep straight where main road bears left. Pass shops on right. Go right after Lloyds Bank (Oliver Street). Factory is 40 yds on left.

From town centre (inner ring road): take A43 north for Kettering. Once on Kettering Road, pass the park on left; go straight at lights (White Elephant pub on far left corner). Take first left. Factory is 40 yds on left.

From M1: take exit 15 on to A45 going north. At a large roundabout, take A5095 (second exit) for Abington. At next roundabout, go left (Abington Avenue). Shortly go right, Abington Grove. At traffic lights (White Elephant pub on far right corner) go right then take first left, Oliver Street. Factory is 40 yds on left.

Open: Mon–Fri 9–5; Sat 9–12.30. Some Bank Holidays. A phone call to let shop know the timing of your visit would be helpful.
Closed: Easter weekend; last week in May; last week July; first week Aug; third week Sept; Christmas–New Year.
Cards: Access, Amex, Visa.
Cars: In street.
Toilets: Yes.
Wheelchairs: Lift to third floor.
Teas: In town.
Groups: Shopping groups welcome, prior phone call appreciated.
Transport: Local buses.
Mail order: Yes.
Catalogue: Yes.

35 Northampton Northants *map earlier page*

Nimbus

Lower Farm Road, Moulton Park NN3 6XF
(01604) 646411

Soaps, shampoos, conditioners, toothpaste, hand creams and novelty soaps.

'Nimbus is a Sheltered Workshop for the Blind, and a registered charity. It manufactures quality toiletry items for major UK retailers and overseas customers. All goods are at factory shop prices, and include ends of runs and redundant stocks.'

Moulton Park Industrial Estate is north of Northampton.

Go north from Northampton on A508 towards Market Harborough. In Kingsthorpe pass Safeway on left, go over traffic lights, pass shopping parade then the Frog & Fiddler on left; turn right in front of The Prince of Wales (sign 'Weight limit 7.5 tonnes'). Pass Nene College and at roundabout take third exit.*

Coming south on A508 towards Northampton: pass cemetery on left then go left at traffic lights into Holly Lodge Drive for Nene Campus Kettering. At roundabout take second exit.*

****At next roundabout take first exit (Lower Farm Road): Nimbus is just over ½ mile on left. Shop in portakabin in car-park.***

Open: Mon–Thur 8–2; Fri 8–1.
Closed: Bank Holidays; Christmas–New Year.
Cards: None.
Cars: On site.
Toilets: No.
Wheelchairs: One step to portakabin.
Teas: None locally.
Groups: Tours by appointment.
Transport: None.
Mail order: No.

36 Northampton Northants *map earlier page*

Piggly-Wiggly Shoe Store

178 Kettering Road NN1 4BH
(01604) 32798 (phone & fax)

Unisex leather walking boots and shoes, including a selection of fashion footwear and work boots. A range of backpacking clothing and equipment.

'Ends of lines with huge reductions; also standard stock ranges at discounted prices.'

On the A43 on north-east side of town centre.

Coming south to town centre from Kettering on A43: cross traffic lights (White Elephant Junction) with The White Elephant pub on right; keep straight, passing tennis courts on right. Shop is on left, just before traffic lights.

From other directions: get on to inner ring road, clockwise or anti-clockwise. Go round till you see detached stone Chronicle and Echo office, on your left if going clockwise or right from other direction. At traffic lights by newspaper, turn off for Kettering, Corby (A43)/St Michael's Car Park. At far end of this one-way street, go left. Go over traffic lights at Talbot Road: shop is third on right.

Open: Mon–Tues 10–5; Wed–Sat 9.30–5.30.
Closed: Bank Holidays. Please phone for Easter and Christmas openings.
Cards: Access, Visa.
Cars: Local streets (double yellow lines immediately outside).
Toilets: Ask if desperate!
Wheelchairs: One step into shop; one step inside. Medium sized shop.
Changing rooms: You are welcome to try on footwear.
Teas: Lots of places in town.
Groups: Shopping groups/ walking clubs please phone first if more than five people.
Transport: Bus nos. 3, 7, 11, 45 pass by. 15 minutes' walk from town centre.
Mail order: Phone shop to enquire about mail order.

Northampton (Cogenhoe) Northants

Late Entry

Ravenna Artworks

Manor Works, Church Street, Cogenhoe NN7 1LR
(01604) 891048

Framed prints, from standard sizes to 48" x 48" in interior designer styles. Themed pictures for restaurants, bar receptions, leisure centres, corridors and hotel chain bedrooms or individually mounted and framed photographs (eg of your pet). Complete bespoke framing service. Gallery open to public.

'Nearly all perfects at up to 70% less than retail prices. Some seconds.'

Cogenhoe is a small village 4 miles east of Northampton.

From Northampton: take A45 north-east for Wellingborough. Take slip road for Great Billing; go right, crossing over A45; pass Aquadome on right, go over river then left into Cogenhoe. Go through village. At end of village turn left into Church Street, (opposite The Royal Oak pub on right). Company is a few hundred yards down on right, with sign in driveway.

Open: Mon–Thur 9–5; Fri 9–1. Occasional weekends and Bank Holidays, please phone.
Closed: Christmas until 2nd week January.
Cards: MasterCard, Visa.
Cars: In street, or limited in own car-park.
Toilets: Ask if required.
Wheelchairs: Ramp next to main entrance.
Teas: Local cafés; leisure centre and pubs nearby.
Groups: Shopping groups welcome, but please phone first.
Transport: Unfortunately none.
Mail order: No.

37 Northampton Northants *map earlier page*

Tricker's

50–60 St Michael's Road NN1 3JY
(01604) 30595

Men's high class shoes; brogues, oxfords, heavy walking shoes and boots. Velvet slippers.

'High quality men's shoes. Ends of lines, seconds and perfects. Discount offered on perfect shoes. Shoes made to special measure, in a variety of leathers of your choice.'

A short distance north of the town centre.

From all directions: get on to the inner ring road, clockwise or anti-clockwise. Go round till you see the detached stone Chronicle and Echo office (on left if going clockwise, on right from other direction). At traffic lights by this newspaper, turn off for Kettering, Corby (A43)/St Michael's Car Park. This is St Michaels Road, a one-way street. Factory is 150 yds on right (just past car-park), in a distinctive brown glazed tiled building. Shop (signposted) is through main entrance.

Open: Mon–Fri 9–12 & 2–4.
Closed: Dec 22–Jan 2 and all factory holidays. Please phone to check.
Cards: Amex, Diners, MasterCard, Visa.
Cars: In street outside; also multi-storey car-park (entrance on right, 20 yds before factory).
Toilets: Yes, on premises.
Wheelchairs: One step up to shop.
Teas: In town centre.
Groups: No.
Transport: Bus depot 200 yds away; Northampton train station 1 mile away.
Mail order: Yes.
Catalogue: Free.

38 Oakham Rutland

Corah

Cold Overton Road LE15 6NB
(01572) 757955

Large selection of clothing for all the family.

Easy to find, half a mile west of Oakham centre.

From the centre of Oakham: go west along the main road for Melton Mowbray. Go over the level crossing and take left fork.*

From Melton Mowbray: turn sharp right in front of level crossing.*

****Pass the hospital and school on right: shop is also on right.***

Open: Mon–Sat 9–5.30; Sun & Bank Holidays 10–4.
Closed: Phone to check.
Cards: Access, Amex, Visa.
Cars: Front of factory.
Toilets: In Oakham.
Wheelchairs: Easy access to huge shop.
Changing rooms: Yes.
Teas: Tea rooms, pubs and cafés.
Transport: 10 minutes' walk from Oakham station.

39 Oakham Rutland

Lands' End Direct Merchants

Pillings Road LE15 6NY
(01572) 722553

Quality casual clothing for men, women and children, including trousers, shorts, shirts, ties, belts, accessories, swimwear, tailored items, sweaters, outerwear, dresses and skirts.

'Mainly firsts, with a few items not quite perfect (further reduced). 25–85% off catalogue prices. All products carry famous unconditional guarantee. If not entirely satisfied, customers can return any item at any time for full refund or exchange.'

On west side of the town centre.

From the town centre: go west along the main street, over the level-crossing towards Melton Mowbray on A606. By Rutland Sixth Form College on right, go right into Pillings Road.*

From Melton Mowbray/west on A606: as you reach town turn left into Pillings Road after Rutland Sixth Form College on left.*

****Drive to shop and car-park clearly marked, shortly on right.***

Open: Mon–Sat 10–6; Sun, Bank Holidays 10–4.
Closed: Christmas Day.
Cards: Access, Amex, Connect, Delta, Switch, Visa.
Cars: Ample free parking on site.
Toilets: Yes.
Wheelchairs: Access ramp to big shop.
Changing rooms: Yes.
Teas: Wide selection of cafés, pubs and restaurants in town.
Tours: Welcome. For tours, please phone PR Department.
Transport: Oakham station 1/3 mile (on Leicester–Peterborough main line).
Mail order: Yes.
Catalogue: Free. Phone 0800 220 106. Monthly catalogue features quality casual wear for all the family.

Thomas Cook

A baptist preacher who spent his adult life in Leicester, one Thomas Cook, was the first person in the world to realise the potential that the new-fangled railways offered in the way of excursions and holidays.

For a fascinating account of the history of Leicester, see 'Discovering Leicester' by John Banner.

His future enterprise came to mind while he was walking from Market Harborough to Leicester to attend a temperance meeting. Why not hire a train to take supporters to the next rally in Loughborough? So, in July 1841, he hired a train with refreshments and entertainment from two brass bands. The fame of his expedition had spread: in addition to the 570 people who travelled (standing up) with 1/- return tickets, as many as 3000 spectators turned out to witness the extraordinary sight.

Within ten years, Thomas Cook was organising train trips on a grand scale. His company transported 165,000 visitors to the Great Exhibition in Hyde Park, London.

At this time, it was becoming perceived wisdom that sea water was beneficial to health, so Thomas carried families to the seaside, as well as to spas around Britain. Then came the international exhibition in Paris along with a demand for organised train travel to get there. One of Thomas's most important breakthroughs was obtaining a monopoly in Nile passenger traffic after the Suez Canal had opened in 1869; he set up his own fleet of Nile steamers which were built in Scotland and shipped out in component parts for assembly in Egypt. The wars in Africa proved a great bonus. Mr Cook was paid £600,000 to supply 650 sailing boats and 50 river steamers to transport 18,000 soldiers and 100,000 tons of supplies up the Nile from Alexandria to Khartoum, where General Gordon was under siege. (Unfortunately the army arrived too late to save the General.)

Thomas Cook was a philanthropist. At one stage he organised soup kitchens and gave away bread. He went blind (his son took over) and died in 1892 at the age of 84. He is buried in Welford Road cemetery.

His company went from strength to strength, and became a household name. He would probably be surprised to learn that it is now German-owned.

The Annie Elizabeth Cook Memorial Hall, built in Archdeacon Lane in 1882 and demolished in 1970 to make way for the St Matthews Way flyover.

See our entry below

40 Oakham Rutland

The Table Place

74 Station Road LE15 6QV
(01572) 722166

Extensive selection of Regency reproduction furniture in mahogany, yew and walnut for dining, sitting and bedrooms. Specialists in Tudor/Jacobean reproduction furniture in oak. Desk chairs, desk lamps, chaises longues, pictures and mirrors etc.

'Showcase for a dedicated company of cabinet makers and french polishers from the heart of Rutland. The quality has to be seen and touched to be appreciated. Individual design commissions welcome. Also colour match to own furniture. Some items not up to high standard sold as seconds. Other showrooms at Fenstanton, Cambs and Kenilworth, Warks.'

See our display advertisement above

This shop is close to the railway station.

Turn off the main road (A606) through Oakham at the level crossing (on the town side) signposted 'Cottesmore, Grantham'. Pass the station on left, follow the road round sharp right bend; clearly marked showroom is about 200 yds along road on right.

Open: Mon–Fri 10–5; Sat 10–4; Sun 11–4.
Closed: Few days over Christmas (phone to check); Bank Holidays.
Cards: Access, Delta, Switch, Visa.
Cars: In forecourt and Station Road.
Toilets: Yes.
Wheelchairs: Access to ground floor but unfortunately not to showroom upstairs.
Teas: Self-service coffee and tea at weekends, or by request. Tea shops, cafés and pubs in Oakham.
Transport: Two minutes from Oakham station and a few minutes' walk from town centre.
Mail order: Yes.
Catalogue: Free relevant photocopy pages available.

Market days

Ashby-de-la-Zouch	Tues, Fri, Sat indoor general retail Mon antiques
Brackley	Fri outdoor general
Beaumont Leys	Wed to Sat outdoor general retail
Bedford	Wed, Sat outdoor general retail
Biggleswade	Sat outdoor general retail
Coalville	Tues, Fri, Sat indoor general retail
Corby	Wed, Fri, Sat outdoor general retail Mon bric-a-brac; Thur antique & bric-a-brac
Dunstable	Wed, Fri, Sat outdoor general retail
Daventry	Tues, Fri outdoor general retail
Hinckley	Mon, Tues, Wed, Fri, Sat indoor general retail Fri bric-a-brac
Flitwick	Fri outdoor general retail
Kettering	Tues, Fri, Sat outdoor general retail Wed antique & crafts
Leicester	Mon to Sat outdoor general retail Tues to Sat indoor general retail
Leighton Buzzard	Tues, Sat outdoor general retail
Loughborough	Thur, Sat outdoor general Fri indoor bric-a-brac, second hand & collectors
Luton	Mon to Sat indoor general retail Thur, Sat outdoor general retail at Purley Centre
Lutterworth	Thur outdoor general retail
Market Bosworth	Wed outdoor general retail
Market Harborough	Tues, Fri, Sat indoor general retail
Measham	Tues outdoor general retail
Melton Mowbray	Tues indoor general retail Wed craft market
Northampton	Tues to Sat outdoor general Thur crafts & bric-a-brac
Oakham	Wed, Sat outdoor general
Oundle	Thur outdoor general
Rothwell	Mon outdoor general
Rushden	Sat outdoor general
Sandy	Fri outdoor general
Shepshed	Fri outdoor general
Tamworth	Tues, Sat outdoor general
Towcester	Fri outdoor general
Uppingham	Fri outdoor general
Wellingborough	Wed, Fri, Sat outdoor general Tues outdoor antiques & bric-a-brac

Information kindly supplied by World's Fair publication (in their useful Markets Year Book)

See our entry below

41 Rothwell Northants

T Groocock & Co.

Gordon Street NN14 6EH
(01536) 714115

High quality men's and ladies' leather shoes. Comfortable and stylish leisure/walking shoes. Ladies sizes 3–9, men's sizes 6–14 including wide fittings.

'All made in our own factory established in 1914. Some discontinued lines and slightly imperfects at greatly reduced prices.'

See our display advertisement above

At the southern end of town.

***Coming south on A6 from Desborough/Market Harborough:** weave through Rothwell until you see the right turn-off to Lamport Hall (but don't turn off); after 150 yds downhill, take first left (Gordon Street).**

***From Kettering:** take A14 west. At exit 4, go north on to A6 for Rothwell. Go uphill for 150 yds and take second right (Gordon Street).**

***Coming east on A14:** at exit 3, turn left for Rothwell then follow road to A6. Go right on to A6. After 150 yds downhill, take first left (Gordon Street).**

****Shop is immediately on the left, clearly marked.***

Open: Mon–Fri 10–5; Sat 9–1.
Closed: Bank Holidays; Christmas–New Year.
Cards: Access, Switch, Visa.
Cars: Outside shop.
Toilets: No.
Wheelchairs: Four steps but wide doors.
Teas: In town.
Groups: Welcome to shop – not necessary to book.
Transport: Buses from Kettering stop on the A6 near the shop.
Mail order: No.

Totectors Trade Shop

Crown Way NN10 6AX
(01933) 410888

Safety footwear and clothing such as overalls, outdoor work clothing, padded jackets, safety gloves etc. Safety shoes and boots for men and women. Wellingtons.

'First quality goods and some seconds at significantly reduced prices. Reject footwear: boots £15, shoes £12, ladies' shoes and occupational footwear £6.50. Always special offers.'

On a new business park north of Rushden, just off the A45.

From A45 going east (from Northampton direction): at roundabout where Lakeside Motel is marked on left, go right round (pass Higham Ferrers turn-off) and exit for Rushden A5001.*

Via the A45 (from Peterborough direction): at roundabout, turn off for Rushden A5001.*

From Rushden on A6 going north: between Rushden and Higham Ferrers, go left (no sign but 100 yds before The Old Swan) into Northampton Road. At far end, go left for superstore.*

****Pass Safeway on right. Totectors are beyond Great Mills on left. Drive to the far end of the building.***

Open: Mon–Thur 9–5; Fri 9–4; Sat 9–12.
Closed: Bank Holidays. Christmas–New Year.
Cards: Access; Visa.
Cars: In company grounds, by shop.
Toilets: In superstore.
Wheelchairs: No steps, medium sized ground floor shop.
Changing rooms: No.
Teas: In town.
Groups: Not really suitable.
Transport: Unfortunately none.
Mail order: Yes.
Catalogue: Free. You can order any item from the catalogue, but no seconds sent.

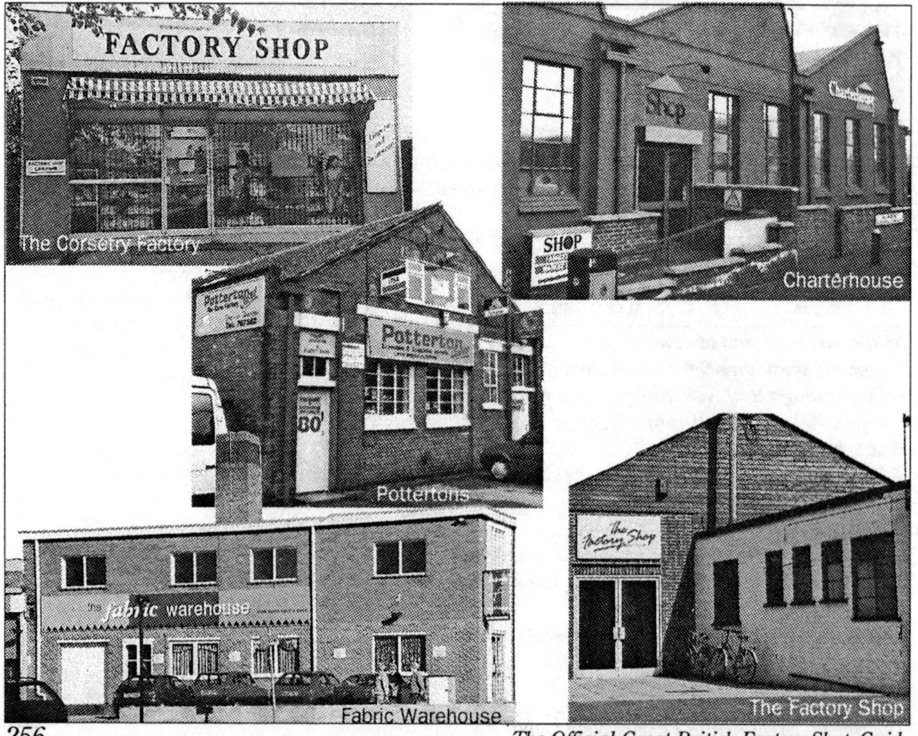

The Corsetry Factory
Charterhouse
Pottertons
Fabric Warehouse
The Factory Shop

See our entry below

43 Shepshed Leics

Charterhouse Holdings

173 Charnwood Road LE12 9NN
(01509) 505050

Huge range of quality family clothing, sportswear, accessories and 'market place' (toiletries, books, towels etc). Many branded and licensed products including footwear.

'Probably the finest manufacturing retail outlet in UK. Free kids' cartoon theatre. Fully equipped playroom. Bottle bank. Public phones. No-quibble exchange/refund guarantee.'

See our display advertisement above

From Loughborough and M1 exit 23: take A512 to Ashby-de-la-Zouch. Go right at second traffic lights (B588 to Hathern).*

From Ashby via A512: go left at first traffic lights (sign to Hathern).*

****Follow road downhill to clearly marked shop on left.***

From Hathern: pass The Crown then The Red Lion on left; go left for Loughborough, Coalville, Cropston. At mini-roundabout (Bull Ring) with NatWest on left and Halifax on right: take Charnwood Road (B588 to Coalville/Ashby). Go uphill to conspicuous company on right.

Open: Tues, Wed 10–5.30; Thur, Fri 10–8; Sat and Bank Holidays 10–5.30; Sun 11–5.
Closed: Monday; Easter Sunday; Christmas & Boxing Days.
Cards: Access, Switch, Visa.
Cars: Large car-park across road. 'Dog park' by shop!
Toilets: Yes, including mother and baby room.
Wheelchairs: Easy access to huge shop. Parking for disabled by shop.
Changing rooms: Yes – extensive and private.
Teas: Own Corner Café in store.
Groups: Coach parties particularly welcome & well catered for. Please book in advance with shop manager on 01509 505050, ext. 340, mentioning this guide.
Transport: Buses from Loughborough and Coalville stop outside.
Mail order: No.

44 Shepshed Leics

Low Woods Furnishings

Low Woods Lane, Belton LE12 9TP *(01530) 222246*

50,000 metres of designer fabrics suitable for curtains and upholstery always in stock. Curtains, blinds and other soft furnishings made in own workrooms.

'Extensive range of quality fabrics mostly off-shade seconds, discontinued lines etc. Fabrics from £2.95–£14 per metre. Most £7.40 per metre. Friendly staff always available to help with measurements or colour schemes. Huge sale twice a year. Children's play area.'

See our display advertisement opposite

Low Woods is a small hamlet north of the A512 and west of M1.

From M1 exit 23: aim west for Ashby on A512. After 4 miles, pass Crossways Garage on right; after 300 yds go right for Low Woods ½ mile.*

From Ashby on A512: pass Grace Dieu Manor School on right; after ⅓ mile, go left for Low Woods.*

****Half a mile down this country lane, go right to shop in first building on right.***

From A6 at Hathern: take B5324 to Belton (4 m). From Belton sign "Please go carefully through our village" stay on B5324. Go straight at two crossroads; at third crossroad (Belton Baptist Church far right corner), go left in front of cottage (far left corner) into Gracedieu Lane. After 200 yds take first left, Low Woods Lane. Shop is ¾ mile along lane in second building on left.

Open: Tues–Sat 9–5.30; Sun 9–1.
Closed: Monday; Christmas and New Year's Days; some Bank Holidays, please phone to check.
Cards: All major credit and debit cards.
Cars: Large car-park next to showroom.
Toilets: Yes.
Wheelchairs: Easy access.
Teas: Local pub serves refreshments all day.
Groups: Welcome everybody! Coach parties with prior phone call please.
Transport: None.
Mail order: No.

45 Sileby Leics

The Factory Shop Ltd.

Newbold Premises, Brook Street LE12 7RE
(01509) 813514

Shoes, bags, toiletries, pottery, silk flowers, pictures, melamine and luggage. Also sell family clothing and a wide range of flight and sports bags.

'Large stock of chainstore items, all at greatly reduced prices. Deliveries of new stock every week to give an ever changing selection.'

If you go down the High Street (B5328): turn left before river into Brook Street (B674). Go under railway arch. Turn left into the main factory gate. Continue for 100 yds to the shop.

Coming into Sileby on B674 from A46 (Fosse Way) or Seagrave: go right into shop car-park just before railway arch.

Coming into Sileby on B5328 from south (Cossington/Rothley direction): pass the thatched Free Trade Inn on right, cross over river, turn right into Brook Street for Seagrave (B674). Go under railway arch; shop on left.

Open: Mon–Sat 9–5.
Closed: Bank Holidays; Christmas, Boxing and New Year's Days.
Cards: Access, Switch, Visa.
Cars: Own free car-park.
Toilets: No. Nearest in village.
Wheelchairs: Easy access to huge shop.
Changing rooms: Yes.
Teas: Tea shop and café in Sileby High Street.
Groups: Shopping groups welcome. For organiser/driver incentives please phone.
Transport: Frequent buses from Leicester and Loughborough.
Mail order: No.

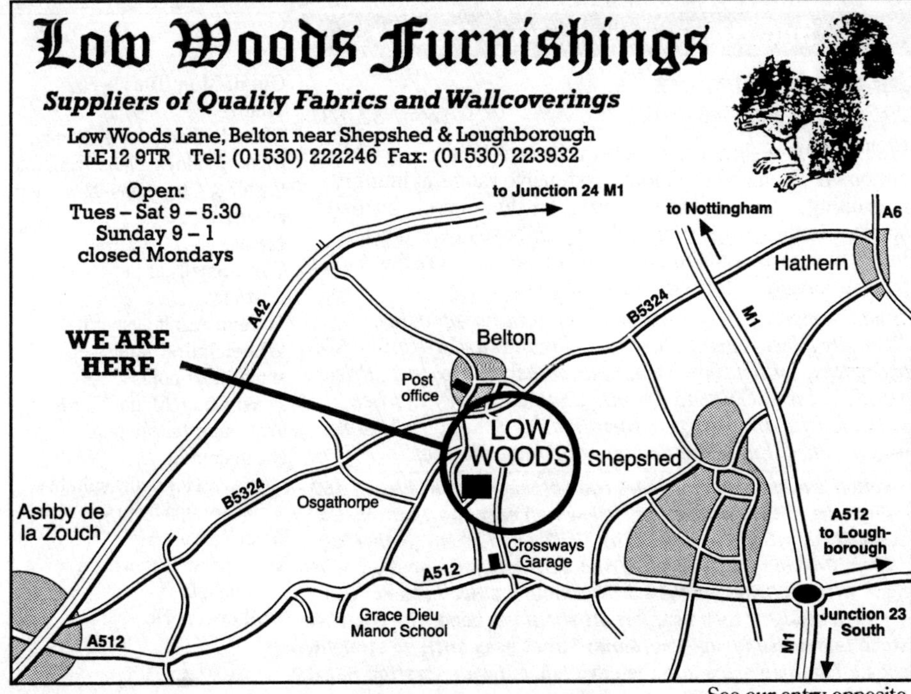

See our entry opposite

46 South Wigston Leics *see map p.233*

Commando Direct

Countesthorpe Road LE8 4PJ
(0116) 278 5288

Men's and ladies' 100% pure wool sweaters made here in traditional designs: Aran, Swaledale and Essex styles (real suede patches many with embroidered motif). 100% wool police jumpers (polycotton patches). Children's jumpers; underwear, men's cushion sole warm socks; men's, ladies' & children's 100% wool gloves; lingerie; hats, walking socks.

'Lots of items for sale are chainstore seconds.'

About 4 miles south of Leicester city centre.

From Leicester on B5366 (Saffron Lane/Road): turn left at far end at mini-roundabout on to A5096 (Blaby Road), then right (Countesthorpe Road).

From Blaby: take A5096 for Oadby; go over mini-roundabout (Esso station and church on corners). Take next right into Countesthorpe Road (bike shop on corner).*

From Wigston Magna & Oadby on A5096: go over railway bridge, through shopping area of South Wigston (across two pedestrian lights) then turn left round bike shop into Countesthorpe Road.*

****Shop 80 yds on left.***

Open: *Sept–Easter:* Fri and Sat 9–4. Please phone any time to check.
Closed: Christmas–New Year period: please phone.
Cards: MasterCard, Switch, Visa, but Fridays only.
Cars: Free large car-park opposite.
Toilets: Yes.
Wheelchairs: Ring first to arrange access through factory.
Changing rooms: Yes.
Teas: Two cafés nearby.
Groups: Shopping groups welcome if they phone first.
Transport: Good bus service from Leicester. Railway station in S Wigston.
Mail order: Yes.
Catalogue: Free on request.

47 Spratton near Northampton Northants

Jane Sale Interiors

29 Smith Street NN6 8HW *(01604) 821831*

Well known designer name curtain fabrics, chintz, printed cottons & linens by the metre. Extensive range of linings, interlinings, heading tapes & other curtain making accessories. Smaller range of upholstery & loose cover fabrics. Individual curtain making and design service. Tracks & poles to order. Fitting can be arranged.

'Small company offering personal service and top value. Carefully selected perfect fabrics & discontinued designs, overstocks, ends of lines, remnants, occasional seconds. Prices greatly reduced (£5–£15 per m). Can also order full price stock (fabrics, trimmings & co-ordinating wallpapers) from huge range of European designer and major brands.'

Spratton is a small village 6 miles north of Northampton, just off A50.

From the A50: at cross-roads, follow sign east into Spratton. Go downhill into village. In front of The King's Head go left (Manor Rd).*

From Brixworth: as you come into Spratton, pass post office on right. After 100 yds, go right after The King's Head (Manor Rd).*

****Keep straight, then bear left. At sharp left bend with thatched stone farmhouse facing you (Smith Street goes left): go straight ahead, following signs into the drive (shared with Spratton Hall School). Shop door is 50 yds on left.***

Open: Mon, Tues 9–8; Thur 9–5.
Closed: Wednesday, Friday; Bank Holidays. Please ring for Easter & Christmas/New Year closures.
Cards: No.
Cars: Small car-park and driveway.
Toilets: Ask if desperate.
Wheelchairs: Four steps, small showroom.
Teas: Coton Manor Gardens; local pubs; tea shop in Northampton.
Groups: Not really suitable (small groups by prior arrangement).
Transport: Buses from Northampton
Mail order: No.

48 Swadlincote Derbys

Webb Ivory

Unit 9, The Rink Shopping Centre DE11 8JL
(01283) 226700

Fascinating variety of surplus catalogue stocks of greetings cards, wrapping papers, household goods, toys and small gifts.

'50% off catalogue prices.'

Situated in town centre pedestrian area 2 minutes' walk from shops and market hall.

Open: Mon–Sat 9.30–5 (Wed 9.30–1). Some Bank Holidays, please check.
Closed: Christmas–New Year.
Cards: Most major credit cards; Switch.
Cars: Free public car-park.
Toilets: No, nearest 3 minutes' walk.
Wheelchairs: Easy access, no steps.
Teas: In Swadlincote.
Groups: No.
Transport: Two minutes' walk from central bus station.
Mail order: No.

49 Tamworth Staffs

Jaeger Sale Shop

43 Church Street B79 7DF
(01827) 52828

Jaeger ladies' and men's wear including ladies' jackets, skirts and blouses; men's suits, jackets, trousers, shirts, ties and socks etc. Ladies' and men's knitwear. *Viyella* ladies' wear including jackets, skirts and blouses, etc.

'High quality merchandise at greatly reduced prices.'

Easy to find in the pedestrianised area of the town centre facing the large church. This huge shop is on a corner site.

Open: Mon–Sat 9.30–5.30.
Closed: Bank Holidays; Christmas and New Year.
Cards: Amex, Access, Visa, Switch & Jaeger Accounts.
Cars: Car-parks nearby.
Toilets: In town.
Wheelchairs: Yes, no steps.
Changing rooms: Yes.
Teas: In town.
Groups: Bus parties welcome by prior arrangement.
Transport: Tamworth rail station ½ mile. Shop is near bus station.
Mail order: No.

50 Tamworth Staffs

Probus Housewares

Watling Street
(01827) 288588

Kitchen tools and icing equipment; co-ordinated kitchen textiles and tinware including oven gloves, tea towels, aprons, tablecloths, bread bins, pedal bins, canisters and biscuit barrels.

'New shop attached to modern factory of company established in 1911 which moves with the times, selling firsts, seconds and ends of lines at reduced prices. Please phone for annual sale dates.'

On the south side of the town centre.

From Brownhills: go east on A5. After Hints village take A453 left, signposted Sutton Coldfield. Follow signs to Sutton Coldfield, going over A5. At traffic lights (Mile Oak pub far left corner) turn left. At next traffic lights go straight; pass Jet petrol on left; go over bridge. Turn right into factory opposite Reliant.

From M42 exit 10: take B5404 west, signposted Drayton Manor; follow signs for Drayton Manor. After 2 miles go over Two Gates traffic lights (The Bull's Head on right corner). Probus is first entrance on left, opposite Reliant.

Open: Thur, Fri, Sat & Sun 10–4; Easter Monday.
Closed: Monday, Tuesday, Wednesday; Christmas–New Year phone for opening times.
Cards: None.
Cars: Own car-park.
Toilets: Yes.
Wheelchairs: Easy access.
Teas: Cafés and pubs nearby.
Groups: Shopping groups welcome; please telephone first.
Transport: Unfortunately none.
Mail order: No.

51 Tamworth Staffs

Webb Ivory

6 Market Street B79 7LV
(01827) 60266

Fascinating variety of surplus catalogue stocks of greetings cards, wrapping papers, household goods, toys, small gifts and clothing.

'50% off catalogue prices.'

In the town centre, easy to find in the pedestrianised shopping area close to Wilkinsons hardware stores and Tamworth Castle. A few yards downhill on the right from the statue of Robert Peel.

Open: Mon–Sat 9–5. Some Bank Holidays, please check.
Closed: Christmas–New Year.
Cards: Most major credit cards; Switch.
Cars: Public car-parks nearby.
Toilets: No; in town centre.
Wheelchairs: Easy access, no steps.
Changing rooms: No.
Teas: In town centre.
Groups: Too small for groups.
Transport: Bus terminal two minutes' walk.
Mail order: No.
Catalogue: No.

52 Uppingham Rutland

Uppingham Yarns

North Street East LE15 9QL
(01572) 823747

Cash & carry warehouse for most industrial machine and handknitting yarns, from silks etc to cottons and acrylics. Machine accessories and buttons.

'Low competitive costs as yarn is contracted direct from industry. Sweaters etc from £5.99. Discounts given for trade, colleges and clubs.'

A large white painted warehouse on the north side of town centre; it is on the main road east of the only traffic lights in town, and adjoins the major town car-park.

From town centre: aim for Oakham; turn right at traffic lights into North Street East. Warehouse is shortly on right.

Coming south from Oakham on A6003: go towards town centre then turn left at traffic lights. Warehouse is shortly on right.

From M1 and places west: best to take A14 to Kettering then go north on A6003. Go into town. Go right at traffic lights into North Street East.

From A1 or Leicester via A47: at the major roundabout north of Oakham, go towards the town centre; at traffic lights, turn left.

Open: Mon–Sat 9–5; Sun and Bank Holidays 10–4.
Closed: Christmas and Boxing Days.
Cards: Visa, MasterCard, Switch.
Cars: Own free parking front & back; adjacent town car-park.
Toilets: Yes.
Wheelchairs: Easy access to ground floor (for handknitting & 4-plys). Huge shop (8,000 sq ft).
Teas: Free tea/coffee on request. Pub lunches locally; also coffee shops in town.
Groups: Specialise in coach visits; welcome in or outside shop hours by arrangement. Discounts given.
Transport: Leicester–Peterborough and Nottingham–Uppingham buses.
Mail order: Yes.
Catalogue: Free to callers; for mail order send SAE. Will try to match any yarn submitted.

53 Whitwick Leics

The Corsetry Factory

North Street LE67 5HD
(01530) 837647

Top quality designer lingerie: bras, bodies, briefs and basques; swimwear; knitted underwear; nightwear.

'Most items are perfect at around 50% off recommended retail prices. Also a few seconds: bras from £3, swimwear from £5. Gift vouchers available.'

Whitwick is just north of the A50, near Coalville.

From M1 exit 22: take the A50 for Coalville. At first roundabout turn right towards Copt Oak. Keep going to double traffic lights and turn left on to the B587 to Whitwick. Continue on the main road through the town past the church (set back on the right). The factory is a red brick building on the right hand side as you begin to come out of the town. Drive into the factory grounds.

Open: Tues, Thur, Fri 10–4; Sat 9–1.
Closed: Monday; Wednesday. For Bank Holidays and factory shutdowns, please phone.
Cards: No.
Cars: Adequate parking in factory grounds.
Toilets: No.
Wheelchairs: No steps to small shop.
Changing rooms: Yes.
Teas: In Whitwick.
Groups: Small groups welcome. Please book in advance with Mrs Sue Healy.
Transport: Bus no. 15 from Coalville every half an hour.
Mail order: No.

54 Wigston Leics

BTM Fabrics

Unit 2, St George's House, Moat Street LE18 2NH
(0116) 281 2383

Now closed

Wide range of knitted fleece fabrics in over 30 different colours; also limited stock of stripes and prints. Ideal for leisurewear, pyjamas etc. Also ribbed collars, cuffs and welts in same wide colour range.

'Plain fleece from £2.64 per metre; stripes and printed slightly less.'

On the south side of Wigston, just off the A50.

Coming south from Leicester on A50: at traffic lights (Texaco on right), turn right for S Wigston/Blaby.*

From Northampton on A50: at traffic lights, turn left for S Wigston/Blaby.*

****After 300 yds look for long, low brick factory on left. Entrance to yard at far end; go through to back left.***

From South Wigston on B582: aim for Wigston. Pass The Plough on left, go over mini-roundabout (large stone church on right).**

From Wigston centre: aim for South Wigston (B582). At mini-roundabout (stone church facing), go left.**

*****Pass the Old Crown on left; after pedestrian crossing turn right at start of long, low brick factory into yard.***

Open: Mon, Wed 12–3; Tues, Fri 11–3; Sat 10–12.
Closed: Thursday; Bank Holidays; two weeks at Christmas.
Cards: None.
Cars: In factory yard.
Toilets: Yes,
Wheelchairs: Easy access to medium-sized shop.
Teas: In Wigston shopping centre.
Groups: Shopping and sewing groups welcome – please contact Jane Measures first.
Transport: Local buses from town centre stop near factory.
Mail order: Yes. Choose from swatches, £2 for set including postage (minimum order £10). Mention this book when requesting.

Towns with factory shops

NUMBERS refer to the ENTRIES, NOT the PAGES

Anstey	1	Bradgate Woollen Mill
Ashby-de-la-Zouch	2	Standard Soap
Bedford	3	Grumbridge
Brixworth near Northampton	4	Haddonstone
Church Gresley	5	T G Green Pottery
Coalville	6	Jaeger
Colston Bassett	7	Colston Bassett & District Dairy
Daventry	8	White and Co.
Desborough	p227	Cheaney
Desborough	9	The Corsetry Factory
Desborough	10	Littlestone & Goodwin
Earl Shilton	11	The Factory Shoe Company
Earls Barton	12	Barker Shoes
Enderby near Leicester	13	Creative Carpets
Hinckley	14	Richard Roberts
Irthlingborough	15	Dr. Martens
Kettering	p232	Countrywear
Kettering	16	Ian M Roberts
Leicester	17	Appliance Centre
Leicester	p234	Dr. Martens
Leicester	18	Potterton Cases
Leicester	19	The Shoe Factory Shop
Leicester	20	Singer Factory Services
Long Buckby	21	Regent Belt Co.
Long Buckby	22	Shades
Loughborough	23	Selective Marketplace
Lutterworth	25	Lady Clare
Market Harborough (Noseley)	p240	Homebirds – The Fabric Trading Company
Market Overton	26	Rutland Lighting
Melton Mowbray	27	Beck Mill
Moira	28	TDP Textiles
Northampton	29	Big L (Levi's)
Northampton	30	Crockett & Jones
Northampton	31	Daro
Northampton	32	Dr. Martens
Northampton	33	The Fabric Warehouse
Northampton	34	J L & Co.
Northampton	35	Nimbus
Northampton	p250	Ravenna Artworks
Northampton	36	Piggly-Wiggly Shoe Store
Northampton	37	Tricker's
Oakham	38	Corah
Oakham	39	Lands' End Direct Merchants
Oakham	40	Table Place
Rothwell	41	T Groocock (Rothwell)
Rushden	42	Totectors
Shepshed	43	Charterhouse Holdings
Shepshed	44	Low Woods Furnishings
Sileby	45	The Factory Shop Ltd.
South Wigston	46	Commando Direct
Spratton near Northampton	47	Jane Sale Interiors
Swadlincote	48	Webb Ivory
Tamworth	49	Jaeger Sale Shop
Tamworth	50	Probus Housewares
Tamworth	51	Webb Ivory
Uppingham	52	Uppingham Yarns
Whitwick	53	The Corsetry Factory
Wigston	54	BTM Fabrics

Western Midlands

D

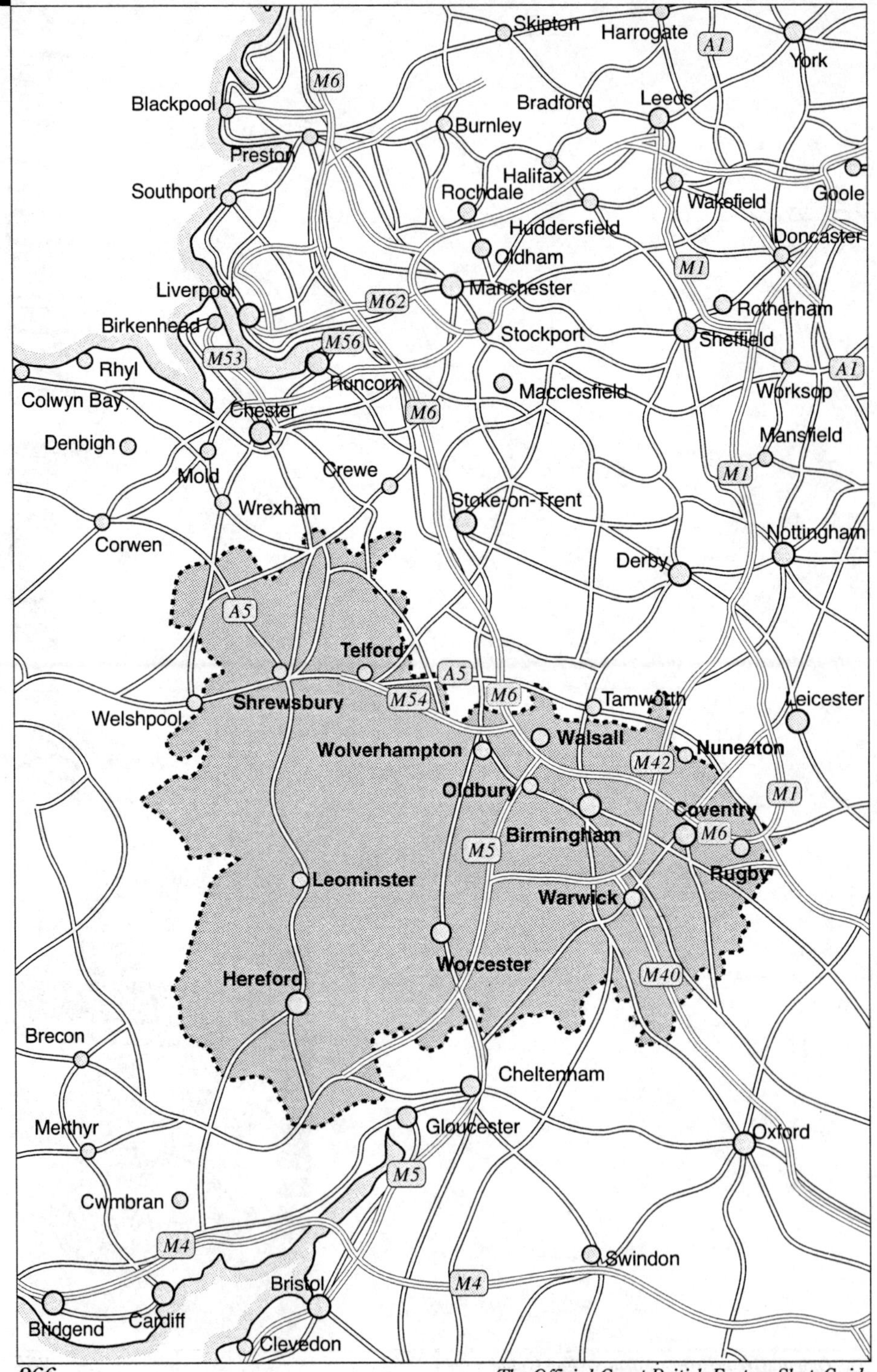

Skipton
Harrogate
A1
York
M6
Blackpool
Bradford
Leeds
Burnley
Preston
Halifax
Goole
Southport
Rochdale
Wakefield
Huddersfield
Doncaster
Oldham
M1
Liverpool
Manchester
M62
Rotherham
Birkenhead
Stockport
Sheffield
M56
M53
Rhyl
Runcorn
A1
Worksop
Colwyn Bay
Macclesfield
Chester
M6
Mansfield
Denbigh
Mold
Crewe
M1
Wrexham
Stoke-on-Trent
Corwen
Nottingham
Derby
A5
Telford
A5
Shrewsbury
M54
M6
Tamworth
Leicester
Welshpool
Walsall
Wolverhampton
Nuneaton
M42
Oldbury
M1
Coventry
Birmingham
M6
M5
Rugby
Leominster
Warwick
Worcester
M40
Hereford
Brecon
Cheltenham
Gloucester
Merthyr
Oxford
M5
Cwmbran
M4
Swindon
Bristol
M4
Bridgend
Cardiff
Clevedon

Western Midlands

The Western Midlands region contains several of the UK's best known industries: glass, carpets and jewellery. The world-famous glass companies are based around Stourbridge, part of which is now designated The Glass Quarter. This is well worth visiting both for your glass purchases and to watch interesting glass-blowing and glass-cutting demonstrations. Kidderminster is the traditional centre of the carpet industry, with several factory shops; another shop, not far away in Craven Arms, specialises in natural fibre floor coverings. In Birmingham you will find the famous Jewellery Quarter, which still manufactures most of the jewellery made in this country. You can buy many hand-crafted pieces, and not only have jewellery made to your own design but have your own jewellery repaired and restored (and necklaces re-strung).

The many other interesting shops in the region will, betweem them, cover everyday and special needs. In Shrewsbury buy high quality brand name clothing for men and women, and cane and wicker furniture; in Telford you find an excellent range of outdoor sportswear and workwear of all kinds; and in Tamworth famous name clothing, greeting cards and wrapping paper, and useful co-ordinated kitchen textiles and tinware. Do not miss the shops in Walsall which sell exceptional quality small leather items. The production of leather goods is a traditional Walsall industry, and there are many locally made leather items on sale in the Walsall Leather Museum shop. Make time to visit the museum itself.

We are delighted to welcome a number of shops which appear in these pages for the first time. Amongst them is a shop in the Brierley Hill area of Stourbridge which sells a fabulous range of furnishing fabrics with all the accessories you are likely to need. As well as carpets, you can buy pine items in Kidderminster – with stressed finishes and in special colours. A shop in Birmingham sells a variety of glass gifts, and they will also personalise paperweights with your own photo while you wait. In Wolverhampton there is a shop selling babywear, and in Lichfield you are faced with a huge choice of wallpapers and co-ordinated fabrics. Should you find yourself near Halesowen, do not miss a shop where you can buy quality candy and boiled sweets, home-made chocolates, including chocolate-covered strawberries, in gift presentations and a range of attractive metal gift containers. If you happen to be on a diet ... well, you can always remember your friends and family!

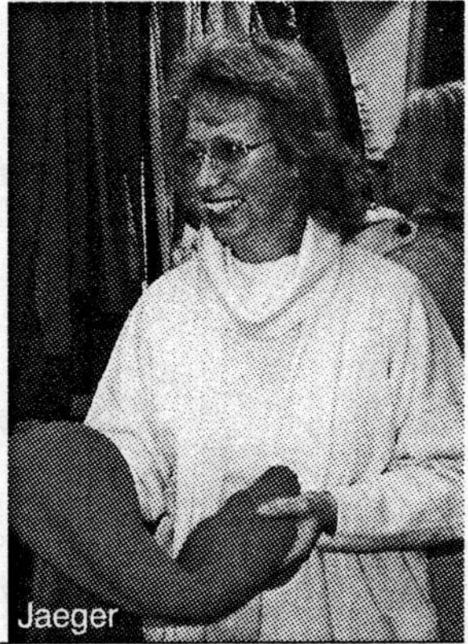
Jaeger

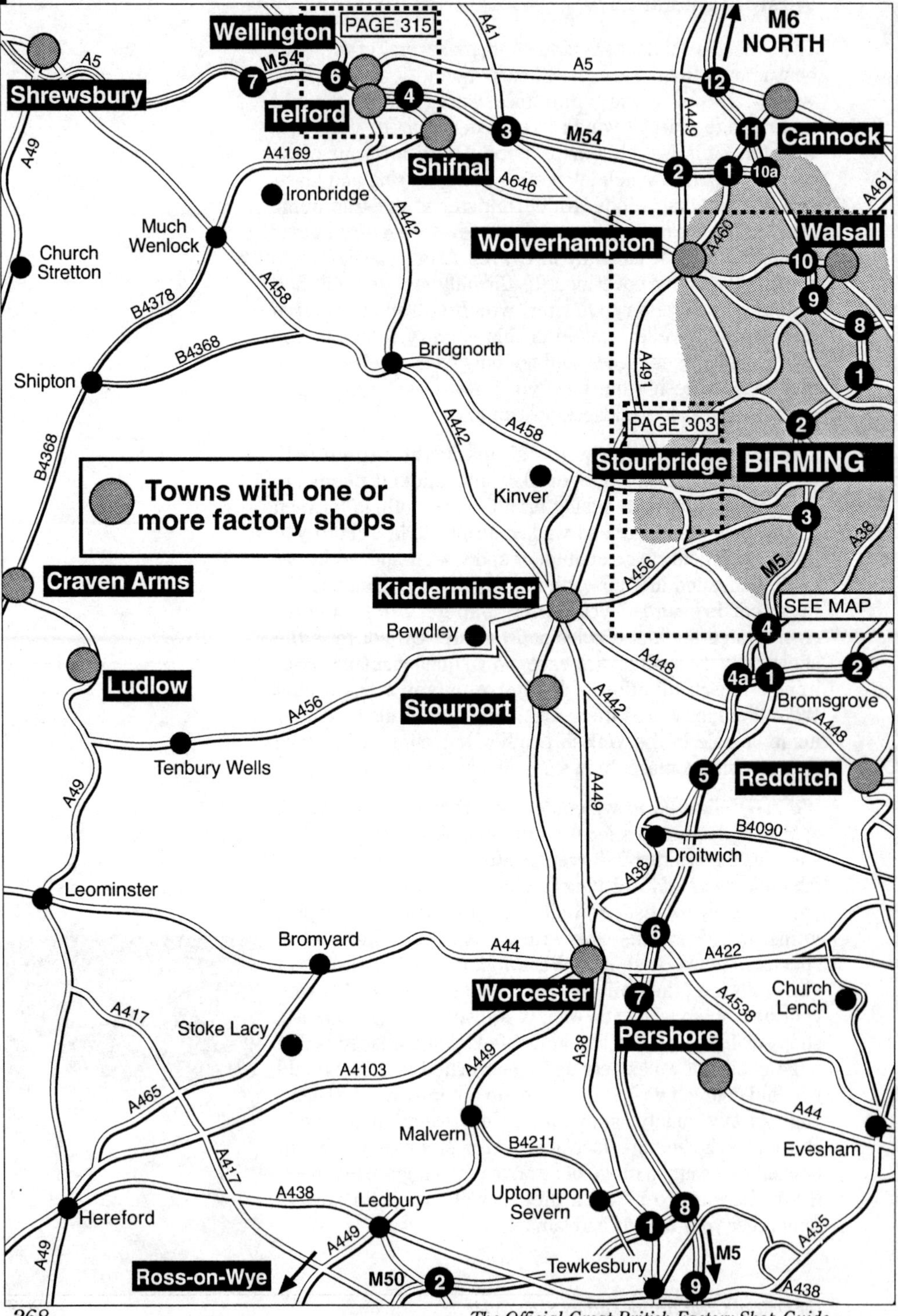

PAGE 315

M6 NORTH

Wellington

Shrewsbury

Telford

Shifnal

Cannock

A5

M54

A41

A449

A4169

A646

A461

A49

Ironbridge

Much Wenlock

Church Stretton

A442

A458

A460

Wolverhampton

Walsall

B4378

B4368

Bridgnorth

Shipton

A491

PAGE 303

Stourbridge

BIRMING

Kinver

Towns with one or more factory shops

Craven Arms

Kidderminster

A456

M5

A38

SEE MAP

Bewdley

Ludlow

A448

Stourport

Bromsgrove

Tenbury Wells

Redditch

B4090

Droitwich

Leominster

Bromyard

A44

A422

Worcester

Church Lench

A417

Stoke Lacy

Pershore

A4538

A4103

A465

Malvern

B4211

Evesham

A438

Upton upon Severn

Hereford

Ledbury

A435

Tewkesbury

Ross-on-Wye

M50

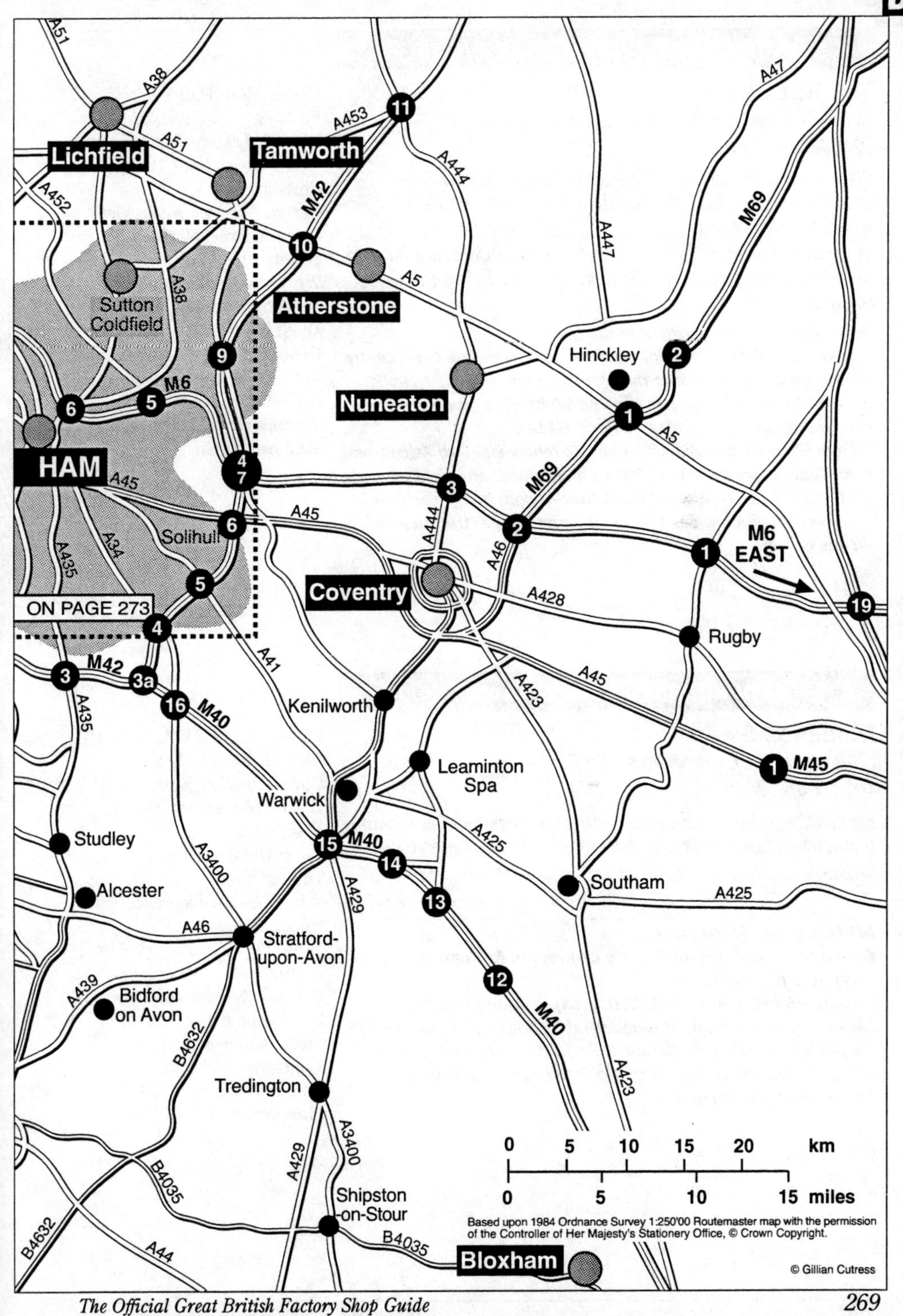
Lichfield
Tamworth
Atherstone
Sutton Coldfield
Nuneaton
Hinckley
HAM
Solihull
Coventry
ON PAGE 273
Rugby
M6 EAST
Kenilworth
Leaminton Spa
Warwick
Studley
Alcester
Southam
Stratford-upon-Avon
Bidford on Avon
Tredington
Shipston -on-Stour
Bloxham
A51
A38
A453
A47
A452
A444
M42
M69
A447
A5
M6
A45
A435
A34
A46
A428
A41
A423
M40
M45
A425
A3400
A429
A439
B4632
B4035
A44
km
miles
Based upon 1984 Ordnance Survey 1:250'00 Routemaster map with the permission of the Controller of Her Majesty's Stationery Office, © Crown Copyright.
© Gillian Cutress

1 Atherstone Warks

The Hat Shop

Coleshill Road CV9 2AA
(01827) 717941

Wide variety of ladies' and men's hats and caps in all colours, shapes and sizes for all seasons, occasions, weddings, Ascot, etc.

'A genuine factory shop with everything manufactured on the premises. Mostly perfects with some seconds. Prices in the range £7–£50.'

South-west of Atherstone, near the canal.

From Tamworth via A5: follow signs to Atherstone town centre. Follow the one-way system through the town. Pass the public car-park/bus station on left and The White Lion on right; at the mini-island turn right (Coleshill Road B4116).*

From Hinckley and Nuneaton on A5: follow signs to Atherstone. Pass Total petrol on left, go left at mini-island, and right at next mini-island. Turn left after 200 yds (mini-island) into Coleshill Rd.*

***Pass Jet petrol, cross the canal hump bridge: the shop is 40 yds on left.**

Open: Mon–Thur 10–4; Fri 10–3.
Closed: Last week July & first week August; Bank Holidays; Christmas–New Year.
Cards: Access, Switch, Visa.
Cars: In street outside.
Toilets: In town.
Wheelchairs: One step to medium-sized shop.
Teas: In town.
Groups: Groups of shoppers welcome by prior arrangement. No factory tours.
Transport: Walk from town.
Mail order: No.

2 Birmingham : Aston W Mids

Moulinex Swan

35 Rocky Lane, Golden Cross B6 5RP
(0121) 380 0635

Electric jugs, kettles, toasters, slow cookers, pots and pans, teasmades, deep-fryers, blenders, microwave ovens etc.

'Seconds, redundant stock and reconditioned items only.'

See our display advertisement opposite

NB This company has moved.

On the north-east side of the city centre, not far from M6 exit 6 (spaghetti junction).

From M6 exit 6: take A38 (Aston Expressway) south-west. Leave at first slip road; At roundabout at end of slip road, go left (Waterlinks Boulevard/Victoria Road). At roundabout go right (A5127, Lichfield Road). At traffic lights at roundabout, go left into Rocky Lane. Shop is on right.

Open: Mon–Fri 9–4; Sat 9–1.
Closed: Bank Holidays; Christmas–New Year.
Cards: Mastercard, Switch, Visa.
Cars: Outside shop.
Toilets: Yes.
Wheelchairs: Easy access for wheelchairs.
Teas: Plenty of places in city centre.
Groups: No tours of the works but shopping groups welcome. Please phone first.
Transport: Short bus ride from city centre.
Mail order: No.

See our entry opposite

3 Birmingham : Central W Mids

Fiesta Glass Factory Shop & Visitor Centre

Upper Marshall Street B1 1LA
(0121) 643 6927

Own manufactured products include worktop savers, glass gifts for anniversaries, birthdays and special occasions. Also personalise paperweights with your own photographs whilst you wait. Many gift items at modest prices.

'Most of our range sells at under £10. Seconds often available.'

In city centre, 400 yds south-west of New Street station/Pallasades shopping centre (on opposite side of A38 dual-carriageway).

From the huge Five Ways roundabout on Hagley Road (A456): exit into Islington Row A4540. Take second left, Bath Row (B4127). Look for Riva Bingo then go left into Granville Street.*

From M6 exit 6: take A38M for city centre. Stay in second lane to end of motorway (1 mile) which becomes A38 for Bromsgrove. Keep straight, go over flyover, down short tunnel (St Chad's) then longer one (Queensway). Stay on inside lane. Emerge from Queensway tunnel; move over one lane to left. Continue to Holloway Circus: take third exit, Holloway Head. Go right at Riva Bingo into Granville Street.*

****Follow official tourist signs. Take first right, Ridley Street. Take second left, Upper Marshall Street. Shop & visitor centre on right.***

Open: Mon–Fri 9–3.30; some Sats before Christmas.
Closed: Christmas–New Year period; Bank Holidays (some extended so phone to check).
Cards: Access, Visa.
Cars: Free parking in Upper Marshall Street outside shop.
Toilets: Yes, and for disabled.
Wheelchairs: Easy access. No steps.
Teas: Complimentary tea/coffee and biscuits. Ample lunch facilities nearby.
Groups: Groups of 10 or more by prior arrangement with Mr Cartwright.
Transport: Bus no. 66 from city. Railway station ½ mile.

Birmingham

Birmingham, Britain's second city, has put great effort and much money over the last few years into modernising its city centre, developing its concert hall, revitalising the canalside and commissioning modern sculptures.

Birmingham was valued at £1 in the Domesday Book in 1086. Since the 12th century it has grown rapidly, helped by a weekly market, when the town's first industries of wool, cloth and leather began to take shape. During the 1400s local smiths made metal cutting tools which they sold to farmers, and it is likely that there was demand for more ornamental metal goods from visiting wealthy landowners.

Long associated with the metal industries, Birmingham has excelled at making what is fashionable – buttons, buckles, toys and, of course, jewellery. When buckles were all the rage in the 18th century, Birmingham produced a huge range – from small buckles on hat bands, to the huge shoe buckle which nearly covered the foot. They cost from one shilling to as much as ten guineas a pair. At its height, the fashion was universal; Birmingham supplied America and the Continent. Alas, however, for the mutability of fashion! In 1790 the buckle was dethroned, the 'effeminate shoe-string' taking its place. In vain did the unfortunate buckle-makers try to arrest the changing fashion. In a petition to the Prince of Wales, they described the newfangled boot-laces as 'void of feeling'. They begged him to help the 20,000 people who worked in the industry and now faced destitution. In response, the Prince and the Duke of York ordered their gentlemen and servants to discard boot-strings and return to buckles. Another petition was presented the following year to the Duke and Duchess of York, but the effort was doomed. So, by the end of the century, one of the great staple trades of the city had died out.

Like most industrial cities, Birmingham has suffered difficult times as traditional trades and industries have closed. But the new city centre, with its restored and renovated buildings, offers much of interest.

Birmingham Tourist Information Office
2 City Arcade B2 4TX
(0121) 643 2514

The history of the buckle making trade was described by Mr Robert Dent in his account dated 1880

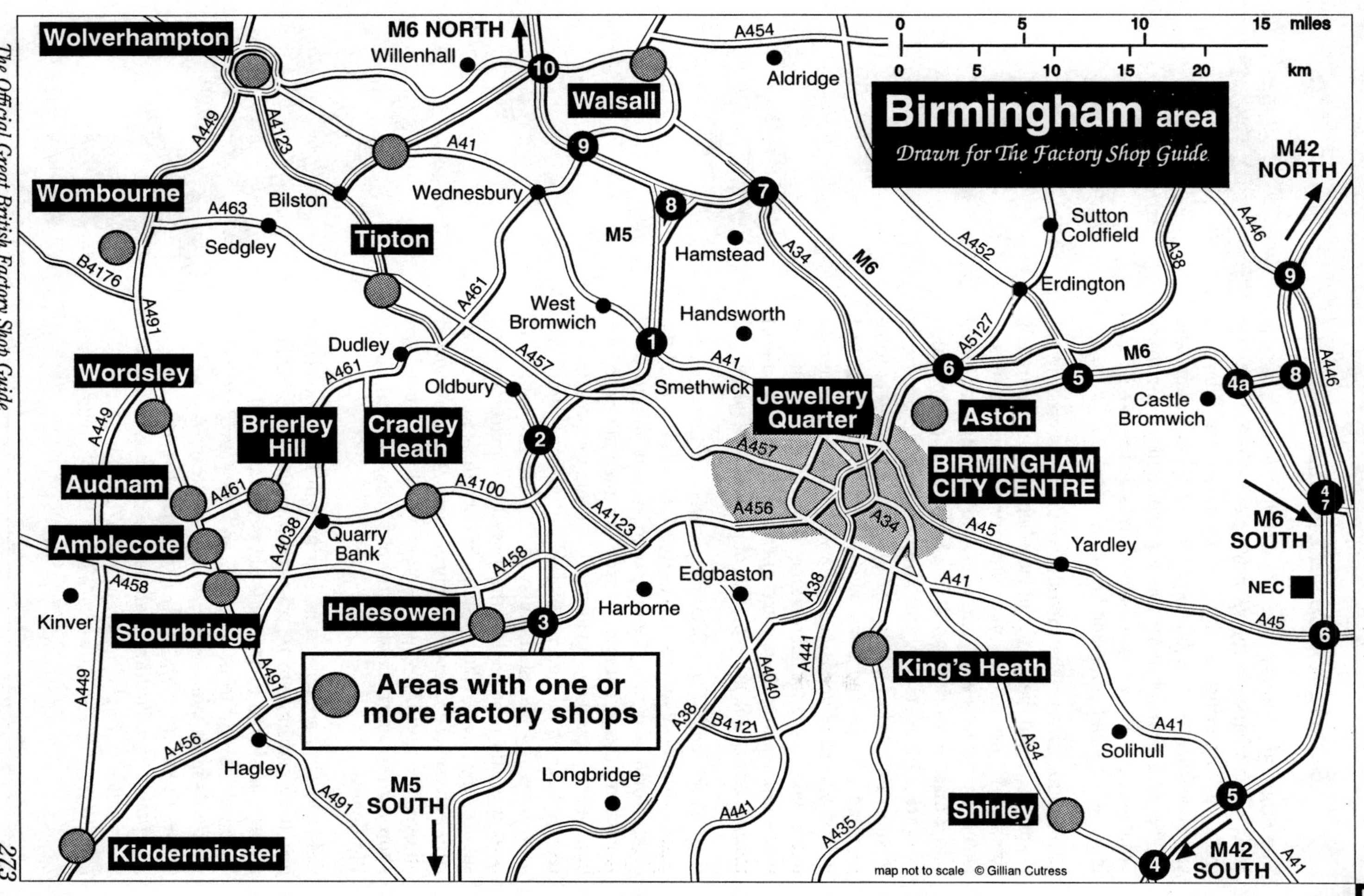

Birmingham area
Drawn for The Factory Shop Guide
0 5 10 15 miles
0 5 10 15 20 km
Areas with one or more factory shops
map not to scale © Gillian Cutress
Wolverhampton
Wombourne
Wordsley
Audnam
Amblecote
Stourbridge
Kidderminster
Brierley Hill
Cradley Heath
Halesowen
Tipton
Walsall
Jewellery Quarter
Aston
BIRMINGHAM CITY CENTRE
King's Heath
Shirley
M6 NORTH
M6 SOUTH
M42 NORTH
M42 SOUTH
M5 SOUTH
M5
M6
NEC
Willenhall
Aldridge
Wednesbury
Bilston
Sedgley
West Bromwich
Hamstead
Handsworth
Sutton Coldfield
Erdington
Dudley
Oldbury
Smethwick
Castle Bromwich
Quarry Bank
Yardley
Kinver
Edgbaston
Harborne
Hagley
Longbridge
Solihull
A454
A449
A4123
A41
A463
B4176
A491
A461
A457
A34
A452
A38
A446
A5127
A4100
A456
A4038
A458
A45
A441
A4040
B4121
A435

Birmingham Jewellery Quarter

The origin of jewellery as a major industry dates back to 1660, when Charles II returned from exile in France after the Civil War, bringing with him a taste for fancy buttons and shoe buckles. The fashion soon spread in Britain, and by the 18th century there was a great demand for these ornaments, as well as small metal boxes and trinkets made in steel, brass and silver, and known as 'toys'.

Goldsmiths, silversmiths and other craftsmen were originally spread around the town, but later began to concentrate in the area known as Jewellery Quarter, which consists of factories of various sizes, and many old buildings converted into a maze of workshops. It is a fascinating conservation area with little streets and alleyways (and some ugly modern buildings too). In the old days the streets were teeming with errand boys whose duty it was to collect bullion and carry goods from one workshop to another, or to the Assay office for hallmarking. It is said that when they met their friends they were apt to stop for a game of marbles or football, using parcels of gold for goal posts.

By the mid 1880's some 3500 people were employed in the trade, a figure which rose to 60–70,000 by 1913. During the First World War many people who stayed behind were employed making munition. Trade resumed after the war, but it never returned to its former level, and the process was repeated during the Second World War. Although trade has now generally declined, most of the jewellery made in Britain is still produced in the Jewellery Quarter, which supplies the most exclusive shops in London as well as high street chainstores. Jewellery made here is also exported all over the world. If you take your watch into your local shop for repair, the work is likely to be carried out in Birmingham.

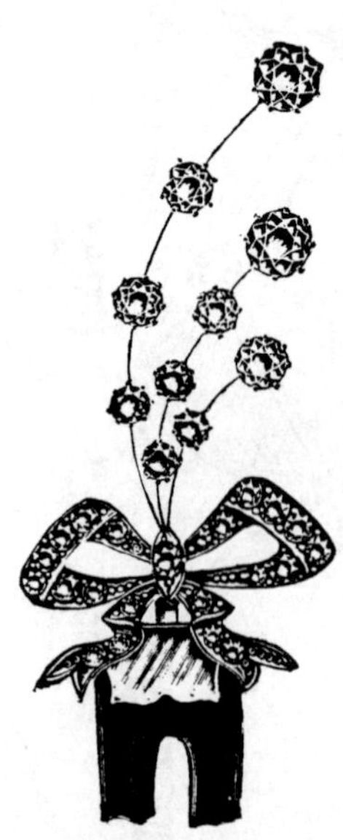

Gold and silver are too soft in their pure form to be used for jewellery and have to be mixed with other metals. The proportion of gold to other metals is measured in 'carats'. Pure gold is said to be 24 carat, and the four acceptable standards in Britain are 22, 18, 14 and 9 carats. Jewellery above a certain weight is checked that it meets a legally acceptable standard and hallmarked by one of the four assay office in England. Birmingham's Assay Office dates back to 1773; its distinctive mark is the Birmingham anchor.

In addition to a huge ready-made selection of jewellery, you will find loose gemstones, antique jewellery, silverware, chased ware, plated items such as sports trophies, hotel ware, tankards and badges, watches and clocks.

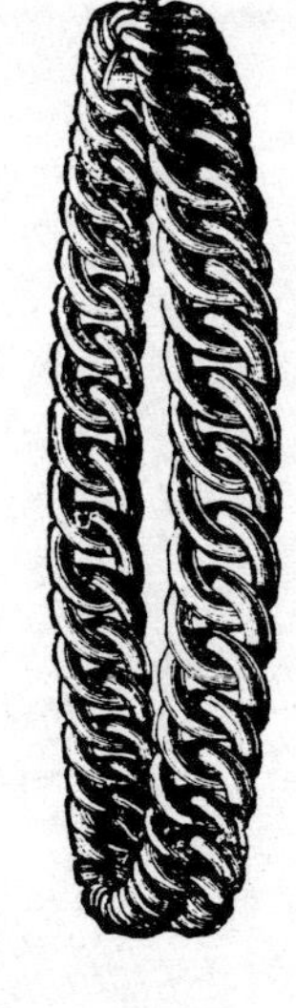

Shops here sell a huge variety of jewellery – rings, brooches, necklaces, earrings, chains, cuff links etc. You can have jewellery valued; and we have found an excellent value service for re-stringing beads. Windows sparkle, and window-shopping is a great pleasure. Many items are in traditional styles, but others are crafted in original designs. You can discuss your ideas with a designer who will make up a unique piece of jewellery for you at no more than the price you would pay for a standard item elsewhere. It is an ideal place to get together to choose a unique engagement ring. Ready-made pieces on offer tend to veer towards the traditional. The Jewellery Quarter Discovery Centre, however, has an interesting display of contemporary pieces.

Shops mentioned here offer an individual service and are only too happy to talk over, without obligation, your own ideas. It is difficult for the public to identify and value jewellery and this is one field where the buyer depends heavily on the integrity of the seller.

Many shops sell their own production but a few shops in the quarter buy in cheap stock and sell it to the public at so-called 'bargain prices'. They are conspicuous by their less-than-subtle posters. Few gold chains are made in this country as the process is time-consuming and expensive; therefore the vast majority of chains are imported.

Facilities in this area are improving. You can eat in a bistro and in several cafés and pubs, including the attractive coffee bar in the Discovery Centre. Toilets can be found at ground level in the Vyse Street multi-storey car-park.

Most excitingly, it is now possible to reach the heart of the Jewellery Quarter by train. The station in Vyse Street has been re-opened and has a direct link to Snow Hill (Centro transport hotline 0121 200 2700). There are buses from the city centre; or it takes about 15 minutes to walk from New Street station.

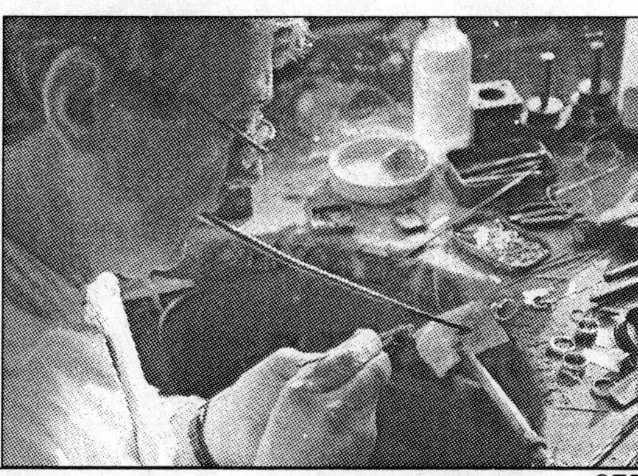

With thanks to the
Jewellery Quarter Discovery Centre
for information and photograph

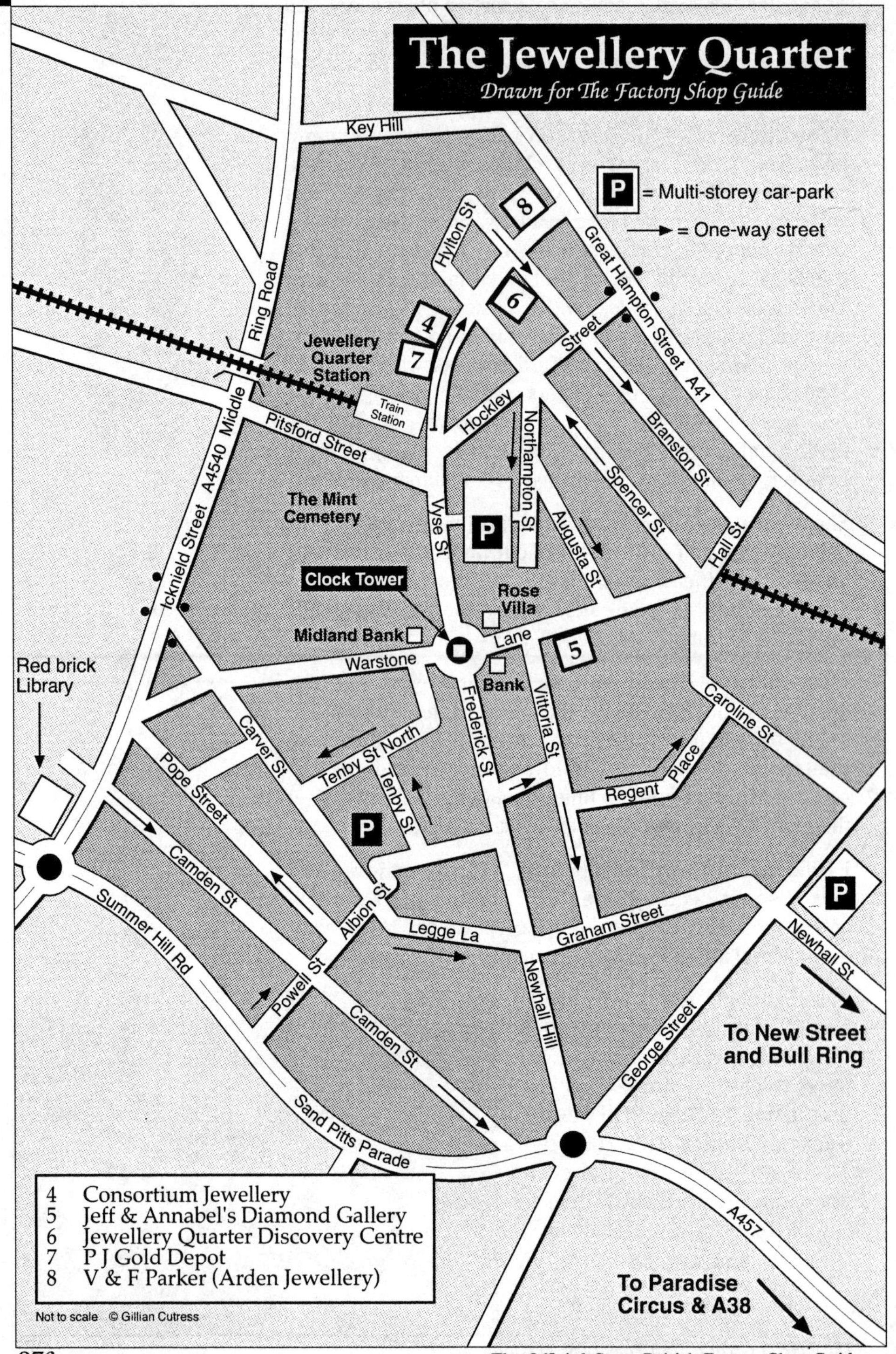
The Jewellery Quarter
Drawn for The Factory Shop Guide
= Multi-storey car-park
= One-way street
Key Hill
Ring Road
Jewellery Quarter Station
Train Station
Hylton St
Great Hampton Street A41
Street
Hockley
Northampton St
Branston St
Spencer St
Augusta St
Hall St
Pitsford Street
Icknield Street A4540 Middle
The Mint Cemetery
Vyse St
Clock Tower
Rose Villa
Midland Bank
Warstone
Lane
Bank
Red brick Library
Carver St
Tenby St North
Tenby St
Frederick St
Vittoria St
Regent Place
Caroline St
Pope Street
Camden St
Summer Hill Rd
Albion St
Legge La
Graham Street
Newhall Hill
Newhall St
Powell St
Camden St
George Street
To New Street and Bull Ring
Sand Pitts Parade
A457
To Paradise Circus & A38
4 Consortium Jewellery
5 Jeff & Annabel's Diamond Gallery
6 Jewellery Quarter Discovery Centre
7 P J Gold Depot
8 V & F Parker (Arden Jewellery)
Not to scale © Gillian Cutress

4 Birmingham : Jewellery Quarter

Consortium Jewellery

39 Vyse Street B18 6JV
(0121) 554 9297

Specialise in diamond rings and sell whole range of gold items including bracelets and chains. Jewellery for ladies and men (cufflinks, tie tacks, bracelets, neck chains & rings).

'Family business which buys and sells all types of jewellery. One-off pieces and commissions welcomed. Prices from £10–£2000. Happy to carry out repairs and give valuations.'

From the clocktower in the middle of the Jewellery Quarter: go down the left side of Vyse Street; go over the railway, with a brick wall on the left, and this is the third shop on the left.

Open: Mon–Sat 9–4. *Also Nov–Dec* Sunday 10–3.
Closed: Bank Holidays; Christmas, Boxing and New Year's Days.
Cards: Access, Amex, Transax (for clearing cheques), Visa .
Cars: Pay-&-display in street and multi-storey car-park.
Toilets: At car-park.
Wheelchairs: Two steps to medium sized shop.
Teas: Local cafés and pubs.
Groups: You are welcome to look into the workshop.
Transport: Bus from city centre. Jewellery Quarter train station nearby.
Mail order: No.

5 Birmingham : Jewellery Quarter

Jeff & Annabel's Diamond Gallery

35 Warstone Lane B18 6JQ
(0121) 236 5799

A small family business specialising in 18ct gold, platinum and 9ct gold hand-crafted quality jewellery, particularly engagement and diamond dress rings, all types of wedding rings etc. Exclusive range of English hand-made chains and bracelets, earrings, etc.

'The first member of the National Association of Goldsmiths in the Jewellery Quarter. Personal friendly service. Free after-sales and cleaning service on all diamond jewellery purchases. Alterations within one hour and repairs carried out on the premises. Take your Factory Shop Guide for a sales discount.'

From the clocktower in the middle of the Jewellery Quarter: go along Warstone Lane (Rose Villa pub on left). Stay on right side. Cross over Vittoria Street: this shop is a few yards on right.

Open: Mon–Sat 9–5; occasional Sundays 10–2 (call first please).
Closed: Christmas, Boxing and New Year's Days; Easter Sunday.
Cards: Access, Amex, Delta, Switch, Visa. Interest free credit (subject to status; details on request).
Cars: Pay-&-display in street. Nearby multi-storey car-park.
Toilets: In Vyse Street.
Wheelchairs: One step to medium sized shop.
Teas: Local cafés and pubs.
Transport: Bus from city centre. Jewellery Quarter train station nearby.
Mail order: No.

6 Birmingham : Jewellery Quarter

Jewellery Quarter Discovery Centre

75–79 Vyse Street B18 6HB
(0121) 554 3598

Jewellery Quarter products made in this factory and selection of contemporary jewellery from Birmingham's talented young designer jewellers. Jewellery books and wide selection of beads and minerals.

'Visit the "time capsule" workshop of Messrs Smith and Pepper, a unique jewellery factory which has hardly changed since the turn of the century. Enjoy a guided tour around the factory and meet skilled jewellers at work. Special events and exhibitions are held throughout the year; please phone for details.'

From the clocktower in the middle of the Jewellery Quarter: go down Vyse Street. This original workshop is towards the bottom on the right, past Spencer Street.

Open: Mon–Fri 10–4; Sat 11–5. Some Bank Holidays.
Closed: Sunday; Christmas, Boxing and New Year's Days.
Cards: Access, Visa.
Cars: On-street parking; multi-storey car-park in Vyse Street.
Toilets: Yes.
Wheelchairs: Good access.
Teas: Own tea room.
Groups: All visitors receive a guided tour around museum. Groups welcome but need to book in advance. £2 adults; £1.50 concessions; £5 family ticket (2 adults + 3 children); 10% discount for groups of ten or more booked in advance. Private evening bookings.
Transport: Bus from city centre. Jewellery Quarter train station almost opposite.
Mail order: No.

7 Birmingham : Jewellery Quarter

P J Gold Depot

37 Vyse Street B18 6JY
(0121) 554 6165

Diamond, wedding and signet rings, pendants and necklets, all made on the premises. Specialist in eternity rings. Hand-made chains; cameos with hand-made gold mountings – which can be worn as either pendants or brooches. Jewellery made to customers' own designs. Wide range of imported chains too.

'This company produced the first ever eternity ring, set in yellow gold with white stones! Immediate re-sizing of rings. VIVAT tax free shopping.'

From the clocktower in the middle of the Jewellery Quarter: go down the left side of Vyse Street; pass new Jewellery Quarter railway station on left then this double-fronted shop with white columns is second company on the left.

From the new 'Jewellery Quarter' railway station: turn left, then this is the second shop on left.

Open: Mon–Sat 9–4; *also Nov and Dec* Sunday 9–4.
Closed: Bank Holidays, Xmas, Boxing and New Year's Days.
Cards: Access, Amex, Diners, Switch, Visa.
Cars: Some street parking; nearby multi-storey car-park.
Toilets: 150 yds along Vyse Street at multi-storey car-park.
Wheelchairs: Two steps to spacious shop; help gladly given. Disabled (incl. groups) also welcome to go behind the scenes and see jewellery made.
Teas: Tea shop almost facing.
Groups: You can see diamond cutter and gemstone mounter at work. Coach parties welcome (also in the evening) – please telephone Mr Hamlington first.
Transport: Bus from city. Jewellery Quarter train station.
Mail order: No.

8 Birmingham : Jewellery Quarter

V & F Parker (Arden Jewellery)

51 Vyse Street (off Gt Hampton Street) B18 6HS
(0121) 554 3587

Ring-making and gemstone setting. Choose both your own stone and mounting from the wide selections of unmounted stones and settings available here. Price range of £10–£4,000 in stock. Large selection of earrings; Victorian and Celtic reproduction jewellery. Company designs to order, undertakes commissions, 'one off' orders and specialises in remaking old gold rings which have become frail with wear.

'Tax free shopping for overseas visitors – please ask for VAT refund form.'

From the clocktower in the middle of the Jewellery Quarter: go along the left hand side of Vyse Street for 300 yards, passing the new 'Jewellery Quarter' railway station on left. Cross over both ends of Hylton Street, then this is the second shop from corner.

Open: Mon–Fri 11–5; Sat 10–3; *also December* Sun mornings. Usually open Bank Holidays – please check.
Closed: Christmas, Boxing and New Year's Days.
Cards: Diners, MasterCard, Visa.
Cars: Pay-&-display in street and multi-storey car-park.
Toilets: 200 yds away, at multi-storey car-park.
Wheelchairs: Rather difficult – four steps to small shop.
Teas: Cafés almost facing.
Groups: Please phone in advance.
Transport: Bus from city centre. Jewellery Quarter train station 100 yds.
Mail order: Yes.
Catalogue: £4.50. No seconds sent, only guaranteed items.

9 Birmingham : King's Heath

Treetops Pine Furniture

76–82 Grange Road B14 7RJ
(0121) 444 8475

Pine furniture, fitted bedrooms and kitchens.

'All furniture made from high quality pine and can be stained and polished to match existing furniture. Seconds and ends of ranges. Measuring and fitting service by our own staff, with free quotes. Nominal charge for delivery.'

King's Heath is south of the city centre. The company is a short way off the High Street.

From Birmingham going south on A435 towards Redditch: pass the town name sign just after roundabout and take the third right (Argos on near right corner).*

Going north on A435 for city centre: go through King's Heath High Street, pass the Crossed Guns on the left and take the next left (Argos on far left corner).*

***The shop is about 250 yds on the right in a white building.**

Open: Mon–Sat 10–6.
Closed: Christmas and Boxing Days.
Cards: Access, Amex, Delta, Switch, Visa.
Cars: Easy parking in road outside factory.
Toilets: Yes.
Wheelchairs: One step.
Teas: In High Street.
Groups: Happy to show pre-booked groups over factory. Please phone in advance.
Transport: Various local buses.
Mail order: No.

10 Bloxham near Banbury Oxon

The Weavers Shop

Barford Road OX15 4HB
(01295) 721225

Wide range of Wilton, broadloom and tufted carpets. New range of natural floor coverings, including sisal, seagrass and coir. Wools for weaving, knitting and tapestry work. Rugs, canvas, carpet-fitting accessories.

'Expert advice willingly given, together with accessories and delivery service. List of recommended fitters. Perfects, seconds and ends of ranges.'

Bloxham is on the A361 (Chipping Norton–Banbury road).

Coming north on A361 from Chipping Norton: as you reach Bloxham, pass Esso station on right then take next right (Barford Road) towards Adderbury.*

From Banbury: take A361 south-west. Keep straight through Bloxham, passing church and Old School House Hotel on left, then go left for Adderbury.*

***Keep going straight till you see Steele's Carpets on left. The shop, clearly marked, is at back.**

From the Barfords: as you reach village outskirts, Steele's are on right.

Open: Mon–Sat 9–5.
Closed: Bank Holidays; Christmas–New Year.
Cards: MasterCard, Visa.
Cars: Large car-park.
Toilets: Yes.
Wheelchairs: Easy access; large shop.
Teas: Pubs in the village and locally.
Groups: Factory tours by appointment. Groups of shoppers welcome but preferably book first.
Transport: Local buses from Banbury.
Mail order: No.

11 Cannock Staffs

Fashion Factory

Unit 5, Wyrley Brook Park, Vine Lane, Bridgetown WS11 3XE
(01543) 466000

Vast selection of quality branded ladies' and men's wear, and shoes.

'Personal shoppers only. Internationally famous brand names at savings of 40–70% off high street prices. 30–40,000 garments of constantly changing merchandise. No chainstore items. Summer and winter sales. Also in Wellington & Shrewsbury.'

See our display advertisement on p. 321

Across the A5 from Cannock, on the south side of this major road. Near B&Q.

Going north-west on A5 from Tamworth: at traffic lights (Texaco on far left corner) at Cannock turn-off, go left (not right for Cannock).*

From M6 exit 12: turn east on to A5 for Cannock/Tamworth. Cross the junction with the A460; at traffic lights (Texaco on near right corner) with Cannock turn-off to left, go right.*

***Shortly turn right into Vine Lane: shop short distance on right.**

Open: Mon–Sat 9.30–5.30; Sun 11–5.
Closed: Easter Sunday; Christmas Day.
Cards: Access, Visa.
Cars: Ample space.
Toilets: Yes.
Wheelchairs: Easy access, no steps to huge ground floor shop.
Changing rooms: Yes.
Teas: Drinks machine, seating.
Groups: Shopping groups welcome, but please phone first.
Transport: Regular bus route via Vine Lane bus stop.
Mail order: No.

12 Cannock Staffs

Lew-Ways

Watling Street WS11 3NB
(01543) 454427

Wide selection of children's to adults' cycles: ATB's, pavement cycles, trikes/scooters. Full range of outdoor play equipment: swings, slides, climbing frames, playmats; swim armbands; sandpits, play sand; goal posts; basketball sets; play homes; baby swings; trampolines; water trays & pools; exercise benches & bicycles. Golf trolleys. Range of garden fish ponds.

'Plenty of room to try the bicycles. All items are used mail order items, factory seconds or slight rejects at considerably reduced prices.'

Clearly marked on the A5, two miles west of Brownhills and 3 miles east of Cannock.

From Brownhills: go west on A5. Look for large signs on the left then follow directions into factory yard.

From Cannock: take A5 east for Brownhills. Go over large roundabout with The Turf Lodge on near left corner (crossing the B4154). Pass The Little Chef on the right, get into the right lane and after 100 yds go right into well marked company.

Well signed shop is at far back of yard.

Open: Mon–Sat 8.30–5; Bank Holidays.
Closed: Christmas–New Year.
Cards: Access, Visa.
Cars: Factory yard immediately outside shop.
Toilets: Yes.
Wheelchairs: Easy access to large sales area on ground floor (no steps).
Teas: Little Chef next door.
Groups: Groups of shoppers welcome.
Transport: None.
Mail order: No.

13 Cannock Staffs

Lighting Bug

173 Walsall Road, Bridgtown WS11 3JB
(01543) 577776

Huge range of domestic lighting: soft shades and table lamps made here; full ranges of polished solid brass light fittings; crystal, wood and panel glass ceiling fittings. Wall lamps to complement ceiling fittings. Outdoor lighting, spot lights, downlighters, low voltage and fluorescent lighting. Light switches, bulbs, doorbells etc.

'Perfects and seconds at discounts of 25–50%. Always special offers on discontinued lines. Gladly pack and post (at cost) if you can't carry purchases home. We are a happy-go-lucky company (biggest lighting shop in the West Midlands) and will do anything to take your money!'

Bridgtown is on the southern side of Cannock, between Cannock town centre and A5.

From Cannock town: take A34 south towards A5. Pass Kwik-Fit on left. Conspicuous shop is on far left corner by roundabout (take first left at roundabout then sharp right into shop car-park).

From A5: at traffic lights, take A34 north for Cannock. Go under railway bridge, then left at T-junction. The conspicuous shop is on the far right corner by the roundabout.

Open: Mon–Sat 9.30–5.30. Bank Holidays.
Closed: Few days during Christmas–New Year period.
Cards: Delta, Eurocard, Mastercard, Visa.
Cars: Free large car-park.
Toilets: Town centre.
Wheelchairs: No steps to large shop.
Teas: Pubs, cafés and McDonald's nearby.
Groups: No factory tours but shopping groups welcome.
Transport: Cannock–Walsall buses stop outside.
Mail order: Yes.
Catalogue: £4, redeemable against purchases of £50+. Please phone for catalogue (with credit card). All items sent by overnight delivery (about £10).

14 Coventry Warks

Nutcracker Factory Direct

1a City Arcade CV1 3HY
(01203) 224602

Home furnishings: quilt covers in many different designs and sizes; percale sheets, *Fogarty* quilts, pillows and cushion inners, cushion covers, curtains, net curtain remnants, towels and bathroom sets. Household linens (tablecloths, napkins, place mats); kitchenware (chainstore melamine bowls, sieves, collanders). In-house seamstress service for curtains, pelmets, Austrian and Roman blinds, alterations.

'Leading chainstore and department store seconds, discontinued lines, overmakes and perfects at up to 75% off RRP. Fogarty quilts from £9, feather pillows & cushions from £3; percale sheets from £8; percale quilt covers from £10; continental pillows from £6; rugs from £2.50, throws from £10.'

In the city centre, within the pedestrian precinct on south side.

From all directions: follow signs for the Coventry inner city ring road. From exit 7, follow signs for the City Arcade parking. Shop is one floor beneath car-park. Follow signs to the arcade.

Open: Mon–Sat 9–5.30.
Closed: Bank Holidays; Christmas, Boxing and New Year's Days.
Cards: Access, Switch, Visa.
Cars: City Arcade car-park.
Toilets: In the City Arcade.
Wheelchairs: Easy access, no steps; wide enough for wheelchairs if shop not very crowded.
Teas: Large cafeteria opposite.
Groups: Small shopping groups welcome, no need to book.
Transport: Five minutes' walk from main bus station and from train station.
Mail order: Yes.

15 Cradley Heath W Mids

Hawk Factory Cycle Stores

Forge Lane B64 5AM
(01384) 636535

Huge range of cycles for all ages: ATB, sports, tandems, BMX, kiddies. Accessories, spares and repairs.

'4,000 sq ft shop. Large range of cycles made in own factory and sold at factory prices plus others from leading UK manufacturers, many at trade prices. Frames guaranteed for life. Prompt after-sales service, all spares available.'

From Merry Hill Shopping Centre: take A4036 south (to Bromsgrove (A491)). At large staggered crossing, turn left at traffic lights on to A4100 for Cradley Heath. Go downhill, pass the right turn to Cradley (B4174); the white building is 400 yds uphill on the left.

From traffic lights in Cradley Heath High Street: take the A4100 downhill (west) for Merry Hill and Brierley Hill. Look for the railway and bus stations on the left, then this white building is on the right.

Open: Mon–Sat 9–6; Sun and Bank Holidays 9–4.30.
Closed: Christmas & Boxing Days; phone to check New Year's Day.
Cards: Access, Delta, JCB, Switch, Visa.
Cars: Ample free parking at factory.
Toilets: Public toilets 50 yds.
Wheelchairs: No steps to large shop.
Teas: In Cradley Heath.
Groups: No factory tours.
Transport: Trains from all areas. Buses from Brierley Hill, Stourbridge and Dudley.
Mail order: No.

16 Craven Arms Shropshire

Crucial Trading

The Market Hall, Market Street SY7 9NY
(01588) 673161

Large selection of conveniently sized natural fibre floor coverings including sisal, seagrass, coir, jute, wool etc at discount prices; also large selection of natural rugs.

'Many ends of rolls, returned orders, discontinued lines etc at half-price. Also list of larger pieces up to whole roll (30 x 4 m) held at factory can be purchased at large discount through this shop. Free measuring service. Fitting can be arranged for most parts of mainland Britain. Complete collection of over 120 natural floorcoverings available for inspection and/or order.'

On the A49, 7 miles south of Church Stretton and 7 miles north of Ludlow.

Coming north from Ludlow on A49: go right on to B4368 in Craven Arms. Market Street is first right; shop is about 100 yds on left, on corner position.

Coming south from Church Stretton: turn left on to B4368. Market Street is first right; shop is about 100 yds on left, on corner site.

Open: Mon–Sat 10–5.
Closed: Bank Holidays; Christmas–New Year.
Cards: Amex, MasterCard, Switch, Visa.
Cars: Easy street parking.
Toilets: By the Craven Arms Hotel.
Wheelchairs: Two steps.
Teas: Local cafés and pubs.
Groups: No tours; unsuitable for group visits.
Transport: Trains and buses from Ludlow and Shrewsbury.
Mail order: Yes. No seconds or factory shop merchandise can be posted.
Catalogue: Free.

17 Halesowen W Mids

The Chambers Candy Co.

Eagle House, Park Road
(01384) 424848

Candy, toffees, boiled sweets, chocolate covered strawberries and pecans etc. Own-made chocolates – in gift boxes and seasonal novelties. Candies and boiled sweets in gift presentations.

'Many unique designs in metal gift containers.'

Park Road is the A458, the main Halesowen–Stourbridge road.

From Halesowen: go west on A458 for 2+ miles towards Lye. Pass Leyland Daf on right then this company is on left.

From Stourbridge: take A458 west. Go through Lye. Cross Hayes Lane then this company is shortly on right, almost opposite Leyland Daf.

Open: Mon–Fri 9–4.30.
Closed: Bank Holidays; Christmas–New Year period.
Cards: All major credit cards.
Cars: Car-park at rear.
Toilets: Yes.
Wheelchairs: Two steps.
Teas: Cafés in Halesowen. Little Chef close by on A456.
Tours: No factory tours.
Transport: Half a mile to Lye train station. Bus no. 9 from Stourbridge and Birmingham.
Mail order: Yes.
Catalogue: Price list and brochure on request.

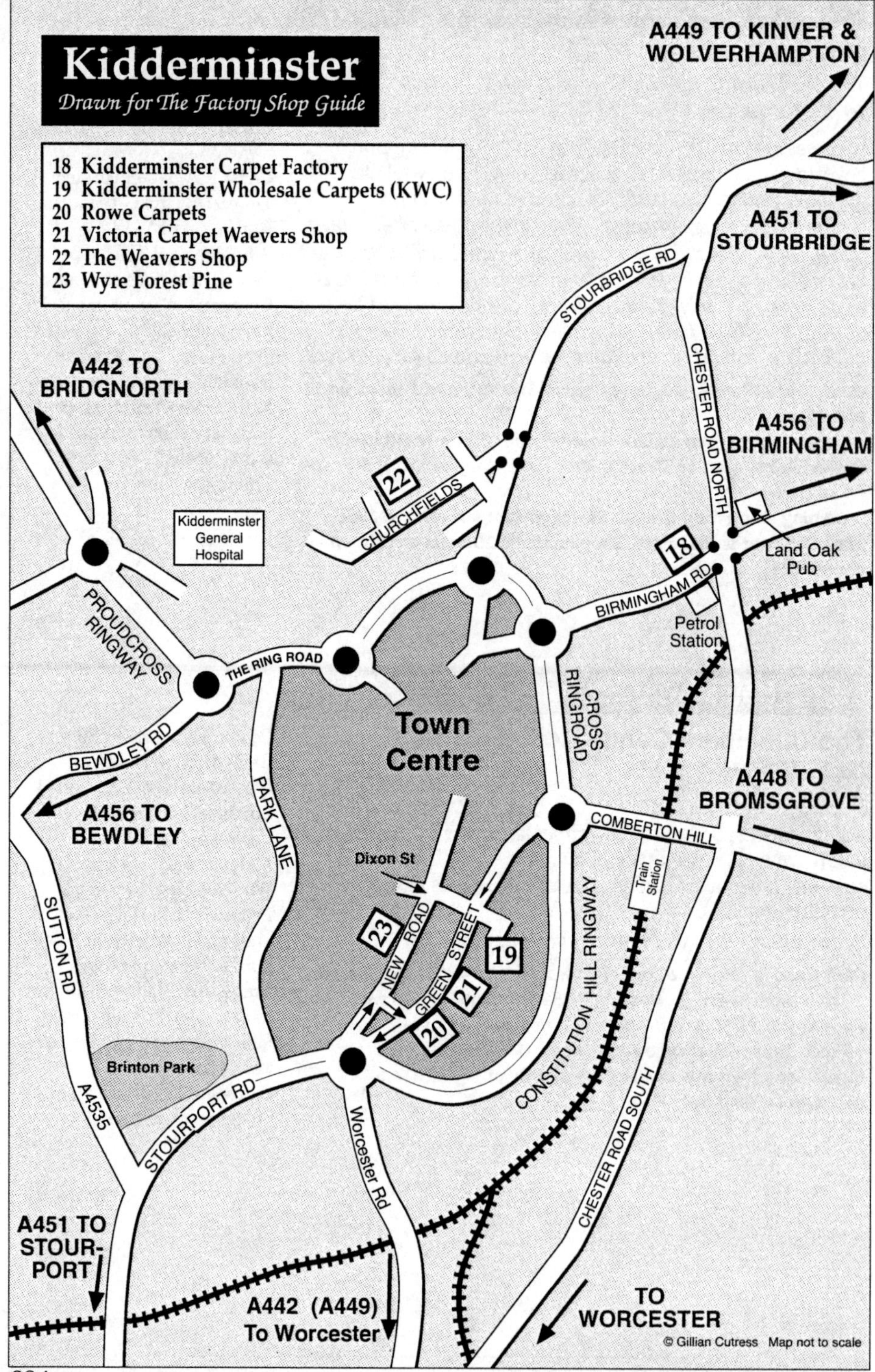
Kidderminster
Drawn for The Factory Shop Guide
18 Kidderminster Carpet Factory
19 Kidderminster Wholesale Carpets (KWC)
20 Rowe Carpets
21 Victoria Carpet Waevers Shop
22 The Weavers Shop
23 Wyre Forest Pine
A449 TO KINVER & WOLVERHAMPTON
A451 TO STOURBRIDGE
STOURBRIDGE RD
CHESTER ROAD NORTH
A442 TO BRIDGNORTH
A456 TO BIRMINGHAM
Land Oak Pub
Petrol Station
BIRMINGHAM RD
CHURCHFIELDS
Kidderminster General Hospital
PROUDCROSS RINGWAY
THE RING ROAD
CROSS RINGROAD
Town Centre
BEWDLEY RD
A456 TO BEWDLEY
PARK LANE
A448 TO BROMSGROVE
COMBERTON HILL
Train Station
Dixon St
NEW ROAD
GREEN STREET
CONSTITUTION HILL RINGWAY
SUTTON RD
Brinton Park
A4535
STOURPORT RD
Worcester Rd
CHESTER ROAD SOUTH
A451 TO STOUR-PORT
A442 (A449) To Worcester
TO WORCESTER
© Gillian Cutress Map not to scale

See our entry below

18 Kidderminster Worcs *see map opposite*

Kidderminster Carpet Factory

Land Oak, Birmingham Road DY10 2DB
(01562) 69204 Fax (01562) 862702

Wide range of Wiltons, Axminsters, tufteds etc in variety of plains, patterns, widths, weights etc. Specialise in coir natural flooring imported directly from India.

'Constantly changing stock of seconds, discontinued lines and bankrupt stock from major UK manufacturers. About half usual prices or less, eg 100% wool berber £9.50 per sq m (£8/sq yd) (normal retail £24–£30 per sq m); 100% wool velvet £12 per sq m (£10/sq yd) (normal retail £24–£36 per sq m); stainfree twist £6 per sq m (£5/sq yd) (normal retail £12 sq m). Nationwide delivery service, £10–£50. Own fitters install carpet bought here (small min. purchase) throughout UK for c. £1.50 per sq yd.'

See our display advertisement above

On eastern side of town, easy to see on Birmingham Road (A456).

From Kidderminster/ring road: aim east for Birmingham. After half a mile, pass Elf petrol on right then go left at traffic lights into Chester Road North, A449. Shop is on this near left corner: car-park entrance is at far side.

Coming west into Kidderminster on A456: at traffic lights (The Land Oak pub near right corner, Elf petrol on far left) go right into Chester Road North A449. After few yards, go left for shop car-park.

Open: Seven days: Mon–Sat 8.30–5.30; Sun and Bank Holidays 10–4.
Closed: Christmas and Boxing Days.
Cards: Access, Connect, Visa.
Cars: Behind shop (entrance to the right of shop).
Toilets: Yes.
Wheelchairs: Easy access, sizeable shop.
Teas: Plenty of places in Kidderminster.
Groups: No factory tours.
Transport: On Kidderminster–Birmingham bus route. Buses from Kidderminster station.
Mail order: No.

19 Kidderminster Worcs *see map previous page*

Kidderminster Wholesale Carpets (KWC)

Unit 23, Meadow Mills, Dixon Street DY10 1HH
(01562) 60811

Wide selection of tufted carpets made on-site. Mainly plain and flecked colours with a few patterned. Specialise in 80% wool heavy weight twist pile carpet.

'Most items perfects at about half high street price (£10 for 80/20% wool/nylon). A few slight seconds at heavily reduced prices. Fitting service in local area. No charge for delivery in Kidderminster and £10–£20 for Birmingham.'

In the centre of town, towards the southern end near the ring road roundabout where the Stourport Road (A451) meets the Worcester Road (A449).

From this ring road roundabout: take exit marked 'Town Centre' then first right and next left. Pass Rowe Carpets and Victoria Carpets on right and continue to crossroads (one-way traffic coming towards you). Go right into Dixon Street then right into factory yard. Clearly marked shop is facing you.

Open: Mon–Fri 9–5.30; Sat 9–5.
Closed: Bank Holidays; Christmas, New Year's Days.
Cards: MasterCard, Visa.
Cars: Beside shop.
Toilets: Yes.
Wheelchairs: No steps, large, spacious shop.
Teas: Plenty of places in town.
Groups: You can see the large tufting machine at the back of the shop.
Transport: Easy walk from town centre bus station; 5 minutes from train station.
Mail order: No.

20 Kidderminster Worcs *see map previous page*

Rowe Carpets

Green Street DY10 1HM
(01562) 820821

Huge selection of Axminster carpets made by this company. Large range of plain colours. Also all types of woven and tufted carpets. Large selection of rugs.

'Factory seconds, roll ends, remnants, perfects. Shop offers a fitting service and nationwide delivery service (free in Kidderminster, about £10 for Birmingham area, up to about £35 throughout the UK).'

Green Street is in the centre of town.

This shop is at the southern end near the ring road roundabout where the Stourport Road (A451) meets the Worcester Road (A449). From this roundabout take the exit marked 'Town Centre' then first right and next left. The shop, clearly visible, is 50 yds on the right.

[Near Victoria Carpets Weavers Shop, see next entry.]

Open: Mon–Sat 8.30–5.30.
Closed: Bank Holidays; Christmas, New Year's Days.
Cards: Access, Amex, Connect, Visa.
Cars: Behind shop (entrance to the left of this huge shop).
Toilets: Yes.
Wheelchairs: Two steps to huge spacious shop.
Teas: Plenty of places in Kidderminster.
Groups: No factory tours.
Transport: Easy walk from town centre bus station; 10 minutes from train station.
Mail order: No.

Understanding Carpets

Despite the large number of advertisements for Axminster and Wilton carpets, few people seem to appreciate the differences between them, and tufted carpets.

Axminsters and *Wiltons* are woven carpets: the pile and backing are woven together simultaneously. In contrast, the pile of *tufted* carpet is inserted into a ready-made backing by needles.

In *Axminster* carpets, tufts are cut in the form of a U and held in place by the weft backing threads. They are usually multi-coloured; but the trend for plain carpeting has made one-colour Axminster more readily available.

The weaving of *Wilton* is costlier because the yarn is continuous and buried into the backing threads. This 'dead' yarn gives Wilton its extra weight and strength. A sculptured texture can be achieved with differing pile heights.

In *tufting*, pile density is determined by the number of needles inserted per inch into the backing, and by the yarn weight. Latex holds the tufts, then a final backing gives extra body. Tufting is speedy and generally cheaper than weaving.

Carpet width used to be restricted to three feet, but sophisticated looms now allow the production of much wider carpets, hence the expression 'broadloom'. These wider carpets eliminate the need for seaming in larger rooms. Tufted carpets can sometimes be made to the exact width required. At some places they can be made to your own colour choice.

Carpet shop managers tell us they wish customers would ask them for advice more often. It is important to purchase both the correct quality floor covering for the room and correct underlay (which can prolong the carpet life significantly).

Kidderminster has five large shops with a huge range of floor coverings (now including plant fibre ranges). Shops in Stourport and Worcester also have large selections. The Craven Arms shop sells sisal, seagrass, coir and jute floor coverings.

The Weavers Shop

Readers often phone us to ask if delivery can be arranged easily – thoughts of transporting large rolls of carpet on top of the car can be somewhat offputting. Yes, reasonably priced delivery can be arranged throughout the country and, in many cases, fitters can be recommended.

The savings incurred make the journey well worthwhile even for shoppers living far afield.

21 Kidderminster Worcs *see map earlier page*

Victoria Carpet Weavers Shop

Green Street DY10 1HL
(01562) 754055

Wide range of Axminsters, Wilton and non-woven carpets, all manufactured in own factories. Excellent selection of colours/designs in variety of qualities and widths for immediate delivery. Also underlays, gripper etc.

'Gladly arrange delivery within West Midlands for £10–£20. List of recommended fitters in the local area.'

Green Street is in the centre of town.

This shop is at the southern end of town near the ring road roundabout where the Stourport Road (A451) meets the Worcester Road (A449). From this roundabout take the exit marked 'Town Centre' then go first right and next left. The shop, clearly visible, is 150 yds on the right.

[Near Rowe Carpets, see earlier entry.]

Open: Mon–Fri 10–5.30; Sat 9–5.
Closed: Four days at Christmas; Bank Holidays.
Cards: Access, Switch, Visa.
Cars: Own car-park at back (drive-in to right of the shop.
Toilets: Yes.
Wheelchairs: Wide doors, no steps to huge, spacious shop.
Teas: Café opposite shop. Plenty of places in town.
Tours: Unfortunately no tours of the works.
Transport: Within easy walking distance of town centre bus station and 10 minutes' walk from train station.
Mail order: No.

22 Kidderminster Worcs *see map earlier page*

The Weavers Shop

Duke Place, Churchfields DY10 2JP
(01562) 820680

Wide selection of Axminster carpets and tufted roll ends, discontinued lines and slight rejects. Also rugs and mats.

'Expert advice available, together with accessories and nation-wide delivery service – about £10 within 20 miles, with rate varying for elsewhere according to amount of carpet bought but always "very reasonable". Recommended fitters' list for West Midlands.'

Just outside the northern section of the ring road.

Going south from Wolverhampton and Kinver (A449) and Stourbridge (A451): after these roads merge (Broadwaters pub on right), continue towards town centre on Stourbridge Road; with Murco petrol on right go right for town centre. Keep straight for ½ mile. Pass the Horsefair pub on right. At traffic lights, go right, then left. Shop is 250 yds on right.

From other directions: get on to ring road, take Stourbridge exit (A451). Go left at traffic lights then go immediately left again to Churchfields. Shop is 250 yds on the right.

Open: Mon–Fri 8.30–5; Sat 9–12.30.
Closed: Bank Holidays; Christmas–New Year.
Cards: No.
Cars: Own car-park in front of shop.
Toilets: Yes.
Wheelchairs: Ramp through double door to huge, spacious shop.
Teas: In Kidderminster.
Tours: No.
Transport: Short walk from the town centre.
Mail order: No.

23 Kidderminster Worcs *see map earlier page*

Wyre Forest Pine

New Road DY10 1AL
(01562) 740599

Large selection of high quality pine items. Specialise in stressed and special colour finishes. Shelving units, book cases, fitted and free-standing kitchen fittings, bedroom furniture and kitchen accessories, eg bread boards, pine boxes etc. Pictures, mirrors and other items of furniture. Ready-made and made to order.

'We don't sell on price, we sell on quality. Free delivery within 20 miles of Kidderminster.'

Open: Mon–Sat 9–5, including Bank Holidays.
Closed: Christmas, Boxing and New Year's Days.
Cards: Eurocard, MasterCard, Visa.
Cars: Own parking area.
Toilets: Yes.
Wheelchairs: Access easy for wheelchair users.
Teas: Cafés in Kidderminster.
Tours: No workshop tours.
Transport: 250 yds from Kidderminster bus station.

On the south side of the town centre, near Kwik Save.

New Road leads off the ring road roundabout where the Stourport Road (A451) meets the Worcester Road (A449). From this roundabout take the exit marked 'Town Centre'. This is New Road. Don't go right into Pump Street. After 50 yds, follow sign for Carpet Warehouse.

Relax, after shopping, on an old steam train

If you have spent your money in Worcester or searched the carpet shops in Kidderminster and need to relax – or if your children are not as keen as you are on buying floor coverings – try the Severn Valley Railway.

The railway, originally part of the Great Western Railway, was restored over recent years by volunteers and is often used for making films, so you might recognize some of the stations. By 1974 only 4½ miles had been restored but the train now wends its way through 16 miles of truly delightful countryside north to Bridgnorth. It calls at Bewdley, a charming small Georgian town on the banks of the Severn, once the principal port for goods shipped from Manchester, via the River Severn, to the trans-Atlantic docks of Bristol and Gloucester; at Arley, a picturesque riverside village; Highley, whose station is a 1860's 'time capsule'; at Hampton Loade, a favourite location for angling, which has a ferry across the river to Dudmaston Hall (National Trust); and it terminates in Bridgnorth, a small hilltop town where you can enjoy wandering round the ancient narrow streets.

At weekends, with enhanced services during the summer and bank holidays. Enjoy Sunday lunch on board. Pre-Christmas Santa trains. For the talking timetable, phone (01299) 401001; for full details, including special events (even your wedding reception), phone (01299) 403816. Adult day returns about £9 (£2 children) and special rates.

24 Lichfield Staffs

Arthur Price of England

Britannia Way, Britannia Enterprise Park WS14 9UY
(01543) 257775 Fax (01543) 414488

Silver plated and stainless steel Sheffield cutlery; tableware and gifts, including tea and coffee sets, trays, tankards, goblets, picture frames, candelabras, condiment sets etc.

'All products British-made in own factories in Birmingham & Sheffield. Items are seconds, ends of ranges or exhibition-soiled.'

See our display advertisement on p. 335

On an industrial estate east of town.

From Lichfield centre: aim for Burton; pass Tesco on left. At roundabout with council depot on right, go right for Birmingham (A38).*

Coming south from Stone/Stafford on A51: go left for Burton/ Birmingham (A38)/Britannia Enterprise Park into Eastern Avenue (A5192). Continue to roundabout: go straight. At next, go left.*

Going south on A38: take first exit to Lichfield. Go over railway, turn left at the roundabout. At next roundabout turn left.*

Going north from Tamworth/A38: follow signs into Lichfield. Go under railway. At traffic lights, go right for Burton (A38). Continue for a mile (pass Lichfield City station on right, Tesco on left). At roundabout (council depot on right), go right for Birmingham A38.*

****At next roundabout, go left for Britannia Way. Look for company on left.***

Open: Mon–Fri 8.30–5; Sat 10–1.
Closed: Bank Holidays; Christmas–New Year.
Cards: Access, Switch, Visa.
Cars: Own spacious car-park.
Toilets: Yes.
Wheelchairs: Unfortunately no access (shop on first floor).
Teas: Tea shops in Lichfield.
Groups: Pre-booked groups welcome to shop. Special films of cutlery and silverware manufacture gladly shown to groups by prior appointment.
Transport: None.
Mail order: Yes. No restrictions on items sent.
Catalogue: Free.

25 Lichfield Staffs

Decor Supplies

Units 21 & 23, Britannia Way WS14 9UY
(01543) 263327

Extensive range of wallpapers, borders, paints, co-ordinated fabrics and some bedlinen. Two huge showrooms on the site, one for discounted ends of designs, etc.

'Thousands of the latest designs and colours. Let us help create your ideal home witih wallpapers that coordinate with borders and fabrics.'

On an industrial estate east of town.

From Lichfield centre: aim for Burton; pass Tesco on left. At roundabout with council depot on right, go right for Birmingham (A38).*

Coming south from Stone/Stafford on A51: go left for Burton/ Birmingham (A38)/Britannia Enterprise Park into Eastern Avenue (A5192). Continue to roundabout: go straight. At next, go left.*

Going south on A38: take first exit to Lichfield. Go over railway, turn left at the roundabout. At next roundabout turn left.*

Going north from Tamworth/A38: follow signs into Lichfield. Go under railway. At traffic lights, go right for Burton (A38). Continue for a mile (pass Lichfield City station on right, Tesco on left). At roundabout (council depot on right), go right for Birmingham A38.*

****At next roundabout, go left for Britannia Way. Look for company on left (on same side as Arthur Price).***

Open: Mon–Fri 9–5.30; Sat 9–5; Sun 10–4. Bank Holidays.
Closed: Easter Sunday; Christmas and Boxing Days.
Cards: Access, Connect, MasterCard, Switch, Visa.
Cars: Own forecourt.
Toilets: Yes.
Wheelchairs: Easy access to two huge showrooms.
Teas: Tea shops in Lichfield.
Groups: Products not really suitable for groups of shoppers.
Transport: None.
Mail order: No.

26 Ludlow Shropshire

Thistle Trading Co.

Lingen Road, Ludlow Business Park SY8 1XE
(01584) 877322

Wide range of clothing with something for all the family. Famous chainstore items at very reasonable prices, especially men's and boys' underwear; polo, rugby and sweat shirts.

'Genuine factory shop with many goods made by this company. The range is expanded by buying in from other manufacturers and clearance outlets.'

About a mile east of Ludlow, off Sheet Road and just inside the bypass (A49).

Via the A49 (Ludlow bypass): find the roundabout where the road goes off to Caynham. From this roundabout, go towards Ludlow. Shortly go right into Parys Road.*

From town centre (Somerfields supermarket): go along Lower Galdeford and continue into Sheet Road. Almost at top, pass Small's Dairy on left then take first left (Parys Road).*

****Take second right (Rover garage on near right corner), Lingen Road. Shop is at far end on left.***

Open: Tues–Sat 9–5.
Closed: Monday; Christmas–New Year; factory holidays (please phone).
Cards: No.
Cars: Own car-park.
Toilets: Yes, on request.
Wheelchairs: Easy access into medium sized shop; no steps.
Changing rooms: Yes.
Teas: Several places in Ludlow; country pubs.
Groups: Shopping groups welcome at any time, but please phone Mrs Lesley Edwards first.
Transport: 15 minutes' walk from town centre.
Mail order: No.

27 Nuneaton Warks

Abbey Textiles

Robinson House, Avenue Road CV11 4LV
(01203) 374141

Wide range of clothing with something for all the family. Famous chainstore items at very reasonable prices.

'Genuine factory shop with a lot of goods made on premises. Also by buying from other manufacturers and clearance outlets the range has been increased to supply customer demand.'

About ¾ mile south of Nuneaton town centre.

From the ring road round the central Nuneaton shopping area: turn off at the large roundabout on to the B4113 for Coventry (Coton Road). At the large roundabout with railway viaduct across it, turn left into Avenue Road (A4254). Company 300 yds on right, opposite a school.

From A5 north-east of Nuneaton: turn south on to the A47; at roundabout turn left on to the A4254 (Eastern Relief Road/ Eastborough Way). Virtually keep straight, pass the Pingles Leisure Centre on the right; this company is shortly on the left.

Open: Tues–Sat 9–5.
Closed: Monday; Christmas, Boxing and New Year's Days.
Cards: No.
Cars: Own car-park.
Toilets: No.
Wheelchairs: Easy access to large, spacious shop.
Changing rooms: Yes.
Teas: Craft Centre 500 yds.
Groups: Shopping groups welcome at any time, but essential to phone first.
Transport: Nuneaton–Coventry Midland Red bus no. 658 stops in Coton Road.
Mail order: No.

28 Pershore Hereford & Worcs

The Factory Shop Ltd.

New Road WR10 1BV
(01386) 556467

Huge range of pottery, footwear, houseware, bedding, lighting, clothing, toiletries, electricals, luggage, basketware and leisurewear. New fashion concessions department with famous brand names on first floor. *Cape Country* pine furniture exclusively produced for The Factory Shop.

'All items at greatly reduced prices. Large stock of chainstore and branded items. Deliveries of new stock every week to give an ever changing selection.'

By the old Infants School close to town centre.

From Upton-on-Severn via A4140: pass Esso petrol on right then take second right (New Road).

From Worcester on A44: shortly after you enter town, go right on to A4104 for Upton.*

From Evesham and town centre: follow A44 for Worcester; go left on to A4104 for Upton.*

****Pass petrol station on left then take second left (New Road). Shop is on right just before New Road bends sharp left.***

Open: Mon–Sat 9–5; Sun and Bank Holidays 10.30–4.30.
Closed: Christmas, Boxing, New Year and Easter Days.
Cards: Access, Switch, Visa.
Cars: Own free car-parks in front and rear of shop.
Toilets: Yes.
Wheelchairs: Easy access to spacious shop on ground floor. Steps to first floor.
Changing rooms: Yes.
Teas: Own coffee shop serving homemade hot and cold food.
Groups: Shopping groups welcome. For organiser/driver incentives please phone.
Transport: Under 5 minutes' walk from town centre.
Mail order: Home delivery service for pine furniture. Please telephone for free catalogue and price list.

29 Redditch Hereford & Worcs

Jaeger Knitwear

c/o Arrow Auctions, Bartleet Road, Washford B98 0DG
(01527) 529029

High quality ladies' knitwear, blouses, skirts, dresses, jackets etc. High quality men's knitwear, suits, jackets, trousers, shirts, ties and socks.

'Quality merchandise at reduced prices.'

On the south-east side of Redditch, just off the B4497 (Icknield Street Drive).

From M42 exit 3/Birmingham: take A435 south for Redditch/Evesham.*

From Redditch town: aim east for 'Birmingham/Coventry (A435)' on A4023 Coventry Highway; keep straight until you meet the A435. Then go south for Alcester/Evesham.*

****Stay on this partly dual carriageway road (do not go right for Redditch town centre) through Mappleborough Green. Pass the Boot Inn on left; after about ½ mile, go right on to B4497 (Icknield Street Drive). Pass Washford Mill pub on left, go over roundabout, take second right (Bartleet Road). Go immediately right into Arrow Auction site. Shop on the right.***

Open: Mon–Fri 10–4.30; Sat 10–3.30.
Closed: Bank Holidays; Christmas and New Year – please phone for dates.
Cards: Access, Connect, Switch, Visa.
Cars: Parking spaces directly outside shop.
Toilets: On site.
Wheelchairs: One step into medium sized shop.
Changing rooms: Yes.
Teas: Café on site weekdays; also in Redditch.
Groups: Shopping groups welcome – prior phone call appreciated.
Transport: None.
Mail order: No.

See our entry below

30 Ross-on-Wye Hereford & Worcs

Barker Shoes Factory Shop at Herrings

17 Gloucester Road HR9 5BV
(01989) 562431

Imperfect and discontinued ranges of high quality men's and ladies' shoes. Brands include *Barkers, Church's, Camel, Cheaney, Ecco, Loakes, Rohde, Van-Dal.* Ladies' widths AA–E and larger sizes.

'Under new management with more quality brands at factory prices. Our Rohde department offers 25% discount on RRP. Many oddments at half price or less to clear, so now is the time to stock up on your fashion, business, walking & casual shoes.'

See our display advertisement above

In the centre of Ross-on-Wye.

From M50 exit 4: turn left at the second roundabout for the town centre. Turn left in the Market Place into Gloucester Road: the shop is 150 yds on the left, opposite Midland Bank.

Open: Mon–Sat 9–5.30. Some Bank Holidays – please phone.
Closed: Christmas–New Year.
Cards: MasterCard, Switch, Visa.
Cars: Limited street parking and local car-parks.
Toilets: Yes.
Wheelchairs: Easy access, wide doors.
Teas: Café opposite.
Groups: No factory tours.
Transport: Any bus to town.
Mail order: No.

31 Ross-on-Wye Hereford & Worcs

Ross Labels

Overross House, Overross HR9 7QJ
(01989) 769000

Ladies' lingerie, hosiery, footwear, hats, mix and match separates, leisure wear, jeans, 18+ section, coats and jackets, handbags, jewellery. Men's underwear, wax and leather hats, wax jackets, golfing/leisure/casual wear, suits, shirts, ties, dinner jackets; also 'king size'. Huge selection of clothing for children of all ages (babies to early teens). Gifts, candles, confectionery, biscuits and jams.

'Famous-label fashions at affordable prices.'

See our display advertisement opposite

North of town on a roundabout near M50 exit 4.

Coming via the M50 from the east: go to the end of M50, pass petrol station on left then shop is on right by next roundabout.

From Wales on A40: bypass Ross-on-Wye, and the shop is on the left by roundabout where the A40 goes right to Gloucester.

From town centre: go north towards M50. At large roundabout with A40, go straight. The shop is on the far right corner.

From Gloucester: stay on the A40. The shop is by the roundabout, on the far right corner where the M50 spur joins the A40.

Open: Mon–Fri 9–5.30; Sat 9–6; Sun & Bank Holidays 10–5.
Closed: Christmas, Boxing and New Year Days.
Cards: All major credit and debit cards.
Cars: Large free car-park.
Toilets: Yes, including for the disabled.
Wheelchairs: Huge ground floor shop on one level.
Changing rooms: Yes.
Teas: Licensed coffee shop for hot and cold dishes, cakes and beverages. Cater for up to 80. Refreshments gladly taken downstairs for the disabled.
Groups: Pleased to accept coach parties by appointment.
Transport: Difficult.
Mail order: No.

32 Shirley, Solihull W Mids

A E Clutterbuck

Cranmore Drive B90 4PG
(0121) 704 3134 x126 Fax (0121) 704 3421
Web site: www.clutterbuck.co.uk

Domestic light fittings; wall and ceiling lights in brass and hand-painted finishes with glass or fabric shades; traditional and contemporary table and floor lamps; outside lighting etc. Large selection of lamp shades (including glass) and bulbs.

'Genuine opportunity to purchase quality domestic lighting for as little as half to two-thirds normal prices. Wide selection of styles from £5.'

See our display advertisement opposite

On the south-west side of Solihull.

From M42 exit 4: take A34 north for Birmingham (on M42 southbound, first sign says 'Henley in Arden A3400'). Turn right off A34 at first roundabout (signs to Cranmore Industrial Estate). At roundabout, go left (Highlands Road); at T-junction at far end go right (Cranmore Boulevard). Go right in front of Bryants Builders office block into Cranmore Drive. Shop in end building on left.

From Birmingham coming south on A34: cross B4102 then shortly turn left into Cranmore Boulevard. Take third right, Cranmore Drive (in front of Bryants Builders office block on right). Shop is in end building on left.

Open: Mon–Fri 8–12.30 & 1–4; Sat 9–12; Good Friday.
Closed: Most Bank Holidays; Christmas Eve, Christmas, Boxing and New Year's Days.
Cards: Access, MasterCard, Visa.
Cars: In road outside.
Toilets: Yes.
Wheelchairs: Easy access to medium-sized sales area within factory.
Teas: In Solihull or Shirley.
Groups: Groups of shoppers welcome; please telephone first.
Transport: Bus nos. 5 and 6 from Birmingham centre to Highlands Road.
Mail order: No.

Discover the exciting world of ROSS LABELS LIMITED, when you visit Ross–on–Wye, the home of famous–label fashions at affordable prices.

Situated by the A40 just outside the historic Herefordshire market town, it couldn't be easier to find.

OPEN 7 DAYS A WEEK

Tel: 01989 769000 Fax: 01989 768855

See our entry opposite

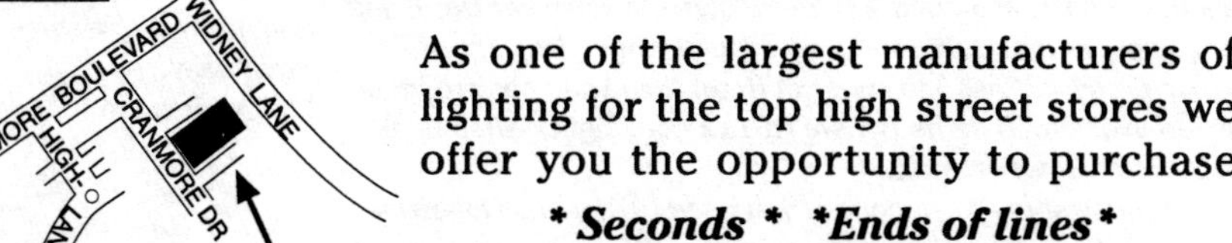

As one of the largest manufacturers of lighting for the top high street stores we offer you the opportunity to purchase

Seconds* * *Ends of lines*

Ex-display / factory samples*

All products fully tested for safety*

See our entry opposite

33 Shrewsbury Shropshire

Cane & Wicker

Hartley Business Centre, 272–284 Monkmoor Road SY2 5ST
(01743) 240261

Huge range of cane and wicker conservatory furniture, including a good selection of occasional items. Sofa beds with wicker arms or fully upholstered; three-piece suites from stock or made to order. Customers' own material service, also fabrics from leading manufacturers such as *Crowson, Sanderson, John Wilman, Ashley Wilde.*

'One of UK's largest importers and suppliers of cane and wicker conservatory furniture. Perfect quality, seconds and prototypes. Individually priced but all at considerable discount. Remnants from £1 per metre.'

See our display advertisement opposite

Monkmoor is a suburb of Shrewsbury, about 2 miles north-east of the town centre and a short distance east off the A49.

Coming west into town on the A5 (from Wellington direction): follow signs to Monkmoor.*

From town centre and all other directions: get on to the A49 north of town. From A49(T): follow signs to Monkmoor.*

****At roundabout in Monkmoor, follow sign to Monkmoor Industrial Estate. After 200 yds, go right into Hartley Business Centre. Well marked, double fronted shop is clearly visible.***

Open: Fri and Sat 9–5; other times by appointment. Some Bank Holidays, please phone.
Closed: Christmas–New Year.
Cards: Access, Visa.
Cars: In forecourt.
Toilets: Yes.
Wheelchairs: No step, huge shop.
Teas: Hot drinks machine; or in town.
Groups: Shopping groups welcome, please phone sales department.
Transport: Bus stop 300 yds; Shrewsbury station 5 minutes by taxi.
Mail order: Yes.
Catalogue: Free. Delivery anywhere in the UK, from £10.

34 Shrewsbury Shropshire

Fashion Factory

172–175 Abbey Foregate
(01743) 356333

Vast selection of quality branded ladies' and men's wear. Footwear and lingerie.

'Internationally famous brand names at savings of 40–70% off high street prices. 20–30,000 garments of constantly changing merchandise (no chainstore items). Summer and winter sales. Personal shoppers only. We are also in Wellington & Cannock.'

See our display advertisement on p. 321

Abbey Foregate, on east side of town centre, is the main road leading into Shrewsbury. Shop is across river from town centre.

From the east, M54 and A5: follow signs to town centre, going along London Road A5064. Go over roundabout with Lord Hill's column on right. Pass the Lord Hill Hotel then Lada showroom on left. Go over traffic lights (where A5112 goes right): shop is on left in former supermarket.

From Shrewsbury town centre: you need to aim east following signs to Telford. Cross the river, go under railway bridge. Shop is on right, just before traffic lights (where A5112 goes left).

Open: Mon–Sat 9.30–5.30; Sun & Bank Holidays 11–5.
Closed: Easter Sunday; Christmas Day.
Cards: Access, Switch, Visa.
Cars: Ample in own car-park.
Toilets: Ask if desperate.
Wheelchairs: Easy access; no steps to huge store.
Changing rooms: Yes.
Teas: Lots of places in town.
Groups: Shopping groups welcome but please phone first.
Transport: Regular bus service from town centre stops a few yards away.
Mail order: No.

Shifnal Shropshire

Ruckley Dried Flowers

Ruckley Estate TF11 8PQ
(01952) 460427 Fax (01952) 462780
e-mail estateoffice@ruckley.co.uk

Dried and preserved flowers, foliage and exotics direct from the grower. Hand-made flowers from around the world. Ready-made arrangements, bouquets, posies and gift-boxed items. For details of made-to-order service, phone (01952) 460428.

'Regular monthly end-of-line clearance sale items.'

Shifnal is 4 miles south-east of Telford. Ruckley is ¼ mile east of Shifnal.

From M54 exit 3: take A41 north for Whitchurch/Newport. Take first left, signposted Shifnal. Continue for 1 mile, passing under M54 (ignore sign to Ruckley and Neachley). Shop entrance is a further ¼ mile on left, clearly signed.

Late Entry

Open: Mon–Fri 8.30–4.30. Occasional weekends, phone (01952) 460428 for details.
Closed: Christmas Eve–1 Jan. Bank Holidays; Whitsun week.
Cards: MasterCard, JCB, Solo, Switch, Visa.
Cars: Free parking on site.
Wheelchairs: Assistance gladly given.
Teas: Hot drinks machine; pubs and cafés nearby.
Groups: Evening group visits can be arranged, phone (01952) 460427 for details.
Transport: Unfortunately no.

AE Clutterbuck

T P Activity Toys

Hawk Cycles

Wrekin Workwear

Rowe Carpets

Whitehouse Cox

Chambers Candy

Lighting Bug

The Stourbridge Area

Stuart Crystal cone

Stourbridge is a small town at the heart of the British glass-making industry. There are seven glass companies in the locality, and we recommend that you take full advantage of the tours which offer you the opportunity to see how glass is blown, cut and engraved. And, of course, there are excellent value pieces for sale. If you have a glass item with a chip it is worth bringing it along, as some of the companies will repair them for you while you wait. You can also have glass engraved with your initials. If you are looking for an individual wedding present, company gift, sports trophy or retirement present, you could consider commissioning a specially engraved piece of glass. For a very reasonable price you will have a unique item, designed and made by a craftsman.

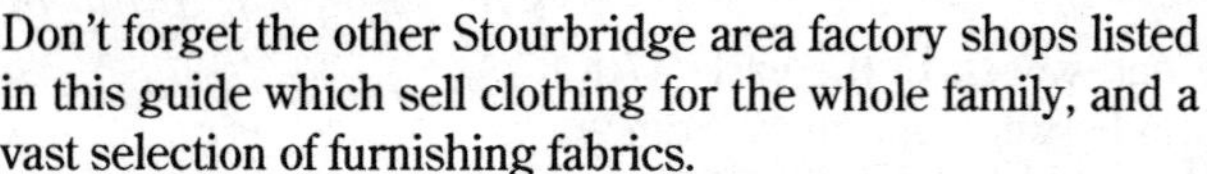

Don't forget the other Stourbridge area factory shops listed in this guide which sell clothing for the whole family, and a vast selection of furnishing fabrics.

The Stourbridge area originally consisted of several villages, which have now merged into an indistinct conglomeration. We have put the villages under the general heading of Stourbridge, and hope the map (on a later page) will help you identify them and find your way around.

Amblecote
Royal Doulton Crystal

Audnam
The Crystal Glass Centre

Brierley Hill
Bairdwear
Brierley Hill Glass Co.
Dennis Hall Tudor Crystal
Midland Fabric Warehouse
Royal Brierley Crystal
Staffordshire Crystal

Wordsley
Stuart Crystal

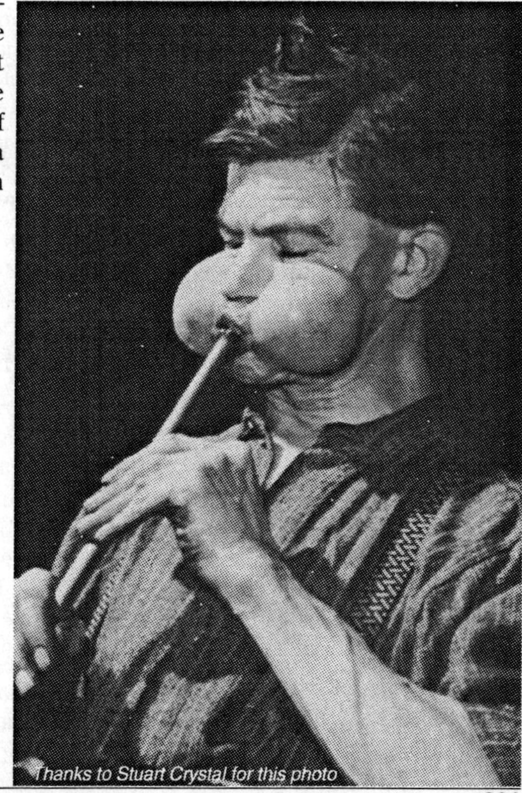

Thanks to Stuart Crystal for this photo

The Glass Quarter

Crystal Glass Centre

In Stourbridge you can indulge yourself in fine glass and crystal. In addition to first quality goods, you will find seconds in the factory shops which are often reduced because of tiny flaws and bubbles – but the imperfections are so minute that the average shopper (and the majority of drinkers) would hardly be able to detect them. On the last few occasions we have visited these shops, there have been some stunning price reductions. As with all factory shopping, stock changes frequently – but we are certain that you will find your visit extremely worthwhile. The factory shops vary in size, from a small company where you can watch the owner blowing the glass, through to one of the largest factory shops we know where you wheel round a shopping trolley. All offer excellent value.

Glassmaking in Stourbridge dates back to the early 17th century when glassmakers from Lorraine in Eastern France arrived in the area, attracted by the rich deposits of fireclay from which they made melting pots, and by the availability of coal. They specialised in making window glass until the discovery in 1676 by George Ravenscroft that if lead oxide is added to the glass composition in significant proportions it resulted in a glass with a rich, lustrous appearance. Until this time, England had relied heavily on imports of fragile Venetian glass for domestic use. From the early 1700s, following the discovery of lead crystal, table glass became an increasingly important part of the Stourbridge industry.

Glass *cutting* first began in Stourbridge in the 18th century, but, after the introduction of steam powered cutting machinery in the 19th century, it became a major – and world famous – part of the local glass industry. Cut lead glass was originally called flint glass but in the 20th century became known as crystal.

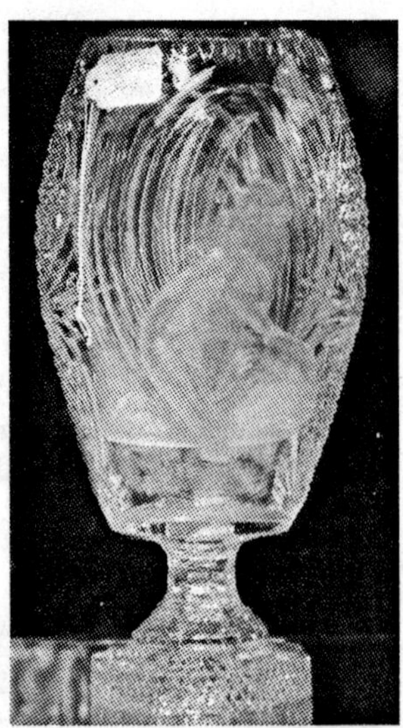
Brierley Hill Crystal

There are two grades of crystal in Britain: full lead crystal containing 30–34% lead oxide, and lead crystal with a minimum content of 24%, both producing the distinctive ringing sound when tapped with the finger. (Note that continental and American glass, although frequently described as 'full lead', generally has a low lead content.) Full lead crystal is more expensive to produce; we have noticed recently that some companies have reduced lead content.

'The Glass Quarter' stretches south from Kingswinford to Stourbridge along the A491, also extending to Brierley Hill and Royal Brierley Crystal. The Himley Hall Glass Museum and Broadfield House Glass Museum are closely linked to the project. The Stourbridge Canal is being given due recognition for the major part it has played in the development of local industries over the centuries. Amongst examples of local heritage is the Red House Cone (at Stuart Crystal), whose 100 ft tall silhouette is a feature of the local skyline. It is the last surviving glassworks cone in the country. In this area is the International Glass Centre, a centre of excellence for training and development in the glass industry.

Make the most of the wonderful ranges of family clothing, curtaining and furnishing fabrics while you are in the area.

With thanks to Dudley Metropolitan Borough Council for this information.

Staffordshire Crystal

Crystal Glass Centre

Broadfield House
Glass Museum

35 Stourbridge area : Amblecote

Royal Doulton Crystal

see map opposite

Coalbourn Lane DY8 4HS
(01384) 552934

Royal Doulton crystal, stemware and giftware.

About ½ mile north of Stourbridge ring road, in a little lane off the A491 (Stourbridge–Wolverhampton road). Look for brown tourist signs.

Going north on A491 from Stourbridge: Coalbourn Lane is on left.

Going south on A491 from Amblecote/Kingswinford: cross the traffic lights at Collis Street (A4102, Dudley/Brierley Hill–Wollaston/Bridgnorth road) and turn into the first little lane on right (large brown 'Royal Doulton' sign opposite).

[Coaches please use Wollaston Road entrance round corner.]

STOP PRESS
Shop has moved to The Crystal Glass Centre (see details below). For further information call (01384) 350134. Free tours are still available at the factory here in Coalbourn Lane.

Open: Mon–Sat 9–5.30.
Closed: Easter Monday; Christmas, Boxing and New Year's Days.
Cards: Access, Amex, Diners, Visa.
Cars: Own car-park beside shop.
Toilets: Yes.
Wheelchairs: Good access.
Teas: Hot-drink machine.
Tours: Free tours Mon–Fri at 10 & 11.15 am. Max 52 people; advisable to book in advance with Mrs Oakes. No children under 10. No tours Saturdays, in Easter week, Spring BH week, August BH or third week September, Xmas–New Year.
Transport: Bus stop 60 yds.
Mail order: Yes.
Catalogue: No.

36 Stourbridge area : Audnam

The Crystal Glass Centre

see map opposite

Churton House DY8 4AJ
(01384) 354400

Vast range of crystal ware from *Edinburgh Crystal*, *Thomas Webb* and other leading British and European makers, incl. *Spiegelau*, *Kristalglas*, *Caithness Glass*, *Tweedmuir Glass*, *Blow-Zone*, *Livanu* and *Swarowski* silver crystal.

'Firsts, seconds, obsoletes, overstocks and promotional ranges. Minimum 30% off RRP for seconds.'

In a large, conspicuous new square glass building in Audnam High Street (A491), the main road north from Stourbridge.

Going north from Stourbridge: the shop is on the left, by traffic lights where Brettel Lane (A461) goes right for Brierley Hill.

From Brierley Hill: take A461 downhill for Stourbridge. At the traffic lights at the bottom, go straight across into little road beside the company (on the right).

Coming south on A491 from Kingswinford towards Stourbridge: at traffic lights where A461 goes left for Brierley Hill, go right into little road beside this conspicuous building.

Open: Mon–Sat 9.30–5.30; Sun 11–5. Bank Holidays. Pre-booked groups welcome evenings.
Closed: Christmas, Boxing and New Year's Days.
Cards: Amex, MasterCard, Switch, Visa.
Cars: Own car-park.
Toilets: Yes.
Wheelchairs: No steps, easy access (plus lift) to all areas. Huge showroom.
Teas: Own 60-seat patisserie/coffee shop for light lunches, home baking, tea, coffee etc.
Tours: Exhibition/video of history of glass in area. Free tours/demonstrations arranged 9.30–4. Coach parties welcome, please book first. Glass cutting workshop (Mon–Fri 10–4), engraving service (Tues–Sat 10–4).
Transport: Stourbridge Town station (train and bus); bus nos. 311 and 313 to Brettel Lane.
Mail order: Yes. Free first quality catalogue and price list.

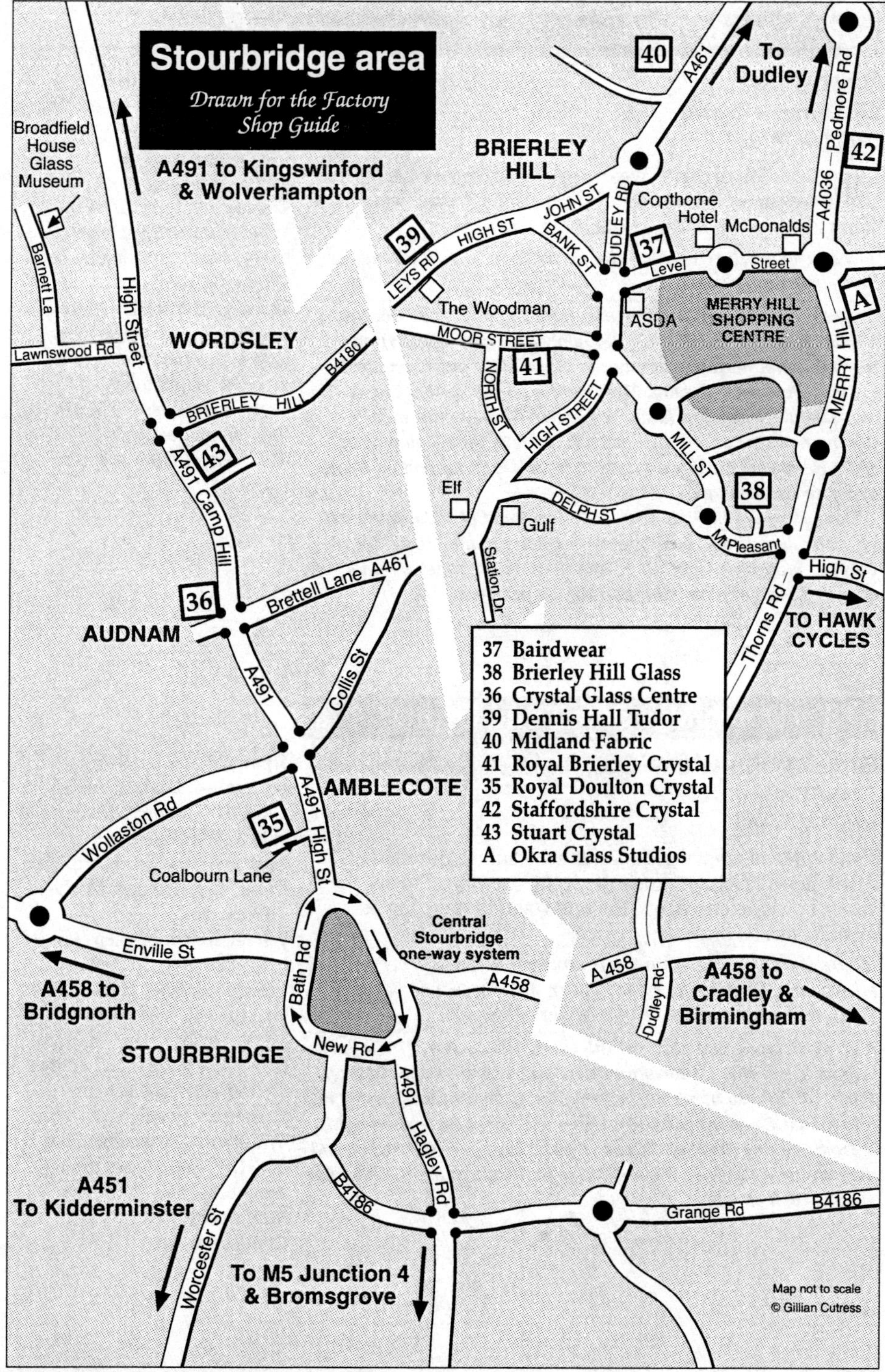
Stourbridge area
Drawn for the Factory Shop Guide
A491 to Kingswinford & Wolverhampton
Broadfield House Glass Museum
BRIERLEY HILL
To Dudley
WORDSLEY
AUDNAM
AMBLECOTE
STOURBRIDGE
MERRY HILL SHOPPING CENTRE
Copthorne Hotel
McDonalds
ASDA
The Woodman
Elf
Gulf
Coalbourn Lane
Central Stourbridge one-way system
TO HAWK CYCLES
A458 to Bridgnorth
A458 to Cradley & Birmingham
A451 To Kidderminster
To M5 Junction 4 & Bromsgrove
Map not to scale
© Gillian Cutress
37 Bairdwear
38 Brierley Hill Glass
36 Crystal Glass Centre
39 Dennis Hall Tudor
40 Midland Fabric
41 Royal Brierley Crystal
35 Royal Doulton Crystal
42 Staffordshire Crystal
43 Stuart Crystal
A Okra Glass Studios

37 Stourbridge area : Brierley Hill

Bairdwear

see map on previous page

Level Street DY5 1UB
(01384) 77102

Large selection of men's wear, especially trousers and jeans; also knitwear and shirts. Ladies' separates, casual wear and some lingerie. Good range of children's wear.

'Famous chainstore overmakes, perfects, seconds and ends of lines at reduced prices.'

On the hill leading up (north-west) from the Merry Hill Centre.

From Pedmore Road (A4036, mainly dual carriageway): at roundabout at north-east corner of Merry Hill Centre, go uphill towards Pensnett, passing McDonald's on the right. At next roundabout go straight (pass Waterside Restaurants then Copthorne Hotel on right). Pass ATS on left, then look for huge silver Bairdwear factory on right: car-park is at far end on right, opposite Asda on left.

From Brierley Hill High Street/Dudley Road (A461): turn east at traffic lights into Level Street for Quarry Bank/Merry Hill Centre. Asda is on right. Bairdwear is the first huge silver factory on left: go left into car-park as soon as possible.

Open: Mon–Sat 10–4.
Closed: Christmas–New Year; most Bank Holidays.
Cards: Access, Visa.
Cars: Own large car-park.
Toilets: In Merry Hill Centre.
Wheelchairs: 22 shallow steps to very large shop on first floor.
Changing rooms: Yes.
Teas: In Merry Hill Centre.
Groups: Groups of shoppers always welcome. Please phone first. No factory tours.
Transport: Buses to Merry Hill then 10 minutes' walk.
Mail order: No.

38 Stourbridge area : Brierley Hill

Brierley Hill Glass Co.

see map on previous page

Mount Pleasant DY5 2YS
(01384) 77486

Hand-cut lead crystal glassware: wine suites, tumblers, vases, jugs etc. Huge range of highly cut punch bowls, vases, bowls, ashtrays etc. Seconds, and first quality at manufacturer's prices.

'There is a large showroom, with one room for perfects and one for seconds. Special sales are held in March, November and December when opening times might be longer.'

A short distance due south of the Merry Hill Centre.

From Merry Hill: go towards Bromsgrove (A491) and 'Quarry Bank A4036'. Go uphill to traffic lights, turn right for Brierley Hill into Mount Pleasant (A4100). Large shop is at far end on right.

From Brierley Hill High Street (A461): turn into Mill Street and stay on the A4100; at the second roundabout turn left. This large shop is then on left.

Open: Mon–Thur 9–5; Fri, Sat 9–4; Bank Holidays.
Closed: Christmas, Boxing and New Year's Days.
Cards: Access, Eurocard, Visa.
Cars: Large car-park by shop.
Toilets: Yes.
Wheelchairs: No steps to large showroom and shop.
Teas: In Brierley Hill.
Groups: Please contact Mrs J. Taylor if you would like to see how glass is cut. Tours are free and last one hour. Coach parties welcome.
Transport: Birmingham bus nos. 137 and 138 pass through Mount Pleasant.
Mail order: Yes.
Catalogue: No.

39 Stourbridge area : Brierley Hill

Dennis Hall Tudor Crystal *see map on previous page*

Chiltern House, Leys Road, Brockmoor DY5 3UR
(01384) 485254

English hand-made full lead (33%) crystal, blown, made and decorated here: wine suites, vases, bowls, glass animals, bells, compotes, christening cups, tankards, sweet dishes, witch bowls and dees (angled vases on stems, ideal for fine sprays of flowers and other floral arrangements).

'First quality, discounted seconds and discounted lines. Special commissions gladly undertaken. Repairs and replacements a speciality. Sherry glasses from £3.75, small bud vases from £4.75, salad bowls from £14.95, 8" vases from £14.75. As supplied to embassies around the world.'

On the B4180 (Leys Road).

At traffic lights at the northern end of Brierley Hill High Street (A461 Stourbridge–Dudley road): turn on to B4179 for Pensett/ Wordsley. Then turn left immediately after The Bridge pub on the left on to B4180 for Wordsley. Shop is on the right, just past West Midland Fabrications Engineering, opposite The Woodman.

From the A491 (Stourbridge–Wolverhampton road): turn on to B4180 at traffic lights in Wordsley. Shop is about a mile on left, 300 yds after BOC on the left, and opposite The Woodman.

Open: Mon–Fri 9–5; Sat 10–4. Bank Holidays 10–4.
Closed: Christmas–New Year.
Cards: Access, Visa.
Cars: Outside shop.
Toilets: Yes.
Wheelchairs: Three steps.
Teas: The Woodman opposite shop for meals.
Groups: Please contact Gordon Noble or John Kimberley. Visitors can see glass blowing and glass cutting. Tours on Mon and Thur 10–12 & 1–3; Tues and Fri 10–12. No restrictions on numbers or ages.
Transport: Local buses.
Mail order: Yes.
Catalogue: Free. No restrictions on items sent.

40 Stourbridge area : Brierley Hill

Midland Fabric Warehouse *see map on previous page*

Units 2 & 3 Oak Park, Dudley Road DY5 1HR
(01384) 482424

Large stock of upholstery and furnishing fabrics: cottons, linens, damasks, velvets etc. Nets, voiles, calico, interlinings, waddings, linings. Haberdashery, fringing. Curtain rails/poles and accessories. Cushion covers and fillers. Ready-made curtains. Foam cut to shape. Dress fabrics.

'Custom-made curtain making service.'

On the north-west side of the Merry Hill Centre.

From Pedmore Road (A4036, mainly dual carriageway): at roundabout at north-east corner of Merry Hill Centre, go uphill for Pensnett, passing McDonald's on right. At next roundabout go straight (pass Copthorne Hotel on right). Pass Bairdwear factory on right. At traffic lights, go right into Dudley Road A461.*

Coming north on Brierley Hill High Street A461: at traffic lights (Asda on right) go straight.*

****Go over roundabout (John Street and fire station on left). Pass Wickes on left; go left for Oak Park estate. Shop clearly visible.***

Open: Seven days a week: Mon–Sat 9.30–5.30 (late night Fri till 8); Sun 10–4. Bank Holidays 10–4.
Closed: Please phone for Christmas closures.
Cards: Access, Connect, Delta, Switch, Visa.
Cars: Own free car-park.
Toilets: Yes, including for the disabled.
Wheelchairs: One easy step, wide aisles, large shop.
Teas: Merry Hill Centre.
Groups: Shopping groups welcome, no need to phone.
Transport: Local buses.

41 Stourbridge area : Brierley Hill

Royal Brierley Crystal

see map on earlier page

Moor Street DY5 3SJ
(01384) 573580 (shop) 70161 (tours)

Huge selection of hand-made, hand-cut crystal such as stemware, tumblers, decanters, jugs, vases, bowls etc. Also *Royal Worcester* porcelain.

'Huge shop – you get a trolley! Stock does not meet company's high standards so prices reduced. Sales in February; mid-June–mid-July; mid-November.'

See our display advertisement opposite

Five minutes' drive from the Merry Hill Shopping Centre, 3 miles north-east of Stourbridge and 3 miles south-west of Dudley in the heart of the British glass-making area.

Moor Street links Brierley Hill High Street (A461, Dudley–Amblecote road) with Brierley Hill Road (B4180, Dudley–Wordsley road). Shop is at Brierley Hill High Street end.

From Brierley Hill High Street (A461): turn off at traffic lights with sign to this company. Go downhill to the huge shop on left.

From Stourbridge: take A491 north; turn right at traffic lights in Amblecote into Brettell Lane (A461). Turn left at signs to shop.

Open: Mon–Sat 9–5; Sun 10–4. Bank Holidays.
Closed: Christmas, Boxing and New Year's Days.
Cards: Access, Amex, Visa.
Cars: Large car-parks, with coach area.
Toilets: Yes.
Wheelchairs: Easy access to huge spacious shop but tour difficult for wheelchairs.
Teas: Coffee shop for light meals, coffee etc Mon–Fri 9–2.30; weekends by arrangement.
Groups: Coach parties, small groups or individuals contact Visits Administrator to arrange tours: £2 adults, £1 children. Groups to shop need not book.
Transport: Bus no. 137 from Birmingham along this road.
Mail order: No.
Catalogue: Retail catalogue only.

42 Stourbridge area : Brierley Hill

Staffordshire Crystal

see map on earlier page

Pedmore Road, Brierley Hill DY5 1TJ
(01384) 77701

33% lead oxide crystal melted in the furnace and mouth-blown on premises: tableware, stemware, tankards, bowls, vases etc. Cutting and engraving. Speciality: glass decanters cut like golf and tennis balls, footballs etc – ideal club prizes.

'Everything hand-made. Prices about 50% less than normal high street prices. Perfects and seconds. Welcome special commissions for clubs, companies. Can engrave while you wait. Repair glass chips on the spot.'

On A4036 Pedmore Road close to Merry Hill Shopping Centre.

From Dudley: take A461 for Stourbridge but turn on to A4036 following signs to Merry Hill Centre. Factory and shop clearly signed on the left about 250 yds before the roundabout.

From Stourbridge: take the A461 north for Brierley Hill. Go along the High Street and turn right at the traffic lights with signs to Merry Hill Centre. Go straight at the first roundabout and left at the second. Staffordshire Crystal is clearly visible on the right but you have to go up to the next roundabout and back-track as this is a dual carriageway.

Open: Mon–Sun 9–5; Bank Holidays.
Closed: Christmas and Boxing Days.
Cards: No.
Cars: Large car and coach park.
Toilets: Yes.
Wheelchairs: Easy access. One small step to shop.
Teas: Teas, restaurants etc in Merry Hill.
Tours: You are welcome to see the glass blown from the Visitor Area.
Transport: Any buses to Merry Hill then short walk.
Mail order: No.

See our entry opposite

Stourbridge area : Brierley Hill

Okra Glass Studios

see map on earlier page

Unit 2, Enterprise Estate, Hurst Lane (off Pedmore Road)
DY5 1TX
(01384) 70000

Unique range of hand-made coloured art glass with decorative iridised effects. Paper weights, perfume bottles, vases, bud vases, ginger jars. Most items signed by the artist.

'Perfects at normal prices, plus a selection of seconds. All items very collectable: phone for details about collectors' club (with newsletter, workshop visits etc).'

On A4036 Pedmore Road facing Merry Hill Shopping Centre.

From Dudley: take A461 for Stourbridge then turn on to A4036 following signs to Merry Hill Centre. At roundabout (HSS hire company on left) go left, then right into Enterprise Estate (then round small one-way system to company).

From Stourbridge: take A461 north for Brierley Hill. Go along High Street; go right at traffic lights (Asda on right) at signs to Merry Hill Centre. Go downhill, straight at first roundabout, pass McDonald's on left and straight at next roundabout. Go right into Enterprise Estate (then round small one-way system to company).

Late Entry

Open: Mon–Sat 10–4. Please phone for Bank Holidays.
Closed: Christmas–New Year; Whit week; last 2 weeks July.
Cards: Major debit and credit cards (not Amex).
Cars: Few spaces in forecourt; large car-park 50 yds walk.
Toilets: Yes; not for disabled.
Wheelchairs: Easy access; one shallow step. All areas one level.
Teas: In Merry Hill centre.
Groups: Free tours may be arranged for up to 6 people – mornings only; workshop can be viewed from shop. Unsuitable for children under 10 years. Please contact Hannah Hughes.
Transport: Any bus to Merry Hill then 5-minute walk.
Mail order: Export only.
Catalogue: £5. Please phone or write for catalogue.

43 Stourbridge area : Wordsley

Stuart Crystal

see map on earlier page

Redhouse Glassworks DY8 4AA
(01384) 261777

Wide range of full lead crystal, best and seconds quality: wine suites, decanters, jugs, vases and extensive range of giftware. Also tantaluses and trays. Often special offers. Personal engraving from 45p per letter.

'Glass repair service available.'

See our display advertisement opposite

On the A491 (Stourbridge–Wolverhampton road), just over a mile north of Stourbridge ring road, and about 1 ½ miles south of the crossroads in Kingswinford. Bottle oven cone is very conspicuous (on the right, if you come north from Stourbridge).

From Brierley Hill via Brettel Lane (A461): at the trafffic lights in Amblecote, turn right on to A491 and continue to company with huge bottle kiln on right.

Open: Mon–Sun 9–5; Bank Holidays.
Closed: Xmas and Boxing Days.
Cards: Access, Amex, Visa.
Cars: Large car & coach parks.
Toilets: Yes, and for disabled.
Wheelchairs: Easy access, huge spacious ground floor shop.
Teas: Coffee shop open seven days 9–5.
Tours: The Redhouse Cone (Mon–Sun 9–5) for an intriguing insight into old and modern glass making. A copper wheel engraver demonstrates his skill Tues–Sat. Factory tours (Mon–Fri).
Transport: Bus nos. 257, 267, 556 (Stourbridge– Wolverhampton) stop near the shop.
Mail order: Yes.
Catalogue: Free stemware catalogue. Firsts & seconds sent.

Broadfield House Glass Museum

If, like us, you enjoy studio glass as well as the more traditional styles, then be sure to visit this museum which has recently been refurbished. It is just off the A491, on the north side of the glass quarter. You enter through the dramatic new entrance, a glass pavilion which is believed to be the largest glass structure of its kind in the world. Here you can buy books about glass and studio pieces by craftspeople working today. The glassmaker in residence might be demonstrating his or her craft. There are excellent examples of Stourbridge glass, cameo glass through the ages, and a multi-screen presentation about personalities behind British glass.

Compton Drive, Kingswinford, DY6 9NS
Open afternoons (not Monday, except Bank Holidays) and longer on Saturdays.
(01384) 812745

Float away after a day's stressful shopping

As serious factory shops know, a full day's bargain hunting can be somewhat exhausting. If you have travelled to the Western Midlands to make the most of the excellent shops here, we suggest that you arrange to stay near Droitwich. Book yourself that evening into Droitwich spa to make a soporific recovery. The water in this luxurious salt 'swimming pool' is gloriously hot and has the same density as the Dead Sea. Therefore you simply cannot sink (but you have to rest your head on a blow-up cushion to lessen the risk of getting salt in your eyes). You are provided with large soft towels then after your relaxing float, you can be served drinks as you relax still further around the pool. Booking is advised although we have turned up and found that they have a vacancy. Cheaper for couples.

(01905) 794894

See our entry opposite

Merry Hill Shopping Centre

Although this book is written especially for people who are seeking reduced price items, some shoppers may from time to time feel drawn to visit high street shops. The Merry Hill Centre, between Dudley and Brierley Hill, should satisfy such urges. With 260 shops, including Debenhams, Marks & Spencer, Sainsbury's, Asda and BHS, there is plenty to tempt you ... as do the 20 places where to eat. Under cover, with its perfectly controlled climate, all facilities and parking space for 10,000 cars, the Merry Hill Centre – 'Europe's finest shopping centre' – does offer convenient shopping. We mentioned in the past that we wished individual shops and the centre management would liaise in reducing the volume of the raucous background music ('shopper-calming'?). It seems that our plea might have reached the right ears ... last time we went to Merry Hill, we were impressed how peaceful it was. Unfortunately the monorail remains out of action as we write. That used to be fun.

Merry Hill Centre, Brierley Hill, DY5 1SY.
(01384) 481141. Open 7 days a week (extra late on Thursday). Free wheelchair loan.

The Black Country
(engraved in 1860)

44 Stourport-on-Severn Worcs *map opposite*

Carpets of Worth

Severn Valley Mills DY13 9HB
(01299) 827222 x 210

Wide range of woven Axminster carpets in good variety of colours and patterns and in different widths; few Axminster rugs; picture rugs; tufted carpets. Mainly wool/nylon.

'All items are seconds, imperfects, overmakes or discontinued lines. Also ends of contract rolls. Regret that children under 14 not allowed into shop. Delivery can be arranged throughout UK; price quoted at time of purchase.'

On the south side of town centre, beside the river Severn. Stourport has rather complicated one-way systems!

From Bewdley (B4195), Kidderminster (A451), Hartlebury (B4193) and Worcester (A4025): don't go right into the town centre but keep going clockwise round the one-way system; in Mitton Street look for sign (on left in a right-hand bend) pointing left to Carpets of Worth and go left.*

From Great Witley: go through town for 'All other routes' or 'Kidderminster'. Pass the adjacent Repsol, Esso and Texaco petrol stations then keep clockwise until you see the sign to the carpet shop. Turn left.*

***The mill is on the left with a clearly marked shop entrance.**

Open: Mon–Fri 9–5; Sat 8–12.
Closed: Bank Holidays; Christmas–New Year.
Cards: None.
Cars: Visitors' car-park.
Toilets: Factory toilets available.
Wheelchairs: Easy access.
Teas: In attractive town of Stourport.
Tours: No factory tours.
Transport: Five minutes from town centre.
Mail order: No.

45 Stourport-on-Severn Worcs *map opposite*

T P Activity Toys

Severnside Works, Severn Road DY13 9EY
(01299) 827300

Own manufacture quality garden toys, climbing frames, slides, trampolines, large swings, netball sets etc. Also large selection of unusual party bag and stocking fillers, and extensive range of *Lego, Playmobil, Galt, Brio* & other brands.

'Play area available. Seconds and ends of ranges of our own products available at greatly reduced prices.'

On the south side of town centre, beside the river Severn. Stourport has rather complicated one-way systems!

From Bewdley (B4195), Kidderminster (A451), Hartlebury (B4193) and Worcester (A4025): don't go right into town centre but keep going clockwise round the one-way system; in Mitton Street look for the sign (on the left in a right-hand bend) pointing left to Carpets of Worth and turn left.*

From Great Witley: go through town for 'All directions' and 'Kidderminster'. Pass adjacent Repsol, Esso,Texaco stations; go clockwise until you see sign on left pointing left to carpet shop.*

***Pass the carpet factory and keep going to the end of Severn Road (long cul-de-sac leading down to the river). T P Activity Toys straight ahead.**

Open: Mon–Fri 9–5; Sat 9.30–4.30.
Closed: Bank Holidays.
Cards: Access, Visa.
Cars: Private car-park across road.
Toilets: Yes.
Wheelchairs: All at ground level.
Teas: In Stourport.
Groups: Groups of shoppers please phone first.
Transport: Easy walking distance of bus station.
Mail order: No.
Catalogue: Free.

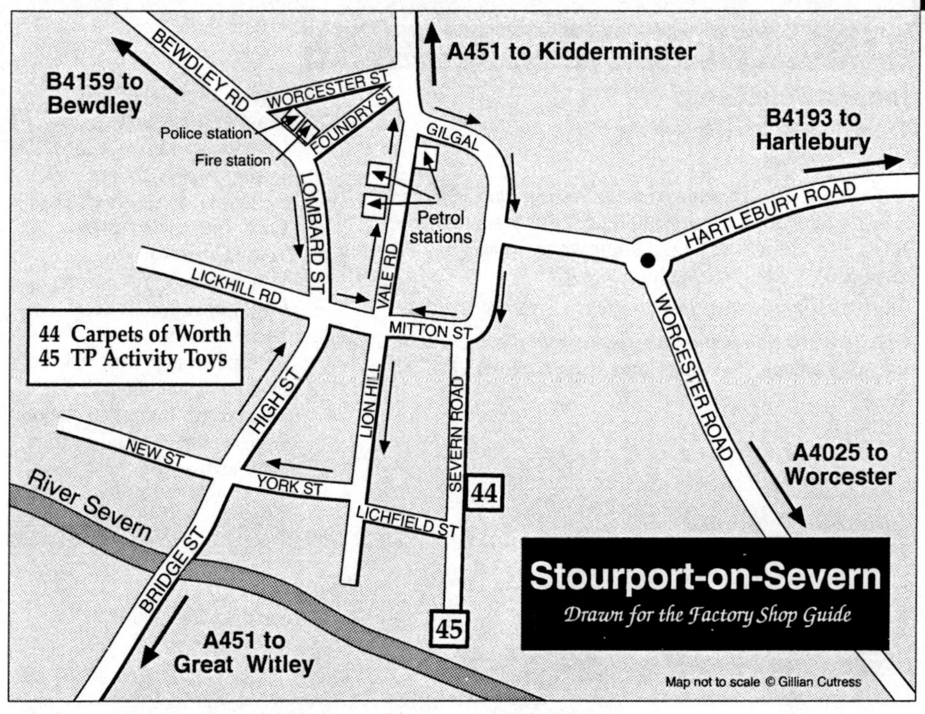

46 Stratford-upon-Avon Warks

Stratford Tile Warehouse

Unit 1 Avenue Farm Industrial Estate, off Birmingham Road
(01789) 299445

Importers of many varieties of natural slate. Hand-made terracotta wall and floor tiles.

'We decorate a wide range of kitchen and bathroom ceramic tiles, and cut and decorate border tiles in a wide range of designs. Slight seconds and discontinued lines available: reductions of up to 50%.'

Birmingham Road A3400 (was A34) is the main road leading north out of Stratford. Company is about two miles north of town.

From Stratford: aim north for Henley-in-Arden and Birmingham. Go over roundabout (Tesco on right). Keep straight for few hundred yards. Go left after large garage (John Yarnold) on left into Avenue Farm.*

Coming south on A3400 (was A34): pass Range Rover garage then turn right into Avenue Farm.*

****At far end, company is on right (behind bed company).***

Open: Mon–Fri 8–5.30 (Thur late till 8); Sat 9–5.30.
Closed: Most Bank Holidays, please phone to check.
Cards: MasterCard, Visa.
Cars: In adjoining car-park.
Toilets: Yes.
Wheelchairs: Unfortunately not suitable for wheelchairs.
Teas: In town.
Transport: 15 minutes' walk from town centre.
Mail order: Yes. Payment by credit card accepted by phone.
Catalogue: No.

47 Tamworth Staffs

Jaeger Sale Shop

43 Church Street B79 7DF
(01827) 52828

Jaeger ladies' and men's wear including ladies' jackets, skirts and blouses; men's suits, jackets, trousers, shirts, ties and socks etc. Ladies' and men's knitwear. *Viyella* ladies' wear including jackets, skirts, blouses etc.

'High quality merchandise at greatly reduced prices.'

Easy to find in the pedestrianised area of the town centre facing the large church. This huge shop is on a corner site.

Open: Mon–Sat 9.30–5.30.
Closed: Bank Holidays; Christmas and New Year.
Cards: Amex, Access, Visa, Switch and Jaeger Accounts.
Cars: Car-parks nearby.
Toilets: In town.
Wheelchairs: Yes, no steps.
Changing rooms: Yes.
Teas: In town.
Groups: Bus parties welcome by prior arrangement.
Transport: Tamworth station ½ mile. Shop near bus station.
Mail order: No.

48 Tamworth Staffs

Probus Housewares

Watling Street B77 1EZ
(01827) 288588

Kitchen tools and icing equipment; co-ordinated kitchen textiles and tinware including oven gloves, tea towels, aprons, tablecloths, bread bins, pedal bins, canisters and biscuit barrels.

'New shop attached to modern factory of company established in 1911 which moves with the times, selling firsts, seconds and ends of lines at reduced prices. Phone for annual sale dates.'

On the south side of the town centre.

From Brownhills: go east on A5. After Hints village take A453 left, signposted Sutton Coldfield. Follow signs to Sutton Coldfield, going over A5. At traffic lights (Mile Oak pub far left corner) turn left. At next traffic lights go straight; pass Jet petrol on left; go over bridge. Turn right into factory opposite Reliant.

From M42 exit 10: take B5404 west, signposted Drayton Manor; follow signs for Drayton Manor. After 2 miles go over Two Gates traffic lights (The Bull's Head on right corner). Probus is first entrance on left, opposite Reliant.

Open: Thur, Fri, Sat, Sun 10–4. Easter Monday.
Closed: Monday, Tuesday, Wednesday; Christmas–New Year phone for opening times.
Cards: None.
Cars: Own car-park.
Toilets: Yes.
Wheelchairs: Easy access.
Teas: Cafés and pubs nearby.
Groups: Shopping groups welcome; please telephone first.
Transport: Unfortunately none.
Mail order: No.

49 Tamworth Staffs

Webb Ivory

6 Market Street B79 7LV
(01827) 60266

Fascinating variety of surplus catalogue stocks of greetings cards, wrapping papers, household goods, toys, small gifts and clothing.

'50% off catalogue prices.'

In the town centre, easy to find in the pedestrianised shopping area close to Wilkinsons hardware stores and Tamworth Castle. Find the statue of Robert Peel: shop is a few yards downhill on the right.

Open: Mon–Sat 9–5. Some Bank Holidays, please check.
Closed: Christmas–New Year.
Cards: Most major credit cards; Switch.
Cars: Public car-parks nearby.
Toilets: In town centre.
Wheelchairs: Easy access, no steps.
Teas: In town centre.
Groups: Too small for groups.
Transport: Bus terminal 2 minutes' walk.
Mail order: No.

Lockmaking in Willenhall

Lockmaking began in this area in Elizabethan times. By the middle of the 19th century it had concentrated in Willenhall, with some 340 self-employed lockmakers in the town, mostly in small workshops. Locks were made entirely by hand, and skills and tools were passed down from father to son. As the industry grew, the population expanded and social conditions deteriorated. Poor housing and sanitation led in 1849 to a cholera epidemic. Nearly 300 people died. The town was shocked into improving conditions: in 1854 the Local Board of Health was founded.

Today only a few backyard locksmiths exist. Locks are no longer made by hand, but mass produced in large factories and sold all over the world.

The fascinating small Lock Museum occupies 54 New Road. This Victorian locksmith's house and workshop, built in 1840, later belonged to John Hodson, whose family had been Willenhall locksmiths since 1792, and John Hodson eventually bought the business from his mother's estate in 1893. With his wife Sarah and their children he moved into No. 54 in 1904. After her husband's death, Sarah Hodson allowed two daughters to open a drapers' shop in the front room, but locks continued to be made in the workshop. In 1983, on the death of the last surviving of the children, the Lock Museum Trust bought and restored the properties.

Most items on display belonged to the Hodson family, and visitors to the gas-lit rooms can experience the life of a turn-of-the century locksmith. A collection of locks and keys is on view, and in the workshops you can often hear the noise of belt driven machinery and see padlocks being made in the traditional way. *Open 4 days a week. £2. (01902 634542)*

50 Telford Salop *see map opposite*

Bairdwear

Halesfield 13 TF7 4QP
(01952) 683700

Large selection of men's wear, especially trousers and jeans; also knitwear and shirts. Ladies' separates, casual wear and some lingerie. Good range of children's wear.

'Famous name chainstore items, perfects, seconds, ends of lines at reduced prices.'

On the south-east side of Telford, Halesfield is off the A442 (Telford–Bridgnorth road).

From Telford town centre or M54 exit 5: get on to A442 (Queensway) for Bridgnorth. At Stirchley Interchange follow signs to Halesfield. At second roundabout go right into Halesfield 13.*

From Ironbridge: take A4169 for Madeley/Shifnal. Go through Madeley, turn right at Halesfield roundabout for Halesfield 17 which becomes Halesfield 13. Shop is in first factory on right; go right into car-park.

From Kidderminster/Bridgnorth via A442: at Brockton roundabout go right for Shifnal into Halesfield 10, then go left into Halesfield 13.*

****Go downhill, pass Halesfield 14; turn left into Bairdwear.***

Open: Mon–Thur 9–4.30; Fri 9–1.
Closed: Christmas–New Year; most Bank Holidays.
Cards: Access, Visa.
Cars: Company car-park.
Toilets: No.
Wheelchairs: One small step, large spacious shop.
Changing rooms: Yes.
Teas: In Madeley and Telford.
Groups: Shopping groups welcome with prior phone call.
Transport: Bus no. 46 from town centre every 20 mins. Get off two stops after last Link 51 then 5 minutes' walk.
Mail order: No.

51 Telford Salop *see map opposite*

Fruit of the Loom

Halesfield 10G TF7 4QR
(01952) 587123 ext 207

T-shirts, sweatshirts, jogging bottoms and polo shirts.

'Firsts, seconds and ends of line sold here from factory in Ireland at discounted prices; minimum discount 25%.'

On the south-east side of Telford, Halesfield is off the A442 (Telford–Bridgnorth road).

From Telford town centre or M54 exit 5: get on to A442 (Queensway) south for Bridgnorth. At the Brockton roundabout turn left for Shifnal, then second right into Halesfield 10G.*

From Ironbridge: follow the A4169 for Madeley and Shifnal. Go through Madeley then turn right at the Coppice Farm roundabout and take the first left after next roundabout into Halesfield 10G.*

From Kidderminster and Bridgnorth north via A442: at the Brockton roundabout turn right for Shifnal into Halesfield 10 and then take second right into Halesfield 10G.

****Shop is at far end of this road, clearly signed.***

Open: Mon–Thur 9.30–4; Fri 9.30–3.30; Sat 9.30–12.30.
Closed: Bank Holidays; Christmas–New Year.
Cards: Delta, MasterCard, Switch, Visa.
Cars: Own car-park.
Toilets: Yes.
Wheelchairs: Level access, wide door.
Changing rooms: Yes.
Teas: In Telford and Madeley.
Groups: Please phone first.
Transport: Bus no. 46 from Madeley; no. 42 from Telford.
Mail order: No.

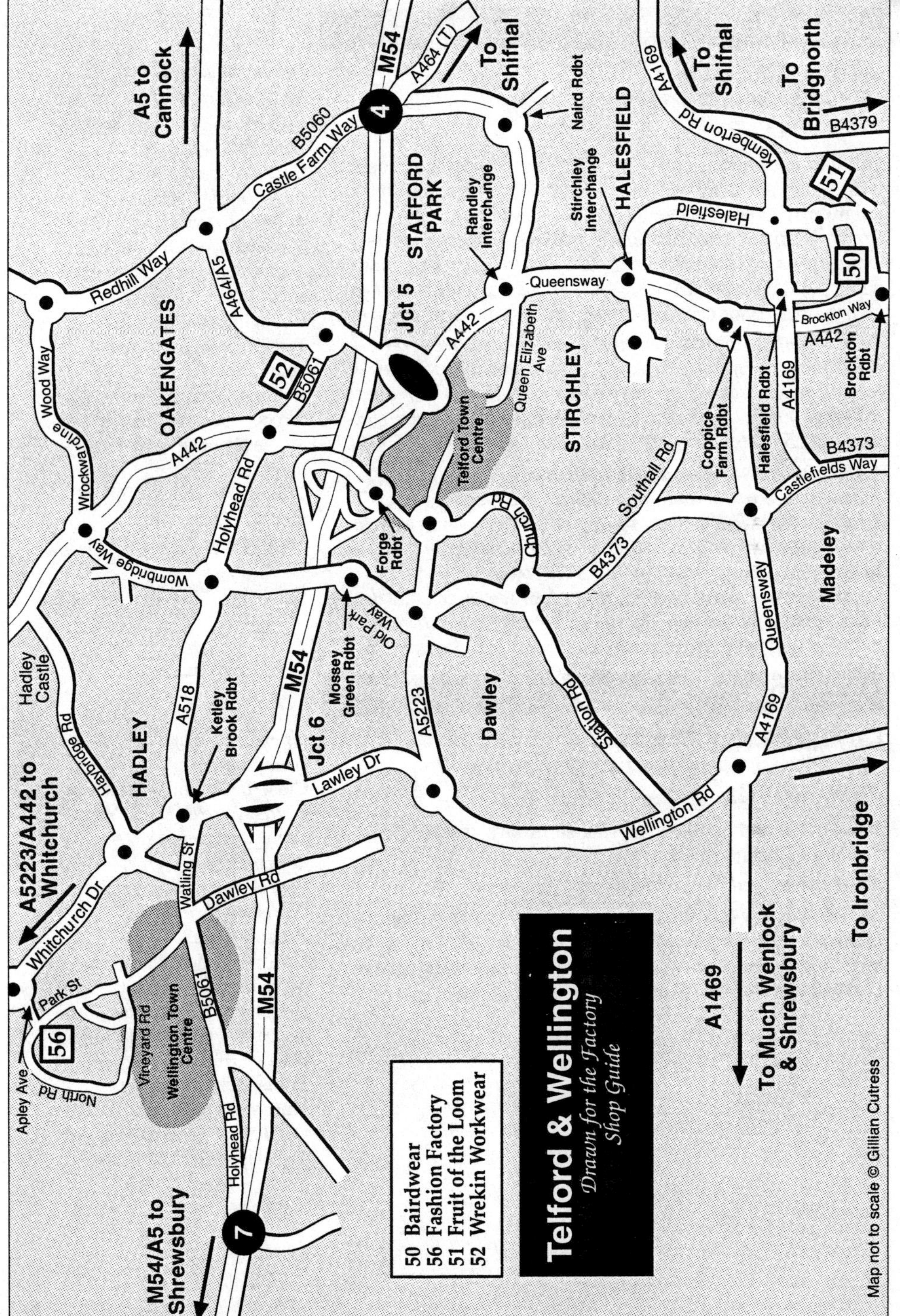
Telford & Wellington
Drawn for the Factory Shop Guide
50 Bairdwear
56 Fashion Factory
51 Fruit of the Loom
52 Wrekin Workwear
A5 to Cannock
To Shifnal
To Bridgnorth
A5223/A442 to Whitchurch
M54/A5 to Shrewsbury
To Much Wenlock & Shrewsbury
To Ironbridge
A1469
OAKENGATES
STAFFORD PARK
HALESFIELD
STIRCHLEY
HADLEY
Dawley
Madeley
Telford Town Centre
Wellington Town Centre
Hadley Castle
Jct 5
Jct 6
M54
A464(T)
B5060
Castle Farm Way
Redhill Way
Wood Way
Wrockwardine
A464/A5
A442
B5061
Holyhead Rd
Wombridge Way
A518
Haybridge Rd
Whitchurch Dr
Watling St
Dawley Rd
Park St
Vineyard Rd
North Rd
Apley Ave
Lawley Dr
A5223
Old Park Way
Church Rd
Southall Rd
B4373
Station Rd
Wellington Rd
Queensway
A4169
Castlefields Way
Brockton Way
Halesfield
Kemberton Rd
B4379
Queen Elizabeth Ave
Naird Rdbt
Randley Interchange
Stirchley Interchange
Coppice Farm Rdbt
Halesfield Rdbt
Brockton Rdbt
Forge Rdbt
Mossey Green Rdbt
Ketley Brook Rdbt
Map not to scale © Gillian Cutress

52 Telford Shropshire *see map earlier page*

Wrekin Workwear

Unit 41, Snedshill Trading Estate
(01952) 615976

Outdoor sportswear and workwear. Waterproof and fleecy jackets; dry socks for walkers, fishermen, golfers; waterproof ski mits; trigger mits; wellies & liners; wax leggings, jackets, trousers; drysuits for sailors/windsurfers. Drivers' jackets, trousers; roundsmen's jackets; safety boots; dustcoats; boiler-suits; painters' overalls; welders' flame retardant workwear; step-in dresses for care assistants; tabards; uniform skirts etc.

'Small-company orders welcome. Made-to-measure service. Embroider logos, staff names etc. Firsts, seconds and ends of lines at much reduced prices: boiler suits £15–£30; breathable waterproof boot liners £9.95 (usual retail £20); carers' step-in dresses £15 (£30); dry suits £190 (£300); dry socks £15 (£30).'

Just north of M54, close to the town centre.

Coming due west into town on A5: as you reach town, go straight at first roundabout, staying on A5 for Town Centre.*

From M54 exit 4: take B5060 north for Donnington Priorslee. At first roundabout, go left on to A5 for Town Centre.*

****At next roundabout, go right (B5061 for Wellington/Snedshill). Keep straight for 0.4 mile. As you go downhill, pass flagpoles on left then turn right into company forecourt.***

Open: Mon–Thur 10–5; Fri 10–3.30.
Closed: Saturday; Whit week; Bank Holidays.
Cards: Access, Amex, Visa.
Cars: In front of shop.
Toilets: In town.
Wheelchairs: One tiny step, double doors to medium sized shop.
Changing rooms: Yes.
Teas: Always happy to put the kettle on!
Groups: Groups of nurses, carers, windsurfers etc welcome. Please phone first. No factory tours.
Transport: Train to Telford then short taxi ride.
Mail order: Yes, on specific items.
Catalogue: Price list on request.

53 Tipton W Mids

Royal Brierley Crystal

Bedford Street, Dudley Port DY4 7PM
(0121) 520 4429

Hand-made and hand-cut crystal, stemware, giftware, tumblers, decanters etc.

'Sales throughout February and mid June–mid July.'

Just off Horseley Heath, the A461 leading from West Bromwich to Dudley. Turn north into Lower Church Lane (A4163 to Tipton) near Dudley Port station. Bedford Street is the second road on the right and the shop is at the far end on the right.

Open: Mon–Sat 9–5; Bank Holidays.
Closed: Christmas–New Year.
Cards: Access, Amex, Visa.
Cars: Own car-park.
Toilets: Yes.
Wheelchairs: One small step to medium sized shop.
Teas: In town.
Groups: Groups of shoppers welcome; prior phone call appreciated. Glassworks tours available at the other factory in Brierley Hill.
Transport: Local buses.
Mail order: No.
Catalogue: Retail catalogue available from Head Office.

A needling experience

One enjoyable part of our travels is the chance to visit unusual local museums. One of these is the needle museum in Redditch. Needles have been the staple manufacturing industry in this town for over 300 years (evidence suggests that they were made in nearby monasteries in the 12th century). The numbers produced are staggering. Millions of needles are exported weekly all over the world.

The museum shows how needles were produced in former times. You would not believe how many processes went into making so simple looking a product, nor how uncomfortable were working conditions.

Until the 19th century there were no special surgical needles. During the Napoleonic wars doctors used sail makers' or glovers' needles with triangular cutting points which could be used on human flesh. Patients were as likely to die from surgery as they were to recover from the ailment! With the discovery of antiseptics and anaesthetics, surgical skills and specialist needle manufacture developed.

The Forge Mill Museum, Needle Mill Lane, Redditch, B97 6RR (01527) 62509. Weekdays and weekend afternoons (closed Friday). Worth confirming times, especially in winter.

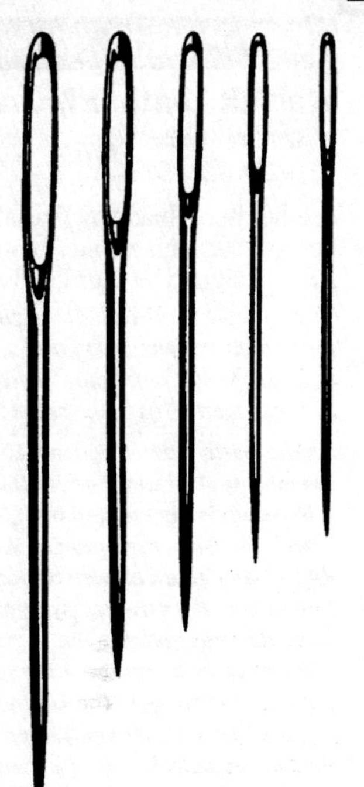

Ironbridge Gorge

South of Wellington and Telford is Ironbridge Gorge, one of Britain's most historical industrial sites and classified as a 'world heritage site'. You need at least a day to explore the six square miles, but if you have limited time, the Ironbridge Passport allows you one visit to each of the nine main attractions on that day or in the future.

The industrial revolution was forged here nearly 300 years ago when iron was first smelted with coke by Abraham Darby. The new process resulted in much purer, carbonised iron which could now be cast more accurately and effectively than ever. This was used to make the first iron bridge (you can still walk across it), iron wheels, rails, boats, steam railway locomotives, steam-engine cylinders etc, thus revolutionising industry and life in general. Coalbrookdale became the most important iron-producing area in the world, and here you will find the **Museum of Iron**.

Coalport China was made in this valley until earlier this century and you can tour the original pottery (no longer active). The Ironbridge shop stocks current ranges (but no seconds!) of Coalport China (which is now made in Stoke-on-Trent). The **Jackfield Tile Museum** has stunning tile exhibits, including Victorian tiles and 1930s tableaux rescued from hospital walls. You can buy or commission tiles from the small tile-making company now based here. Seconds were available on our last visit.

Ironbridge Gorge Museums Trust (01952) 433522. Open nearly every day of the year. Separate tickets for each museums or buy a reduced price joint ticket.

Tourist Information Centre (01952) 432166.

54 Walsall W Mids

Walsall Leather Museum

Wisemore WS2 8EQ
(01922) 721153

Leather items made by Walsall factories: belts, purses, wallets, personal organisers etc. Leather jewellery, horse brasses. Also 'designer' leather goods. Firsts and seconds from £3.

'Walsall is Britain's leather goods capital specialising in the manufacture of saddlery and small leather items. The museum, with authentic workshops, tells the story of Walsall's leather history and acts as a showcase for the best of the industry today.'

On the north side of Walsall, this museum is on the ring road (where the A34 turns off for Cannock and Stafford).

Museum is signposted from M6 exits 7, 9, 10. From M6 exits 9 and 10, Wolverhampton or Wednesbury: get on to the ring road A4148 and go clockwise. When you reach a public car-park in the middle of a one-way system, turn right into it opposite the large Renault garage. The Leather Museum is opposite.

From Cannock on the A34: you join the ring road just before the Renault garage. The Leather Museum is opposite.

From Birmingham via A34 or Aldridge via A454: get on to ring road anti-clockwise. Half a mile after large roundabout by arboretum turn right into car-park with brown sign 'Leather Museum'.

Open: Tues–Sat 10–5; Sun 12–5 (*Nov–March* closes at 4); Bank Holiday Mondays.
Closed: Most Mondays; Easter Sunday; Christmas & New Year.
Cards: Yes.
Cars: Public car-park. Limited street parking in Lord's Drive behind museum.
Toilets: Yes, and for disabled.
Wheelchairs: Ramps and special lifts.
Teas: Saddle Room café for home made cakes and meals (open to all, not just museum visitors).
Groups: Demonstrations in museum most days. Group tours welcome at no charge, but please book first.
Transport: 5 minutes' walk to town. Short walk from station.
Mail order: No.

55 Walsall W Mids

Whitehouse Cox & Co.

Crown Works, Marsh Street WS2 9LE
(01922) 24661

Top quality small leather goods: wallets, purses, coin purses, notecases, jewel boxes, belts, photo frames, coasters, shaving sets, shoeshine kits, briefcases, luggage, rucksacks and handbags.

'Manufacture for chainstores and also for leading designer names. Large selection of ends of lines and cancelled orders at average discounts of 50%. Many belts at £5. Special commissions for orders over £200. Summer sale in July.'

In the middle of town, in a pedestrianised street near the station.

Walsall has undergone major road and traffic alterations so best to follow signs to the railway station and park in Bridgeman Street multi-storey car-park. Then 200 yds walk to shop (with large new window in old red-brick industrial building).

Open: Mon 9.30–4; Tues–Thur 9.30–5; Fri 9.30–4; Sat 9–4.
Closed: Bank Holidays; Whitsun week; first week in August; Christmas–New Year. Please phone for exact dates.
Cards: Access, Amex, Mastercard, Visa.
Cars: Bridgeman St car-park.
Toilets: Ask if desperate.
Wheelchairs: Easy access; no steps.
Teas: Druckers Saddle Centre; Walsall Leather Museum.
Groups: No factory tours, but shopping groups very welcome (over age 18); please book with Jenny Chapman.
Transport: Walsall station 200 yds from shop.
Mail order: No.
Catalogue: Brochures £4 each.

The Leather Industry of Walsall

Walsall Leather Museum

Originally it came as a surprise to us to discover that many of the highly desirable (and highly expensive) fine leather items one finds in top department stores are made in Walsall. The making of leather goods is the traditional industry of this particular town, which specialises in two main fields: light leather goods, such as wallets, purses and belts, and heavy goods, such as saddlery and riding equipment. It has never been significantly involved in the manufacture of leather clothing, upholstery or footwear. Walsall leather manufacturers make goods for many famous name retailers around the country, as well as essential surgical supplies for the National Health Service and a variety of items for industry such as gaskets and washers.

It is estimated that 2500 people are employed in the Walsall leather industry in firms of widely varying sizes. A few employ 200 or more people, but the majority are much smaller. Most are family owned, and several present day directors can trace family connections with the leather trade to the early 19th century.

Whitehouse Cox

In spite of modern labour saving devices, such as computerised sewing machines, the manufacture of leather goods remains labour intensive and dependent on manual skills. This makes it possible for skilled leather workers to establish their own firms with limited equipment.

Traditionally, men and women did different jobs in the industry, with women undertaking most of the stitching, and men doing most of the heavier work, such as cutting and making saddles and harness. These days, however, the sexual division of labour has become more blurred, and there are now several women saddlers!

For an excellent insight into this industry (and some well priced small leather goods to buy) allow an hour to tour the Leather Museum. It explains the different processes and leathers and has interesting replica workshops showing the old tools and working conditions. Allow time to enjoy the food in the café. (Or simply go there for lunch.) The Whitehouse Cox factory shop had such excellent items at such reasonable prices when we visited that we stocked up with presents for the next few months.

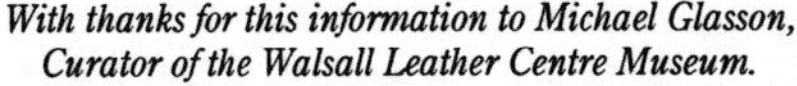

With thanks for this information to Michael Glasson,
Curator of the Walsall Leather Centre Museum.

Walsall Leather Museum

56 Wellington Shropshire *see map on earlier page*

Fashion Factory

Park Street/King Street TF1 3AF
(01952) 260489

A variety of constantly changing, quality branded ladies' wear.

'Savings of between 40–70% off high street prices. Stock always perfect unless indicated (99% first quality). No chainstore items. Summer and winter sales. Personal shoppers only.'

See our display advertisement opposite

On the north side of Wellington town centre, easily reached from the major road going north from M54 exit 6 (Whitchurch Drive, A442/A5223).

From M54 exit 6: take A442/A5223 north. At the third roundabout (Telford hospital on far right), go left into Apley Avenue.*

From Telford going west on A5061/A518: aim for Wellington. At the first (huge) roundabout, go right on to A442/A5223 north. At the second roundabout (Telford hospital on far right), go left into Apley Avenue.*

****At T-junction (school on right corner), go left in to Whitchurch Road which becomes Park Street. Turn into car-park of The Red Lion on right. Large shop is a few yards further down road.***

Open: Mon–Sat 9.30–5.30; Sun 11–5.
Closed: Easter Sunday; Christmas Day.
Cards: Access, Visa.
Cars: At Red Lion Inn next door.
Toilets: Nearest at Red Lion Inn next door.
Wheelchairs: Huge shop on two floors, access to ground floor only (no steps).
Changing rooms: Yes, on both floors.
Teas: Red Lion Inn next door.
Groups: Evening shopping by appointment. Please contact Denise Wagg.
Mail order: No.

57 Wolverhampton W Mids

Grasshopper Babywear

Spring Road, Ettingshall WV4 6JA
(01902) 353666

Babywear from 0–2 years. Sleepsuits, pyjamas, rompers, bodysuits, vests, bibs, underwear.

'Superior quality, value for money babywear direct to the public at factory prices. Perfects and seconds.'

About 2 miles south-east of Wolverhampton, on west side of Bilston.

From Wolverhampton ring road: at the roundabout, take A41 (Bilston Road) south. After nearly a mile, go right at roundabout into A4126 Ettingshall Road. Go over traffic lights then under railway into Spring Road. Look for company signs shortly on left.

Coming north on A4123 Birmingham New Road: at traffic lights, go right on to A4126 Spring Road. Company is on left, shortly before railway bridge across road.

Open: Mon–Fri 10–4; Sat 10–12.
Closed: Bank Holidays; Christmas–New Year.
Cards: No.
Cars: Car-park at rear.
Toilets: Yes.
Wheelchairs: Two very small steps to large shop.
Changing rooms: No.
Teas: Café in Spring Road.
Groups: No factory tours, but shopping groups welcome.
Transport: Bus nos. 125 and 126 from Wolverhampton to Essington and Bilston.
Mail order: No.

58 Wolverhampton W Mids

Yarnolds

106 Birmingham Road WV2 3NZ
(01902) 459321

Wide range of soft furnishings, various curtains including velvets, nets and blinds. All made to measure. Ends of rolls and discontinued lines.

'Firsts, slight seconds and remnants sold here.'

About ½ mile south of Wolverhampton along Birmingham Road (A4123) which leads off the ring road.

If you come south from Wolverhampton: the shop is on the right where the road bends slightly to the left. Huge signs on factory with flags on top.

Open: Mon–Sat 9–5.
Closed: Bank Holidays; Christmas–New Year.
Cards: Access, Eurocheque, Switch, Visa.
Cars: Outside factory.
Toilets: During week, not Saturday.
Wheelchairs: Easy access to huge spacious shop.
Teas: In Wolverhampton.
Groups: Shopping groups welcome. No need to book.
Transport: Bus nos. 581 (to Dudley) & 126 (to Birmingham) from Wolverhampton bus station pass the door.
Mail order: No.

59 Wombourne W Mids

Pifco Salton Carmen Russell Hobbs Tower Mountain Breeze

Heath Mill Road, Wombourne Industrial Estate WV5 8AO
(01902) 324123

Small electrical appliances: kettles, toasters, irons, kitchen appliances, hairdryers and stylers, electrical housewares, Christmas tree lights, cookware, air cleaning products.

'Most items at factory prices.'

West of Wombourne on the B4176.

Wombourne Industrial Estate is signposted at traffic lights at the crossing of A449 (Stourbridge–Wolverhampton road) and B4176 (Dudley–Bridgnorth road). Take the B4176 for Bridgnorth. Pass the Waggon and Horses on the right, then turn left into industrial estate. Company is first on left: shop is inside the gates on the left, clearly marked.

From Bridgnorth on B4176: pass Wombourne Ford on right; keep going till you see industrial estate on right; turn right into it. Company is first on left: shop is inside the gates on the left, clearly marked.

Open: Tues–Fri 9–4.30; Sat 9–12.30.
Closed: Monday; Bank Holidays; Christmas–New Year.
Cards: Mastercard, Visa.
Cars: In factory yard.
Toilets: Yes.
Wheelchairs: One step to large, spacious shop.
Teas: Local pubs.
Groups: Groups of shoppers welcome by appointment. No factory tours.
Transport: Not easy.
Mail order: No.

60 Worcester Worcs

Rowe Carpets

Castle Street WR1 3AV
(01905) 619515

Wide selection of Axminster carpets made by this company. Large range of plain colours. Also all types of woven and tufted carpets. Large selection of rugs. Three-piece suites, beds and mattresses from well known manufacturers.

'Factory seconds, 700 roll ends, remnants, perfects. Expert fitting service for local area and a nationwide fitting and delivery service (local deliveries free, up to about £35 throughout the rest of the UK).'

To the north side of town centre, opposite the Royal Infirmary.

Coming south from M5 exit 6 on A449, or on A38 from Droitwich: go towards town along first Barbourne Road then The Tything. Pass Grammar School on left; at traffic lights go right into Castle Street. Shop 200 yds on right directly opposite Royal Infirmary.

From the west: go over River Severn; go left into one-way system. Keep straight, with river on left. Go under railway. Pass race-course on left: shop is 50 yds on left.

From town centre: go north along Foregate Street and under multi-coloured railway bridge; pass Odeon on left; after 150 yds, go left at traffic lights into Castle Street. Shop is 200 yds right.

Open: Mon–Sat 9–5.30.
Closed: Bank Holidays; Christmas, Boxing and New Year's Days.
Cards: Access, Amex, Connect, Visa.
Cars: Own large car-park to front and side of shop.
Toilets: Yes (but not for disabled).
Wheelchairs: No step, huge shop (19,000 sq ft).
Teas: Tea or coffee made on request for customers!
Groups: No factory tours.
Transport: 5 minutes' walk from bus station; 5 minutes' walk from train station.
Mail order: No.

61 Worcester Worcs

Royal Worcester Porcelain

Severn Street WR1 2NF
(01905) 23221

Four shops for bone china tableware, porcelain, oven-to-table ware, wall plates, gifts and souvenirs. Best ware shop for current range. Large seconds shop, including *Royal Brierley* and *Dartington Crystal*. Clearance shop for white-ware. Souvenir shop. Also sell *Spode*, *Caithness Glass*, *Country Artists*, *Arthur Price* cutlery, *Pimpernel* mats.

'January & July sales. Museum of Worcester Porcelain currently closed for refurbishment (please phone for information).'

In city centre off A44 (Evesham–Leominster road) by cathedral.

On foot or by car: aim for the cathedral.

If cathedral is on your left (you come from Evesham/Upton/M5): go left at traffic lights into Edgar Street towards imposing cathedral archway.*

If you are going towards Evesham/Upton, cathedral is on right. This main road is dual-carriageway – you must double back; then go left at lights into Edgar St towards imposing cathedral archway.*

From M5 exit 7: follow city centre signs. At third traffic lights, go left into Edgar Street towards imposing cathedral archway.*

****Turn left in front of arch into Severn Street; company 150 yds on left.***

Open: Mon–Sat 9–5.30; Bank Holidays.
Closed: Xmas and Boxing Days.
Cards: Access, Amex, Diners, Visa.
Cars: Own car–park.
Toilets: Yes.
Wheelchairs: Easy access to shops.
Teas: Own restaurant. Parties to book in advance.
Tours: Frequent 1-hour tours Mon–Fri (not Bank Holidays). £3.50. Book in advance with Mrs Savage. Unsuitable for elderly and disabled; children over 8. 'Connoisseurs Tour' (£11) at 10.15 & 1.15 Mon–Thur (give 2 days' notice). Coaches please phone.
Transport: Easy walk city centre.
Mail order: Yes. Any package can be mailed world-wide.
Catalogue: No.

D

Towns with factory shops

NUMBERS refer to the ENTRIES NOT the PAGES

Town	No.	Shop
Atherstone	1	The Hat Shop
Birmingham : Aston	2	Moulinex Swan
Birmingham : Central	3	Fiesta Glass
Birmingham : Jewellery Quarter	4	Consortium Jewellery
Birmingham : Jewellery Quarter	5	Jeff & Annabel's Diamond Gallery
Birmingham : Jewellery Quarter	6	Jewellery Quarter Discovery Centre
Birmingham : Jewellery Quarter	7	P J Gold Depot
Birmingham : Jewellery Quarter	8	V & F Parker (Arden Jewellery)
Birmingham : King's Heath	9	Treetops Pine Furniture
Bloxham	10	The Weavers Shop
Cannock	11	Fashion Factory
Cannock	12	Lew-Ways
Cannock	13	Lighting Bug
Coventry	14	Nutcracker Factory Direct
Cradley Heath	15	Hawk Factory Cycle Stores
Craven Arms	16	Crucial Trading
Halesowen	17	The Chambers Candy Co.
Kidderminster	18	Kidderminster Carpet Factory
Kidderminster	19	Kidderminster Wholesale Carpets
Kidderminster	20	Rowe Carpets
Kidderminster	21	Victoria Carpet Weavers Shop
Kidderminster	22	The Weavers Shop
Kidderminster	23	Wyre Forest Pine
Lichfield	24	Arthur Price of England
Lichfield	25	Decor Supplies
Ludlow	26	Thistle Trading Co.
Nuneaton	27	Abbey Textiles
Pershore	28	The Factory Shop Ltd
Redditch	29	Jaeger Knitwear
Ross-on-Wye	30	Barker Shoes Factory Shop at Herrings
Ross-on-Wye	31	Ross Labels
Shifnal	p297	Ruckley Dried Flowers
Shirley, Solihull	32	A E Clutterbuck
Shrewsbury	33	Cane & Wicker
Shrewsbury	34	Fashion Factory
Stourbridge area : Amblecote	35	Royal Doulton Crystal
Stourbridge area : Audnam	36	The Crystal Glass Centre
Stourbridge area : Brierley Hill	37	Bairdwear
Stourbridge area : Brierley Hill	38	Brierley Hill Glass
Stourbridge area : Brierley Hill	39	Dennis Hall Tudor Crystal
Stourbridge area : Brierley Hill	40	Midland Fabric Warehouse
Stourbridge area : Brierley Hill	p307	Okra Glass Studios
Stourbridge area : Brierley Hill	41	Royal Brierley Crystal
Stourbridge area : Brierley Hill	42	Staffordshire Crystal
Stourbridge area : Wordsley	43	Stuart Crystal
Stourport-on-Severn	44	Carpets of Worth
Stourport-on-Severn	45	T P Activity Toys
Stratford-upon-Avon	46	Stratford Tile Warehouse
Tamworth	47	Jaeger Sale Shop
Tamworth	48	Probus Housewares
Tamworth	49	Webb Ivory
Telford	50	Bairdwear
Telford	51	Fruit of the Loom
Telford	52	Wrekin Workwear
Tipton	53	Royal Brierley Crystal
Walsall	54	Walsall Leather Museum
Walsall	55	Whitehouse Cox
Wellington	56	Fashion Factory
Wolverhampton	57	Grasshopper Babywear
Wolverhampton	58	Yarnolds
Wombourne	59	Pifco Salton Carmen Russell Hobbs Tower Mountain Breeze
Worcester	60	Rowe Carpets
Worcester	61	Royal Worcester Porcelain

Staffordshire & The Potteries

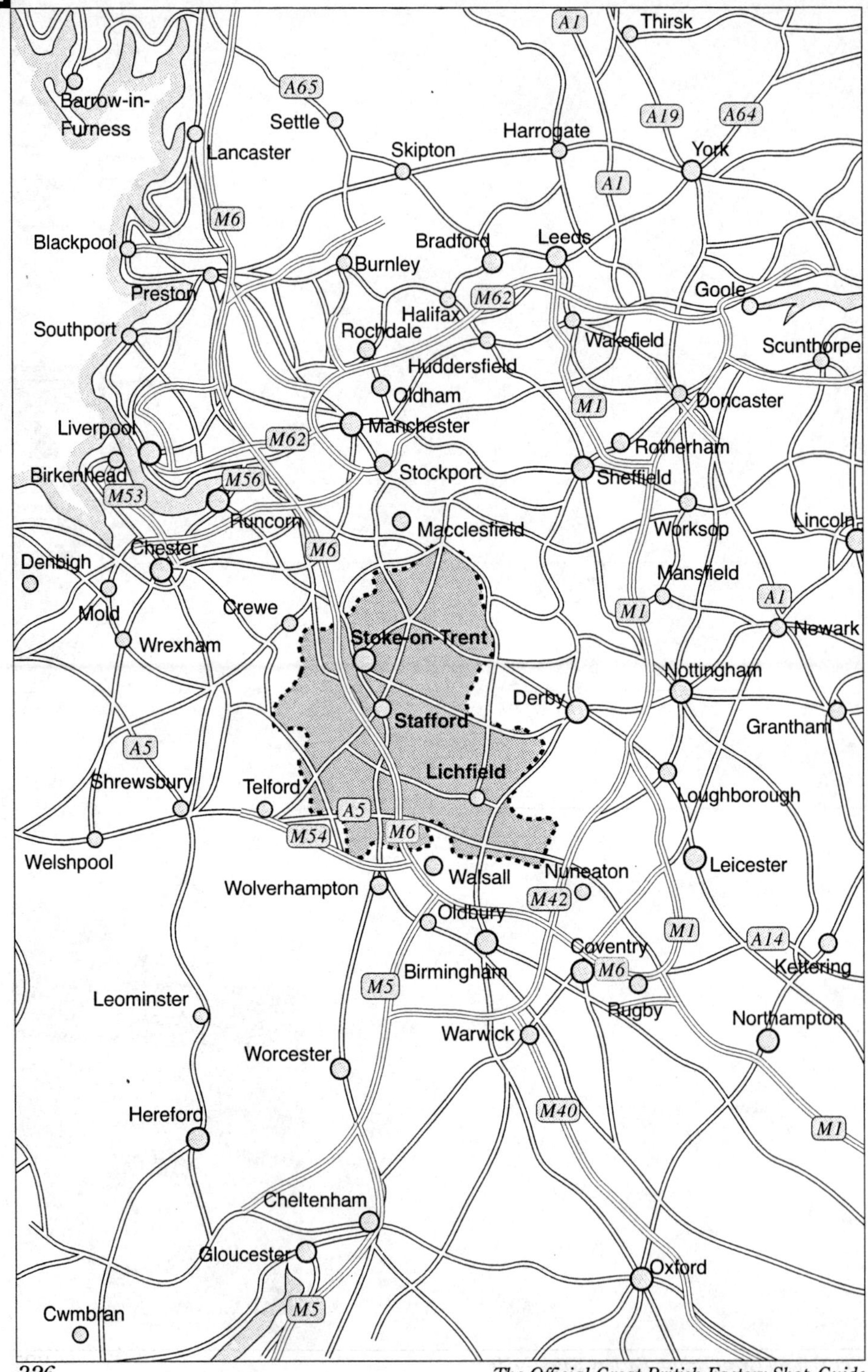
A1
Thirsk
A65
Barrow-in-Furness
Settle
A19
A64
Lancaster
Harrogate
Skipton
York
A1
M6
Blackpool
Bradford
Leeds
Burnley
Preston
Halifax
M62
Goole
Southport
Rochdale
Wakefield
Scunthorpe
Huddersfield
Oldham
M1
Doncaster
Liverpool
Manchester
M62
Rotherham
Birkenhead
Stockport
Sheffield
M56
M53
Runcorn
Worksop
Macclesfield
Lincoln
Chester
M6
Denbigh
Mansfield
Mold
Crewe
M1
A1
Newark
Wrexham
Stoke-on-Trent
Nottingham
Derby
Stafford
Grantham
A5
Lichfield
Shrewsbury
Telford
Loughborough
A5
M54
M6
Welshpool
Leicester
Walsall
Nuneaton
Wolverhampton
M42
Oldbury
M1
A14
Coventry
Kettering
Birmingham
M6
M5
Rugby
Leominster
Northampton
Warwick
Worcester
M40
M1
Hereford
Cheltenham
Gloucester
Oxford
M5
Cwmbran

Staffordshire & The Potteries

Information about the Stoke-on-Trent area is given on pp. 343–379. Factory shops in other Staffordshire towns appear on pp. 330–341.

This area incorporates two distinct, but equally important aspects of factory shopping: on the one hand a wonderful variety of shops in the county as a whole, on the other the world famous potteries centred in the Stoke-on-Trent area. All these offer excellent value, whether they sell perfect goods at reduced prices, or ends of lines, overmakes or slight seconds (which failed the strictest quality controls).

Across Staffordshire you will find an exciting variety of shops selling quality clothing for the family (including fashion garments, lingerie, shoes, famous name waxed, showerproof and quilted country wear), as well as a huge choice of luxury and everyday items for the home (such as silver plated cutlery and tableware, lighting, useful bathroom accessories and tiles for both floors and walls). Featuring in this book for the first time are shops selling wallpapers and co-ordinated curtain fabrics, terracotta planters, men's and women's clothing, hand-decorated tableware evoking the charms of old farmhouse kitchens, etc. A more unusual shop belongs to a brewery, which sells beers, spirits and wines, together with brewery gift merchandise, direct to the public. We are delighted to welcome them all.

Over 30 well-known potteries are located within a short distance of one another in Stoke-on-Trent. Between them they represent all that is coveted by lovers of quality china and ceramics in the UK and abroad. This is the place to stock up on all your china needs, whether you are in the mood to swap your old crocks for a gleaming new design, or whether you are setting up home for the first time, or, indeed, buying a wedding present for someone else. Some of the companies have opened additional branches, which shows just how popular this kind of shopping has become. As pottery is heavy and tedious to carry, we include a chart showing how various companies help get purchases home (in the UK and abroad). It is reassuring to know that, should any of your precious purchases suffer a mishap, one company in this book undertakes not only china and glass repairs, but will also restore paintings, jewellery, clocks and all types of furniture, regardless of age and value.

One very special bonus for shoppers in this part of the world is the opportunity to join the many tours on offer. Do allow enough time for these (at least an hour); you will be amazed by the skills involved in china production and decoration.

Should you be tempted to go into competition, one shop specialises in artists' supplies and whiteware for china painters.

Royal Doulton

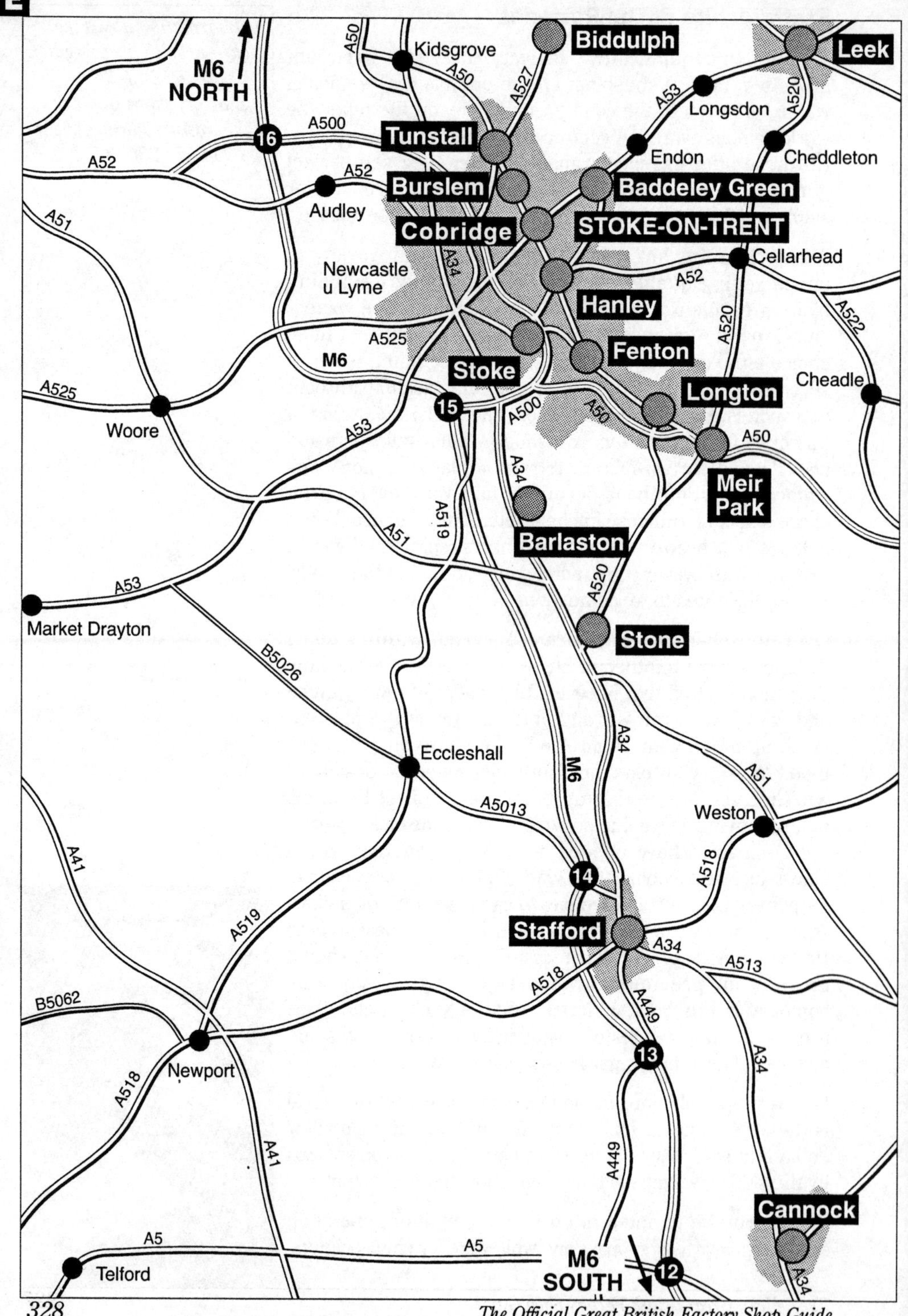

M6
NORTH
Kidsgrove
Biddulph
Leek
A50
A527
A53
Longsdon
A520
Tunstall
16
A500
Endon
Cheddleton
A52
Burslem
Baddeley Green
Audley
A51
Cobridge
STOKE-ON-TRENT
Cellarhead
Newcastle
u Lyme
A34
A52
Hanley
A522
A525
A520
Fenton
M6
Stoke
Cheadle
A525
15
Longton
A500
A50
Woore
A53
A50
Meir
Park
A34
A519
Barlaston
A51
A520
A53
Market Drayton
Stone
B5026
A34
Eccleshall
M6
A51
A5013
Weston
A41
A518
14
A519
Stafford
A34
A513
A518
B5062
A449
13
Newport
A518
A34
A41
A449
Cannock
A5
A5
Telford
M6
SOUTH
12
A34

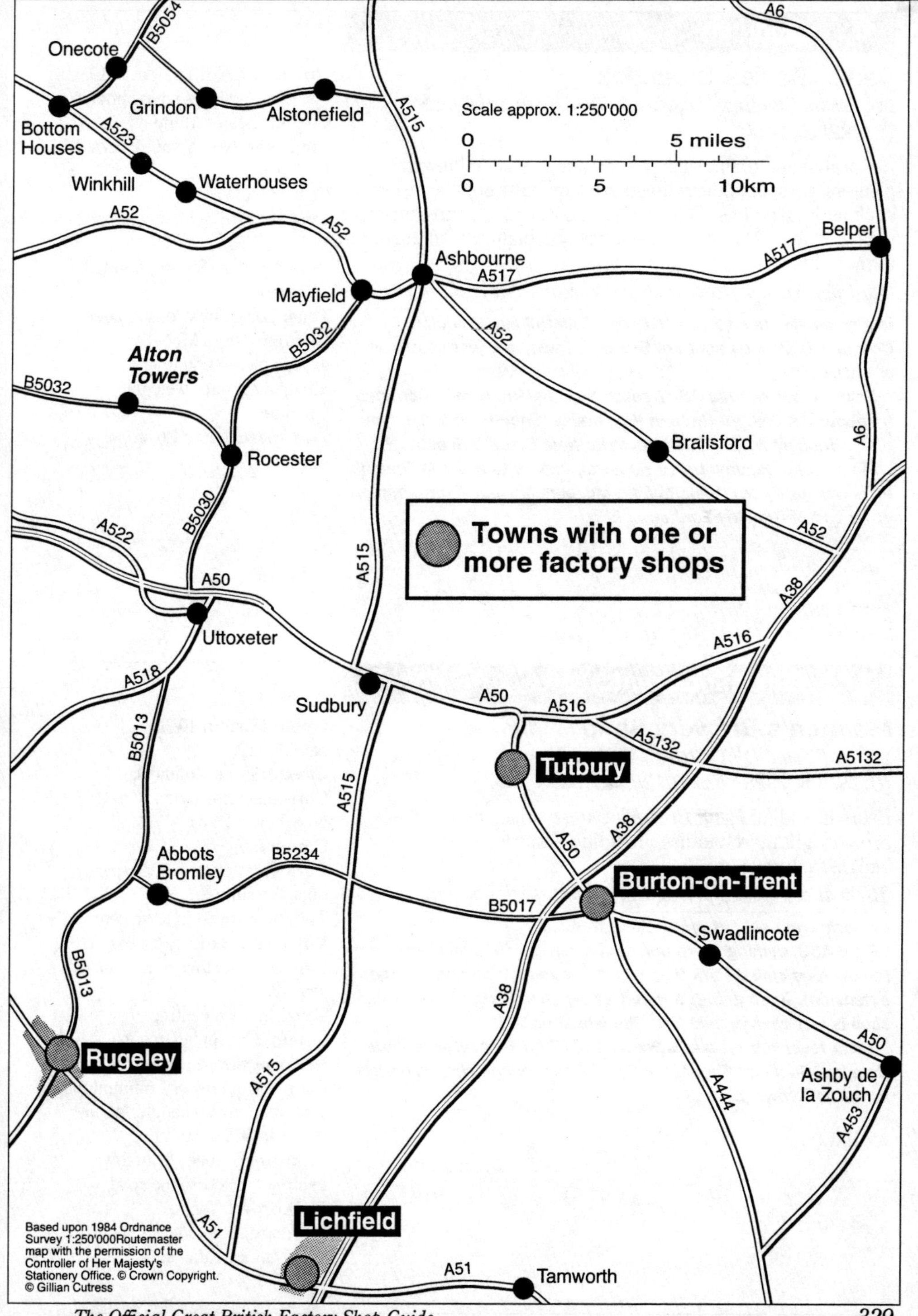
Onecote
B5054
Grindon
Alstonefield
A515
A6
Bottom Houses
A523
Winkhill
Waterhouses
Scale approx. 1:250'000
0
5 miles
0
5
10km
A52
A52
Belper
A517
Ashbourne
A517
Mayfield
A52
B5032
Alton Towers
B5032
Rocester
Brailsford
A6
Towns with one or more factory shops
B5030
A522
A515
A52
A50
A38
Uttoxeter
A516
A518
Sudbury
A50
A516
A5132
B5013
A5132
Tutbury
A515
A50
A38
Abbots Bromley
B5234
Burton-on-Trent
B5017
Swadlincote
B5013
A38
A50
Rugeley
Ashby de la Zouch
A515
A444
A453
Based upon 1984 Ordnance Survey 1:250'000Routemaster map with the permission of the Controller of Her Majesty's Stationery Office. © Crown Copyright. © Gillian Cutress
A51
Lichfield
A51
Tamworth

1 Biddulph Staffs

Carter Davies Ceramics

Old School Buildings, Outclough Road, Brindley Ford ST8 7QD
(01782) 514744

Decorated and plain earthenware made here: tableware, planters, pots, pot-pourri dishes etc and bathroom accessories such as soap dishes. Range of eggcups, cruets, cups and tea pots with feet. Also sell some terracotta planters, oil burners, night lights etc.

'Most items are perfects, with some seconds, at reduced prices.'

In a small village on A527 between Tunstall and Biddulph. Company is 2 miles south of Biddulph town hall, just south of Knypersley.

From Biddulph: take A527 south for Burslem/Stoke. Continue for about 2 miles, go through Knypersley. Shop is on left as you reach Brindley Ford, almost opposite New Black Bull pub.

From Stoke/Hanley: take A50 north; fork on to A527 in Tunstall. Pass Chatterley Whitfield Mining Museum on your right; shop is at far end of Brindley Ford on right.

Open: Mon–Fri 7–4; Sat 7–12. For Bank Holidays please phone.
Closed: Easter Monday; Christmas–New Year; Potters Holidays.
Cards: None.
Cars: In yard behind company.
Toilets: Yes.
Wheelchairs: Six steps, small showroom.
Teas: Local pubs; teas in Leek.
Groups: Tours Mon–Sat, groups please phone first. Shopping groups welcome any time.
Transport: Route B6 stops outside.

2 Burton-on-Trent Staffs

Marston's Brewery Shop

Shobnall Road DE14 2BW
(01283) 507328 Fax (01283) 510378

Beers including *Head Brewer's Choice*, wines and spirits; brewery gift merchandise including T-shirts, glasses, badges, ashtrays etc.

'Beers at discounted prices. Occasional special offers.'

On north-west side of town, close to A38.

From A38, coming north and south: turn off for Branston (a new road called Park Way which becomes Wellington Street extension). Keep going; turn left at big island into Shobnall Road; shop is just over ½ mile from the island on left.

From town centre: aim west on B5017 for Uttoxeter/Abbots Bromley. Go along Shobnall Road. Go over canal, shop is on left in front of brewery.

Open: Mon-Fri 10–3; Sat 9.30–12.
Closed: Bank Holidays; Christmas, Boxing and New Year's Days.
Cards: No.
Cars: Brewery's own car-park opposite shop.
Toilets: Nearest in town centre.
Wheelchairs: Easy access to small shop; tiny step, help available.
Teas: In town centre.
Groups: Shopping groups welcome, please phone first. For tours of brewery (minimum 12, maximum 30 people) phone H Clark (01283 507440).
Transport: Buses from town centre stop across the road.
Mail order: Yes.
Catalogue: No. Please phone if you want anything sent.

3 Burton-on-Trent Staffs

Webb Ivory

Queensbridge Works, Queen Street DE14 3LP
(01283) 506371

Fascinating variety of surplus catalogue stocks of greetings cards, wrapping papers, household goods, toys, small gifts and clothing.

'50% off catalogue prices.'

Close to the centre of town, on the south-west side.

From Tutbury: go into town, proceed along Guild Street and Union Street. At traffic lights (Comet on near left corner) go right into New Street.*

From shopping precinct with W H Smith car-park: turn left; at traffic lights go right (New Street).*

***At next lights, go left (Uxbridge Street); cross next lights (Evershed Way); take third left (Queen Street). The company is 100 yds on left.**

From other places in town centre: find Safeway and pass it on left; at roundabout go right into Evershed Way; at traffic lights turn left into Uxbridge Street (Keepmere Engineering on far left corner). Go left at Queen Street. The company is 100 yds on left.

Open: Mon–Fri 9–5; Sat 9–2; Some Bank Holidays, please check.
Closed: Christmas–New Year.
Cards: Most major credit cards; Switch.
Cars: Own car-park.
Toilets: Yes.
Wheelchairs: Yes; ground level shopping, no steps.
Changing rooms: Yes.
Teas: In Burton.
Groups: Pre-booked shopping groups welcome.
Transport: 15 minutes' walk from town centre.
Mail order: No.

4 Cannock Staffs

Fashion Factory

Unit 5 Wyrley Brook Park, Vine Lane, Bridgetown WS11 3XE
(01543) 466000

Vast selection of quality branded ladies' and men's wear, and shoes.

'Personal shoppers only. Internationally famous brand names at savings of 40–70% off high street prices. 30–40,000 garments of constantly changing merchandise. No chainstore items. Summer & winter sales. We are in Wellington & Shrewsbury too.'

See our display advertisement on p. 321

Across the A5 from Cannock, on south side of this major road. Near B&Q.

Going north-west on A5 from Tamworth: at traffic lights (Texaco far left corner) at Cannock turn-off, go left (not right for Cannock).*

From M6 exit 12: turn east on to A5 for Cannock/Tamworth. Cross junction with A460. At traffic lights (Texaco on near right corner) with Cannock turn-off to left, go right.*

***Shortly turn right into Vine Lane: conspicuous shop is short distance on right.**

Open: Mon–Sat 9.30–5.30; Sun 11–5. Bank Holidays.
Closed: Easter Sunday; Christmas Day.
Cards: MasterCard, Visa.
Cars: Ample.
Toilets: Yes.
Wheelchairs: Easy access, no steps to huge ground floor shop.
Changing rooms: Yes.
Teas: Drinks machine and seating.
Groups: Shopping groups welcome; please phone first.
Transport: Regular bus route via Vine Lane bus stop.
Mail order: No.

5 Cannock Staffs

Lew-Ways

Watling Street WS11 3NB
(01543) 454427

Wide selection of children's to adults' cycles: ATB's, pavement cycles, trikes/scooters. Full range of outdoor play equipment: swings, slides, climbing frames, playmats; swim armbands; sandpits, play sand; goal posts; basketball sets; play homes; baby swings; trampolines; water trays and pools; exercise benches and bicycles. Golf trolleys. Full range of garden fish ponds.

'Plenty of room to try the bicycles. All items are used mail order items, factory seconds or slight rejects at considerably reduced prices.'

Clearly marked on A5, 2 miles west of Brownhills and 3 miles east of Cannock.

From Brownhills: go west on A5. Look for large signs on left then follow directions into factory yard.

From Cannock: take A5 east for Brownhills. Go over large roundabout with The Turf Lodge on near left corner (crossing the B4154). Pass The Little Chef on right, get into right lane and, after 100 yds, go right into well marked company.

Well signed shop is at far back of yard.

Open: Mon–Sat 8.30–5; Bank Holidays.
Closed: Christmas–New Year.
Cards: MasterCard, Visa.
Cars: Factory yard immediately outside shop.
Toilets: Yes.
Wheelchairs: Easy access to large sales area on ground floor (no steps).
Teas: Little Chef next door.
Groups: Groups of shoppers welcome.
Transport: None.
Mail order: No.

6 Cannock Staffs

Lighting Bug

173 Walsall Road, Bridgtown WS11 3JB
(01543) 577776

Huge range of domestic lighting: soft shades and table lamps made here; full ranges of polished solid brass light fittings; crystal, wood and panel glass ceiling fittings. Wall lamps to complement ceiling fittings. Outdoor lighting, spot lights, downlighters, low voltage and fluorescent lighting. Light switches, bulbs, doorbells etc.

'Perfects and seconds at discounts of 25–50%. Always special offers on discontinued lines. Gladly pack and post (at cost) if you can't carry purchases home. We are a happy-go-lucky company (biggest lighting shop in the West Midlands) and will do anything to take your money!'

Bridgtown is on the southern side of Cannock, between Cannock town centre and A5.

From Cannock town: take A34 south towards A5. Pass Kwik-Fit on left. This conspicuous shop is on far left corner by the roundabout (take first left at roundabout then go sharp right into shop car-park).

From A5: at traffic lights, take A34 north for Cannock. Go under railway bridge, then left at T-junction. Conspicuous shop is on far right corner by roundabout.

Open: Mon–Sat 9.30–5.30. Bank Holidays.
Closed: Few days during Christmas–New Year period.
Cards: Delta, Eurocard, MasterCard, Visa.
Cars: Free large car-park.
Toilets: Town centre.
Wheelchairs: No steps to large shop.
Teas: Pubs, cafés and McDonald's nearby.
Groups: No factory tours but shopping groups welcome.
Transport: Cannock–Walsall buses stop outside.
Mail order: Yes.
Catalogue: £4, redeemable against purchases of £50+. Please phone for catalogue (with credit card). All items sent by overnight delivery (about £10).

Cannock Staffs

Cannock Gates

Martindale, Hawks Green
(01543) 462500

Wrought iron and timber gates from the UK's largest direct manufacturer, and garden products such as obelisks, gazebos, arbours, rose arches, etc.

'Perfects; and ends of ranges, sale items, discontinued lines, slightly imperfect, out of season products and much more. Overflowing with price buster bargains. Please check availability before long journeys. Outdoor garden designed by the BBC's late Geoff Hamilton, so our products can be seen in situ.'

North-east of town, just south of A460 (to Rugeley).

From Cannock centre/other directions: take A460 north for Rugeley. Pass fire station with tower on left. After ¼ mile, before railway bridge, go right (Hawks Green Lane) at bottom of hill.*

From Rugeley on A460: go through Hednesford. Go under railway bridge then take first left (Hawks Green Lane).*

****Go under another railway bridge; take first right (Martindale). Follow road round left: Cannock Gates is on left, clearly signed.***

From A5: on Brownhills side of Cannock, go north on new road for Hednesford/Rugeley. Cross A5190. At second roundabout, go left in front of petrol station. Take next left. Shop on right.

Late Entry

Open: Mon–Sat 9–5; Sun 10–4. Bank Holidays 9–5.
Closed: Christmas and New Year's Days; phone to check.
Cards: Major credit and debit cards.
Cars: Own car-park.
Toilets: Yes, including for the disabled.
Wheelchairs: Easy access; no steps.
Teas: Local pubs and cafés.
Groups: No tours, but shopping groups welcome.
Transport: Bus from town stops 10 minutes' walk away.
Mail order: Yes.
Catalogue: Yes. Free gates and garden products catalogue.

7 Leek Staffs

Joshua Wardle

Cheadle Road, Leekbrook ST13 7AY
(01538) 382451

Ladies' wear, men's wear, children's wear, underwear and lingerie; homewares. In-store *Dannimac* shop sells off-price merchandise.

'Famous name chainstore perfects, seconds, ends of lines at reduced prices. Phone to check current range details.'

A mile and a half south of Leek.

From Leek: take A520 south towards Stone. After you pass under railway bridge, shop is on factory site 600 yds on right.

From the south: take A520 towards Leek. Go through Cheddleton and pass St Edwards Hospital. 200 yds after you go over railway bridge, clearly marked site is on left, opposite farms and The Travellers Rest. Turn left into estate: shop is in main building, facing you.

Open: Mon–Fri 9.30–4; Sat 10–3.
Closed: Easter; Christmas, New Year and Bank Holidays. Last full week in July (+ previous Fri and Sat) and following week; also one week end Sept (please check exact dates).
Cards: MasterCard, Switch, Visa.
Cars: Own car-park for 100 cars. Spaces reserved for disabled.
Toilets: On site at the canteen.
Wheelchairs: Ramps leading to shop, no steps. Large shop.
Changing rooms: Yes.
Teas: On site at canteen or at the Travellers Rest (nearby pub).
Groups: No factory tours. Phone for shopping groups.
Transport: Buses from Leek, Hanley and Cheadle pass front of factory.
Mail order: No.

8 Leek Staffs

Leek Factory Shop

2 Westwood Road ST12 8DH
(01538) 385340

Well known branded names ladies' clothing including lingerie, knitwear, skirts, blouses, nightwear etc. Also wide range of branded names men's clothing – shirts, leisurewear, trousers, knitwear.

'New goods on a weekly basis. The majority of items are perfects sold at discount prices. Special offer of 10% discount for senior citizens every Thursday.'

From Macclesfield: come south on A53, pass 'The Jester' on the right and continue uphill. Turn right, around octagonal red brick toilets, into West Street.*

From Ashbourne: go right at war memorial; left at traffic lights into Stockwell Street. Continue straight, past top of Market Place. Go left in front of red-brick octagonal toilets into West Street.*

From Buxton: go straight at traffic lights, along Stockwell Street. Pass top of Market Place. Go left in front of red-brick octagonal toilets into West Street.*

****Continue into Westwood Road: shop 300 yds on right.***

From Stoke: go north on A53. Pass Churnet Valley Pub on right. By Safeway, go left into Burton St. At far end, go right (Spring Gardens). Go to end: go right into Westwood Road. Shop on left.

Open: Mon–Sat 9–5.15. Bank Holidays.
Closed: Christmas Day; New Year's Day.
Cards: MasterCard, Switch, Visa.
Cars: Local streets.
Toilets: In town centre.
Wheelchairs: One small step, assistance gladly given.
Changing rooms: Yes.
Teas: Cafés, pubs, and fish & chip shops in Leek.
Groups: Coach groups very welcome to shop any time.
Transport: Ten minutes' walk from Leek bus station.

9 Leek Staffs

Lotus Shoes

36 Derby Street ST13 5AB
(01538) 383700

Shoes: ladies' courts, sandals, leather casuals. Men's city shoes, top grade all-leather men's welted brogues, leather casuals, sandals. Also seasonal products such as slippers, ladies' fashion boots, warm-lined boots. Handbags, purses and shoe cleaning products.

'No factory tours but small shopping groups welcome. Prior phone call please.'

In the centre of town, in the main shopping street.

Derby Street leads from the lower end of the Market Place to the war memorial. If you come from the Market Place, the shop will be on your right.

Open: Mon–Sat 9–5.30. Good Friday.
Closed: Bank Holidays; Christmas, Boxing and New Year's Days.
Cards: MasterCard, Switch, Visa.
Cars: Town car-parks.
Toilets: In the Market Place.
Wheelchairs: Two steps; easier access to shop in Stone.
Teas: Several cafés, pubs and eating places in town.
Groups: No factory tours as not on factory site, but groups of shoppers welcome. Prior phone call appreciated. Please contact Mrs Gidman.
Transport: Easy walking distance from bus station.
Mail order: No.
Catalogue: Branded catalogue can be viewed in shop but is not for distribution.

See our entry below

10 Lichfield Staffs

Arthur Price of England

Britannia Way, Britannia Enterprise Park WS14 9UY
(01543) 257775 Fax (01543) 414488

Silver plated and stainless steel Sheffield cutlery; tableware and gifts including tea & coffee sets, trays, tankards, goblets, picture frames, candelabras, condiment sets etc.

'All items British-made in own factories in Birmingham and Sheffield. Items are seconds, ends of ranges or exhibition-soiled.'

See our display advertisement above

On an industrial estate east of town.

From Lichfield centre: aim for Burton; pass Tesco on left. At roundabout (Council Depot on right), go right for Birmingham (A38).*

Coming south from Stone/Stafford on A51: go left for Burton/ Birmingham (A38)/Britannia Ent. Park into Eastern Ave (A5192). Continue to roundabout; go straight. At next roundabout go left.*

Going south on A38: take first exit to Lichfield. Go over railway, turn left at the roundabout. At next roundabout turn left.*

Going north from Tamworth/A38: follow signs into Lichfield. Go under railway. At lights, go right for Burton (A38). Keep straight for a mile (pass Lichfield City station on right, Tesco on left). At roundabout (council depot on right), go right for Birmingham (A38).*

****At next roundabout, go left for Britannia Way. Company on left.***

Open: Mon–Fri 8.30–5; Sat 10–1.
Closed: Bank Holidays; Christmas–New Year.
Cards: MasterCard, Switch, Visa.
Cars: Own spacious car-park.
Toilets: Yes.
Wheelchairs: Unfortunately no access as shop is on first floor.
Teas: Tea shops in Lichfield.
Groups: Pre-booked groups welcome to shop. Special films of cutlery and silverware manufacture gladly shown to groups by prior appointment.
Transport: None.
Mail order: Yes, no restrictions.
Catalogue: Free.

11 Lichfield Staffs

Decor Supplies

Units 21 & 23, Britannia Way WS14 9UY
(01543) 263327

Extensive range of wallpapers, borders, paints, co-ordinated fabrics and some bedlinen. Two huge showrooms on the site, one for discounted ends of designs, etc.

'Thousands of the latest designs and colours. Let us help create your ideal home witih wallpapers that coordinate with borders and fabrics.'

Open: Mon–Fri 9–5.30; Sat 9–5; Sun 10–4. Bank Holidays.
Closed: Easter Sunday; Christmas and Boxing Days.
Cards: Connect, MasterCard, Switch, Visa.
Cars: Own forecourt in front of shop.
Toilets: Yes.
Wheelchairs: Easy access to two large showrooms.
Teas: Tea shops in Lichfield.
Groups: Product not really suitable for groups of shoppers.
Transport: None.
Mail order: No.

On an industrial estate east of town.

From Lichfield centre: aim for Burton; pass Tesco on left. At roundabout (Council Depot on right), go right for Birmingham (A38).*

Coming south from Stone/Stafford on A51: go left for Burton/ Birmingham (A38)/Britannia Ent. Park into Eastern Ave (A5192). Continue to roundabout; go straight. At next roundabout go left.*

Going south on A38: take first exit to Lichfield. Go over railway, turn left at the roundabout. At next roundabout turn left.*

Going north from Tamworth/A38: follow signs into Lichfield. Go under railway. At lights, go right for Burton (A38). Keep straight for a mile (pass Lichfield City station on right, Tesco on left). At roundabout (council depot on right), go right for Birmingham (A38).*

****At next roundabout, go left for Britannia Way. Company on left. (on same side as Arthur Price).***

The City of Lichfield

Probably best known for its beautiful three-spired cathedral, and for the fact that it is the birthplace of Samuel Johnson, Lichfield is a pleasant (and historic) town in which to have tea after you have visited the factory shops here. It is an ideal town for walking – amble round Minster Pool and through the 13th century close, and call in at Johnson's birthplace museum. The market is worth spending some money in too. We make a point of staying near Lichfield whenever we can, partly because the countryside towards Kings Bromley is so attractive and partly because of the several excellent farmhouse B&Bs nearby.

Further south is the interesting Hungry Horse Craft Centre (Weeford Road, a mile north of Sutton Coldfield, and a mile west of the A38) with its stables converted into small specialist shops for reduced price lingerie, engraved glass, dried flowers, tapestry materials etc. A café serves light meals. One of the best quality crafts shops (Artifex 0121 323 3776) in the country is here – be tempted by the sculpture, carved stone, wooden furniture, ceramics, glass etc.

See our entry below

12 Rugeley Staffs

John Partridge

Power Station Road, Trent Meadows WS15 2HS
(01889) 584438

John Partridge waxed cotton jackets, trenchcoats, waistcoats. Showerproof classic town coats. Casual, *Goretex*, tweed coats. Waistcoats, waxed & quilted jackets for children. Ladies' fashions. Moleskin, cord, waterproof trousers and leggings. Shooting sticks. Hats & caps. New riding department: boots, jodhpurs, hats, whips, jackets, stocks, hunt shirts etc.

'All garments sold here slightly imperfect or discontinued lines. Spring & autumn sales in marquee – phone for details.'

On an industrial estate on north-east edge of town.

Coming south-west into Rugeley from Uttoxeter/Abbots Bromley via B5013: as you reach Rugeley, go under railway, over river bridge; take first left (Power Station Rd). Shop 200 yds on right.

Coming south-east from Stafford (A513) or Stone (A51): as you enter town, fork left at first roundabout. At double mini-roundabout, go left for Uttoxeter B5013.*

From Cannock, Lichfield, Armitage: go into Rugeley. Keep straight to roundabout with Little Chef/Shell. Go into Elmore Lane (Little Chef on left; The Globe on right). Stay on this road, pass police station on left. Go straight at double mini-roundabout.*

****Pass church on right, take first right. Shop 200 yds on right.***

Open: Mon–Fri 9–5; Sat 9–4. Good Friday, Easter Monday and some other Bank Holidays – phone to check.
Closed: Christmas & Boxing Days. Some Bank Holidays.
Cards: Amex, MasterCard, Visa. During clearance sales cheques and cash only.
Cars: Outside shop.
Toilets: Yes.
Wheelchairs: One step to large shop.
Changing rooms: Yes.
Teas: In town.
Groups: No tours but groups of shoppers welcome.
Transport: None.
Mail order: No.

Early industry in Rugeley

In 1992 the remains of the 15th century Wolseley Glass Works were discovered during a quarrying operation some two miles from Rugeley. It was here that some of the world's finest stained glass was produced in 1417 for the windows of York Minster. The site has been excavated and the artifacts removed to the glass museum in Dudley.

Rugeley – today dominated by the huge cooling towers of the power station – has long been an industrial town. In the 1760s, a happy accident brought prosperity: when plans, backed by industrialists such as Josiah Wedgwood, were made to build canals linking the country's major rivers, it happened that Rugeley was on the Trent and Mersey canal route (the eighteenth century equivalent of a motorway). Construction was a major engineering feat which included an aqueduct across the river Trent in Rugeley. It brought commercial prosperity, and the new ease of transport gave a tremendous boost to coal mining.

Cannock Chase, near Rugeley, was used for hunting by Plantagenet kings. In later centuries, many trees in this forest were cut down in order to fire the many iron blast furnaces located between Rugeley and Hednesford.

This century Cannock Chase – now a country park – has claimed fame for a totally different reason. During both world wars, especially the first, Rugeley camp was a final base for soldiers leaving for the front. For many thousands of men who died in action in France, Rugeley was their last English town.

City Museum & Art Gallery, Hanley

For details about leisure activities within Cannock Chase, contact the Valley Heritage Centre (01543) 877666.

Stafford Tourist Office (01785) 240204

Thanks to Staffordshire County Council for this information

John Partridge

13 Stafford Staffs

Antique and Ceramics Restoration Studio

Ye Olde Post Office, Newport Road
(01785) 780424 Fax (01785) 780157
e-mail: ars@uk-hq.demon.co.uk

Specialist restorers of all types of ceramics, including bone china, porcelain and pottery regardless of age. Also specialist restorers of glassware, paintings, jewellery, clocks and all types of furniture, regardless of age and value.

'Personal callers and mail order repair service. Written quotations are given for all work (which is inclusive of five-year guarantee). Full reports and valuation for insurance claims prepared.'

On the south-west side of town, near the railway station.

Please ask for precise directions when you phone for appointment.

Open: Mon–Sat 9–5 by appointment only. (As this is a small, specialist business, you must phone in advance.)
Closed: Bank Holidays. Christmas–New Year.
Cards: All major cards.
Cars: Own limited parking space, or public car-park nearby.
Toilets: Yes.
Wheelchairs: One step, assistance given.
Teas: In town nearby.
Groups: No groups or tours.
Transport: Train and buses to Stafford.
Mail order: Mail order or courier repair service for all ceramics, glassware and paintings.

14 Stafford Staffs

Schott-UK

Drummond Road, Astonfields Industrial Estate ST16 3EM
(01785) 222707

Over 20 complete suites of stemmed glasses in cut, plain and coloured crystal, boxed presentation sets, decanters, jugs, a range of exclusive hand-made crystal, barware and some heat-resistant glassware. Wide selection of crystal giftware – vases, bowls and ornaments.

'Perfect quality unless otherwise stated. Continuous special offers. Wedding list service. Four sales a year, please phone for dates.'

On the north side of Stafford.

From north, south, west: approach from M6 exit 14. Follow A513. After ¾ mile, go straight over roundabout for Uttoxeter. After ½ mile go right at sign to Common Road/Astonfields Industrial Estates. After one mile the road swings left into Astonfields Road. Drummond Road is first left.*

From east: approach via A518 from Uttoxeter. At the roundabout by Staffordshire University go right on to A513 for M6. After 1⅓ miles go left just after traffic lights by the RAF into B5066 (Sandon Road). After ½ mile go right into Astonfields Road. Drummond Road is first right.*

****The shop is on right at end of Drummond Road.***

Open: Wed–Fri 10–4.30; Sat 10–3. Please enquire for Bank Holidays.
Closed: Monday; Tuesday; Christmas, Boxing and New Year's days.
Cards: MasterCard, Visa.
Cars: Free large parking area with coach access.
Toilets: Yes.
Wheelchairs: One step to sizeable shop; willing assistance given.
Teas: In Stafford.
Groups: No factory tours but coach parties welcome to shop by prior arrangement: please contact Mrs Sue Cope, mentioning this book.
Mail order: Yes.
Catalogue: No.

15 Stone Staffs

Lotus Shoes

27 High Street ST15 8AJ
(01785) 812915

Shoes: ladies' courts, sandals, leather casuals. Men's city shoes, top grade all-leather welted brogues, leather casuals, sandals. Also seasonal products such as slippers, ladies' fashion boots and warm-lined boots. Handbags, purses and shoe cleaning products.

'Quality footwear at discounted prices. Occasional sales on selected footwear.'

This shop is in the main shopping street (now pedestrianised) of Stone opposite the Crown Hotel. If you go down High Street, the shop is on the left.

Via A34 from Stafford: you come into the one-way system. Park in car-park on left then walk through Adie's Alley into High Street: Lotus is directly opposite.

Open: Mon–Sat 9–5.30. Good Friday.
Closed: Easter Monday and other Bank Holidays.
Cards: MasterCard, Switch, Visa.
Cars: In town car-parks.
Toilets: In Stone.
Wheelchairs: Easy access, no steps into medium sized shop.
Teas: Pubs and cafés in Stone.
Groups: No factory tours but small shopping groups welcome. Prior phone call please.
Transport: Any bus or train to Stone.
Mail order: No.
Catalogue: Branded catalogue can be viewed in shop but is not for distribution.

16 Tutbury Staffs

Georgian Crystal (Tutbury)

Silk Mill Lane DE13 9LF
(01283) 814534 Fax (01283) 520186

English full-lead crystal glassware: wine glasses, tumblers etc, honey pots, vases and small gift items.

'Firsts and seconds. Engraving service. Please mention this book if asking for a leaflet. Mail order service.'

This clearly signposted glassworks is in a small lane near the centre of Tutbury.

From the High Street: turn off by the post office and then take first left. Follow the sign to 'The Silkmill'.

Open: Mon–Sat 9–5; Sun 10–3; Bank Holidays.
Closed: Christmas & New Year.
Cards: Amex, Diners, MasterCard, Switch, Visa.
Cars: Outside shop or car-park in village.
Toilets: Yes.
Wheelchairs: Access possible to sales area (from where you can see the furnace) but space is tight.
Teas: Tea rooms and pubs in the pleasant village of Tutbury.
Tours: Morning tours of the glassworks. Group visits very welcome. Shop is beside and above the glass-blowing area.
Transport: Trent bus no. 104 from Burton. Stephensons buses from Uttoxeter via Tutbury.
Mail order: Yes. No restrictions.
Catalogue: Free price lists.

See our entry below

17 Tutbury Staffs

Tutbury Crystal Glass

Burton Street DE13 9NC
(01283) 813281

Hand-crafted, hand-decorated full lead crystal glassware, stemware, tumblers, decanters, bowls, paperweights etc.

'All items on sale are slight seconds. Engraving service available. A gift for every occasion.'

See our display advertisement above

Almost in the centre of Tutbury, on the main road through the town by the mini-roundabout at the bottom of the hill. The company is clearly marked.

Open: Mon–Sat 9–5; Sun 11–4; Bank Holidays.
Closed: Christmas–New Year.
Cards: Delta, MasterCard, Switch, Visa.
Cars: Own car-park; coach parking available.
Toilets: Yes.
Wheelchairs: Easy access.
Teas: Own tea room on the premises Mon–Fri 9.30–4. Also tea shops in village.
Tours: Groups to shop please arrange in advance with reception. Glassworks tours: please book ahead, mentioning this guide. Tours Mon, Tues, Thur 9.30, 11.30 & 1.30. Fri 9.30 only. Phone reception for dates. Max 60 (min 12) at 50p per person. Children must be accompanied.
Transport: Trent bus no. 104 from Burton. Stephensons buses from Uttoxeter & Burton.
Mail order: Yes. No restrictions.
Catalogue: Free.

W Moorcroft

Collecting china becomes a passion, made even more absorbing when coupled with specialised knowledge. Some Stoke pottery manufacturers have formed clubs for their devotees; other clubs are run independently. Amongst benefits are membership packs, magazines, newsletters, a free gift on joining, organised visits, special offers and exclusive pieces for members, and valuations. Annual fees range from £12–£25 in the UK. Factory shops in this book will be glad to give details. Here is a summary of the clubs we are aware of.

Clubs for china collectors

Aynsley Collectors' Society – *From UK*: Freepost (ST1663), Stoke-on-Trent ST3 1BR. *From elsewhere*: Portland Works, Longton, Stoke-on-Trent ST13 1HS.

Coalport Collectors Society - Laura Collingwood, Coalport Collector, PO Box 99, Sudbury, Suffolk CO10 6SN.

Moorcroft Collectors Club – Maggie Williams, W Moorcroft plc, Sandbach Road, Burslem, Staffs ST6 2DQ.

Portmeirion Collectors' Club – Dawn Shufflebotham, Portmeirion Potteries Ltd., London Road, Stoke-on-Trent, Staffs ST4 7QQ.

Royal Doulton International Collectors Club – Royal Doulton (UK) Ltd., Minton House, London Road, Stoke-on-Trent, Staffs ST4 7QD.

The Royal Winton International Collectors' Club – Ken Glibbery, Dancer's End, Northall, Beds LU6 2EU.

Spode Society – Mrs R Pulver, PO Box 1812, London NW4 4NW.

The Official International Wade Collectors' Club – Royal Works, Westport Road, Burslem, Staffs ST6 4AP.

The Wedgwood International Society – Admail 981, Stoke-on-Trent, Staffs ST12 9JW.

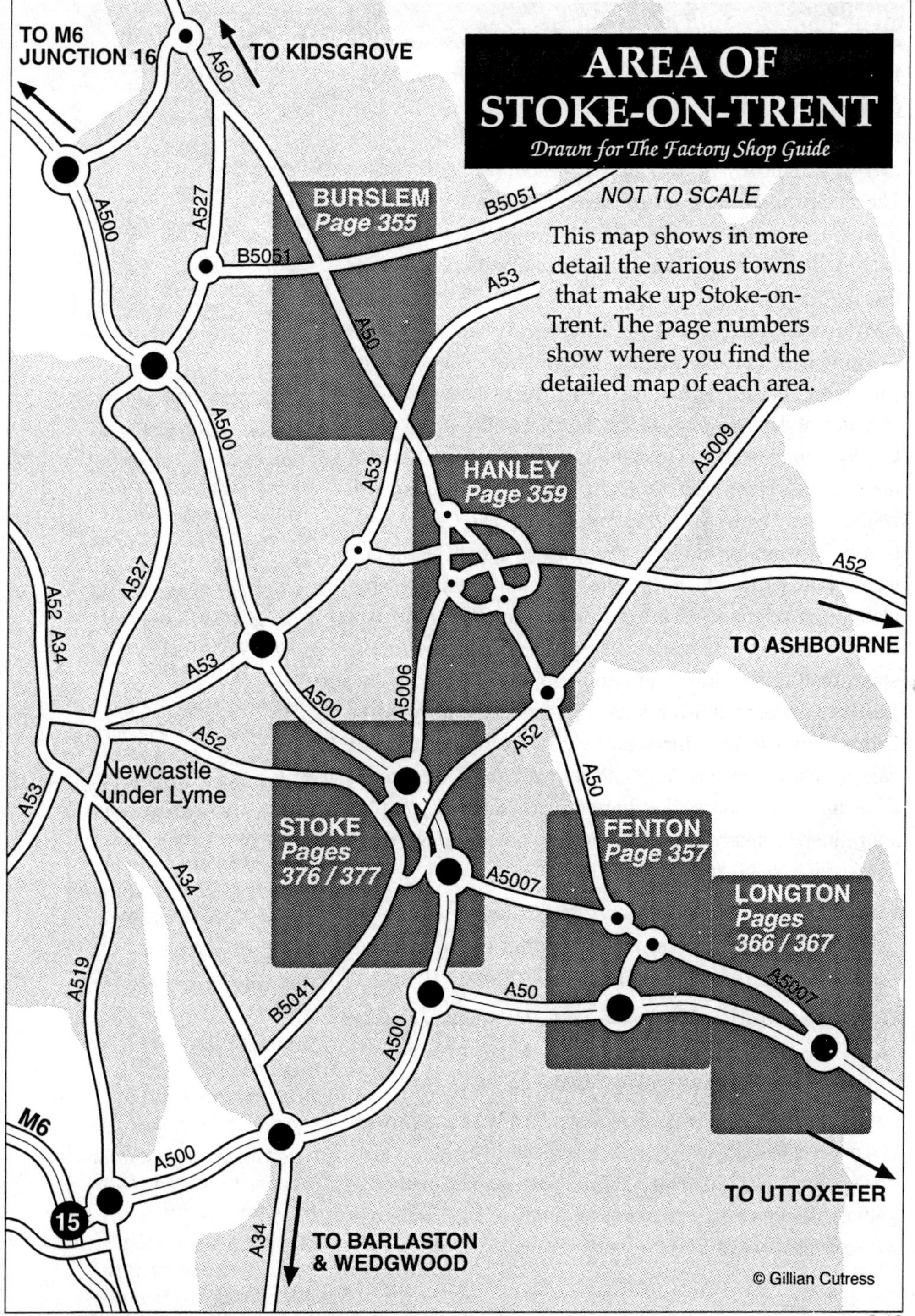
AREA OF
STOKE-ON-TRENT
Drawn for The Factory Shop Guide
NOT TO SCALE
This map shows in more detail the various towns that make up Stoke-on-Trent. The page numbers show where you find the detailed map of each area.
TO M6
JUNCTION 16
TO KIDSGROVE
A50
A500
A527
B5051
BURSLEM
Page 355
A53
HANLEY
Page 359
A5009
A52
TO ASHBOURNE
A52 A34
A5006
STOKE
Pages
376 / 377
Newcastle
under Lyme
FENTON
Page 357
LONGTON
Pages
366 / 367
A5007
A34
A519
B5041
M6
15
TO BARLASTON
& WEDGWOOD
TO UTTOXETER
© Gillian Cutress

Welcome to Stoke-on-Trent

Churchill Tableware

Before you go Stoke-on-Trent is an agglomeration of six old industrial towns (Tunstall, Burslem, Hanley, Fenton, Longton and Stoke), which have merged together. Visitors may have difficulty in working out exactly where they are. The factory shops themselves are not always easy to find as most are still in the original potteries off the beaten track in narrow back streets. The recent proliferation of brown tourist signs has reduced some of the guesswork, but navigation around Stoke is still daunting. British roads take longer to negotiate than similar roads in the US or Australia, and progress round Stoke is slowed down by heavy traffic at all times of day. Road signs can be misleading. Road signs to 'City Centre' lead you to Hanley, the busiest part of town, not to Stoke which visitors might (with reason) assume to be the centre. Signs to 'The Potteries Shopping Centre' lead to a prize-winning modern shopping precinct in Hanley which houses four factory shops but no manufacturing plants. Construction of the major new bypass (A50) is a long-term project (several years) but should eventually streamline traffic. Much is complete; but do not be surprised to encounter diversions, part-finished slip roads or paltry signposting. Thirty pottery factory outlets merit considerable browsing time and a tour behind the scenes takes up to two hours. We therefore recommend you plan your itinerary in advance. The detailed directions and maps in this guide will help you unravel the maze.

Getting there From London it takes about 3½ hours by car and 2 hours by train. Fast trains from London, Birmingham and Manchester go direct to Stoke station.

Getting around The area is linked by two major roads:

the new A50 (currently subject to major roadworks) runs east–west, linking Uttoxeter to the A500.

the A500 (Queensway, known locally as the D-road) is a major dual-carriageway which runs north–south. It joins up with the M6 at both ends and provides a quick method of getting from one part of the area to another. The skill lies in recognising at which roundabout you should get off!

Factory holidays

'Potters' Holidays' are the times when all potteries in the area traditionally closed down so that the furnaces could be cleaned. 'Potters' Holidays' are to Stoke what 'Wakes Weeks' are to other industrial manufacturing towns in Britain.

Factory tours are not available during factory holidays. Most factory shops remain open, but we advise you to check before you travel. Visitor centres are open throughout the year except Christmas week and New Year's Day.

Week after Easter

May Day: *(first Monday in May).*

Summer: *last week in June (plus previous Thursday and Friday) and first week in July.*

Late Summer: *last week in August (plus previous Thursday and Friday).*

Christmas–New Year *period (some shops might open during this time).*

If you arrive in Stoke by train, or prefer not to drive around the narrow congested streets yourself, it is best to take a cab. Local buses offer a link service between the major outlets, but you must remember that their timetables will not always coincide with yours; and that any pottery you buy will become increasingly heavy as the day wears on.

Minton

About the shops The shops vary greatly in style. While some have beautiful brightly lit displays, others have a less professional look and give you a chance to 'rummage'. An increasing number of companies are offering 'visitor experiences'. You never quite know what you will find but you can be certain that you'll have fun during the search.

Prices Most items in the Stoke factory shops are of a slightly substandard quality sold at a significantly reduced price. Collectors' items such as character jugs tended, in the past, to be perfects sold at full price but on recent visits we have noticed that these items may be reduced in price too. Each company has its own policy. *Royal Doulton* (which includes *Minton, Royal Albert, Coalport, Johnston Bros., Mason's Ironstone, John Beswick* and *Royal Crown Derby*) sells both perfect quality and seconds in their six shops in Stoke. Perfects of current ranges may sell at full price while seconds and ends of lines, in our experience, sell at 30%–50% less than normal British retail prices. *Wedgwood Best* in Barlaston sells only perfect items from the current range at full price. Their seconds are sold at *The Waterford Wedgwood Factory Shop* in Fenton. Other well known companies sell substandard items or discontinued designs at up to 50% less than perfect or current ranges. You are likely to find excellent special offers. We recently came across 80% reductions on some of the best known tableware designs. Note too that if you can plan your trip for the right time (especially after Christmas), you will find stunning bargains in factory shop sales.

Pottery tours are an absolute must for anyone visiting the Potteries. The tours are fascinating, if exhausting, and allow you to see how the goods are produced. You will soon become aware of the old family links within the pottery industry. All companies ask you to book tours in advance. But if you are travelling alone or in winter it is worth

For details please phone Hanley Tourist Information Centre on (01782) 284600.

enquiring if there is a vacancy. Many companies show how tableware is moulded and decorated. It is also interesting to see how figurines and floral studies are designed and constructed. A tour which shows contrasting techniques is the one at *Moorcroft*. Some companies have special visitor centres where their skilled craftspeople demonstrate techniques directly to the public and are happy to answer questions. These are found at *Wedgwood Best*, *Spode* and *Royal Doulton* in Burslem. Many potteries are still housed in ancient buildings and manufacture takes place on several levels linked by staircases. Such tours are not recommended for the less-than-agile.

City Museum & Art Gallery

Museums Several companies (eg *Wedgwood, Royal Doulton, Moorcroft, Spode, John Beswick*) have their own museums. *The City Museum* in Hanley has a fine collection of ceramics and 18th century Staffordshire earthenware, while the *Gladstone Museum* in Longton – with its original 'bottle ovens' – shows how work was carried out.

City Museum & Art Gallery

How the shops are arranged in this book

The historic but confusing area of Stoke comprises several towns. For the purpose of this book, we group them under the name *Stoke-on-Trent* and list them alphabetically within it. We take the liberty of treating Barlaston in this way too.

We list the shops in the following order:

Stoke-on-Trent : Baddeley Green
Stoke-on-Trent : Barlaston
Stoke-on-Trent : Burslem
Stoke-on-Trent : Cobridge
Stoke-on-Trent : Fenton
Stoke-on-Trent : Hanley
Stoke-on-Trent : Longton
Stoke-on-Trent : Meir Park
Stoke-on-Trent : Stoke
Stoke-on-Trent : Tunstall

Individual detailed street maps will help you to navigate in Burslem and Cobridge; Fenton; Hanley; Longton; Stoke.

To see which towns are home to which shops, please turn to the two pages at the back of this section on Stoke.

Royal Doulton

Value Added Tax (VAT) is charged at a uniform rate of 17.5% in the UK and is payable on just about everything except children's clothes, food and books. Under the Retail Export Scheme, VAT may be reclaimed by overseas visitors (except for visitors from other EU countries) for a minimum purchase of £30. However, this does tend to vary from shop to shop and £50 seems to be the average minimum purchase price for which shops give exemption certificates. In practice, the process is complicated and time-consuming.

How to reclaim VAT You will need an Exemption Certificate which is available from the shop on purchase of the goods. You may be asked to show your passport to confirm you are not a local resident. The next step is to take your purchases and Exemption Certificate to Customs for validation when you leave the country. Make sure they stamp your Exemption Certificate.

Cash refund In order to receive an immediate VAT cash refund take your validated Exemption Certificate to the VAT refund desk or appointed agent located at major UK airports. £1000 is the maximum cash refund. **NB**. This service is not necessarily available for customers of all retail outlets.

Reclaiming after departure from the UK If you are unable to cash your Exemption Certificate before you leave the UK you can claim VAT by posting your certificate in the pre-paid envelope provided by the shop. Remember, the certificate must be validated by UK Customs. It is probably worth asking for a refund to be made to your credit card account, otherwise you might have the added (expensive) complication of receiving a refund cheque in sterling.

Insurance may or may not be included when items are posted or shipped to customers. Some companies do not offer an insurance service but replace, free of charge, any items broken in transit. A photograph of the damaged goods will help any claim.

The above information is a summary of the reclaim process. VAT rules are complicated and liable to change, so we cannot take responsibility for any details which prove to be faulty.

Please check the exact regulations at the time of purchase.

Some companies ship anything anywhere in the world while others do not have the facilities to do so. There is no standard policy. Those who organise an overseas shipping service usually deduct VAT then charge for carriage and insurance (usually a similar sum). Others have a set charge according to the number of items sent; some charge exact postage.

Factory shops can advise you about export procedures from the UK but – since regulations on importing goods into other countries are complicated – it is unlikely the shops will be able to advise you on import rules that you will meet on your arrival back home. 'Cookware' and 'tableware', for example, are classified differently for import tax by at least one major foreign country! The best solution is to clarify the situation for yourself, before you leave home or from your embassy in the UK.

Please see the following two pages for a summary.

Company	Number	Ship abroad	Overseas shipping charges	Insurance
Arthur Price of England	10	Yes	At freight cost.	By request
Aynsley China	28, 35	Yes	By weight.	Automatic
Ceramic World	36	No		By request
Churchill Tableware	22, 37	Yes	By weight and destination.	Automatic
Georgian Crystal (Tutbury)	16	Yes		Automatic
John Beswick	39	Yes	Tableware & stemware: 1–9 pieces £14 (min charge) then £1.30 per piece; oven-to-tableware 1–9 pieces £17 (min) then £2.20 per piece; Figures 1–3 pieces £20 (min) then £6.60 per item.	Automatic
Lotus	9, 15	Yes		
Minton	47	Yes	Tableware & stemware: 1–9 pieces £14 (min charge) then £1.30 per piece; oven-to-tableware 1–9 pieces £17 (min) then £2.20 per piece; Figures 1–3 pieces £20 (min) then £6.60 per item.	Automatic
Moorcroft	23	No		
Portmeirion	25, 41, 48	Yes	Parcel Force rates.	By request
Queen's Fine Bone China	49	Yes	By weight and destination.	Automatic
Royal Doulton Baddeley Green	18	Yes	Tableware & stemware: 1–9 pieces £14 (min charge) then £1.30 per piece; oven-to-tableware 1–9 pieces £17 (min) then £2.20 per piece; Figures 1–3 pieces £20 (min) then £6.60 per item.	Automatic
Royal Doulton Burslem	20	Yes	Tableware & stemware: 1–9 pieces £14 (min charge) then £1.30 per piece; oven-to-tableware 1–9 pieces £17 (min) then £2.20 per piece; Figures 1–3 pieces £20 (min) then £6.60 per item.	Automatic
Royal Doulton Fenton	26	Yes	Tableware & stemware: 1–9 pieces £14 (min charge) then £1.30 per piece, oven-to-tableware 1–9 pieces £17 (min) then £2.20 per piece, figures, character jugs & crystal giftware £20 (min) then £6.60 per item.	Automatic
Royal Worcester	32	Yes	First piece £17 + £2 each extra piece.	Automatic
Spode	50	Yes	According to destination.	Automatic
Staffordshire Enamels	44	Yes	By weight and destination.	Automatic
Tutbury Crystal Glass	17	Yes	At cost at time of purchase.	No
Wade Ceramics	21	Yes	By weight.	Automatic
Wedgwood	19, 27	Yes	By the piece.	Automatic

Min purchase for VAT refund	Post in UK	Postage charges in UK	Other Comments
No minimum	Yes	As per Royal Mail charges.	Complete telephone enquiry service.
£50	Yes	By weight (eg, £6.50 anywhere in UK for large box).	Customers can ring for stock availability. If out of stock, items can be ordered from factory.
No VAT charged	Yes	By weight + packing, or Amtrax minimum cost.	Happy to pack parcel for customer to take to post office direct. Accept travellers' cheques.
£30	Yes	Parcel Force minimum postal charge £3.95.	Sterling travellers' cheques.
£40	Yes	By weight + cost of packaging.	
£50	Yes	According to size.	
	Yes	Usually £3 per pair of shoes.	
£50	Yes	Min £4.60 for 9 pieces + 30p per each extra piece.	
£100	No		
£50	Yes	Parcel Force rates.	No shipping orders after 4 weekdays or 12.30 Saturday.
£55	Yes	Minimum postal charge: £3.95 (also for phone orders).	
£50	Yes	£4.60 for 6 items + 40p for each extra item sent.	
£50	Yes	According to type of item and number of pieces.	
£50	Yes	1–7 pieces £3.50 + 50p–£1 for each extra item.	Seconds and firsts sent.
£50	Yes	£5 first piece + 50p each extra piece, fully insured.	Sterling travellers' cheques.
£50	Yes	£6.50 up to 6 items; £8.50 up to 10 items; then as advised.	
£60	Yes	£1.95 per postal address in UK.	Send perfects but not seconds quality.
£40	Yes	At cost at time of purchase.	Goods damaged in post replaced free of charge.
£100	Yes	By weight.	Accept US dollars.
£30	Yes	By size of box & number of pieces.	Shipping/packing/insurance quotation given.

How to get the best out of your shopping

We hope that the following hints will not only add an extra streak of practicality to china shopping but will enhance your pleasure and comfort too. We learned them from a group of five delightful American women with whom we shared a table for breakfast one morning in a farmhouse not far from Stoke. These women were professional shoppers – on their fourth two-day trip to Stoke to stock up with superb Staffordshire china. Their rules of attack are indelibly printed in our minds. We repeat them here for the benefit of others following in their wake. We do not suggest that all rules should be followed ardently (and we take no responsibility for any untoward reactions from shop managers arising from Rule no. 5!)

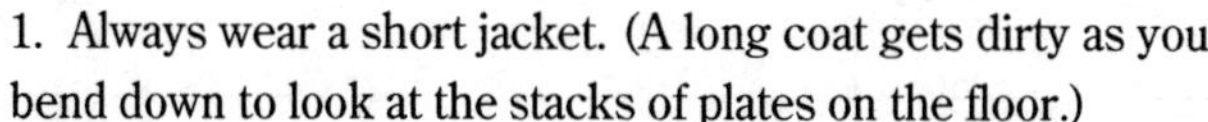

1. Always wear a short jacket. (A long coat gets dirty as you bend down to look at the stacks of plates on the floor.)

2. Kit yourself out with a waist bag for money, cheque book etc. (A shoulder bag is likely to swing round into a fragile display of plates and knock it over; a handbag can easily be left behind if you put it down in order to pick something up to look at closely.)

3. Wear warm, flat and comfortable shoes. (Some pottery outlets still retain the original cobbled floors; a surprising amount of walking can be fitted into a day of serious factory shopping; not all car-parks are beside the shop.)

4. Wear your Factory Shop Hair-Do. (Tie your hair back so that it doesn't flop into your eyes as you bend forward to inspect the bargains.)

Cauldon Works

5. Our favourite – but please don't jeopardise our excellent relationship with factory shop managers by telling them that we let you into this secret – don't forget your little polythene bag. (In this little bag you store your damp sponge, to be taken out whenever you inspect a dusty piece of crockery. Give the item a quick wipe and you will easily see if there are any flaws!)

What is bone china?

Porcelain was first made by the Chinese in the 7th century AD, and for the next 1000 or so years the technique remained a closely guarded secret. Porcelain was brought to Europe by Arab merchants in the twelfth century, but only the richest people could afford it. European pottery, at that stage, was heavier, dull grey or reddish brown earthenware. No one in Europe knew how porcelain was made.

The Chinese secret ingredient was kaolin, a perfectly white clay found high on a mountain. Kaolin, or 'china clay', is a result of the partial decomposition of the feldspar in granite which has changed into a fine white powder. Deposits were found in Saxony and France, which eventually led to the production of true porcelain in Europe, first at Meissen (in 1709), then at other potteries.

William Cookworthy, a Quaker apothecary from Plymouth, found small deposits of kaolin in Cornwall. In 1768 he patented his process and started a pottery at Plymouth. He was not entirely successful and eventually retired, but when his partner attempted to renew the patent in 1782, he was opposed by the Staffordshire potters. who also wanted to use china clay. Eventually the major Staffordshire potters moved into Cornwall and opened their own pits.

Production increased slowly but steadily in the first quarter of the 19th century, and once the clay began to be used for other purposes – mainly for the paper industry – demand increased dramatically. New methods speeded up extraction, refining and drying. It took six to eight months in Cookworthy's day to get the clay from the pit to the port; by 1870 this was reduced to three months. Today the process takes a few days.

Production of fine bone china, the English form of porcelain, began around 1800 when someone in Staffordshire added ashes of animal bone to the china clay, achieving startling results. Credit for the experiment generally goes to Josiah Spode. The new bone china was perfectly white, translucent and very strong, and, moreover, could be made using the traditional kilns and methods of Staffordshire.

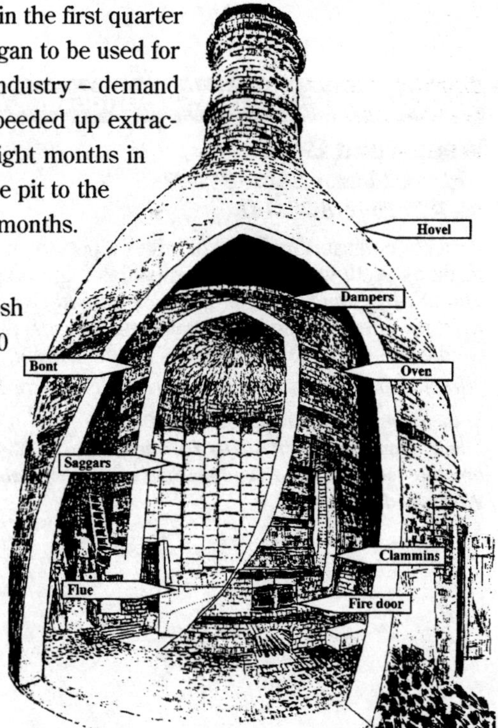

Thanks to Royal Doulton.

18 Stoke-on-Trent : Baddeley Green

Royal Doulton

Leek New Road ST2 7HR
(01782) 291700

Large range of *Royal Doulton* figures, character jugs, giftware, nursery items. Wide selection of seconds in tableware and crystal.

'Good range of seconds in tableware.'

See our display advertisement on p. 373

On the A53 north-west of Baddeley Green.

From Leek on A53: pass left turn-off A5009 and Elf petrol station on left. Pass the Victoria pub on the right then shop is at the end of factory on the right.

From Burslem: take A53 towards Leek. Enter Baddeley Green, pass large Partners (stationery) warehouse on left; shop is in next factory on left.

Open: Mon–Sat 9–5.30, Sun 10-4; Bank Holidays.
Closed: Christmas & New Year.
Cards: Amex, Diners, MasterCard, Switch, Visa.
Cars: Car spaces next to shop. Coach parking available.
Toilets: Yes.
Wheelchairs: Easy access to large shop. No steps.
Teas: In town.
Groups: Coach parties welcome to shop. For pottery tours and *Royal Doulton* display visit the factory in Burslem; for times and reservations contact Yvonne Wood (017820) 292434.
Transport: PMT bus no. 218 (Hanley to Leek) every half hour
Mail order: Yes. Bests and seconds sent.
Catalogue: Free tableware price lists; £3.50 for catalogue of current figurines.

19 Stoke-on-Trent : Barlaston *map p. 343*

Wedgwood Best

Wedgwood Visitor Centre ST12 9ES
(01782) 204218 204141

Perfect goods at normal retail prices – pottery and glass made by Wedgwood Group companies (eg, *Coalport, Mason's Ironstone, Johnson Bros., Waterford Crystal, Stuart Crystal*): fine china and glass tableware, vases, dishes, candlesticks, jewellery, figurines and florals etc.

'The shop for Wedgwood Group seconds is now in Fenton.'

In the countryside 6 miles south of Stoke.

Full signposting from M6 exit 15 and from the A34 (also signs on other local roads). Keep following signs once you reach the Wedgwood Estate.

Open: All year Mon–Fri 9–5; Sat 10–5; Sun 10–4. Most Bank Holidays: phone to check.
Closed: Xmas, Box. & NY Days.
Cards: Amex, Diners, MasterCard, Visa.
Cars: Large car and coach park.
Toilets: Yes, and for disabled.
Wheelchairs: Large Visitor Centre on one level.
Teas: Own restaurant.
Groups: Museum, cinema and demonstration area. £3.25 adults, £1.60 children, students & OAPs. £7.95 family ticket. Reduced for groups of 12+. Book in advance & mention this guide. Entrance to shop and refreshments free. Connoisseur Tour with own guide £7.25, book in advance.
Transport: Trains from Stafford or Stoke to Wedgwood Halt. Bus nos 46, 47 from Hanley bus station.
Mail order: Yes, incl. overseas. No restrictions.
Catalogue: Free.

20 Stoke-on-Trent : Burslem *map on p. 355*

Royal Doulton

Nile Street ST6 2AK
(01782) 292451

Royal Doulton figures, character jugs, giftware, nursery items. Wide selection of best ware and seconds in tableware. Range of glassware (gifts and stemware).

See our display advertisement on p. 373

Close to Burslem centre, effectively behind the large Food Giant supermarket on the A50.

This company is clearly marked, with conspicuous brown signs, from all directions.

Open: Mon–Sat 9–5.30, Sun 10–4. Most Bank Holidays.
Closed: Xmas, Boxing, NY days.
Cards: Amex, Diners, MasterCard, Visa, Switch.
Cars: Limited company parking. Car-park opposite.
Toilets: Yes, also for disabled.
Wheelchairs: Easy access.
Teas: Own new restaurant.
Tours: 75-min tours Mon–Fri 10.30 & 1.15 (not in Potters Holidays) incl. visitor centre, adults £5.50. Visitor centre only (7 days a week) with large figure display, video, demonstrations, *Minton* fine art studio, adults £2.75. Concessions. Book in advance Yvonne Wood (01782) 292434. (Tours not for infirm; children to be 10+ yrs.)
Transport: Five minutes' walk from Burslem bus station.
Mail order: Bests and seconds.
Catalogue: Free tableware price lists; £3.50 for catalogue of current figurines.

21 Stoke-on-Trent : Burslem *map on p. 355*

Wade Ceramics

Greenhead Street ST6 4AF
(01782) 524218

Novelty tea pots, whimseys, lamps, figurines, tea caddies, breakfast cups and saucers, casual dining ware. Small range of collectable items.

'Mainly seconds but some firsts and discontinued lines. Collectable items. Teapots from £1.99.'

On the north-west side of Burslem.

From the centre of Burslem: go north on the A50; pass Barratts Pottery on left, go left into Overhouse Street (in front of large car-wash) then left into Greenhead Street. Clearly visible shop is on right (go 40 yds further on to company car-park on right).

From the D-Road (A500): take A527 for Burslem. Go right at first roundabout, over next roundabout (Kwik Save on right) then turn left opposite Duke William and immediately after pelican crossing outside ornate NatWest bank on left into Westport Road. Take first right: after 100 yds turn left into Wade car-park.

Open: Mon–Fri 10–5.15; Sat 10–4.
Closed: Bank Holidays; Christmas–New Year.
Cards: Amex, Eurocard, MasterCard, Switch, Visa.
Cars: Own car-park.
Toilets: Yes.
Wheelchairs: Five steps to sizeable shop on ground floor.
Teas: In Burslem.
Groups: Pre-booked shopping groups welcome.
Transport: Bus nos. 92, 94 from Newcastle; 22, 24 from Stoke. Short walk from Burslem bus station.
Mail order: Yes, unrestricted. Regular limited editions directly from shop or by mail order. Free price lists.

22 Stoke-on-Trent : Cobridge *map on p. 355*

Churchill Tableware

Crane Street ST1 5RR
(01782) 268870 Fax (01782) 260051

Mugs, plates, cups, salt and pepper pots, dishes, meat platters, gravy boats, soup tureens, vegetable dishes, teapots and coffee pots in many patterns.

'Good quality seconds. Most prices 40–50% discounted from normal retail prices. Bargain basement items from 10p.'

North of Hanley, just off (on east side) the A50 Waterloo Road, south of the large junction with the A53.

Going north from Hanley on A50: go right into small side road (about 100 yds before traffic lights at major junction with A53).*

Going south along A50: at traffic lights, cross A53 then take first little road left.*

From A500: take A53 for Leek/Tourist Information Centre. At major junction traffic lights, go right on to A50 for Hanley. Take first little road left.*

***Follow large signs to shop on left through large iron gates.**

Open: Mon–Sat 9–5. Bank Holidays 9–5.
Closed: Christmas–New Year; please phone for details.
Cards: Amex, MasterCard, Switch, Visa.
Cars: Own car-park.
Toilets: Nearest are in Hanley.
Wheelchairs: Easy access to large shop; four steps to bargain basement.
Teas: In city centre.
Groups: No pottery tours but coaches welcome to shop. Please mention this guide.
Transport: On a main bus route to Hanley.
Mail order: Yes. Best and seconds by mail order.
Catalogue: Free.

23 Stoke-on-Trent : Cobridge *map on p. 355*

Moorcroft

Sandbach Road ST6 2DQ
(01782) 207943

Traditional *Moorcroft* designs: hand-made ornamental pottery, beautiful rich designs on vases, bowls, plates, table lamps (with matching lampshades) etc.

NB This company does not sell tableware.

'Best quality and seconds. Prices to suit most budgets.'

Between Hanley and Burslem, just off the A53.

Via A50 coming north from Hanley or south from Burslem: at major junction with traffic lights, turn east on to A53 for Leek.*

From A500: take A53 for Leek/Tourist Information Centre/ Moorcroft. Cross major junction with A50 (traffic lights).*

***Pass Jet petrol on right. After 50 yds take left fork (opposite Focus Home Centre). After 150 yds go left into well marked pottery with bottle kiln.**

Open: Mon–Fri 10–5; Sat 9.30–4.30 incl. Bank Holidays.
Closed: Christmas–New Year.
Cards: MasterCard, Switch, Visa.
Cars: Own large car-park.
Toilets: Yes, and for disabled.
Wheelchairs: No step, wide door, spacious showroom.
Teas: Hot drinks machine. Restaurants & cafés in Hanley.
Tours: Welcome to wander round restored bottle oven to see how pottery was fired. Tours Mon, Wed, Thur at 11 & 2 and Fri at 11 by appointment only. Adults £2.50, OAP's & children £1.50. Museum with beautiful examples of 'Old Moorcroft' – open daily, same times as shop. Coach parties welcome to shop.
Transport: Keele–Leek bus nos. 218 & 24. Short walk from Hanley–Burslem bus routes.
Mail order: No.
Catalogue: £3.50.

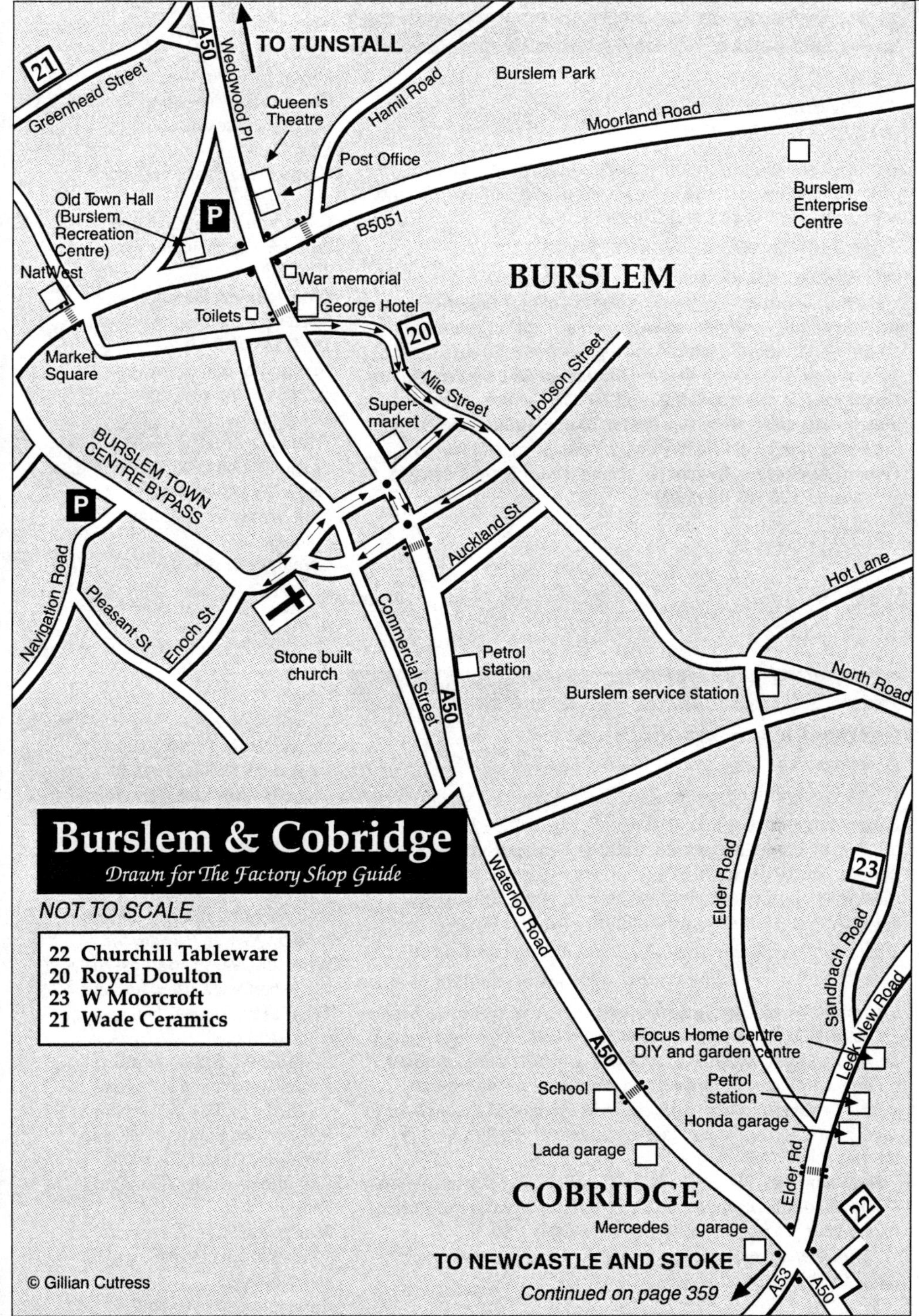
TO TUNSTALL
21
A50
Wedgwood Pl
Greenhead Street
Queen's Theatre
Hamil Road
Burslem Park
Moorland Road
Post Office
Old Town Hall (Burslem Recreation Centre)
P
B5051
Burslem Enterprise Centre
NatWest
War memorial
BURSLEM
Toilets
George Hotel
20
Market Square
Hobson Street
Nile Street
Super-market
BURSLEM TOWN CENTRE BYPASS
P
Auckland St
Hot Lane
Navigation Road
Pleasant St
Enoch St
Commercial Street
Stone built church
Petrol station
North Road
Burslem service station
A50
Burslem & Cobridge
Drawn for The Factory Shop Guide
NOT TO SCALE
22 Churchill Tableware
20 Royal Doulton
23 W Moorcroft
21 Wade Ceramics
Waterloo Road
Elder Road
23
Sandbach Road
Leek New Road
Focus Home Centre DIY and garden centre
A50
School
Petrol station
Honda garage
Lada garage
Elder Rd
COBRIDGE
22
Mercedes garage
TO NEWCASTLE AND STOKE
A53
A50
© Gillian Cutress
Continued on page 359

24 Stoke-on-Trent : Fenton *map on p. 357*

Lalco

4 Elsing Street ST4 2PR
(01782) 844858

White china and porcelain; artists' supplies such as colours, precious metals, brushes etc; photo-glazing machines and ware; decorated ware and transfers.

'Perfects and seconds all at factory prices.'

Off City Road (A5007) which links A500 to Fenton.

From A500: exit at large roundabout east for Ashbourne A52 & Fenton. Go under railway, then straight at roundabout on City Road A5007. After ½ mile, go left into Elsing Street.*

From new A50, Heron Cross exit: aim for City Centre/Fenton. Follow road to roundabout: go left for City Centre. At next roundabout, keep straight for Newcastle. Elsing Street third on right.*

Coming south from Hanley on old A50: at roundabout in Fenton, go right for Newcastle. Elsing Street is third on right.*

****Lalco is 100 yds on right.***

Open: Mon–Fri 9–5.
Closed: Bank Holidays; Christmas, Boxing and New Year's Days.
Cards: Most major credit and debit cards.
Cars: Ample space in street.
Toilets: Yes, including for disabled.
Wheelchairs: Easy access, no steps to medium sized shop.
Teas: In Hanley.
Groups: Shopping groups welcome; larger groups please phone.
Transport: Bus nos. 5, 24, 27 and 28 along City Road, stop a few yards away.
Mail order: Yes. Minimum order £5.
Catalogue: Free.

25 Stoke-on-Trent : Fenton *map on p. 357*

Portmeirion Seconds Shop

Dewsbury Road, off Victoria Road ST4 2TE
(01782) 743460

Large range of seconds at significantly reduced prices – tableware, cookware, vases, plant pots, porcelain jugs, trays, chopping boards, textiles and novelty teapots. First quality glassware, porcelain handled cutlery, porcelain-on-steel cookware, place mats and miniature hinged boxes.

'Special offers always available. Please phone for details.'

See our display advertisement on p. 369

Off Victoria Road, the old A50 linking Hanley with Fenton/Longton.

From Hanley: go south on A50 for 1¼ mile. Pass retail parks on left and right. After MEB on right, go left (Dewsbury Road).*

From A500: exit at large roundabout east for Ashbourne A52 & Fenton. Go under railway, then straight at roundabout on City Road A5007. At next large roundabout, go left for City Centre, Hanley A50.*

From new A50, Heron Cross exit: aim for City Centre, Fenton. Follow road to next roundabout: go left for City Centre. At next roundabout, go right for City Centre, Hanley A50.*

****After ⅓ mile, pass Queen Victoria pub on left. Take next right, Dewsbury Road.***

Open: Mon–Sat 9–5.30; Sun 10–4. Bank Holidays 9–5.30.
Closed: Christmas–New Year. Please ring to confirm dates.
Cards: Amex, MasterCard, Switch, Visa.
Cars: Own car-park, including spaces for disabled and coaches.
Toilets: Yes, and for disabled.
Wheelchairs: Easy access to large shop, wide aisles; no steps.
Teas: Main Hanley shopping centre and other local cafés.
Groups: No pottery tours. Parties welcome to shop (one coach at a time) – please phone Mrs Barbara Hobson in advance. Allow extra time for a group.
Transport: Hanley/Longton buses.
Mail order: Yes. No restrictions. Will post throughout UK and overseas.
Catalogue: Free leaflets.

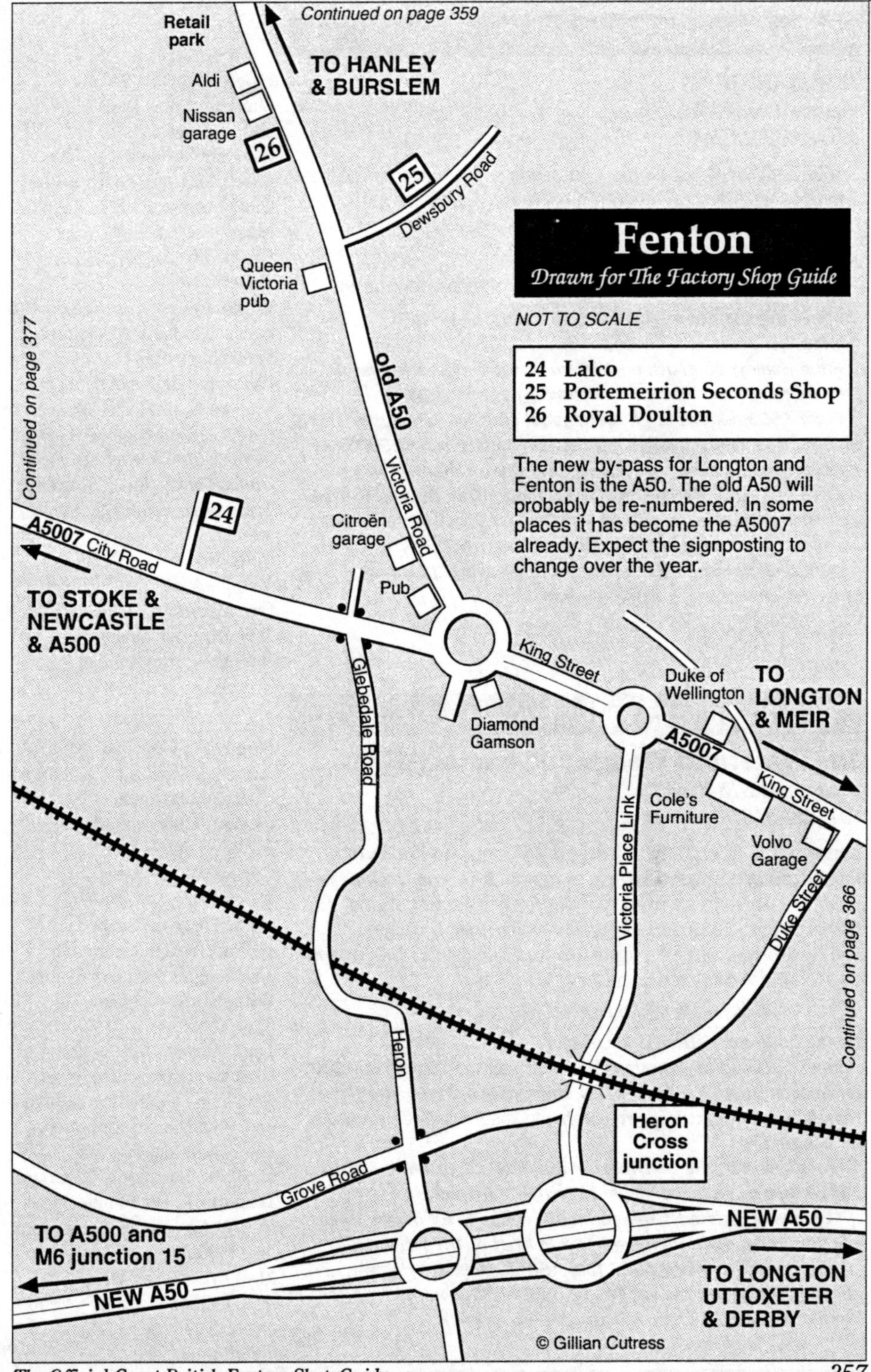

Continued on page 359
Retail park
Aldi
Nissan garage
26
TO HANLEY & BURSLEM
25
Dewsbury Road
Fenton
Drawn for The Factory Shop Guide
NOT TO SCALE
24 Lalco
25 Portemeirion Seconds Shop
26 Royal Doulton
The new by-pass for Longton and Fenton is the A50. The old A50 will probably be re-numbered. In some places it has become the A5007 already. Expect the signposting to change over the year.
Queen Victoria pub
old A50
Victoria Road
Continued on page 377
24
A5007 City Road
Citroën garage
Pub
TO STOKE & NEWCASTLE & A500
King Street
Glebedale Road
Diamond Gamson
Duke of Wellington
TO LONGTON & MEIR
A5007
King Street
Cole's Furniture
Victoria Place Link
Volvo Garage
Duke Street
Continued on page 366
Heron
Heron Cross junction
Grove Road
NEW A50
TO A500 and M6 junction 15
NEW A50
TO LONGTON UTTOXETER & DERBY
© Gillian Cutress

26 Stoke-on-Trent : Fenton *map on p. 357*

Royal Doulton

Victoria Road ST4 2PH
(01782) 291869

Wide range of *Royal Doulton* tableware, including dinner and tea services, and selection of figures, giftware and nursery items. *Royal Albert* design a speciality.

'Excellent choice of seconds.'

See our display advertisement on p. 373

Victoria Road is the original A50 linking Hanley with Fenton/Longton.

From Hanley: go south on A50 for about a mile. Pass retail park on right then Nissan. Company is next on right.

From A500: exit at large roundabout east for Ashbourne A52 & Fenton. Go under railway; straight at roundabout on A5007. At next large roundabout, go left for City Centre, Hanley A50.*

From new A50, Heron Cross exit: aim for City Centre, Fenton. Follow road to next roundabout: go left for City Centre. At next roundabout, go right for City Centre, Hanley A50.*

****Continue for ¾ mile. Go over zebra crossing: this shop is on left, immediately before Nissan.***

Open: Mon–Sat 9–5.30; Sun 10–4. Most Bank Holidays: phone to check.
Closed: Christmas and New Year: please phone to check.
Cards: Amex, Diners, JCB, MasterCard, Switch, Visa.
Cars: Own car-park.
Toilets: No.
Wheelchairs: Three steps with handrail to fairly spacious shop.
Teas: In Hanley.
Groups: Groups of shoppers very welcome to this shop; prior phone call appreciated. For pottery tours, please see *Royal Doulton* entry under *Burslem*.
Transport: Hanley/Longton buses.
Mail order: Yes. Bests and seconds sent.
Catalogue: Free tableware price lists; £3.50 for catalogue of current figurines.

27 Stoke-on-Trent : Fenton *map on p. 357*

The Waterford Wedgwood Factory Shop

King Street ST4 3DQ
(01782) 316161

Large range of slightly sub-standard goods and ends of lines from Wedgwood Group companies (*Coalport, Johnson Brothers, Mason's Ironstone, Waterford Crystal & Stuart Crystal*): fine china and glass tableware, vases, dishes, candlesticks, jewellery, figurines and florals etc. *Dartington Crystal* and *Arthur Price* cutlery.

'All items at 25–75% off high street prices.'

On the border of Fenton and Longton.

From A500: at large roundabout exit east on City Road A5007 for Ashbourne A52 & Fenton. Go under railway, then straight at roundabout. At next large roundabout, keep straight on A5007 for Longton.*

From new A50, Heron Cross exit: aim for City Centre, Fenton. Follow road to next roundabout: go right for Longton.*

****Company is about 1 mile on right, opposite Elf petrol. Pass the factory on right: go sharp right in front of The Potter pub.***

From Longton: take A5007 (old A50) for Fenton/Hanley; shop is 400 yds on the left (opposite Elf petrol on right). After The Potter pub, go sharp left to car-park at back.

Open: Mon–Sat 9–5.30; Sun 11–5. Most Bank Holidays – please phone to check.
Closed: Christmas, Boxing and New Year's Days.
Cards: Amex, Delta, MasterCard, Switch, Visa.
Cars: Large car-park.
Toilets: Yes, including for disabled. Baby changing area.
Wheelchairs: No steps to huge shop.
Teas: Crown Hotel in Longton.
Groups: Groups of shoppers welcome – please ring shop to book in advance. For pottery demonstrations visit the *Wedgwood* factory in *Barlaston*.
Transport: Ten minutes' walk from Longton train station; local buses along King Street.
Mail order: Yes. On all products, including seconds. Export anywhere in the world.
Catalogue: Free.

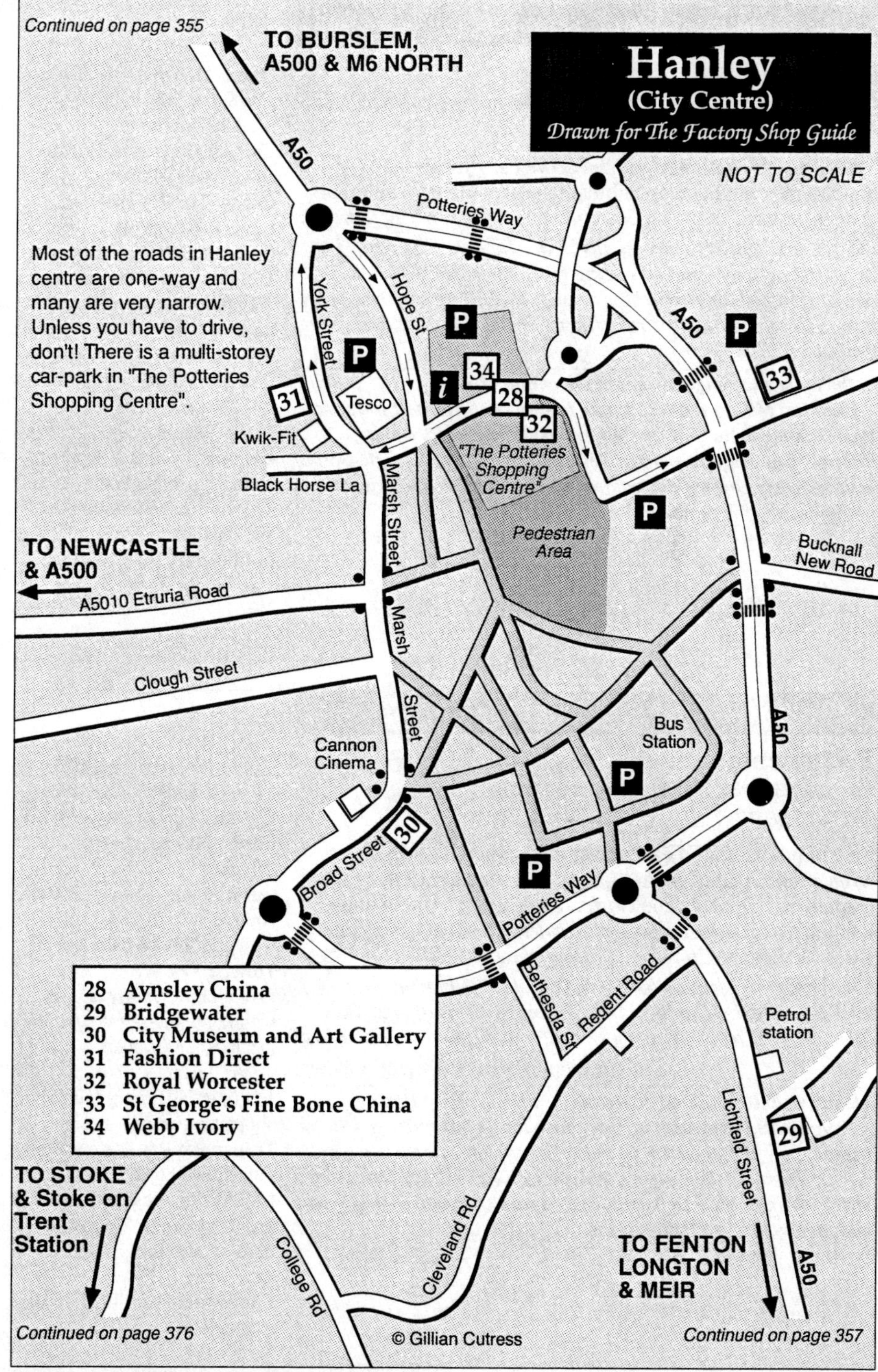
Hanley
(City Centre)
Drawn for The Factory Shop Guide
NOT TO SCALE
Continued on page 355
TO BURSLEM, A500 & M6 NORTH
A50
Potteries Way
Most of the roads in Hanley centre are one-way and many are very narrow. Unless you have to drive, don't! There is a multi-storey car-park in "The Potteries Shopping Centre".
York Street
Hope St
P
Tesco
31
34
28
32
33
Kwik-Fit
Black Horse La
"The Potteries Shopping Centre"
Pedestrian Area
Marsh Street
TO NEWCASTLE & A500
A5010 Etruria Road
Bucknall New Road
Clough Street
Marsh
Street
Cannon Cinema
Bus Station
30
Broad Street
Potteries Way
Bethesda St
Regent Road
Petrol station
29
Lichfield Street
28 Aynsley China
29 Bridgewater
30 City Museum and Art Gallery
31 Fashion Direct
32 Royal Worcester
33 St George's Fine Bone China
34 Webb Ivory
TO STOKE & Stoke on Trent Station
College Rd
Cleveland Rd
TO FENTON LONGTON & MEIR
Continued on page 376
© Gillian Cutress
Continued on page 357

28 Stoke-on-Trent : Hanley *see map on p. 359*

Aynsley China

Unit N, Lewis's Arcade, The Potteries Shopping Centre ST1 1PS
(01782) 204108

Fine bone china dinner and tea services; giftware and hand-made china flowers; china-handled cutlery. Tablemats, textiles, trays & chopping boards to match best-selling designs.

'We sell best quality and seconds in most items, plus bargains in perfect obsolete lines. Wedding gift service. Most patterns can be adapted for corporate use with initialling and company logo. Seconds at massive reductions. Special offers all year. Collectors' Club.'

In the large shopping precinct in the centre of Hanley (NOT Stoke).
From the M6 via the A500: aim for Stoke-on-Trent at first and then pick up signs to 'City Centre' and 'Potteries Shopping Centre'. You come to Hanley. Follow signs to the car-park. Shop is underneath Lewis's department store. Look for the Body Shop entrance: shop is on that level.

Open: Mon–Sat 9–5.30; *also Nov & Dec* late night Tues to 8. Bank Holidays.
Closed: Christmas, Boxing and New Year's Days.
Cards: MasterCard, Visa.
Cars: Potteries Shopping Centre multi-storey car-park.
Toilets: In the Potteries Shopping Centre, including for disabled.
Wheelchairs: Easy access to Potteries Shopping Centre and this shop (no steps).
Teas: Nearby cafés.
Groups: Groups welcome to shop; no need to book.
Transport: Train to Stoke station, then any bus to Hanley.
Mail order: No restrictions.
Catalogue: £3.

29 Stoke-on-Trent : Hanley *see map on p. 359*

Bridgewater

Eastwood Works, Lichfield Street ST1 3EJ
(01782) 201328

Fine hand-decorated earthenware designed by *Emma Bridgewater*: plates, platters, cups and saucers, mugs, jugs, teapots etc. Ceramic cookware. Range of table linen and kitchen accessories. Also *Matthew Rice* designs in stationery, cards, decorative tin boxes, picture frames, address books etc.

'Our ceramic pieces recall the charm of period farmhouse kitchens. Slight seconds and discontinued items at least 30% below normal retail prices on sale; also additional special offers.'

See our display advertisement opposite

Clearly visible on the original A50, ¼ mile south of Hanley.
From Hanley ring road: from roundabout go downhill on A50 for Fenton/Longton. Pass UK petrol then turn left into factory yard.
From Fenton: follow signs for Hanley on A50. Cross the round-about with the A52. Go uphill for a quarter of a mile then go right into clearly marked factory yard.

Open: Mon–Sat 9.30–4.30.
Closed: Bank Holidays; for Christmas times please phone.
Cards: Major cards (not Diners).
Cars: Ample parking at side of shop. Coach parking preferably with prior phone call.
Toilets: Yes.
Wheelchairs: Easy access with ramp, but regret no toilet facilities for disabled.
Teas: In Hanley.
Groups: No factory tours, but shopping groups welcome.
Transport: Bus station at top of Lichfield Street.
Mail order: Yes. Telephone orders welcome. No restrictions on mail order. Export worldwide.
Catalogue: Free illustrated catalogue.

30 Stoke-on-Trent : Hanley *see map on p. 359*

City Museum and Art Gallery

Bethesda Street ST1 3DW
(01782) 232323

Museum shop stocks a wide range of books, particularly ceramic related publications, and gifts, including ceramic and craft items, children's souvenirs and greetings cards.

'This purpose-built museum and art gallery houses the finest collection of Staffordshire pottery in the world. Over 5000 pieces on display, ranging from early slipware to contemporary factory products and studio pottery. Highlights include slipware by Thomas Toft, rare 18th century ceramics by Wedgwood and his contemporaries, sumptuous Minton porcelain, pottery by Bernard Leach, and the famous Owl Jug featured on BBC TV's Antiques Roadshow. Other attractions include a Spitfire and a lively programme of changing exhibitions. Free information service, and identification for up to five items (no valuations).'

Easy to find in the centre of Hanley in the large square glass fronted building.

If you park in The Potteries Shopping Precinct car-park: museum is about 5 minutes' walk (on corner of Bethesda Street, Broad Street and Warner Street). Main entrance is on Bethesda Street.

Open: Mon–Sat 10–5; Sun 2–5.
Closed: Christmas–New Year.
Cards: MasterCard, Visa.
Cars: Many pay-&-display car-parks.
Toilets: Yes, including for disabled people.
Wheelchairs: Easy access; two wheelchairs available.
Teas: Own tearoom.
Groups: Admission free. Tours for groups only: Mon–Fri 10–12 or 2–4. Please book in advance.
Transport: Any bus to Hanley centre. Train to Stoke, then short bus or taxi ride.
Mail order: On request. Fragile items not sent.
Catalogue: Free (for books on ceramics only).

31 Stoke-on-Trent : Hanley *see map on p. 359*

Fashion Direct (Hanley)

151 Marsh Street ST1 5QE
(01782) 266660

Quality fashion clothing for men and women direct from UK and Europe's leading manufacturers. Over 10,000 perfect garments; also handbags, scarves and other accessories.

'This season's overmakes, cancelled orders, designer samples etc. We take huge deliveries of garments every week; most with 30% off and 100's at half price.'

Easy to find in Hanley centre, opposite Tesco. Marsh Street is part of the 'inner ring road' which encircles The Potteries Shopping Centre and pedestrianised town centre.

Either: go through Hanley centre, following signs for Burslem/Tunstall via the A50. Pass Kwik-Fit on left, then this clearly marked company is on left (opposite Tesco).

or: follow signs to The Potteries Shopping Centre, park in multi-storey car-park then walk downhill for 200 yds (ask for Tesco).

Open: Mon–Sat 9.30–5.30; Sun 11–5. Bank Holidays.
Closed: Easter Sunday; Christmas and Boxing Days.
Cards: Major credit and debit cards.
Cars: Own large car-park. Space for one coach, otherwise coach park 100 yds.
Toilets: Yes, including for the disabled.
Wheelchairs: Easy access to huge shop; no steps.
Changing rooms: Yes, with ample space for wheelchair.
Teas: Not at present, but cafés and restaurants in town.
Groups: Shopping groups welcome but no factory tours.
Transport: Any bus to Hanley; or train to Stoke then short bus or taxi ride.
Mail order: No.

32 Stoke-on-Trent : Hanley *see map on p. 359*

Royal Worcester

Lewis's Arcade, Potteries Shopping Centre ST1 1PS
(01782) 204276

Now closed

Porcelain, fine bone china and giftware. Also *Spode, Worcester Ornamental Studios, Royal Brierley, Country Artists, Fo-Frame, Heredities, Cloverleaf* mats, *Pimpernel* mats, *Paw Prints, Lakeland Studios, Arthur Price* cutlery, *Caithness Glass.*

'25% off high street prices.'

In the large shopping precinct in the centre of Hanley (NOT Stoke).

From M6 via the A500: aim for Stoke-on-Trent at first and then pick up signs to 'City Centre' and 'Potteries Shopping Centre'. You come to Hanley. Follow signs to car-park. Shop is underneath Lewis's department store. Look for Body Shop entrance: shop is on same level.

Open: Mon–Fri 9–5.30; Sat 9–6. Some Bank Holidays – please phone to check.
Closed: Christmas and Boxing Days.
Cards: All major cards.
Cars: Potteries Shopping Centre multi-storey car-park.
Toilets: In shopping centre.
Wheelchairs: No steps if you enter shop by Body Shop.
Teas: Café opposite, and various restaurants in shopping centre.
Groups: Shopping groups welcome.
Transport: Stoke train station, then bus to Hanley. All local buses stop at shopping centre.
Mail order: Any package, large or small, can be mailed world-wide.
Catalogue: No.

33 Stoke-on-Trent : Hanley *see map on p. 359*

St George's Fine Bone China

77 Upper Huntbach Street ST1 2BV
(01782) 263709

Fine bone china: mugs, beakers, tankards, jugs, vases, plant pots, cachepots, loving cups, miniature cups and saucers, table lamps, thimbles, flower arrangements, even bone china greetings cards! Items personalised with names/messages.

'From 50p–£30. Main store and mail order rejects available.'

In Hanley centre: easy to walk from the pedestrian area.

By car: go clockwise round Hanley to be on correct side of dual carriageway.

Coming south on A50 from Burslem: go to first major roundabout then left so that you go clockwise round Hanley; go uphill, underneath bridge; go left after first and immediately before second pedestrian lights. Shop 100 yds on left.

Open: Mon–Fri 9–5.30; Sat 9–2.
Closed: Phone to check Bank Holidays.
Cards: Access, Visa.
Cars: Own car-park.
Toilets: In town centre.
Wheelchairs: One small step, fairly small compact shop.
Teas: In Hanley.
Groups: Please phone first, mentioning this book.
Transport: Near bus station.
Mail order: Yes.

34 Stoke-on-Trent : Hanley *see map on p. 359*

Webb Ivory

Unit 2, Quadrant Road, Potteries Shopping Centre
(01782) 202570

Fascinating variety of surplus catalogue stocks of greetings cards, wrapping papers, household goods, toys, small gifts and clothing.

'50% off catalogue prices.'

In the large shopping precinct in the centre of Hanley (NOT Stoke).

From M6 via the A500: aim for Stoke-on-Trent at first and then pick up signs to 'City Centre' and 'Potteries Shopping Centre'. You come to Hanley. Follow signs to the car-park. Shop is between the Tourist Information Centre and TK Maxx with access by lift and escalator from other floors.

Open: Mon–Sat 9–5.30; *also Oct–Dec* Sun 11–5. Some Bank Holidays, please check.
Closed: Christmas–New Year.
Cards: Most major credit cards; Switch.
Cars: Public car-park within shopping centre complex.
Toilets: In shopping centre.
Wheelchairs: Shop on ground floor, accessible from other floors by lifts.
Teas: In shopping centre.
Groups: No.
Transport: Stoke-on-Trent train station. All local buses stop outside shopping centre.
Mail order: No.

Stoke-on-Trent : Longton

The Gladstone Pottery Museum (01782) 319232. Open 7 days a week. Visit this restored working Victorian pottery. Charge made.

These splendid bottle ovens (Gladstone Pottery Museum) are nearly the only ones which remain out of the hundreds that dominated the smoke-filled skyline of the Stoke area. The museum has fascinating old photographs, and information about the appalling living and working conditions for pottery families in former times. The air was dense with smoke (except for two weeks a year when furnaces were allowed to go cold for cleaning); the kilns were dangerous; and materials used were poisonous. So much for the 'good old days'!

Longton roads are special

Longton, one of the most important pottery producing towns, and the area with most factory shops, has now been bypassed by the new A50. This dual carriageway runs east–west on the south side of Longton, linking Uttoxeter in the east to the A500 (the major north–south artery through the Stoke-on-Trent area) and M6.

Construction of the new A50 has been in operation for several years. Local people are heartily sick of building works, the cones and the mud. Businesses have suffered – road works have impeded access to their premises; visitors either couldn't find them, or couldn't be bothered to negotiate the maze of road diversions to get there.

The new road should improve the situation greatly.

The new road is still incomplete, without its full quota of signposts. Shoppers should be aware of several points:

1. two roads are officially called the A50
2. the newly built A50 is signposted A50
3. the original A50 is still called the A50 along the Hanley–Fenton stretch
4. the old A50 in Fenton–Longton is now the new A5007 (but still signposted A50 in some places)
5. the new A5007 appears on few signposts.

[*Honest!*]

We hope the following advice is helpful for finding Longton shops:

The new A50 has three main exits.

The exits are (from west to east, ie from the A500):

Heron Cross exit
convenient for Fenton (*Lalco; Portmeirion, Fenton; Royal Doulton, Fenton; Waterford Wedgwood; Hadida; Churchill*).

Longton exit
convenient for all shops in Longton (including *John Beswick* and *Hartley Greens*), and those near Gladstone Pottery Museum (*Royal Winton; Portmeirion, Longton; Ceramic World; Aynsley*).

Normacot exit
convenient for shops in Longton East (*Staffordshire Enamels; Royal Doulton, Longton*).

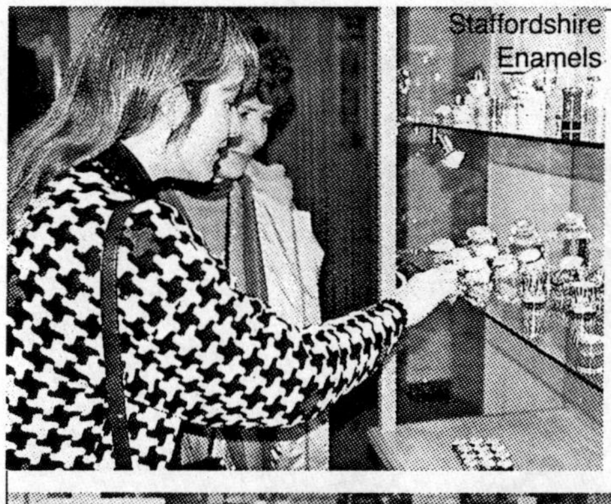

Stoke-on-Trent : Longton

see map on p366

Late Entry

Hartley Greens

Leeds Pottery, Anchor Road ST3 5EP
(01782) 599959

Traditional pierced Leedsware, hand-made to 18th century designs. Wide choice of ornamental pieces and tableware. Also creamware dinner services, both plain and decorated, classic and casual.

'All items are seconds (made in own factory) at up to 50% off best quality price.'

Anchor Road B5039 leads north off the one-way system in central Longton.

From new A50, Longton exit: aim for Normacot/Longton East. Follow signs for Gladstone Pottery Museum. At T-junction (museum on right), go left into Uttoxeter Road (old A50). Take first right. At bottom, go left into Sutherland Road. At T-junction, go right into Anchor Road. Go under railway. Shop is ½ mile on right, on corner of Amison Street.

Coming south on King Street (old A50) from Fenton: go under railway bridge into the Longton one-way system; go left at traffic lights in front of Lloyds Bank into Anchor Road. Go under railway. Shop is ½ mile on right, on corner of Amison Street.

Open: Mon–Thur 8.30–4.30; Fri 8.30–2; some Bank Holidays. Weekends by arrangement.
Closed: Easter; Christmas–New Year; last week June & first week July; first week September. Phone for dates.
Cards: Major credit/debit cards.
Cars: Factory car-park.
Toilets: Ask if required.
Wheelchairs: 15 steps to shop, but staff gladly assist visitors in wheelchairs to view display on ground floor and to purchase.
Teas: Local cafés and pubs.
Groups: Shopping groups welcome. Factory tours for small groups by prior arrangement, £1 (refundable against purchase); children aged 10+. Phone Cynthia Whitehurst.
Transport: Buses or trains to Longton then walk.
Mail order: No.

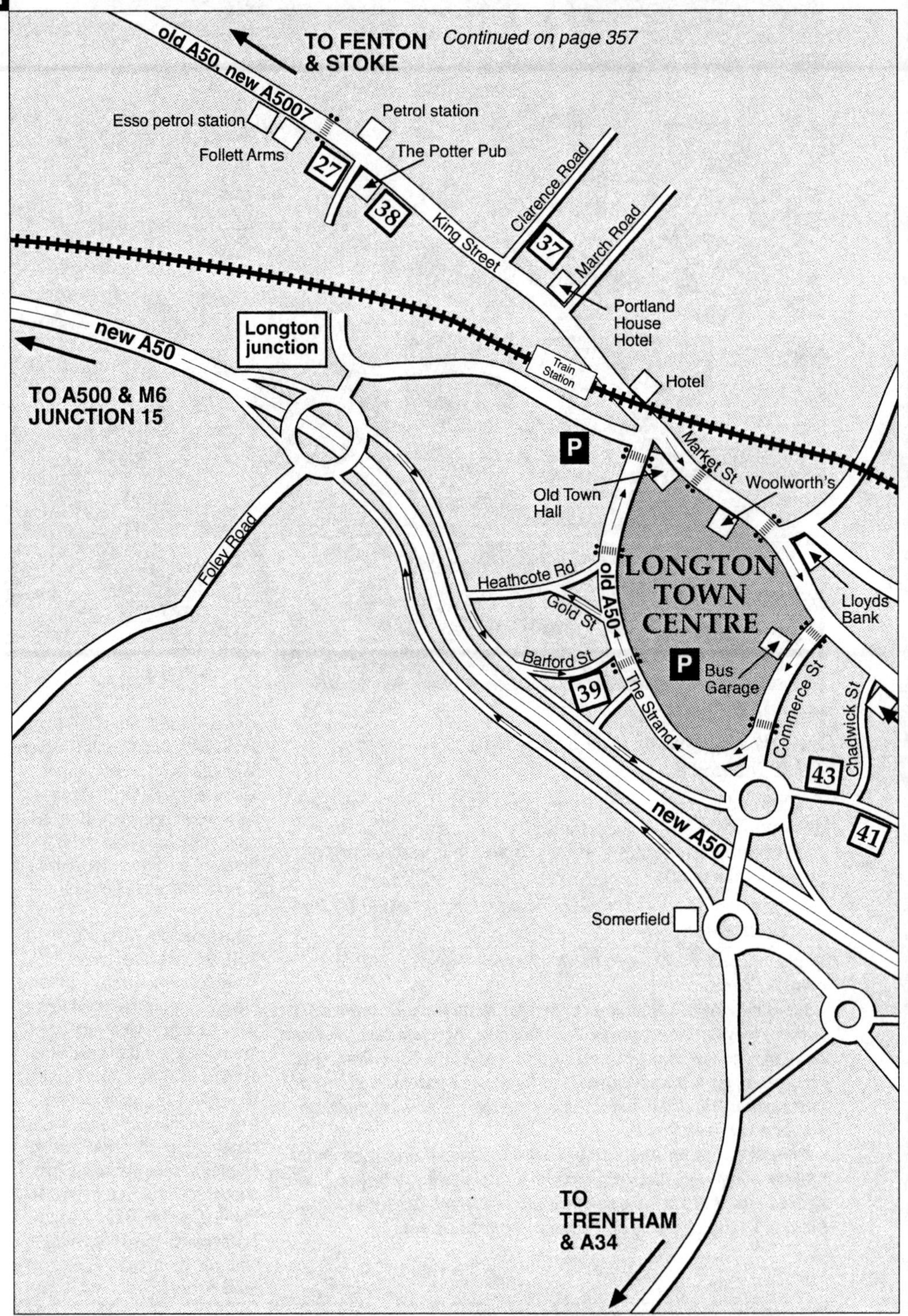

TO FENTON & STOKE
Continued on page 357
old A50, new A5007
Esso petrol station
Petrol station
Follett Arms
The Potter Pub
27
38
Clarence Road
March Road
37
King Street
Portland House Hotel
Longton junction
new A50
TO A500 & M6 JUNCTION 15
Train Station
Hotel
P
Market St
Old Town Hall
Woolworth's
Foley Road
Heathcote Rd
old A50
LONGTON TOWN CENTRE
Lloyds Bank
Gold St
Barford St
P
Bus Garage
39
The Strand
Commerce St
Chadwick St
43
41
new A50
Somerfield
TO TRENTHAM & A34

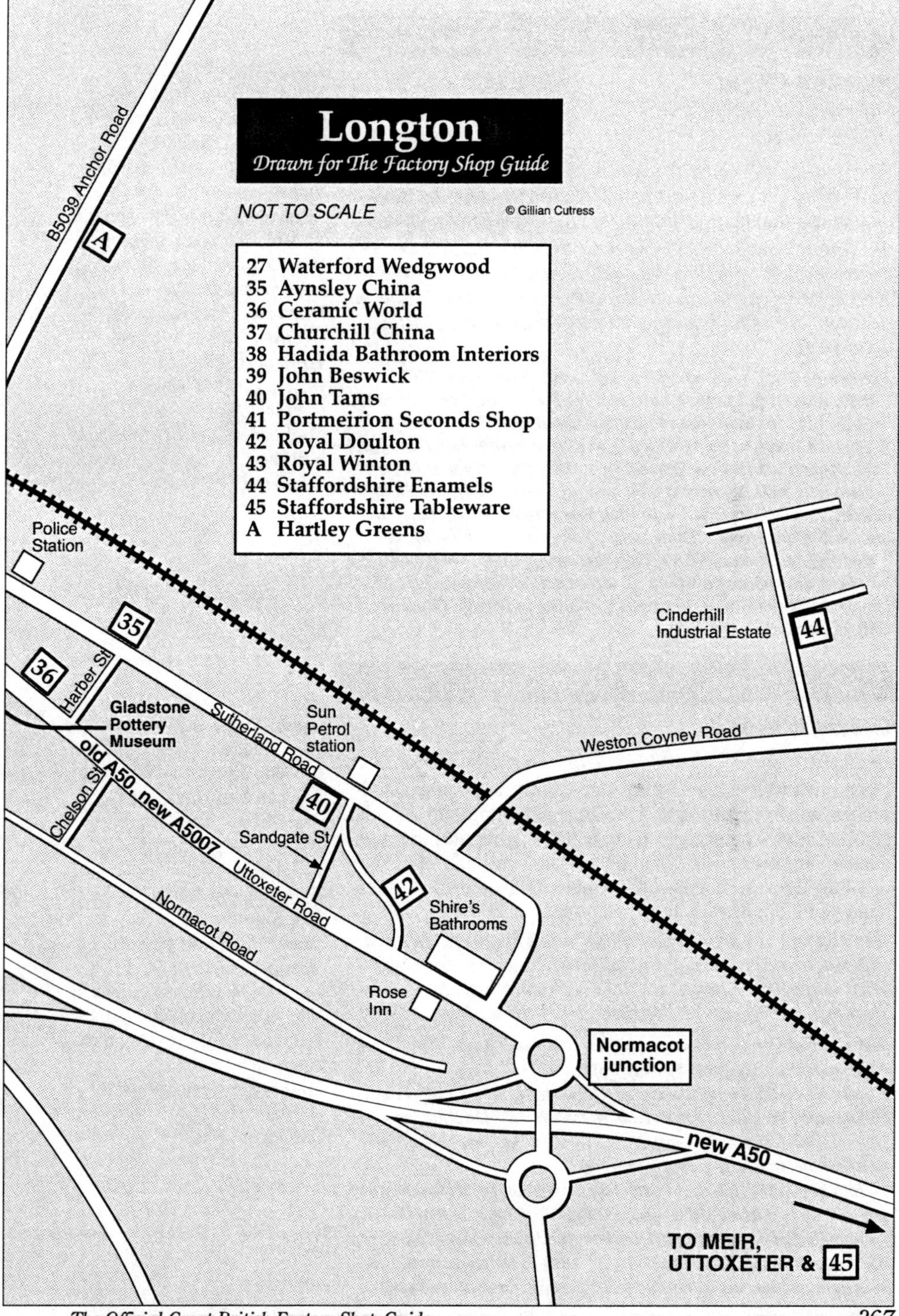

Longton
Drawn for The Factory Shop Guide
NOT TO SCALE
© Gillian Cutress
27 Waterford Wedgwood
35 Aynsley China
36 Ceramic World
37 Churchill China
38 Hadida Bathroom Interiors
39 John Beswick
40 John Tams
41 Portmeirion Seconds Shop
42 Royal Doulton
43 Royal Winton
44 Staffordshire Enamels
45 Staffordshire Tableware
A Hartley Greens
B5039 Anchor Road
A
Police Station
35
36
Harber St
Gladstone Pottery Museum
Sutherland Road
Sun Petrol station
old A50, new A5007
Chelson St
40
Sandgate St
Uttoxeter Road
42
Shire's Bathrooms
Normacot Road
Rose Inn
Normacot junction
Cinderhill Industrial Estate
44
Weston Coyney Road
new A50
TO MEIR, UTTOXETER & 45

35 Stoke-on-Trent : Longton *map on p. 366*

Aynsley China

Sutherland Road ST3 1HR
(01782) 593536

Fine bone china dinner & tea services. Giftware – vases, hand-made china flowers, china-handled cutlery. Textiles, trays, tablemats, chopping boards to match best-selling patterns.

'Best quality and seconds in most items, plus bargains in perfect obsolete lines. Wedding gift service. Collectors' Club. Most patterns can be adapted for corporate use with initialling and company logo. Seconds at massive reductions. Special offers all year.'

Sutherland Road runs parallel to Uttoxeter Road (old A50).

From new A50, Longton exit: aim for Normacot/Longton East. Follow signs for Gladstone Pottery Museum. At T-junction (Gladstone Museum on right), go right into Uttoxeter Road (old A50). Take second left (Harber Street). Aynsley is facing you at bottom.

From new A50, Normacot exit: aim for Weston Coyney. Go right in front Shire's Bathrooms into Meir Hay Road which bends round into Sutherland Road. Clearly marked shop is ½ mile on right.

Coming south on old A50 from Fenton: go under railway bridge into Longton one-way system; go left at traffic lights in front of Lloyds Bank then take first right (Sutherland Road). Shop is 250 yds on left.

Open: Mon–Sat 9–5.30. Sun 11–4. Bank Holidays.
Closed: Christmas, Boxing and New Year's Days.
Cards: Amex, MasterCard, Visa.
Cars: Own coach and car-park.
Toilets: Yes, and for disabled.
Wheelchairs: Ramp to huge, spacious shop.
Teas: Local cafés and pubs.
Groups: Groups welcome.
Transport: Five minutes' walk to Longton bus and train stations.
Mail order: Yes. Seconds and bests sent.
Catalogue: £3.

36 Stoke-on-Trent : Longton *map on p. 366*

Ceramic World

31 Uttoxeter Road ST3 1NY *(01782) 593433*

Decorative wall plaques (humorous, flowers, animals, land-scapes, works of art, Royal Family, coal mining etc). Special commissions – personalised china items, christening mugs, anniversary plates, etc. Plant pots, vases, jardinières. Range of mugs, figures, military collectibles, local souvenirs, some hand-painted, giftware items, all prices.

'The factory shop for several "small" manufacturers. Limited editions, exclusive designs unavailable elsewhere. £1–£300 price range with plaques at £2–£15. Best and second qualities. Your own photos can be transfered on to china. January sale.'

Just south of Longton town centre, on Uttoxeter Road (A5007, old A50) opposite Gladstone Pottery Museum.

From new A50, Longton exit: aim for Normacot/Longton East. Follow signs for Gladstone Pottery Museum. At T-junction (Gladstone Museum on right), go right into Uttoxeter Road (old A50). Shop is on left, facing museum.

From new A50, Normacot exit: aim for Gladstone Museum. Keep straight for ½ mile downhill: shop on right (facing museum on left).

From Fenton on old A50: aim for Longton, go clockwise round one-way system – turn off for A5007 (old A50) to Uttoxeter, following sign for museum; shop shortly on left (facing museum on right).

Open: Mon–Sat 10–4. Some Bank Holidays – please phone.
Closed: Christmas–New Year (re-open with January sale).
Cars: In side streets and Longton car-park.
Toilets: In Longton.
Wheelchairs: One step into shop; one inside.
Teas: Oatcake shop next door.
Groups: Phone call first appreciated. Demonstrations in shop by arrangement.
Transport: Close to Longton bus station.
Mail order: Mainly for wall plaques.
Catalogue: No.

See our entries nos. 25, 41 & 48

37 Stoke-on-Trent : Longton *map on p. 366*

Churchill China

King Street ST3 1ET
(01782) 329785 Fax (01782) 598063

Fine bone china tableware, including dinner, tea and coffee sets. China mugs galore. Collectors' cups and saucers. *Dartington Crystal.*

'At least 40% savings. Perfect quality items available to order.'

On border of Longton and Fenton (ie, on west side of Longton).

From A500: at large roundabout exit east for Ashbourne A52 & Fenton on City Road A5007. Go under railway, straight at roundabout. At next large roundabout, keep straight on A5007 for Longton.*

From new A50, Heron Cross exit: aim for City Centre, Fenton. Follow road to next roundabout: go right for Longton.*

***Company is about 1¼ mile on left. Pass Elf petrol on left. Go left (in front of Standish) into Clarence Road. Shop entrance on right.**

From Longton: take A5007 (old A50) for Fenton/Hanley. Go under Longton railway bridge. After 300 yds (beyond hotel on right), go right into Clarence Road. Shop entrance on right.

Open: Mon–Sat and Bank Holidays 9–5.
Closed: Christmas–New Year; please phone for details.
Cards: Access, Visa.
Cars: Own car-park.
Toilets: Nearest in Longton centre.
Wheelchairs: Ramp; easy access to small shop.
Teas: Crown Hotel in Longton.
Groups: No pottery tours but coaches welcome to shop. Please mention this guide.
Transport: Five minutes' walk from train station; local buses along King Street.
Mail order: Yes. Contact Queen's at Stoke (01782 745899) or Churchill's at Cobridge (01782 268870).
Catalogue: Free.

38 Stoke-on-Trent : Longton *map on p. 366*

Hadida Bathroom Interiors

Old Foley Pottery (Est. 1686), King Street ST4 3DG
(01782) 597700

Co-ordinating china bathroom accessories. Traditional jugs and bowls and wide selection of giftware. Some of the *Hadida* fabric collection.

'Seconds and best ware.'

See our display advertisement opposite

On border of Longton and Fenton (ie, on west side of Longton).

From A500: at large roundabout exit east for Ashbourne A52 & Fenton on City Road A5007. Go under railway, straight at roundabout. At next large roundabout, go straight on A5007 for Longton.*

From new A50, Heron Cross exit: aim for City Centre, Fenton. Follow road to next roundabout: go right for Longton.*

***Company is about 1 mile on right. Pass Elf petrol on left then go right after about 50 yds (after traffic island).**

From Longton: take A5007 (old A50) for Fenton/Hanley. Go under Longton railway bridge. Shop is 350 yds on left (100 yds before Elf petrol on right). Go sharp left (before traffic island) through large, green iron gates.

Open: Mon–Sat 9–4.30.
Closed: Bank Holidays; Christmas–New Year.
Cards: MasterCard, Switch, Visa.
Cars: Factory car-park.
Toilets: Yes.
Wheelchairs: Two steps, but assistance gladly given.
Teas: Local cafés and pubs.
Groups: Shopping groups welcome any time.
Transport: Five minutes from station. Local buses along King Street.
Mail order: Yes.
Catalogue: No.

39 Stoke-on-Trent : Longton *map on p. 366*

John Beswick

Barford Street ST3 2JR
(01782) 291237

John Beswick animal sculptures. Also *Royal Doulton* figures, character jugs, nursery and giftware. Selection of seconds in tableware.

A small one-way street in the middle of Longton. Barford Street leads INTO The Strand, the road which forms part of the one-way system encircling Longton.

From new A50, Longton exit: aim for Normacot/Longton East. At roundabout at end of slip road, go left for Town Centre. Go clockwise around one-way system.*

From Hanley/Fenton on A5007 (old A50) or from direction of Gladstone Pottery Museum: aim for Longton town centre. You come into the one-way system. Keep going round town.*

***After Barford Street on left (no entry) take next left, Gold Street. Take two more left turns – you are in Barford Street, with shop clearly visible on right.**

Open: Mon–Fri 9–4.30. Might open Sat before Xmas & Easter.
Closed: Easter week, last week June (+ previous Thur, Fri) and first week July; late Summer Bank Holiday week (+ previous Thur, Fri); Christmas–New Year.
Cards: Amex, Diners, MasterCard, Switch, Visa.
Cars: Own car-park in front.
Toilets: In shopping precinct.
Wheelchairs: Five large steps, so access not really possible to medium sized shop.
Teas: Local pubs, cafés.
Tours: Arrange in advance, mentioning this book. Tours (£2.50) incl. museum visit last 90 minutes. Mon–Thur at 10.15 & 2; Fri 10.15 & 1. Please book, only available on request.
Transport: 5 minutes' walk from Longton bus and train stations.
Mail order: Phone for details. Minimum order £3.50.
Catalogue: Free tableware price lists; £3.50 catalogue includes figurines.

40 Stoke-on-Trent : Longton *map on p. 366*

John Tams

Sutherland Road ST3 1JB
(01782) 599667

Wide range of china tableware, dinner, tea and coffee sets, vases etc.

Sutherland Road runs parallel to Uttoxeter Road, the former A50.

From new A50, Normacot exit: aim for Longton East. Go right in front of Shire's Bathrooms into Meir Hay Road (becomes Sutherland Road). Clearly marked shop ¼ mile on left, facing petrol station.

Coming south on A50 from Fenton: go under railway bridge into Longton one-way system; go left at traffic lights in front of Lloyds Bank; take first right (Sutherland Road). Shop ½ mile on right.

Open: Mon–Fri 9–4.30; Sat 9–3.
Closed: Phone to check.
Cards: Access, Amex, Diners, Visa.
Cars: Easy parking.
Wheelchairs: No steps to large shop.
Teas: Hotels and cafés in Longton.
Groups: Please phone.
Transport: 10 minutes' walk to bus station.

41 Stoke-on-Trent : Longton *map on p. 366*

Portmeirion Seconds Shop

Sylvan Works, Normacot Road ST3 1PV
(01782) 326412

Large range of seconds at significantly reduced prices – tableware, cookware, vases, plant pots, porcelain jugs, trays, chopping boards, textiles and novelty teapots. First quality glassware, porcelain handled cutlery, porcelain-on-steel cookware, place mats and miniature hinged boxes.

'Special offers always available. Please phone for details.'

See our display advertisement on p. 369

A short way south-east of Longton town centre.

From new A50, Longton exit: aim for Normacot/Longton East. From roundabout, follow sign for Gladstone Pottery Museum. You come into Normacot Road. After 150 yds, Portmeirion is facing you on far right corner.

From new A50, Normacot exit: follow signs to Gladstone Pottery Museum; after museum, downhill on left, go left into Chadwick St.*

From Fenton on old A50: aim for Longton, go clockwise round the one-way system – turn off for A5007 (old A50) to Uttoxeter following sign for Gladstone Pottery Museum; go right in front of museum on right into Chadwick Street.*

****Turn left at cross-road: shop is immediately on right.***

Open: Mon–Sat 9–5.30; Sun 10–4. Bank Holidays 9–5.30.
Closed: Christmas–New Year. Please ring to confirm holidays.
Cards: Amex, MasterCard, Visa, Switch.
Cars: Side-roads or factory car-park.
Toilets: In Longton centre.
Wheelchairs: Ramp to large shop.
Teas: Local hotels and cafés.
Groups: No pottery tours but parties welcome to shop – please contact Mrs Doreen Bath in advance. Please allow extra time for a group.
Transport: Near Longton train and bus stations.
Mail order: Yes. No restrictions. Will post throughout the UK and overseas.
Catalogue: No.

42 Stoke-on-Trent : Longton *map on p. 366*

Royal Doulton

Lawley Street ST3 2PH
(01782) 291172

Biggest and best selection of seconds tableware from the *Royal Doulton, Royal Albert* and *Royal Crown Derby* ranges. Also best quality discontinued figurines.

See our display advertisement opposite

Off the north side of Uttoxeter Road (A5007, old A50).

From new A50, Normacot exit: follow signs to Gladstone Pottery Museum; pass the Rose Inn on left and after Shires Bathrooms on right, go right to clearly visible shop in side road.

From new A50, Longton exit: aim for Normacot/Longton East. Follow signs for Gladstone Pottery Museum. At T-junction (museum on right), go right into Uttoxeter Road (A5007, old A50).*

From Fenton on old A50: aim for Longton. Go clockwise round the Longton one-way system – keep straight on to A5007 (old A50) for Uttoxeter, following sign for Gladstone Pottery Museum.*

****Continue for a few hundred yards: in front of Shires Bathrooms, go left to clearly visible shop.***

Open: Mon–Sat 9–5.30; Sun 10–4. Bank Holidays.
Closed: Christmas, Boxing and New Year's Days.
Cards: Amex, Diners, MasterCard, Switch, Visa.
Cars: For cars and coaches.
Toilets: Yes, including for disabled.
Wheelchairs: Easy access.
Teas: Refreshments available.
Groups: Shopping groups welcome, no need to book. For pottery tours and *Royal Doulton* display visit factory in Burslem; contact Yvonne Wood (01782) 292434.
Transport: Half a mile from Longton bus station.
Mail order: Best and seconds sent within UK and abroad.
Catalogue: Free tableware price lists; £3.50 for catalogue of current figurines.

See our entry opposite

43 Stoke-on-Trent : Longton *map on p. 366*

Royal Winton

Normacot Road ST3 1PJ
(01782) 598811

Decorated earthenware storage jars, planters, vases, bathroom ware (pitchers and basins, soap dishes etc), candlesticks, apothecary/ginger jars, loving cups. Chintz design. Classic jugs and vases.

'Perfects at trade prices plus seconds at about 30% reductions. Sometimes available – surplus items in our limited edition range made for the collectors' club.'

A short way south-east of Longton town centre.

From new A50, Longton exit: aim for Normacot/Longton East. From roundabout, follow sign for Gladstone Pottery Museum. You come into Normacot Road. After 100 yds, company is on left.

From new A50, Normacot exit: follow signs to Gladstone Pottery Museum; after the museum downhill on left, go left into Chadwick Street.*

From Fenton on old A50: aim for Longton. Go clockwise round the Longton one-way system – turn off for A5007 (old A50) to Uttoxeter, following sign for Gladstone Pottery Museum; go right in front of museum on right into Chadwick Street.*

****Turn right at cross-road: shop is immediately on right.***

Open: Mon–Thur 10–4; Fri 10–3. Sat by appointment.
Closed: Bank Holidays and Potters' Holidays.
Cards: Amex, Delta, Eurocard, MasterCard, Switch, Visa.
Cars: Cars in own car-park; coaches in street facing shop.
Toilets: Yes.
Wheelchairs: Three steps, fairly small shop.
Teas: In Longton town centre.
Groups: No factory tours but shopping groups welcome if you phone first.
Transport: Buses to Longton bus station then short walk.
Mail order: Yes. Charge postage and packing fee.

44 Stoke-on-Trent : Longton *map on p. 366*

Staffordshire Enamels

Cinderhill Estate, Weston Coyney Road ST3 5JT
(01782) 599948

Extensive collection of fine hand-painted enamels including traditional snuff and pill boxes, musical boxes, travel alarm clocks and *Chelsea Bonbonnières.*

'Renaissance of the traditional 18th century art of enamelling. Perfects and seconds on sale. Shop air-conditioned all year.'

A mile east of Longton, near junction of new A50 and A520.

From new A50, Normacot exit: aim for Weston Coyney. Go right in front Shire's Bathrooms into Meir Hay Road which bends round into Sutherland Road. Take first right, Weston Coyney Road. Follow brown signs ½ mile to estate on left.

Coming south on old A50 from Fenton: go under railway into Longton one-way system; go left at traffic lights in front of Lloyds Bank, take first right (Sutherland Road). After ½ mile, go left into Weston Coyney Road. Follow brown signs ½ mile to estate on left.

From Stone going north on A520: in Meir, cross new A50, staying on A520 north for Leek. After ¾ mile, go left into Weston Coyney Road: follow brown signs.

From Leek: take A520 south for Stone. In Weston Coyney follow brown signs.

Open: Mon–Fri 9–5; Sat 10–4. Some Bank Holidays.
Closed: Christmas and New Year: please check.
Cards: All major cards.
Cars: Outside shop.
Toilets: Yes.
Wheelchairs: Ramp access; double door.
Teas: Drinks machine.
Groups: Groups to shop welcome. Tours Mon–Fri 11 & 2 (Fri 11 only), maximum 6 people. Booking advised for groups and tours. Other factory shops nearby, so large groups can be split.
Transport: Local buses.
Mail order: Yes. Mail order for best quality items only.
Catalogue: Free.

45 Stoke-on-Trent : Meir Park *map p. 343*

Staffordshire Tableware

Uttoxeter Road ST3 7AB
(01782) 315251

Large selection of mugs. 18, 20 and 30-piece earthenware dinner sets, plus open stock plates, cups, saucers, tea and coffee pots etc. Crystal glass. Porcelain gift items.

'Seconds with additional permanent special offers. January sale.'

Conspicuous well-signed shop in large factory premises in Whittle Road, just off A50 (Uttoxeter Road) about 2 miles south-east of Longton.

From Longton on A50: watch for Little Chef on left; the company is almost opposite, on the right. Continue to roundabout then double back and take first left, Whittle Road. Shop is on left.

From Uttoxeter: take A50, mostly dual carriageway. As you come towards Meir go over the roundabout, pass factory on left. After pedestrian lights go left into Whittle Road. Shop is on left.

Open: Mon–Fri 9.30–5; Sat 9.30–4.30. Some Bank Holidays including Good Friday, Easter Monday. Potters' Holidays.
Closed: Christmas–New Year.
Cards: MasterCard, Visa.
Cars: Large customer car-park.
Toilets: Yes, and for disabled.
Wheelchairs: Ramp into new, larger shop.
Teas: Hot drinks machine; Little Chef opposite.
Groups: No pottery tours but coaches welcome to shop. Please book with Keith Wilshaw, Shop Manager.
Transport: Bus stop outside shop. Blythe Bridge/Uttoxeter/Cheadle service.
Mail order: Existing customers can contact Consumer Services for odd stock (no seconds), eg additional pieces for your existing set, or to replace breakages.

46 Stoke-on-Trent : Stoke see map on p. 376

Blakeney Pottery

Wolfe Street ST4 4DA
(01782) 847244

Range of planters, jardinières and traditional decorative ware such as ewers and bowls in plain glazes and unique flow blue underglaze printed patterns.

'High quality seconds and discontinued lines at very reasonable prices.'

In the centre of Stoke.

From M6 exit 15: take A500. Take slip road signposted Campbell Road & Michelin. Continue on Campbell Road for about 1 mile into Stoke. After petrol station, fork left into Boothen Road. After police station go left into Wolfe Street: pottery is straight ahead.

From the A500: follow signs into Stoke (marked Minton). Go clockwise round large one-way system. Pass large churchyard on left; keep going clockwise, over pedestrian lights then take small road left, Wolfe Street – almost opposite Job Centre and Fleming Road pay-&-display car-park. (NB Company on left before Minton.)

Open: Mon–Thur 9–4.30; Fri 9–3.30; late Spring Bank Holiday.
Closed: Bank Holidays; Potters' Holidays; Christmas–New Year.
Cards: MasterCard, Switch, Visa.
Cars: In factory yard.
Toilets: Nearest 50 yds in the market square.
Wheelchairs: One small step to fairly small showroom.
Teas: In Stoke.
Groups: No pottery tours, but groups welcome to shop if they phone first.
Transport: Any bus to Stoke (NOT Hanley). Stoke train station 20 minutes' walk.
Mail order: No.

47 Stoke-on-Trent : Stoke see map on p. 376

Minton

London Road ST4 7QE
(01782) 292121

Minton bone china dinner and tea services (available as sets and tea services), best quality and seconds merchandise. Also best quality *Royal Doulton* figures, character jugs, nursery and giftware.

In the centre of Stoke.

From M6 exit 15, Trent Vale, A34: take B5041 for Stoke. In Stoke, look for Minton on right by traffic lights. Either park here and walk across; or go right round Stoke one-way system.*

From the A500: at roundabout, follow signs to Stoke ¼, Minton and Spode.*

****Go clockwise round one-way system. Pass large churchyard on the left. Keep going clockwise then over pedestrian lights. Pass Job Centre on right: this clearly marked pottery is on left, before traffic lights. Park in one of the nearby public car-parks.***

Open: Mon–Sat 9–5.30. Good Friday.
Closed: Bank Holidays; Christmas, Boxing and New Year's Days.
Cards: Diners, MasterCard, Switch, Visa.
Cars: Town car-parks and visitors' car-park in Fleming Rd.
Toilets: No.
Wheelchairs: One step to medium sized shop.
Teas: A limited selection of cafés in Stoke.
Transport: Any bus to Stoke (NOT Hanley). Stoke train station 20 minutes' walk.
Mail order: Yes. Bests and seconds sent.
Catalogue: Free tableware price lists; £3.50 catalogue includes figurines.

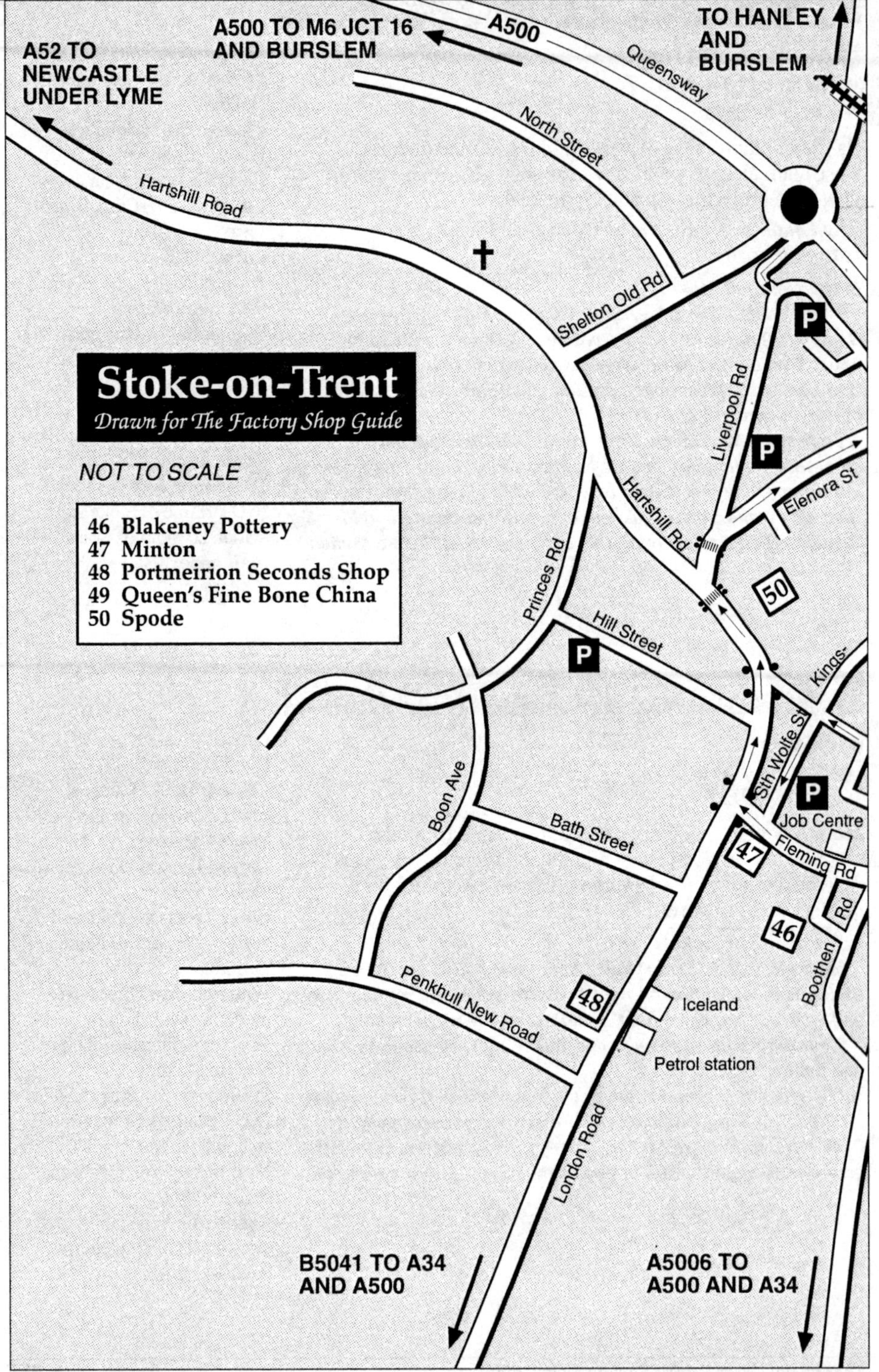

A52 TO NEWCASTLE UNDER LYME
A500 TO M6 JCT 16 AND BURSLEM
A500
TO HANLEY AND BURSLEM
Queensway
North Street
Hartshill Road
Shelton Old Rd
Stoke-on-Trent
Drawn for The Factory Shop Guide
NOT TO SCALE
46 Blakeney Pottery
47 Minton
48 Portmeirion Seconds Shop
49 Queen's Fine Bone China
50 Spode
Liverpool Rd
Elenora St
Hartshill Rd
Princes Rd
Hill Street
Kings-
Sth Wolfe St
Job Centre
Fleming Rd
Rd
Boon Ave
Bath Street
Boothen
Penkhull New Road
Iceland
Petrol station
London Road
B5041 TO A34 AND A500
A5006 TO A500 AND A34

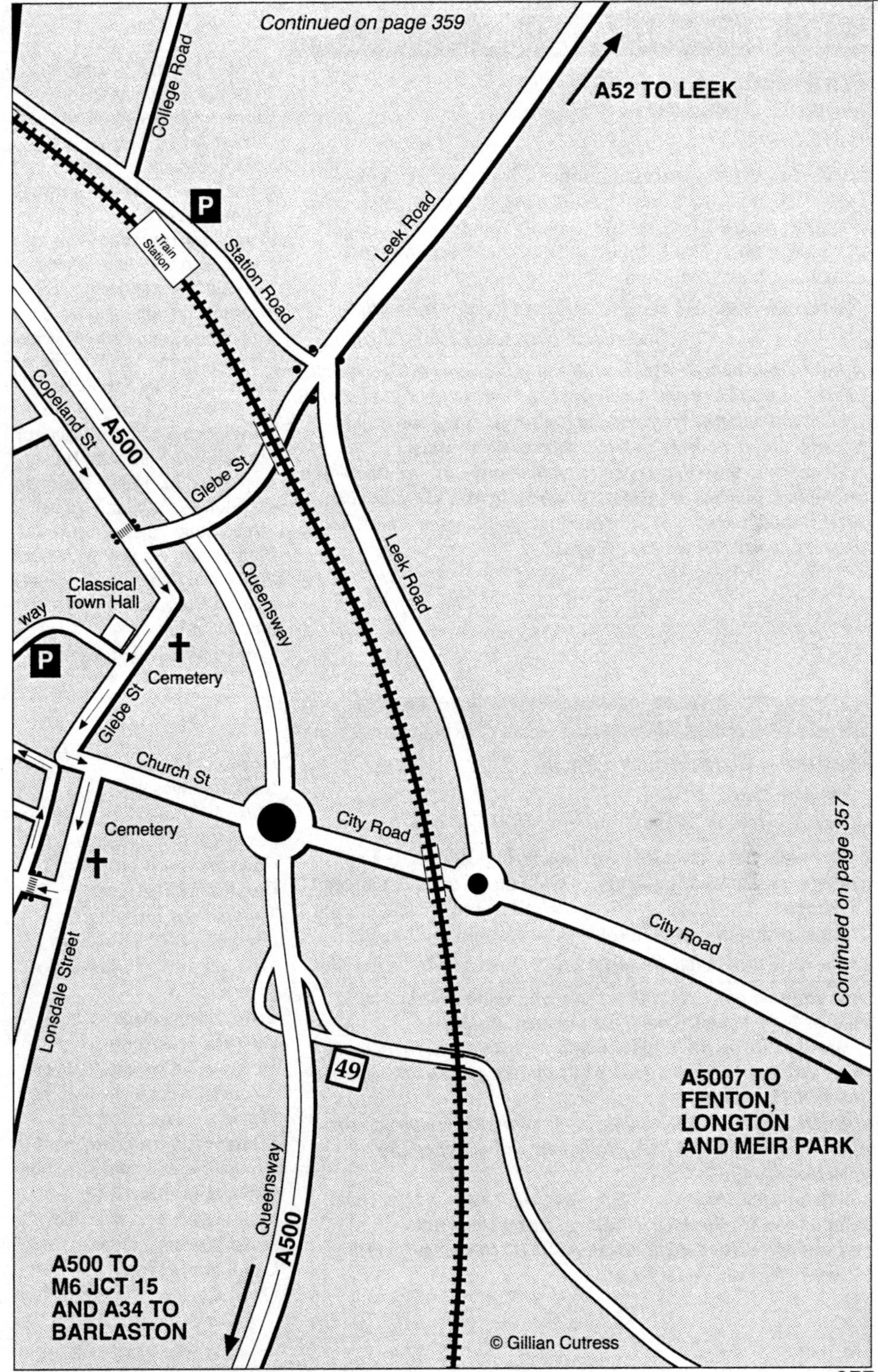

Continued on page 359
A52 TO LEEK
College Road
P
Train Station
Station Road
Leek Road
Copeland St
A500
Glebe St
Queensway
Leek Road
Classical Town Hall
way
P
Cemetery
Glebe St
Church St
City Road
Cemetery
City Road
Continued on page 357
Lonsdale Street
49
A5007 TO FENTON, LONGTON AND MEIR PARK
Queensway
A500
A500 TO M6 JCT 15 AND A34 TO BARLASTON
© Gillian Cutress

48 Stoke-on-Trent : Stoke *see map on p. 376*

Portmeirion Seconds Shop

London Road ST4 7QQ
(01782) 411756

Large range of seconds at significantly reduced prices – tableware, cookware, vases, plant pots, porcelain jugs, trays, chopping boards, textiles and novelty teapots. First quality glassware, porcelain handled cutlery, porcelain-on-steel cookware, place mats and miniature hinged boxes.

'Special offers always available. Please phone for details.'

See our display advertisement on p. 369

About ¼ mile outside Stoke centre in large converted red-brick chapel on B5041 (going south-west to Trent Vale, M6, Stafford).

From M6 exit 15, Trent Vale and A34: go along the B5041 towards Stoke. Shop is on left, opposite Elf services.

From Stoke town centre: go round one-way system! By Minton on the left, turn left at pedestrian traffic lights (at T-junction). After ¼ mile, the shop is on right, just past Iceland on left and almost opposite Elf service garage.

Open: Mon–Sat 9–5.30; Sun 10–4. Bank Holidays 9–5.30.
Closed: Christmas–New Year.
Cards: Amex, MasterCard, Switch, Visa.
Cars: Factory car-park or nearby.
Toilets: Yes.
Wheelchairs: Small steps at entrance to very large shop.
Teas: In Stoke shopping centre.
Groups: No pottery tours. Shop welcomes groups (one coach at a time) – phone Mrs Win Hobson in advance. Large shop, but allow extra time for a group.
Transport: 5 minutes' walk from Stoke. Bus no. 22 from Hanley stops outside; or take bus opposite Stoke station into Glebe Street, Stoke, then short walk.
Mail order: Yes. No restrictions. Post throughout the UK & overseas. MasterCard & Visa taken for mail order.
Catalogue: Leaflets available.

49 Stoke-on-Trent : Stoke *see map on p. 376*

Queen's Fine Bone China

Whieldon Road ST4 4ST
(01782) 745899/747555 Fax (01782) 744778

Fine bone china and tableware, including dinner, tea and coffee sets. China mugs galore. Collectors' cups & saucers. *Dartington Crystal*. Also *Pimpernel* place mats, coasters and trays at reduced prices and *Cloverleaf* chopping boards.

'At least 40% savings. Perfect quality items available to order.'

Just off (east of) the A500, a short way south-east of Stoke. Access is from south-bound carriageway of A500.

Going south on A500: go straight at roundabout (Ashbourne A52/City Road turn-off) After short distance, take left slip road (for Whieldon Road).*

Going north on A500: double back at large roundabout (the turn-off for Ashbourne A52). Take next left slip road (for Whieldon Road).*

****Factory and shop are on right: at end of slip road, go sharp right on to site. Go through barrier, entrance on left.***

If you come west along Whieldon Road: this is last building on left before you go under A500.

Open: Mon–Sat 9–5.
Bank Holidays 9–5.
Closed: Christmas–New Year; please phone for details.
Cards: MasterCard, Visa.
Cars: In front of shop.
Toilets: Yes, including for disabled.
Wheelchairs: No steps, large shop.
Teas: Drinks machine in shop and seating area.
Groups: No pottery tours but coaches welcome to shop. Please mention this guide.
Transport: 15 minutes' walk to bus station; 15 minutes to train station. Bus nos. 45, 47.
Mail order: Yes. Best and seconds by mail order.
Catalogue: Free.

50 Stoke-on-Trent : Stoke *see map on p. 376*

Spode

Church Street ST4 1BX
(01782) 744011

Wide range of slightly imperfect fine bone china, and earthenware, in tableware (in sets or as individual pieces) and giftware.

'Firsts and seconds at bargain prices on sale. Sales in January and July. For special commissions please contact Stephen Riley.'

In the centre of Stoke.

From roundabout on A500: follow signs to Stoke, Spode, Minton. Go clockwise, right round town. At T-junction traffic lights (Minton on left), go right into London Road; at far end, turn left into Church Street, pass Spode main entrance on right; follow the road round to the right, bear right into Elenora Street, then go right into Spode grounds.

From Newcastle: take A52 downhill into Stoke; you have to turn left into the one-way system. Shortly bear right into Elenora Street then turn right into Spode factory grounds.

Open: Mon–Sat 9–5; Sun 10–4. Bank Holidays.
Closed: Christmas, Boxing and New Year's Days.
Cards: Amex, MasterCard, Visa.
Cars: Free parking on site.
Toilets: Yes.
Wheelchairs: Easy access, large shop.
Teas: Blue Italian restaurant on site for lunches and teas.
Tours: Tours by prior arrangement (weekdays only). Please book in advance with Tours Organiser. Include visitor centre, factory tour and museum: adults £3.75, concessions £2. Limited access for disabled. Children 11+ only. Visitor centre (7 days a week): adults £2.25, concessions £1.25. Connoisseur's tour by prior arrangement £6.
Transport: Short walk from main Stoke bus stop.
Mail order: Yes, best & seconds sent. Free catalogue.

51 Stoke-on-Trent : Tunstall *see map p. 343*

H & R Johnson Tiles

Harewood Street ST6 4JY
(01782) 524040

Slight seconds in wall and floor tiles and ends of range tiles. Ceramic giftware, mirrors, tiled trays, clocks. Also some chainstore giftware such as trays, lamps, vases, pictures, candlesticks. Tile adhesives, grouts etc.

'Seconds and discontinued firsts. Most prices reduced by 50% off normal retail price. 6" x 6" tiles @ £6.49 per sq metre carton, 8" x 6" tiles @ £7.99 per sq metre carton, flooring tiles at £4.99 per carton. Prices might vary.'

West of Tunstall town centre.

From the south (Burslem) via A50: at the roundabout in front of 'Dewhirst Ladieswear', fork left. After 400 yds (where main road goes left) go right, then immediately left into Connaught Street.*

From A500: take A527 for Tunstall. Pass Price & Kensington on left; at next roundabout follow signs left to Tunstall. Go under H & R Johnson overpass then over pedestrian lights. Where main road goes right, keep straight. Go immediately left into Connaught Street (Office Stationery on corner, Lloyds Bank opposite).*

****At far end turn left then follow signs to car-park and shop.***

Open: Mon–Wed and Fri–Sat 9–4.
Closed: Thursday; Bank Holidays. Ten days at Christmas.
Cards: Yes.
Cars: Own adjacent car-park.
Toilets: Public toilets in Tunstall near Town Hall.
Wheelchairs: Two bays for the disabled outside factory door; seven steps from car-park to huge shop.
Teas: At Three Cooks in High Street, Tunstall.
Groups: Shopping groups welcome, no need to book.
Transport: Buses to centre of town, shop 5 minutes' walk.
Mail order: No.

Towns with factory shops

	Biddulph	1	Carter Davies Ceramics
	Burton-on-Trent	2	Marston's Brewery Shop
	Burton-on-Trent	3	Webb Ivory
	Cannock	4	Fashion Factory
	Cannock	5	Lew-Ways
	Cannock	6	Lighting Bug
	Cannock	p333	Cannock Gates
	Leek	7	Joshua Wardle
	Leek	8	Leek Factory Shop
	Leek	9	Lotus Shoes
	Lichfield	10	Arthur Price of England
	Lichfield	11	Decor Supplies
	Rugeley	12	John Partridge
	Stafford	13	Antique and Ceramics Restoration Studio
	Stafford	14	Schott-UK
	Stone	15	Lotus Shoes
	Tutbury	16	Georgian Crystal (Tutbury)
	Tutbury	17	Tutbury Crystal Glass
Stoke-on-Trent	**Baddeley Green**	18	Royal Doulton
	Barlaston	19	Wedgwood Best
	Burslem	20	Royal Doulton
	Burslem	21	Wade Ceramics
	Cobridge	22	Churchill Tableware
	Cobridge	23	W Moorcroft
	Fenton	24	Lalco
	Fenton	25	Portmeirion Seconds Shop
	Fenton	26	Royal Doulton
	Fenton	27	The Waterford Wedgwood Factory Shop
	Hanley	28	Aynsley China
	Hanley	29	Bridgewater
	Hanley	30	City Museum and Art Gallery
	Hanley	31	Fashion Direct
	Hanley	32	Royal Worcester
	Hanley	33	St George's Fine Bone China
	Hanley	34	Webb Ivory
	Longton	p365	Hartley Greens
	Longton	35	Aynsley China
	Longton	36	Ceramic World
	Longton	37	Churchill China
	Longton	38	Hadida Bathroom Interiors
	Longton	39	John Beswick
	Longton	40	John Tams
	Longton	41	Portmeirion Seconds Shop
	Longton	42	Royal Doulton
	Longton	43	Royal Winton
	Longton	44	Staffordshire Enamels
	Meir Park	45	Staffordshire Tableware
	Stoke	46	Blakeney Pottery
	Stoke	47	Minton
	Stoke	48	Portmeirion Seconds Shop
	Stoke	49	Queen's Fine Bone China
	Stoke	50	Spode
	Tunstall	51	H & R Johnson Tiles

North-West England & North Wales

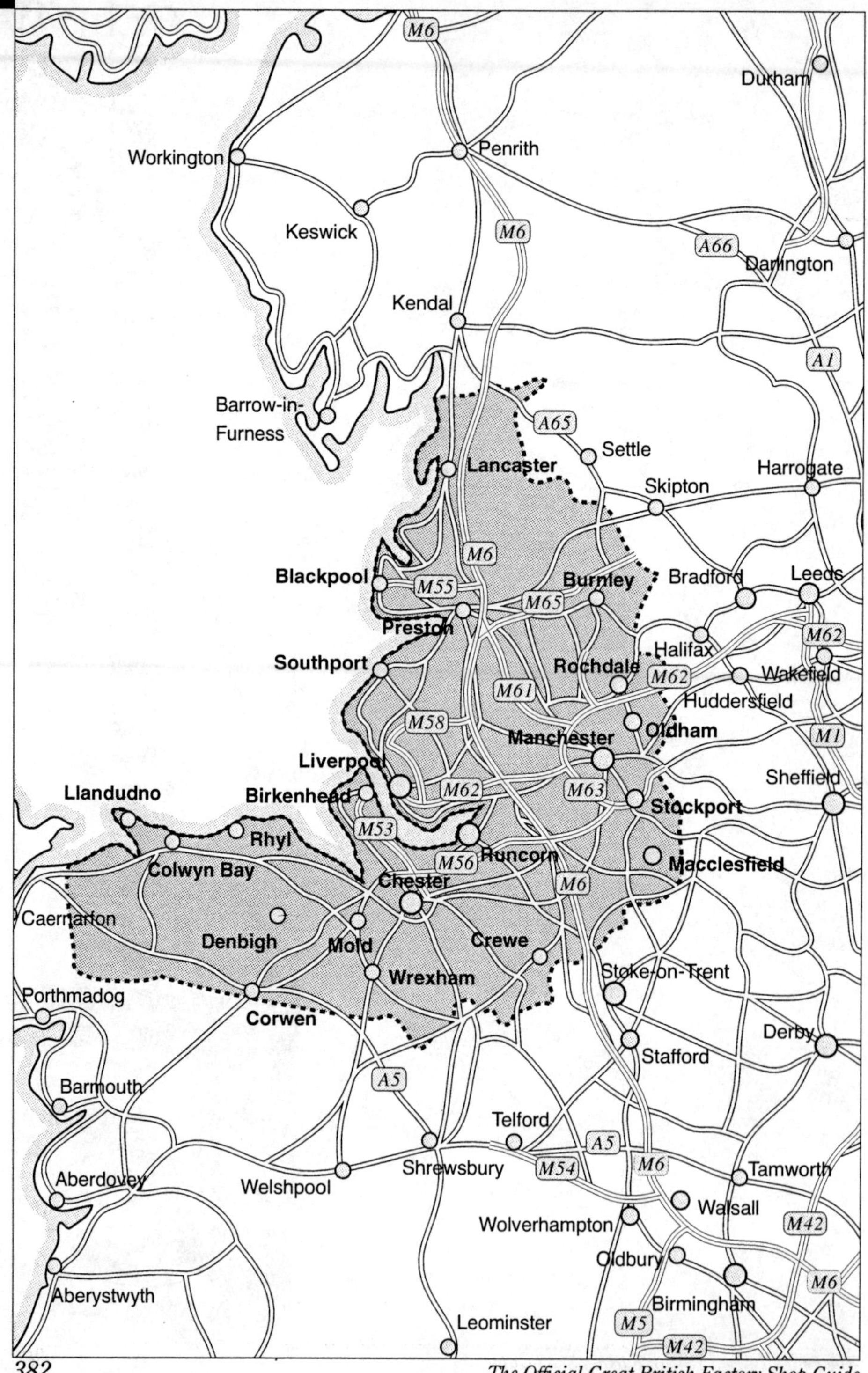
M6
Durham
Workington
Penrith
Keswick
M6
A66
Darlington
Kendal
A1
Barrow-in-
Furness
A65
Settle
Lancaster
Harrogate
Skipton
M6
Blackpool
M55
Burnley
Bradford
Leeds
M65
Preston
M62
Halifax
Southport
Rochdale
M62
Wakefield
M61
Huddersfield
M58
Oldham
Manchester
M1
Liverpool
Sheffield
Llandudno
Birkenhead
M62
M63
Stockport
M53
Rhyl
Runcorn
M56
Colwyn Bay
Macclesfield
Chester
M6
Caernarfon
Denbigh
Mold
Crewe
Wrexham
Stoke-on-Trent
Porthmadog
Corwen
Derby
Stafford
A5
Barmouth
Telford
A5
Shrewsbury
M54
M6
Tamworth
Aberdovey
Welshpool
Walsall
Wolverhampton
M42
Oldbury
M6
Aberystwyth
Birmingham
Leominster
M5
M42

F

North-West England & North Wales

It is always a pleasure to visit this area with its great industrial tradition. Sadly, so many of the old mills are now abandoned and have fallen into disrepair, but it is always heartening to find others beautifully restored for a variety of industrial and other uses.

From a factory shopper's point of view, this area is near to heaven. The variety of goods on offer is colossal, and you are never far from one of these delightful shops where you will find perfects at reduced prices, ends of lines, seconds, overmakes and cancelled orders, all offering wonderful value for money.

So many excellent value items for the home ... carpets, wall-papers, what are claimed to be the cheapest blinds in England, the largest disposal centre for decorative lighting in Europe, lampshades made in your own fabric, silk and dried flower arrangements, electrical goods, towels woven in Lancashire, cushions covered and buttoned with co-ordinating fabric, leather sofas, pine kitchen fittings (including butcher's chopping blocks and island work tops), Welsh unglazed quarry tiles and gardening equipment. But, above all, this is the area for dress, furnishing and upholstery fabrics. Wherever you travel in the region one of these shops is within easy reach. If you are a keen dressmaker, or aiming to spruce up your home with new curtains or upholstery, this is where you should be. It goes without saying that all kinds of family fashions and footwear are catered for too, with many famous brand name and chainstore fashion garments.

There is a wealth of specialist items too, such as spectacles, accessories for those suffering from disabilities, shoes in a range of extra wide fittings, plus sewing threads in an unbelievable range of colours, thicknesses and materials for all types of hand and machine sewing.

As ever, we are delighted to welcome companies who feature in this book for the first time. Amongst them are one of the best known names in the luggage world, a shop for rugby jerseys, a company specialising in hill walking and backpacking clothes, upmarket clothing shops, a company supplying foam cut to any size, and another selling baby bedding and baby goods.

We know you'll have a money-saving and very enjoyable experience.

Oakmount

F

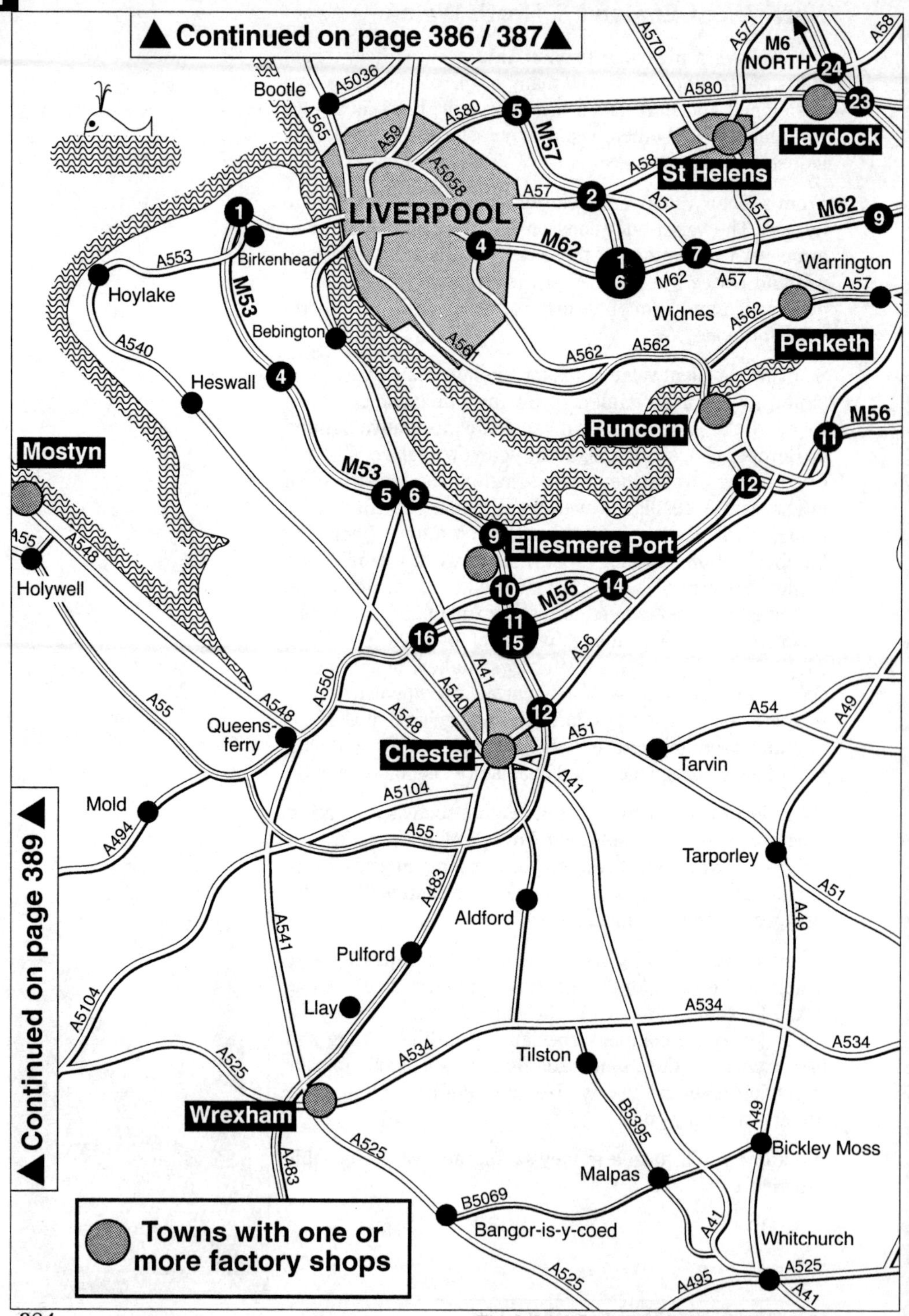
▲ Continued on page 386 / 387▲
▲ Continued on page 389 ▲
LIVERPOOL
Bootle
Birkenhead
Hoylake
Bebington
Heswall
Mostyn
Holywell
Queens-
ferry
Mold
Chester
Ellesmere Port
Runcorn
Widnes
Penketh
Warrington
St Helens
Haydock
M6
NORTH
Tarvin
Tarporley
Aldford
Pulford
Llay
Tilston
Wrexham
Malpas
Bickley Moss
Bangor-is-y-coed
Whitchurch
M53
M56
M57
M62
A5036
A565
A59
A580
A5058
A57
A58
A570
A571
A553
A540
A561
A562
A548
A55
A550
A41
A56
A54
A49
A51
A5104
A494
A483
A541
A534
A525
B5395
B5069
A495
Towns with one or
more factory shops

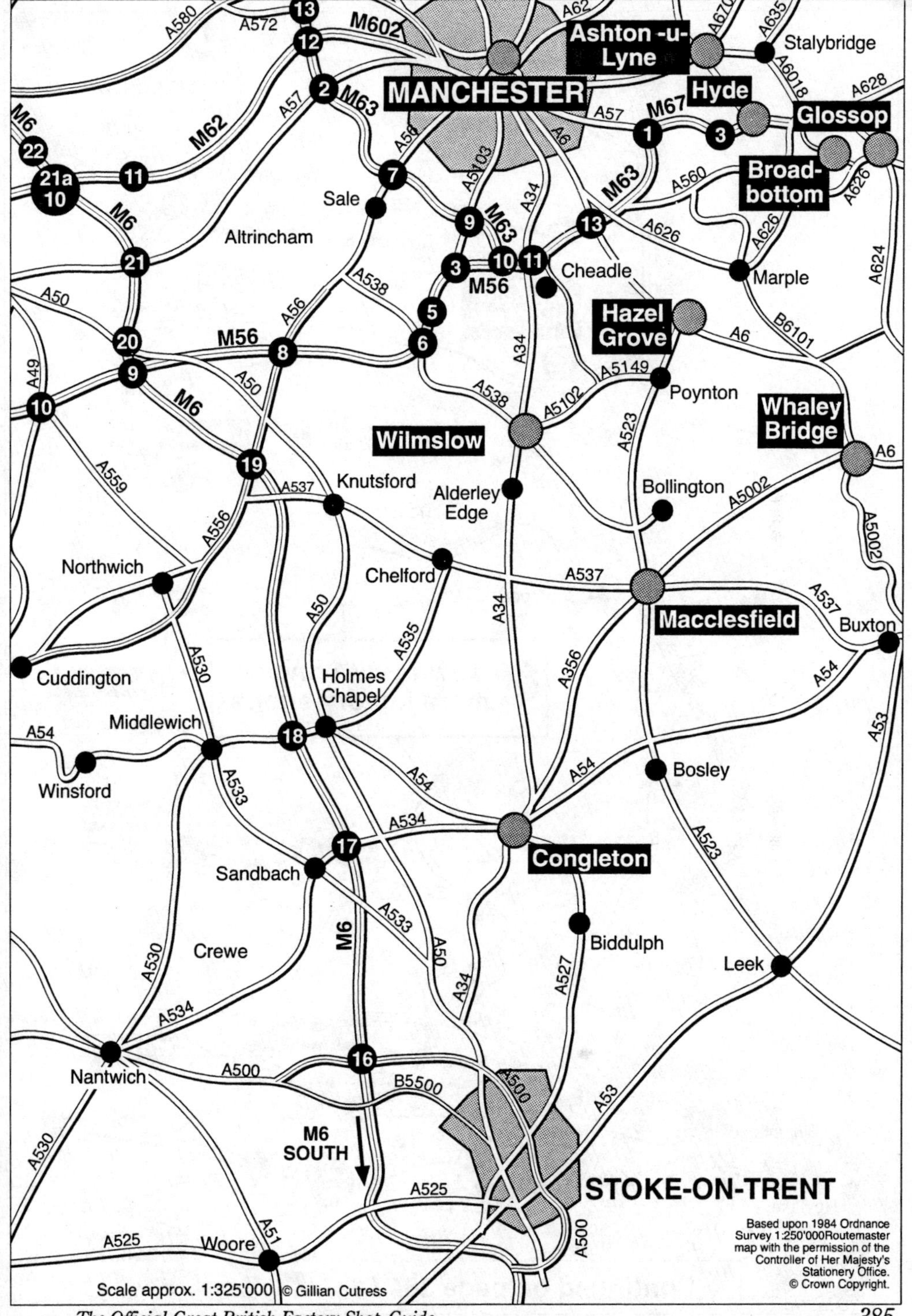
MANCHESTER
Ashton -u-Lyne
Stalybridge
Hyde
Glossop
Broad-bottom
Sale
Altrincham
Cheadle
Marple
Hazel Grove
Poynton
Wilmslow
Whaley Bridge
Knutsford
Alderley Edge
Bollington
Northwich
Chelford
Macclesfield
Buxton
Cuddington
Holmes Chapel
Middlewich
Winsford
Bosley
Congleton
Sandbach
Biddulph
Crewe
Leek
Nantwich
M6 SOUTH
STOKE-ON-TRENT
Woore
Scale approx. 1:325'000 © Gillian Cutress
Based upon 1984 Ordnance Survey 1:250'000Routemaster map with the permission of the Controller of Her Majesty's Stationery Office. © Crown Copyright.

▲Continued on page 388▲

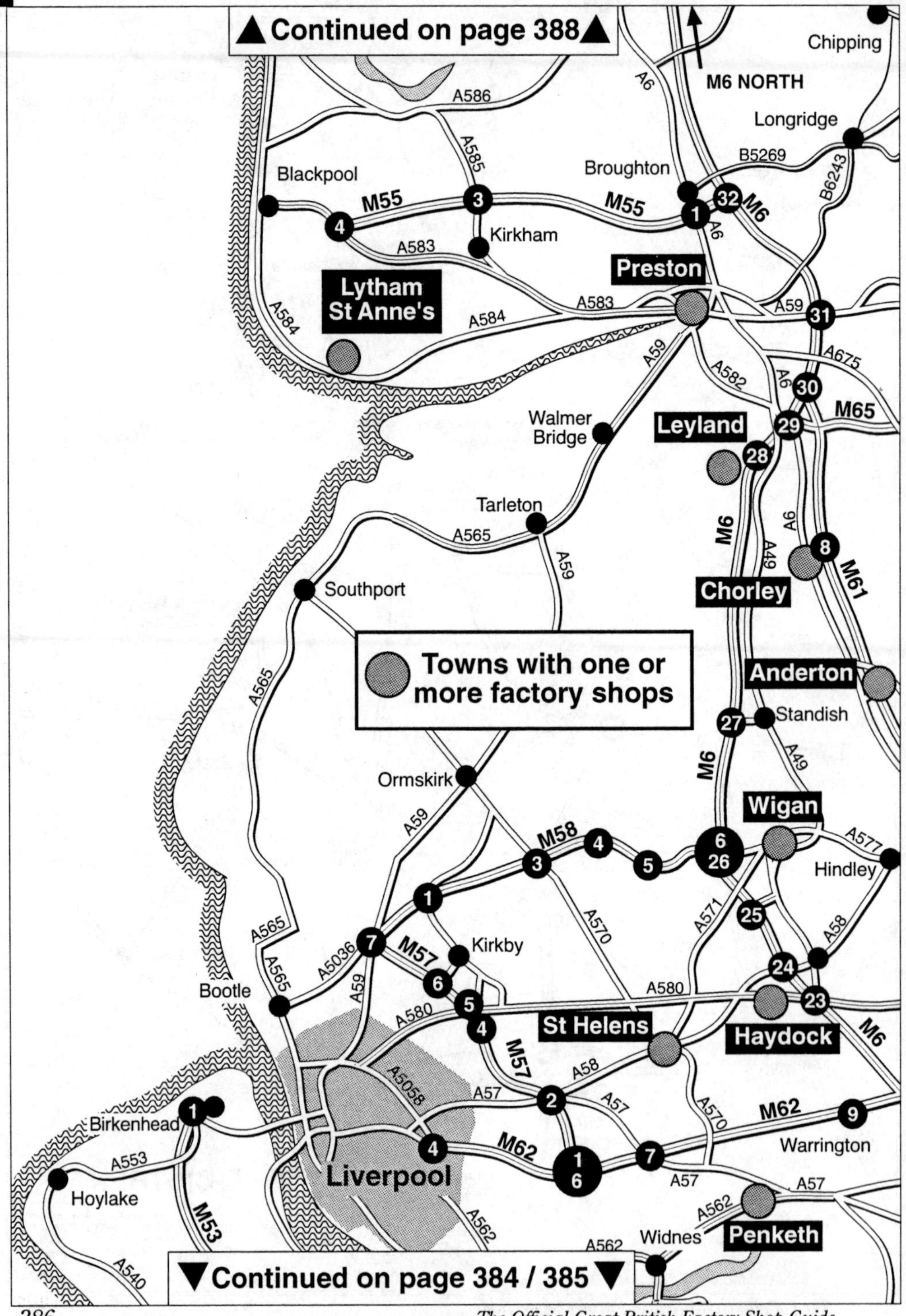

▼Continued on page 384 / 385▼

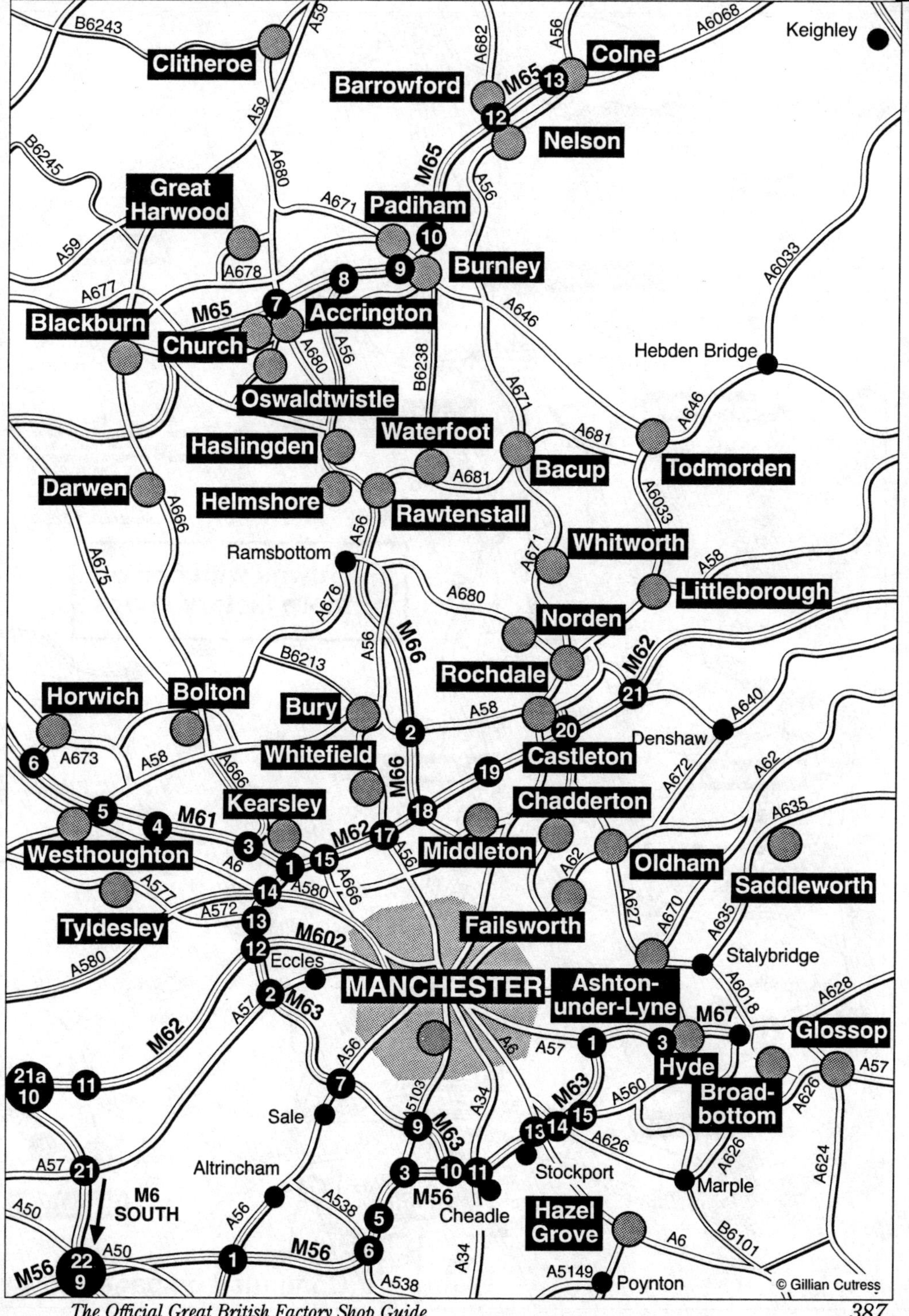
B6243
A59
Clitheroe
A682
A56
A6068
Keighley
Colne
Barrowford
M65
13
12
Nelson
A59
B6245
A680
M65
A56
Great Harwood
A671
Padiham
10
A59
Burnley
9
A678
8
A677
7
M65
Accrington
Blackburn
Church
A56
A680
B6238
A646
A6033
Hebden Bridge
Oswaldtwistle
A671
Waterfoot
A681
A646
Haslingden
Bacup
Todmorden
A681
Darwen
Helmshore
Rawtenstall
A666
A6033
A56
Whitworth
A675
Ramsbottom
A671
A58
A680
Littleborough
A676
M66
Norden
A56
B6213
M62
Rochdale
Horwich
Bolton
Bury
21
A58
A640
2
20
Denshaw
A673
A58
Whitefield
Castleton
6
A666
19
A672
M66
Chadderton
A62
5
4
M61
Kearsley
18
A635
3
M62
17
Middleton
Westhoughton
1
15
A6
A56
A62
Oldham
A577
A580
A666
Saddleworth
14
A627
A670
A572
Tyldesley
13
Failsworth
A635
M602
12
Eccles
Stalybridge
A580
MANCHESTER
Ashton-under-Lyne
A6018
A628
2
M63
M67
A57
A56
A6
A57
1
3
Glossop
M62
Hyde
A57
21a
10
11
7
A5103
M63
A34
15
A560
Broad-bottom
A626
14
13
Sale
9
A626
M63
A624
A57
21
Altrincham
3
10
11
Stockport
A626
Marple
M6
SOUTH
M56
A56
A538
A50
5
Cheadle
Hazel Grove
22
9
A50
M56
1
6
A6
B6101
M56
A34
A5149
A538
Poynton
© Gillian Cutress

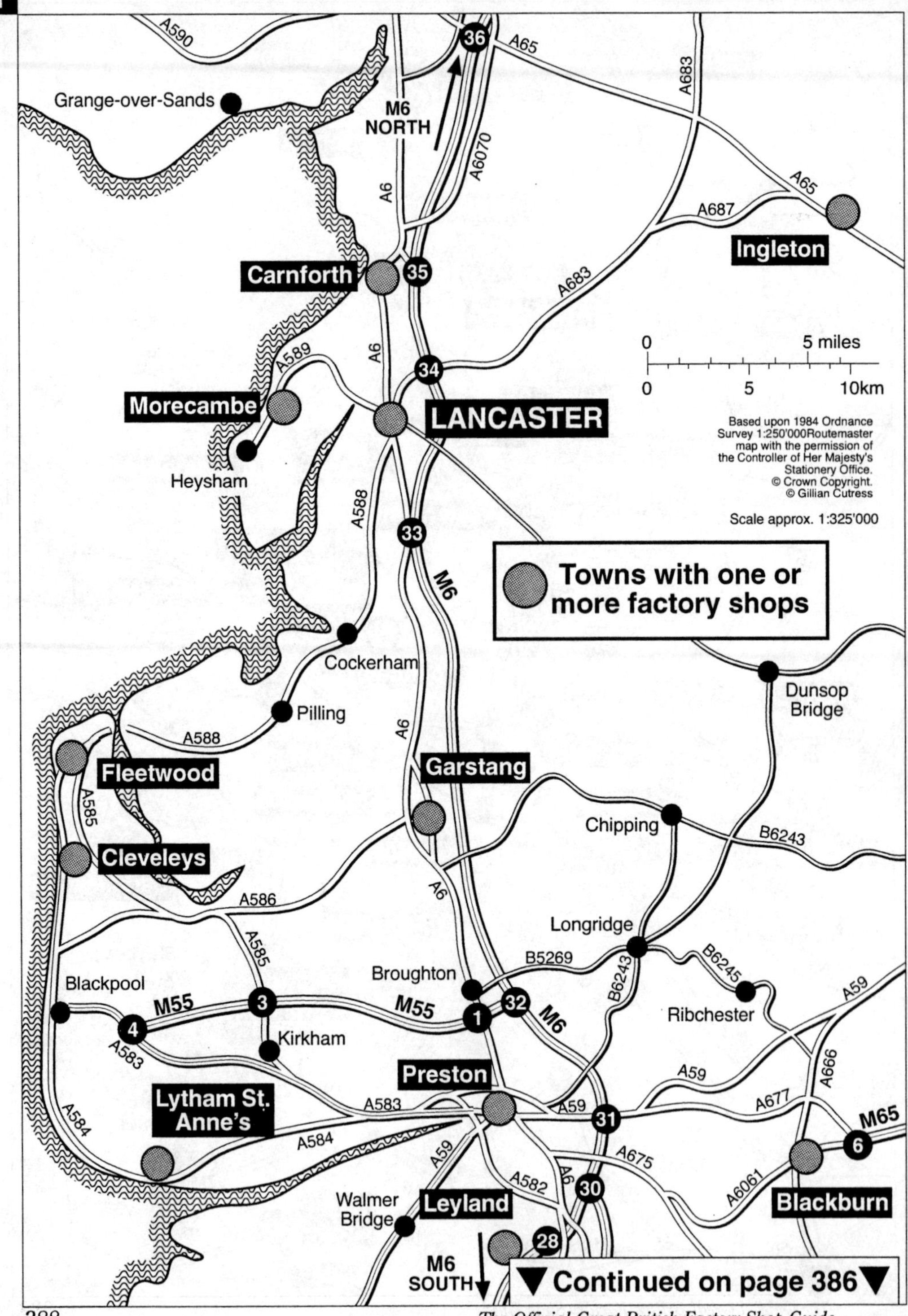

▼ Continued on page 386 ▼

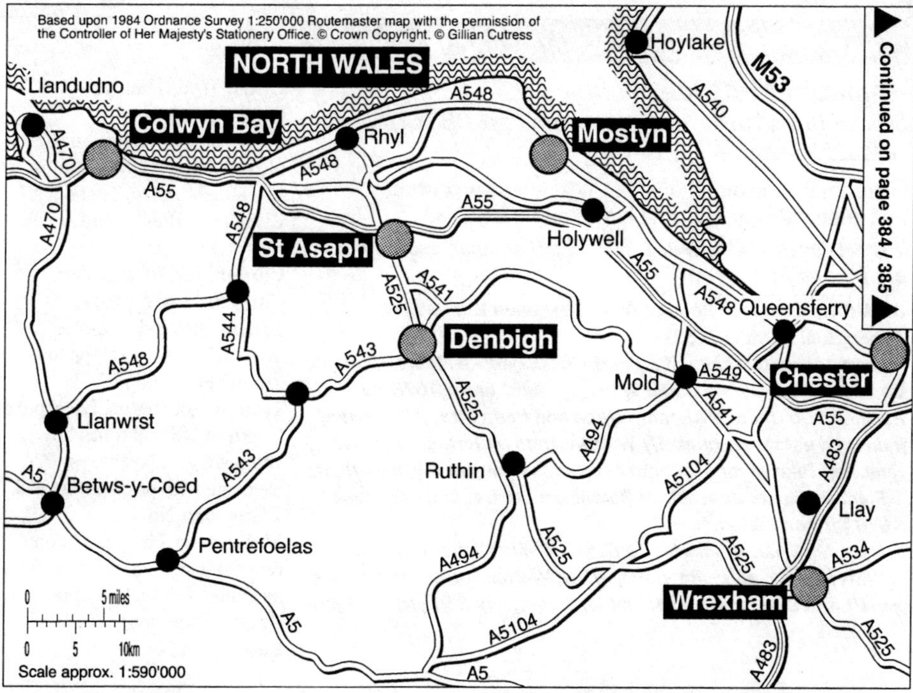

Based upon 1984 Ordnance Survey 1:250'000 Routemaster map with the permission of the Controller of Her Majesty's Stationery Office. © Crown Copyright. © Gillian Cutress
NORTH WALES
Llandudno
Colwyn Bay
Rhyl
Mostyn
Hoylake
M53
A540
A548
A470
A55
St Asaph
Holywell
A525
A541
Denbigh
A544
A543
Queensferry
Chester
Mold
A549
Llanwrst
Ruthin
A494
A5104
A483
Llay
A5
Betws-y-Coed
Pentrefoelas
A534
Wrexham
0 5 miles
0 5 10km
Scale approx. 1:590'000

Continued on page 384 / 385

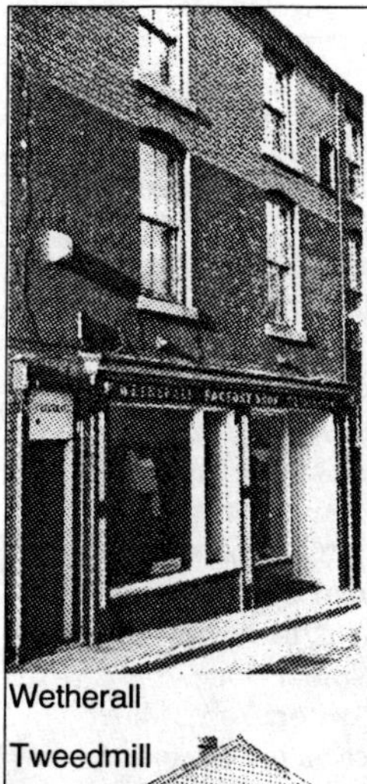

Wetherall

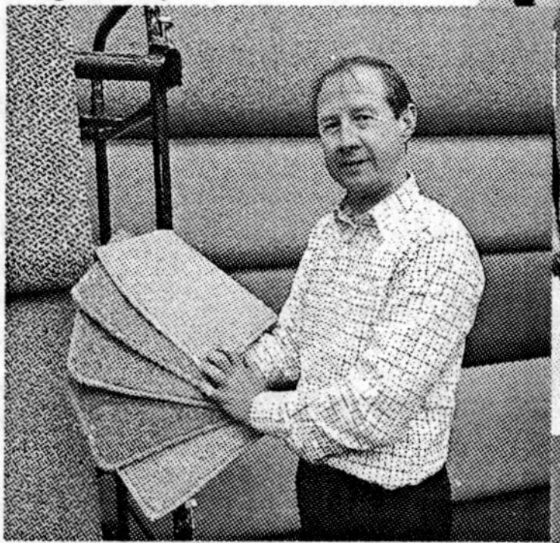

Jorgus Carpets

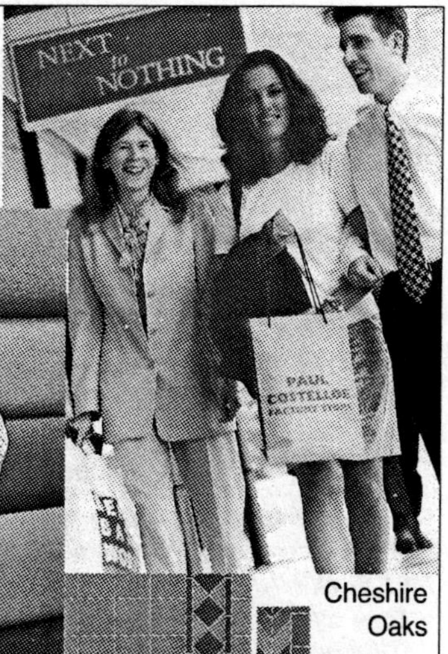

NEXT to NOTHING
PAUL COSTELLOE

Cheshire Oaks

Tweedmill

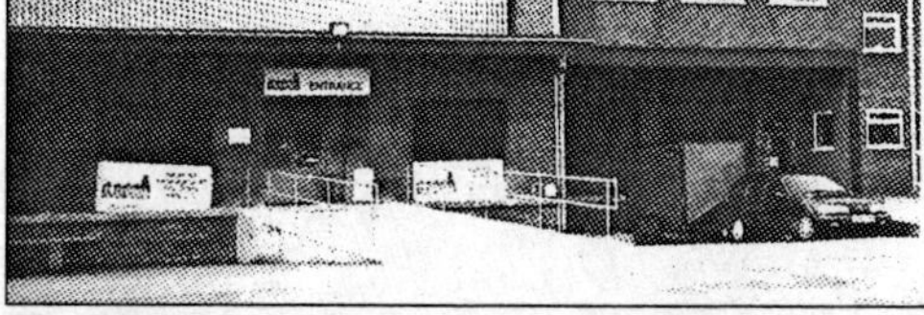

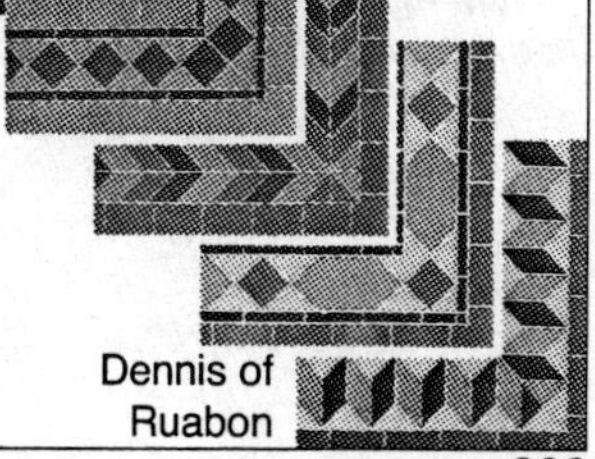

Dennis of Ruabon

1 Accrington Lancs see map on p. 428

Hamilton McBride

Shorten Brook Drive, Altham Business Park BB5 5YR
(01282) 858206

Co-ordinated fashion home textiles, featuring curtains, bed linen, table linen, table lamps and cushions.

'Perfect goods; discontinued lines; slight seconds and imperfects at about half price.'

On Altham Business Park on A678 (between Burnley and Accrington, north of M65).

From Accrington: take A680 north for Clayton-le-Moors/Clitheroe. Go over motorway. At traffic lights, go right on to A678 for Padiham. Go through Altham village and keep straight, passing industrial estate on right. By Walton Arms on left, go right for Huncoat. Take second left into estate: company 150 yds on right.

From Padiham: go west for Blackburn. At traffic lights, take A678 for Accrington.*

From M65 exit 8: aim for Padiham. At first lights turn left.*

***After ½ mile, opposite green/white Walton Arms pub on right, go left into estate. Take second left: company 150 yds on right.**

Open: Wed, Thur, Fri 10–5; Sat & Sun 12–5. Most Bank Holidays, but please phone to check times.
Closed: Monday, Tuesday; Christmas, Boxing and New Year's Days.
Cards: MasterCard, Visa.
Cars: Factory car-park.
Toilets: Ask if desperate.
Wheelchairs: No steps to ground level shop.
Teas: In Accrington. Local pubs.
Groups: No mill tours but shopping groups always welcome with prior phone call.
Transport: No.
Mail order: Photos sent on request if anyone has problems locating a product in stores. Only perfects sent.
Catalogue: No.

2 Accrington Lancs see map on p. 428

Karrimor International

Petre Road, Clayton-le-Moors BB5 5JZ
(01254) 388466

Rucksacks, child carriers, cycle bags, outdoor garments including waterproofs. *Trangia* stoves, *Karrimats*. Footwear for outdoor activities.

'Perfects, seconds, ex-display, samples and ends of lines. Gore-Tex perfects and seconds; cycle clothing range; Phoenix ski clothing.'

See our display advertisement opposite

Clayton-le-Moors is on north-west side of Accrington.

From Accrington: follow signs to M65/Rishton. Cross under M65 at exit 7.*

From M65 exit 7: follow signs to Clitheroe (A6185).*

***Turn right at traffic lights opposite GEC Industrial Estate; Petre Road is first on left. Karrimor is at end of road.**

Open: Mon–Thur 11–7.30; Fri 11–5; Sat 9–12.30.
Closed: Bank Holidays; Christmas–New Year.
Cards: MasterCard, Switch, Visa.
Cars: Own car-park.
Toilets: Yes.
Wheelchairs: Yes.
Changing rooms: Yes.
Teas: In Accrington.
Groups: Groups welcome to shop but please ring first.
Transport: None.
Mail order: Yes. 24-hour service on most items.
Catalogue: £2.50.

3 Accrington Lancs *see map on p. 428*

Optical Direct (Clayton-le-Moors)

5 Cunliffe Court off Petre Road, Clayton Enterprise Park, Clayton-le-Moors BB5 5JF
(01254) 395725

Over 1300 budget and designer frames. From £14.95 including s/v lenses. Designer styles at reduced prices. Contact lenses from £35. Free spectacles/eye tests for children & people on income support/family credit; choose from special collection.

*'Professional advice on all types of lenses, single vision to complicated bifocals & varifocals. Save up to 50%. Registered family health service authority practice. Half price eye tests for senior citizens. Tests by appointment or bring own prescription. **Free tints with this advertisement.**'*

Open: Mon–Sat 9–5.
Closed: Christmas, Boxing and New Year's Days. Please check for Bank Holidays.
Cards: MasterCard, Switch, Visa.
Cars: Car-park.
Toilets: Yes.
Wheelchairs: Easy access; no steps.
Teas: Tea and coffee free on request. Cafés and pubs.
Groups: Groups welcome to the shop. Contact Karen Worswick for eye-test appointments. Please phone for groups over 20.
Transport: None.
Mail order: Gladly post spectacles if we have details of prescription and measurements.
Catalogue: No.

Clayton-le-Moors is north-west of Accrington.

From Accrington: follow signs to M65 and Rishton. Cross under M65 at exit 7. Turn right at traffic lights opposite GEC Industrial Estate.*

From M65 exit 7: follow signs to Clitheroe (A6185). Go right at traffic lights opposite GEC Industrial Estate.*

****Petre Road is first left. Cunliffe Court is on right with Unit 5 clearly visible.***

4 Accrington Lancs see map on p. 428

Red Rose Velvets

Royal Mill, Victoria Street BB5 OPO
(01254) 392059

Curtain velvet fabric, clothing velvet fabric, velvet curtains made-to-measure, all in cotton. Also cushions, curtain linings, tie backs etc.

'We only sell what we weave on the premises. Genuine low prices. 48" wide curtain velvet in 30 colours from £5.50 per yd; 60" wide dress velvet £7.50 per yd, 54" wide £6.50 per yd.'

In town, on the south-west side of main shopping area.

From Baxenden/Haslingden/Rawtenstall (A680): go into town, pass the fire station on left. After adjacent large square stone magistrates' court/police station, go left (Spring Gardens).*

From Blackburn/Burnley via A679, or M65 exit 7: go over huge roundabout with the railway viaduct across it then follow signs round town for Haslingden/Baxenden. Look for The Swan on the left, then go right into Spring Gardens (in front of the square stone police station).*

****Take third left, Nuttall Street (ie, go uphill where road swings right), which becomes Mount Street. Keep straight almost to far end; go right into Victoria Street. Company is 300 yds on right, clearly marked.***

Open: Mon–Fri 9.30–5; *also Sept–Dec* Sat 10–1.
Closed: Easter three days; last week May; last two weeks July; third week September; Christmas–New Year.
Cards: MasterCard, Visa.
Cars: Outside shop in street.
Toilets: Ask if desperate.
Wheelchairs: One step only.
Teas: In town.
Tours: Small groups welcome to shop; may also be able to see round mill if visit is arranged beforehand.
Transport: Not far to walk from town centre.
Mail order: Yes.
Catalogue: No.

5 Anderton Lancs

Jorgus Carpets

Grimeford Mill, Grimeford Lane PR6 9HK
(01257) 482636

Plain wool carpets made on the premises. Special colours gladly made to order. Twist piles in plain and tweeds. Velvets etc. 80/20% wool/nylon mixtures in 12' to 13'6" and 15' widths. Sculptured wool in 50oz per sq yd.

'Genuine mill shop (3,000 sq ft) with everything made here. 80–100 rolls displayed in shop. Twist piles and velvets, 80/20% plains and berbers from £7.50 per sq yd. Reduced price roll ends. Fitting service.'

Short distance south of Adlington and almost in the shadow of M61; between A6 and A673 (Grimeford Lane links these 2 roads).

Going north on A6 to Chorley: look for The Drunken Duck pub on left – immediately go right (Grimeford Lane). Keep going; pass under motorway; after 100 yds go left into small factory complex.

Coming north on A673 from Horwich: pass The Millstone on right; take next left (Grimeford Lane): factory complex is 100 yds on right.

Via A673 from Chorley: go under motorway, take next right (Grimeford Lane). Factory complex is 100 yds on right; Jorgus is at far back left.

Open: Mon–Fri 8–12 & 1–5; Sat 9.30–3; Sun 11–3.
Closed: Bank Holidays; Christmas–New Year.
Cards: None.
Cars: Large car-park in yard.
Toilets: Yes.
Wheelchairs: Easy access, ground floor sales area.
Teas: Nearby pubs; cafés and tea shops in Chorley, Adlington, Horwich.
Tours: No tours but you can see carpets being made.
Transport: Horwich–Chorley buses stop near the end of Grimeford Lane.

6 Ashton-under-Lyne Lancs

Barden Mill Shop

Cavendish Street OL6 7QL
(0161) 343 7696

Full range of discount clothing for men, ladies and children. Some items debranded. Most garments are overmakes for chainstores or ex-high street merchandise. Over 1500 men's suits in stock at all times.

'Perfects and overmakes all at substantial savings. Ex-catalogue department for ladies' larger sizes (up to 32). Men's suits from £39, suit jackets £15 and suit trousers £10!'

See our display advertisement on page 401

On the south edge of Ashton town centre, towards Dukinfield.

From Oldham coming south on A627: at Wellington Road traffic lights, go straight over into one-way system on Oldham Road. At second lights go right at Alty & Co. Barden Mill is on the right, opposite the traffic lights.

From other directions: (A635 from Manchester, A635 from Stalybridge, A670 from Mossley, A627 from Dunkinfield) you arrive at Asda roundabout on edge of town centre. Take exit for Oldham (Oldham Road). At first traffic light Barden Mill is on left.

Open: Mon–Sat 10–5.
Closed: Bank Holidays.
Cards: MasterCard, Delta, Switch, Visa.
Cars: Up to 50 cars in own car-park.
Toilets: Yes.
Wheelchairs: Easy access, no steps.
Changing rooms: Yes.
Teas: In town.
Groups: Coach trips welcome, both pre-booked and 'just calling'.
Transport: Two minutes' walk from bus station; bus no. 219 runs past.

7 Bacup Lancs

E Sutton & Sons

Newchurch Road OL13 0DP
(01706) 875578

Men's, ladies' and children's fashion shoes in leather and synthetic materials.

'Massive range of branded footwear from own factory and all over the world. Stock changes daily. Prices from £1 to £100. Special lines at lowest prices in the country. January and July sales.'

Easy to see on the Bacup–Rawtenstall road (A681), on the edge of Bacup.

As you leave Bacup for Rawtenstall: this clearly marked shop is on the left, immediately after Total petrol.

Coming into Bacup from Rawtenstall: pass Lee Mill Post Office on left; after ½ mile, as you come into Bacup, this shop is clearly visible on the right.

Open: Mon–Fri 10–5.30; Sat 9–5.30; Sun and Bank Holidays 10–4.
Closed: Christmas, Boxing and New Year's Days.
Cards: Access, Style, Visa.
Cars: Own large car-park.
Toilets: In town or pub next door.
Wheelchairs: Easy access; no steps to large shop.
Teas: Cold drinks machine. Coffee in Bacup.
Groups: No factory tours. Groups of shoppers always welcome.
Transport: Bus no. 464 within 20 metres (every 15 minutes).
Mail order: No.

8 Barrowford near Nelson Lancs

East Lancashire Towel Company

Park Mill, Halstead Lane BB9 6HK
(01282) 612193

Jacquard woven hand towels, bath towels, bath sheets, babies' nappies, face cloths, tea towels, roller towels. Also cotton and poly/cotton sheets, pillowcases, handkerchiefs, dusters, dishcloths. Specialise in souvenir and promotional towels.

On northern side of town, just off the main road.

From M65: take exit 13 for Nelson then follow signs into Barrowford. Go north along main road through Barrowford. Pass White Bear Inn on left; take first left just after 'Elderly People Crossing' sign.

Coming south on A682: go right into Halstead Lane soon after you reach Barrowford and 100 yds after 'Elderly People' sign.

Coming west on B6247: pass left turn-off to Pendle Heritage Centre, go over river bridge, turn left, take the third right, Halstead Lane (phone box on the corner).

Open: Mon–Fri 8.30–5; Bank Holidays.
Closed: One week Easter; first three weeks July; one week Sept; two weeks at Christmas.
Cards: None.
Cars: Outside mill.
Toilets: Yes; also for disabled.
Wheelchairs: Easy access, ground floor shop.
Teas: Teas and traditional Lancashire meals served between 10–2. Pre-arranged meals gladly prepared for evening group visits.
Tours: To see towels made: contact Mrs R Hobson. You will probably be shown round by leading British towel expert! Pre-booked coach parties welcome.
Transport: Regular local buses.
Mail order: No seconds posted.
Catalogue: Free. Please mention this guide.

9 Blackburn Lancs *see map opposite*

Graham & Brown

Daveyfield Road, Roman Road Industrial Estate BB1 2NR
(01254) 582229

Wide selection of wallpapers, including ready-pasted vinyls and blown vinyls (embosssed designs) and borders; decorating accessories including paints and brushes.

'Ends of lines and seconds in current ranges at significantly reduced prices.'

About 1½ miles south of Blackburn.

From Blackburn: take road for Haslingden. Pass Blackburn Arena, retail park and Asda on left. Keep straight at mini-roundabouts. At traffic lights, go straight (Blackamoor pub on far right corner). Go right into Davyfield Industrial Estate. Take first right.

Coming north to Blackburn from Edgeworth: pass right turn-off to Waterside village and papermill; continue for ½ mile. Go left at sign to Davyfield Industrial Estate. Take first right.

Open: Mon–Fri 9.30–5.30; Sat 9.30–5; Sunday 10–4.
Closed: Christmas–New Year period.
Cards: Access, Switch, Visa.
Cars: Own large car-park.
Toilets: No.
Wheelchairs: Three steps at front; gentle ramp at side.
Teas: Local pubs and in Blackburn.
Groups: No factory tours.
Transport: Bus service.
Mail order: No.

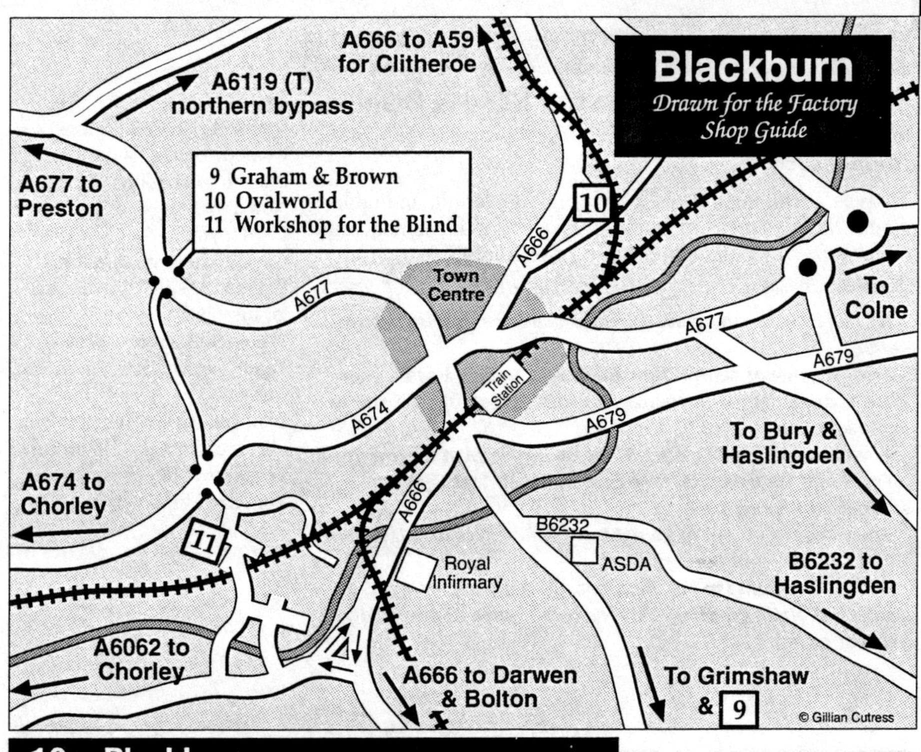

10 Blackburn Lancs see map above

Ovalworld

Bastfield Mill, Beach Street, Little Harwood BB1 6LT
(01254) 582735

Huge selection of wallcoverings (vinyls, papers, tile-on-a-roll, embossed vinyls, borders, lining papers, anaglypta); full range of decorating accessories (paint, paste, filler, brushes etc). Paint mixed to any colour.

'Slight imperfects, DIY superstore returns & manufacturers' end-of-line clearances at a fraction of usual price (from 50p a roll).'

Little Harwood is on the north-east side of Blackburn.

From town centre: take A666 north for Whalley. At mini-roundabout (Peugeot on left), fork right into Whalley Old Road. At next junction (100 yds before railway bridge) go sharp left into yard.

Coming south for Blackburn on A666 from outer ring road: go down hill for town centre. At traffic lights (Bastwell post office near left corner) go left, Plane Street. Just before railway bridge, go right, Beach Street. Shop clearly marked at far right end.

From M6/north: follow Blackburn ring-road A6119 clockwise to traffic lights at Philips Road (tall chimney with PHILIPS).*

From M65 exit 6: take Blackburn ring-road A6119 north to Preston. After 0.7 mile, go left at lights, Philips Rd (tall PHILIPS chimney).*

****Stay on this road, go under railway. At mini-roundabout at bottom of hill, Ovalworld is ahead.***

Open: Mon–Fri 9–5.30; Sat 9.30–5; Sun 10–4; Bank Holidays.
Closed: Christmas and Boxing Days.
Cards: Access, Connect, Switch, Visa.
Cars: Own ample car-park.
Toilets: No.
Wheelchairs: No steps, huge ground floor shop.
Teas: Blackburn town centre.
Groups: No factory tours but coach enquiries welcome.
Transport: Bus nos. 212, 213, 214 and Outer Circle.
Mail order: Product type and constantly changing range make mail order inappropriate.

11 Blackburn Lancas *see map on previous page*

Sheltered Workshop for the Blind & Disabled

Mill Hill Street BB2 2RA
(01254) 52666

Textiles, including curtains, bedding, household and table linens. Made-to-measure curtains. 95% of goods manufactured on premises by blind and disabled workforce.

'Some seconds and ends of lines available at factory shop prices.'

Near Mill Hill station, about 1½ miles south-west of Blackburn centre.

From Blackburn centre: take A674 for Chorley. Pass Citroën showroom on right with church opposite, go left at next traffic lights into Spring Lane.*

From Preston (A677): pass Moat House Hotel at start of town, go over first traffic lights, take first right. At next lights go straight into Spring Lane.*

From Chorley on A674: go right at traffic lights for Blackburn Royal Infirmary into Spring Lane.*

****Take third right (to Mill Hill), pass Mill Hill pub on right, go straight at offset crossing. Take next left: shop at end of low building on left.***

Open: Mon–Fri 9–12.30 & 1.30–4 (Fri 1.30–3); Sat 9–12.
Closed: Bank Holidays; last two weeks July; Christmas–New Year.
Cards: No.
Cars: Own large car-park.
Toilets: Ask if desperate; also for disabled.
Wheelchairs: Easy access.
Teas: Tea available for booked parties.
Groups: By arrangement only. Please contact Ian Ainsworth.
Transport: Regular services from Blackburn centre.

12 Bolton Gr Manchester *see map opposite*

AP Supplies

Unit 7 Lever Bridge Mills, Radcliffe Road, Darcy Lever BL3 1RV
(01204) 394981 Fax (01204) 531767

Twist pile carpets in 80/20% wool/nylon – 12ft, 4m and 15ft widths. Wide selection of colours.

'Reduced prices on ends of rolls. Special colours gladly made to order. Full fitting service. Free delivery under 5 miles; reasonable price further afield.'

On the south-east side of Bolton.

From north or south: take A666. Turn off this dual carriageway for A579 to Bury/Bolton South: if going north – at lights at top of slip road, go right; if going south – turn left at top of slip road. After 400 yds go right at lights into Castle Street.*

From Bury via A58: at traffic lights, bear left on to A579 for town centre. At lights go left into Castle Street.*

From Bolton centre: follow signs for Bury A579/(A58). Cross A666; go right at lights into Castle Street.*

****Go straight. After railway bridge, company is in mill on left.***

Open: Mon–Fri 8–4.30; Sat 9–3. Other times by arrangement.
Closed: Bank Holidays; Christmas, Boxing and New Year's days.
Cards: Access, Visa.
Cars: Own yard in front of shop.
Toilets: Yes.
Wheelchairs: Easy access to spacious medium sized shop.
Teas: Nearby pubs, cafés; teashops in Bolton.
Tours: No factory tours.
Transport: Buses from Bolton town centre.
Mail order: No.

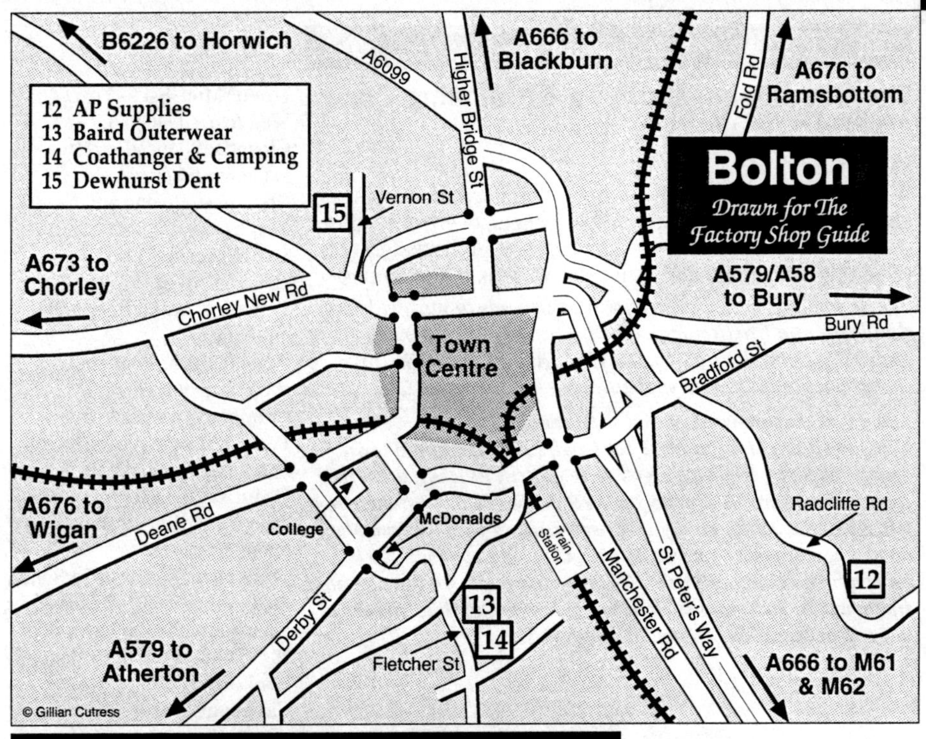

13 Bolton Gr Manchester *see map above*

Baird Outerwear Brands

Fletcher Street BL3 6PR
(01204) 32311

Ladies' and men's rainwear and casual wear. Brand names include: *Dannimac, Telemac, Baracuta, Cloud Nine* and *Thomas Marshall.*

'Perfects, seconds, ends of lines on sale.'

About ¼ mile south-west of Bolton station.

You need to get on to A579 for Leigh (although in the town centre, begin by following signs to Wigan/St Helens). At traffic lights with McDonald's restaurant on one corner and Institute of Technology opposite, go left (Fletcher Street). Follow road round. Go through next traffic lights. Company is on the left.

Open: *New times.* Mon–Sat 10–4. Worth phoning first to confirm if travelling far.
Closed: Christmas–New Year.
Cards: Access, Switch, Visa.
Cars: In street outside shop.
Toilets: No.
Wheelchairs: One small step. Spacious shop.
Changing rooms: No.
Teas: In Bolton.
Groups: If groups wish to attend the monthly sale, please phone first.
Transport: 15 minutes' walk from centre of town.
Mail order: No.

14 Bolton Gr Manchester *map previous page*

The Coathanger Clothing & Camping Co.

215 Fletcher Street BL3 6NG
(01204) 397886

Wide range of high quality outdoor clothing and camping equipment. Waterproof breathable jackets, overtrousers, wax jackets, body warmers, riding capes, fleece jackets, boots, rucksacks, sleeping bags, tents etc. Various brand names.

'We design and manufacture many garments to market leader standards at a fraction of the cost. Brand name seconds, ex-displays, samples and ends of lines. We exhibit at many shows around the country: please ring for current list.'

About ⅛ mile south-west of Bolton Station.

You need to get on to A579 for Leigh (although in the town centre, begin by following signs to Wigan/St Helens). From the town centre, you will probably pass Sainsbury's on left: then bear left. At traffic lights, go right. At traffic lights with McDonald's on one corner and the Institute of Technology opposite, go left for Leigh into Fletcher Street. Follow road round. Go through next traffic lights. This shop is on left, just before the third street on left and opposite the Queen Elizabeth pub.

Open: Mon–Sat 9–5 except Wed (closed all day).
Closed: Wednesday; Bank Holidays; first week Sept; Christmas, Boxing and New Year's Days.
Cards: Access, Visa.
Cars: In street.
Toilets: Use of factory toilet on request.
Wheelchairs: Four steps to shop on ground floor.
Changing rooms: Yes.
Teas: Tea served at no charge. Cafés, pubs, restaurants in town.
Groups: No factory tours but groups welcome to shop if they phone first.
Transport: Bus/train to Bolton then bus nos. 569/572 from Moor Lane bus station to Lever St or 10/15 mins' walk from station.
Mail order: Yes.
Catalogue: No.

15 Bolton Gr Manchester *map previous page*

Dewhurst Dent

Union Mill, Vernon Street
(01204) 399619

Ready-made curtains; plain and printed curtain and furnishing fabrics by the metre. Suitings. Velours and devoré velvets. Printed and plain dress fabrics in many weaves: colour-woven checks, gingham, winceyette, children's and Christmas prints, stretch fabrics; bridal fabrics, brocades. Trimmings, linings.

'Most products, including chainstore items, are perfects. About 40% off normal retail prices.'

In a large mill close to the city centre (on the north-west side) Vernon Street leads off St George's Road (B6226/A673).

From city centre and inner ring road: aim for Horwich/Chorley A6226 or Chorley A673. At traffic lights at a major junction, you come into St George's Road. Take first right, Vernon Street.*

Coming south into Bolton from Horwich/Chorley on B6226. Go downhill into Bolton. Go over traffic lights at junction (where Chorley New Road A673 comes in from right) into St George's Road. Take last road on left (Vernon Street) before traffic lights.*

Coming east into Bolton from Horwich/Chorley on A673: bear right at traffic lights into St George's Road; go downhill for short distance. Take last road on left (Vernon St) before traffic lights.*

****Take first left (past The Royal pub) to large, impressive mill.***

Open: Mon–Wed 10–5; Thur 10–7.30; Fri, Sat 10–5; Sun 10–4.
Closed: Some Bank Holidays; phone for Christmas–New Year period and Easter dates.
Cards: Delta, MasterCard, Switch, Visa.
Cars: Own large car-park.
Toilets: Yes.
Wheelchairs: Five steps to large shop. Please phone in advance if assistance required.
Teas: Various cafés in town.
Groups: Shopping groups welcome: please phone the shop manager in advance.
Transport: Bus nos. 501, 502, 518, 519, 575 from town centre or train station.

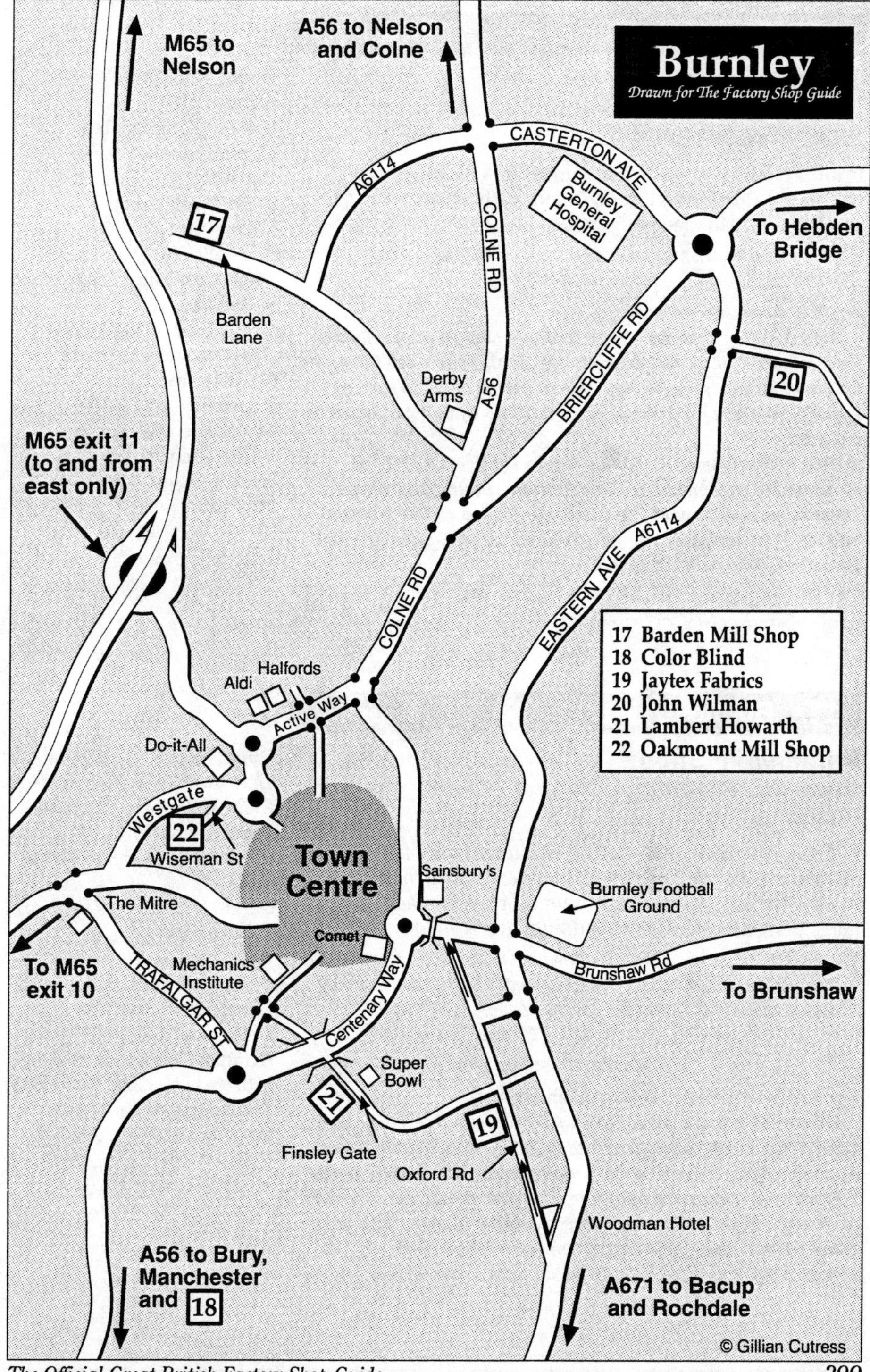
Burnley
Drawn for The Factory Shop Guide
M65 to Nelson
A56 to Nelson and Colne
CASTERTON AVE
A6114
COLNE RD
Burnley General Hospital
17
Barden Lane
To Hebden Bridge
BRIERCLIFFE RD
20
Derby Arms
A56
M65 exit 11 (to and from east only)
COLNE RD
EASTERN AVE A6114
17 Barden Mill Shop
18 Color Blind
19 Jaytex Fabrics
20 John Wilman
21 Lambert Howarth
22 Oakmount Mill Shop
Halfords
Aldi
Active Way
Do-it-All
Westgate
22
Wiseman St
Town Centre
Sainsbury's
Burnley Football Ground
The Mitre
To M65 exit 10
Comet
Mechanics Institute
TRAFALGAR ST
Centenary Way
Brunshaw Rd
To Brunshaw
Super Bowl
21
Finsley Gate
19
Oxford Rd
Woodman Hotel
A56 to Bury, Manchester and 18
A671 to Bacup and Rochdale
© Gillian Cutress

16 Broadbottom near Hyde Gr Manchester

Tiviot Prints

Lymefield Mill SK14 6AF
(01457) 764399

Printed cloth cut-outs of oven gloves, tea cosies, aprons, bags etc. Tablecloths, towels (hand, bath, sheet, children's and beach). Also made-up textiles, towel sets, bathrobes.

'New items and designs always on offer. Rummage boxes. 25p to £15. Ideal for charity fund-raising.'

About 3 miles west of Glossop.

From Glossop: take A57 west for Manchester; after railway viaduct go left on to A626 for Marple. In Charlesworth take road for Broadbottom, go over very narrow bridge beneath railway viaduct, continue for 100 yds, turn left into Lymefield. Go left in mill yard.

From M67, Hyde or Stalybridge: turn south off A57(T) at Mottram in Longdendale to Broadbottom. Go through village, under railway arch, past The Cheshire Cheese on left and turn into track immediately on right. Turn left at mill. Shop in small detached stone building to left.

Open: Thur, Fri 10–4; Sat 10–3.30.
Closed: Bank Holidays; Christmas–New Year.
Cards: None.
Cars: Outside shop.
Toilets: Yes.
Wheelchairs: One step.
Teas: Local pubs. Tea rooms in Glossop.
Groups: Shopping groups please phone beforehand. No mill tours.
Transport: Trains from Manchester/Glossop to Broadbottom; buses from Hyde/Glossop.
Mail order: No.

17 Burnley Lancs *see map on previous page*

Barden Mill Shop

Barden Lane BB12 0DY
(01282) 420333

Full range of discounted clothing for men, ladies and children. Some items debranded. Over 3000 men's suits in stock at all times. *Musbury Fabrics* department for ready-made and made-to-measure curtains, bedding, quilts and towels.

'Most garments are overmakes for chainstores or ex-high street merchandise. Perfects and overmakes at substantial savings. Ex-catalogue department for ladies' larger sizes (up to 32). Men's suits from £39, suit jackets £15 and suit trousers £10!'

See our display advertisement opposite

North of town between the canal and railway.

From M65 exit 12: go south on A56 through Brierfield. After Oaks Hotel on left, go right at traffic lights (Windermere Avenue). At end go right (Barden Lane). Shop on right, after railway bridge.

From town centre and southern/western directions: take A56 for Nelson. In small one-way system about half mile north of canal hump bridge, pass Derby Arms on left then fork left for Fence. Shop is in large mill, ½ mile on right, after railway bridge.

Open: Mon–Sat 10–5 *(May–Oct: Thur late night to 8);* Sun 11–5.
Closed: Christmas Day and Easter Sunday.
Cards: Access, Delta, Switch, Visa.
Cars: Large car-park by shop.
Toilets: Yes.
Wheelchairs: Easy access, no steps. Huge shop on one level.
Changing rooms: Yes.
Teas: Jack Moore's tea room.
Groups: Coach trips welcome, both pre-booked and 'just calling'.
Transport: Wizzard bus no. 5 from town centre to Reedley Hallows.
Mail order: Not yet.

18 Burnley Lancs *see map on previous page*

Color Blind

Farrington Road, Rossendale Road Industrial Estate
BB11 5ST *(01282) 425504*

Blinds in large range of styles, colours, textures including washable. Vertical, roller, pleated; conservatory roof blinds; Venetian blinds in four slat widths. For DIY and commercial fitters.

'Blinds also made to order. Fitting at nominal price within 30 miles. We only charge for width and believe our blinds are cheapest in England. Vertical blinds £7 per ft width, any length drop (eg patio door 6ft wide x 7ft for £42 + vat); roller blinds trim-&-fit or made-to-measure £3 per ft width.'

South-west of Burnley town centre.

From town centre: take A679 west for Hapton/Accrington.*

From M65 exit 10: aim for town centre. At large roundabout, go right for Hapton/Huncoat/Accrington (A679).*

****At traffic lights, go left into Rossendale Road (A646). After ½ mile, go right into Farrington Road. Shop 200 yds on left.***

From Rawtenstall on A56: at lights, go left into Rossendale Road (A646). After ¾ mile, go left into Farrington Road.

From Bacup on A671/Todmorden on A646: where these two roads meet, south of town, go west on A646 for 2+ miles; go left into Farrington Road.

Open: Mon–Fri 10–5.30; Sat 10-4.
Closed: Bank Holidays; Christmas–New Year.
Cards: Access, Switch, Visa.
Cars: Outside shop.
Toilets: Yes.
Wheelchairs: Easy access at rear.
Teas: Refreshment kiosk nearby.
Groups: Maximum 8 people – phone Mr Donnelly prior to visit.
Transport: From town on each half-hour: bus no. 1 to Rose Grove/Whitegate; ask for Farrington Road.
Mail order: Phone first to clarify samples and swatches required – many colourways and fabric samples for all types of blinds. Usual price + carriage. No seconds, fully guaranteed.
Catalogue: No.

19 Burnley Lancs *see earlier map*

Jaytex Fabrics

129 Oxford Road BB11 3HM *(01282) 428291*

Quality materials at bargain prices; lining, tapes, rails etc. Local measuring service. Make-up service: swags, tails, festoon valances, plaited tie backs, etc. Upholstery materials: fabrics, webbing, cushions, foam sheet, dacron sheet, filling. Seat webbing for cottage suites made up.

'Run by trained upholsterer – gladly gives professional advice. Upholstery service for dining suites, headboards etc. Good quality at mill shop prices.'

On the south-east side of Burnley centre.

From Bacup (A671)/Todmorden (A646): take A671 for Burnley; look for The Woodman Hotel on left and go left after it. Shop is on left just below church on right.

From town centre: find Sainsbury's.*

From M65 exit 10: take A671 to Town Centre (Happy Eater on right). Get in right lane for 'Through traffic'. At lights, go straight (The Mitre on right) into Trafalgar Street. At next roundabout bear left (not sharp left, Manchester Street) into Centenary Way; continue to roundabout with Sainsbury's.*

***Pass Sainsbury's on left. Go right (Yorkshire St). Go under canal bridge, right at lights (Todmorden Rd), straight at next set; take first right, first left. Shop 200 yds on right on corner with Brunswick St.**

Open: Tues–Fri 9.30–5; Sat & Bank Holidays please phone.
Closed: Monday; Christmas–New Year. Variable summer holidays, please ring.
Cards: No.
Cars: Outside.
Toilets: In Burnley.
Wheelchairs: One step, extended shop.
Teas: Towneley Hall, and park and café 500 yds away.
Groups: Not suitable for groups.
Transport: None.
Mail order: Yes.
Catalogue: No.

20 Burnley Lancs *see earlier map*

John Wilman

Widow Hill Road, Heasandford Industrial Estate BB10 2TK (01282) 427008

Wide range of co-ordinated wallpapers, furnishing fabrics, lampshades, paint and textiles.

'Always special offers. Curtaining from £3.50 per metre, vinyl wall coverings from £2.99 per roll, papers from £1.99. All stock discontinued or slightly imperfect.'

See our display advertisement on p. 409

Off Eastern Avenue (A6114), major road on north-east side of town.

Coming north on A671 from Bacup: keep straight. At third traffic lights in Burnley, go right into this well marked estate.

From Burnley/Nelson via A56: go east at traffic lights into Casterton Avenue (A6114); pass Burnley General Hospital on right; go over roundabout (for Rochdale A6114/Bacup (A671)) into Eastern Avenue; go left at traffic lights into this estate.*

From M65 exit 10: take A671 to Town Centre (Little Chef on right). Get in right lane for 'Through traffic'. At traffic lights, go straight (The Mitre on right) into Trafalgar Street. At roundabout, take second exit (Centenary Way, for Nelson A682). At roundabout take third exit, in front of Sainsbury's; go left at traffic lights; go right at lights into estate.*

***Company 150 yds on right.**

Open: Mon–Fri 9.30–5.30; Sat 9–5; Sun 10–4. Bank Holidays 10–5.
Closed: Christmas Eve; Christmas & Boxing Days; New Year's Day; Easter Sunday.
Cards: MasterCard, Switch, Visa.
Cars: Own large car-park.
Toilets: Yes, including for disabled.
Wheelchairs: Easy access, wide door and aisles, huge shop.
Teas: Own coffee shop.
Groups: No factory tours. Shopping groups welcome, no need to book.
Transport: Bus to bottom of Widow Hill Road then walk.
Mail order: No.

21 Burnley Lancs *see earlier map*

Lambert Howarth & Sons

Finsley Mill, Finsley Gate BB11 2HI
(01282) 425641 switchboard, 471283 shop.

Men's, ladies' and children's shoes, boots, slippers, training shoes. Towels, bags. Ladies', men's and children's wear, and accessories.

'Seconds and ends of lines at considerably reduced prices. Thursday 10% discount for OAPs. Canal enthusiasts (from Burnley Canal) can step off their boat into our shop!'

Close to town centre, backing on to canal. Probably easiest to look for tall black chimney with red stripes and water tank on roof with large sign 'Osbornia Shoes'.

Finsley Gate runs under the A56 overpass. Shop is opposite Superbowl.

From town centre: go up Manchester Road, pass Mechanics Institute on right, go left at next traffic lights into Finsley Gate.*

From M65 exit 10: take A671 to Town Centre (Happy Eater on right). Get in right lane for 'Through traffic'. At lights, go straight (The Mitre on right) into Trafalgar Street. By next roundabout go left (Manchester Street); at lights go right into Finsley Gate.*

***Go under A56: shop on right opposite Superbowl.**

Open: Mon–Fri 9.30–5; Sat 9–4. Some Bank Holidays, phone to check.
Closed: Good Friday–Easter Monday; Christmas–New Year.
Cards: Yes.
Cars: Parking available.
Toilets: Ask if desperate.
Wheelchairs: Ramp to sizeable shop.
Changing rooms: Yes.
Teas: Coffee in Superbowl across the road. Cafés in town.
Groups: No factory tours. Shopping groups always welcome with prior phone call.
Transport: Easy walking distance from centre of town.

22 Burnley Lancs *see earlier map*

Oakmount Mill Shop

Wiseman Street BB11 1RV
(01282) 414950

Wide range of dress fabrics (including bridal fabrics), patterns, haberdashery. Large selection of curtain and furnishing fabrics – cottons, calicos, moirés, dupions, linings, nets, sheeting etc plus wadding and toy filling. Curtain and sewing accessories and *American Craft* cottons for patchwork.

'First and seconds at prices between 30–40% lower than recommended retail prices. Curtain-making service. Children's play area.'

Close to the town centre, on the west side.

From Burnley town centre: aim for Blackburn A679/M65/ Padiham. Pass Do It All on right. At roundabout, go right (Westgate). Pass The Plane Tree on left. Take next left, Wiseman Street.*

From M65 exit 10: aim for Burnley town centre. Pass HSS Hire Shop on left then take next right, Wiseman Street.*

***Shop is 100 yds on right, beneath tall chimney.**

Open: Mon–Sat 9.15–5.
Closed: Bank Holiday Mondays; Christmas, Boxing and New Year's Days.
Cards: MasterCard, Switch, Visa.
Cars: Private car-park just outside mill shop.
Toilets: Yes.
Wheelchairs: No steps to shop, but four steps inside. Separate entrance without steps may be used.
Teas: Good café at Asda.
Groups: Shopping groups welcome; larger groups please phone shop in advance.
Transport: Burnley–Padiham buses pass end of Wiseman Street. Burnley train station about 400 m.
Mail order: No.

23 Bury Lancs

Antler

Pilot Works, Alfred Street BL9 9EF
(0161) 764 5241

Wide selection of luggage, cases and bags, attaché cases, picnic hampers and leather goods.

'End of season ranges; quality seconds and samples.'

See our display advertisement opposite

South-east of Bury town centre, not far from M66 exit 2.

From Bury town centre ring road: take A58 east for Heywood/Rochdale. Shortly turn right at traffic lights (Crown Hotel on right) into Heywood Street, B6219.*

From M66 exit 2: take A58 for Bury. At traffic lights (Crown Hotel on left) turn left into Heywood Street, B6219.*

****Take second or third left; after 100 yds or so, go right into Alfred Street. Go over the railway hump bridge. Clearly marked shop is in huge mill on left.***

Coming north on A56 into Bury: cross pedestrian lights, pass The Swan & Cemetery on left. After a few hundred yards, go right at sign to football ground into Gigg Lane. After half a mile, go left (Alfred Street). Antler are in huge mill on right.

Open: Tues–Sat 10–4.
Closed: Monday; Easter Friday & Saturday; Christmas–New Year.
Cards: Delta, MasterCard, Switch, Visa.
Cars: Own car-park.
Toilets: No.
Wheelchairs: No access as shop is down a flight of stairs.
Teas: In town centre.
Groups: Coach parties welcome to the shop Tuesday–Friday. Please contact Alan Holden before arrival.
Transport: Train or bus to Bury then local buses 92, 93, 70, 135, 136, 138, 790.
Mail order: No.

24 Bury Lancs

Whitfords Bury Boot & Shoe Co.

Brandlesholme Road BL8 1BQ
(0161) 238 4209

Shoes for people who have difficulty finding correct fitting footwear: wide fittings D, E–EEEE in sizes 3–9 for ladies; ultra wide for men in sizes 6–12. Heavy duty corsetry. Dresses, coats, underwear and nightwear. Also items for people with disabilities, eg clothing with velcro fastening, button-through, long handled toe nail scissors, incontinence pants/pads/mattress covers, heat pads for arthritic pain, bedding, curtains and travel goods.

'Slippers and shoes from £6.99–£40. Sales in January and July with prices reduced by 25–50%.'

On the B6214 north-west of Bury.

From M66 exit 2: take slip road for Bury/Heywood. At end of slip-road follow signs on Bury bypass for Bolton, Ramsbottom, Tottington. Go along dual carriageway, signposted A58 Bolton. Get into outside lane. Follow Ramsbottom signs. At traffic lights take right fork for A676 Tottington/Ramsbottom; pass B&Q; at next lights go right for Ramsbottom (The Dusty Miller pub on left). Go along Brandlesholme Road, and immediately before BPgarage on right, go right. Company is on right (car-park at end).

Open: Mon–Sat 9–5.
Closed: Bank Holidays; Christmas–New Year period.
Cards: Access, Visa.
Cars: Own car-park.
Toilets: Yes.
Wheelchairs: Wheelchair available from shop if required.
Changing rooms: Yes.
Teas: In town.
Groups: No guided tours, but shopping groups welcome – phone Mrs Pam Pearson, especially for 52-seater coaches.
Transport: Bus no. 474 (to Ramsbottom) from Bury Interchange: ask for Whitfords Bury Boots.
Mail order: No seconds by mail order.
Catalogue: Free.

See our entry opposite

25 Carnforth (Holme) Lancs

Abbey Horn of Lakeland

Units 6a & 6b Holme Mills, Holme LA6 1RD
(01524) 782387

Shoe horns, spoons, spatulas, salad servers, soldiers' mugs, paperweights, bottle openers, corkscrews, walking sticks, all made of ox horn. Also horn ships, brushes, combs.

'All items perfect with prices reduced by a third.'

Holme is 6 miles north of Carnforth (west of M6) between M6 exits 35 & 36. Company is in industrial estate south of Holme.

From M6 exit 36: go towards Kirkby Londsale; after 150 yds go right for Holme on A6070. After 2 miles go right for Holme over motorway. In Holme, go left opposite The Smithy pub.*

From Milnthorpe on A6: turn towards Holme at traffic lights; once out of Milnthorpe, fork right for Holme. In Holme turn right opposite The Smithy.*

****Continue until you pass mill pond on left and first entrance to industrial estate. Take second entrance after about 200 yds. Park on right in marked spaces. Walk down 80 yds between the units: units 6A and B are on right.***

Open: Mon–Fri 9–4.
Closed: Bank Holidays; Christmas–New Year.
Cards: None.
Cars: Small area in front of factory.
Toilets: No.
Wheelchairs: Access to factory for self-guided tour but not to shop (16 steps).
Teas: Local pub.
Tours: Abbey Horn, established in 1749, is the oldest working horn works and the only one open to public. Factory visits free. Groups welcome – please call Heather McKellar first.
Transport: Bus no. 55 from Kendal.
Mail order: No.
Catalogue: Only wholesale catalogue.

26 Castleton near Rochdale Lancs

Vectase Lighting

Unit 4B Gorrels Way, Trans-Pennine Trading Estate
OL11 9XY
(01706) 341636

Light fittings: wall, ceiling and picture lights; lamp bases, lampshades, Christmas lights, security lights, bulbs etc.

'Both perfects and seconds on sale at wholesale prices.'

A short distance north of M62 exit 20 and two miles south of Rochdale centre.

From M62 exit 20: take A627M north for Rochdale. At first roundabout, go right; at next roundabout go right for Castleton.*

Coming south on A58 from Rochdale: at a large roundabout, turn left on to A664. Go over next roundabout and right at third on to Queensway (A664) for Castleton.*

****Go right, before Honda garage & overpass, into Gorrels Way.*****

From Middleton via A664: follow signs to Rochdale, bear right in Castleton towards estate, go under the overpass, past Honda garage and turn left.**

*****Once on estate, keep left. Company is on right, with shop on far side.***

Open: Mon–Thur 9.30–4.30; Fri 9.30–2.45.
Closed: Bank Holidays; Christmas–New Year period.
Cards: None.
Cars: In front of shop.
Toilets: Yes.
Wheelchairs: One step to medium sized shop.
Teas: In Castleton.
Groups: No tours.
Transport: None.
Mail order: No.

27 Chadderton Gr Manchester

Gorse Mill Lighting

Gorse Mill, Gorse Street, Broadway OL9 9RK
(0161) 628 4202

Modern and traditional light fittings, lamps, silk lampshades, spots, glass panel pendants, wall washers, track 12v halogen and recess lighting, crystal chandeliers, security and outdoor lighting.

'Europe's largest decorative lighting disposal centre. 240,000 sq ft with £1 million stock! Perfects unless otherwise marked. Average saving 50% off normal retail. Lighting displayed amongst reproduction artefacts and furniture, also for sale.'

See our display advertisement opposite

Between Middleton and Oldham off A663 in a huge, conspicuous mill.

From M62 exit 20: go south on A627(M) for Oldham. This road becomes the A663; keep straight (do not take slip road for Oldham). Cross B6189 at traffic lights; take first right after pedestrian lights. Go to far corner of Gorse Mill following signs.

From Manchester: take A62 towards Oldham then turn left at traffic lights on to A663 for Rochdale. At end of dual carriageway, cross A6104 at lights, pass Boat and Horses pub on left and take next left. Gorse Mill factory shop is at end of mill on right.

Open: Mon–Fri 9–4.30; Sat, Sun 10–4; Bank Holidays 10–4.
Closed: Easter Sunday; Christmas, Boxing and New Year's Days.
Cards: Access, Amex, Switch, Visa.
Cars: Own car-park for 300 cars.
Toilets: Yes.
Wheelchairs: Six steps or ramp to very large shop.
Teas: Own coffee shop.
Tours: Four tours a year – ask for details. Shopping groups always welcome.
Transport: Buses from Oldham and from Manchester–Chadderton.
Mail order: No.

28 Chester Cheshire

Montgomery Tomlinson

Broughton Mill Road, Bretton CH4 0BY
(01244) 661363

Curtains, valances, tie-backs and cushions in printed cottons, velvet and woven fabrics. Lining material by the metre.

'Company manufacturing soft furnishings. Prices up to 50% off normal prices. Mainly cancelled orders; some seconds.'

About 3 miles west of Chester.

From city centre: take A5104 for Saltney. Drive through Saltney, under railway bridge, then keep straight. Pass right turn-off for Queensferry (B5129). After ½ mile (50 yds before Iveco Trucks), turn right into road.*

From A55 (Chester southerly by-pass): exit for Broughton, follow signs for A5104 for Saltney/Chester. Pass Iveco Trucks on left and immediately turn left into road.*

***Drive to end of road; factory is on left. Go left in front of factory to car-park at rear.**

Open: Tues–Fri 10–12.30 & 1–4.30; Sat 9.30–4.30.
If travelling far, please phone to confirm times.
Closed: Bank Holidays.
Cards: No (possibly in future, please check).
Cars: In factory yard.
Toilets: No.
Wheelchairs: Ramp to medium sized shop on ground floor.
Teas: Chester city centre or local pubs.
Tours: No guided tours.
Transport: Buses from city centre.

29 Chorley Lancs

Curtain Choice

Corporation Street PR6 0HK *(01257) 622290*

Ready-made curtains including cotton velvets. Full range of made-to-measure curtains & accessories. Nets, fabric by the metre. Curtain poles, tracks. Also bedding, quilts, towels etc.

'Don't forget your window measurements! Clearance lines and slight seconds. Perfects to order.'

A short way north-east of Chorley town centre and equidistant from A6 (Park Road) and B6228 (Eaves Lane), which both run north–south.

Coming south on A6: go left to Highfield Industrial Estate; pass B&Q on left; take second exit at double roundabout (Harpers Lane).*

From Chorley Town Hall (tall pointed clock tower): take A6 for Preston. At first roundabout go right (B&Q on left); take second exit (Harpers Lane).*

****Go over railway, take first right (Railway Road). Pass factory on left, go left into Corporation Street. Shop is on right.***

Coming along Eaves Lane (B6228): turn west into Geoffrey Street beside Select Wine Co.; go right at bottom (Doris Street), then first left (Corporation Street). Shop is on corner. Take care – many small streets are blocked off, others are one way!

Open: Mon–Fri 10–4.30; Sat 10–4.
Closed: Bank Holidays; Spring Bank Holiday week; last two weeks July; Christmas–New Year.
Cards: Access, Visa.
Cars: In nearby streets.
Toilets: Town centre.
Wheelchairs: Access possible.
Teas: In Chorley centre.
Groups: Welcome small groups of shoppers.
Transport: 15 minutes' walk from town centre.
Mail order: No.

30 Chorley Lancs

John Wilman

George Street PR7 2BE
(01257) 264011

Wide range of co-ordinated wallpapers, furnishing fabrics, lampshades and textiles. Always special offers.

'Curtaining from £3.50 per metre, vinyl wall coverings from £2.99 per roll, papers from £1.99. All stock discontinued or slightly imperfect.'

See our display advertisement opposite

On the south side of the town centre, just off the A6.

Coming south: get on to the A6 and stay on this road through town. Pass the railway station on left. Take next right, George Street. John Wilman is clearly visible on left. Go left into car-park.

Coming north on A6: pass Ford on left and Morrisons supermarket on right. Go left into George Street. John Wilman is clearly visible on left. Go left into car-park.

Open: Mon–Fri 9.30–5.30; Sat 9–5; Sun 10–4; Bank Holidays 10–5.
Closed: Christmas Eve; Christmas, Boxing and New Year's Days; Easter Sunday.
Cards: MasterCard, Switch, Visa.
Cars: Own large car-park.
Toilets: Yes, including for disabled.
Wheelchairs: Easy access, wide doors and aisles, huge shop.
Teas: In Chorley.
Groups: No factory tours. Shopping groups welcome, no need to book.
Transport: Train station almost facing shop, 10 minutes' walk to bus station.
Mail order: No.

F

See our entry opposite & no. 20

Market days

Accrington	Mon, Tues, Thur, Fri, Sat, indoor general
Ashton-in-Makerfield	Tue, Sat, outdoor general
Bacup	Wed, Sat, outdoor general
Biddulph	Mon, Thur, outdoor general
Blackburn	Mon to Sat, indoor general; Wed, Fri, Sat, outdoor general
Blackpool	Mon to Sun (summer), Mon to Sat (winter), indoor general
Bolton	Tues, Thur, Sat, indoor/outdoor general
Burnley	Mon, Wed, Thur, Fri, Sat, indoor general Mon, Thur, Sat, outdoor general; Wed antiques/bric-à-brac
Bury	Mon, Wed, Thur, Fri, Sat, indoor general Wed, Fri, Sat, outdoor general; Mon to Sat, indoor fish and meat
Cheadle	Tues, Fri, Sat, outdoor general
Chester	Mon to Sat, indoor general
Chorley	Tues, Fri, Sat, outdoor general
Clitheroe	Tues, Sat, outdoor general
Colne	Wed, Sat, outdoor general; Mon, Wed, Thur, Fri, Sat, indoor general
Congleton	Tues, Sat, indoor/outdoor general
Ellesmere Port	Tues, Fri, Sat, indoor general
Farnworth	Mon, Fri, Sat, outdoor general
Fleetwood	Mon, Tues, Fri, Sat, indoor/outdoor general
Great Harwood	Fri, outdoor
Haslingden	Tues, Fri, outdoor general
Horwich	Tues, Fri, indoor/outdoor general
Hyde	Wed, Thur, Fri, indoor/outdoor general
Kirkby	Tue, Fri, Sat, outdoor general
Lancaster	Mon, Tues, Thur, indoor general; Thur, Fri, Sat indoor bric-à-brac/ antiques; Tues, Fri, Sat, indoor/outdoor general
Liverpool	Mon to Sat, indoor general (St John's); Mon to Sat, indoor general (Broadway); Thur, Sat, outdoor general (Monument Place)
Macclesfield	Tues, Fri, Sat, outdoor general; Tues to Sat indoor general
Middleton	Fri, Sat, outdoor general
Morecambe	Tues, Thur, indoor general
Nelson	Mon to Sat, indoor general; Fri, Sat outdoor general
Oldham	Mon to Sat, indoor general; Mon, Fri, Sat, outdoors general (Tommyfield); Wed, second-hand market (Tommyfield) Wed, outdoor (Chadderton); Thur, outdoor (Hollinwood, Shaw)
Padiham	Wed, Fri, outdoor general; Sat bric-à-brac
Preston	Mon, Wed, Fri, Sat, outdoor; Mon to Sat, indoor general
Radcliffe	Tue, Fri, Sat, indoor general
Rawtenstall	Thur, Sat, indoor/outdoor general
Rochdale	Mon to Sat, indoor general
Runcorn	Tues, Thur, Sat, indoor/general
St Helens	Sat, indoor general
Stockport	Fri, Sat, outdoor general; Tues, flea market
Westhoughton	Thur, Sat, indoor general
Wigan	Mon to Sat, indoor/outdoor general
Wrexham	Mon to Sat, indoor general; Mon, outdoor general

This information was kindly supplied by World's Fair Publications (in their useful Markets Year Book)

See our entry below

31 Chorley Lancs

R B Contacts (Wholesale)

Churchill Road, Brinscall PR6 8RO
(01254) 832188/832177

Huge range of curtain fabrics by the yard – designer prints, plains, velvets, chintz, jacquards, damasks and moirés. 70 shades of linings. Full fitting and making-up service on site for curtains and accessories, eg tie-backs, cushion covers, loose suite covers etc.

'Fabrics from 99p per yd. Free samples, quotes and delivery. Free expert advice.'

See our display advertisement above

Five miles north-east of Chorley.

From Chorley: take A674 north-east for Blackburn. Go right for Brinscall. Go through the village, passing the post office on left. Go downhill and follow road round to left (long railings on right). Churchill Road is fourth on left.*

From Blackburn or Bolton on A675: follow signs into Brinscall. Drive along by railings on left. Pass car repair yard on right then Churchill Road is second on right.*

****Company clearly marked 50 yds on left.***

Open: Mon–Fri 9–5; Sat 10–3; Sun 11–1; Bank Holidays 9–5.
Closed: Christmas and New Year's Days.
Cards: Major credit and debit cards.
Cars: Ample free parking beside shop.
Toilets: Yes.
Wheelchairs: Full access at front.
Teas: In Brinscall.
Groups: Shopping groups welcome with prior phone call.
Transport: Hourly bus service from Chorley and Blackburn.
Mail order: No.

32 Church near Accrington Lancs

The Card & Gift Factory Shop

see map on p. 428

Church Bridge Works, Mill Street BB5 4EF
(01254) 237324

Wide range of greetings cards, toys, gifts, wrapping paper, Christmas decorations, bedside lamps, tie racks, fruit juice holders and many household items etc. Stock constantly changing.

'All items are excess orders or returned items from catalogues sold off at very low prices.'

Special offer: 10% discount to anyone who shows this book!

From big roundabout underneath railway viaduct on west side of Accrington: follow signs for (M65 Blackburn)/Church. Go left at second traffic lights; take first right in front of huge cream windowless warehouse. Turn left immediately into small lane.*

From M65 exit 7: aim for Accrington; go right at first traffic lights and immediately right again; turn left into slip road.*

From Blackburn/Oswaldtwistle via A679: go under railway then left at both traffic lights, on to B6231 (for Clayton-le-Moors/M65). Pass Hyndburn Sports Centre on right, turn left into slip road.*

***Look for Factory Shop sign. Shop behind building on left.**

Open: Mon–Fri 9.30–4.45.
Closed: Bank Holidays; Christmas–New Year.
Cards: No.
Cars: Car-park.
Toilets: In Accrington.
Wheelchairs: Easy access, ramps only. Medium sized shop.
Teas: Oswaldtwistle Mill; cafés in Accrington.
Groups: Welcome.
Transport: Bus nos. 5, 6, 7, 8. Church & Oswaldtwistle train station 5 minutes' walk.

The Mill Fabric Shop

Cheshire Oaks Designer Outlet Village

See our entry below

33 Cleveleys near Blackpool Lancs

Cresta Factory Outlet

8–12 Nutter Road FY5 1BG *(01253) 823257*

Vast range of famous chainstore ladies', men's and children's clothing. Pottery, household goods and shoes. Also genuine, authentic designerwear by *Armani, Calvin Klein, Ralph Lauren, Versace, Valentino, Boss* and many more.

'Cancelled contracts and last year's stock, saving up to 40% on high street designer store prices. Air-conditioning in summer in this huge 14,000 sq ft shop. Blackpool's most popular tourist attraction for chainstore and designer clothing.'

See our display advertisement above

Nutter Road leads off the central shopping street in Cleveleys.

Going north from Blackpool on coast road (A584) or inland road (A587): aim for Cleveleys. Tram line moves into middle of road. Go left at traffic lights (Royal Bank of Scotland on near right corner, NatWest far right) for sea/Tourist Information Centre.*

Coming south on Fleetwood on A587: at traffic lights in Cleveleys (Royal Bank of Scotland on far left corner, NatWest on near left corner), go right towards the sea.*

****Take first right (Nutter Road), in front of clocktower. Huge shop is 50 yds on right.***

From the sea: go inland on Cleveleys main street (Victoria Rd). Nutter Rd last turning on left before lights. Shop 50 yds on right.

Open: Mon–Sat 9.30–5.30 (Wed, Thur until 6); Sun 10.45–4.45.
Closed: Christmas, Boxing and New Year's Days.
Cards: Most major cards.
Cars: Own car-park to right of shop.
Toilets: Nearest 300 yds.
Wheelchairs: Easy access, no step, to ground floor (men's wear and household) but stairs to first floor (ladies' wear).
Changing rooms: Yes (16 for ladies, 8 for men).
Teas: Lots of cafés in Cleveleys.
Groups: Shopping groups, including coaches, welcome any time.
Transport: Lots of buses from Blackpool stop nearby.
Mail order: No.

34 Clitheroe Lancs

Shireburn Carpets

Primrose Works, Primrose Road BB7 1BS
(01200) 429066

Large range of quality tufted carpets, mainly plain colours, in all yarns and mixes from light domestic through to heavy domestic and contract weight. Most widths available. Patterned Axminsters and Wiltons. Large selection of room-sized roll ends, many at less than trade prices.

'Genuine mill shop with almost everything made on premises. Free measuring service and expert fitting available. Seconds generally on sale. Annual sale early in the New Year.'

On the southern edge of town.

Leave town for 'Preston and Whalley' (turn out of main street, Market Place, beside NatWest bank); at T-junction go right and follow signs for Whalley. Pass Shell petrol and Barkers Garden Centre, on left, then take second right, immediately before bridge at bottom of hill.*

From Padiham via A671: Primrose Road is on left as you reach Clitheroe, just after bridge and immediately before town sign.*

****Mill is 100 yds on left. Park near clearly visible shop.***

Open: Mon, Tues 9–5; Thur 9–8; Fri 9–4.30; Sat 10–4. Bank Holidays.
Closed: Wednesday; Easter; Christmas–New Year.
Cards: None.
Cars: In front of main showroom.
Toilets: Ask if desperate.
Wheelchairs: Easy access.
Teas: In Clitheroe.
Groups: You can see work in progress in the mill (no tours or coach parties).
Transport: Buses from Clitheroe – get off at Primrose Bridge.
Mail order: No.

35 Colne Lancs *see map opposite*

Boundary Mill Stores

Burnley Road BB8 8LS *(01282) 865229*

Ladies' and men's quality garments from all over Europe. Over 100 brands: *Alexon, Austin Reed, Christian Dior, Dannimac, Double Two, Farah, Fruit of the Loom, Jaeger, Laura Ashley, Lyle & Scott, Timberland, Viyella, Windsmoor, Wolsey, Wrangler*. Shoes & boots by *Bally. Equator* luggage. *Warners, Charnos, Gossard* lingerie. New home furnishings building: *Coloroll, Dorma, Laura Ashley, Sheridan.* Crystal from *Dartington, Edinburgh, Royal Doulton, Spiegelau. Wedgwood, Hornsea* and *Staffordshire China. Arthur Price* and *Oneida* cutlery.

'The largest quality mill store in the country.'

See our display advertisement inside front cover

A few yards off the A56, between Colne and Nelson, beside Asda.

From Colne: go south-west towards Nelson, under railway bridge and follow signs to Whitewalls Industrial Estate/Superstores. Turn left in front of Asda.

From Nelson coming north-east on A56: pass Jet petrol then Golden Ball Inn on left; at mini-roundabout, go left into Corporation Street. Boundary Mill is on left.

From the end of M65: follow signs to Whitewalls Industrial Estate/Superstores. Turn left in front of Asda.

Open: Mon–Fri 10–6; Sat and Bank Holidays 10–5; Sun 11–5.
Closed: Easter Sunday and Christmas Day.
Cards: Mastercard, Switch, Visa.
Cars: Massive car-park on all sides; reserved area for coaches.
Toilets: Yes.
Wheelchairs: Easy access with lift to first floor.
Changing rooms: Yes.
Teas: In-house BB's coffee shop; Bannisters restaurant at rear for meals.
Groups: Welcome to shop.
Transport: Main Colne–Burnley bus route; 2 minutes' walk from Asda bus stop.
Mail order: No.

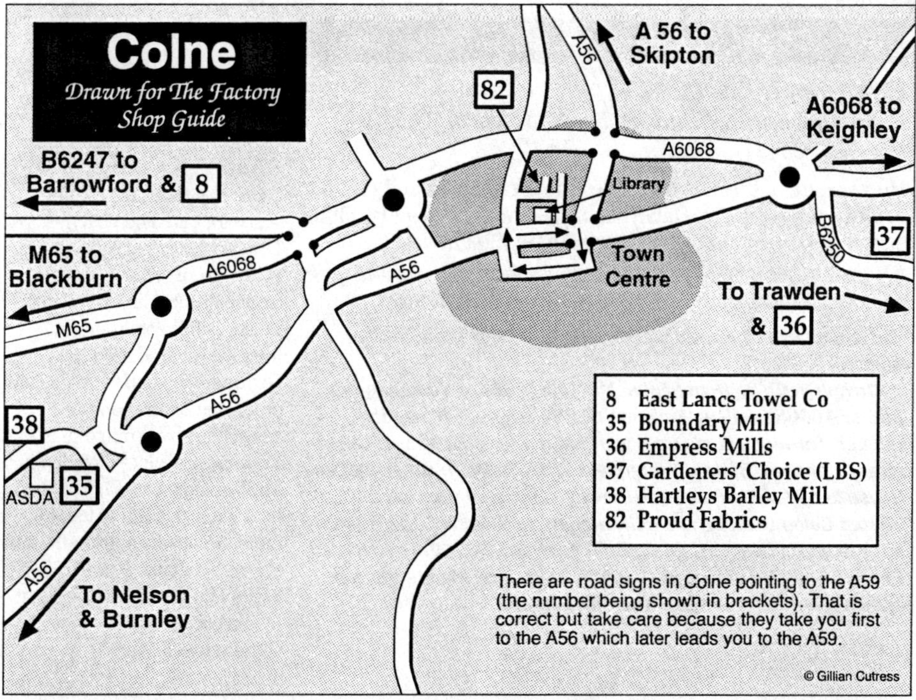

Colne

Drawn for The Factory Shop Guide

B6247 to Barrowford & 8

M65 to Blackburn

A 56 to Skipton

A6068 to Keighley

82

Library

Town Centre

37

To Trawden & 36

38

ASDA 35

To Nelson & Burnley

A56 A6068 M65 B6250

- 8 East Lancs Towel Co
- 35 Boundary Mill
- 36 Empress Mills
- 37 Gardeners' Choice (LBS)
- 38 Hartleys Barley Mill
- 82 Proud Fabrics

There are road signs in Colne pointing to the A59 (the number being shown in brackets). That is correct but take care because they take you first to the A56 which later leads you to the A59.

Shireburn Carpets

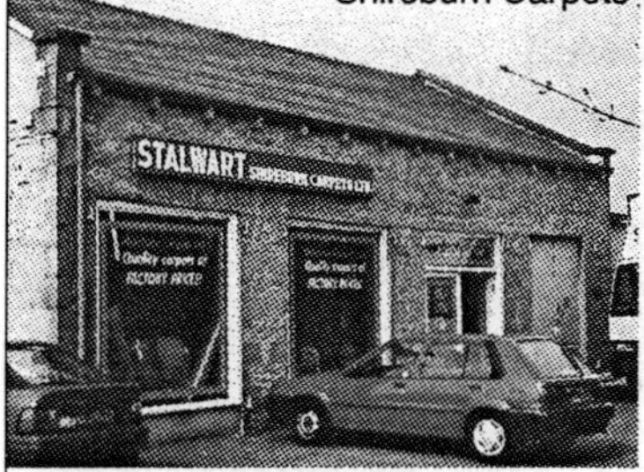

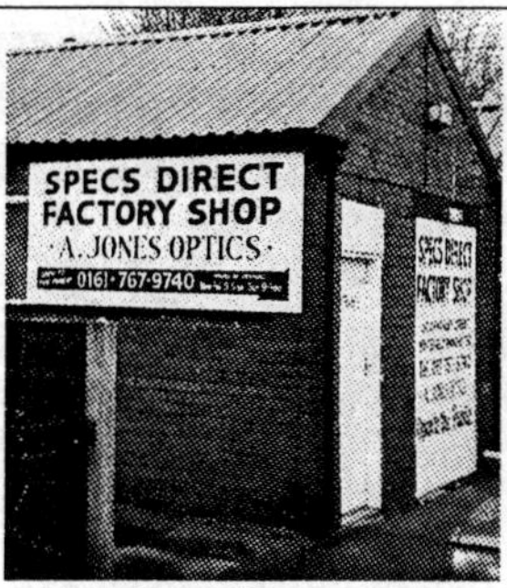

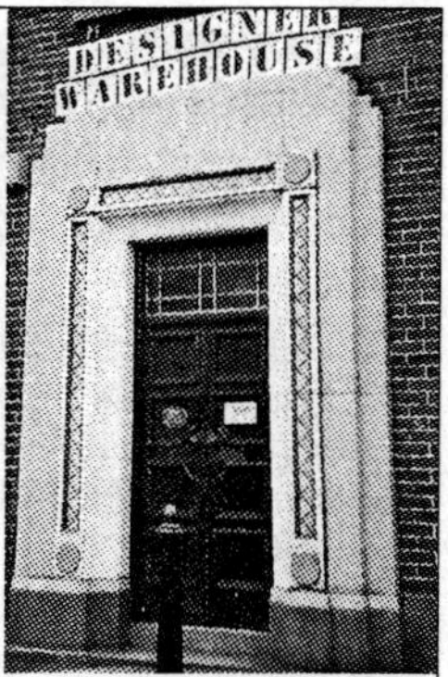

Designer Warehouse

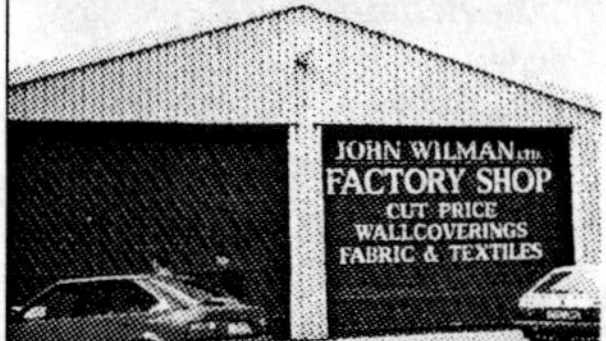

John Wilman

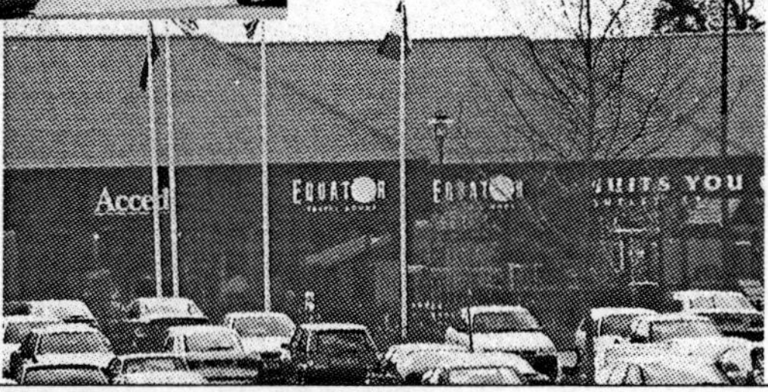

Cheshire Oaks Village

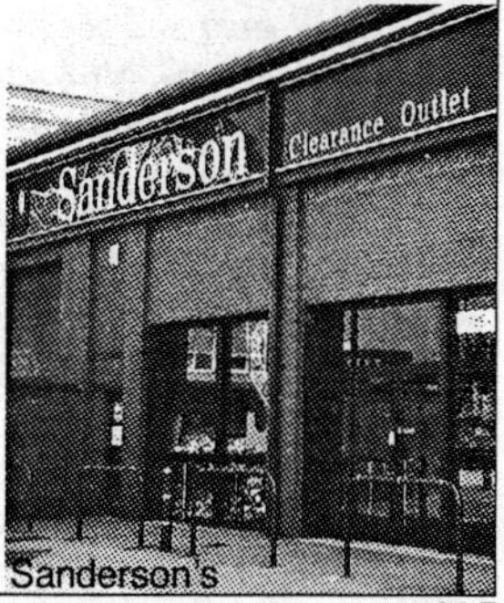

Sanderson's

36 Colne Lancs

see map on previous page

Empress Mills (1927)

Hollin Hall Sewing Centre, Hollin Hall Mill BB8 8SS
(01282) 863181

Huge range of threads for all sewing techniques and crafts manufactured on site. Haberdashery, embroidery and quilting supplies, fabric paints etc. Exclusive textile giftware.

'Contact us for a calendar of workshops for beginners and advanced sewing enthusiasts. Regular exhibitions held.'

This company has moved to Trawden, a village south-east of Colne.

Arriving in Colne from Lancashire (via M65) or Yorkshire (via A56 or A6068): follow 'Trawden B6250' signs. Follow road through Trawden village until you reach a fork (St Mary's Church straight ahead). Bear left (signposted Hollin Hall). Go along Lane House Lane until you see the Sewing Centre on your left.

From Colne town centre: follow signs to Keighley. Immediately after large roundabout, go right for Trawden B6250. Follow road through Trawden village, fork left in front of St Mary's Church and look for the Sewing Centre on your left.

Open: Mon–Fri 9–5; Sat and Sun 10–4.
Closed: Christmas Eve–4 Jan.
Cards: Access, Visa.
Cars: Own car-park. Ample space for cars and coaches.
Toilets: Beautiful toilets here.
Wheelchairs: Easy access to large mill shop; lift to workshop.
Teas: Café/restaurant for freshly prepared food.
Groups: To shop welcome any time. Demonstrations and workshops by arrangement.
Transport: Colne–Trawden bus.
Mail order: Yes. Mail Order Fact Pack also full of helpful hints. Advice from friendly staff always available. Fax (01282) 870935 for details. No seconds by mail order.
Catalogue: Free.

37 Colne Lancs

see map on previous page

Gardeners' Choice Mill Shop (LBS Group)

Standroyd Mill, Cotton Tree BB8 7BW
(01282) 873341

'A–Z' range of horticultural supplies and gardening sundries. Also many houseware, picnic ware and patio ware items. Outdoor clothing. Large florist sundries section to cover all enthusiasts' needs. Wide range of unusual gifts for all occasions.

'Amazing offers available on horticultural supplies from the largest horticultural polythene products distributors in the country.'

At the south-east end of town.

From town centre, M65 and A561: aim for Keighley. Cross major roundabout; immediately after this, turn right on to B6250 to Trawden.*

From Keighley coming west on A6068: turn left on to B6250 just before big roundabout at beginning of Colne.*

****Go down to bottom of hill: you shortly see LBS on left. Go through gates; shop porch entrance is at rear of building.***

Open: Mon–Fri 9–5; Sat 9–4; Sun and Bank Holidays 10–4.
Closed: Christmas and New Year's Days.
Cards: MasterCard, Switch, Visa.
Cars: Own car-park.
Toilets: Yes, and for disabled.
Wheelchairs: No steps, easy access.
Teas: In town.
Groups: Groups and coaches welcome by appointment with Mrs Hill.
Transport: Bus no. 21 Colne/Trawden.
Mail order: Yes. No seconds by post.
Catalogue: £1.

 see map on previous page

Hartleys Barley Mill Shop (& Mail Order)

Regent House, Whitewalls Industrial Estate BB8 8LJ
(01282) 868587 Fax (01282) 870679

Large selection of quality silks, dress, curtain and sheeting fabrics; bedding (sheets, quilts, bedspreads, pillows), towels. Other textile bargains. Curtain-making service (don't forget your measurements). Wadding, patchwork squares, craft-work fabrics, remnants.

'An Aladdin's cave. Most fabrics and special offers way below high street prices. Savings galore, come and explore. Company established 35 years.'

Off the A56, between Nelson and Colne.

From Colne on A56: go south-west for Nelson, under railway bridge, follow signs to Whitewalls Industrial Estate.*

From Nelson: take A56 for Colne; go left at sign to Whitewalls Industrial Estate.*

From M65: follow signs to Whitewalls Industrial Estate.*

****Pass Asda on left then shop is 300 yds on right.***

Open: Mon–Fri 9.30–4.30; Sat 9.30–12.30.
Closed: Bank Holidays; Christmas–New Year (please phone to check).
Cards: MasterCard, Visa.
Cars: Huge car-park outside.
Toilets: Ask if desperate.
Wheelchairs: No steps; large shop, one level.
Teas: Nearby pub for lunch.
Groups: No mill tours. Coaches by appointment.
Transport: On main Nelson–Colne bus route, 3 minutes' walk from Asda bus stop.
Mail order: Yes.
Catalogue: Send five 2nd-class stamps for free mail-order catalogue and free samples – please mention this book. 95%+ are perfects. If imperfect or any doubt, customers are advised accordingly.

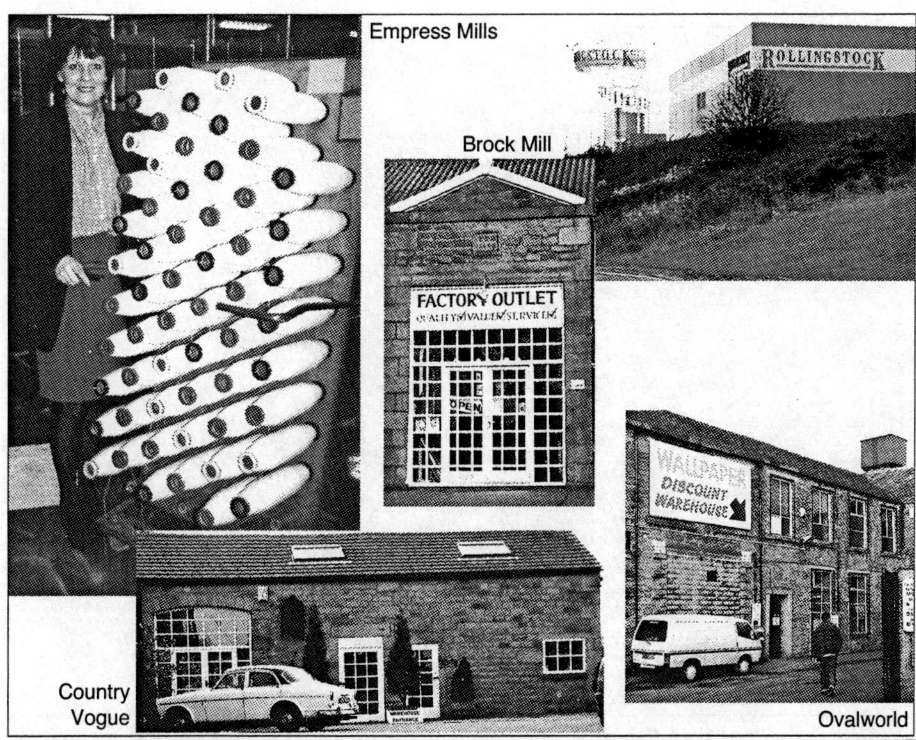

Empress Mills

Brock Mill

Country Vogue

Ovalworld

Hughes Lighting

Mochdre Business Park LL28 5HA
(01492) 547789

As well as manufacturing table lamps and lampshades (from your own choice of materials/trim should you wish), company stocks a comprehensive range of light fittings and ancillaries for most indoor and outdoor applications.

'You will find our prices very competitive and if you cannot see what you want on display, please ask.'

See our display advertisement opposite

South-west of Colwyn Bay off the A547.

From the A55 west bound (North Wales Expressway): exit on to A470 (Betws-y-coed and Llandudno); take first left at sliproad roundabout on to A547 for Mochdre.*

From A55 east bound: exit on to A470 (Betws-y-coed and Llandudno); take fourth left at sliproad roundabout on to A547 for Mochdre.*

****Proceed for just over one mile until you see 30mph signs. On entering 30mph zone immediately turn left: shop straight ahead.***

Open: Mon–Sat 10–4.
Closed: Bank Holidays.
Cards: Access, Switch, Visa.
Cars: Car-park outside shop.
Toilets: Ask if desperate.
Wheelchairs: Ground floor shop; no steps.
Teas: Plenty of places in nearby Conwy, Rhos-on-Sea and Llandudno.
Groups: No factory tours.
Transport: No reliable bus service.
Mail order: No.

Liverpool in the 1870s

See our entry opposite

40 Congleton Cheshire

Florakits

Worrall Street CW12 1DT
(01260) 271371

Ready-made and made-to-order silk and dried flower arrangements. Full range of artists supplies, materials for parchment craft, stencilling, candlemaking, silk and glass painting, découpage, baskets, ribbons, glass, pottery, picture frames.

'Silk flowers and foliage from 20p. Dried flowers from 99p per bunch (commercial size bunch). Ribbon from 2p per yard. (All plus VAT.)'

On north-east side of Congleton, ¼ mile from town centre.

From Macclesfield/Buxton/Leek on A54: as you reach Congleton, pass BFL petrol then large St Stephen's church on right, and Berisford Ribbons on left; take first right, Foundry Bank (where road bends sharp left). Park at bottom of hill, walk right.

From other directions: aim for A54 Buxton/Macclesfield. Get on to the dual-carriage Mountbatten Way on the north side of town. At traffic lights near Safeway, exit north into Worrall Street opposite towards leisure centre. Pass leisure centre on left. Continue to company on right.

Open: Mon–Sat 8–5 (late night Thur to 8); Sun 9–12.
Closed: Christmas & Boxing Days; some Bank Holidays, please phone to check.
Cards: All major cards except Amex.
Cars: Own car-park.
Toilets: Yes, but difficult for disabled.
Wheelchairs: No steps to shop but stairs leading to upper floor.
Teas: Hot drinks machine in shop, café 200 yds, several wine bars & cafés in walking distance.
Groups: Shopping groups welcome but please phone in advance. Tours of factory by arrangement.
Transport: Congleton train station ½ mile, bus station 300 yds.
Mail order: No.

41 Congleton Cheshire

R H Lowe

The Roldane Mills, Mill Green CW12 1JO
(01260) 277911

Wide range of children's wear, ladies' and men's fashions; lingerie and nightwear; leisurewear; footwear; luggage and leather goods. Homeware including towels and bedding. Chainstore ends of lines and seconds.

'Great reductions from original chainstore prices.'

On north side of Congleton, ¼ mile from town centre.

From Congleton centre: go towards A34 on A54 signposted 'Nantwich and M6'; cross cast-iron bridge over river, then turn sharp right (sign to Congleton Park).*

Via A34: at traffic lights go towards town. Go down Rood Hill for 200 yds: Mill Green leads off left immediately before cast-iron bridge over river (look for magnificent copper beech tree).*

***Company drive is 20 yds on right: shop at back.**

Open: Mon–Sat 9.30–4.30; Sun 12–4.30; Bank Holidays 9.30–4.30.
Closed: Christmas, Boxing and New Year's Days.
Cards: Switch, Visa.
Cars: In road or car-park.
Toilets: Yes.
Wheelchairs: Easy access; ramp to huge ground floor shop.
Changing rooms: Yes, six.
Teas: In town. Good café for light lunches 100 yds up road.
Groups: Parties of shoppers welcome – please telephone in advance.
Transport: Easy walk from town centre.
Mail order: No.

42 Congleton Cheshire

Victoria Lighting / The Clothes Peg

Victoria Mill, Foundry Bank CW12 1DT
(01260) 281071 & 297593

This mill encompasses several shops including:
Victoria Lighting (01260) 281071 – Traditional and pleated lampshades (all sizes) in plain and patterned fabrics, silks, flounced etc from UK's largest lampshade manufacturer; ceramic and wood lamp bases, chandeliers, wall lights etc. Hand make to order. *'Seconds about half price.'*
The Clothes Peg (01260) 297593 – Ladies' and men's wear, light outerwear clothing. *'Famous named merchandise at best value prices coupled with high fashion branded merchandise offering superb value.'*

'Enjoy shopping in a recently refurbished Victorian Mill.'

On north-east side of Congleton, ¼ mile from town centre.

From Macclesfield/Buxton/Leek on A54: as you reach Congleton, pass BFL petrol then large stone St Stephen's church on right, and Berisford Ribbons on left; take first right (where road bends sharp left). Mill is few yards down steep hill on right.

From all other directions: aim out of town on A54 Buxton/ Macclesfield. From the roundabout continue 100 yds then bear left down steep hill where main road goes right. Mill is on right.

Open: Mon–Sat 9–5.
Closed: Christmas and Boxing Days; Bank Holidays.
Cards: All major credit and debit cards accepted.
Cars: Ample space outside shop or by leisure centre.
Toilets: Yes.
Wheelchairs: Six steps into mill.
Changing rooms: Yes.
Teas: Café in mill.
Groups: Welcome, but phone to book first.
Transport: 10 minutes' walk from the town centre.
Mail order: No.

43 Darwen Lancs

Silk Mill Shop

Anchor Mill, Moss Fold Road SK14 1LU
(01254) 873333

Bridal and evening dress fabrics in a range of fibres, by the metre. Bridal patterns, bridal trimmings and suitable sewing threads. Tie fabric fents by the metre. Range of ties, bows, cummerbunds, shirts and waistcoats.

'Our speciality is manufacturing jacquard bridal fabrics (50") and jacquard tie fabrics (25"), both of which have a wide range of craft uses. Fabric is £5 to £25 per metre. Most items are perfects, with a few seconds and fents.'

At the north end of Darwen, just off the A666.

Coming north on the A666 from Darwen: pass The Anchor on the right. After 300 yds, go left (opposite the off-licence) into Mossfold Road. The company is 50 yds on the left.

Coming south on A666 from Blackburn: go under the new motorway, pass Moss Bridge Post Office on right then take second right, Mossfold Road. The company is 50 yds on the left.

Open: Mon–Fri 10–5; Sat 10.30–4.
Closed: Christmas–New Year. Please phone for other bank holiday closures.
Cards: MasterCard.
Cars: Car-park in mill yard.
Toilets: No.
Wheelchairs: Four steps to small shop. Please phone ahead to ensure someone available to help.
Changing rooms: No.
Teas: The Anchor pub, about ½ mile up the road, for lunch.
Transport: Any bus on the main Blackburn–Darwen route. Bus stop about 100 m from shop.
Mail order: No.

44 Denbigh Denbighshire

Wetherall

Diamond Buildings, Love Lane LL16 3LF
(01745) 815592

Please phone first

Top quality ladies' wear, especially reversible garments in pure wool: long coats, short jackets, rainwear, suits, capes, waistcoats. Sizes 8–28. Selection of jumpers, dresses and blouses. Co-ordinated accessories such as berets, travel rugs.

'Will gladly make garments to your own size, including mail order. Significant price reductions – all items at factory prices.'

Easy to find in a one-way street which leads off the main road through town.

From Ruthin on A525 or St Asaph on A525: follow signs to town centre. Go uphill to centre of town, passing library/museum on left. Go over pedestrian lights. Go round Halifax Building Society on left into Highgate, which becomes Love Lane.*

From the west on the A543: go into Denbigh and uphill. Pass The Plough pub on the left then go right opposite Woolworths into Highgate, which becomes Love Lane.*

***Shop is 50 yds on right.**

Open: Mon–Sat 9–5. Bank Holidays.
Closed: Christmas–New Year.
Cards: Access, Visa.
Cars: In street nearby; local car-parks.
Toilets: Yes.
Wheelchairs: Access into medium sized ground floor shop.
Changing rooms: Yes.
Teas: Several places in town.
Groups: Shopping groups welcome with prior phone call.
Transport: Any bus to Denbigh.
Mail order: Yes. All first class; no seconds by post.
Catalogue: Free if you write or phone.

45 Ellesmere Port Cheshire

Cheshire Oaks Designer Outlet Village

Cheshire Oaks, Kinsey Road L65 9JJ
(0151) 357 3633

Over 120 individual stores selling top brand names like *Donna Karan, Paul Costelloe, Viyella, Nike, Timberland* and *Levi.* Women's, men's and children's fashions, casualwear, sportswear, footwear, glassware and electrical goods.

'Discounts of 30% or more off retail prices.'

See our display advertisement inside back cover

Easy to find, 6 miles north of Chester city centre and a short distance south of Ellesmere Port.

From M53 exit 10: follow signs to Cheshire Oaks. This huge new development is next to Sainsbury's, with the entrance on the roundabout.

From Runcorn/Liverpool direction on the M56, follows signs to North Wales (this brings you to M53 exit 10), then as above.

Open: Mon–Sat 10–6 (Thur late night to 8); Sun & Bank Holidays 11–5.
Closed: Christmas Day.
Cards: All shops accept major credit cards.
Cars: Free parking for over 2000 cars and 20 coach bays.
Toilets: Yes.
Wheelchairs: Easy access to entire shopping area and free wheelchairs.
Changing rooms: In clothes shops.
Teas: Site includes Garfunkel's and McDonald's and coffee bar La Brioche Dorée.
Groups: Coach parties always welcome. For group bookings please phone for details.
Transport: Buses from Ellesmere Port and Chester.

46 Ellesmere Port Cheshire

Velmore

Thornton Road Industrial Estate L65 5ER
(0151) 357 1212

Ladies' wear: dresses, skirts, jackets, trousers, suits, shorts.

'Leading chainstore seconds only sold here, at factory shop prices.'

About ¾ mile east of town centre.

From M53 exit 9: go south into town centre along Station Road; go over railway bridge; go left at traffic lights for stadium. Keep following signs to stadium.*

From Council Offices in town centre: go east along Stanney Lane (B5132); take fourth left (Wolverham Road). Go towards motorway until you can turn right into Thornton Road.*

****Turn left into Telford Road between Evason's and Wolverham Social Club. Shop is the fourth unit on the right.***

Open: Tues–Thur 10.30–3; Fri 10.30–2; Sat 9–1.
Closed: Monday; Bank Holidays; Christmas–New Year.
Cards: Access, Switch, Visa.
Cars: In streets outside factory.
Toilets: In town.
Wheelchairs: One step to large shop.
Changing rooms: No.
Teas: In town.
Groups: Welcome to shop but must telephone first.
Transport: Local buses; Ellesmere Port train station.

See our entries F49, F59, F89, F96, G18, H27, H30, H32, H46, H62, H95, H100, H106, J106

47 Failsworth Gr Manchester

Pifco Salton Carmen Russell Hobbs Tower Mountain Breeze

Princess Street M35 0HS
(0161) 681 8321

Small electrical goods – hairdryers, tongs, electric kettles, irons, toasters; kitchen appliances; Christmas tree lights; torches; cookware; travel items; air cleaning products.

'Most of our goods are at factory prices.'

On the A62 Manchester–Oldham road.

From Oldham going south on A62: keep straight on this road. Go through Hollinwood. Pass the ornate red brick library on left and look for the huge Pifco tower on left. The shop is on a corner site on left, facing Save petrol on right.

From Manchester: take A62 east for Oldham; go over traffic lights where A663 (Broadway) goes off left. Shop is on right, facing Save petrol on left.

From M62 exit 20: follow signs to Oldham (A627M); continue down A627M on to A663. Turn left on to A62. Stay on A62 for ¼ mile. After traffic lights and just before Save petrol on left, look for huge Pifco Tower (set back) and shop in street on right.

Open: Mon, Wed–Fri 9–5.30; Sat 9–1.
Closed: Tuesday; Bank Holidays; Christmas–New Year.
Cards: Access, Visa.
Cars: Car-park behind shop.
Toilets: Ask if desperate.
Wheelchairs: No steps; easy access.
Teas: In Failsworth.
Groups: No tours, but pre-booked groups of shoppers welcome.
Transport: Three minutes' walk from Failsworth train station. Oldham–Manchester buses stop nearby.
Mail order: No.

Fleetwood

With the recent decimation of the British fishing fleet, it is refreshing to find that one can buy fish and shellfish from the quayside in Fleetwood. This town developed after 1836 when it was established as a railway/ship transfer port for Scotland and Ireland. It became a staging post to the Isle of Man. The building of Fleetwood bankrupted Sir Peter Hesketh-Fleetwood, its initiator, and his dream was never fully realised. Some of the layout devised by his architect Decimus Burton has survived, however, and at the north end you can stay in the wonderful curved hotel looking across the bay. Before the day of the car, Fleetwood was popular for holidays and day trips; you can still enjoy the tram ride from Blackpool to Fleetwood (via Cleveleys) which is the northern end of the line. Today Fleetwood has lost its former glory, but does have a new factory shop centre which – open to the elements, hence somewhat windy – attracts many shoppers, especially at weekends.

In the old Custom House is the Fleetwood Museum with displays on deep sea fishing and inshore fishing (for prawns, cockles, mussels, etc) related to Fleetwood. Several trawlers are on display. Other galleries illustrate the naval patrol services etc.

Fleetwood lighthouse

Fleetwood Museum, Queens Terrace (01253) 876621 Easter–October, afternoons, some mornings.

48 Fleetwood Lancs

Briggs & Shoe Mines

Freeport Shopping Village SK14 1LU
(01253) 773355

Regular clearance and sub-standard footwear for all the family. Self-selection with expert help and advice available. Small range of clothing and accessories.

'Family footwear by famous makers at greatly reduced prices.'

See our display advertisement on p. 651

Easy to find in the outlet centre at the 'top right of the Fleetwood peninsula', adjacent to the marina.

Going north on the A585: follow brown signs then signs for Fleetwood town centre. At the roundabout with Kwik Save on right, go right then follow signs into this shopping complex behind Kwik Save.

Coming north from Cleveleys on the coast road (A587): once you get to Fleetwood probably best to follow the main road round town then turn off at the roundabout by Kwik Save. Then follow signs into the shopping complex behind Kwik Save.

This conspicuous shop is at far end, facing on to the marina.

Open: Seven days 10–6 (Thur & Fri late nights to 8)
Closed: Christmas and Boxing Days.
Cards: Access, Amex, Connect, Switch, Visa.
Cars: Extensive free car-park for cars and coaches.
Toilets: Yes.
Wheelchairs: Easy access.
Teas: Restaurant for meals and light refreshments, snack facilities, ice-cream parlour.
Groups: Groups welcome, please contact manager to book. £2 reduction per member of a coach party on purchase.
Transport: Public transport from Blackpool to Fleetwood.
Mail order: Gladly supply items in stock if customer knows size, fitting and style. Ask for shop manager.

49 Fleetwood Lancs

Wynsors World of Shoes

Dock Street FY7 6JW
(01253) 779871

Ladies' fashion and comfort shoes in leather and synthetic. Girls' fashion shoes in leather and synthetic. All types of men's, boys', ladies', girls' and kids' shoes. Also handbags, sportsbags and accessories.

'Massive range of branded footwear from own factory and all over the world. Stock changes daily. Mainly perfects, some seconds. Prices from £1.99 to £100. Special lines at lowest prices in the country.'

See our display advertisement on previous page

Easy to find at the 'top right of the Fleetwood peninsula'.

Going north on the A585: signs for Fleetwood town centre. At the roundabout with Kwik Save on right, go straight.*

If you come north from Cleveleys on the coast road (A587): once you get to Fleetwood probably best to follow the main road loop round the north of the headland. At the roundabout with Kwik Save, go left into Dock Street.*

****Shop is 400 yds on right.***

Open: Mon, Tues, Wed, Sat 9–5.30; Thur, Fri 9–8; Sun 10–4. Bank Holidays 10–4.
Closed: Easter Sunday; Christmas, Boxing and New Year's Days.
Cards: Access, Style, Switch, Visa.
Cars: Own large car-park.
Toilets: Nearest 200 yds.
Wheelchairs: Easy access, but assistance given if required.
Teas: Own drinks machine; cafés, fish & chip shops, pub – all within 200 yds.
Groups: Shopping groups welcome. Prior phone call appreciated.
Transport: Bus and tram stops at Pier Head, 100 yds.
Mail order: No.

50 Garstang Lancs

Brock Mill Factory Outlet

119 Garstang Road, Claughton-on-Brock PR3 0PJ
(01995) 640778

Now closed

Men's, ladies' and children's classic wool and cotton jumpers, cardigans, shirts, plus co-ordinated mix 'n' match skirts, sweatshirts, trousers, shirts and jackets. Also a large range of wax, fleece and anorak style jackets.

'Up to 50% off normal retail prices.'

Just off the A6, south of Garstang.

From Garstang centre: go south on B6430 for Preston. This clearly marked shop is on the left, about 300 yds after village sign 'Claughton-on-Brock'.

From the north: stay on the A6 (Garstang bypass). Go through Catterall, then take second left after Claughton-on-Brock sign. Go left at end: pass timber yard then continue 200 yds to clearly marked shop on right.

From Preston going north on A6: go right at sign to Garstang B6430 – continue until you see this clearly marked shop on right.

Open: Tues–Sun 10–5. (including Bank Holidays).
Closed: Monday; Christmas and Boxing Days.
Cards: Access, Delta, Switch, Visa.
Cars: Large car-park in front.
Toilets: In Garstang nearby.
Wheelchairs: Shop upstairs.
Changing rooms: Yes.
Teas: In Garstang nearby.
Groups: All welcome.
Transport: Any bus to Garstang; stop in front of shop.
Mail order: No.

51 Garstang Lancs

Country Vogue

Garstang Road, Claughton-on-Brock PR3 0PH
(01995) 640622

Quality upmarket ladies' clothing: cashmere & wool jackets and coats, blazers, trousers, skirts, dresses, knitwear, shoes and handbags. Country clothing and children's wear.

'Reductions of 30–50% on all our stock. Perfects and overmakes. "Classics For Less" range gives excellent value.'

Just off the A6, south of Garstang.

From Garstang centre: go south on B6430 for Preston. This clearly marked shop is on the right, about 300 yds after village sign 'Claughton-on-Brock'.

From the north: stay on the A6 (Garstang bypass). Go through Catterall, then take second left after Claughton-on-Brock sign. Go left at end: pass timber yard on right then continue 200 yds to clearly marked shop on left.

From Preston going north on A6: go right at sign to Garstang B6430 – continue until you see this clearly marked shop on the left opposite the Brockholes Arms pub.

Open: Seven days 10–5; Bank Holidays.
Closed: Christmas–New Year period.
Cards: Connect, MasterCard, Switch, Visa.
Cars: Own forecourt.
Toilets: Yes.
Wheelchairs: One step to ground floor, stairs to upstairs showroom.
Changing rooms: Yes.
Teas: Tea shops and pubs in Garstang.
Groups: Shopping groups welcome, please phone first.
Transport: Buses from Lancaster, Blackpool and Preston stop outside the Brockholes Arms pub.
Mail order: Any products posted on request.
Catalogue: Yes.

52 Glossop Derbys

Abris Outdoor Clothing

3 Wren's Nest, High Street West SK13 8EX
(01457) 863966 Fax (01457) 854712

Manufacturers of specialist high quality clothing for hill walking and backpacking; breathable waterproof jackets, overtrousers, fleece jackets, polycotton walking trousers and shorts, microfibre trousers and shorts.

'Reps' samples, ends of lines, last year's colours and factory specials all at reduced prices.'

On western end of town behind Telegraph petrol station.

From Manchester on A57: turn left immediately after Telegraph petrol station and before Tesco. Drive in through petrol station exit. Shop is clearly signed.

From town centre and the east on A57: go over traffic lights which lead to Tesco on right and immediately turn right as if you went on to Telegraph forecourt, but proceed around the right and follow signs to shop.

Open: Tues–Thur 10–5; Fri, Sat 10–3.
Closed: Monday; usual Christmas/New Year holidays. Phone about Bank Holidays.
Cards: Eurocard, MasterCard, Switch, Visa.
Cars: Communal car-park.
Toilets: Ask if desperate.
Wheelchairs: One small step into shop, help available if necessary.
Changing rooms: Yes.
Teas: Numerous local cafés.
Groups: Phone ahead.
Transport: 15 minutes' walk from Glossop train station. Buses to Glossop from Manchester and Sheffield.
Mail order: Yes.
Catalogue: Free.

53 Glossop Derbys

Glossop Factory Shop

Howard Town Mills SK13 8LR
(01457) 866039

Well known branded names ladies' clothing including lingerie, knitwear, skirts, blouses, nightwear etc. Also wide range of branded names men's clothing – shirts, leisurewear, trousers, knitwear.

'New goods on a weekly basis. The majority of items are perfects sold at discount prices. Special offer of 10% discount for senior citizens every Thursday.'

Close to centre of town, easy to find.

From traffic lights in town centre: take road (Victoria Street) for Chapel-en-le-Frith. This large mill on left is 100 yds from these traffic lights almost opposite post office and across road from market. Go left into car-park: shop is immediately on right.

Open: Mon–Sat 9–5.15. Bank Holidays 9–5.15.
Closed: Christmas and New Year's Days.
Cards: Access, Switch, Visa.
Cars: Free car-park outside shop.
Toilets: In town.
Wheelchairs: Easy access, no steps to large ground floor shop.
Changing rooms: Yes.
Teas: Several places in town.
Groups: Coach groups very welcome to shop any time.
Transport: Easy walk from town centre. Trains to Glossop. Buses from Manchester stop in Henry Street, 2 minutes' walk from shop.

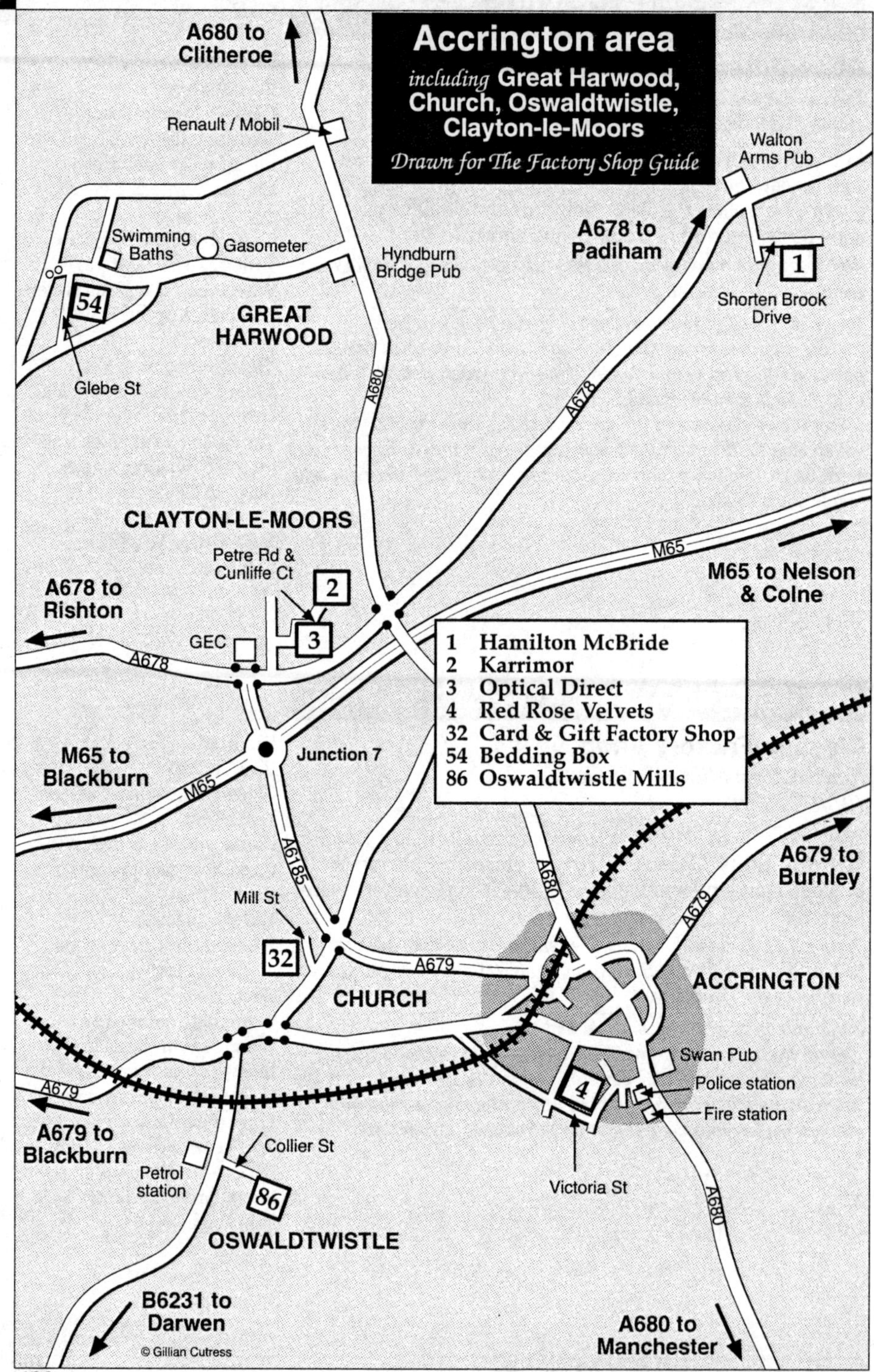

Accrington area
including Great Harwood, Church, Oswaldtwistle, Clayton-le-Moors
Drawn for The Factory Shop Guide
A680 to Clitheroe
Renault / Mobil
Walton Arms Pub
Swimming Baths
Gasometer
Hyndburn Bridge Pub
A678 to Padiham
1
Shorten Brook Drive
54
GREAT HARWOOD
Glebe St
A680
A678
CLAYTON-LE-MOORS
Petre Rd & Cunliffe Ct
2
3
A678 to Rishton
GEC
A678
M65
M65 to Nelson & Colne
1 Hamilton McBride
2 Karrimor
3 Optical Direct
4 Red Rose Velvets
32 Card & Gift Factory Shop
54 Bedding Box
86 Oswaldtwistle Mills
Junction 7
M65 to Blackburn
M65
A6185
A680
A679 to Burnley
A679
Mill St
32
A679
CHURCH
ACCRINGTON
Swan Pub
Police station
Fire station
4
A679
A679 to Blackburn
Collier St
Petrol station
86
Victoria St
A680
OSWALDTWISTLE
B6231 to Darwen
A680 to Manchester
© Gillian Cutress

F

See our entry below

54 Great Harwood Lancs *see map opposite*

The Bedding Box

Harwood House, Glebe Street BB6 7AF
(01254) 888338

Continental quilts, pillows, duvet covers, pillowcases; curtains made to measure; tie backs, lampshades, mattress covers. Also fabrics by the yard.

'Perfects and seconds on sale. Chainstore items at very reasonable prices. Seven-day make-up service for curtains.'

See our display advertisement above

In the centre of town.

From M65 exit 7: take A678 (A680) north for Clitheroe. At T-junction traffic lights, go right. At major junction traffic lights, go left on to A680. Follow sign left into Great Harwood. This road becomes Queen Street. Pass the large classical building (swimming baths) set back from road on right. Continue to Barclays bank on far left corner: turn left into Glebe Street in front of bank. Shop is on left.

From Accrington and Rishton: take B6535 north into Great Harwood. In town, turn right at two small roundabouts into Queen Street, then first right into Glebe Street: shop is on left.

Open: Mon–Fri 9–5; Sat 9.30–4.30. Sun 11–4.30.
Closed: Christmas, Boxing and New Year's Days.
Cards: Mastercard, Switch, Visa.
Cars: Private car-park at the rear of building.
Toilets: Yes.
Wheelchairs: Ramp leading into the shop.
Teas: Tea shops and pubs in town.
Transport: Any bus to town.
Mail order: Yes.
Catalogue: Free.

55 Haslingden Lancs

Winfields

Hazel Mill, Blackburn Road BB4 5DB
(01706) 227916

A vast range of discounted footwear and clothing for men, women and children, including sports footwear and clothing, accessories and ex-catalogue goods. Manufacturers and retailers of slippers.

'Perfects, seconds and clearance lines in a wide variety of quality goods at value-for-money prices; many items are at half the usual high street price.'

About a mile north of Haslingden, on the A680.

From the roundabout where the A680 and A56 (extension of the M66 from Manchester) join: turn south towards Haslingden. After a few yards, Winfield's entrance is clearly signposted on left.

From Haslingden: take A680 north of Accrington. As you leave town, look for Winfields clearly marked on your right. The drive entrance is further along on right, just before roundabout.

Open: Mon–Fri 10–5.30 (Thur late to 8); Sat 9–5.30; Sun 11–5.
Closed: Easter Sunday; Christmas Day.
Cards: MasterCard, Switch, Visa.
Cars: Free parking for 400 cars & coaches. Parking for disabled.
Toilets: Yes, with baby changing facilities and for disabled.
Wheelchairs: Easy access to all departments, limited number of chairs provided.
Changing rooms: Yes.
Teas: 174 seater restaurant with high chair facilities and a children's menu. Also takeaway service and Pick 'N' Mix.
Groups: No need to book, although preferred (telephone Teresa or Mandy).
Transport: Bus nos. 4 (Accrington–Bacup), 464 (Accrington–Rochdale), 701 (Clitheroe–Manchester).

56 Haydock Merseyside

CBS

Rollingstock Factory Outlet Centre, Andover Road WA11 9FA
(01942) 402520

Now closed

Huge range of mail order surplus items: clothing, fashions, household, footwear, hardware, furniture, electrical, toys and gifts. Separate unit for furniture; another unit for leathers and labels.

'Large savings from original catalogue prices. Firsts & seconds.'

Inside Rollingstock Factory Outlet Centre, one mile west of M6 exit 23 and just north of the A580.

From M6 exit 23: take A580 for Liverpool. Continue for about a mile. Pass the large blue Rollingstock building on the right. After the Travelodge/Elf petrol, take slip road left for Haydock Ind. Est. Follow the road round (go under the A580), keeping left, and pass Sainsbury's Distribution Centre on the right. Go sharp left at the sign to this centre.

From Liverpool on A580: aim for M6; after left turn-off for Haydock Industrial Estate, pass Gulf petrol. Look for Rollingstock on left. Take next left. At the roundabout, go straight. Take first left into Rollingstock.

Open: Mon–Sat 10–6 (Thur till 8); Sun 11–5. Bank Holidays.
Closed: Easter Sunday; Christmas Day.
Cards: Delta, MasterCard, Switch, Visa.
Cars: 600 parking spaces in complex.
Toilets: Yes, including for the disabled.
Wheelchairs: Easy access to huge shop (and to the shopping centre).
Changing rooms: Four changing rooms.
Teas: On-site diner for coffee, lunch and tea.
Groups: Large groups welcome any time.
Transport: Buses from St Helen's stop 10 minutes' walk away; buses from Ashton stop 3 minutes' walk away.
Mail order: No.

Port Sunlight

'Sunlight', as in soap, must be one of the world's best known cleansing products. The name of this product gave rise to the remarkable village of Port Sunlight on the Wirral peninsula.

For a fascinating account of Port Sunlight, see 'Sunlighters: The Story of a Village' by Sue Sellers. This book, and other information, are available from the Port Sunlight Heritage Centre, 95 Greendale Road (0151) 644 6466.

Readers tempted to stay on the Liverpool side of the Mersey should make the effort to go through the tunnel to Birkenhead then south to explore this garden village with its wide streets, green verges and intriguing architecture. Leave half an hour or so to wander round the village and to call in at the heritage centre. Its famous Lady Lever Gallery, with Lord Lever's own eclectic and remarkable collections of art, furniture, ceramics, ethnic items etc will take you as long as you wish to browse (good tea shop too).

Purpose designed for the factory workers by Lord Leverhulme when he needed a new site to expand manufacturing in the late 1880s, this garden town was built on uninspiring marshy land. It remains substantially the same as in 1925 when its founder died. The factory, hidden behind a decorative wall, is at the end of the village.

The village reflected Lord Lever's philosophy 'A child that knows nothing of God's earth, of green fields, of sparkling brooks ... but knows only the drunkenness prevalent in the hideous slums it is forced to live in ... cannot be benefited by education. Such children grow up depraved and become a danger to the state, wealth destroyers instead of wealth producers ... Work people [in Port Sunlight] will learn more about the science of life than they can in a back slum and they will learn there is more in life than the mere going to and returning from work and looking forward to Saturday night to draw their wages.'

"One day in seven the house was filled with the odour of nauseating suds. Odd scraps served for meals, the housewife looked weary and worried, the inmates fretful ... it was wash day! Sunlight Soap has changed all that! You merely rub the soap well on the clothes, roll them up for a couple of hours and rinse them out."

The Illustrated London News, June 1902

He encouraged games, recreations and organisations promoting art, literature, science and music. He financed the church, technical institute and art gallery and introduced schemes to promote the welfare, education and pleasure of his workers. The gymnasium and open-air swimming pool (warm water came from the glycerine works) demonstrated his concern for workers' health – as did the building of the cottage hospital. His most instantly noticeable achievement was the extraordinary range of architecture: from half-timbered to mock Gothic, with gables, twisted chimneys, ornate mouldings, gargoyles and a host of features from different styles. Nearly 30 architects were employed, including Edward Lutyens when he was only 21.

Rent for a three bedroom house in 1909 was 5/9d – below the usual rate. Houses were let to employees, widows and pensioners until recently. Now they are on the open market.

57 Haydock Lancs

Now closed

Rollingstock Factory Outlet Centre

Haydock Retail Park, North Florida Road WA11 9UB
(01942) 402500

Huge range of brand name merchandise: men's, ladies' and children's wear. Footwear, sportswear, leatherwear, ski and outdoor wear. Soft furnishings, electrical goods, furniture, tableware, crystal, greetings cards, luggage, travel goods, toys and books.

'One of the largest discount outlet shopping centres in the north-west with huge savings against the original prices. 25 stores with over 50,000 sq ft of selling space. Goods are mainly catalogue surplus, ends of ranges, discontinued lines, overmakes and slight impefects.'

One mile west of M6 exit 23, just off the A580.

From M6 exit 23: take A580 for Liverpool. Continue for about a mile. Pass large blue Rollingstock building on right. After the Travelodge/Elf petrol, take slip road left for Haydock Ind. Est. Follow the road round (go under the A580), keeping left and pass Sainsbury's on the right. Go sharp left at the sign to this centre.

From Liverpool on A580: aim for M6; after left turn-off for Haydock Industrial Estate, pass Gulf petrol. Look for Rollingstock on left. Take next left. At the roundabout, go straight. Take first left into Rollingstock.

Open: Mon–Sat 10–6; (late night Thur till 8); Sun and Bank Holidays11–5. Special Christmas times.
Closed: Phone to check Christmas.
Cards: All shops take credit and debit cards.
Cars: Free for 600 car spaces.
Toilets: Yes, including for the disabled. Baby changing facilities.
Wheelchairs: Easy access to large ground floor and all shops; lift to diner.
Teas: 250-seat diner.
Groups: Coach parties always welcome. Please phone first.
Transport: Buses from St Helen's stop 10 minutes' walk away; buses from Ashton stop 3 minutes' walk away.

58 Hazel Grove Gr Manchester

Mood Factory Shopping

36/38 London Road SK12 1LF
(0161) 456 9876/482 4544

Ladies' and gents' clothing: blouses, jackets, skirts, trousers, dresses, knitwear, coats.

'Most of our stock is current season's lines, with about 80% manufactured by ourselves. Prices on average are 30% lower than high street. Fashion shows can be arranged for local groups and clubs.'

In the centre of Hazel Grove.

Coming north from Macclesfield via A523(T) and Sheffield via A6015: these roads become the A6 which goes straight through Hazel Grove. Pass the Co-op Superstore on left. This shop, in a detached two-storey building on left, is just before traffic lights. Go sharp left before shop to car-park, or go left at next traffic lights to rear entrance (signposted).

Coming south on A6 from Stockport: pass Stepping Hill Hospital then go right at traffic lights for Co-op Superstore. Take first left: after 100 yds go left into rear car-park by sign.

Open: Mon–Sat 9.30–5.30; Sun 11–4.
Closed: Christmas and New Year's Days. Bank Holidays.
Cards: Access, Connect, Style, Switch, Visa.
Cars: Own car-park at rear (entrance at front left or from Co-op feeder road at rear).
Toilets: Yes.
Wheelchairs: Easy access to large shop.
Changing rooms: Yes.
Teas: Nearby Co-op superstore and local cafés.
Groups: Shopping groups welcome.
Transport: Hazel Grove train station; bus no. 192 stops outside shop.
Mail order: No.

59 Hazel Grove Gr Manchester

Wynsors World of Shoes

56/57 London Road SK12 1LF
(0161) 456 2632

Men's, ladies' and children's fashion shoes in both leather and synthetic fabrics.

'Massive range of branded footwear from own factory and all over world. Stock changes daily; monthly offers at lowest prices in the country. Shoes from £1 to £100.'

See our display advertisement on p. 423

In the centre of Hazel Grove.

Coming south from Stockport via A6: look for Shopping Giant and Gospel Church on right; go left into Angel Street to park; Kwik Save car-park behind well marked shop.

Coming north from Macclesfield via A523(T) and Sheffield via A6015: these roads become the A6. Look for Shopping Giant and Gospel Church on left: turn right into Angel Street to park in the Kwik Save car-park behind the well marked shop.

Open: Mon–Wed 9–5.30; Thur, Fri 9–8; Sat 9–5.30; Sun and Bank Holidays 10–4.
Closed: Christmas and New Year's Days.
Cards: MasterCard, Style, Visa.
Cars: In Kwik Save car-park adjacent.
Toilets: Opposite.
Wheelchairs: Easy access to large shop. No steps.
Teas: In Co-op Shopping Giant.
Groups: Shopping groups welcome
Transport: Hazel Grove train station; bus no. 192 stops outside shop.
Mail order: No.

60 Helmshore Lancs

Musbury Fabrics

Park Mill, Holcombe Road BB4 4NQ
(01706) 221318

Co-ordinated household textiles, duvet covers, valances, sheets etc from most top household names. Huge selection of towels. Always remnants and sale lines.

'Firsts, seconds and ends of runs at keen factory prices. Special emphasis on top brands in furnishing fabrics and sheeting. Sewing service for quality furnishings and special size bedding. Everything a mill shop should be!'

Six miles south of Accrington and eight miles north of Bury.

Shop is in the red mill opposite Helmshore Textile Museum which is well signposted.

Follow brown road signs to this museum from the area of Haslingden and Rawtenstall. Take care because signs on A56 are at actual exits, with no advance warning.

Open: Seven days a week 9.30–4.30, including Bank Holidays.
Closed: Christmas, Boxing and New Year's Days.
Cards: MasterCard, Switch, Visa.
Cars: In road, or public car park opposite.
Toilets: Yes.
Wheelchairs: Easy access, no steps, huge shop.
Teas: Helmshore Textile Museum.
Groups: No mill tours but shopping groups welcome: prior phone call appreciated. Charity events by arrangement.
Transport: Helmshore Circular buses from Rawtenstall and Haslingden stop outside.
Mail order: Household textiles only.
Catalogue: Free.

61 Horwich Gr Manchester

Halbro Sportswear

Lee Lane BL6 7JG
(01204) 696476

Huge range of rugby jerseys, including replicas of UK and overseas teams. Own ranges in large selection of colours and styles and in different thickness acrylics and cottons. Can supply sets for teams and schools, and embroider logos, motifs etc.

'Most items are slight imperfects at greatly reduced prices at about £5–£15.'

At the west end of Horwich on the B6226.

From Chorley coming south via A673: as you reach Horwich, fork left at the roundabout (in front of red brick Crown Hotel) for town centre, B6226. After 100 yds go right at Original Bay Horse pub, Hampson Street: shop at rear left.

From Bolton coming north on A673, and M6 exit 6: go through Horwich. At far end, pass Halbro on right. At roundabout, go right for town centre, B6226. After 100 yds go right at Original Bay Horse pub, Hampson Street: shop at rear left.

Open: Tues, Thur, Fri 10–5; Sat 10–2.
Closed: Monday, Wednesday; Easter; Christmas–New Year period; Bank Holidays. Please phone to check as dates vary.
Cards: MasterCard, Visa.
Cars: Unrestricted within the locality.
Toilets: Ask if desperate.
Wheelchairs: Large ground floor shop.
Changing rooms: Yes.
Teas: Lots of local cafés, pubs and restaurants.
Groups: By arrangement.
Transport: Any bus to Horwich.
Mail order: No.

62 Horwich Gr Manchester

The Towel Mill Shop

Victoria Mill, Chorley New Road BL6 6ER
(01204) 695611

Wide range of towels of all colours and sizes. Bathrobes, skirts, blouses, knitwear, tops and men's shirts.

'Near-perfects and current stock manufactured by this company sold here at discounted prices.'

A short way south of the town centre.

From Horwich town centre/Chorley: keep going south-east on A673 through town centre towards Bolton. Go over hump bridge, pass Texaco station on left, take second small road to right (in front of mill).*

From M61 exit 6: go north. This road meets A673 from Bolton at large roundabout. Continue north-west on A673 towards Horwich for about ½ mile; 200 yds after Elf petrol station take small turning left (past mill).*

****Shop 70 yds on left.***

Open: Mon–Fri 9–4.30 (Thur late night to 7); Sat 10–3.
Closed: Christmas–New Year; some Bank Holidays so please phone to check.
Cards: MasterCard, Switch, Visa.
Cars: Large car-park.
Toilets: No.
Wheelchairs: One step up then five steps down.
Changing rooms: Yes.
Teas: In Horwich.
Groups: Shopping groups welcome with prior phone call.
Transport: Local buses.
Mail order: No.

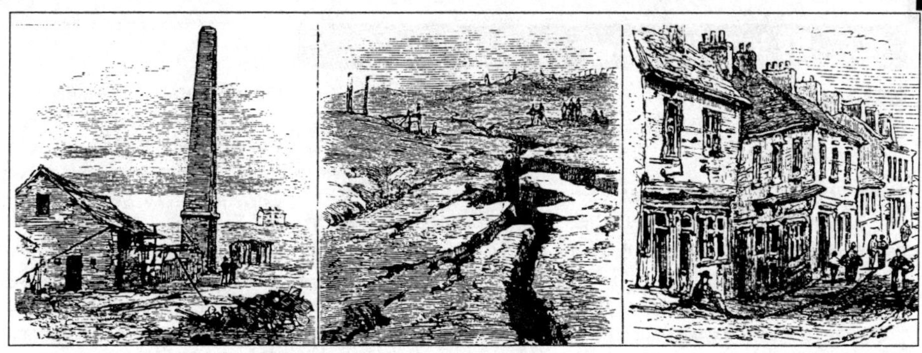

Cheshire Salt Mines

An intriguing picture of a large two-storey building lying almost on its side forms part of the collection of The Salt Museum in Northwich. Another study shows a boat stranded in mud after a canal had burst its banks. Both the house and the canal were victims of subsidence resulting from uncontrolled pumping out of brine beneath the town. It is interesting to note, however, that local building practices – as in earthquake torn countries – made allowance for this potential hazard and that many buildings were constructed in timber so they could be jacked up, or even moved, if afflicted by subsidence. *[What a boon that would have been over our last 10 years of drought.*]

The largest salt deposits in Britain occur deep beneath the Cheshire countryside, especially in the Nantwich, Middlewich, Northwich and Winsford region, and have given rise to the extensive alkali and chlorine-based industries in the area – producing bleach, soap, glass, dyes and PVC, to name a few products.

There were many small family-run saltworks. Underground conditions were dry, with an even temperature – in contrast to coal mines no noxious fumes or explosive gases pervaded the air so tallow candles could be used to illuminate the mines. The companies gradually merged, and today just one rock salt mine remains, in Winsford. Blasting dislodges many hundreds of tonnes of salt at a time and the Salt Union Co. produces over two million tons of rock salt each year. Most is used for road clearance in winter.

The world's first salt museum opened in Northwich in 1889.
Its successor is The Salt Museum, 162 London Road, Northwich CW9 8AB (01606 41331). Open all year, Tuesday–Sunday (longer in August).

63 Hyde Gr Manchester

Ashtons

Newton Street SK14 4NP
(0161) 368 1961

Towels: hand and bath sheet sizes, plain colours. *Ashtons'* and embroidered and embellished *Christy* brands. Bed linen. Baby products – nappies, cot quilts and bumpers, cot duvet covers and matching curtains. Sheets and blankets.

In the huge mill just north of M67 exit 3.

Coming east from Manchester on M67: turn left at top of slip road; coming west, go right at end of the slip road. Turn right at second traffic lights and go straight uphill: mill is on right.*

Coming south from Ashton/Oldham on Dukinfield Road (A627): go left at roundabout into Newton Street (B6170), go 100 yds uphill.*

****Shop is opposite stone church.***

Open: Mon–Wed 9–4.30; Thurs 9–6.30; Fri 9–12.30.
Closed: Bank Holidays; Easter; Fri & Mon first week in October; Christmas–New Year.
Cards: None.
Cars: In side roads or company parking facility (but not, please, within the site).
Toilets: Please ask if desperate.
Wheelchairs: Easy access to small shop. No steps.
Teas: In Hyde.
Tours: Unfortunately no factory tours any more.
Transport: Local trains and buses.
Mail order: No.

64 Hyde Cheshire

The Mill Fabric Shop

Cartwright Street, Newton SK14 4QU
(0161) 367 9337

Printed cotton and satin furnishing fabrics, curtain fabrics including plain dyed satin and chintz; curtain linings; ready-made and made-to-measure curtains. Scatter cushions, tablecloths, tea cosies, oven gloves, aprons and placemats.

'Perfects and seconds, most at half price or less, eg slightly imperfect fabric from £1.50 per yd.'

See our display advertisement opposite

On the north-east side of Hyde.

From Manchester/the west: take M67 exit 3 for Dukinfield/ Hyde town centre. Turn left for Dukinfield at traffic lights at top of slip road then right at next traffic lights into Clarendon Road.*

From Hyde centre: follow signs for Newton; continue as below when on Clarendon Road.*

Going east on M67: exit for Hyde, go over motorway; at traffic lights go right into Clarendon Road.*

****Keep straight, through next traffic lights into Victoria Street. After ½ mile fork left, Cartwright Street. Shop entrance is on right side opposite Park House, before junction with Talbot Road.***

Open: Mon 10–5; Tues–Sat 9–5; Sun 10–4; Most Bank Holidays (phone to check).
Closed: Easter Sunday; Christmas–New Year.
Cards: Access, Switch, Visa.
Cars: In nearby streets.
Toilets: No.
Wheelchairs: Ten steps to shop; entry through warehouse by arrangement with shop manager.
Teas: Pub on the corner.
Groups: Shopping groups by prior arrangement with Mr P Roberts.
Transport: Hyde Central train station. Bus nos. 209 and 346 from bus station.
Mail order: No.

See our entry opposite

65 Hyde Gr Manchester

Providence Reproductions

Providence Mill, Alexandra Street SK14 1DX
(0161) 366 6184

Vast selection of period style furniture for bedrooms, dining and living rooms in mahogany, yew and oak finishes. Specialists in solid mahogany dining tables and chairs.

'Special service to stain/polish pieces to your own requirements in own workshop on premises. Repair and re-polishing services.'

West side of Hyde, south of M67 exit 3, near Hyde Central station.

Via A627 from south and A57 from east: go into town centre. From Market Street (main shopping area) in central Hyde go left into small Croft Street at sign to this company. At far end, go left into Alexandra Street.

Via M67 from east: exit for Hyde and turn right over motorway.*

From Manchester: exit for Hyde and turn left.*

****Go round long left bend, go through two traffic lights and over motorway again. At next lights go straight; by station turn left (Gt Norbury St).*****

Via A57 from Denton/Manchester: go right (sign to station) immediately before railway bridge into Gt Norbury Street.**

*****Take first right (Railway Street), go right (Croft Street) and left (Alexandra Street). Go right for huge red-brick mill. Entrance on left side.***

Open: Mon–Sat 9–5; Sun 10–4; Bank Holidays 10–4.
Closed: Christmas and Boxing Days.
Cards: Access, Visa.
Cars: In mill yard.
Toilets: Yes.
Wheelchairs: Huge shop on first floor up stone staircase. Lift (enquire at office).
Teas: In Hyde.
Transport: 10 minutes' walk from town centre.

66 Hyde Gr Manchester

Super Seconds

24 Reynold Street SK14 1LU
(0161) 368 3376

High quality men's and women's designer and high street chainstore wear.

'Enormous range of high street and designer fashions at least 25% off high street prices. Men's suits from £40, shirts from £12.99. Huge range of ladies' chainstore and designer coats. New stock. Perfects and seconds.'

See our display advertisement opposite

In the town centre at the side of the covered market. Next door but one to Iceland.

Reynold Street is a small one-way street leading into the main road, Market Street (A627). Best to park in public car-park or in street and walk.

Open: Mon–Sat 10–5 (closed Tues).
Closed: Tuesday; Bank Holidays; Christmas, Boxing and New Year's Days.
Cards: No.
Cars: Large car-park a minute away, facing Iceland.
Toilets: In shopping mall two minutes away.
Wheelchairs: Two steps into large shop. Help given to wheelchair users.
Changing rooms: Yes.
Teas: Plenty of places in shopping mall and locally.
Groups: Groups welcome but please phone in advance.
Transport: Five minutes' walk to bus station. Bus no. 330 Stockport–Hyde and Ashton-under-Lyne. Bus nos. 210 & 211 Hyde–Manchester.
Mail order: No.

67 Ingleton N Yorks

Daleswear Factory Shop

High Street LA6 3AD
(015242) 42373

High quality outdoor and leisurewear. Fleece jackets and pullovers, both lined and unlined, jumpers, pants, salopettes and accessories. Fleece jackets, pullovers, jumpers and pants for children. Extended *Polartec* range of fleeces. Extended waterproof range including more 2-layer and 3-layer *Porelle* (formerly *Aquatex)* jackets, also overtrousers and salopettes. *Kingsdale* caving oversuits and undersuits, *Gold Flash* tackle, *SRT* bags etc. Stockist of *Altberg Boots* at factory prices.

'Mostly firsts, competing in standard and design with market leaders, at much lower prices. Also prototypes, clearance, seconds and bargain lines.'

Ingleton Village is on the A65, 28 miles north-west of Skipton and 6 miles south-east of Kirkby Lonsdale.

Follow one-way system up through the village centre. The High Street is up from the square and the shop is next to the Wheatsheaf pub.

Factory shop may move to Laundry Lane at edge of village, with own car-park.

Open: Mon–Sat 9–5 (including Bank Holidays); Sun 9.30–5.
Closed: Christmas, Boxing and New Year's Days.
Cards: MasterCard, Switch, Visa.
Cars: Limited High Street parking; main parking at community centre.
Toilets: Ask if desperate.
Wheelchairs: Three steps; large shop.
Changing rooms: Yes.
Teas: In Ingleton.
Groups: Shopping groups welcome; group factory tours by arrangement.
Transport: None.
Mail order: Anything available in the shop can be bought by mail order.
Catalogue: Free. As we are continually working on new designs, our current catalogue does not always reflect our full range.

See our entry opposite

Kearsley Gr Manchester

Ebac

221 Manchester Road BL4 8QX
(01204) 707953

Range of domestic de-humidifiers, electrical appliances which remove excess moisture from the air and help prevent condensation. New and graded stock. Humidex 4, Homedry, 440, 660, 670, 870, 880 and Hi-Dri.

'Firsts and seconds. Prices from under £100. Various discounts on graded and end-of-line goods.'

Kearsley is north of M61 exits 2 and 3. Manchester Road is A666.

Going north on M61: take exit 2 for Bolton A666. Take first slip road (for Farnworth) then third exit, for Kearsley (crossing dual-carriageway you have just left). Go along A666 Bolton Road.*

Going south on M61: take exit 3 for Bolton A666. Take first slip road left (for Farnworth) then 3rd exit, for Kearsley (crossing dual-carriageway you have just left). Go along A666 Bolton Road.*

From Bolton: take A666 south. From this dual-carriageway, take slip road for Kearsley; go left at top on to A666 Bolton Road.*

****Ebac is 1½ miles on left.***

Late Entry

Open: *October–March* only. Thur 10–7; Fri 10–5; Sat 9–5.
Closed: *April–September*. Also Monday, Tuesday, Wednesday during rest of year.
Cards: Delta, MasterCard, Visa.
Cars: Opposite and in side street.
Toilets: Available if required.
Wheelchairs: Difficult; two steps.
Teas: Mineral water, coffee and tea available; sandwich shop next door.
Groups: Small shopping groups welcome.
Transport: Bus nos 22, 28, 8, 9 from Bolton or Manchester stop 200 yds away.
Mail order: Yes.

68 Lancaster Lancs

The Factory Shop Ltd.

Lancaster Leisure Park, Wyresdale Road LA1 3LB
(01524) 846079

Clothing and footwear for all the family. Toiletries, cosmetics, luggage and bags. Good range of branded bedding and towels. Housewares and kitchenware. Posters and toys. Fashion concessions department with famous brand names. *Cape Country* pine furniture exclusively produced for The Factory Shop.

'Deliveries of new stock every week to give an ever changing selection. Antique centre, animals, children's attractions and ride a train. Golf driving range and club house. Indoor children's play area. Site shops and restaurant areas free – other attractions charged individually.'

On the east side of town.

From the A6: go into town and follow signs to the Ashton Memorial; turn right when you see sign for 'Cattle Market'. Pass the abattoir and this leisure park is on the right.

From the M6: go into the city centre; from here follow signs to 'Ashton Memorial', pass it and take next left downhill.

Open: Mon–Sat 10–5; Sun 11–5.
Closed: Christmas and Boxing Days.
Cards: Eurocard, MasterCard, Switch, Visa.
Cars: Ample free car and coach parking.
Toilets: On the leisure site.
Wheelchairs: Good access into and around the shop.
Changing rooms: Yes.
Teas: Café and restaurant on leisure site.
Groups: Shopping groups welcome. For organiser/driver incentives please phone.
Transport: Bus no. 253 from Lancaster bus station.
Mail order: Home delivery service available for pine furniture.
Catalogue: Please telephone for free catalogue and price list.

69 Lancaster Lancs

Standfast

Caton Road LA1 3PB
No phone in shop.

Seconds in printed fabrics, including many well known designer names for curtains and upholstery (cottons, linens, chintz and sateens). Also sell small pieces suitable for cushions or patchwork.

Nearly 1 mile north of the town.

From Lancaster: follow signs to M6 (northbound). You go along A683 (Caton Road). Pass the clock-tower on left, then Standfast is 100 yds on left, with name clearly displayed.

From M6 exit 34: follow signs to Lancaster. Company is about a mile on right, after Shell petrol.

Please do NOT park inside main gate (hinders emergency access). Park in car-park across road.

Open: Mon–Fri 9.30–1; Sat 10–12.30.
Closed: Bank Holidays; Christmas–New Year.
Cards: None.
Cars: Special car-park across the road.
Toilets: Yes.
Wheelchairs: Five steps into shop. You can arrange to go in via the warehouse for easier access.
Teas: In Lancaster.
Groups: No mill tours.
Transport: None.
Mail order: No.

See our entry below

70 Leyland Lancs

Holmes For Foam

Heald House Road PR5 2JB
(01772) 422377

Foam cut to any size and shape. Also cushions and cushion covers in quality materials, with matching curtains if required, for boats, caravans and horse boxes. Upholstery fabrics, ready-made curtains, roller blinds, futons, chairs, suites, cushions, pillows and ironing board covers.

'Most of the moquette, dralon and flat weave fabrics are woven in Yorkshire or Lancashire. Our prices are for full covers, with zip fastenings. No stretch covers. We supply buttons in same material. Send us your own cushions and backs and we will recover and button them.'

See our display advertisement above

Off the B5248 south of town centre and next to M6.

From M6 exit 28: turn on to B5256 east for Chorley.*

From town centre: follow signs east to M6, M55 via B5256. Go under the motorway.*

****At first traffic lights turn right on to A49 for Wigan. At next crossing, go right on to B5248. Go over motorway: after 20 yds turn right. Shop is at the end of drive.***

Open: Mon–Thur 8.30–5; Fri–Sat 8.30–4.
Closed: Bank Holidays; Christmas–New Year period.
Cards: Mastercard, Visa.
Cars: Own car-park.
Toilets: Yes.
Wheelchairs: No steps, easy access into shop.
Teas: Plenty of places in nearby village or at Charnock Farm Garden Centre.
Groups: No.
Transport: Bus nos. 298 from Blackburn and 109 from Chorley stop 300 yds from shop; 2 miles from Leyland train station.
Mail order: Yes.
Catalogue: No.

Littleborough Gr Manchester

New England Design

Sladen Wood Mill, Todmorden Road OL15 9EW
(01706) 371343

Fabric three-piece suites made here; covers can be chosen from more than 100 pattern books, or can use customers' own fabric. Specialise in made-to-measure suites. Also stock leather suites, beds, wrought iron and brass bedsteads, dining suites, occasional furniture and pictures, mirrors and accessories (such as *Austin* sculptures), and modern candelabra and chandeliers.

'Our motto is furniture with a difference! Perfects at reduced price, also some seconds. Three-piece suites from £499 (leather from £1100); beds: single from £99, double from £299; dining suites from £299. "Bargains of the week", some at half price. Sales after Christmas and early July; occasional mid-season sales.'

North of Littleborough (which is about 3 miles north-east of Rochdale).

From Rochdale: take A58 north-east. Go through Littleborough then left on to A6033 for Todmorden. Company is 1½ miles on right, well posted with signs and large vertical flags.

From Burnley or Halifax: take A646 south to Todmorden. Continue south on A6033 towards Littleborough. Go through Walsden. Company is about 3 miles from Walsden on left, in old mill on main road, with signs and flags.

Late Entry

Open: Seven days: Mon–Sat 10–5 (Thur late till 8); Sun 11–4; Bank Holidays 10–5.
Closed: Christmas, Boxing and New Year's Days.
Cards: Major credit and debit cards. Credit facilities.
Cars: Large free car-park at side, or by main entrance.
Toilets: Yes.
Wheelchairs: Easy access; no steps to large ground floor showroom.
Teas: Tea rooms in Littleborough and Todmorden; fish & chip shops in vicinity.
Groups: Shopping groups welcome anytime without prior arrangement.
Transport: On main Halifax/Burnley and Rochdale bus route. Bus stop outside.
Mail order: For small range of the most popular suites at competitive prices.

71 Lytham Lancs

Fylde Footwear

Units A & B, Waterfront Marine, Dock Road FY8 5AQ
(01253) 730060

Fashion footwear for all the family. Branded names and well known high street shoes. Good selection of leather goods and handbags. Household goods including crockery, towels and bedding, all up to 75% off RRP.

'Some seconds available. Prices start from as little as £1 for toiletry bags.'

Customers will receive 10% off their purchases on production of this book.

In the industrial estate east of town centre.

From M55 exit 3: take A583, which becomes B5259, always following signs for Lytham. Go through Wrea Green. At roundabout, bear left for Lytham. Go over railway, at mini-roundabout go right. At traffic lights, go left into Dock Road.*

From Preston on A584: enter Lytham, go straight at roundabout (signposted B5259 to right) and turn left at first traffic lights.*

From town centre and Blackpool on A584: pass Lytham Hospital on left and at next traffic lights turn right (fish & chip shop on far right corner).*

***Continue to the end and shop is on left.**

Open: Mon–Fri 9.30–5; Sat 9–4; Sun 10–4.
Closed: Bank Holidays; Christmas–New Year (phone to check.)
Cards: Access, Switch, Visa.
Cars: Car-park to the side.
Toilets: Please ask if necessary.
Wheelchairs: One small step through double doors to medium sized shop.
Teas: Good range of eating places in Lytham.
Groups: Coaches welcome. Please book if visiting at the weekend.
Transport: Bus nos. 11, 11a and 22 from Blackpool and Lytham to the end of Dock Road, then 10-minute walk.
Mail order: Only on request.
Catalogue: No.

72 Macclesfield Cheshire see map next page

Designer Warehouse

Paradise Mill, Park Lane SK11 6TJ
(01625) 511169 Fax (0161) 449 7842

Ends of lines and samples, cancelled orders and overmakes of up-to-the-minute designer wear: coats, skirts, dresses, evening wear, blouses. Top designer labels from British, Italian, German, French, Danish and Finnish manufacturers.

'Clothing for that special occasion. At least 50% off normal retail prices. Sizes 8–XOS. Stock changes weekly.'

In the town centre, next to Paradise Mill Silk Museum which is well signed.

From Leek on A523: as you come into town, at traffic lights with the Sun Inn on left, go left; at next traffic lights, go straight. After the Register Office on left, go left into Park Lane.

From Stockport/Manchester via A523: at roundabout (Tesco on left) keep straight; follow new Silk Road; go right at lights, under railway lines, to station.*

From Buxton on A537: at traffic lights at bottom of hill, go straight under railway for station.*

****Pass station on your left; continue to traffic lights, go right. After the Register Office on left, go left into Park Lane. Shop is 150 yds on left.***

Open: Mon–Sat 9.30–5.30.
Closed: Bank Holidays; Christmas, Boxing and New Year's Days.
Cards: MasterCard, Switch, Visa.
Cars: In street.
Toilets: No.
Wheelchairs: One step, large ground floor shop.
Changing rooms: Yes.
Teas: Café 200 yds via walkway.
Groups: Groups welcome to shop if they arrange visit first.
Transport: 10 minutes' walk from train station; 5 minutes from bus station. Regular services from all routes.
Mail order: No.

73 Macclesfield Cheshire see map next page

The Fent Shop

Pickford Street Mill, Pickford Street SK11 6HY
No telephone in shop.

Huge range of haberdashery, crafts items and fabrics for dresses, clothing, curtains and upholstery. Some toys, sheeting and evening wear.

'Large range of rolls and remnants at vastly reduced prices.'

In the tangle of little streets in old town centre, facing and on downhill side of The Pickford Centre (Discount Giant) supermarket car-park.

From Stockport/Manchester via A523: at roundabout (Tesco on left) keep straight; follow new Silk Road; go right at lights, under railway lines, to station.*

From Buxton on A537: at traffic lights at bottom of hill, go straight under railway for station.*

****Pass station on your left; continue into Sunderland Street. Pass bus station and George & Dragon, both on right, then go right into Pickford Street. Shop immediately on left.***

From Leek on A523 or Congleton on A536: from traffic lights where these road converge at bottom of main road through town (Mill Street), aim for station. Pass the Jolly Sailor on left then go left (Pickford Street). Shop immediately on left.

Open: Mon, Tues, Thur 9.30–4.30; Wed 9.30–12.30; Fri 9.30–3.30; Sat 9–1.
Closed: Bank Holidays; Christmas, Boxing and New Year's Days.
Cards: None.
Cars: Public car-park 20 yds.
Toilets: In supermarket next door.
Wheelchairs: No steps. Easy access to ground floor show-rooms crammed with items.
Teas: In supermarket next door.
Groups: Shopping groups welcome.
Transport: Easy walk from bus and train stations.
Mail order: No.

74 Macclesfield Cheshire *see map opposite*

Room Service Interiors

38 Charlotte Street SK11 6JA
(01625) 613955

Curtain and upholstery fabrics by top British & international designers. Curtain trimmings. Interior design service, plus curtain make up and upholstery services.

'Ends of lines and seconds. Cut lengths at quarter of usual retail price, rolls at half usual price. A small company offering personal service.'

In tangle of little streets in old town centre, facing & on downhill side of The Pickford Centre (Discount Giant) supermarket car-park.

From Stockport/Manchester via A523: at roundabout (Tesco on left) keep straight; follow new Silk Road; go right at lights, under railway lines, to station.*

From Buxton on A537: at traffic lights at bottom of hill, go straight under railway for station.*

Pass station on your left; continue into Sunderland Street. Pass bus station and George & Dragon, both on right; go right after Animal World into Pickford Street.*

From Leek on A523/Congleton on A536: from lights where these roads converge at bottom of main road through town (Mill St), aim for station. Pass the Jolly Sailor on left, go left (Pickford St).**

****Go right into Charlotte Street. Shop 50 yds on right.**

Open: Mon, Tues 9.30–5; Wed 10–5; Thur–Sat 9–5.30.
Closed: Bank Holidays; Christmas, Boxing and New Year's Days.
Cards: Access, Visa.
Cars: Public car-park facing.
Toilets: In supermarket.
Wheelchairs: Access to ground floor showrooms; three small showrooms upstairs.
Teas: Good local cafés.
Groups: Not suitable for groups.
Transport: Easy walk from bus and train stations.
Mail order: No.

75 Macclesfield Cheshire *see map opposite*

A Shufflebotham & Son

8 Gunco Lane SK11 7JK
(01625) 423304

Exclusive designer seconds in furnishing and upholstery fabrics, and high class dress fabrics such as silk, wool challis and wool worsted. Some wool shawls and scarves.

Near south-eastern end of town.

From Leek on A523: turn right at first traffic lights for Sutton Langley (Byrons Lane).*

From town centre and all other directions: follow signs to Leek A523. Pass the Three Crowns pub (in a road fork on the left); turn left at the next traffic lights for Sutton Langley (Byrons Lane).*

***Go over railway bridge and take first left (opposite the Railway View pub). Go around the right hand bend and after 30 yds turn right through gate into yard.**

Open: Mon–Fri 9–5.30; Sat 10–1.
Closed: Bank Holidays & Christmas – please phone to check.
Cards: None.
Cars: Ample parking.
Toilets: Yes.
Wheelchairs: Easy access for wheelchair users and prams. No steps.
Teas: Arighi Bianchi coffee shop five minutes away.
Groups: Shopping groups welcome.
Transport: 10 minutes' walk from train station.
Mail order: We can post fabrics to customers if they know specific requirements.

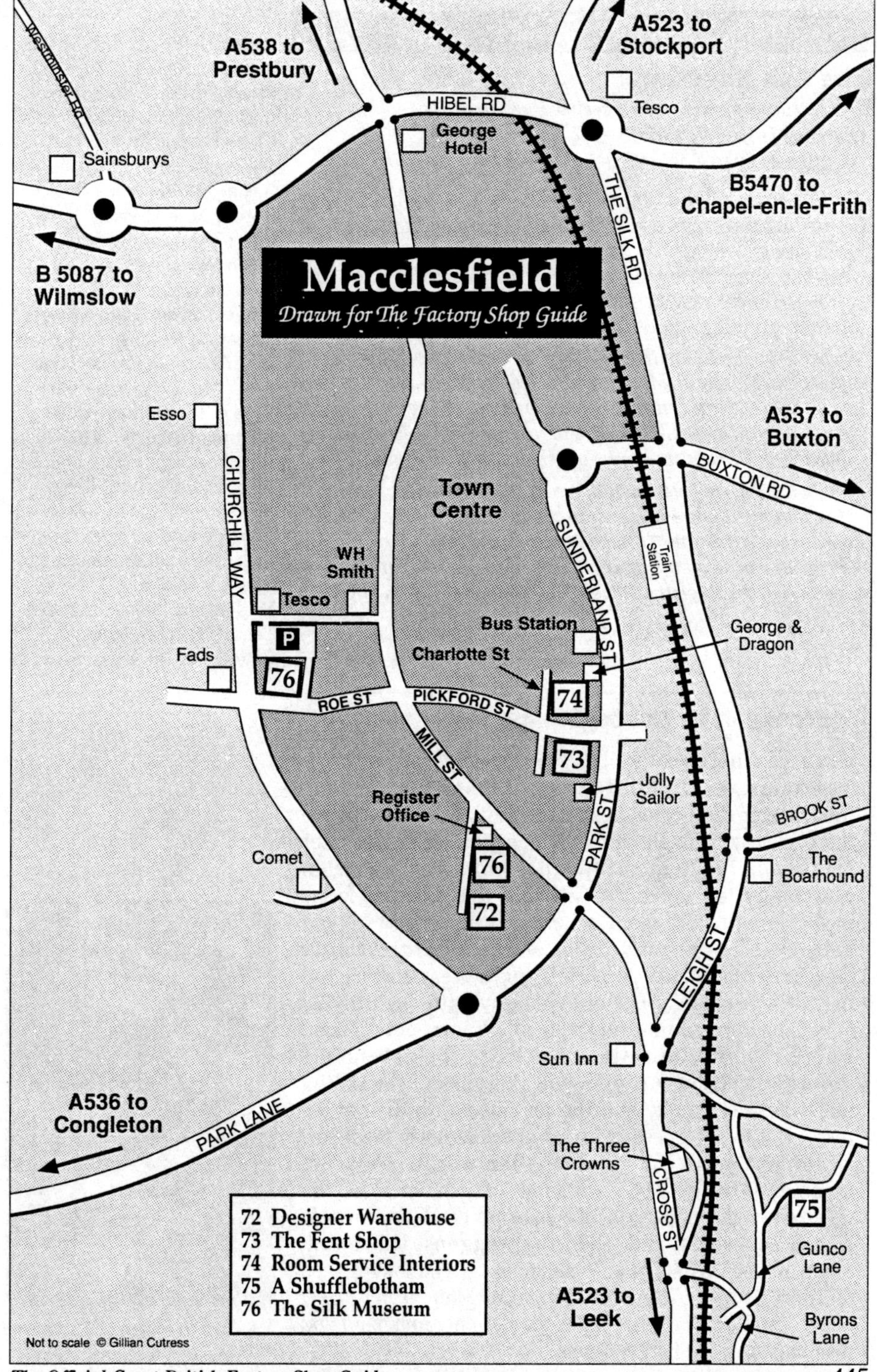
Macclesfield
Drawn for The Factory Shop Guide
A538 to Prestbury
A523 to Stockport
B5470 to Chapel-en-le-Frith
B 5087 to Wilmslow
A537 to Buxton
A536 to Congleton
A523 to Leek
HIBEL RD
THE SILK RD
CHURCHILL WAY
BUXTON RD
SUNDERLAND ST
ROE ST
PICKFORD ST
MILL ST
PARK ST
BROOK ST
LEIGH ST
PARK LANE
CROSS ST
Tesco
George Hotel
Sainsburys
Esso
Town Centre
WH Smith
Tesco
P
Fads
Bus Station
Charlotte St
George & Dragon
Train Station
Jolly Sailor
Register Office
Comet
The Boarhound
Sun Inn
The Three Crowns
Gunco Lane
Byrons Lane
72 Designer Warehouse
73 The Fent Shop
74 Room Service Interiors
75 A Shufflebotham
76 The Silk Museum
Not to scale © Gillian Cutress

76 Macclesfield Cheshire *map previous page*

The Silk Museum

The Heritage Centre, Roe Street & Paradise Mill, Old Park Lane SK11 6UT
(01625) 613210

The Silk Museum is on two sites, with displays in The Heritage Centre and the original working hand-looms in Paradise Mill. There are two shops (the larger is located in The Heritage Centre) selling silk by the yard, silk handkerchiefs, ties and scarves of both first and second qualities. In addition general giftwear, greetings cards, books and souvenirs.

'A visit to both sites, with exhibition on the history of the silk industry in Macclesfield, and working looms, gives an excellent insight into the silk industry which operated in the town for over 200 years and still survives on a much reduced scale. Joint tickets for both museums or single site tickets available.'

Both buildings, well signposted, are in the centre of town.

The Heritage Centre faces on to the central car-park, across from Tesco, WH Smith, TJ Hughes and Homestyle.

Paradise Mill is on the downhill side of town. Turn into Old Park Lane beside the Register Office. The mill is 100 yds on left.

Open: Heritage Centre: Mon–Sun 11–5; Bank Holidays 1–5. Paradise Mill: Tues–Sun 1–5 (including Bank Holidays)
Closed: Good Friday; Christmas Eve, Christmas, Boxing & New Year's Days.
Cards: Access, Visa.
Cars: Town car-parks and coach park close by.
Toilets: Yes.
Wheelchairs: Lift to 5th floor displays at Paradise Mill. Chair lift to displays at Heritage Centre.
Teas: Mulberry Tree Coffee Shop in The Heritage Centre.
Groups: Groups welcome; for party bookings, please phone in advance. Pre-booked light refreshments can be organised.
Transport: Both sites 10 mins' walk from train station; 5 mins from bus station.
Mail order: Phone the Heritage Centre for information.
Catalogue: No.

Stockport at the beginning of this century

Our favourite travel writer Mr Harper wrote in 1907, 'Stockport would probably resent being lumped with Manchester (and Manchester itself might object) but to the passerby, it is all one with the great city. The river Mersey here divides Stockport in Cheshire from Manchester in Lancashire: Cheshire of the cheese farms in the great fertile plain, where mild-eyed cows stand knee-deep in pastures [*what would Mr Harper have thought of Manchester Airport?*]; and a great manufacturing town is entirely out of sympathy with such idyllic scenes. There are no idylls in Stockport: only a road where the granite setts are greasy; the pavements thronged with busy people and the girls of the cotton mills; the sky smoky and the air filled with distracting noise. But to see a less crowded and less noisy Stockport would be a sorry thing, for it is the wealth-producing commerce of the place that makes it what it is, the times when the railway lorries cease to crash and rumble along the streets, and when the waggons, laden with mountainous heights of grey shirtings, are no longer seen on their way from the cotton mills to Manchester warehouses, will be troublous times for not only mill-hand and manufacturer, but for every one.'

A loom in action at The Silk Museum in Macclesfield

See our entry below

77 Manchester : Ancoats

Sanderson Clearance Outlet

2 Pollard Street M4 7DR
(0161) 272 8501

Huge range of seconds and remnants in *Sanderson* printed and plain furnishing fabrics from current and discontinued collections. Also carpets, wallcoverings, bedlinen, ready-made curtains, and extensive range of gift items.

See our display advertisement above

Conspicuous shop in central Manchester, ¼ mile north-east of Piccadilly Station. Pollard Street is the A662, off Great Ancoats Street (A665).

From Piccadilly Station: with station entrance on your right, go along Store or Ducie Street. Follow road round to traffic lights. Go right into Great Ancoats Street at T-junction.*

Coming south into Manchester on A62 (Oldham Road): go towards city centre. At traffic lights, go left into Great Ancoats Street (A665).*

****Pass new retail park on left. At second traffic lights go left (Pollard Street, A662 to Ashton): shop on right.***

From Ashton and places east: take A662. Shop on left just before traffic lights in city centre.

Open: Tues, Wed, Fri 10–6; Thur 10–7.30; Sat 10–5.30; Sun 10–4.
Closed: Monday; Bank Holidays.
Cards: Access, Visa.
Cars: Large car-park in front of shop.
Toilets: Yes, and for disabled.
Wheelchairs: Easy access to vast, spacious shop, no steps.
Teas: City centre.
Groups: Groups of shoppers welcome but please pre-book.
Transport: Bus nos. 216 & 217; trains to central Manchester.
Mail order: Yes.
Catalogue: No.

Market Street, Manchester, showing Lewis' good house of business, where the public are provided with the very best articles, all at fair prices.
Illustrated London News, February 1883

78 Middleton Gr Manchester

Color Blind

Unit 6, Middleton Central Industrial Estate, Oldham Road M24 1AS (0161) 643 3800

Blinds in large range of styles, colours, textures including washable. Vertical, roller, pleated; conservatory roof blinds; Venetian blinds in four slat widths. Ideal for DIY or commercial fitters.

'Blinds also made to order. Fitting at nominal price within 30 miles. Only charge for width and we believe our blinds are the cheapest in England. Vertical blinds £7 per ft width, any length drop (eg patio door 6ft wide x 7ft £42 + vat); roller blinds trim and fit or made-to-measure £3 per ft width.'

Easy to find in small industrial estate along road from huge Warwick mill on Oldham Road, A669, through Middleton.

Going north on Manchester New Road (A664): at first roundabout go right; double back at next roundabout. Pass huge mill on left.*

Coming west from Oldham on A669: at first roundabout go straight; pass huge mill on left.*

Via Manchester Old Road (A576) going east: keep straight; pass Arndale Centre and bus station on left. At roundabout go straight; at next roundabout double back. Pass huge mill on left.*

****Go left (by road sign), just before next roundabout, into estate.***

Open: Mon, Tues, Wed, Fri 10–5; Sat 10–4.
Closed: Thursday; Bank Holidays and Christmas period.
Cards: Access, Switch, Visa.
Cars: Outside shop.
Toilets: Nearest at bus station.
Wheelchairs: One step.
Teas: Café in Arndale Centre.
Groups: Up to 8 people – phone Mr Donnelly prior to visit.
Transport: Bus nos. 17, 163, 59 from Manchester.
Mail order: Phone first to clarify samples and swatches required – many colourways and fabric samples for all types of blinds. Usual price + carriage. No seconds, fully guaranteed.
Catalogue: No.

79 Morecambe Lancs

Briggs & Shoe Mines

205 Marine Road West LA3 1TE (01524) 419293

Wide selection of branded clearance and substandard shoes at reduced prices for all the family. A section of the store is dedicated to first quality international brands, with services and fitting from trained staff.

'Sub-standard and clearance goods directly from K factories in Kendal. About 60 other famous brand products at substandard and clearance prices.'

See our display advertisement on p. 651

On the promenade between Victoria Pavillion and old railway station (now Tourist Information Centre), and next to Woolworths.

From Lancaster: follow signs to central area or town centre. Pass Morrisons and turn right at the coast. The shop is about 200 yds on right.

Open: *Summer:* Mon–Sat 10–8; Sun 10.30–4.30. *Winter:* Mon–Sat 10–5.30; Sun 10.30–4.30.
Closed: Christmas Day.
Cards: Access, Amex, Connect, Switch, Visa,
Cars: Festival Market car-park next to shop.
Toilets: Yes.
Wheelchairs: Full access.
Teas: Many cafés and bars along the promenade.
Groups: Coach parties welcome: please book with the manager beforehand, mentioning this guide. Organised parties get £2 voucher per person towards purchases.
Transport: Morecambe train station 5 minutes' walk.
Mail order: Pleased to supply by mail order items in stock if customers know size, fitting and style. Ask for manager.

80 Mostyn Clwyd

Abakhan Fabrics

Coast Road, Llanerch-y-Mor CH8 9DX
(01745) 560312

One of the largest selections of fabrics, needlecrafts and knitting yarns in the North-West, housed in a carefully restored 100 ft main building on a 10-acre site.

'This former lead smelting shed was winner of the Prince of Wales Award 1988. Fabric and wool shops, crafts and gifts, children's play area, coffee shop and free parking. Company does not make anything but specialises in clearing lines, job lots etc. Special offer fabric rolls from 5p per m. Also in Liverpool, Manchester, Birkenhead.'

Large, conspicuous converted industrial building on the coast side of Coast Road (A548), 5 miles north of Flint and 2 miles south of Mostyn.

Open: Mon–Sat 9–5.15 (Thur 9–8); Sun 9–4.30; Bank Holidays.
Closed: Easter Sunday; Christmas Eve; Christmas, Boxing and New Year's Days.
Cards: Access, Connect, Switch, Visa.
Cars: Own large car-park.
Toilets: Yes and for disabled.
Wheelchairs: Ramp to ground floor. Access to 60% of public areas.
Teas: Own coffee shop for snacks, light meals. Children's play area.
Groups: Pre-booked coach parties welcome, discounts given.
Transport: Trains to Flint and Rhyl stations. Bus nos. A8, A18, X1 to Llanerch-y-Mor (Mostyn).
Mail order: Only specific orders or repeat items sent.

Nelson Lancs

Late Entry

Pendle Village Mill

Hollin Bank, Brierfield BB9 5NF
(01282) 605004

Wide range of quality clothes; first class footwear. Household textiles, three-piece suites, carpets, Oriental rugs and other floor coverings. Wool Shoppe, Pine Shoppe, Ice Cream Parlour, Sweetie Shoppe etc.

'Excellent value, variety and very very friendly service all under one roof. We also have a picnic area in canal-side setting. Pay us a visit soon.'

Brierfield is between Nelson and Burnley. This mill is close to M65 exit 12.

From M65 exit 12: aim for Brierfield/Nelson A682. Cross the Leeds & Liverpool Canal. At the next roundabout, follow road to rear of B&Q. Pendle Village Mill is to your right.

From Brierfield: take Colne Road A682 north for Nelson. At roundabout go left for M65.*

From Nelson: take Manchester Road A682 south for Burnley. At roundabout go right for Lomeshay Industrial Estate/M65.*

****Go along Churchill Way. At roundabout, follow road to rear of B&Q. Pendle Village Mill is to your right.***

Open: Mon–Sat 9–5.30; Sun 10–4. Bank Holidays 10–4.
Closed: Easter Sunday; Christmas Day.
Cards: MasterCard, Switch, Visa.
Cars: Large car-park; coaches welcome.
Toilets: Yes.
Wheelchairs: Easy access; ramp to large main retail area.
Changing rooms: Yes.
Teas: Meals & snacks on site.
Groups: Shopping groups welcome: please phone first.
Transport: 5–10 minutes' walk from town centre.
Mail order: No.

81 Nelson Lancs

The Card & Gift Factory Shop

Reedyford Mill, Westfield Road, off Scotland Road BB9 7YM
(01282) 605500 x 7506

Wide range of greetings cards, toys, gifts, wrapping paper, Christmas decorations, bedside lamps, tie racks, fruit juice holders and many household items etc. Stock constantly changing.

'All items are excess orders or returned items from catalogues sold off at very low prices.'

Special offer: 10% discount to anyone who shows this book!

Open: Mon–Fri 9.30–4.45.
Closed: Bank Holidays; Christmas–New Year.
Cards: No.
Cars: In street.
Toilets: In town.
Wheelchairs: Seven steps down inside.
Teas: In Nelson.
Transport: Bus no. 10.
Mail order: No.

Next to M65 exit 13.

From M65 exit 13: go towards Nelson; go right into small street as soon as you come off roundabout on Nelson side of motorway.*

From Nelson: take A682 for Gisburn. Go over humped canal bridge, go left just before roundabout.*

****Shop is clearly visible straight ahead on corner.***

82 Colne Lancs

Proud Fabrics (moved from Nelson)

Empress Mill, Empress Street BB8 9HV
(01282) 866575

Huge selection of high-class dress, bridal, curtaining and craft fabrics from leading companies (including *Liberty's, Rose & Hubble* etc). Special bridal section. Curtains and soft furnishings made to requirements.

'Very low prices. Perfects and seconds from £2 per m. January and July sales. Discount section all year with prices up to 50% off rrp.'

Open: Mon–Fri 9–5; Sat 9–4.
Closed: Bank Holidays; Xmas, Boxing and New Year's Days.
Cards: Delta, MasterCard, Switch, Visa.
Cars: Free car-park behind library close to mill.
Toilets: Yes.
Wheelchairs: Easy access to shop with ramp.
Teas: Cafés in town.
Groups: Shopping groups welcome, including coach parties. Phone Susan Proud to book if more than 10 people. Carpeted play area for children.
Transport: Near bus station, one mile from railway.
Mail order: Yes.
Catalogue: Send two 1st-class stamps. Catalogues issued spring/summer, autumn/winter, plus sale catalogue/bargains throughout year.

NB Shop has moved from Nelson to Colne town centre.

From Lancashire (via M65) or Yorkshire (via A56 or A6068): follow 'Town centre' signs. The town centre is a one-way system – keep going clockwise till you see the market hall on right and library on left. Go left after library into Dockray Street. Take third left, King Street (first and second left turns take you into car-parks). Empress Mill is 100 yds on right, on corner.

83 Norden near Rochdale Gr Manchester

Alexander Drew and Sons

Rainshore Mill Shop OL12 7TK
(01706) 42671

Screen-printed cotton and satin furnishing fabrics for curtains etc. Fire-retardant upholstery fabrics; cushions. Make-up service available.

'Always special prices on some goods. Note Monday and Wednesday late-night shopping.'

Going north-west from Rochdale on A680: in Norden turn right immediately after The White Lion into private road.*

Coming south-east on A680 towards Rochdale: go through double-bend at start of Norden. Slow down as you see tall square chimney, turn left in front of The White Lion.*

****Continue for 350 yds, passing row of terraced houses; take right fork to mill gates. Inside gates, turn left, go up hill. Clearly signposted.***

Open: Mon, Wed 1–8; Tues, Thur 1–4; Fri closed; Sat, Sun 10–4.
Closed: Friday. Please phone to check June and Sept holidays.
Cards: Access, Visa.
Cars: In mill yard.
Toilets: No.
Wheelchairs: One small step.
Teas: In The White Lion.
Groups: No tours of the works but groups welcome to shop.
Transport: Buses stop at end of the lane, ¼ mile from shop.
Mail order: No.

84 Norden near Rochdale Gr Manchester

Cudworth of Norden

Baitings Mill OL12 7TQ
(01706) 41771 (phone & fax)

Extensive range of top quality and value outdoor and leisurewear, mainly for adults. Exclusive quality moleskin and corduroy garments – trousers, breeches, shirts. Bodywarmers, jackets, children's wax-jackets. New ranges, eg lightweight walking trousers, fleeces and breathable waterproofs.

'Most stock perfect; some seconds. Orders taken by phone. Visit us at many country shows in April–September.'

Going north-west from Rochdale on A680: in Norden, go right immediately after The White Lion into private road.

Coming south-east on A680 towards Rochdale: go through double-bend at beginning of Norden. Slow down as you see tall square chimney, go left in front of The White Lion into private road. Shop is immediately behind pub.

Open: Sat 10.30–1.30 Usually in shop Mon–Fri too, but phone to confirm. Happy to open other times, including Sunday, by arrangement.
Closed: Saturday in *July* and *August*.
Cards: MasterCard, Visa.
Cars: Outside shop.
Toilets: Yes.
Wheelchairs: Access to small shop not really possible.
Changing rooms: Yes.
Teas: Cafés in vicinity. Pub in front of shop.
Groups: No mill tours. Shopping groups welcome if they phone first.
Transport: Local buses stop just across main road.
Mail order: Yes.
Catalogue: Free. Write or phone for catalogue, mention this guide.

85 Oldham Gr Manchester

Baird Outerwear Brands

Victor Street/Albert Street, Hollinwood OL8 3QN
(0161) 681 2060

Ladies' and men's rainwear and casual wear. Brand names include: *Dannimac, Telemac, Baracuta, Cloud Nine* and *Thomas Marshall.*

'Perfects, seconds, ends of lines.'

Two miles south-west of central Oldham.

From Oldham: take Manchester Road south (A62). At major junction, go left (after Roxy Cinema) into Albert Street. Shop is on left.

From central Manchester going north-east on A62: at major junction, go right (before Roxy Cinema) into Albert Street. Shop is on left.

From Ashton-under-Lyne: go north on Oldham Road (A627); go left at traffic lights into Hathershaw Lane (A6104) which becomes Hollins Road. Continue to junction with A62 where you go left after Roxy Cinema into Albert Street. Shop is on left.

Open: First Saturday of month 9–11. (If a Bank Holiday weekend, please phone as sale might be on different weekend.)
Closed: Christmas–New Year.
Cards: Access, Switch, Visa.
Cars: Outside company.
Toilets: Yes.
Wheelchairs: Easy access to ground floor shop.
Changing rooms: Yes.
Teas: In Hollinwood.
Groups: No guided tours of the works. For coach party visits to shop please contact Mr Ashworth first, mentioning this guide.
Transport: Local buses.
Mail order: No.

86 Oswaldtwistle near Accrington Lancs

Oswaldtwistle Mills

see map p. 428

Moscow Mill, Collier Street BB5 3DF
(01254) 871025

Fabrics woven on premises – Egyptian cotton, household textiles etc plus huge selection of pottery, crafts, antiques, interior design items, sweets, domestic cleaning products etc.

On the north-east side of Oswaldtwistle.

From Blackburn Road (A679): go south at traffic lights in Church into Market Street (B6231) to Oswaldtwistle.*

From Accrington: go west on A679 for Blackburn. In Church, go over first traffic lights then left at second lights into Market Street (B6231) for Oswaldtwistle.*

****This becomes Union Road. Go under railway; by Total on right, go left (Collier Street). Mill clearly visible 100 yds ahead.***

From south of town (Union Street): keep straight on main road. By Total on left, go right. Mill clearly visible 100 yds ahead.

Open: Mon–Sat 9–5; Sun 10–5; Bank Holidays.
Closed: Please check.
Cards: Yes.
Cars: Own car-parks.
Toilets: Yes; for disabled too.
Wheelchairs: Easy access, no steps, huge warehouse.
Teas: Own coffee shop.
Tours: Weaving shed tours by appointment.
Transport: Hyndburn bus.

87 Padiham Lancs

Sherry's Towel Mill

Stockbridge Mill BB12 7HA
(01282) 778416

Wide range of towels made here plus huge selection of household textiles: duvets, bedding, bathroom sets, flannelette sheet pieces and sets. Large range of ready-made curtains, perfumed candles and interesting gifts, silk flowers, bakeware, dressing gowns etc.

'Genuine factory shop, lots of bargains. Please browse without obligation.'

See our display advertisement opposite

Close to centre of town.

From Burnley, or M65 exit 10: take main road (A671) to Padiham. Pass Gawthorpe Hall on right. As main road turns sharp right over river, go left round The Bridge Inn for Hapton.*

Coming east from Blackburn along Padiham main road (A671): go through town, pass Kwik Save on left, go sharp right over river. Main road then goes left but you go ahead for Hapton (Bridge Inn on left).*

****Go under railway: shop on left on corner of Stockbridge Road.***

Open: Mon–Fri 9.30–5.30; Sat 10–5; Sun 10–4. Bank Holidays (usually with 'open weekend'.)
Closed: Christmas, Boxing and New Year's Days.
Cards: Access, Switch, Visa.
Cars: Ample parking for cars and coaches.
Toilets: Yes (but inaccessible for disabled visitors).
Wheelchairs: Easy access, no steps.
Teas: New 30-seater coffee shop for light snacks; lunch or supper menus for pre-arranged groups.
Groups: Pre-booked groups (maximum 50) may see towels woven (phone Iris to arrange). Free. Individuals please ask at the time.
Transport: Buses from Burnley.
Mail order: Yes.
Catalogue: Leaflet.

88 Padiham Lancs

Winchester Furniture

Clover Croft Mill, Higham Hall Road, Higham BB12 9EZ
(01282) 778783

Wide range of leather upholstered furniture in traditional and modern designs: sofas, settees, chairs, recliners, pouffes, stools etc.

'Prices are far lower than high street retailers and include delivery. All items perfects and we also have ex-display furniture at low prices. Special offers.'

See our display advertisement opposite

Higham is a couple of miles north-east of Padiham, a tiny village just off the A6068.

From the A6068: follow signs into Higham. The company is in the centre of the village, in a stone mill next to The Four Alls Inn.

Open: Mon–Fri 9–5; Sat 10–5; Sun 11–4; Bank Holidays.
Closed: Christmas–New Year period.
Cards: Access, Switch, Visa.
Cars: Own car-park.
Toilets: Yes.
Wheelchairs: Staircases to first & second floor showrooms.
Teas: Pub next door.
Tours: Customers can see suites being made Mon–Fri.
Transport: Buses from Burnley, Nelson, Colne, Accrington and Blackburn.
Mail order: No.

See our entry opposite

See entry opposite for details

89 Penketh Lancs

Wynsors World of Shoes

74 Warrington Road WA5 2EV
(01925) 727481

Men's, ladies' and children's fashion shoes, both leather and synthetic.

'Massive range of branded footwear from own factory and all over the world. Stock changes daily. Prices from £1 to £100. Special lines at lowest prices in the country.'

See our display advertisement on p. 423

Warrington Road is the main A562, linking Widnes to Warrington.

From Warrington: take A57. At roundabout in Great Sankey take left fork for Widnes. Continue into Warrington Road. Shop is on left, on same forecourt as Mobil petrol station.

Open: Mon, Tues, Wed, Sat 9–5.30; Thur, Fri 9–8; Sun 10–4. Bank Holidays 10–4.
Closed: Christmas, Boxing and New Year's Days.
Cards: Access, Style, Visa.
Cars: Own car park in front and behind shop.
Toilets: Locally.
Wheelchairs: Easy access, no steps to large shop.
Teas: Take-away 100 yds. Many places in Warrington.
Groups: Welcome to shop.
Transport: Stop nearby for bus nos. 12, P1, P2, 302, T10, A1, A2.
Mail order: No.

90 Preston Lancs

Maitland Enterprises

Paul Catterall Mill, Maitland Street PR1 1QF
(01772) 703169

Picture framing to your own requirements; screen-printing including T-shirts. Indoor and outdoor signs; badges; packing and collating (of interest to businesses, hotels etc).

'Unit in Essex Street (01772 556036) just round corner from old Infirmary specialises in wooden items – rocking horses (from £53), dolls houses, bird tables, picnic tables. Some items on display and for sale; others gladly made to order. Furniture restoration service.'

Maitland Street is on east side of town centre, a small road on north side of and parallel to New Hall Lane, the busy road linking town centre to M6 exit 31.

From town: follow signs to M6. Go left at first traffic lights then right. Shop is on left.

From M6 exit 31: go towards town. Do not go right for ring road but go right at first lights after roundabout.

Open: Mon–Fri 8.30–4.30.
Closed: Bank Holidays; Christmas–New Year.
Cards: None.
Cars: In street.
Toilets: No.
Wheelchairs: No access (first floor).
Teas: In town.
Transport: Local buses along New Hall Lane.

91 Rawtenstall Lancs

P B A Mill Shop

Unit 5, New Hall Hey Road BB4 6HL
(01706) 222146

Big range of clearance lines and seconds from leading fabric manufacturers – *Romo, Crowson, Ametex, Sanderson* etc. Plain chintz and lining. All major names to order from pattern books at discounted prices. Making-up service.

'Roll ends from £2.13 per metre. Full rolls from £3.83 per metre. Perfects also available.'

On the south-west side of Rawtenstall.

From town centre/all directions: find huge roundabout with Asda on one corner and Shell on far side. With Asda on left, take Bury Road for Edenfield. Take first right (New Hall Hey Road), pass Kwik Save on right. Shop at far end on left before level crossing.

If you miss above turn-off, take A682 for Bury/Manchester. After 400 yds go left on to slip road for New Hall Hey Industrial Estate. Go left in front of mill, over level crossing: shop in first building on right.

Open: Mon–Fri 10–5; Sat 10.30–4; Sun 11–4. Bank Holidays as normal.
Closed: Easter Sunday; Christmas and New Year's Days.
Cards: Access, Visa (2% extra).
Cars: Own yard.
Toilets: On first floor.
Wheelchairs: One step to large ground floor showroom; upstairs showroom.
Teas: Two minutes' walk to Cobblers Inn.
Groups: Shoppers welcome if they phone first.
Transport: Any bus to town then 10 minutes' walk.
Mail order: Customers can order by manufacturers' code any of the ranges. Seconds stock more difficult. Happy to supply cuttings by post. Linings, chintz, heading tape etc can be sent.

Rochdale Lancs

Comfy Quilts

Lowfield Mill, Belfield Lane OL16 3AZ
(01706) 345868

Quilts, pillows, bedspreads, comforters, sleeping bags. Full range of plain and printed bedding and curtains. Most items made on site.

'All items at factory prices. Ends of lines and slight seconds. Designs and styles constantly changing.'

Just over a mile east of Rochdale town centre, just off the A640.

From Rochdale town centre: follow signs for Milnrow, taking A640 east towards M62. Cross traffic lights at junction with A664 Kingsway. Take second left, Belfield Road (in front of the Lord Nelson pub). Company is on left.

From M62 exit 21: take A640 north-west for Rochdale. Continue for just over a mile. Go right immediately after the Lord Nelson pub on right. Company is on left.

Late Entry

Open: Tues, Wed, Thur 10.30–3.30; Fri 10.30–2.30.
Closed: Monday; Bank Holidays; Christmas–New Year.
Cards: No.
Cars: Ample free parking opposite.
Toilets: No.
Wheelchairs: Easy access; no steps to small shop.
Teas: Lord Nelson pub for lunch; and in Rochdale.
Groups: No factory tours; small shopping groups welcome by prior arrangement.
Transport: Rochdale buses stop 2–3 minutes' walk away.
Mail order: No.

92 Runcorn Cheshire

Velmore

Picow Farm Road WA7 4UJ
(01928) 560169

Ladies' wear: skirts, dresses, jackets, trousers, suits, shorts.

'Leading chainstore seconds only sold here, at factory shop prices.'

Just off the A557 on the west side of Runcorn.

From M56 exit 12: take A557 north towards Runcorn.

From either Liverpool or Chester: turn off A557 (Runcorn Expressway) at sign 'Westfield Docks/Runcorn Station' then:

from Liverpool direction: go left at top of slip road; large factory is clearly visible, 200 yds on right.

from Chester: turn right at end of slipway, go over a small bridge; factory is 200 yds on right.

Open: Tues, Thur, Fri 10.30–3.
Closed: Monday; Wednesday; Bank Holidays; last week July and 2 weeks in Aug; Christmas–New Year. Phone first to check dates.
Cards: Access, Switch, Visa.
Cars: Own car-park.
Toilets: In Runcorn.
Wheelchairs: 12 steps to shop.
Changing rooms: No.
Teas: In Runcorn.
Groups: Groups welcome to shop but must phone first.
Transport: None.

93 Saddleworth Moor near Oldham Lancs

Adept Pine

Tame Water Mill, Delph New Road, Dobcross OL3 5BF
(01457) 877155

Large range of pine furniture: tables, chairs, windsor chairs, cupboards, wardrobes, bookcases, towel rails, dressers, mirrors, station clocks, video holders, butchers' blocks, kitchen fittings and island work tops/draws for kitchens etc.

'All items can be made, stained, polished or painted to customers' requirements. Delivery arranged at reasonable price. Children's play area.'

See our display advertisement opposite

Dobcross is a small village about 7 miles east of Oldham, on Saddleworth Moor.

From the A62 (Oldham–Huddersfield road): turn south on to A6052 for Uppermill/Ashton. Continue for half a mile, passing Saddleworth Yarn Dyers on left, to well marked company, with tall chimney, on right.

From Oldham via A669: go through Uppermill then go left at sign to Dobcross. At mini-rounabout at T-junction, go left, down-hill and over the river. Follow this road round for several hundred yards to clearly marked company (tall chimney) on left.

Open: Mon–Fri 9–5 (Thur late opening to 8); Sat, Sun 10–4.
Closed: Christmas and New Year's Days.
Cards: Connect, MasterCard, Switch, Visa.
Cars: Own large car-park.
Toilets: Yes.
Wheelchairs: Ramp into huge, spacious shop.
Teas: Tea shops in Uppermill. Local pubs.
Groups: Shopping groups welcome with prior phone call.
Transport: Plenty of buses go past the shop.

See our entry opposite

94 St Asaph Denbighshire

Tweedmill Factory Shopping

Llannerch Park LL17 0UY
(01745) 730072

Quality fashion clothing for men and women direct from UK and Europe's leading manufacturers. Over 15,000 perfect garments; also handbags, luggage, shoes, accessories etc. Hats, scarves and picnic rugs woven at the mill.

'This season's overmakes, cancelled orders, designer samples etc. We take delivery of over 1000 garments a week; most with 30% off and 100's at half price.'

Two miles south of St Asaph, just off A525 (St Asaph–Denbigh road).

From St Asaph: take A525 south for Denbigh. Go left at brown signs to Golf Driving Range.*

From Denbigh: go north on A525. In Trefnant, go straight over traffic lights. Follow road round then go right at conspicuous brown sign to Golf Driving Range.*

****After 50 yds, go straight through gates then left to large building.***

Open: Mon–Sat 10–6; Sun 11–5.
Closed: Christmas Day
Cards: Access, Switch, Visa.
Cars: Large car and coach park.
Toilets: Yes.
Wheelchairs: Ramp to vast shop.
Changing rooms: Yes.
Teas: Own café open till 5 pm.
Groups: Shopping groups always welcome. Large groups please book first.
Transport: Bus stop at end of lane.
Mail order: No.

95 St Helens Merseyside

Ena Shaw

Eurolink Road WA10 2JR
(01744) 816186

Large selection of ready-made curtains in wide range of fabrics, drops, widths and headings. Curtain fabrics by the metre. Tie-backs and curtain accessories. Cushions and cushion covers. Carpet roll ends.

'Most items are perfects: end-of-line fabrics and cancelled orders. A few seconds on sale. From as little as half price.'

South of St Helens, near the link road with the M62 (exit 7).

From M62 exit 7: take A570 north for St Helens. From the roundabout at the end of the slip road, keep straight for about a mile. At the roundabout (Micklehead Green pub on right), go right for Lee Green & Lowfield Industrial Estates. Clearly marked shop is 300 yds on left, set back from road.

From St Helens: take A570 south for M62. At roundabout, go left for Lee Green & Lowfield Industrial Estates (Micklehead Green pub on far left). Clearly marked shop is 300 yds on left, set back from road.

Open: Mon–Sat 9.30–5.
Closed: Bank Holidays; Christmas–New Year period.
Cards: Access, Connect, Switch, Visa.
Cars: Own car-park by shop.
Toilets: Ask if desperate.
Wheelchairs: Ramp to huge shop.
Teas: Micklehead Green pub 300 yds.
Groups: No tours of factory but shopping groups welcome.
Transport: Bus nos. 23 and 24 from St Helens town centre. Bus stop 50 yds.
Mail order: No.

96 St Helens Merseyside

Wynsors World of Shoes

Boundary Road WA10 2PV
(01744) 454983

Men's, ladies' and children's fashion shoes in both leather and synthetic fabrics.

'Massive range of branded footwear from own factory and all over the world. Stock changes daily; monthly offers reduced by at least 50%.'

See our display advertisement on p. 423

A short distance west of town centre.

From town centre: take Westfield Street towards Prescot; after first roundabout take first right, Eccleston Street.*

From Prescot on A58: pass Pilkington offices on right, go left into Boundary Road just as you enter one-way system. Shop 200 yds on right.

From east on A58: go over railway, go left at third roundabout. Take first right, Eccleston Street, just before TA centre.*

From A580 (Liverpool–Manchester road): take A570 into St Helens. At first roundabout go right and next right again, Eccleston Street.*

****At traffic lights go left around Nags Head. Shop in third building on left.***

Open: Mon, Tues, Wed 9–5.30; Thur, Fri 9–8; Sat 9–5.30; Sun 10–4. Bank Holidays 10–4.
Closed: Christmas, Boxing and New Year's Days.
Cards: Access, Style, Visa.
Cars: Own large car-park.
Toilets: Locally.
Wheelchairs: Easy access (no steps) to large shop.
Teas: Pub and café within 150 yds.
Groups: Groups welcome to shop. No need to book but prior phone call appreciated.
Transport: Five minutes from town centre by local bus.
Mail order: No.

97 Todmorden Lancs

Bottoms Mill

Rochdale Road, Walsden OL14 7UB
(01706) 812691

This company makes flannelette and cotton sheets with matching pillowcases; polycotton sheets; tea towels, dusters, chamois cloths, dishcloths, dust sheets, terry towels, counterpanes; cleaning rags and large cloth remnants.

'Small family company which weaves a range of cotton cloths. Perfects and seconds available.'

Walsden is about 7 miles north-east of Rochdale.

From Burnley or Halifax: take the A646 to Todmorden. Then go nearly 2 miles south on the A6033 (towards Littleborough). The shop is on the right, opposite Gordon Rigg's garden centre. Walk through the arch and follow signs.

Open: Mon–Fri 9.30–5; Sat, Sun 10.30–4.30.
Closed: Christmas & Boxing Days, 31 Dec & 1 January.
Cards: Major debit & credit cards..
Cars: Ample space.
Toilets: At the garden centre.
Wheelchairs: Easy access to medium sized shop on ground floor.
Teas: Drinks machine at garden centre. Pubs, and fish & chips nearby.
Tours: Groups welcome to shop. Small numbers can also visit weaving sheds. Please arrange in advance, mention this book.
Transport: Bus nos. 589 and 590 pass door from Rochdale to Halifax.
Mail order: Goods gladly forwarded by post or carrier.

98 Tyldesley Gr Manchester

Curtain Choice

Tyldesley Road M29 9AT
(01942) 891182

Ready-made curtains including cotton velvets. Full range of made-to-measure curtains and accessories. Roller blinds. Nets, fabric by the metre, curtain poles, tracks. Also bedding, quilts, towels etc.

'Large spacious shop. Don't forget your window measurements! Clearance lines and slight seconds. Perfects to order.'

On the A577.

Coming east from Atherton: pass the Rectella factory on the right, then go into the first lane on the right – in front of the Smiley garage and just after the town sign 'Tyldesley'.

If you are going west towards Atherton: pass the Smiley garage on the left shortly after the end of the one-way system, and turn left immediately into the little lane.

Open: Mon–Fri 10–4.30; Sat 10–4.
Closed: Bank Holidays; Spring Bank Holiday week; last week June and first week July (check); Christmas–New Year.
Cards: Access, Visa.
Cars: Outside shop, along the small lane.
Toilets: In Tyldesley and Atherton.
Wheelchairs: Access possible. No steps.
Teas: In Tyldesley and Atherton.
Groups: Small groups of shoppers welcome.
Transport: 10 minutes' walk from Tyldesley centre. Wigan–Manchester and Leigh–Bolton buses stop nearby.

99 Waterfoot Lancs

Gaghills Mill & Footwear Museum

Burnley Road East BB4 9AS
(01706) 215417

Men's, ladies' and children's shoes, boots, slippers and training shoes. Towels, bags, and ladies', men's and children's wear and accessories.

'Perfects and ends of lines at greatly reduced prices. Thursday 10% discount for senior citizens.'

Burnley Road East (B6328) is only road going north along the valley from Waterfoot north towards Burnley.

From traffic lights in Waterfoot: at this T-junction, turn off Bacup Road (A681) into Burnley Road East (B6328). Go north for 400 yds then turn right at sign to 'Gaghills Factory Shop & Museum'. Clearly marked company is 50 yds on right.

Coming south from Burnley on Burnley Road East (B6328): go downhill towards Waterfoot. Pass Edge Side Post Office on the left; after several hundred yards go left at sign 'Gaghills Factory Shop & Museum'.

Open: Mon–Thur 10.30–5; Fri 10–1; Sat 9.30–3.30; Bank Holiday Mondays 10–5.
Closed: Easter; Christmas–New Year.
Cards: None.
Cars: Large car-park.
Toilets: Yes.
Wheelchairs: Lift available.
Changing rooms: Yes.
Teas: Locally.
Tours: Groups welcome to shop, please phone first. Allow extra time to visit fascinating small museum in original shoe company premises.
Transport: Buses: Rochdale–Accrington and Rawtenstall–Todmorden go to main bus stop in Waterfoot (4 minutes' walk from mill). Rawtenstall–Burnley and Blackburn–Burnley (via Rawtenstall) stop at top of drive.

100 Westhoughton, Bolton Gr Manchester

Brunel (By Testall) Upholstery

Perseverance Mill, Bolton Road BL5 3DZ
(01942) 814461

Showroom for three-piece suites, settees and chairs in any combination. Two, three and four-seater settees and chairs all made to order on site. Wide choice of fabrics. Curtains made to match; customers' own fabrics made up in any design.

'Curiosity does pay off. Come and visit us today. Genuine factory shop. See your own suite being made. Friendly and helpful staff.'

Fifteen miles north-west of Manchester city centre, 5 miles south-west of Bolton.

From M61 exit 5: follow signs to Westhoughton A58. Go to roundabout, go right (A6, signposted 'Chorley'). After ½ mile, go left at traffic lights (White Horse pub on far left); pass the Grey Mare on left (about 400 yds) and clearly marked mill is ¼ mile on right (look for yellow sign).

Open: Mon–Fri 9–4.30; Sat 10.30–4; Sun 11–3;
Closed: Bank Holidays; Christmas–New Year.
Cards: No.
Cars: Large yard at front.
Toilets: Yes.
Wheelchairs: Easy access to ground floor showroom.
Teas: In Westhoughton.
Tours: Customers welcome to see furniture being made; unsuitable for groups.
Transport: Buses from Bolton, Wigan and Manchester 100 yds.
Mail order: No.

Pilkington Glass Museum

Readers of our guides will have gathered over the years that we love glass. Naturally we visit Pilkington's glass museum in St Helen's. A fairly small museum, it shows the technical, rather than aesthetic, history of glass from ancient Egypt to the present day, and it needs about an hour to enjoy.

The most interesting parts of the museum for us explain more modern developments such as window glass. Early window glass was made by blowing cylinders which were then split, opened up and flattened in a kiln. Crown glass, with its traditional bull's eye, was a large hand-spun disc. Improved cylinder blown glass enabled a million square feet of glass to be manufactured in just six months for the Crystal Palace. Newly devised rolled glass became a feature of magnificent Victorian railway station roofs.

TV tubes, ovenware and high voltage insulators are moulded, a process developed from the production of inexpensive 'reproduction' cut glass tableware.

Glass reinforced cement is a new building material containing glass fibres: amazingly (to us) this strengthened cement can be sprayed, cast, moulded, or applied as rendering to walls. Glass is also used to reinforce plastics and rubber.

The museum has a fine collection of old glass, dating back as far as 4th century Naples. Interesting Victorian and Venetian pieces are on display, with examples of cameo work, sand-blasting, engraved and etched glass etc. A few pieces of modern studio glass are shown.

Prescot Road, St Helen's, Merseyside (01744) 692014. Weekdays and weekend afternoons. On the A58 south-west of town.

101 Westhoughton, Bolton Gr Manchester

The Carpet Company

Perseverance Mill, Bolton Road BL5 3DZ
(01942) 815532

Quality carpets all made here: plain tufted and berbers 80/20% wool/nylon; hand tufted 100% wool rugs; also vinyl and some patterns available. Underlays, door trims, roll ends etc. Fitting service.

'All carpets at factory prices. Oriental rug service. Please ring first.'

Fifteen miles north-west of Manchester city centre, 5 miles south-west of Bolton.

From M61 exit 5: follow signs to Westhoughton A58. Go to roundabout, go right (A6, signposted 'Chorley'). After ½ mile, go left at traffic lights (White Horse pub on far left); pass the Grey Mare on left (about 400 yds) and clearly marked mill is ¼ mile on right (look for yellow sign).

Open: Thur–Fri 11.30–5; Sat and Sun 11.30–4. Worth phoning first.
Closed: Monday, Tuesday, Wednesday; Bank Holidays; Christmas–New Year.
Cards: No.
Cars: Large yard at the front.
Toilets: Yes.
Wheelchairs: No steps to large showroom and factory.
Teas: Westhoughton.
Groups: Not suitable for groups. You can see carpets being made from the showroom.
Transport: Buses from Bolton, Wigan and Manchester 100 yds.
Mail order: We can post small samples on request. Nationwide service available.
Catalogue: Free brochure available on request.

102 Whaley Bridge High Peak

The Factory Shop

Wharf Road SK12 7AD
(01663) 734589

Duvets and covers, sheets, pillow cases, towels, household linens; ladies' dresses, skirts, blouses, nightwear, knitwear, underwear, hosiery. Men's trousers, shirts, ties, underwear, knitwear, socks. Children's wear, leisure and sportswear.

'Firsts, seconds and ends of ranges of well-known brand names and chainstore items.'

Shop is about 300 yds from the train station and bus stop (opposite the station).

Coming out of the station: turn right along Market Street (the main street). Wharf Road turns off Market Street. Shop is on left, next to old NatWest Bank; customer car-park is at rear of shop.

Open: Mon–Fri 9–5; Sat 9–4.
Closed: Bank Holidays; Christmas, Boxing, New Year's Days.
Cards: Access, Switch, Visa.
Cars: Free public car-park.
Toilets: Yes.
Wheelchairs: Shop on two floors.
Changing rooms: Yes.
Teas: Local cafés.
Groups: Groups welcome to shop; please phone first.
Transport: Station (Manchester–Buxton line) 300 yds from shop. Bus stop 150 yds from shop.
Mail order: No.

103 Whitefield Gr Manchester

Specs Direct

31 Charnley Street M45 6BF
(0161) 767 9740

Over 1000 spectacle frames in stock which can be fitted with bifocal, varifocal, photochromic, tinted or plastic lenses. Simple prescriptions made up on the spot. On-site sight tests available now.

'Prices from £25–£75, as much as half off prices elsewhere. Spend £35 and get a second pair free (standard prescription) from selected range up to £25 in value!'

Short distance north of M62 exit 17.

From M62 exit 17 and Prestwich: aim for Bury/Radcliffe along Bury New Road A56. Pass McDonald's on left. Go over traffic lights. Go over pedestrian lights; opposite New Grove Inn on left, take second right (Charnley Street). Shop is 100 yds on left.

Coming south along Bury New Road A56 towards M62: pass police station on left, cross Moss Lane traffic lights then take first left (Charnley Street). Shop is 100 yds on left.

Open: Mon–Fri 9–5.30; Sat 9–3.
Closed: Bank Holidays; Christmas–New Year period.
Cards: Yes.
Cars: In street outside shop.
Toilets: Yes.
Wheelchairs: One step.
Teas: Irresistible patissier/chocolatier (Slattery) for snacks and cakes only 200 yds away in Bury Road.
Transport: From Bury and Manchester; 5 minutes' walk from Whitefield tram station.
Mail order: No.

104 Whitworth Lancs

Anglo Felt

Tong Lane OL12 8BG
(01706) 853513

Carpet underfelt sold by roll only. 1.37m (54") wide x 12.5m (13.67yds) long, totalling 17.13 sqm (20.5 sq yds). Minimum quantity one roll.

'Six weights in two qualities of underfelt. Prices from £1.70 per sq m (ie, £1.42 per sq yd).'

About four miles north of Rochdale.

Via the M62: coming from the east, take exit 21; from the west, exit 20. Follow signs to Rochdale town centre. Leave Rochdale on A671, Burnley Road. Whitworth is 3 miles north. Pass Lords Caterers (large blue sign) on right: after 100 yds go left into Tong Lane. Factory 100 yds on right.

Open: Mon–Fri 9–12.30 & 1.15–5. Bank Holidays.
Closed: Easter; Christmas–New Year.
Cards: None.
Cars: In mill car-park.
Toilets: Yes.
Wheelchairs: No access to first floor office, but to works on ground floor.
Teas: In Whitworth.
Tours: Individuals welcome to see underfelt being made.
Transport: Not applicable as own transport needed for bulky rolls.
Mail order: No.

Dinner time, Healy Wood Road, Burnley, in earlier times. *(Thanks to Burnley Archives)*

105 Wigan Gr Manchester

Courtaulds Home Textiles

Trencherfield Mill, The Pier WN3 4EF
(01942) 501331

Duvet covers, pillowcases, sheets, bedspreads, valances, continental quilts, pillows. Curtains, towels, baby bedding (bumpers, cot and pram sheets), changing bags, nappies. Thread, ribbon, lace, fabric and remnants.

'Genuine mill seconds plus end of line bedding at factory shop prices.'

See our display advertisement opposite

Half a mile from town centre. This magnificent brick mill is on the banks of the canal in the Wigan Pier tourist area.

As you come into Wigan from any direction follow signs 'Wigan Pier'. This mill shop, signposted, is on the ground floor of the huge mill on your left as you go round the one-way system; it is tucked away at back, next to staff car park and opposite the café.

Open: Mon–Fri 9.15–4.30; Sat, Sun & Bank Holidays 10–3.30.
Closed: Christmas–New Year.
Cards: Access, Visa.
Cars: In mill yard and all public car-parks at Wigan Pier.
Toilets: In cafeteria across yard.
Wheelchairs: No steps; easy access.
Teas: Cafeteria; Wigan Pier tea shop; George Orwell pub by canal.
Groups: Groups welcome to shop – please ring shop manager to arrange.
Transport: Close to both train stations and town centre.
Mail order: No.

106 Wigan Gr Manchester

Flax Mill

Bretherton Row, Wallgate WN1 1LL
(01942) 242102

Huge range of curtain and dress fabrics from leading manufacturers. Ready-made curtains, nets. Second floor for latest fashion fabrics including bridal materials and evening wear. Dress patterns from leading manufacturers. Haberdashery section.

'Incredible selection. 1000's of rolls to choose from at bargain prices that are hard to beat. Made-to-measure service.'

In centre of town near the post office.

From M6: follow signs to Wigan Pier.*

From other directions: follow signs 'Through traffic'/Wigan Pier.*

****Follow signs to station. Go under viaduct into car-park on right just after station. Walk up to town centre (3 minutes), go right into narrow lane opposite post office and Bees Knees pub. Shop clearly marked 50 yds on left.***

Open: Mon, Tues, Thur, Fri, Sat 9.30–5.15.
Closed: Wednesday; Bank Holidays; Christmas, Boxing and New Year's Days.
Cards: None.
Cars: Town centre car-parks within easy reach.
Toilets: In town centre.
Wheelchairs: Two steps to large ground floor shop. Please ask for assistance.
Teas: In town centre.
Groups: Shopping groups and coach parties welcome. Please phone first. Discounts available.
Transport: Any bus to town centre. Close to Wallgate and Northwest train stations.
Mail order: No.

See our entry opposite

107 Wigan Lancs

Wharf Mill Textiles

Caroline Street WN3 4EZ
(01942) 825352 Fax (01942) 825322

Over 3000 different rolls of top brand curtain fabric always in stock. New: Fabric Market. Hundreds of rolls direct from the printers. Also discount tracks, poles, brasswear, trimmings, linings, tiebacks, cushions, beanbags etc.

'One of the largest selections of quality curtain and soft furnishing fabrics in Lancashire. Examples of prices: Wilson Wilcox printed Panamas £7.99 (rrp £11.99); slight seconds from 99p per m on fabrics with rrp of £7.99. Curtain-making service. As recommended by Homes & Ideas Magazine.'

Near Wigan Pier. From all directions, follow signs to the Pier.

From the west/M6 exit 26: go into town. Pass Wigan Pier on right. At traffic lights before railway bridge, go right into Queen Street (one way); at far end traffic lights, go right into Chapel Lane.*

From other directions/M6: follow signs to Wigan Pier. You come into dual carriageway (Chapel Lane). Pass MFI on right. Go under large railway bridge.*

****Get into right lane. At next lights, go right into Caroline Street. Shop immediately on right, opposite Carpet World & Upholstery.***

Open: Seven days Mon–Sat 9–5 (Thur late night to 8); Sun 10–4.
Closed: Phone for Christmas and New Year dates.
Cards: Access, Switch, Visa.
Cars: Own huge car-park.
Toilets: Yes, including for disabled.
Wheelchairs: All on one level, large shop, easy access.
Teas: Nearby in Wigan Pier or in town.
Groups: Shopping groups welcome, but for larger groups phone call first would be appreciated.
Transport: Train stations and bus stop 5 minutes' walk.
Mail order: Will post goods if customers can send sample, or if they know which design they want.

108 Wilmslow Cheshire

Abris Outdoor Clothing

Courthill House, 60 Water Lane SK9 5AP
(01625) 548803

Manufacturers of specialist high quality clothing for hill walking and backpacking; breathable waterproof jackets, overtrousers, fleece jackets, polycotton walking trousers and shorts, microfibre trousers and shorts.

'Reps' samples, ends of lines, last year's colours and factory specials all at reduced prices.'

In shopping parade in centre of Wilmslow on A538 to Altrincham.

From M56 exit 6: take A538 for Wilmslow; go over first pedestrian lights, pass Mazda garage on right then shop is 50 yds on left in modern shopping parade.

From A34: north or southbound, turn on to A538 at lights for Altrincham/Manchester Airport. The shop is 300 yds on right in modern shopping parade.

Open: Mon–Sat 10–5.
Closed: All Bank Holidays.
Cards: Access, MasterCard, Switch, Visa.
Cars: Nearby public car-park.
Toilets: No.
Wheelchairs: Easy access to medium sized shop.
Changing rooms: Yes.
Teas: In town.
Groups: No tours of the factory.
Transport: 15 minutes' walk from Wilmslow train station. On the main bus routes from Altrincham and Hale.
Mail order: Yes.
Catalogue: Free.

109 Wrexham Clwyd

Dennis of Ruabon

Hafod Tileries, Ruabon LL14 6ET
(01978) 840233

First and second quality traditional Welsh quarry unglazed clay tiles in a variety of colours, shapes and sizes (including traditional border tiles etc); clay pavers suitable for drives and patios; *Keope* Italian porcelain floor tiles in a large and varied selection of sizes and colours. Grouts, adhesives and cutters are also available; garden pots and wall tiles.

'Tiles and pavers made from local clay. Prices for own tiles from about £12 + vat per square yard. Please phone or call in for full details.'

About 4 miles south-west of Wrexham.

From Wrexham: take A483 dual carriageway south for Oswestry. Take exit signposted B5426 Bangor-On-Dee/The Plassey. At top of slip road go right, then over bypass to crossroad: turn right (B5605). Shop 500 yds on left, after offices.

From Oswestry go north on A483. Take slip road to Johnstown (B5426). After 50 yds turn right. Shop is 500 yds on left, after offices.

Open: Mon–Fri 8–12.45 & 1.15–4; Sat 8–1 & 1.30–3.30.
Closed: Christmas–New Year. Most Bank Holidays but phone to check.
Cards: MasterCard, Visa.
Cars: At front of shop.
Toilets: Yes.
Wheelchairs: Three steps, no ramp.
Teas: Facilities and pubs nearby.
Tours: Tours of the factory by prior arrangement only.
Transport: None.
Mail order: Will send items by post (carriage paid by customer).
Catalogue: Free.

F

110 Wrexham Clwyd

Velmore

Holt Road LL13 9DY
(01978) 363456

Ladies' wear; dresses, suits, jackets, skirts, trousers, shorts.

'Leading chainstore seconds only sold here, at factory shop prices.'

On east side of Wrexham.

From Wrexham: take road east for Holt and Nantwich (A534)/ Wrexham Ind. Est. Pass The Hand on left; Velmore 400 yds on left.

From Chester via A483: take slip road for Wrexham Ind. Est. (A534); at first roundabout take first turn 'Wrexham Ind. Est.' Follow road to end; at next roundabout take second exit ('Town Centre'). Go over mini-roundabout (Greyhound Inn on corner).*

Going west on A534: keep straight, look for mini-roundabout with Greyhound Inn.*

****Pass Brooklands garage on left – clearly marked factory 200 yds on right.***

Open: Mon, Wed, Fri 10.30–3.
Closed: Tuesday and Thursday; Bank Holidays; Christmas–New Year. Please phone to check.
Cards: Access, Switch, Visa.
Cars: Yes.
Toilets: In Wrexham.
Wheelchairs: Eight steps to shop.
Changing rooms: No.
Teas: In Wrexham.
Groups: Groups welcome to shop but must telephone first.
Transport: Local buses.

111 Wrexham Clwyd

Vossen

D5 Dutton Rd, Redwither Ind. Est. LL13 9UL (01978) 661155

Wide range of quality towels and bathrobes in plain, patterned and printed designs including beach towels, gift sets, velours, bath mats and children's towels and bathrobes. Also pillows, quilts and bedding.

'Perfects and selected imperfects. Buy from Europe's largest manufacturer of towels and bathrobes and save up to 50%.'

Three miles east of Wrexham in huge, well marked Ind. Estate.

From Wrexham: go east for Holt/Nantwich (A534), Wrexham Ind. Estate. Go right at signs for Wrexham Ind Est.*

Going west towards Wrexham on A534: go left at sign for Wrexham Ind. Est.*

From Chester via A483: take slip road for Wrexham Ind. Est.; go south-east on A5156 following signs to estate. At next roundabout go left on to A534. After ¾ mile go right for Wrexham Ind. Est.*

****At roundabout go straight. Take next left, Abbey Road. Go right (First Avenue) for Redwither Tower. Go round back of tower. Vossen faces rear car-park.***

Going north-west to Wrexham on A525: at Cross Lanes go right at traffic lights then first left for Wrexham Ind. Est. At roundabout (after ¾ mile) go right, Bridge Road South. Cross two roundabouts to T-junction. Go right then left, Bridge Road North. Go left (Second Avenue) for Redwither Tower. Go round back of tower. Vossen faces rear car-park.

Now closed

Open: Mon–Fri 10.30–5.30.
Closed: Bank Holidays; Christmas–New Year.
Cards: None.
Cars: Own forecourt.
Toilets: In town.
Wheelchairs: No steps, easy access, large shop.
Teas: In town.
Groups: No factory tours. Shopping groups always welcome – prior phone call appreciated.
Transport: None.

Towns with factory shops

NUMBERS refer to the ENTRIES, NOT the PAGES

Town	No.	Shop
Accrington	1	Hamilton McBride
Accrington	2	Karrimor
Accrington	3	Optical Direct (Clayton-le-Moors).
Accrington	4	Red Rose Velvets
Anderton	5	Jorgus Carpets
Ashton-under-Lyne	6	Barden Mill Shop
Bacup	7	E Sutton & Sons
Barrowford near Nelson	8	East Lancashire Towel Co.
Blackburn	9	Graham & Brown.
Blackburn	10	Ovalworld
Blackburn	11	Sheltered Workshop for the Blind & Disabled
Bolton	12	A P Supplies
Bolton	13	Baird Outerwear Brands
Bolton	14	The Coathanger Clothing & Camping Co.
Bolton	15	Dewhurst Dent
Broadbottom near Hyde	16	Tiviot Prints
Burnley	17	Barden Mill Shop
Burnley	18	Color Blind
Burnley	19	Jaytex Fabrics
Burnley	20	John Wilman
Burnley	21	Lambert Howarth & Sons
Burnley	22	Oakmount Mill Shop
Bury	23	Antler
Bury	24	Whitfords Bury Boot & Shoe Co.
Carnforth (Holme)	25	Abbey Horn of Lakeland
Castleton near Rochdale	26	Vectase Lighting
Chadderton	27	Gorse Mill Lighting
Chester	28	Montgomery Tomlinson
Chorley	29	Curtain Choice
Chorley	30	John Wilman
Chorley	31	R B Contacts (Wholesale)
Church near Accrington	32	The Card & Gift Factory Shop
Cleveleys near Blackpool	33	Cresta Factory Outlet
Clitheroe	34	Shireburn Carpets
Colne	35	Boundary Mill Stores
Colne	36	Empress Mills.
Colne	37	Gardeners' Choice Mill Shop (LBS Group)
Colne	38	Hartleys Barley Mill Shop (& Mail Order)
Colne	82	Proud Fabrics
Colwyn Bay	39	Hughes Lighting
Congleton	40	Florakits.
Congleton	41	R H Lowe
Congleton	42	Victoria Lighting / The Clothes Peg
Darwen	43	Silk Mill Shop
Denbigh	44	Wetherall
Ellesmere Port	45	Cheshire Oaks Designer Outlet Village
Ellesmere Port	46	Velmore
Failsworth	47	Pifco Salton Carmen Russell Hobbs Tower Mountain Breeze
Fleetwood	48	Briggs & Shoe Mines
Fleetwood	49	Wynsors World of Shoes
Garstang	50	Brock Mill Factory Outlet
Garstang	51	Country Vogue
Glossop	52	Abris Outdoor Clothing
Glossop	53	Glossop Factory Shop
Great Harwood	54	The Bedding Box
Haslingden	55	Winfields
Haydock	56	CBS

Towns with factory shops

NUMBERS refer to the ENTRIES, NOT the PAGES

Town	No.	Shop
Haydock	57	Rollingstock Outlets
Hazel Grove	58	Mood Factory Shop
Hazel Grove	59	Wynsors World of Shoes
Helmshore	60	Musbury Fabrics
Horwich	61	Halbro Sportswear
Horwich	62	The Towel Mill Shop
Hyde	63	Ashtons
Hyde	64	The Mill Fabric Shop
Hyde	65	Providence Reproductions
Hyde	66	Super Seconds
Ingleton	67	Daleswear
Kearsley	p439	Ebac
Lancaster	68	The Factory Shop Ltd.
Lancaster	69	Standfast
Leyland	70	Holmes For Foam
Littleborough	p442	New England Design
Lytham	71	Fylde Footwear
Macclesfield	72	Designer Warehouse
Macclesfield	73	The Fent Shop
Macclesfield	74	Room Service Interiors
Macclesfield	75	A Shufflebotham & Son
Macclesfield	76	The Silk Museum
Manchester : Ancoats	77	Sanderson Clearance Outlet
Middleton	78	Color Blind
Morecambe	79	Briggs & Shoe Mines
Mostyn	80	Abakhan Fabrics
Nelson	p450	Pendle Village Mill
Nelson	81	The Card & Gift Factory Shop
Norden near Rochdale	83	Alexander Drew and Sons
Norden near Rochdale	84	Cudworth of Norden
Oldham	85	Baird Outerwear Brands
Oswaldtwistle	86	Oswaldtwistle Mills
Padiham	87	Sherry's Towel Mill
Padiham	88	Winchester Furniture
Penketh	89	Wynsors World of Shoes
Preston	90	Maitland Enterprises
Rawtenstall	91	P B A Mill Shop
Rochdale	p457	Comfy Quilts
Runcorn	92	Velmore
Saddleworth Moor	93	Adept Pine
St Asaph	94	Tweedmill Factory Shopping
St Helens	95	Ena Shaw
St Helens	96	Wynsors World of Shoes
Todmorden	97	Bottoms Mill Co
Tyldesley	98	Curtain Choice
Waterfoot	99	Gaghills Mill & Footwear Museum
Westhoughton near Bolton	100	Brunel (By Testall) Upholstery
Westhoughton near Bolton	101	The Carpet Company
Whaley Bridge	102	The Factory Shop
Whitefield	103	Specs Direct
Whitworth	104	Anglo Felt
Wigan	105	Courtaulds Home Textiles
Wigan	106	Flax Mill
Wigan	107	Wharf Mill Textiles
Wilmslow	108	Abris Outdoor Clothing
Wrexham	109	Dennis of Ruabon
Wrexham	110	Velmore
Wrexham	111	Vossen

Empress Mills

Adept Pine

G

Derbyshire Nottinghamshire & Lincolnshire

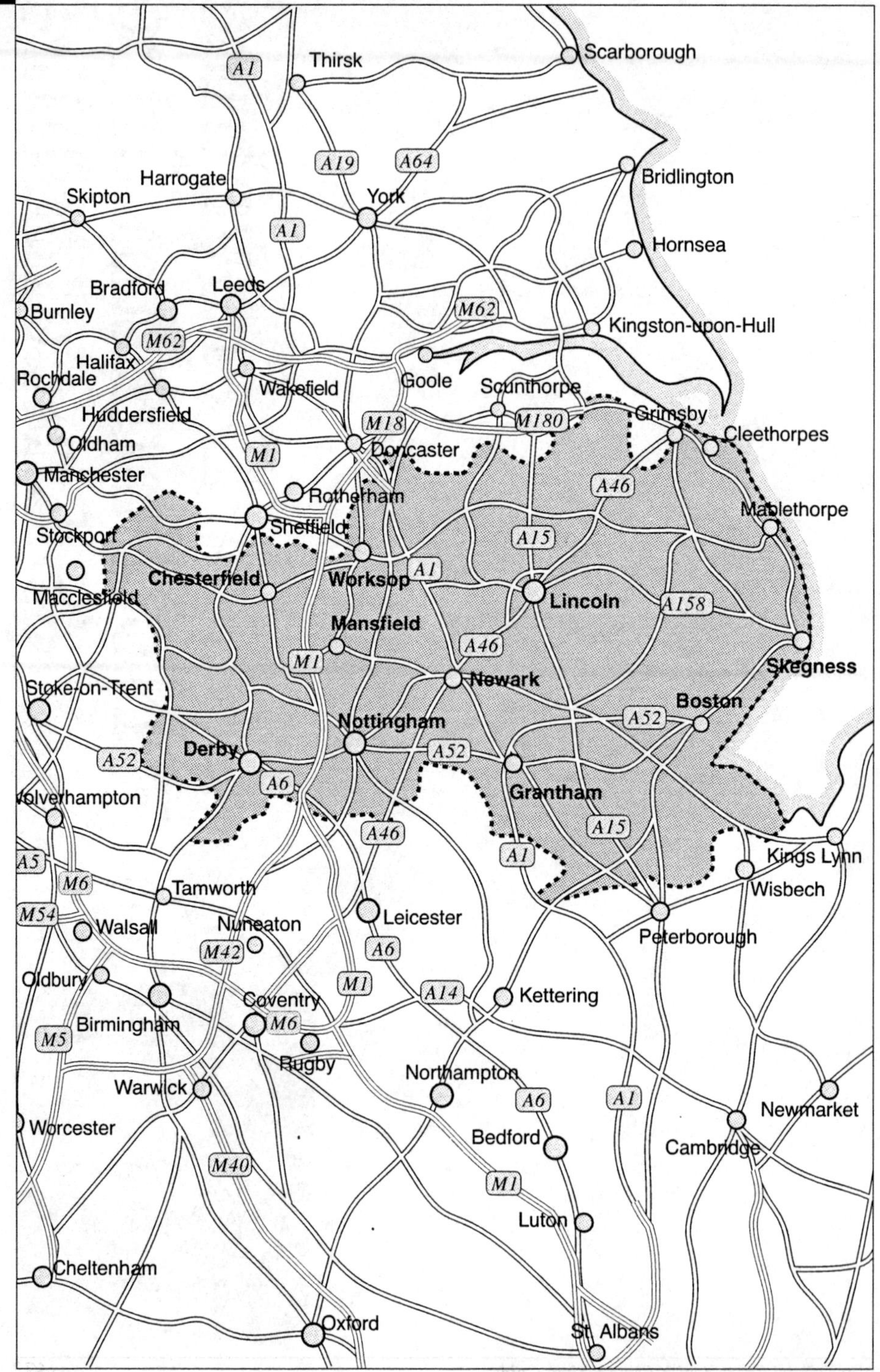
Scarborough
Thirsk
A1
A19
A64
Harrogate
Skipton
York
Bridlington
A1
Hornsea
Bradford
Leeds
Burnley
M62
M62
Kingston-upon-Hull
Halifax
Rochdale
Wakefield
Goole
Scunthorpe
Huddersfield
M18
M180
Grimsby
Cleethorpes
Oldham
M1
Doncaster
Manchester
A46
Rotherham
Mablethorpe
Stockport
Sheffield
A15
Macclesfield
Chesterfield
Worksop
A1
Lincoln
A158
Mansfield
A46
M1
Skegness
Newark
Stoke-on-Trent
Boston
A52
Nottingham
Derby
A52
A52
A6
Grantham
Wolverhampton
A46
A15
A1
Kings Lynn
A5
M6
Tamworth
Wisbech
M54
Walsall
Nuneaton
Leicester
Peterborough
M42
A6
Oldbury
M1
A14
Kettering
Coventry
Birmingham
M6
M5
Rugby
Northampton
Warwick
A6
A1
Newmarket
Worcester
Bedford
Cambridge
M40
M1
Luton
Cheltenham
Oxford
St. Albans

Derbyshire, Nottinghamshire & Lincolnshire

Returning to the factory shops in this part of the world is like coming home. Nottinghamshire is where we lived when we first discovered factory shops, and where we carried out our initial exploratory expeditions. We remember early research trips there in deep snow in February. The darkness and bitterness of winter were compounded by road verges blackened with coal dust from the fleets of lorries operating during the miners' strike – a very significant event here.

These three counties have long been some of the best in Britain for factory shops. With traditional industries that produce items which can be sold direct – textiles, knitwear, lingerie, upholstered furniture, pottery – they lend themselves to this special type of shopping.

We always look forward to returning to the East Midlands factory shops, our only regret being that we don't *need* new curtains or a new sofa when we come across something exciting and good value. Over the years we have collected a great many bargains. Our garden is lined with a regimental display of terracotta lions' heads (filled with flowers in summer). Under our pure lambswool sweaters we wear fine undies, all made here. Our three-piece suite was re-covered in Derbyshire, while our curtains originated in Nottinghamshire. This is the area, too, for tights.

On recent visits we have noticed that northern Nottinghamshire has become ablaze with factory shop signs; we are a little sceptical about so many new claims to the title. Even companies without the hint of a showroom advertise themselves as 'factory shops'. In some instances we rejected the 'factory shop' claim when a more accurate description was 'cheap import shops'. Several shops, while offering a good service to people in the immediate area, are too small or disorganised to tempt shoppers from further afield. The definition of 'factory shop' has become ever more diffused over the years, but often this is because some shops buy in an increasing percentage of stock complementary to their own, thus offering a greater range.

With new shops for hand-decorated earthenware (including tiles and handbasins), for kitchen gadgets, curtaining, curtain-making, shoes and branded wallpapers at discounted prices – along with literally thousands of other great value items to buy – make sure you spend time (and money) on the excellent items for sale here.

Nottingham Castle seen from the meadows in Ruddington 1866

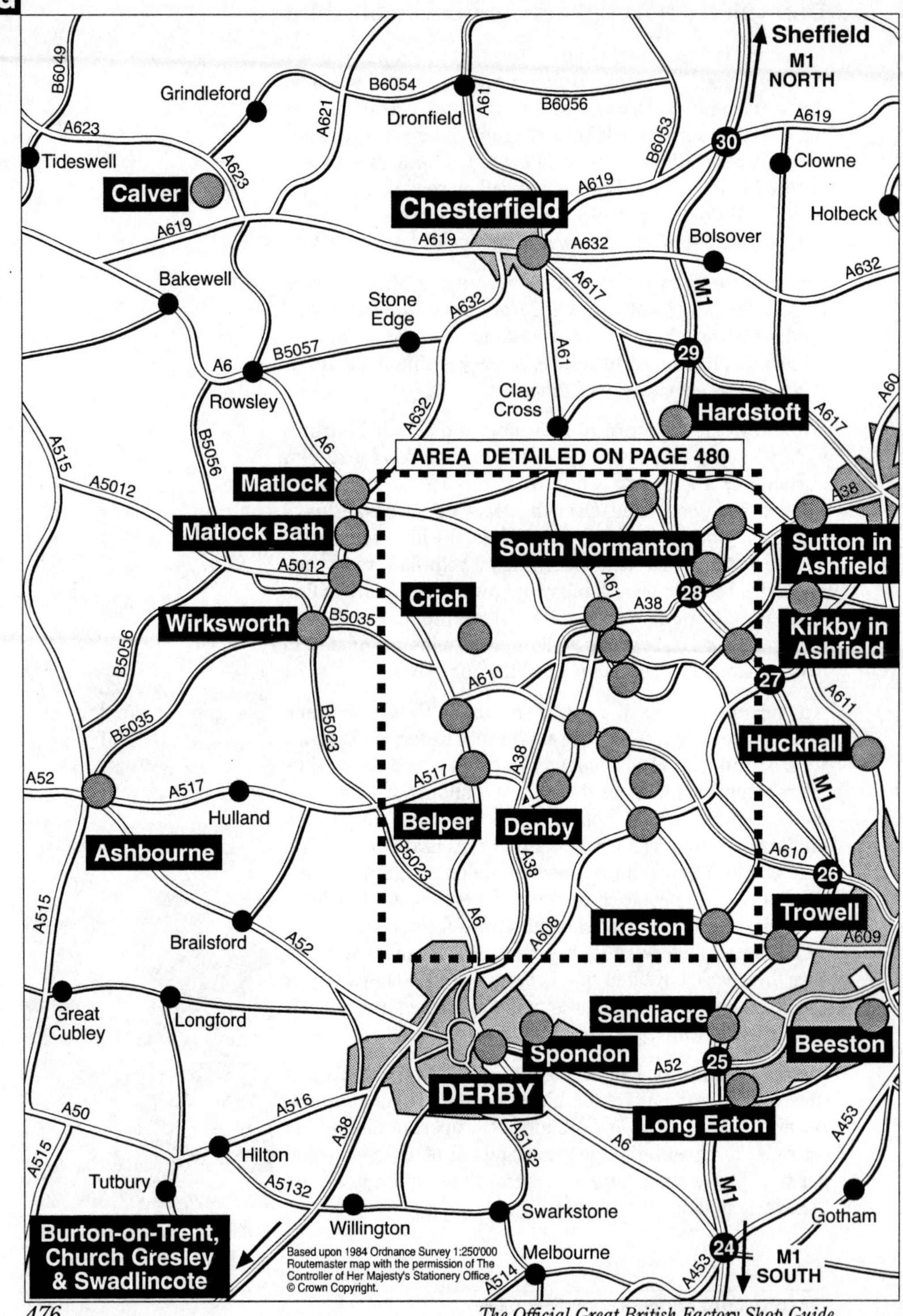

Sheffield
M1 NORTH
B6049
Grindleford
B6054
A621
Dronfield
A61
B6056
B6053
A619
30
Clowne
A623
Tideswell
Calver
Chesterfield
Holbeck
A619
A632
Bolsover
Bakewell
Stone Edge
A617
M1
A632
A6
B5057
A61
29
Rowsley
Clay Cross
Hardstoft
A515
B5056
A6
AREA DETAILED ON PAGE 480
A5012
Matlock
Matlock Bath
South Normanton
Sutton in Ashfield
A5012
28
Crich
A61
A38
Wirksworth
B5035
Kirkby in Ashfield
B5056
A610
27
A611
B5035
B5023
Hucknall
A52
A517
A38
A517
M1
Hulland
Belper
Denby
Ashbourne
A610
26
B5023
A38
A515
A6
Trowell
Ilkeston
Brailsford
A52
A608
A609
Great Cubley
Longford
Sandiacre
Spondon
Beeston
A52
25
DERBY
Long Eaton
A50
A516
A5132
A453
A515
Hilton
A38
A6
Tutbury
A5132
M1
Swarkstone
Willington
Gotham
Burton-on-Trent, Church Gresley & Swadlincote
Melbourne
24
M1 SOUTH
A514
A453

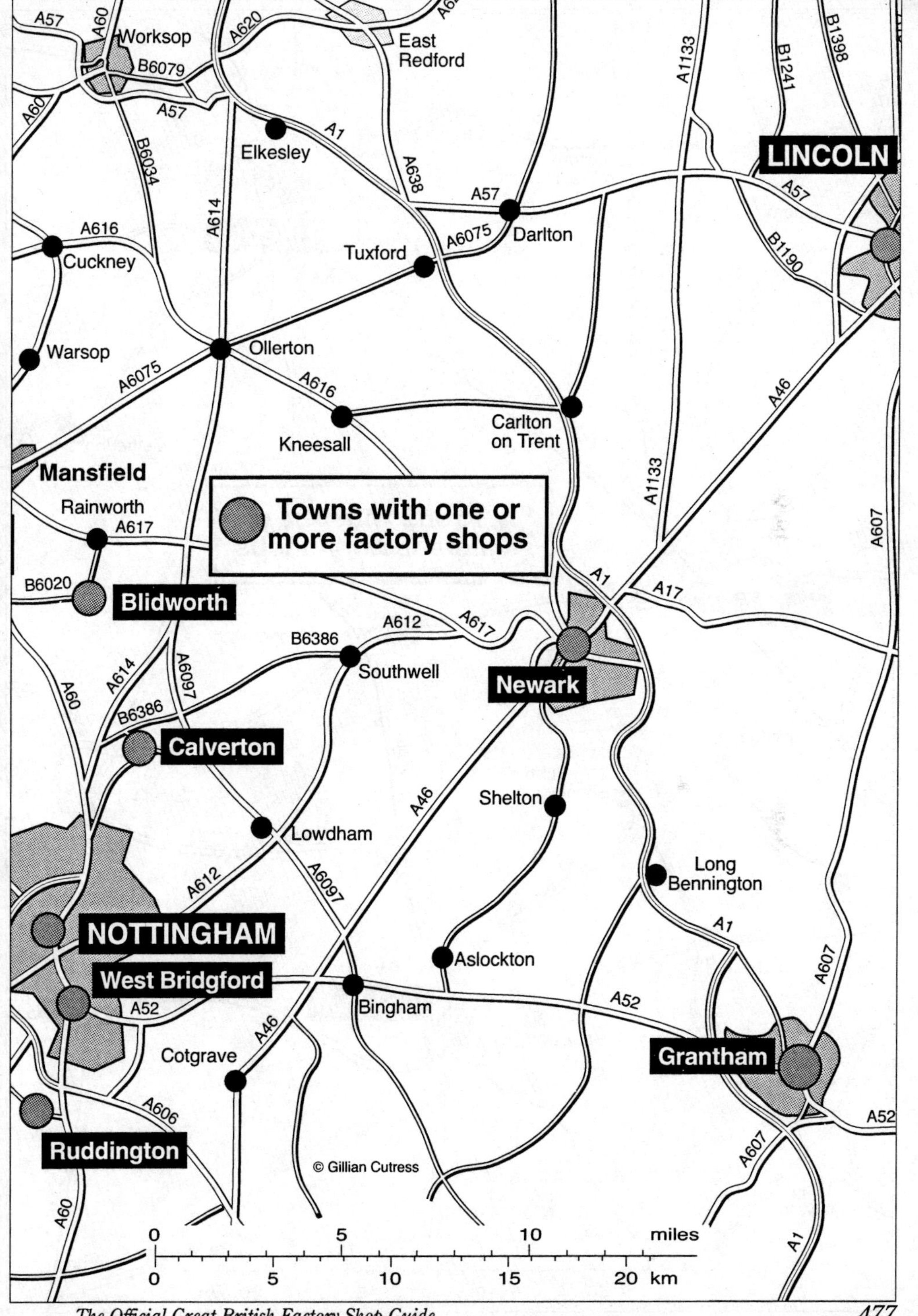

Worksop
East Redford
Elkesley
LINCOLN
Darlton
Tuxford
Cuckney
Warsop
Ollerton
Kneesall
Carlton on Trent
Mansfield
Rainworth
Towns with one or more factory shops
Blidworth
Southwell
Newark
Calverton
Shelton
Lowdham
Long Bennington
NOTTINGHAM
Aslockton
West Bridgford
Bingham
Grantham
Cotgrave
Ruddington
© Gillian Cutress
0 5 10 miles
0 5 10 15 20 km

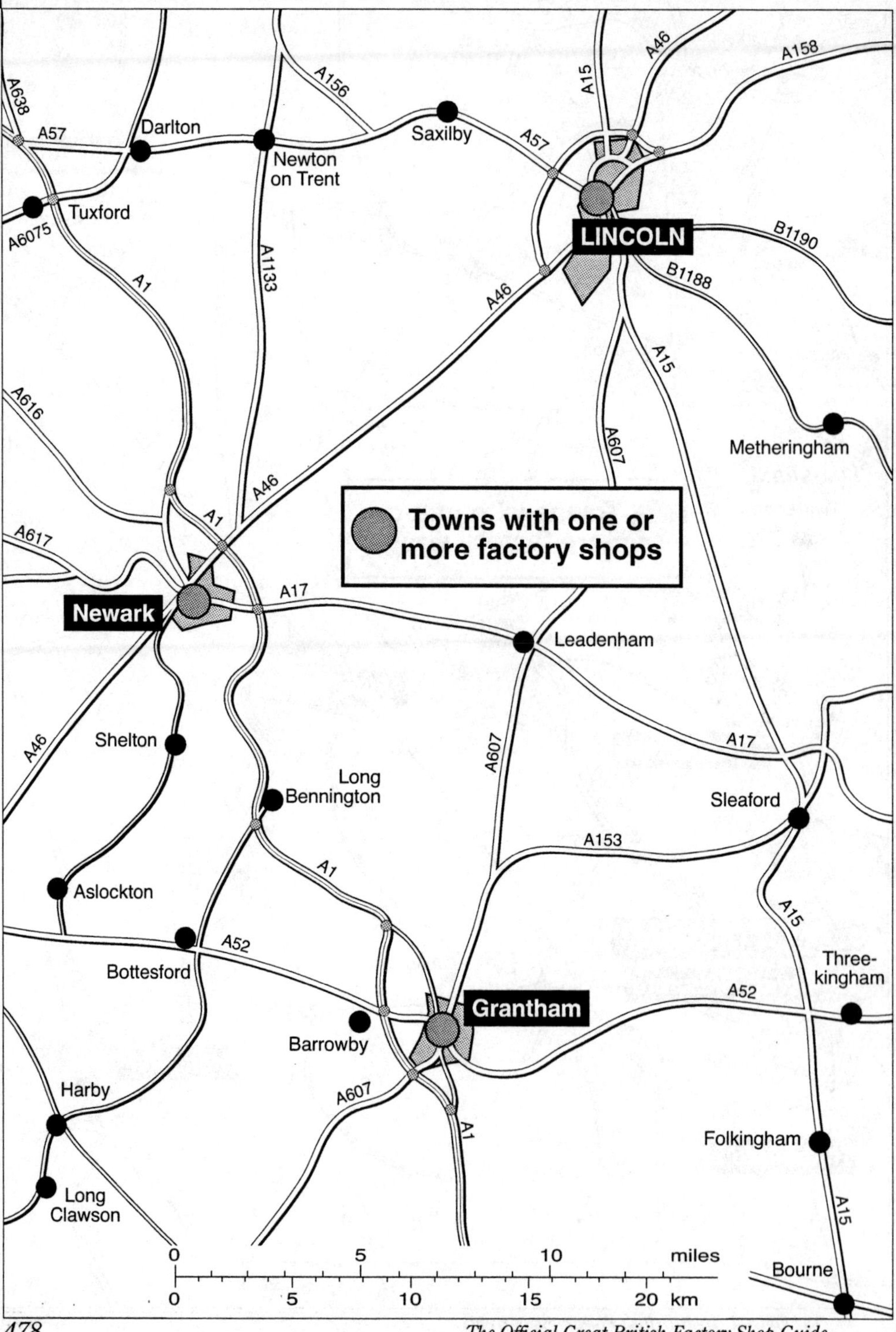

Towns with one or more factory shops

LINCOLN
Newark
Grantham
Darlton
Newton on Trent
Saxilby
Tuxford
Metheringham
Leadenham
Shelton
Long Bennington
Sleaford
Aslockton
Bottesford
Three-kingham
Barrowby
Harby
Folkingham
Long Clawson
Bourne

A638
A57
A156
A46
A15
A158
A6075
A1
A1133
B1190
B1188
A616
A607
A617
A17
A153
A52

0 5 10 miles
0 5 10 15 20 km

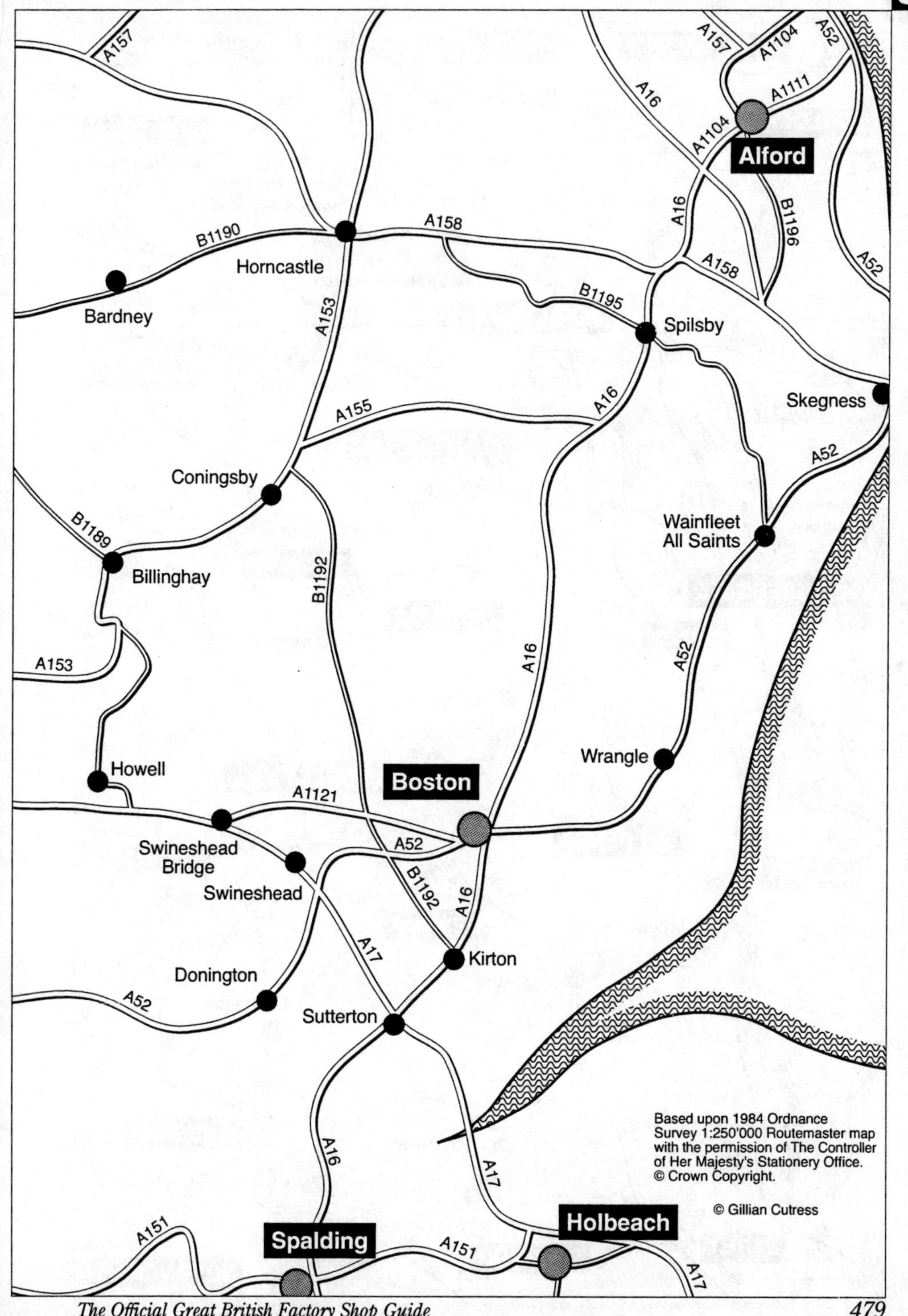

A157
A157
A1104
A52
A16
A1111
A1104
Alford
A16
B1196
A158
B1190
Horncastle
A158
A52
Bardney
B1195
Spilsby
A153
Skegness
A155
A16
A52
Coningsby
B1189
Wainfleet
All Saints
Billinghay
B1192
A16
A52
A153
Wrangle
Howell
Boston
A1121
A52
Swineshead
Bridge
Swineshead
B1192
A16
A17
Kirton
Donington
A52
Sutterton
A16
A17
Based upon 1984 Ordnance
Survey 1:250'000 Routemaster map
with the permission of The Controller
of Her Majesty's Stationery Office.
© Crown Copyright.
© Gillian Cutress
A151
Spalding
A151
Holbeach
A17

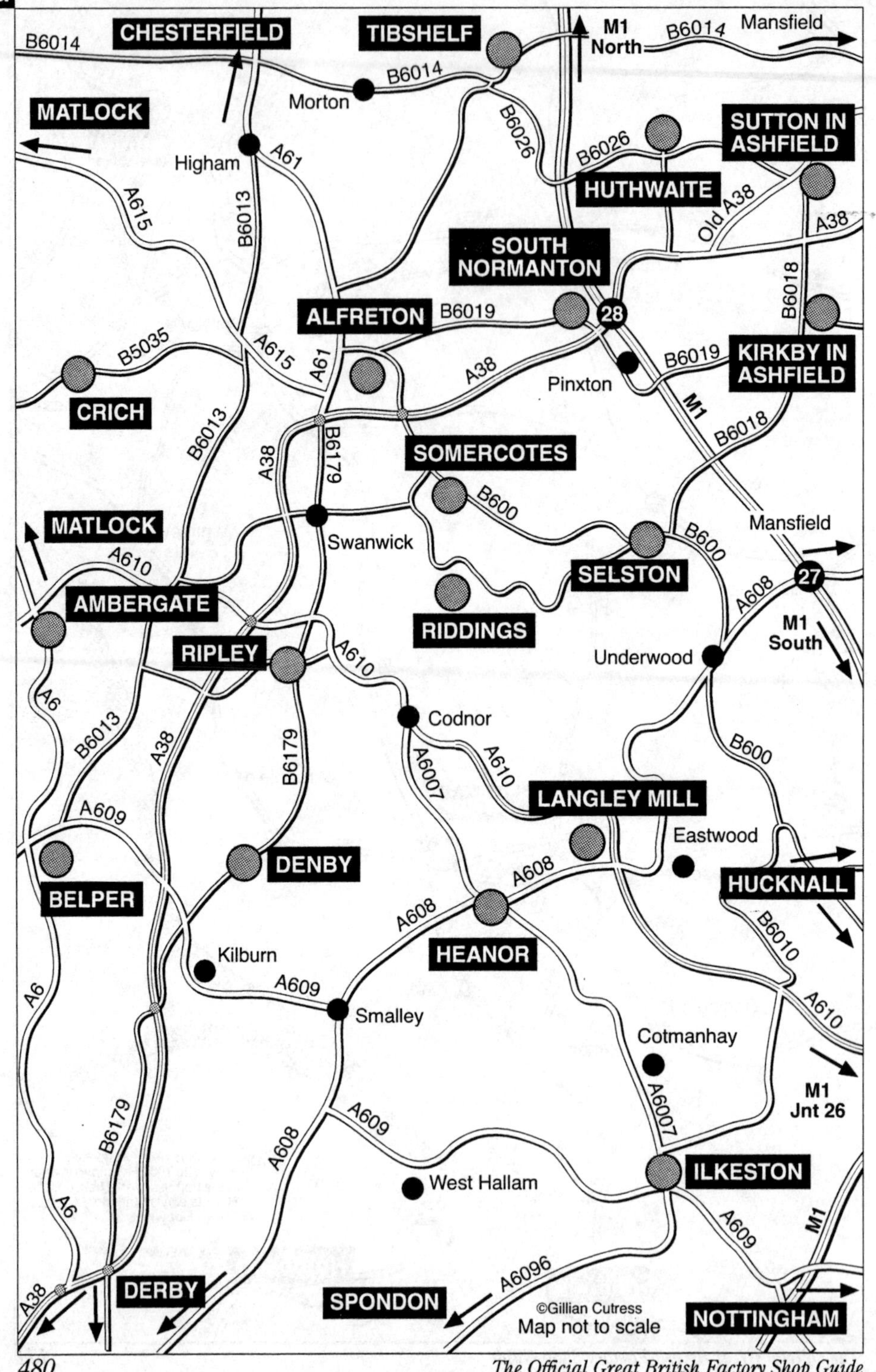

CHESTERFIELD
TIBSHELF
M1 North
B6014
Mansfield
Morton
MATLOCK
Higham
A61
B6026
SUTTON IN ASHFIELD
HUTHWAITE
A615
B6013
Old A38
A38
SOUTH NORMANTON
B6018
ALFRETON
B6019
28
B5035
Pinxton
KIRKBY IN ASHFIELD
CRICH
M1
SOMERCOTES
B6179
B600
Swanwick
Mansfield
MATLOCK
A610
SELSTON
A608
27
AMBERGATE
RIDDINGS
M1 South
RIPLEY
Underwood
A6
Codnor
A6007
LANGLEY MILL
A609
Eastwood
DENBY
BELPER
HEANOR
HUCKNALL
B6010
Kilburn
Smalley
Cotmanhay
M1 Jnt 26
West Hallam
ILKESTON
A6096
DERBY
SPONDON
©Gillian Cutress
Map not to scale
NOTTINGHAM

Wirksworth Factory Shop

HOT AND COLD DRINKS CHILDREN'S PLAY AREA

OPEN SEVEN DAYS A WEEK
9.00am – 5.00pm
LATE NIGHT THURSDAYS UNTIL 8.30pm

WE HAVE 'WORKING' MACHINES ON DISPLAY

HUGE RANGE OF STYLES & SIZES FROM THE FAMILY'S FAVOURITE CLOTHES SHOP

Jackets · Coats · Shirts · Skirts · Jeans · Bodywarmers · Trousers · Dresses · Jumpers · Cardigans · Blouses · Leggings · Shorts · T-shirts · Jog suits · Sweatshirts · Workwear · Schoolwear · Sportswear · Nightwear · Underwear · Swimwear · Babywear · Baby linen · Towels · Duvets · Pillows · Oven mitts · Aprons

See our entry no 91

1 Alford Lincs

Straven

Beechings Way LN13 9DH
(01507) 463223 (phone & fax)

Fully fashioned knitwear in natural fibres for men and women, made here. Also sell high quality ladies' skirts.

'Perfects and slight seconds on sale. We have a reputation for high quality. We operate a mailing list for forthcoming special events.'

17 miles north-west of Skegness and 18 miles south-east of Louth.

From the coast: go through centre of Alford towards A16; take first left after petrol station on the right.*

From A16 & Ulceby Cross coming north-east on A1104: come down the hill into Alford. Take first right just after the S-bend at very beginning of town.*

****In Beechings Way take first left: Straven is at far end on right.***

Open: Mon–Thur 9.30–4; Fri 9.30–3.
Closed: Bank Holidays; Christmas–New Year.
Cards: MasterCard, Switch, Visa.
Cars: Own car-park.
Toilets: Ask if desperate.
Wheelchairs: One step to small shop; access via office ramp on request.
Changing rooms: Yes.
Teas: Cafés in Alford.
Groups: Shopping groups welcome, but please telephone first.
Transport: None.
Mail order: No.

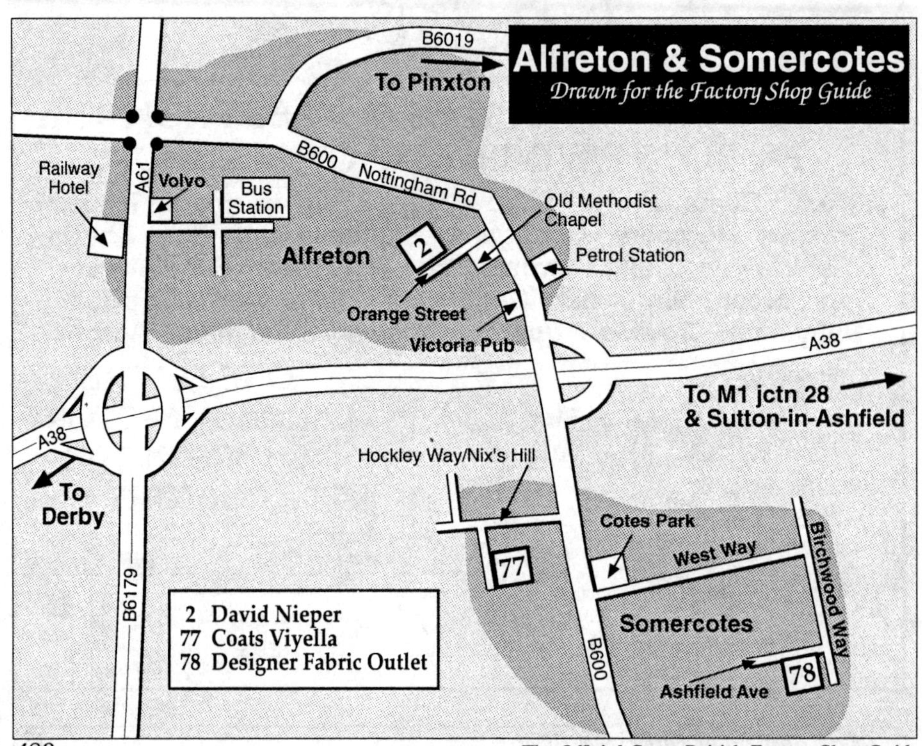

See our entry below

2 Alfreton Derbys

David Nieper

Orange Street, Nottingham Road DE55 7LE
(01773) 833335

Finest quality designer lingerie, nightwear and leisurewear, dressing gowns and bed jackets, full slips, slippers, swimwear and high class daywear. Fabrics and laces. Design room samples; discontinued lines and slight imperfects.

'An Aladdin's cave – unlike any other factory shop.'

See our display advertisement above

About ½ mile east of Alfreton on B600 and 5 minutes from M1 exit 28.

From M1 exit 28: take A38 west, signposted Matlock. Take first main exit to Alfreton (B600); at top of slip road, turn right then go straight for Alfreton. Pass petrol station on right: take next left (Orange Street).*

From Alfreton town centre: go towards Somercotes on Nottingham Road. Take the right fork, signposted Selston (not B6019 to Pinxton). Turn into the third right (Orange Street) opposite Watson's paint shop.*

****Shop at bottom right of car-park.***

Open: Mon–Sat and Bank Holidays 9–5.
Closed: Christmas and New Year's Days.
Cards: All major cards.
Cars: Own large car-park.
Toilets: Yes.
Wheelchairs: One step.
Changing rooms: Yes, spacious.
Teas: Tea, coffee, light refreshments usually available in canteen.
Groups: Welcome to shop, but please telephone first.
Transport: Alfreton/Somercotes buses stop at factory entrance.
Mail order: Yes. No seconds, but the entire perfect range. Ring (01773) 836000.
Catalogue: Free.

3 Ambergate Derbys

End of the Line Furniture

32 Derby Road DE56 2GF
(01773) 856082

Top quality upholstered, sprung furniture: sofas, armchairs etc.

'Perfect quality items which are factory direct. Fully guaranteed. At prices at least 40% lower than rrp. Fabric samples available.'

See our display advertisement opposite

On the main road (A6) through Ambergate, a short distance south of the traffic lights where the A610 turns off for Nottingham.

The shop is in the old Co-Op beside the pedestrian lights, almost opposite the White House pub (black and white building).

Open: Wed–Sat 10–5; Sun 1–5.
Closed: Monday, Tuesday. Christmas, Boxing & New Year's Days.
Cards: MasterCard, Visa.
Cars: On forecourt.
Toilets: In pub across the road.
Wheelchairs: Three shallow steps.
Teas: Little Chef and pub meals along road.
Groups: No tours; large shopping groups please phone first.
Transport: Any bus through Ambergate.
Mail order: Yes. Free photos and fabric samples available.

4 Ashbourne Derbys

Derwent Crystal

Shaw Croft Car Park DE6 1GH
(01335) 345219

English full-lead crystal glassware: wine glasses, tumblers and fancy gift items. Sandblasting and hand engraving.

'Factory shop prices. Special offers always available.'

In the major car-park in the centre of Ashbourne.

The company is clearly visible and well marked.

Open: Mon–Sat 9–5. Bank Holidays.
Closed: Christmas–New Year.
Cards: Amex, Diners, MasterCard, Switch, Visa.
Cars: Own small car-park and huge public car-park.
Toilets: In car-park.
Wheelchairs: Easy access to small shop.
Teas: Several tea-shops within easy walking distance.
Groups: Always welcome to shop. Free tours for individuals around glassworks in the mornings. Coach parties (maximum 50 people) welcome but must book in advance.
Transport: Take any bus to Ashbourne.
Mail order: Yes. Phone for free price list.

See our entry opposite

5 Ashbourne Derbys

The Elite Factory Clothes Shop

Elite Buildings, Market Place DE6 1ES
(01335) 344065

Many branded names in a large and varied selection of clothing and shoes for ladies, men and children; chainstore garments; designer knitwear; underwear etc.

'Mainly perfects, some seconds and clearance lines.'

Clearly marked in the centre of Ashbourne on the market square, 50 yds down from the town hall.

Much of Ashbourne is a one-way system. Go clockwise until you see the market square sloping uphill on the left then take the next left.

Open: Mon–Sat 9–5; Sun 11–5.
Closed: Christmas, Boxing and New Year's Days.
Cards: Delta, MasterCard, Visa.
Cars: Opposite shop on market square.
Toilets: 200 yds.
Wheelchairs: One small step to large shop.
Changing rooms: Yes.
Teas: Several attractive cafés in town.
Groups: No tours, but shopping groups welcome; please phone to arrange.
Transport: Any bus to Ashbourne.
Mail order: No.

Ashbourne

This small town, which has a couple of factory shops, is very pleasant to walk around. Much of the road system is one way so, to park, keep going till you see the entrance to the Ashcroft car-park. On summer weekends, Ashbourne can become very crowded.

During the Napoleonic wars, Ashbourne enjoyed phenomenal prosperity. Due entirely to the fact that it is situated in the midst of England, making access to the sea rather a long and tiresome business (at that time, anyway), the government decided to station 200 captured French officers in town. They were not supposed to venture further than a mile out of town but, other than the nine o'clock curfew, the officers had little to complain about apart from enforced idleness. They are said to have spent £30,000 a year here.

We came across this extraordinary engraving of the vicar of Ashbourne being hauled up the church steeple to add the finishing touch after repairs in 1873. We are not aware that such a frightening undertaking is a normal part of a vicar's duty so we congratulate him on having had the nerve to carry the weather cock up to the tip. Apparently a more recent vicar turned down an offer to repeat the experience.

Ashbourne Tourist Office
(01335) 343666

6 Beeston Notts

Floral Textiles

Unit 1, Lilac Grove NG9 1PF
(0115) 925 2556 Fax (0115) 925 5258

Wide range of nets and lace curtains, ready-made and made-to-measure. Net curtaining by the metre. Selection of lace tablecloths. Curtains ready-made and made-to-measure, and some curtaining. Also some sheets, pillow and duvet covers.

'Perfects, ends of lines and seconds available.'

On the south side of Beeston, near the station.

From the town centre: follow signs to the station and Beeston Marina. Go along Station Road and over the railway. Go immediately left into Lilac Grove. Keep straight for 400 yds to company on left, facing Lilac Grove Garage.

From Nottingham ring road: take A6005 for Long Eaton. Pass the university on the right. At roundabout go left, staying on A6005. At traffic lights, go left for Boots. At roundabout in front of Boots, go right into Lilac Grove. Keep straight to company clearly visible on right, facing Lilac Grove Garage.

Open: Mon–Fri 10–4; Sat 9.30–1.
Closed: Bank Holidays, Christmas–New Year.
Cards: Connect, MasterCard, Switch, Visa.
Cars: Own large car-park.
Toilets: At Beeston bus station.
Wheelchairs: No steps, sizeable ground floor shop.
Teas: In Beeston.
Groups: Shopping groups welcome.
Transport: 5-minute walk from train station; 20-minute walk from Beeston bus station.
Mail order: No.

7 Beeston Notts

The Mill Factory Shop

Queens Road East NG9 2FE
(0115) 922 3312

Good selection of roller blinds, ready-made net and lace curtains, ruffs, fabric curtains, accessories, pelmets, tie backs, cushion covers, lace tablecloths and shower curtains made on site. Also pillows, duvets and bedding.

'Net curtains from 50p a yard, ready-made curtains from £5 per pair (slight substandards at about half usual price). Shower curtains from £5 each.'

On the east side of Beeston, on the A6005.

From Nottingham outer ring road: exit for Long Eaton A6005. Pass the university on the right. At roundabout, continue left for Long Eaton. At next traffic lights (left turn to Boots and Boulevard Industrial Estate.) go sharp right directly into factory yard.

From Beeston centre: take A6005 (Queen's Road) east for Nottingham. Pass Total petrol on left. After 100 yds, at traffic lights with Coldseal on left (and right turn for Boots) go left into the factory yard. Shop at back right.

Open: Mon–Sat 10–5. Spring & August Bank Holidays; May Day.
Closed: Christmas–New Year.
Cards: None.
Cars: Adjacent to shop.
Toilets: No.
Wheelchairs: No steps.
Teas: The Coffee Parlour (from 9.30 am) five minutes from the top of Humber Road.
Groups: Shopping groups welcome, please phone in advance.
Transport: Beeston–Nottingham buses go past: City bus no. 13 from Queens Road; Bartons bus nos. 18, 32, R5; Middle Street city bus nos. 1, 506, R5, R5b.
Mail order: No.

8 Belper Derbys

De Bradelei Mill Shops

De Bradelei House, Chapel Street DE56 1AP
(01773) 829830

Women's clothing: *Jaeger* knitwear shop; *Windsmoor, Planet, Précis Petite, Country Casuals, Elvi, Naf Naf, Dutch Casual* jeans, top German and American designer labels and many more. Men's: *Jaeger* knitwear shop; *Wolsey, HOM, Ralph Lauren; Robert Leonard's Menswear* selling *Greiff, Pierre Cardin, Gabicci, Gurteen, Oakman, Savile Row, John Slim* and many more. Shoes for all the family: *Lilley & Skinner, Roland Cartier, Hush Puppies, Cable & Co., Studio* and many more.

'Ends of lines, end of season, surplus stock, providing many bargains for all the family. Up to 70% discount in four shops in an attractive courtyard setting. Excellent service, friendly staff.'

See our display advertisement opposite

On the A6 on southern side of the town centre.

From Derby via A6: as you reach Belper, go left at roundabout for Safeway.*

From Heanor via A609: stay on this road downhill to roundabout with A6. Go straight over for Safeway.*

From Matlock on A6: keep straight through town, over traffic lights, past bus station on left. At roundabout, go right for Safeway.*

****Pass Shell petrol on right: shop is on right.***

Open: Mon–Fri (including Bank Holidays) 9.30–5.30; Sat 9.30–6; Sun 11–5.
Closed: Easter Sunday; Christmas and New Year's Days.
Cards: MasterCard, Switch, Visa.
Cars: Own car-park.
Toilets: Yes.
Wheelchairs: Easy access, no steps, large shops.
Changing rooms: Yes.
Teas: Safeway coffee shop, tea shop in town.
Groups: Shopping groups welcome, but if over 25 people please phone first.
Transport: Bus nos. R30, 31, 32. Belper train station.
Mail order: No.

9 Belper Derbys

Derwent House

The Bridge, Milford DE56 0RR
(01773) 880404

Large range of pottery and decorative items for the home. Collectable novelty teapots and jugs. Glassware, planters, dough fruit and figures. Brassware and fireside accessories, cast iron doorstops. *Henry Watson* terracotta kitchenware, *Hornsea Pottery* tableware, *Tienshan Trading Company* tableware, *Gleneagles of Edinburgh* crystal. Greetings cards, gift wrap. Throws and cushions. Cookshop.

'Perfects and seconds available, together with 'bargain basement' for ex-mail order items, ends of lines and seconds. Prices from 20–50% below high street.'

Milford is a couple of miles south of Belper on the A6. This shop is almost below the tall brick chimney in the large mill complex.

Coming south on the A6 from Belper: after the road goes sharp right over the river, go right into the mill complex.

Coming north on the A6 from Derby/Duffield: pass The Strutt Arms on the right then shortly go left into the clearly marked mill complex (immediately before the stone bridge).

Open: Mon–Sat 9.30–5; Sun 10.30–5.
Closed: Christmas, Boxing and New Year's Days.
Cards: Delta, MasterCard, Switch, Visa.
Cars: Large car-park.
Toilets: Yes.
Wheelchairs: Five steps to shop.
Teas: Own coffee shop (upstairs) for breakfasts, light lunches, afternoon tea and home-made cakes.
Groups: Groups welcome, please book in advance with Linda Bowley.
Transport: Bus nos. 30, 31 and 32 from Derby and Belper to Milford. Bus stop two minutes from shop.
Mail order: No.

See our entry opposite

10 Belper Derbys

George Brettle and Co.

Chapel Street DE56 1AR
(01773) 821532

Ladies', men's and babies' wear; many well known high street brands such as *Vedonis* in a large variety of sizes, including hosiery, socks. Comprehensive range of household textiles. Own manufacture and from other factories.

'Very competitive prices. Seconds and perfects. Many miscellaneous items make regular visits well worthwhile.'

On A6 close to town centre and Safeway.

From Derby via A6: go straight at roundabout (Safeway on left).*

From Heanor via A609: stay on this road downhill to roundabout with A6 (Safeway opposite). Go right.*

****Shop is 50 yds on right, before bus station.***

From Matlock on A6: keep straight through town, over traffic lights, past bus station on left. Clearly marked shop is a few yards on left.

On foot from main shopping street: go downhill to bottom, turn left into Chapel Street; shop 100 yds on left.

Open: Mon–Fri 9–4; Sat 9–2.30; Sun *(Dec only)* 10–4.
Closed: Bank Holidays; Christmas, Boxing and New Year's Days.
Cards: MasterCard, Visa.
Cars: Own car-park behind shop. Coaches please phone first.
Toilets: Locally.
Wheelchairs: No steps, easy access to medium-sized shop.
Changing rooms: Yes.
Teas: In town and in Safeways.
Groups: No factory tours but glad to have coaches and shopping groups. Please phone first.
Transport: Almost next to bus station.
Mail order: No.

11 Blidworth Notts

The Major Oak Clothing Company

Dale Lane NG21 0SB
(01623) 793073

Quality men's wear manufactured for high street multiple shops: suits, jackets, and trousers.

'Prices 30–50% less than high street on ends of lines. Most items are perfects, with a very few seconds.'

See our display advertisement opposite

Clearly visible near the centre of town.

From A620 (main Blidworth–Kirkby road): turn off between Fina petrol and Forest Folk pub towards Sherwood Forest (brown sign) into Dale Lane. Clearly marked shop is 150 yds on left in converted chapel.

Open: Mon–Sat 9–4; Fri 9–2.
Closed: Bank Holidays; Christmas–New Year.
Cards: MasterCard, Visa.
Cars: Easy, by shop.
Toilets: Yes.
Wheelchairs: Unsuitable, 11 stairs.
Changing rooms: Yes.
Teas: Pubs in village.
Groups: Most welcome. Prior phone call to notify shop is appreciated.
Transport: Regular bus route.
Mail order: No.

12 Boston Lincs

Ashcroft Fabrics

Unit 1, Cowbridge PE22 7AY
(01205) 360888

Cane furniture, fabric by the metre, curtains, cushion covers, lampshades, bedding, cushions, made-to-measure service.

'Extensive range of co-ordinating products at factory shop prices. Special offers always available.'

On the north side of Boston.

From Boston centre: take the B1183 towards Horncastle. Go over level-crossing then canal about one mile further on. Shop is about 100 yds past bridge on right.

From Horncastle: stay on B1183 through Frithville. The shop is about 1½ miles on left after this village, shortly before the bridge over the canal.

Open: Mon–Fri 10–6; Sat 9–5; Sun 12–5; Bank Holidays 12–5.
Closed: Two weeks at Christmas, please phone to check.
Cards: All major credit and debit cards.
Cars: Large car-park.
Toilets: Yes.
Wheelchairs: One step to large shop.
Teas: In Boston.
Groups: Shopping groups welcome; group factory tours by appointment.
Transport: None.
Mail order: No.

See our entry opposite

13 Burton-on-Trent Staffs

Webb Ivory

Queensbridge Works, Queen Street DE14 3LP
(01283) 506371

Fascinating variety of surplus catalogue stocks of greetings cards, wrapping papers, household goods, toys, small gifts and clothing.

'50% off catalogue prices.'

Close to the centre of town, on the south-west side.

From Tutbury: go into town, proceed along Guild Street and Union Street. At traffic lights (Comet on near left corner) go right into New Street.*

From shopping precinct with W H Smith car-park: turn left; at traffic lights go right (New Street).*

****At next lights, go left (Uxbridge Street); cross next lights (Evershed Way); take third left (Queen Street). The company is 100 yds on left.***

From other places in town centre: find Safeway and pass it on left; at roundabout go right into Evershed Way; at traffic lights turn left into Uxbridge Street (Keepmere Engineering on far left corner). Go left at Queen Street. The company is 100 yds on left.

Open: Mon–Thur 9.30–5.30; Fri 9.30–5; Sat 9.30–2. Some Bank Holidays, please check.
Closed: Christmas–New Year.
Cards: Most major credit cards; Switch.
Cars: Own car-park.
Toilets: Yes.
Wheelchairs: Yes; ground level shopping, no steps.
Changing rooms: Yes.
Teas: In Burton.
Groups: Pre-booked shopping groups welcome.
Transport: 15 minutes' walk from town centre.
Mail order: No.

14 Calver Derbys

Peaklander Footwear (Heginbotham Bros.)

Peaklander Works S30 1XH
(01433) 630317

Wide range of footwear for men, women and children: safety boots and shoes, hiking boots and shoes, casual and formal shoes, casual boots, slippers, trainers, wellingtons, sandals etc. Brands include *Regatta, Padders, Sterling & Hunt, Equity* and *Rieker*. Also anoraks, country clothing etc.

'We buy in bulk from factories both local and worldwide and pass the savings on to our customers. 90% of stock comprises perfect current seasonal items.'

Five miles north of Bakewell, 12 miles south-west of Sheffield and 11 miles west of Chesterfield, at crossroads of A623 and B6001.

From Sheffield: take A625 south-west. After Fox House Inn, take second road on left to Grindleford (B6521), then join B6001 to Bakewell. The shop is on right at traffic lights with A623.

From Chesterfield: take A619 to Baslow, then A623 to traffic lights. Shop is on left, a few yards beyond lights.

Open: Mon–Sat 9–5; Sun, Bank Holidays 10–5.
Closed: Christmas and Boxing Days.
Cards: MasterCard, Switch, Visa.
Cars: Own large car-park at the side of the factory.
Toilets: No; nearest 100 yds.
Wheelchairs: Access with no steps from car-park; one small step inside medium-sized shop. Assistance gladly given.
Changing rooms: One.
Teas: Across the road.
Groups: Groups welcome to shop, booking not necessary; no factory tours.
Transport: Bus nos. 65, 66, 67, 175, 460, 795, X67 stop outside.
Mail order: Yes. Free leaflets. Hiking and shooting boots, and *Equity* shoes sent; other items by arrangement.

15 Calverton Notts

The Wrangler Factory Outlet

Pepper Road NG14 6GC
(0115) 965 4043

Large selection of men's, ladies' and youths' jeans. Also sweatshirts, jackets, T-shirts and shirts.

'Seconds and ends of lines at greatly reduced prices.'

A large village a couple of miles north of Arnold and mid-way between the A60 (Nottingham–Mansfield road) and A6097 (Lowdham–Ollerton road). Shop is in centre of village (near Co-Op) but can be tricky to find. Please use the landmarks below to orientate yourself.

Coming north from Arnold: cross the B684 and continue into village. At junction in village, go right (Main Street) for Epperstone. Immediately go left, opposite Happy Shopper general stores into Mews Lane. At far end (Cherry Tree pub on left), go right (Collyer Road) then left (Co-Op on left) into Flatts Lane. By William Lee School Annexe on right, take first left (Pepper Road). Shop is 50 yds on left.

Open: Mon–Sat 9.30–5.30; Bank Holidays 10–4.
Closed: Christmas, Boxing and New Year's Days.
Cards: All major credit cards.
Cars: Outside shop.
Toilets: No.
Wheelchairs: Ramp to sizeable shop on ground floor.
Changing rooms: Yes.
Teas: Local pubs.
Groups: Groups of shoppers welcome but please phone beforehand.
Transport: Bartons buses from Nottingham.
Mail order: No.

16 Chesterfield Derbys

Demaglass Tableware

Pottery Lane West S41 9BI
(01246) 274201

Plain and decorated moulded glassware made here. Also sell wide range of lead crystal (*Edinburgh Crystal* and continental).

'Ends of ranges, discontinued lines, some seconds. Sales usually held at Easter (including Easter Monday), August and early November.'

About two miles north of Chesterfield.

From town:

EITHER, take A61 north for Sheffield; go left at roundabout (Tesco superstore on right) for Newbold/Stonegavels. Keep straight for ½ mile to mini-roundabout; go right on to B6057.*
OR, take B6057 (old Sheffield Road) north, following signs to Whittington Moor.*

Coming south on A61: at roundabout with Tesco, go right for Newbold/Stonegavels. Keep straight for ½ mile to roundabout; go right on to B6057.*

****Pass fire station on left. Go right into Pottery Lane (small cul-de-sac). Shop, with clear sign, is at far right.***

Open: Mon, Tues, Wed, Fri 9.30–4; Thur 9.30–8; Sat 9.30–1.30.
Closed: Bank Holidays; Christmas–New Year.
Cards: MasterCard, Switch, Visa.
Cars: Outside shop.
Toilets: Yes.
Wheelchairs: Easy access, large shop and warehouse area.
Teas: Little Chef nearby.
Groups: Please contact Mrs Shaw, mentioning this guide.
Transport: Bus nos. 19, 20, 21, 22 and 36 every 5 minutes from Chesterfield; X11 from Sheffield.
Mail order: No.

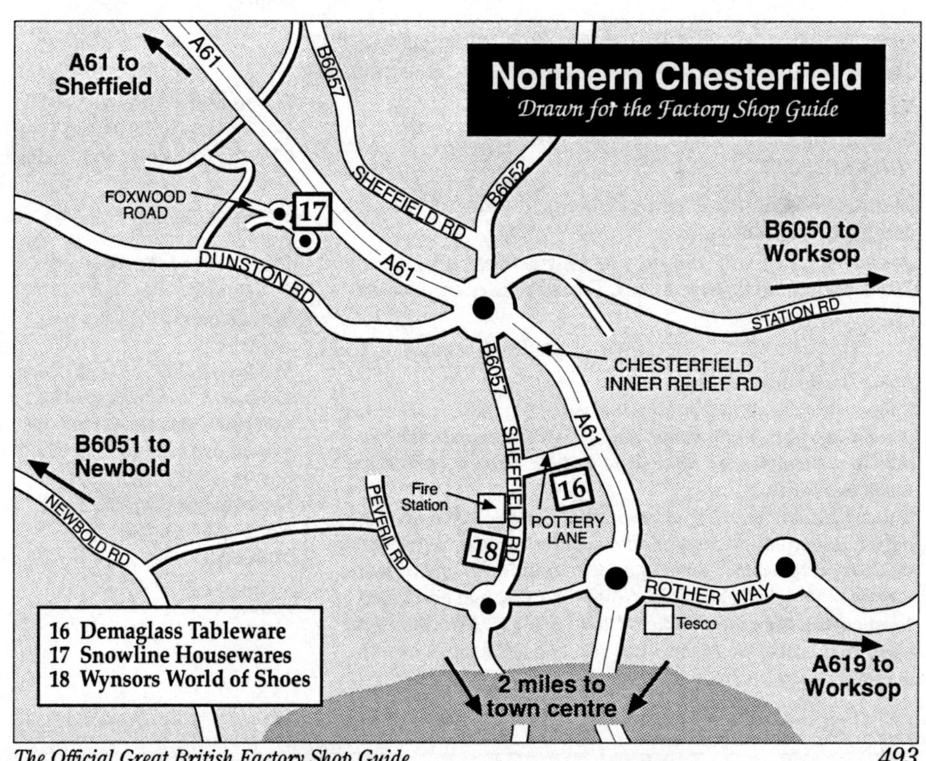

17 Chesterfield Derbys *see map previous page*

Snowline Housewares

Foxwood Industrial Park, Sheepbridge S41 9RN
(01246) 260500

Manufacturers of kitchen gadgets, utensils, knives, cutlery and woodware gift sets.

'We have many guest lines on offer to complement our own products, together with many special offers, discounts and promotions.'

North of Chesterfield, in large industrial park off A61.

Going north via A61: bypass Chesterfield then turn left at sign to Chesterfield Trading Estate Sheepbridge. At the end of slip road, go left.*

From Sheffield going south on A61: turn off right at sign to Chesterfield Trading Estate Sheepbridge. At the bottom of the slip road turn right under the A61.*

****Take first left into Sheepbridge Lane, pass Sheepbridge Centre on right and after 200 yds turn left into Foxwood Road. At roundabout, go straight over. Snowline Housewares is in the first building on the left.***

Open: Mon–Thur 10–4.30; Fri 10–4; Sat 10–1. Some Bank Holidays for special events, advisable to check first.
Closed: Please phone to check Christmas trading hours.
Cards: MasterCard, Visa.
Cars: Own large car-park.
Toilets: Yes, and for disabled.
Wheelchairs: Easy access to small shop.
Teas: In town.
Groups: Shopping groups welcome, please phone in advance.
Transport: Special early bus no. 120. from Chesterfield. Bus nos. 42 & 44 terminate at The Sandpiper pub, ½ mile from shop.
Mail order: Yes.
Catalogue: Trade catalogue only, prices quoted at time of enquiry.

18 Chesterfield Derbys *see map previous page*

Wynsors World of Shoes

Netto Retail Development, Sheffield Road S41 8JT
(01246) 276690

Men's, ladies' and children's fashion shoes in both leather and synthetic fabrics.

'Major sales January and July. Mainly perfects, a few seconds. 30% less than high street prices. Promotions every 6 weeks offering at least 50% off.'

See our display advertisement on p. 423

About ¾ mile north of town.

From town: take A61 north for Sheffield: go left at roundabout (Tesco on right) for Newbold/Stonegavels. Keep straight for ½ mile to roundabout: go right on to B6057. Shop is on left, past Mobil and Netto.

Coming south on A61: at roundabout with Tesco on left, go right for Whittington Moor. Follow road for ½ mile to roundabout: go right on to B6057. Shop is on left, past Mobil and Netto.

From large one-way system (Holywell Cross) on north side of town centre: take old Sheffield Road (B6057), following signs north to Whittington Moor. After roundabout, shop is on left, past Mobil and Netto.

Open: Mon, Tues, Wed, Sat 9–5.30; Thur, Fri 9–8; Sun 10–4.
Closed: Christmas and Boxing Days.
Cards: MasterCard, Style, Visa.
Cars: Large car-park at shop.
Toilets: No.
Wheelchairs: Easy access, no steps.
Teas: Café 200 yds from shop.
Groups: Shopping groups welcome with prior phone call.
Transport: Chesterfield bus nos. 14, 15, 19, 20, 21, 22, 36; Sheffield bus nos. 203, 204, X11 stop outside shop.
Mail order: No.

19 Church Gresley Derbys

T G Green Pottery

John Street DE11 8EE
Mon–Fri: (01283) 217981; weekends: 226696

Large selection of decorated pottery; plain coloured cookware and tableware; *Cornish* kitchenware. Table mats, trays, coasters, melamine food preparations, co-ordinated linens and small gifts.

'Please ring for special sale dates.'

Five miles south-east of Burton upon Trent, just off the A50, on south side of Swadlincote.

From Burton: take A50 south-east for Ashby. In Woodville, go right on to A514 for Swadlincote; take first left to Church Gresley/ Nuneaton A514; go left at roundabout for Measham B586. After 100 yds go left into private road; pottery is 200 yds on right.

From Swadlincote: take B586 south for Measham. Go uphill, past artificial ski slope on left; go straight at roundabout. After 100 yds, go left through vehicle welder's yard into private road; pottery is 200 yds on right.

From Moira: go north on B586: pass Q8 petrol on left. After ½ mile, go right into private road (100 yds before roundabout at A514).

From M42 exit 11: go north through Overseal to Castle Gresley. Take A514 east; go right on to B586; after 100 yds go left.

Open: Mon–Fri 9.30–5; Sat 9.30–4.30; Sun 10–4.
Closed: Easter Monday; please phone for Christmas opening.
Cards: MasterCard, Switch, Visa.
Cars: Own car-park.
Toilets: Yes.
Wheelchairs: Access to fairly spacious shop.
Teas: In Burton and Swadlincote.
Groups: To shop only by prior arrangement. Arrangements can be made for parties of 15 people or more to tour factory at £2 each. Mon–Thur only. Must be pre-booked: please contact Brenda Maddock.
Transport: None.

20 Crich Derbys

Crich Pottery

Market Place DE4 5DD
(01773) 853171

Large range of unique stoneware pottery with hand-decorated colourful designs in unusual glazes: oven-to-tableware, platters, lampbases, vases, jugs, flagons, cheese dishes, candle holders, book ends, salt pots, giant storage jars, plant pots, wall pots, handbasins and some tiles.

'Full price perfect items on ground floor; upstairs for slight seconds and discontinued designs at 30–50% off.'

Crich is a village about five miles north of Belper and six miles south-east of Matlock; the pottery is in the village square (about half a mile from the National Tramway Museum).

From the A6 (Matlock–Derby road): follow signs east into Crich. In the village, go right for Fritchley/Bullbridge. The pottery is 100 yds on left.

If you pass the National Tramway Museum on your left: continue downhill into village. At the stone cross, go right. At the crossing in the village, go left for Fritchley/Bullbridge. The pottery is 100 yds on left.

Open: Seven days a week 10–6, please phone to check.
Closed: Christmas, Boxing and New Year's Days.
Cards: Eurocheques, MasterCard, Visa.
Cars: Courtyard in front of shop.
Toilets: Yes, including for the disabled.
Wheelchairs: 1 step to downstairs showroom; staircase to upper floor.
Teas: Tea shop across the road.
Groups: Groups welcome, please phone in advance.
Transport: Buses from Alfreton, Matlock and Ripley.
Mail order: Yes.
Catalogue: Please phone for free brochure. Telephone orders taken with credit cards.

21 Denby Derbys

Dartington Crystal

Denby Pottery DE5 8NX
(01773) 513116

Wide selection of second quality *Dartington* crystal: clear crystal wine glasses, matching decanters, bowls, vases and gift ideas.

'All crystal at discounted prices.'

Within the Visitors Centre at Denby Pottery, on the B6179, two miles south of Ripley and eight miles north of Derby (but not in Denby village).

The pottery is clearly signposted on a sharp bend in the road (on the right if you come from Derby, on the left from Ripley).

From A38: the pottery is signposted where B6179 turns off.

From Belper: take A609 for Ilkeston. Go under A38; at traffic lights go left on to B6179 to Ripley. Pottery is shortly on right .

Open: Mon–Sat 9–5; Sun 10–5. Bank Holidays.
Closed: Christmas, Boxing and New Year's Days.
Cards: MasterCard, Visa.
Cars: Large car/coach park.
Toilets: Yes.
Wheelchairs: Easy access, large shop, no steps.
Teas: Restaurant in complex.
Groups: Shopping groups welcome.
Transport: Bus nos. 243 and 245 from Ripley
Mail order: No.
Catalogue: Free.

22 Denby Derbys

Denby Pottery Visitors Centre

DE5 8NX
(01773) 740799

Denby tableware, cookware and mugs – best and second qualities. Wedding list service. Also a speciality cookshop with a full scale demonstration kitchen, the *Dartington* crystal factory shop and gift and florist shop.

'Sales in January and June.'

On the B6179, two miles south of Ripley and eight miles north of Derby. The pottery is clearly signposted on a sharp bend in the road (on the right if you come from Derby, on left from Ripley).

From the A38: the pottery is signposted before the turning for Kilburn and Denby on the B6179.

From Belper: take A609 for Ilkeston. Go under A38; at traffic lights go left on to B6179 for Ripley. Pottery is shortly on right .

The visitor centre is by the main entrance.

Open: Mon–Sat (inc. Bank Holidays) 9.30–5; Sun 11–5.
Closed: Xmas, Boxing Day.
Cards: Connect, MasterCard, Switch, Visa.
Cars: Large car/coach-park.
Toilets: Yes.
Wheelchairs: Easy access to spacious shop, restaurant, Craftsman's Workshop, toilets. Regret wheelchairs cannot take part in full factory tour (safety).
Teas: Goodalls restaurant 9.30–4.30: home-made lunches etc.
Tours: Mon–Thur 10.30 & 1; Fri 10.30. Adults £3.50, children/OAPs £2.50. Groups welcome, please book for factory tours. Craftsman's Workshop open Mon–Sun 10–3.15: adults £2.50, children/OAPs £1.75. Phone Tours Reception.
Transport: Bus nos. 243 and 245 from Derby.
Mail order: No.

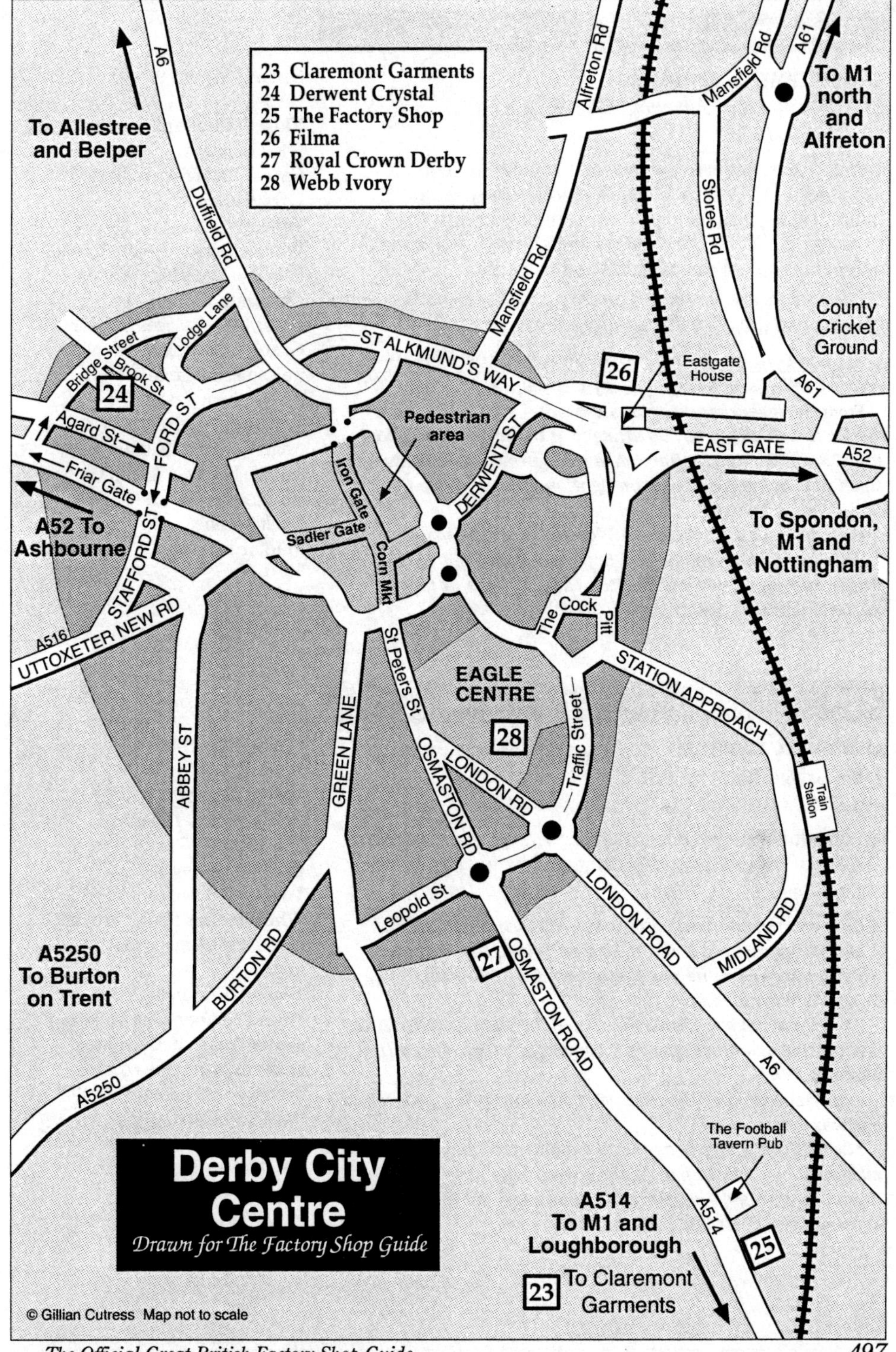
23 Claremont Garments
24 Derwent Crystal
25 The Factory Shop
26 Filma
27 Royal Crown Derby
28 Webb Ivory
To Allestree and Belper
A6
Duffield Rd
Alfreton Rd
Mansfield Rd
Stores Rd
To M1 north and Alfreton
A61
County Cricket Ground
Lodge Lane
Bridge Street
Brook St
24
FORD ST
Agard St
Friar Gate
A52 To Ashbourne
ST ALKMUND'S WAY
26
Eastgate House
EAST GATE
A52
To Spondon, M1 and Nottingham
Pedestrian area
Iron Gate
Sadler Gate
Corn Mkt
DERWENT ST
STAFFORD ST
A516
UTTOXETER NEW RD
The Cock Pit
STATION APPROACH
EAGLE CENTRE
28
St Peters St
Traffic Street
Train Station
ABBEY ST
GREEN LANE
OSMASTON RD
LONDON RD
LONDON ROAD
MIDLAND RD
Leopold St
A5250 To Burton on Trent
BURTON RD
27
OSMASTON ROAD
A6
A5250
The Football Tavern Pub
A514 To M1 and Loughborough
A514
25
23 To Claremont Garments
Derby City Centre
Drawn for The Factory Shop Guide
© Gillian Cutress Map not to scale

23 Derby Derbys *see map on previous page*

Claremont Garments

399 Boulton Lane, Allenton DE21 9TA
(01332) 691909

Ladies' wear: lingerie, swimwear, casualwear (bodies, leggings etc), dresses, blouses, skirts, trousers, and tailored suits, coats and jackets. Schoolwear: boys' trousers and shirts; girls' skirts and shirts. Boys' wear: a limited range of casual shirts and trousers.

'All garments are leading chainstore perfects, seconds or ends of lines, and are offered at greatly reduced prices.'

See our display advertisement on p. 539

About 3 miles south-east of Derby city centre.

From the inner ring road: take the A514 (Osmaston Road) signposted 'Melbourne'. Go straight at the major roundabout into Chellaston Road; after ½ mile turn left at traffic lights into Boulton Lane: the factory is on right, just past Jubilee Road (first turning on right).

From M1 exit 24: take the A6 for Derby. At the major roundabout in Alvaston (where Shardlow Road joins London Road), turn sharp left into Boulton Lane. Shop is at far end on left, almost opposite park.

Open: Mon–Fri 9–4.30; Sat 9–3.
Closed: Please phone about Bank Holidays.
Cards: All major credit cards.
Cars: On site.
Toilets: No.
Wheelchairs: Ramp to ground floor, but steps to first floor.
Changing rooms: Yes.
Teas: Lots of places in Derby.
Groups: Shopping groups welcome, but large groups please phone first.
Transport: Regular buses from Derby to Melbourne and Shelton Lock go down Chellaston Road and stop at Boulton Lane.
Mail order: No.

24 Derby Derbys *see map on previous page*

Derwent Crystal

Little Bridge Street DE1 3LF
(01332) 360186

English full-lead crystal glassware: wine glasses, tumblers and fancy gift items. Sandblasting and hand engraving.

'Factory shop prices. Always special offers.'

A third of a mile north-west of Derby Museum/Art Gallery.

Little Bridge Street is a tiny lane off Bridge Street, part of which comprises a one-way system on the A52, main Derby–Ashbourne road.

From Derby: aim for Ashbourne; go right off Friar Gate (A52) just outside inner ring road as if coming back into Derby (to Matlock A6).*

From Ashbourne via A52: as you come into town, go left into one-way system.*

****Go 100 yds along Bridge Street then keep straight (where main road bends right into Agard Street; take little lane to right (factory shop sign) – a narrow cul-de-sac leading to canal. At canal, go sharp left into yard.***

Open: Mon–Sat 9–5.
Closed: Bank Holidays; Christmas–New Year.
Cards: Amex, Diners, MasterCard, Visa.
Cars: In nearby streets.
Toilets: In town centre.
Wheelchairs: Rough ground to small showroom so a little tricky.
Teas: Café round the corner.
Tours: Not here, but you can see the action at Ashbourne glassworks of same company.
Transport: 20 minutes' walk from city centre.
Mail order: Yes.
Catalogue: Phone for free price list.

25 Derby Derbys see map on previous page

The Factory Shop

Osmaston Works, Osmaston Road DE3 8LE
(01332) 360045

Waxed jackets, ladies', gents' and children's anoraks and waterproofs. Golfwear, sweatshirts, bodywarmers, dress shirts, workwear, high visibility clothing, microthermal jackets etc.

'Shop under new management.'

About ¾ mile south-east of the city centre.

Osmaston Road (A514), signposted Melbourne, runs south from the inner ring road.

If you come south from Derby: the shop is just past The Football Tavern on left.

If you come north into Derby: go over the railway, then the shop is about 100 yds on right.

Open: Tues–Fri 12–4.30; some Saturdays 10–1, please phone to check.
Closed: Mondays; Bank Holidays; Christmas–New Year.
Cards: None.
Cars: Free parking at rear (enter through archway beside shop).
Toilets: No.
Wheelchairs: One step to medium-sized shop.
Changing rooms: Yes.
Teas: Pub next door but one.
Groups: Groups welcome to shop but must phone first.
Transport: Buses from bus station or The Spot, Osmaston Road. Get off at Ivy Square.

26 Derby Derbys see map on previous page

Filma

Clarke Street DE1 2BU
(01332) 347571

Lingerie made here: full and half-slips, bras, french knickers, teddies, nightdresses, negligées, thermals, corselettes, girdles, cami-tops, suspender belts and briefs. Range of large sizes.

'Almost all stock is perfect, with some seconds in bras, girdles and corselettes. Party plan and small traders welcome.'

Not far from city centre, just outside north-east section of the inner ring road.

Best to go clockwise round the ring road: turn off for A52 (towards Nottingham) then take first left, immediately in front of huge glass Eastgate House. Clarke Street is opposite and the shop is on the left, next to The New Station pub.

If you find yourself going anti-clockwise round the ring road: turn off to Nottingham (A52) (you will see huge glass Eastgate House on left). Turn left at first roundabout; keep going left until you see The New Station pub: turn beside it into Clarke Street; shop is on left.

Open: Mon–Fri 10.30–4.30.
Closed: Bank Holidays; Christmas–New Year.
Cards: None.
Cars: Limited parking outside shop.
Toilets: In town.
Wheelchairs: One tiny step to small shop.
Changing rooms: No.
Teas: In town.
Tours: No.
Transport: 10 minutes' walk from the city centre.
Mail order: Yes. Please phone for details.

27 Derby Derbys *see map on earlier page*

Royal Crown Derby

194 Osmaston Road DE3 8JZ
(01332) 712800

Finely decorated bone china tableware; giftware such as paperweights. Wide selection of seconds.

'Some best quality but mainly seconds for sale.'

About ½ mile south of the city centre.

From inner ring road: take A514 (Osmaston Road) signposted to Melbourne. The pottery is about ¼ mile on right, set slightly back but clearly visible.

If you come north into Derby on A514: go almost into city centre and look for this clearly marked company set back on left.

Open: Mon–Sat 9–5.30; Sun 10–4.
Closed: Most Bank Holidays – please check prior to visit.
Cards: Amex, Diners, JCB, MasterCard, Visa.
Cars: Limited car-park; in road.
Toilets: Yes (not weekends!).
Wheelchairs: Easy access to shop but tour is unsuitable for the less-than-agile.
Teas: Drinks machine (not weekends). Refreshments for groups by prior arrangement.
Tours: Please arrange in advance mentioning this book. Up to 45 people (must be over 10 yrs). £3 pp, £2.75 OAP's & students. Tours Mon–Thur 10.30 & 1.45; Fri 10.30 & 1.15. None weekends or late Spring Bank Holiday week.
Transport: Many buses from Derby Market Place.
Mail order: No.

28 Derby Derbys *see map on earlier page*

Webb Ivory

38 Main Centre DE1 2PF
(01332) 204078

Fascinating variety of surplus catalogue stocks of greetings cards, wrapping papers, household goods, toys, small gifts and clothing.

'50% off catalogue prices.'

In the city centre.

In the pedestrian area adjacent to the Eagle Centre (main shopping precinct) and opposite Argos and Wilkinsons.

Open: Mon–Sat 9–5. Some Bank Holidays, please check.
Closed: Christmas–New Year.
Cards: Most major credit cards; Switch.
Cars: Public car-parks close by.
Toilets: In town centre.
Wheelchairs: Easy access to ground floor shop.
Teas: In town centre.
Groups: No.
Transport: Five minutes' walk from central bus station.
Mail order: No.

Market days

Alford	Mon to Sat indoor general
Arnold	Tues, Fri, Sat outdoor general
Ashbourne	Thur, Sat outdoor general
Bakewell	Mon outdoor general
Belper	Sat outdoor general
Boston	Wed, Sat outdoor general
Burton-on-Trent	Thur, Fri, Sat outdoor general
Buxton	Tues, Sat outdoor general
Castle Donnington	Sun indoor general
Chesterfield	Mon, Fri, Sat outdoor general. Thur flea market
Creswell	Mon outdoor general
Derby	Tues to Sat indoor general and flea market
Dronfield	Thur outdoor general
Gainsborough	Tues, Sat outdoor general
Grantham	Sat outdoor general
Heanor	Fri, Sat outdoor general
Holbeach	Thur, Sat outdoor general
Horncastle	Mon (Jun to Aug), Thur outdoor general
Hucknall	Fri outdoor general
Ilkeston	Thur, Sat outdoor general. Thur outdoor second-hand
Kirkby-in-Ashfield	Fri, Sat indoor general
Lincoln	Mon to Sat indoor general
Long Eaton	Wed, Fri, Sat outdoor general. Tues outdoor second-hand
Louth	Wed, Fri, Sat outdoor general
Mabelthorpe	Mon (Jun to Aug) Thur outdoor general
Mansfield	Mon, Thur, Fri, Sat outdoor general Tues, Wed outdoor flea market
Market Rasen	Tues outdoor general
Matlock	Tues, Fri indoor general
Newark	Wed, Fri, Sat outdoor general. Mon antiques, crafts
Nottingham	Mon to Sat indoor/outdoor general (city centre)
Retford	Thur, Fri, Sat outdoor general. Fri antiques/bric à brac
Ripley	Sat outdoor general
Scunthorpe	Fri, Sat indoor/outdoor general
Sheffield	Mon, Tues, Wed, Fri, Sat indoor general
Shepshed	Fri outdoor general
Shirebrook	Wed, Fri outdoor general. Wed flea market
Sleaford	Mon, Fri, Sat outdoor general
South Normanton	Tues outdoor general
Spalding	Tues, Sat outdoor general
Spilsby	Mon outdoor general
Staveley	Fri outdoor general
Sutton-in-Ashfield	Tues, Fri, Sat outdoor general. Mon to Sat indoor general
Swadlincote	Tues, Fri, Sat indoor general
Wirksworth	Tues outdoor general
Worksop	Wed, Fri, Sat outdoor general

Thanks to World's Fair Ltd. for allowing us to copy information from their useful Markets Yearbook.

29 Grantham Lincs

Boundary Mill Stores

Gonerby Moor NG32 2AA
(01476) 591001

Vast range of ladies' and men's quality garments from all over Europe. Over 100 brands including *Centaur, Dannimac, Double Two, Farah, Fruit of the Loom, J H Collectibles, Levi, Liz Claiborne, Lyle & Scott, Pierre Cardin, Timberland, Whimsy, Windsmoor* and *Wolsey*. Shoes and boots by *Kurt Geiger* and *Carvela. Charnos, Gossard, Jockey* and *Naturana* lingerie.'

See our display advertisement on inside front cover

Fronting on to the A1, north of Grantham.

At roundabout, turn off for Grantham on the B1174. Shortly turn right. Boundary Mill is conspicuous building on left.

Open: Mon–Sat 9.30–5.30; Sun and Bank Holidays 11–5.
Closed: Easter Sunday and Christmas Day.
Cards: MasterCard, Switch, Visa.
Cars: Massive space on all sides with reserved area for coaches.
Toilets: Yes.
Wheelchairs: Easy access to huge ground floor shop, with lift to first floor.
Changing rooms: Yes.
Teas: Coffee shop on first floor within Downtown.
Groups: Coach groups welcome to shop.
Transport: No local buses.
Mail order: No.

30 Grantham Lincs

Designer Fabric Superstore

91–93 Westgate NG31 6PG
(01476) 570022

Huge selection of furnishing fabrics. Plain & patterned sheeting. Curtain poles, tracks and fittings, roller blinds, tapes, bean bags, pet beds, floor and scatter cushions.

'8000 rolls of fabric in stock. Custom-made curtain service available. Perfects, seconds and ends of lines sold here.'

See our display advertisement on p. 195

In centre of town opposite the Westgate exit of The George Shopping Centre.

From the south: follow the main road through town: pass Marks & Spencer on right then turn left at next lights.*

From the north: go into town. Pass Kwik-Fit on right then go right at next lights.*

****Take first left (Market Cross on right) into Westgate. Shop is about 100 yds on right.***

Open: Mon–Sat 9.30–5.30; Sun 10–4. Bank Holidays.
Closed: Easter Sunday, Christmas and Boxing Days.
Cards: MasterCard, Switch, Visa.
Cars: In market square nearby. Car-park to rear of shop can be reached via Union Street into Greyfriars.
Toilets: In The George Shopping Centre opposite.
Wheelchairs: Easy access to huge shop.
Teas: Own restaurant and coffee house 'Goodfellows'.
Groups: Groups welcome, please phone in advance.
Transport: Any bus or train to Grantham.
Mail order: No.

31 Grantham Lincs

Rutland Lighting

10–12 Watergate NG31 6PP
(01476) 591049

Full range of lampshades in many different styles and fabrics; table lamps, standard lamps, chandeliers, pendants; accessories.

'Items made by this company. Also chainstore returns and ends of lines.'

On the main road through town.

From the High Street, with the ancient Angel & Royal Hotel on right: go 200 yds along High Street/Watergate; clearly marked shop is on right, 100 yds before Gateway on left.

Coming south into Grantham from A1: take old A1 into town centre. This brings you into Grantham in southerly direction. Pass Gateway on right; clearly marked shop is 100 yds on left.

Open: Mon–Sat 9–5.30.
Closed: Christmas and Boxing Days.
Cards: MasterCard, Switch, Visa.
Cars: 25 yds from shop.
Toilets: No.
Wheelchairs: Access easy, one small step to large shop.
Teas: In town.
Groups: No guided tours; coach parties of shoppers welcome but please phone first.
Transport: Regular buses from outlying towns and villages.
Mail order: No.

32 Grantham Lincs

Witham Contours

Harlaxton Road NG31 7SA
(01476) 565268

Ladies' high fashion underwear, night and swimwear for the young at heart.

'Won Designer of Year Award 1990.'

See our display advertisement opposite

A short distance from town centre towards A1.

From town centre: follow A607 towards Melton Mowbray. Go under railway to the end of a long row of terraced houses. Pass Eddison factory on left and go to end of tree-lined section of this road: Witham Contours is on left.

From A1: turn towards Grantham at junction with A607 (second turn-off from south or third from north). Go over traffic lights; Witham Contours is on right.

Open: Mon–Thur 10–5; Fri 10–3; Sat 10–1.
Closed: Bank Holidays; Christmas–New Year.
Cards: No.
Cars: Outside shop.
Toilets: Yes.
Wheelchairs: Two steps to medium-sized shop.
Changing rooms: Yes.
Teas: Pub next door (open all day) and in town.
Transport: Buses every 20 minutes to Earle's Field. About 15 minutes' walk from station.
Mail order: No.

33 Hardstoft near Chesterfield Derbys

Yew Tree

Yew Tree Farm, S45 8AE
(01246) 853614

Summer: Swedish garden furniture and outdoor lighting, indoor lighting, indoor and outdoor candles, terracotta and glazed planters, barbecues. *Winter*: Swedish/English electrical Christmas decorations, Swedish candlesticks and all other Christmas decorations.

'Perfects and seconds at up to 30% less than high street prices.'

Hardstoft is 6 miles south-east of Chesterfield.

From M1 exit 29: follow signs to Clay Cross. After 250 yds go left for Hardwick Hall. Continue for 2 miles, pass Hardwick Hall turning and go under M1. Turn right for Hardstoft and Tibshelf at junction. Go uphill for 1 mile and Yew Tree Farm is first building on right.

Open: *April–Aug* and *Oct–Dec*: Mon–Fri 1–5; Sat–Sun 9–5. Bank Holidays. Welcome to phone for special opening any time.
Closed: *Sept; Jan–end March*. Please phone for opening hours between Christmas and New Year.
Cards: No.
Cars: Own large car-park.
Toilets: Yes.
Wheelchairs: Two steps to shop, please ask for assistance.
Teas: Local pubs.
Groups: Small groups welcome to shop.
Transport: Buses from Chesterfield and Alfreton stop on main road, 300 yds from shop.
Mail order: No.

See our entry opposite

34 Heanor Derbys

The Fabric Factory (Nottingham)

Loscoe Road, DE7 7FE
(01773) 718911

Large range of curtaining, upholstery and furnishing fabrics. Dress fabrics, fleece, T-shirting, lycra, cottons, linens, jerseys. Large bridal and haberdashery departments.

'Lowest possible prices on all fabrics in the area.'

See our display advertisement on next page

On the A6007 between Heanor and Codnor.

From centre of Heanor: go north on A6007 for Loscoe/ Codnor/ Ripley. Go downhill out of town and road bends to left: this conspicuous shop (brick building with silver roof) is on the right.

From Ripley/Codnor: at traffic lights in Codnor, go south on A6007 for Heanor. Go through Loscoe then, at start of Heanor, pass Total petrol station and Kwik-Fit on left. This building is immediately past them.

Open: Mon–Sat 9.30–5.30; Sun 10–2. Please phone to check Bank Holiday opening times.
Closed: Easter Sunday and Christmas Day.
Cards: MasterCard, Switch, Visa.
Cars: Own car-park.
Toilets: Yes.
Wheelchairs: One small step to huge shop.
Teas: Self-service cafeteria with vending machines for hot and cold drinks and snacks. Also Sky TV lounge.
Groups: Groups of shoppers always welcome.
Transport: Buses from Ripley, Heanor and Alfreton.

35 Heanor Derbys

Langley Furniture

Delves Road, Heanor Gate Industrial Estate DE75 7SJ (01773) 765544

A comprehensive, distinctive range of furniture made individually in selected quality pine by traditional carpentry methods. Stained to client's colour choice with exclusive mixes of natural pigments and finished with high quality wax polish. The *Langley Collection* is a complete range of bedroom, lounge & dining room furniture & individually designed fitted or free-standing kitchen units.

'Also made-to-measure service to clients' designs & dimensions. For commercial clients stand-alone display & merchandiser units & other specialist fixtures can be designed & manufactured. Free delivery within 25 miles of Heanor for orders over £150. Competitive rates for deliveries within UK. Also in Joseph Street, Belper (01773) 820410 and Digby Street, Ilkeston Junction (0115) 944 1040.'

On the industrial estate west of Heanor: enter from Derby Road (A608).

From Derby direction, coming east along Derby Road (A608) towards Heanor: in Smalley, go downhill, and right after Heanor Gate school for Shipley Country Park and Heanor Gate Industrial Estate. Langley Furniture is in first factory on the right.

From Heanor: take A608 for Smalley/Derby. Pass The Jolly Colliers on the right. After Total petrol on left, turn left into Heanor Gate Road (sign to Heanor Gate Industrial Estate). Shop is 100 yds on right.

Open: Mon–Fri 8–6; Sat 8–5; Sun and Bank Holidays 10.30–4.
Closed: Christmas and Boxing Days.
Cards: Delta, MasterCard, Switch, Visa.
Cars: Own car-park.
Toilets: Yes.
Wheelchairs: Ramp to medium-sized shop.
Teas: Complimentary coffee and biscuits.
Groups: Small groups welcome to shop (but not to factory itself).
Transport: Nottingham and Derby buses stop nearby; 2 miles from station at Langley Mill.
Mail order: Yes.
Catalogue: Telephone for free brochure and price list.

36 Heanor Derbys

The Wallpaper Factory Shop

10 High Street, Red Lion Square DE75 7PB (01773) 711422

Wallpapers, borders and paints: *Zen* and *Coloroll* wall coverings; *Fine Art, Holden, Primose Gallery, Country Decor* and *Distinctive* wallpapers; *Leyland* and *Dulux* paints. Decorating sundries.

'Most items are perfect ends of designs; others are slightly substandard, direct from manufacturers. Wallpapers and borders from £1 per roll. Dado rails from 45p per ft. 5-litre coloured emulsion silk £10; matt £8; white emulsion from £5. End of range clearance sale in January.'

Near the town centre, 150 yds from the market square.

From Ilkeston coming north: at traffic lights, go left into centre of Heanor. Pass the market place on your left.*

***From Heanor market place: go downhill (Boots and Woolworths on your right). After pedestrian lights, the clearly marked shop is on the right corner (facing The Red Lion) at the junction where the A608 goes left for Smalley/Derby.**

Coming south from Codnor: go uphill into Heanor. At the junction where the A608 goes right for Smalley/Derby, this shop is on the left.

From Derby via A608: at the T-junction as you come into Heanor, this shop is facing you.

Open: Mon–Tues and Thur–Sat 9.30–5; Wed 9.30–1.
Closed: Wed pm. Christmas, Boxing & New Year's Days.
Cards: Amex, Delta, MasterCard, Switch, Visa.
Cars: Car-park at rear.
Toilets: In nearby market square.
Wheelchairs: Easy access to ground floor; stairs to anaglyptas and embossed papers.
Teas: Café two doors away.
Groups: Groups welcome to shop although probably not very suitable.
Transport: Buses from Ripley, Derby, Mansfield, Nottingham and Eastwood.
Mail order: No.

See our entry no 34

37 Holbeach Lincs

The Factory Shop Ltd.

51 Fleet Street PE12 7AU
(01406) 422180

Clothing and footwear for all the family. Toiletries, cosmetics, luggage and bags. Good range of branded bedding and towels, housewares, kitchenware and toys. Several concessions selling quality merchandise.

'Large stock of branded and chainstore items, all at greatly reduced prices. Deliveries of new stock every week to give an ever changing selection.'

On the east side of town, about ½ mile from the town centre on the site of the old bus garage.

From the north on A17 and the west on A151: follow signs into Holbeach. At the only traffic lights in town take the B1515 towards Fleet Hargate and King's Lynn. The shop is about ½ mile on the left, set back from the road 10 yds after the sign pointing right to Holbeach Community Centre.

From King's Lynn on A17: turn on to B1515 for Holbeach. Pass the Burmah petrol station on left and the shop is about 500 yds on the right, set back from the road.

Open: Mon–Sat 9–5; Sun 10–4.
Closed: Christmas and Boxing Days.
Cards: MasterCard, Switch, Visa.
Cars: Ample free car-parking.
Toilets: No.
Wheelchairs: Good access into and around shop.
Changing rooms: Yes.
Teas: Cafés and restaurants in Holbeach.
Tours: Shopping groups welcome. For organiser/driver incentives please phone.
Transport: Buses from Boston, King's Lynn and Spalding.
Mail order: No.

38 Hucknall Notts

Jaeger

39 Watnall Road NG15 7JR
(0115) 963 9334

High quality ladies' and men's knitwear together with ladies' blouses, skirts and dresses etc; men's suits, jackets and trousers etc.

'Ends of lines and slight substandards.'

In the town centre.

From Hucknall High Street (A611): at traffic lights near Boots, turn off towards Watnall B6009 and 'Police'. Shop is 300 yds on left, on corner of Watnall Road and Beardall Street.

From Watnall: take B6009 for Hucknall. Pass the Flying Bedstead pub on right; after ¼ mile, Police Headquarters is on left; Jaeger (with broad white fascia) is on the right, on the near right corner of Beardall Street.

Open: Tues–Fri 9.45–4.45; Sat 10–1.
Closed: Monday; Bank Holidays; Christmas–New Year.
Cards: Connect, MasterCard, Switch, Visa.
Cars: Local side streets.
Toilets: In town centre.
Wheelchairs: Four steps to sizeable shop.
Changing rooms: Yes.
Teas: Locally.
Tours: Shoppers please phone Mrs Dorothy Hill.
Transport: Any bus to Hucknall.
Mail order: No.

39 Huthwaite, Sutton-in-Ashfield Notts

B & B Factory Shop

see map on p. 545

19/21 Sutton Road NG17 2NZ
(01623) 554061

Safety footwear – shoes, boots and *Rigger* boots for men and women. Also hiking boots for all. Fashion, leisure and sports footwear, slippers and sandals for men and women. Some protective clothing and workwear for industry.

This is the main road (B6026) through Huthwaite leading into Sutton-in-Ashfield.

From M1 exit 28: take A38 in direction of Mansfield. Go left at first traffic lights, then right at cross-roads. Shop is ½ mile on left, just before Fina petrol.

From Mansfield: follow signs into Sutton-in-Ashfield (at roundabout by hospital on right, go straight, not left on to new A38 towards M1/Derby); go through Sutton then at large roundabout follow signs to Huthwaite. Shop is on right, 1 mile from Sutton centre and shortly after Fina petrol on right.

Open: Mon–Fri 9–5.30; Sat 9–5.
Closed: Bank Holidays; Christmas–New Year. Phone to confirm exact dates.
Cards: MasterCard, Switch, Visa.
Cars: Unlimited parking in side streets.
Toilets: No.
Wheelchairs: Easy access.
Teas: Several cafés in Sutton-in-Ashfield.
Tours: No.
Transport: Bus stop outside for bus nos. 1, 1A, 30, 341, 342, 345 from Sutton. Nearest rail station is Alfreton Parkway.

40 Ilkeston Derbys

see map on next page

Charnos

Corporation Road DE7 4BR
(0115) 944 0301

Wide range of ladies' lingerie, hosiery, underwear, knitwear, dresses, skirts and blouses; children's wear; men's wear; sportswear; household linens.

See our display advertisement on p. 535

At the southern end of Ilkeston, just off the A609.

From Nottingham/Trowell via A609: cross railway and canal. After Rutland Windows showroom take first left (Thurman Street) which leads to Corporation Road. Charnos is at far end on left.

From Derby/Spondon via A6096: turn right for Little Hallam half way up Little Hallam Hill. This is Quarry Hill Road. Take first left (Longfield Lane) then seventh left, Corporation Road. Charnos is large building on right.

From Ilkeston and other directions: continue downhill on the A609, over the pedestrian crossing and right in front of Rutland Window into Thurman Street which leads to Corporation Road. Charnos is at far end on left.

Open: Tues–Fri 10–4; Sat 9.30–1.
Closed: Monday; Christmas–New Year.
Cards: MasterCard, Visa.
Cars: In factory yard and Corporation Road.
Toilets: No.
Wheelchairs: Easy access to large shop.
Changing rooms: Yes.
Teas: Cafés in Ilkeston.
Groups: Tours of factory for organised groups – please contact Suzie Sheldon (0115 932 2191) to arrange. Shopping groups welcome, prior phone call appreciated.
Transport: Trent bus no. 235 from Nottingham; Trent bus nos. 253 and 254 from Ilkeston Market Place – stop on Corporation Road.
Mail order: No.

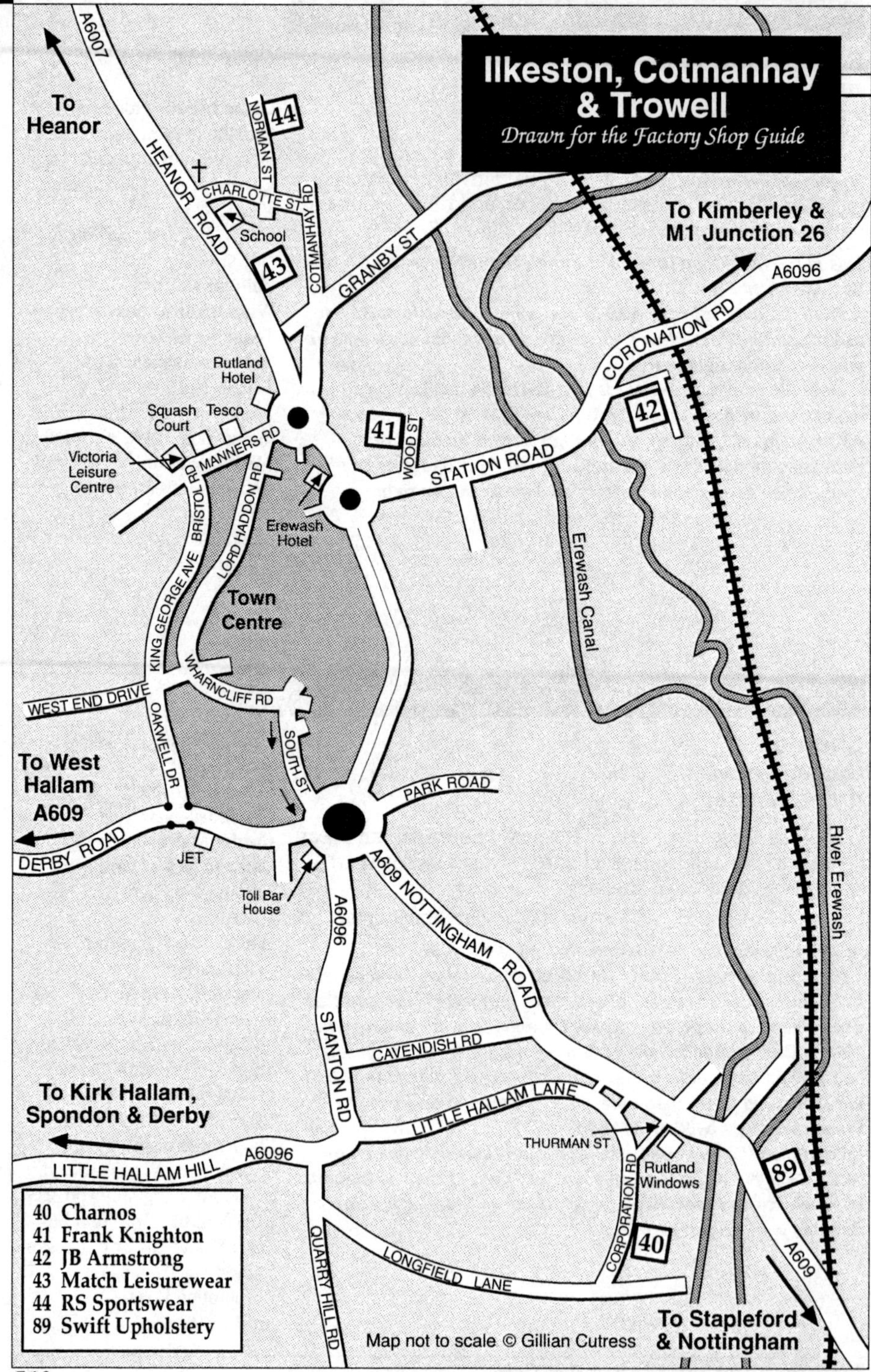

40 Charnos
41 Frank Knighton
42 JB Armstrong
43 Match Leisurewear
44 RS Sportswear
89 Swift Upholstery

41 Ilkeston Derbys *see map opposite*

Frank Knighton & Sons

Critchley Court, Wood Street DE7 8GF
(0115) 930 6567

Wide selection of leather chairs and suites, and also upholstered suites.

'Leather suites from £999 to £2,500. Coil sprung fabric suites from £1,399 to £1,999. Also at Castle Boulevard, Nottingham (0115 950 9940).'

See our display advertisement above

From M1 exit 26: follow signs to Ilkeston. Stay on A6096 into town. You come into Station Road; Wood Street is second to last turning on right before roundabout.*

From Nottingham/Derby: go uphill in town; at roundabout get on to new Ilkeston bypass. At next roundabout go right for M1 north/Kimberley/Awsworth; take first left, Wood Street.*

From Heanor: come downhill into town; at roundabout, take second exit on to Ilkeston bypass. At next roundabout, go left for M1 north/Kimberley/Awsworth. Take first left, Wood Street.*

Shop is in old large red-brick building 50 yds on left.

Open: Mon–Sat 9–6; Sun 11–1 (viewing only). Bank Holidays.
Closed: Christmas, Boxing and New Year's Days.
Cards: MasterCard.
Cars: Space for 100.
Toilets: Yes.
Wheelchairs: Two steps; help gladly given. Large shop.
Teas: In Ilkeston.
Groups: You can always ask to see your suite being made. Group visits to shop welcome – no need to book.
Transport: Easy walking distance from town centre.
Mail order: No.

42 Ilkeston Derbys *see map on previous page*

J B Armstrong & Co.

Armstrong's Mill, Middleton Street, off Station Road DE7 5TT
(0115) 932 4913

Men's suits, jackets, trousers and accessories. Ladies' suits, jackets, skirts, blouses and accessories.

'Perfects and seconds at very competitive prices.'

See our display advertisement opposite

East of town centre near railway line.

From Nottingham & M1 exit 26: take A610, following signs for Ilkeston; go left at first intersection (A6096); enter Ilkeston over railway bridge; turn immediately sharp left. Armstrong's Mill is on right.

From Nottingham/Trowell on A609: as you reach town centre, go straight at large roundabout on to dual carriageway; turn right at next roundabout into Station Road for Kimberley/M1.*

From Derby on A609: turn left at large roundabout at top of town centre into dual carriageway, then right at next roundabout into Station Road for Kimberley/M1.*

From Heanor on A6007: as you enter Ilkeston at first island follow sign to Nottingham, then turn left at next roundabout into Station Road for Kimberley/M1.

****Pass Vauxhall dealership on left then veer right before going over railway bridge. Armstrong's Mill is straight ahead on right.***

Open: Mon–Fri 9.15–5 (Wed late night till 6); Sat 9.30–5.30; Sun 10.30–4.30. Bank Holidays.
Closed: Christmas Day.
Cards: MasterCard, Switch, Visa.
Cars: Own large free car-park.
Toilets: Yes.
Wheelchairs: Difficult, but assistance gladly given.
Changing rooms: Yes.
Teas: Own coffee shop.
Groups: Groups including coaches welcome to shop. Please phone first.
Transport: Any bus to Ilkeston.
Mail order: No.

43 Ilkeston Derbys *see map on previous page*

Match Leisurewear Manufacturers

Norton Buildings, 10 Heanor Road DE7 8EP
(0115) 944 4554

Top quality clothing: jackets, trousers, skirts, lingerie; schoolwear, leisurewear, sportswear, including golf, gym, bowls, football strips; reversible school rugby tops. Also fleece cardigans, jumpers and tracksuits.

'Sizes from 1 yr to 60" chest. Most things made on premises. Orders taken. Embroidery service and screen printing. School orders.'

On the northern edge of Ilkeston.

From Ilkeston: take A6007 north for Heanor.*

From M1 and directions south: at roundabout in town, get on to new bypass. Go over three roundabouts, exiting for Heanor A6007 and American Adventure.*

****Shop is 50 yds on right, on second floor of Norton Buildings, opposite Wileda.***

From Heanor: take A6007 south to Ilkeston. Pass Texaco then Rutland Cottage, both on left. After red brick church on left, continue down Heanor Road about ½ mile. Shop is on left on second floor of Norton Buildings (big sign 'Norton Plastics'), opposite Wileda.

Open: Mon–Sat 9–5. Bank Holidays 10–4.
Closed: Christmas, Boxing and New Year's Days. Phone Mrs Smedley to confirm times.
Cards: MasterCard, Visa.
Cars: At front of shop on main road.
Toilets: Yes.
Wheelchairs: Shop on second floor.
Changing rooms: Yes.
Teas: Local cafés.
Groups: Coach parties welcome any time.
Transport: Buses from Heanor and Ripley.
Mail order: Yes.
Catalogue: No.

See our entry opposite

44 Ilkeston Derbys *see map on previous page*

R S Sports & Leisurewear

192–194 Norman Street, Cotmanhay DE7 8NR
(0115) 932 3865

Sports and leisurewear for all the family: jogging suits, sweatshirts, bottoms, cardigans, ski pants and leggings; school wear. Wide range of exclusive styles all made on premises in choice of over 15 colours from stock or made-to-measure. All sizes from 1–2 years to XXXXL (54" chest, 60" waist). No size too big! Customers' own designs.

'Small family business welcoming party planners and traders. Best local prices since 1984. Sweatshirts from £3; jog suits from £6; cardigans from £3.75; jog bottoms from £3.'

On the northern edge of Ilkeston.

From Ilkeston: take A6007 north for Heanor. Cross brick railway bridge, look for Apricot Nursing Home on left and school on right: take next right, before red brick church on right, into Charlotte Street.*

From Heanor: take A6007 south to Ilkeston. Pass Texaco then Rutland Cottage, both on left. After red brick church on left, go left (Charlotte Street).*

****Turn left again (Norman Street); go almost to far end. Well marked entrance is through archway on right; follow signs to back.***

Open: Mon–Fri 9–4; Sat 10–2 (phone to confirm).
Closed: Bank Holidays; Christmas–New Year. Ring to check.
Cards: None, but school vouchers accepted.
Cars: In street.
Toilets: Ask if desperate!
Wheelchairs: One small step, small shop.
Changing rooms: Yes.
Teas: Local cafés.
Groups: Not really able to cope with groups.
Transport: Ilkeston/Heanor bus: get off at nursing home then 10 minutes' walk.
Mail order: Yes.
Catalogue: Phone for free price list, mentioning this guide. No seconds available by mail order.

45 Kirkby-in-Ashfield Notts *see map on p. 545*

Claremont Garments

Portland Street NG17 7AB
(01623) 720240

Ladies' wear: lingerie, swimwear, casualwear (bodies, leggings etc), dresses, blouses, skirts, trousers, and tailored suits, coats and jackets. Schoolwear: boys' trousers and shirts; girls' skirts and shirts. Boys' wear: a limited range of casual shirts and trousers.

'All garments are leading chainstore perfects, seconds or ends of lines, and are offered at greatly reduced prices.'

See our display advertisement on p. 539

In the centre of Kirkby.

From the traffic lights in Kirkby (The Nag's Head on left): go a short distance north along Lowmoor Road South towards Sutton. Pass Solo then the doctors' surgery on the left. Go left into Portland Street. Shop is at far end on right.

From the M1 exit 28/west: take A38 towards Mansfield. At the fifth traffic lights, go right on to B6021 then right again one mile further at T-junction into Lowmoor Road. Keep straight for Kirkby. Pass Esso petrol on left, then fish & chip shop, and go immediately right. Shop is at far end on right.

Open: Mon–Fri 9–4.30; Sat 9–3.
Closed: Please phone about Bank Holidays.
Cards: Most major credit cards.
Cars: Own car-park.
Toilets: Nearby supermarket.
Wheelchairs: Ramp to medium sized shop.
Changing rooms: Yes.
Teas: Nearby supermarket.
Transport: 5-minute walk from town centre.
Mail order: No.

46 Kirkby-in-Ashfield Notts *see map on p. 545*

Forget-Me-Not Lingerie

Southwell Lane NG17 8EY
(01623) 750599

Ladies' nightwear, pyjamas, negligées, underwear, briefs, camitops and sets. Most garments in polyester satin. Girls' nightwear and underwear.

'Ends of lines plus seconds of chainstore items at about half price.'

On the west side of Kirkby.

From traffic lights in Kirkby (Barclays Bank on left, The Nag's Head on right): take Station Road (B6020) for Pinxton. Keep straight. Pass Victoria Road Post Office on right then take third right, Southwell Lane. Shop is 20 yds on right.

Coming south from Sutton on B6018: pass Elf petrol on left; go left at mini-roundabout into Chapel Street (for Portland Park Visitor Centre).*

Coming north from Pinxton on B6018: pass The Duke of Wellington on right; go right at mini-roundabout into Chapel Street (for Portland Park Visitor Centre).*

****Pass Sherwood House Inn on right; take third left, Southwell Lane. Shop 20 yds on right.***

Open: Mon, Wed & Fri 9–12.30 & 1.30–4.30.
Closed: Tuesday & Thursday; Bank Holidays; Christmas–New Year.
Cards: None.
Cars: In street outside.
Toilets: Yes.
Wheelchairs: Two steps. Fine for prams, tricky for wheelchairs.
Changing rooms: No.
Teas: In Sutton or Kirkby.
Groups: No tours of factory; groups welcome to the shop, please ring beforehand.
Transport: Trent bus nos. 41 & 42 (Mansfield–Nottingham).
Mail order: No.

47 Kirkby-in-Ashfield Notts *see map on p. 545*

Paul Steiger

Byron Avenue, Lowmoor Industrial Estate NG17 7LB
(01623) 721628

Curtain lace, by the yard and all types of ready-mades; also enlarging range to cover a collection of roller blinds, shower curtains, display tables with tablecloths and matching all-lace window sets. All made on site.

'First quality at factory prices and good quality seconds.'

Between Kirkby and Sutton-in-Ashfield.

From M1 exit 28: take A38 for Mansfield. Go right at fifth traffic lights (for Kirkby-in-Ashfield Industrial Estates); at next lights go right on to B6021 (Lowmoor Road); after 100 yds go left (Byron Avenue).*

From traffic lights in centre of Kirkby (Nag's Head pub on left): take B6021 for one mile: stay on Lowmoor Road. Pass Romo factory on left, then go right into Byron Avenue.*

****Go left after Paul Steiger factory into Prospect Close: factory shop on left.***

Open: Mon–Fri 10–4. Some Bank Holidays – please phone.
Closed: Saturday; Christmas–New Year.
Cars: Street parking and own car-park.
Toilets: In town.
Wheelchairs: Ramp to door.
Teas: In town.
Groups: Groups welcome; please phone Dorothy Adkin first.
Transport: Bus no. 120 to Lowmoor Road.
Mail order: No.

48 Kirkby-in-Ashfield Notts *see map on p. 545*

White Angel

Unit 38, Unity Road, Lowmoor Industrial Estate NG17 7LF
(01623) 722290

Net curtaining by the yard and ready-made net curtains. Printed and plain curtain fabrics and ready-made curtains. Curtain track, accessories, roller blinds, tablecoths, towels, home furnishings, quilt covers and quilts.

'Well stocked shop with friendly service.'

From M1 exit 28: take A38 for Mansfield. Go right at fifth traffic lights into Oddicroft Lane (for Kirkby-in-Ashfield Industrial Estates); at next lights go right on to B6021 (Lowmoor Road); after 100 yds go left (Byron Avenue).*

From Kirkby centre traffic lights (Nag's Head pub on left): take B6021 north for one mile; continue along Lowmoor Road; pass Romo factory on left; go right into Byron Avenue.*

****Go right into Unity Road. Company is immediately on right, clearly marked.***

Open: Mon–Thur 10–4; Fri 10–5; Sat 10–2.
Closed: Bank Holidays; Christmas–New Year.
Cards: MasterCard, Visa.
Cars: Own large car-park.
Toilets: By request.
Wheelchairs: No steps, big shop.
Teas: In town.
Groups: Shopping groups welcome, but please telephone first.
Transport: Bus no. 120 to Lowmoor Road.

49 Langley Mill Derbys

Coppice Side Pottery

North Street NG16 4EV
(01773) 716854

Terracotta garden pots including troughs, jardinières and many wall planters. New range of coloured garden pottery and novelty garden gifts.

'All pots sold at discounted prices. Some seconds.'

Just off the A608 (Station Road) which links Heanor & Eastwood.

From Heanor: take A608 downhill towards Langley Mill/ Eastwood. Pass Langley Mill garage, go over pedestrian lights and go left into North Street (sign to railway station).*

From M1 exit 26/Eastwood: take A610 for Heanor/Derby. After 4 ½ miles, take left slip road for Heanor; go about ½ mile, uphill into Langley Mill, under railway bridge. After pedestrian crossing go right into North Street (opposite large stone church).*

****Go 400 yds, past Aristoc factory on right; road bears left then right to Canlin Castings Yards. Pottery is on left in yard.***

Open: Mon–Fri 9–5; Sat 9–2.
Closed: Bank Holidays, Christmas–New Year.
Cards: MasterCard, Visa.
Cars: Own car-park.
Toilets: Ask if desperate.
Wheelchairs: Access difficult.
Teas: Local pubs.
Groups: You can see the potters at work. Small groups by prior arrangement with Mr Alan Woolley.
Transport: Bus nos. 120, 125 from Derby and R11 from Nottingham; or to Langley Mill station.
Mail order: Pots can be sent, please ask for details.

50 Langley Mill Notts

One Stop Factory Shop

North Street NG16 4BR
(01773) 717111

Wide range of textiles and household goods from local manufacturers. Men's, ladies' and children's clothing; sportswear.

'High quality perfects and seconds with substantial reductions on normal high street prices. Ladies' fitness wear is a speciality.'

Just off the A608 (Station Road) which links Heanor & Eastwood.

From Heanor: take A608 downhill towards Langley Mill/ Eastwood. Pass Langley Mill garage, go over pedestrian lights and go left into North Street (sign to railway station).*

From M1 exit 26/Eastwood: take A610 for Heanor/Derby. After 4 ½ miles, take left slip road for Heanor; go about ½ mile, uphill into Langley Mill, under railway bridge. After pedestrian crossing go right into North Street (opposite large stone church).*

****Shop entrance is in Ebenezer Street, fourth road on the left. Shop is 50 yds on right.***

Open: Mon–Fri 9–5.30; Sat 9–5; Sun 10–4.
Closed: Christmas, Boxing and New Year's Days.
Cards: Delta, MasterCard, Switch, Visa.
Cars: In street.
Toilets: Yes.
Wheelchairs: Easy access via ramp to large ground floor sales area.
Changing rooms: Yes.
Teas: Local pubs in Langley Mill 100 yds away.
Groups: Shopping groups welcome, but large groups please phone first. No factory tours.
Transport: Bus nos. 120, 125 from Derby and R11 from Nottingham; or to Langley Mill station.
Mail order: No.

Alternative shopping

One of our pleasures while researching factory shops is to sneak off to do another sort of 'buying direct' from the maker: visiting the local craftspeople and crafts galleries. The East Midlands has an excellent choice. Here is a small selection. For more details, contact the local tourist offices. Britain has a wealth of crafts people working from small workshops and in general the quality is outstanding.

One of those most off-the-beaten-track is the Pea Room Craft Centre in Heckington, Lincolnshire (on the A17, three miles east of Sleaford) (01529 460765). It has regular exhibitions of crafts, ceramics, textiles etc, and offers demonstrations and short courses.

Uppingham has the Magpie crafts gallery (01572 8222120) and also a gallery exhibiting sculpture and paintings.

Near Calverton (go factory shopping there for jeans) are pleasant farm buildings converted to a gallery and tea rooms/restaurant (open day and evening). Patching's Farm Art Centre (0115 965 3479) offers you the opportunity to paint in the countryside too.

The Harley Gallery (01909 501700) in Welbeck, Nottinghamshire, is located on the site of the former nineteenth century estate gas works. Set in a water garden, this fine building, built by a specially recruited team of local craftsmen, houses exhibitions of arts and crafts (March–early November).

Probably the most famous crafts gallery (one of our favourites, with top quality items) is at Rufford Abbey (01623 824153) near Ollerton. Leave enough time to enjoy the good food in the restaurant, and the sculpture park.

Inside Nottingham castle (be sure to go on a tour of the underground tunnels while you are there) is a top quality craft shop (0115 948 3504).

Ashbourne, Derbyshire, recently acquired an excellent art and crafts gallery (01335 346742). In the centre of town on the one-way system, it also has a tempting café. An ideal place to drop into when you are buying glassware from the factory shop a few yards away at the rear.

In Rowsley, a north Derbyshire village near Bakewell and Matlock, are a famous silk picture embroider, artist, furniture maker and stringed instrument maker.

51 Lincoln Lincs

The Curtain Factory Shop

279 High Street LN2 1JG
(01522) 522740

Full range of *Filigree* products. Lace and net curtains; ready-made curtains; custom-made voiles. Curtain rails and accessories also available.

'Filigree factory seconds at less than half perfect price.'

See our display advertisement opposite

The High Street (pedestrianised) is the main shopping street (running north–south) in Lincoln, on the south side of the cathedral hill. This shop is 20 yds north of Corporation Street, next to the Job Centre and 50 yds from Binns Department Store.

Open: Mon–Sat 9–5.
Closed: Bank Holidays; Christmas, Boxing and New Year's Days.
Cards: MasterCard, Switch, Visa.
Cars: Public car-park 200 yds away.
Toilets: Ask if desperate.
Wheelchairs: Easy access; no steps.
Teas: Many cafés in town.
Groups: Small shopping groups welcome.
Transport: Any bus or train to Lincoln, then walk.
Mail order: No.

52 Lincoln Lincs

Tanya

Ferry Road, Fiskerton LN3 4HV
(01522) 595955

Men's and ladies' high quality fully fashioned knitwear in natural fibres.

'Classic and fashion styles in wide range of sizes. Genuine factory shop, all knitwear made on site. Perfects and seconds.'

Four miles east of Lincoln.

From Lincoln: take A158 for Skegness; go right after 1 mile (signposted Reepham, Cherry Willingham, Fiskerton); continue to Fiskerton, through village towards Bardney. Factory is on left, ½ mile outside the village.

Open: Mon–Fri 10–1 & 1.30–4; Sat 10–2.
Closed: Bank Holidays; Whit week; Christmas Eve–New Year.
Cards: None.
Cars: Own car-park.
Toilets: No.
Wheelchairs: Ramp to shop in large portakabin.
Changing rooms: No.
Teas: Nearby pubs.
Groups: No factory tours. Shopping groups by appointment.
Transport: Bus no. 15 hourly from Lincoln terminates at factory.

See our entries nos. 51 & 80

Lincolnshire Distractions

Lincoln is famous for its stunning cathedral, medieval steep hill and old gaol (make sure you visit the curved prison chapel, where prisoners attended services without being able to see one another).

A lesser known fact, maybe, is that Lincoln was the centre of the British aircraft industry during the Great War, with companies such as Shuttleworth engaged in the manufacture of nearly 5000 aeroplanes. The county of Lincolnshire had – by the end of that war – 37 military aerodromes.

The county again acquired great significance during the Second World War with 49 air bases, more than any other county in Britain. It was from here that Commander Guy Gibson undertook the famous 'dam busters' raid' in May 1943. This county is home to the Red Arrows.

Because of intense interest (including from thousands of Americans, Canadians, Australians, New Zealanders, Poles, Rhodesians etc who served here) several leaflets on aviation heritage, air force memorials and aviation history, and an Air Force trail, are available from tourist offices.

Lincs Tourism (01522) 526450 Gainsborough TIC (01427) 615411

Tours can be organised (written applications please) for recognised groups to the Royal Air Force College at Cranwell, near Sleaford.

The Lincolnshire Aviation Heritage Centre, East Kirkby near Spilsby (01790 763207) has a large visitor centre with the original control tower, RAF Escaping Society, air raid shelter etc. Open all year (not Sunday)

The Battle of Britain Memorial Flight Visitor Centre, Coningsby (01526 344041)

Newark Air Museum (01636 707170)

Many other sites and museums are open too.

53 Long Eaton Derbys

Charnos

Nottingham Road NG9 6GE Now closed
(0115) 973 0345

Ladies' lingerie, hosiery, underwear, knitwear, dresses, skirts and blouses; children's wear; men's wear; sportswear; household linens.

See our display advertisement on p. 535

One of the easiest shops to find.

It is on the main road (A6005) from Long Eaton to Nottingham, about 300 yds east of the town centre and superstore.

From Long Eaton: go over the railway: the shop is immediately on left, in a clearly marked red-brick building.

Open: Tues–Fri 10–5; Sat 9.30–1.
Closed: Monday; Christmas–New Year.
Cards: MasterCard, Visa.
Cars: On side road.
Toilets: No.
Wheelchairs: Access to large shop through rear door.
Changing rooms: Yes.
Teas: In Long Eaton (easy walking distance).
Groups: Groups of shoppers always welcome – prior phone call appreciated. For organised group tours of the Ilkeston factory – please contact Suzie Sheldon (0115 932 2191).
Transport: Within easy walking distance of town centre so take any bus to Long Eaton.
Mail order: No.

54 Long Eaton Derbys

Harrington Bridal Fabrics & Laces

Turret E, Harrington Mills, Leopold Street NG10 4QE
(0115) 946 0766

All kinds of bridal fabrics in pure silk or low cost polyester. Plain fabrics or brocades, damasks, jacquards and embroideries. Bridal laces including guipures, corded, beaded, gold etc. Veiling and skirt tulles, petticoat dress nets, beads and ribbons.

'Prices below usual retail, eg pure silk dupion from £5.39 + vat per metre. Please telephone for catalogue and samples.'

Off the A6005, Derby Road, west of town centre. (Phone for free easy map.)

From M1 exit 25: follow signs to Long Eaton (not Nottingham).*

From Nottingham: take A52 Derby Road to M1 exit 25; follow signs to Long Eaton.*

****At large roundabout turn left into A6005 Derby Road. Pass Trent College on right. After ½ mile, go right into Leopold Street, immediately before Harrington Arms on right. Showroom entrance 200 yds to the right.***

From town centre: take A6005 towards Derby. Go over canal and go left into Leopold Street immediately after Harrington Arms on left. Showroom entrance about 200 yds on right.

Open: Mon–Fri 9–5; Sat 9–12.
Closed: Most Bank Holidays (phone previous week); Christmas–New Year.
Cards: Eurocard, MasterCard, Visa.
Cars: Free car-park on opposite side of road.
Toilets: Yes.
Wheelchairs: Regret access too difficult.
Teas: Many places in nearby town centre.
Groups: No tours or large shopping groups.
Transport: Long Eaton station. Buses to The Green, Long Eaton.
Mail order: Yes.
Catalogue: £3.95. Samples available. Please phone for free list of fabrics.

55 Long Eaton Derbys

P F Collections

Oakleaf House, Acton Road NG10 1FY
(0115) 946 1282

Luxury upholstered traditional country house sofas and chairs in a large selection of fabrics.

'Large savings, eg chairs from £250–£500; sofas from £400–£1200.'

See our display advertisement above

On the southern side of town.

From M1 exit 25: follow signs to Long Eaton. At large roundabout go left into A6005 Derby Road. Pass Trent College on right.*

From places west: take A6005 (Derby Road) into Long Eaton.*

****Go to mini-roundabout in town centre (superstore on left). Go straight; take first right (Waverley Street).*****

From Nottingham on A6005: go over railway, take first left (Waverley Street).**

*****Keep straight, pass Co-op and The Old Stillage on left; at roundabout with The Tapper's Harker go straight on to Field Farm Road. After ¼ mile (road bends left), company is on far right corner of Acton Road.***

From south on A6540: at roundabout at Long Eaton station, go right into Field Farm Road. Continue for one mile. Shop is on left.

Open: Mon–Fri 10–4; Sat 10–1.
Closed: Most Bank Holidays; last week July & first two weeks August; Christmas–New Year.
Cards: None.
Cars: Car-park at front.
Toilets: Yes.
Wheelchairs: One step to large shop.
Teas: Vending machine. Cafés in town.
Groups: 3–4 visitors can see around at a time. Please phone J. Campbell.
Transport: 10 minutes' walk from town centre. 1 mile from station.
Mail order: No.
Catalogue: Free.

56 Matlock Derbys

John Smedley

Lea Mills, Lea Bridge (near Cromford) DE4 5AG
(01629) 534571

High quality knitwear for men and women. Sea Island cotton casual shirts, day shirts, socks (own yarn), handkerchiefs, tights, ties etc.

'Knitwear and cotton shirts made by this company.'

Lea Bridge is a small village south-east of Matlock.

Turn off A6 (Derby–Matlock road) east to Cromford Mill and continue for about two miles towards Holloway. At junction in Lea Bridge, go left. You see the large mill ahead; the clearly marked shop is on the left.

From Crich: follow signs to the Tramway Museum (pass it on your right) then Holloway. Go straight for ½ mile to Lea Bridge. This large mill is on the right; park downhill; the shop is a few yards up on left.

NB. Lea Bridge is about a mile south-west of Lea.

Open: Seven days a week 10–4.
Closed: Christmas, Boxing and New Year's Days.
Cards: MasterCard, Visa.
Cars: Own car-park downhill from shop.
Toilets: No.
Wheelchairs: One step. Large shop with ramps.
Changing rooms: No.
Teas: Teas in Lea, Matlock, Wirksworth.
Tours: For 12–20 persons by prior arrangement with Meg Hatton; no charge. Tours all year on Wed and Thur at 1.30. Group visits welcome to sizeable shop: please book as above.
Transport: Matlock–Crich bus passes through Lea Bridge.
Mail order: No, but willing to post orders to customers.

The most advanced industrial buildings in the world ...

The Derwent Valley, which links Matlock, Cromford, Belper and Derby, saw some of the most exciting industrial developments in the world – such as the first water-powered cotton mills – in the 1770s. By the early 1880s, Belper was the second largest town in Derbyshire. Even now, you cannot fail to be impressed by the splendid old mills in this small town – especially the astonishing brick mill (built in 1912) at the northern end. Beside it is a cotton mill which now houses the Derwent Valley Visitor Centre. When constructed in 1804, this mill was the most technically advanced building of its time. Because its predecessor on the site had been destroyed by fire, this one incorporated an iron frame and brick arches to make it fireproof. It had a warm air central heating system, a goods lift between floors – and a school room in the roof. It housed the great breast-shot water wheel, also of advanced design. The mill was built by William Strutt, a member of the famous family of benefactors in Belper: for 150 years, they provided work, housing, education and good food from model farms. William's father, Jedediah Strutt invented the ribbed cotton machine and went into partnership with Richard Arkwright.

The Visitor Centre (01773 880474) in Belper, open several afternoons a week, is being established with local photographs and other material by volunteers. To get a feel of the significance of mills and textiles in this area, do drop in. Also be sure to visit Cromford Mill Visitor Centre (01629 824297) just south of Matlock Bath.

Tramways were installed from Ambergate to Crich to link the limestone quarries into the important canal network. You can ride a variety of old trams at the National Tramway Museum in Crich (01773 852565).

57 Matlock Derbys

Matlock Shoe Sales

Paxton Warehouse DE4 3BX
(01629) 583105

Men's and women's footwear including fashion and designer shoes, casuals, boots, slippers, trainers, hiking boots, wellingtons, sandals etc.

'We buy in bulk from factories all over the world and pass the savings on to our customers. 90% of stock current season and perfect.'

See our display advertisement above

On the A615, half a mile east of Matlock town centre (ie, from roundabout at end of bridge).

From Matlock: take A615 for Alfreton. Continue for ½ mile; pass Total petrol on right and after 100 yds go sharp left into company drive (signposted).

Coming into Matlock on A615: pass Matlock town sign on left; after 200 yds go sharp right into private drive (100 yds before Total petrol on left). Shop clearly marked.

Open: Mon–Sat 9–6; Sun 10–5; Bank Holidays 9–6.
Closed: Christmas, Boxing and New Year's Days.
Cards: MasterCard, Visa.
Cars: Own large car-park behind shop.
Toilets: Yes.
Wheelchairs: Easy access, parking for disabled by door.
Teas: Lots of places locally.
Groups: Large shopping groups welcome, but please phone first.
Transport: 10 minutes' walk from town centre and Matlock station.
Mail order: No.

58 Matlock Bath Derbys

Denby Factory Shop

44 North Parade DE4 3NS
(01629) 56408

Denby tableware, mugs and cookware – best and second qualities. Wedding list service.

'Sales in January and June.'

The shop is situated in the long parade of shops on one side of the river, approximately 200 yds from the railway station.

Open: Mon–Sat (including Bank Holidays) 9–5; Sun 10–5. Additional hours in summer, please ring for details.
Closed: Christmas, Boxing and New Year's Days.
Cards: Connect, MasterCard, Switch, Visa.
Cars: Limited parking outside and nearby public car-parks.
Toilets: By the Tourist Office.
Wheelchairs: Small shop; access difficult.
Teas: Plenty of cafés along the parade.
Tours: Please see entry under 'Denby' for tours of the pottery.
Transport: Trains to Matlock Bath. Many buses to the area.
Mail order: No.

59 Matlock Bath Derbys

Fabric Design

10–12 North Parade DE4 3NS
(01629) 584747

Leading supplier of designer furnishing fabric seconds: linens, cottons, damasks, moirés and chintz.

'Phone for dates of special sales. Cottons from £4.25 per metre, plain linen £5.99 per metre. Majority of fabrics reduced up to 80%. Seconds and clearance lines.'

Easy to find in long parade of shops in Matlock Bath.

From Matlock: as you reach Matlock Bath, look for detached, square stone Midland Hotel on left; shop is almost opposite.

From Cromford/Derby on A6: go through Matlock Bath to far end of shops. Shop on left.

Open: Tues, Wed, Fri, Sat 10–5; Mon, Thur, Sun 1.30–5.
Closed: Bank Holidays; Christmas, Boxing and New Year's Days.
Cards: Amex, MasterCard, Visa.
Cars: Limited parking outside; car-park across road near station.
Toilets: Opposite shop.
Wheelchairs: Two small steps; assistance if needed.
Teas: Lots of places in Matlock Bath.
Groups: Shopping groups welcome with prior notice.
Transport: Any bus or train to Matlock Bath.
Mail order: Yes.
Catalogue: Free brochure. No restrictions.

60 Newark Notts

Weston Mill Pottery

Navigation Yard, Millgate NG24 4TV
(01636) 76835

Terracotta pottery for gardens and interiors – garden planters, patio pots, wall pots, herb pots. Cookware such as chicken bricks, tandoori pots, egg racks, storage jars and wine racks. Vases, cache-pots, perfume burners and lamp rings.

'Factory shop prices for perfects, plus seconds and discontinued lines at bargain prices.'

Close to centre of town, near river and castle.

Coming north on A46: at first roundabout, go right on to B6166 for Newark. Go over river by Newark Marina (on left). Take first left, in front of Spring House pub. After 500 yds go left into Navigation Yard: pottery, signposted here, is facing you, 20 yds ahead. (If you miss this little turning, best to park and walk back.)

From the market place: easiest to walk. Head for river and follow riverside walk in opposite direction from castle.

Open: Mon–Sat 9–5; Sun and Bank Holidays 11–5.
Closed: Please telephone for Christmas–New Year closures.
Cards: None.
Cars: Adjacent car-park and town car-parks.
Toilets: Yes.
Wheelchairs: Two flights of stairs.
Teas: Great variety of places in Newark.
Groups: Shopping groups welcome, please be sure to notify in advance.
Transport: Any bus to Newark.
Mail order: Yes.
Catalogue: Free (leaflet and photographs). Only perfect stock items supplied, ie cannot hand throw to specific requirements.

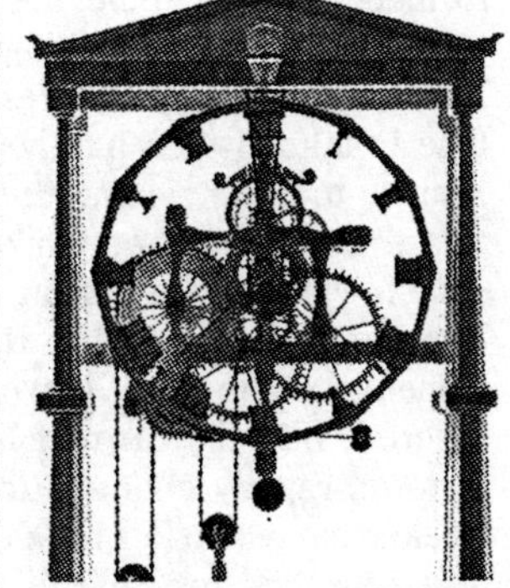

Famous Names of Nottinghamshire

After the first world war, changing fashions meant that demand for lace – a major product of Nottinghamshire – dropped dramatically. This would have hit the city badly had it not been not been for the great growth of three other major industries.

May 1902

Jesse Boot, founder of the famous chemist shop chain, started his career helping his mother run a medical herbalist shop at no. 6 Goose Gate in the city. Completely self taught and with a life long interest in herbs and wild flowers, he built up a number of shops and provided many jobs. His philosophy was to sell a wide range of products cheaply. His shop was one of the first in Nottingham to be lit by the newly invented electric light. Fierce opposition from competitors failed to prevent his expansion, and Boots 'department stores' spread to other cities such as Leeds and Sheffield – selling books, stationery, artists' materials, fancy goods and cosmetics as well as pharmaceuticals. Boots became American owned in 1920. But after the disastrous Wall Street crash, it was bought back again. The huge factory is in Beeston, near Nottingham University.

John Player began by setting up an agency for the sale of manures and seeds in Nottingham in 1861. As a service to his customers (and extra income) he kept tins of tobacco handy to sell in 'screws' at a few pence each. Appreciating that there was a market for ready-made cigarettes instead of loose tobacco, Player bought a factory in Broadmarsh in 1877. His cigarettes were sold in convenient sized paper packets with card stiffeners which later evolved into pictorial cigarette cards. His manufacturing business grew rapidly towards the end of the 19th century to become one of the major employers in the region with a workforce of well over a thousand. Two hundred girls were nicknamed 'Players Angels', each making 2000 cigarettes per day by hand.

At much the same time, the manufacture of bicycles began to emerge: at least 60 Nottingham firms were in the business. The best known (and longest lasting) of these was Raleigh. One Frank Bowden had become terminally ill; he visited France, took up cycling then miraculously recovered. He traced the makers of the bike he had used to a small workshop in Nottingham making three machines a week. Frank Bowden bought the firm. By 1896 the Raleigh Cycle Co., named after the street in which the original premises were located, had the largest bicycle factory in the world. Bowden rapidly changed from making 'bone shakers' to sleeker models using the new Dunlop pneumatic tyre. He also made tandems. Raleigh, sadly, is no longer British.

For further details on the industrial background, see Ian Brown's fascinating book 'Nottinghamshire's Industrial Heritage' from which we gathered this information.

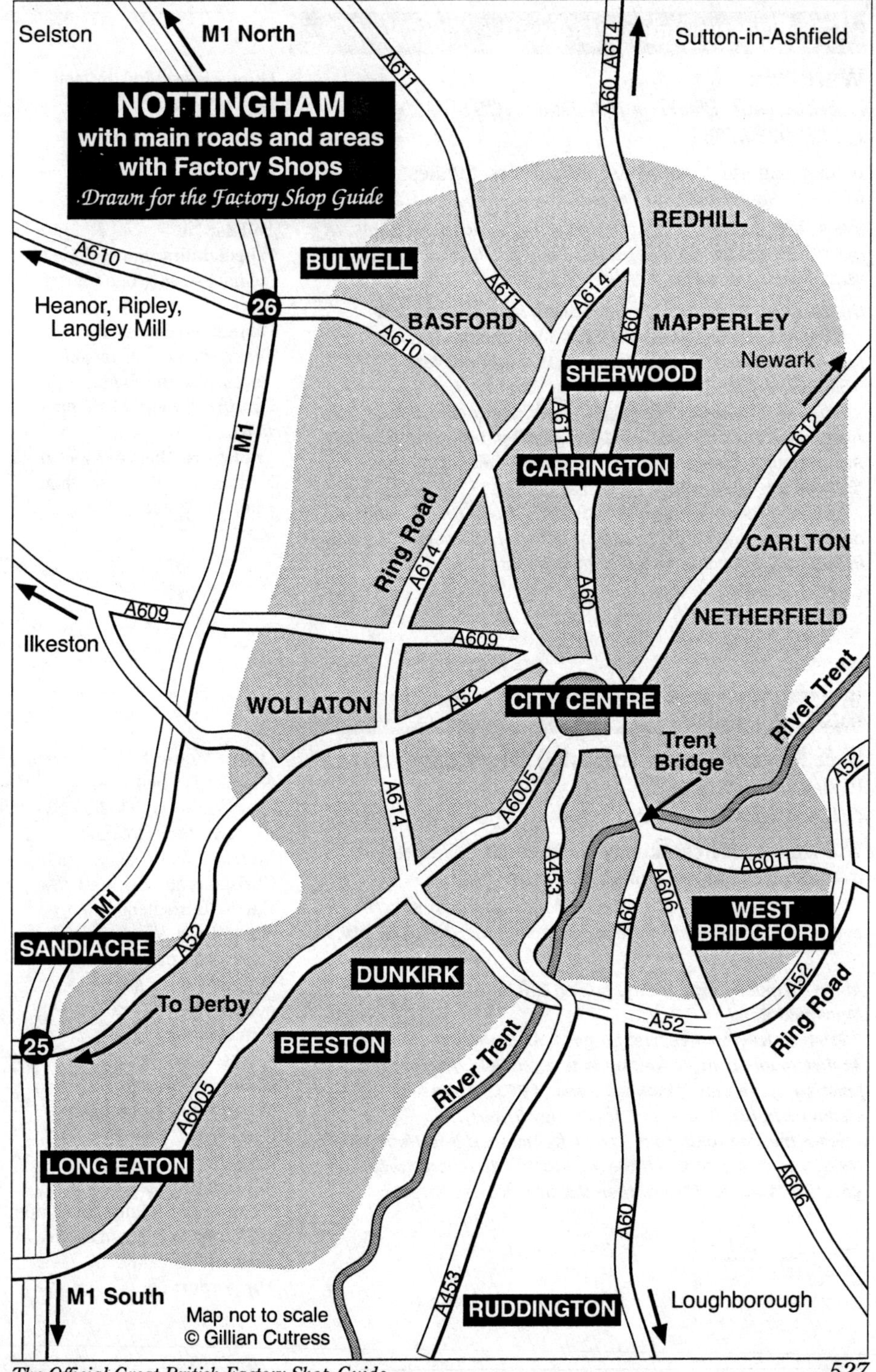
NOTTINGHAM
with main roads and areas with Factory Shops
Drawn for the Factory Shop Guide
Selston
M1 North
Sutton-in-Ashfield
A611
A60. A614
REDHILL
A610
BULWELL
Heanor, Ripley, Langley Mill
26
BASFORD
A611
A614
A60
MAPPERLEY
Newark
A610
SHERWOOD
A611
M1
CARRINGTON
A612
Ring Road
A614
CARLTON
A60
A609
Ilkeston
NETHERFIELD
A609
River Trent
A52
CITY CENTRE
WOLLATON
Trent Bridge
A52
A614
A6005
A453
A6011
A606
A60
WEST BRIDGFORD
M1
SANDIACRE
A52
DUNKIRK
A52
To Derby
A52
Ring Road
25
BEESTON
River Trent
A6005
LONG EATON
A606
A60
A453
M1 South
RUDDINGTON
Loughborough
Map not to scale
© Gillian Cutress

61 Nottingham : Bulwell see map p. 527

Warner's

Dabell Avenue, Blenheim Ind. Estate NG6 8WA
(0115) 979 5796

Ladies' lingerie: bras, pants, suspenders, teddies, nightwear. Men's designer label underwear.

'Firsts and seconds sold here, including chainstore items, at approx 40% reductions. Special weekend sales throughout the year. Please phone for details.'

On the north-west side of Nottingham, near M1 exit 26.

From M1 exit 26: take A610 for Nottingham. At next roundabout, take second exit (Low Wood Road) for 'Bullwell 2 ½' & Blenheim Industrial Estate.*

From Nottingham: take A610. Cross ring road. Go over first roundabout marked 'Bulwell 1'; pass BP petrol station on left. At next huge roundabout, take fifth exit (Low Wood Road) for 'Bulwell 2 ½' & Blenheim Industrial Estate.*

****At next roundabout go left (Seller's Wood Drive) and right at next (Bennerley Road). Take first left, Dabell Avenue: company in large grey building on left with large letter W.***

Open: Tues, Wed, Fri and Sat 10–5; Thur 10–7.
Closed: Monday; Bank Holidays.
Cards: Yes.
Cars: Outside shop.
Toilets: No.
Wheelchairs: Small slope to medium-sized ground floor shop.
Changing rooms: Yes.
Teas: Pub nearby; lots of places in Nottingham.
Groups: Groups of shoppers welcome.
Transport: Bus no. 84 from Nottingham city centre then 8 minutes' walk.
Mail order: No.

62 Nottingham : Carrington see map p. 527

K & M (Leather Clothing) Mnfg. Co.

Wesley Street NG5 2BJ
(0115) 960 9474

Wide range of sheepskin and leather coats, jackets, trousers, hats, gloves, mitts, moccasins etc.

'Items all made by this company. Made-to-measure service. Professional garment alterations and repair. Post-Christmas sale.'

About 1½ miles north of city, behind Bristol Street Motors, Mansfield Road.

From Nottingham centre: go north on Mansfield Road (A60). At first roundabout, follow signs to Mansfield. At next major junction, go left into Hucknall Road (A611). Take first right (Jenner Street), then first left (Wesley Street).

From the ring road: turn off by City Hospital into Hucknall Road (A611) to city centre. After a mile (100 yds before traffic lights), go left into Jenner Street, then left into Wesley Street.

Open: Mon–Sat 10–4; also *Oct–Jan* Sun 11–4; New Year's Day 11–2.30.
Closed: Bank Holiday Mondays; Whit week; Christmas and Boxing Days.
Cards: Eurocheque, MasterCard, Visa.
Cars: Easy parking.
Toilets: Please ask if necessary.
Wheelchairs: Easy access to large shop.
Changing rooms: No.
Teas: Hot drinks available if required.
Groups: Coach parties welcome – please arrange in advance, mentioning this guide.
Transport: Plenty of buses along Mansfield Road.
Mail order: No.

63 Nottingham : City Centre *see map p. 527*

Denby Factory Shop

Drury Walk, Broadmarsh Centre NG1 7LL
(0115) 948 3932

Denby tableware, mugs and cookware – best and second qualities. Wedding list service.

'Sales in January and June.'

Broadmarsh Centre is one of the two major shopping precincts in the centre of Nottingham.

The shop is on the upper level near The Caves exhibition.

Open: Mon–Sat 9–5.30 (Tues 9.30–5.30).
Closed: Bank Holidays; Christmas, Boxing and New Year's Days.
Cards: Connect, MasterCard, Switch, Visa.
Cars: Huge public car-park in the Broadmarsh Centre.
Toilets: In Broadmarsh Centre.
Wheelchairs: Lifts and escalators in shopping centre; limited access in the shop due to shortage of space.
Teas: Opposite shop.
Tours: Please see the company's entry under 'Denby' for details of factory tours.
Transport: Shop is above Broadmarsh bus station. Easy walk from rail station.
Mail order: No.

64 Nottingham : City Centre *see map p. 527*

H. Jackson Fabrics

243 Lower Parliament Street *(0115) 958 2184*

Huge range of continental and British fashion fabrics for day and evening wear. Also coat fabrics.

'We have always been known for a vast range of top quality fashion fabrics at low prices. All our stock is bought in bulk from the largest suppliers in the EEC. A full range of haberdashery means we provide a complete service to the home dressmaker. All our spare stocks are next door so we can always hunt for that something special or off-season item.'

In a major, busy one-way road on the south-east of city centre.

From city centre (Victoria Centre): go clockwise round town, into the one-way Lower Parliament Street (inner ring road) towards Trent Bridge, passing the ice rink on the right.**

From Southwell: at traffic lights as you reach the town centre (ice rink facing you), go left for Broadmarsh Centre and Loughborough A60.*

****From the city centre (Broadmarsh Centre): aim for Trent Bridge. At large roundabout with traffic lights, go left into one-way system, go up the hill and turn right, effectively doubling back on yourself. Look for the ice rink on right.*****

*****Go over the traffic lights, pass Texaco on left: shop is immediately past it, on corner site.***

Open: Mon–Fri 10–4; Sat 9–12.
Closed: Bank Holidays; Christmas to New Year.
Cards: None.
Cars: Own garage during week; local side streets on Sats.
Toilets: Ask if desperate.
Wheelchairs: Two large steps to large shop.
Teas: Lots of places in town.
Groups: Groups of shoppers always welcome. Prior phone call appreciated.
Transport: Any bus or train to Nottingham city.

65 Nottingham : Sherwood see map p. 527

The Factory Shop

313 Hucknall Road NG5 1FJ
(0115) 962 0458

Ladies' wear: blouses, skirts, jackets, trousers, ski pants, knitwear, coats and leisurewear. Items mainly produced in own factories.

'Perfects and seconds on sale. We aim to be cheaper than our main rivals.'

On the north side of city centre.

From Nottingham: take Mansfield Road (A60) north. Go over first large roundabout and turn left at traffic lights (A611 for Hucknall). Pass Sunblest Bakery; go over traffic lights at Haydn Road. Shop is 100 yds on left.

From the ring road: turn south by City Hospital on to A611 (Hucknall Road) for city centre; go over first traffic lights and downhill. Shop is on right, 100 yds before traffic lights (at Haydn Road).

Open: Mon–Sat 9.30–4.30.
Closed: Bank Holidays; Christmas–New Year.
Cards: Eurocard, MasterCard, Visa.
Cars: Outside shop.
Toilets: No.
Wheelchairs: One step to medium-sized shop.
Changing rooms: Yes.
Teas: Cafés within easy walking distance.
Groups: Tours of factory and shopping groups welcome. No need to pre-book.
Transport: Bus nos. 15, 16, 17, 18, 19 from Trinity Square. All stop almost directly outside shop.
Mail order: No.

66 Nottingham : Sherwood see map p. 527

Florentine Trading Co.

Sherwood Mills, 20 Victoria Road NG5 2NB
(0115) 960 5444

This company makes net curtains, jardinières, Austrian swags, Austrian blinds, café nets, macramé nets, lace tablecloths & mats, and napery. Also sell household linens.

'Some ends of lines and seconds usually available. Quick alteration service on non-standard size nets. Extra wide jardinières available. Made-to-measure service.'

On the north side of city centre.

From Nottingham: take Mansfield Road (A60) north. Go over first large roundabout and turn left at traffic lights (A611 for Hucknall). Pass Sunblest Bakery, go right at traffic lights into Haydn Road.*

From the ring road: turn south by City Hospital on to A611 (Hucknall Road) for city centre; at second traffic lights, go left (Haydn Road).*

****After 300 yds go left in front of pink glass building into Victoria Road. Shop in low white building on right.***

Open: Mon–Fri 9.15–4; Sat 9.15–1, please phone first to confirm.
Closed: Bank Holidays; Christmas–New Year.
Cards: None.
Cars: In street.
Toilets: In Sherwood.
Wheelchairs: Four steep steps.
Teas: Café in Sherwood.
Groups: Not suitable for group visits.
Transport: Bus nos. 55–59 from Nottingham to Haydn Road.
Mail order: No.

Visit of the Prince of Wales to Nottinghamshire in October 1891

67 Nottingham : Sherwood *see map p. 527*

John D Maltby

Hartley House, Haydn Road NG5 1DM
(0115) 960 3063

Now closed

Lace net curtains, ready made and piece lengths. Various designs – jardinières, flounces, brise bise, side curtains, voile panels – plain and printed. Lace tablecloths, runners, bedspreads, cushion and pillow covers. Printed woven drape fabrics, curtain tracks, poles & window furnishing accessories.

'Mostly perfects. with some seconds. Lace net curtains in piece lengths from £1 per m; ready-made curtain lace sets from £1.95. On average 40% less than high street. Alterations at modest cost.'

Two miles north-west of Nottingham city centre, in the large building at the junction of Haydn and Hucknall Roads.

From Nottingham: go north on Mansfield Road (A60). At roundabout, keep straight. At next major junction, go left into Hucknall Road (A611). Keep straight for ⅔ mile, passing huge Sunblest bakery on left. Go downhill. Pass Burmah petrol on left. After 80 yds (before traffic lights on Haydn Rd) go left into car-park.

From the ring road: turn off by City Hospital into Hucknall Road (A611) towards the city centre. After ½ mile, cross Haydn Road traffic lights then go immediately right into company car-park.

Open: Mon–Sun 9–5. Some Bank Holidays (please phone to check, or see local press).
Closed: Christmas & Boxing Days; New Year's Eve & Day.
Cards: MasterCard, Visa.
Cars: Factory car-park at rear.
Toilets: Yes.
Wheelchairs: Six steps then lift to 3rd floor. Assistance gladly given on request (or phone beforehand).
Teas: Café opposite, and in nearby factory shop.
Groups: No tours, but shopping groups welcome, no need to book.
Transport: Bus nos. 17 & 19 and Hucknall bus from city centre. Stop across the road; or 5 minutes by cab.
Mail order: Yes. Goods can be sent anywhere in UK or abroad.

68 Nottingham : Sherwood see map p. 527

Meridian

Haydn Road NG5 1DH
(0115) 924 6100

Huge range of clothing for all the family. Household linens.

Two miles north of the city centre. Haydn Road links Mansfield Road (A60), Hucknall Road (A611) and Nottingham Road (B682).

From Nottingham: take Mansfield Road (A60) north. Go over first large roundabout, left at traffic lights (A611 for Hucknall). Go left at traffic lights into Haydn Road: shop 200 yds on right.

From the ring road: turn off to Nottingham along Hucknall Road. Go right at traffic lights into Haydn Road.

Open: Mon–Sat 9–5.30 (Wed until 7.30); Sun and Bank Holidays 10.30–4.30.
Closed: Please phone to check.
Cards: Yes.
Cars: Huge car-park.
Toilets: Yes.
Wheelchairs: Easy access to vast shop.
Changing rooms: Yes.
Teas: Own café.
Groups: Coaches phone first.
Transport: Buses going north from the city cross Haydn Road.

Also see Nottingham entries nos. 93 & 94

69 Nottingham : Sherwood see map p. 527

Please phone first

Regency Furniture Direct

Unit 18, Hartley House Business Centre, Haydn Road NG5 1DM
(0115) 985 6949

High quality reproduction Regency and Georgian cabinets, dining tables, chairs, chests, desks, occasional furniture, bookcases, TV and video cabinets.

'All items are perfects, at prices about 15% less than the high street. This company sells off the floor and also undertakes specialist polishing; they will gladly make items to fit your room and stain them to match your furniture. New luxury curtain-manufacturing service. Free delivery locally, and at reasonable cost elsewhere.'

Two miles north-west of Nottingham city centre, behind the large building at the junction of Haydn and Hucknall Roads.

From Nottingham: go north on Mansfield Road (A60). At roundabout, keep straight. At next major junction, go left into Hucknall Road (A611). Keep straight for ⅔ mile, pass Sunblest bakery on left. Go downhill. Pass Burmah petrol on left. After 80 yds (just before traffic lights, Haydn Road) go left into car-park.*

From the ring road: turn off by City Hospital into Hucknall Road (A611) towards city centre. After ½ mile, cross Haydn Road traffic lights then go immediately right into company car-park.*

Shop is at back of car-park.

Open: Mon–Sun 10–4. Bank Holidays.
Closed: Christmas Eve, Christmas and Boxing Days.
Cards: MasterCard, Visa.
Cars: In factory car-park at rear.
Toilets: Yes.
Wheelchairs: No steps.
Teas: Café opposite, and in nearby factory shop.
Groups: Customers welcome to watch their pieces stained and polished.
Transport: Bus nos. 17 & 19 and Hucknall bus from city centre. Stop across the road; or 5 minutes by cab.
Mail order: Yes. Goods can be sent to anywhere in the UK or abroad.

Where & when to use which tiles

The huge range of floor and wall tiles available in the UK (including the wide range available in factory shops) means that it is most important to buy the correct quality. The National Tile Association (NTA, 0181 663 0946) offers free leaflets including one on the correct technique for laying tiles. The NTA categorises tiles according to how hard-wearing they are with various symbols:

Class 1 (symbolised by a bare foot) comprises tiles for 'soft soled footwear and bare feet areas, bathrooms and bedrooms without direct access from the outside'.

Class 2 tiles (denoted by a mule, the slipper that is, not the animal) are suitable for 'living areas of homes but with the exception of kitchens, entrances, and other rooms which may have a lot of traffic'.

Class 3 (shown by a slip-on shoe) is for 'residential kitchens, halls, corridors, balconies and terraces'.

Class 4 (with a man's lace-up shoe) for 'regularly used areas, entrances, commercial kitchens, hotel bathrooms'.

Class 5 (a boot) are for heavy duty tiles suitable for hotel foyers etc'.

Modern clothes sizing

In Nottingham, where textile industries have long played such an important part in the local (and national) economy, innovative computer techniques are coming to the advance of fashion. Nottingham Trent University has devised a virtual reality cat-walk with software programs which respond to the human voice. They can now design clothes interactively, looking at the model from every angle, swapping materials, raising or lowering hems and making other changes according to whim or style. The department has also carried out a survey recently to discover whether standard clothing sizes are correct for the modern figure. They measured 2500 women and came to the conclusion that the classic hour-glass figure has gone into decline – with the parallel rise of the pear-shaped. The previous industry-wide survey of women's vital statistics was carried out in 1954; these latest figures, compiled for a group of large national chains of clothing shops, indicate that clothing sizes might be changed in the near future – enabling those of us who have had problems in finding correctly proportioned garments to be satisfied! Maybe a shoe manufacturer could follow suit ...

70 Riddings Derbys

Charnos

Amber Business Centre, Greenhill Lane DE55 4BP
(01773) 540408

Now closed

Ladies' lingerie, hosiery, underwear, knitwear, dresses, skirts and blouses; children's wear; men's wear; sportswear; household linens.

See our display advertisement opposite

The clearly marked entrance to this estate is in Greenhill Lane, the main road going uphill through Riddings.

From Somercotes: go downhill; entrance to estate is on right.

If you go uphill towards Somercotes: look for entrance to Greenhill Industrial Estate on left.

Charnos is at far end of first large building on right, beyond huge car-park.

Open: Tues–Fri 10–4; Sat 9.30–1.
Closed: Monday; Christmas–New Year.
Cards: MasterCard, Visa.
Cars: Own car-park.
Toilets: No.
Wheelchairs: Easy access to large shop.
Changing rooms: Yes.
Teas: Local cafés.
Groups: Groups of shoppers always welcome – prior phone call appreciated. Organised group tours of the Ilkeston factory – please contact Suzie Sheldon (0115) 932 2191 to arrange.
Transport: Trent bus nos. 148 (Ripley–Mansfield), 330 (Heanor–Alfreton), 333 (Alfreton–Nottingham) pass through Riddings.
Mail order: No.

71 Riddings Derbys

Standard Soap

Amber Business Centre, Greenhill Lane DE55 4BR
(01773) 604063

Soaps, talc powder, bath grains. Also deodorants, hand cream, flannels, bath foam and novelty soaps.
'We mainly sell end-of-line toiletries plus a selection of soap especially produced for sale direct to the public.'

The clearly marked entrance to this estate is in Greenhill Lane, the main road going uphill through Riddings.

From Somercotes: go downhill; entrance to estate is on right.

If you go uphill towards Somercotes: look for entrance to Greenhill Industrial Estate on left.

Go into the estate, then after 400 yds the shop, easily visible, is on the right.

Open: Mon–Thur 9.30–1.30 and 2–4; Fri 9.30–2.45.
Closed: Bank Holidays; Whitsun week; Christmas–New Year.
Cards: None.
Cars: In road.
Toilets: No.
Wheelchairs: Yes.
Teas: Several places within a mile.
Groups: No factory tours. Groups welcome to small shop: please contact Miss Helen Sharpe in advance.
Transport: Trent bus nos. 148 (Ripley–Mansfield), 330 (Heanor–Alfreton), 333 (Alfreton–Nottingham) pass through Riddings.
Mail order: No.

72 Ripley Derbys

Chelsee Design

Prospect Court, 194 Nottingham Road DE5 3AY
(01773) 570057

Pine chests of drawers, wardrobes, bookcases, farmhouse tables, coffee tables, bedside cupboards. Shelves, display racks, plate racks, dressing tables, desks, dressers, bathroom cabinets etc. Also linen and soft furnishings, mirrors, pictures, bric-a-brac, teddies.

'All items perfect, at prices considerably up to 50% less than street shops. Items can be made to size and colour matched.'

On the south-east side of Ripley, a few yards off the A610.

Going north on A610 (Nottingham Road): pass Moss Cottage pub on left; after ¼ mile, go sharp left into track into small industrial estate. Sign over entrance says Prospect Court.*

From Ripley town centre: follow signs to M1 (south)/ Nottingham A610. Go right at roundabout (Sainsbury's on left). After 150 yds go right into track (sign says Prospect Court).*

From A38: take A610 for Nottingham. Continue round bypass. At roundabout (Sainsbury's on right), go left for Nottingham. After 150 yds go right under tall arch into track.*

****Company is 150 yds at back left.***

Open: Mon, Tues, Thur–Sun 10–4.
Closed: Wednesday; some Bank Holidays.
Cards: Eurocard, MasterCard, Switch, Visa.
Cars: Beyond shop.
Toilets: Ask if desperate.
Wheelchairs: No steps; easy access.
Teas: In town (5 minutes' walk).
Groups: No factory tours, but shopping groups welcome. Please phone Carol Free or Janice Murray.
Transport: Bus no. R11 (Derby–Nottingham).
Mail order: No.

Lace and bricks

The lace industry in Nottingham has been famous world-wide since the 19th century when up to a third of the working population of the city was employed in the trade. Until 1770 all lace was hand-made, but by the late 18th century, bobbin and carriage machines had been designed, and by 1865 there were more than 120 lace factories in Nottingham. Most of the lace was produced by small firms who rented space within large factories. Conditions were not good for lace makers; the industry expanded so rapidly that they were crammed into attics and cellars in an effort to keep up with demand. Nottingham developed appalling slums – 'almost the worst in the empire'. After the Great War, the sale of lace collapsed because of the change in fashion. and the Lace Market area of central Nottingham, with its magnificent facades, was allowed to run down. Even ten years ago parts of the Lace Market were derelict. (*See our Scottish information for another story of how change in fashion can devastate a manufacturing industry: in that case the market for Paisley shawls went into sudden decline with the advent of bustles in Victorian times – shawls did not fall gracefully over bustles although they had been ideal with crinolines.)*

The Lace Market is now a conservation area, and the old buildings, perched above the city, have been converted into offices and residential units. It is worth walking round the area with the 'Lace Trail' leaflet and looking at the splendid buildings of the lace merchants. Visit The Lace Hall (0115 948 4221) to see how lace was made and to buy examples. Note that there is no street market here, despite the name.

Interestingly, the unprecedented expansion of the lace and hosiery industries of Nottingham in the 1850s and the construction of the huge Lace Market complex of offices and warehouses led to another booming industry: brick making. Brickworks sprang up like mushrooms in the Carlton, Mapperley and Arnold districts. Some of them produced several million bricks a year. At one stage, 20 or so brickyards were on the north-east side of Nottingham, some of them continuing to operate until the 1960s. The Nottingham Patent Brick Co., with excellent rail links, provided the 60 million bricks used to build St Pancras station in London.

Thanks to Ian Brown's 'Nottinghamshire's Industrial Heritage'.

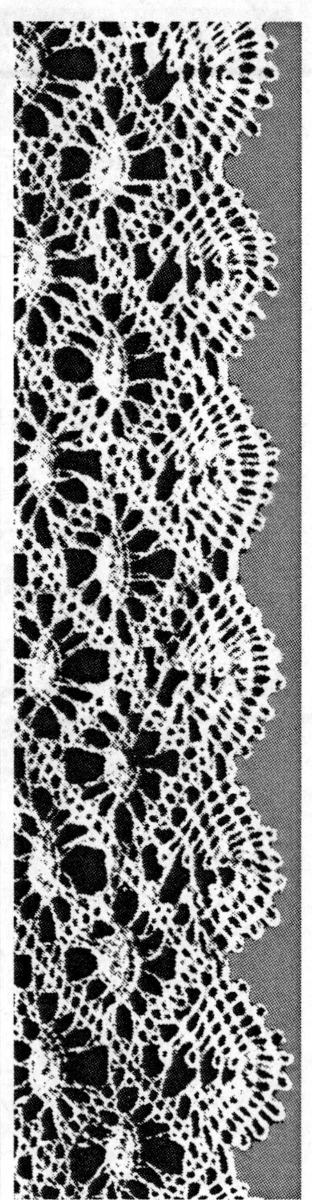

Nottingham Tourist Information Centre

Nottingham Smith Row, Nottingham NG1 2BY (0115) 915 5330

73 Ripley Derbys

Nuthall Lighting

High Holborn Road, Codnor Gate Industrial Estate DE5 3NL
(01773) 570000

All types of decorative lighting products – table lamps, centre lights, wall lamps, glass and fabric shades etc. A fine selection of jugs, storage jars and vases. Also soft furnishings, from wallcoverings to beddings.

About a mile east of Ripley, and the A38, just off Nottingham Road (A610).

Turn off Nottingham Road near the Fina petrol station (on your left if you travel in the Ripley–Heanor direction) into Brittain Drive, on industrial estate.*

Going north towards Ripley on A610: pass Fina petrol on right; after 100 yds go right into Brittain Drive, on the industrial estate.*

****Take first right (High Holborn Road): clearly visible shop is 200 yds on left.***

Open: Mon–Sat 9–5; Sun 10–4.
Closed: Christmas–New Year.
Cards: MasterCard, Visa.
Cars: Company car-park.
Toilets: No.
Wheelchairs: Easy access to larger new shop on ground floor.
Teas: Cafés in Ripley.
Groups: No factory tours but groups welcome to shop. Please arrange first with Kath Mee in the shop.
Transport: Bus nos. 231, 232, 330 from Ripley; then 5 minutes' walk.
Mail order: No.

74 Ruddington Notts

Cooper & Roe

Pasture Lane NG11 6AJ
(0115) 921 6766

Huge range of all-wool knitwear for men and women. Ladies' clothing – blouses, skirts, underwear, lingerie, hosiery; children's wear, leisurewear etc.

'Almost all items are made by this company. Seconds and export overmakes. Extended opening before Christmas.'

South of Nottingham, between Ruddington and Clifton.

From West Bridgford/Nottingham: easiest to take A60 south for Loughborough. Go right at traffic lights into Ruddington. Then go right along main street towards West Bridgford (but not along A60); shortly turn left opposite The Victoria Tavern for Clifton. After ¼ mile go over old railway bridge, then left into Pasture Lane. Shop clearly signposted.

From A453: follow signs into Clifton. From Clifton you need to go east for Ruddington: follow Green Lane. Go over brook, then after about ½ mile Pasture Lane is on right.

Open: Mon–Fri 9–5; Sat 9–4.
Closed: Bank Holidays; Christmas–New Year.
Cards: MasterCard, Switch, Visa.
Cars: Car-park behind factory.
Toilets: Yes.
Wheelchairs: Easy access to large shop. Special opening times can be arranged.
Changing rooms: Yes.
Teas: Tea rooms and small restaurant in village.
Groups: No tours of works but groups always welcome to shop – no need to book but phone call appreciated.
Transport: Bus no. 14 (from Broadmarsh Centre, Nottingham, to Ruddington) then ½ mile walk or no. 54 (Nottingham–Ruddington–Clifton).

75 Sandiacre Derbys

Claremont Garments

Derby Road NG10 5HU
(0115) 949 1188

Ladies' wear: lingerie, swimwear, casualwear (bodies, leggings etc), dresses, blouses, skirts, trousers, and tailored suits, coats and jackets. Schoolwear: boys' trousers and shirts; girls' skirts and shirts. Boys' wear: a limited range of casual shirts and trousers.

'All garments are leading chainstore perfects, seconds or ends of lines, and are offered at greatly reduced prices.'

See our display advertisement opposite

On B5010 less than 1 mile from M1 exit 25.

From M1 exit 25 roundabout: turn towards Sandiacre (on Derby side of M1). Go right at the T-junction. Go over the motorway: Claremont is 300 yds on the right.

From Stapleford: go over the hump bridge over the canal. Pass Texaco on right and shop is 100 yds on left.

Open: Mon–Fri 10–5; Sat 9–5; Sun 10–4.
Closed: Please phone about Bank Holidays.
Cards: Most major credit cards.
Cars: In street.
Toilets: In town centre.
Wheelchairs: Unfortunately not, shop is in basement.
Changing rooms: Yes.
Teas: In town centre.
Groups: Groups welcome; please phone first.
Transport: On direct bus route.
Mail order: No.

76 Selston Notts

Claremont Garments

Dove Green, Nottingham Road NG16 6DF
(01773) 863094

Ladies' wear: lingerie, swimwear, casualwear (bodies, leggings etc), dresses, blouses, skirts, trousers, and tailored suits, coats and jackets. Schoolwear: boys' trousers and shirts; girls' skirts and shirts. Boys' wear: a limited range of casual shirts and trousers.

'All garments are leading chainstore perfects, seconds or ends of lines, and are offered at greatly reduced prices.'

See our display advertisement opposite

On Nottingham Road (B600).

From Somercotes on B600: pass the Bull & Butcher on left and the turning for Jacksdale to the right. Go uphill, pass the Crown Inn on right and the entrance to the factory is 70 yds on right.

From Nottingham on B600: go through the only pedestrian lights, go to the top of the hill and the shop is on the left. Follow signs to shop.

Open: Mon–Fri 9–4.30; Sat 9–3.
Closed: Some Bank Holidays.
Cards: All major credit cards.
Cars: Own car-park.
Toilets: None in the vicinity.
Wheelchairs: Easy access.
Changing rooms: Yes.
Teas: Pub nearby.
Groups: Shopping groups welcome, but large groups please phone first.
Transport: On local bus route.
Mail order: No.

Claremont Garments

See our entries B230, G23, G45, G75, G76, G84, H66, H82, J11, J99, J103, J109, J112, K47

77 Somercotes Derbys *see map p. 482*

Coats Viyella

Nottingham Road DE55 4JM
(01773) 727590

Large range of men's shirts, trousers, knitwear; *Viyella* and *Jaeger* ladies' knitwear, skirts, blouses, jackets etc; children's wear, high quality household linens.

'Seconds, ends of lines etc from several companies in this group.

The factory is on the B600, between Alfreton and Somercotes.

From Leabrooks going north towards Alfreton: pass this large factory on left, then turn left into Hockley Way.*

From Alfreton coming south: pass slip road to A38 on the left, then take first right (Hockley Way).*

****Turn left through first gate into grounds and go round to clearly marked shop at rear.***

Open: Mon–Fri 10–4; Sat 9–4.
Closed: Bank Holidays. Please phone for Christmas closures.
Cards: MasterCard, Visa.
Cars: Close to shop in factory yard.
Wheelchairs: Ramp to huge shop on ground floor.
Changing rooms: Yes.
Teas: In Alfreton.
Groups: Coach parties welcome to shop. Prior phone call appreciated.
Transport: Leabrooks–Alfreton buses stop outside.

78 Somercotes Derbys *see map p. 482*

Designer Fabric Outlet

Birchwood Way DE55 4QO
(01773) 602555

Now closed

Huge stock of upholstery and furnishing fabrics: cottons, linens, damasks, velvets etc. Nets, voiles, calico, interlinings, waddings, linings. Haberdashery and fringing. Curtain rails, poles and accessories. Cushion covers and fillers. Ready-made curtains. Curtain-making service. Any size foam cut to shape.

'Discontinued lines from £2 per metre. Many upholstery fabrics at £4.99–£12.99. Voiles £3.99–£6.99 per metre. Approximately 5000 rolls available.'

See our display advertisement on p. 195

On an industrial estate on the east side of Nottingham Road (B600, Alfreton–Leabrooks).

From M1 exit 28: exit west for Alfreton. Take left slip road for Alfreton. At top of slip road, go left on to B600. After Cotes Park Inn on left, go left into West Way.*

Coming from Leabrooks north on B600 towards Alfreton: take right turn immediately before Cotes Park Inn (West Way).*

From Alfreton going south on B600: after Cotes Park Inn on left, go left into West Way.*

****At far end, go right at T-junction (Birchwood Way); take first right (Ashfield Avenue). Shop in first building on left.***

Open: Mon–Fri 10–5; Sat 9.30–5; Sun and Bank Holidays 10–4.
Closed: For Christmas closures please phone; open New Year's Day.
Cards: Access, Delta, Switch, Visa.
Cars: Own car-park.
Toilets: Yes.
Wheelchairs: Easy access to large shop; one step.
Teas: In Alfreton. Nearby pubs.
Groups: Shopping groups welcome, no need to phone.
Transport: Bus nos. 242/3, 245, 330, 332/3 from Alfreton, Derby, Nottingham.
Mail order: No.

See our entry below

79 South Normanton Derbys

Fabric Corner

Market Street Centre, Market Street DE55 2AB
(01773) 863700

Huge selection of top quality curtain fabrics, curtain linings and chintz. Plain, patterned and coloured voiles and muslins. Remnant section with thousands of metres of designer name fabrics.

'Chintz from £2.50 per m; regular and designer fabrics, voiles and muslins from £1.99 and linings from £1.50. Children's area with toys and videos.'

See our display advertisement above

In the centre of South Normanton.

From M1: take exit 28 then follow sign B6019 to South Normanton. After ¾ mile turn right immediately before Mobile petrol into Market Street. Shop is 300 yds on left.

Open: Mon–Sat 9.30–5; Sun 10–2.
Closed: Christmas, Boxing and New Year's Day.
Cards: Amex, MasterCard, Switch, Visa.
Cars: Own car-park.
Toilets: Yes.
Wheelchairs: Ramp; easy access.
Teas: Cafés 200 yds away.
Groups: Shopping groups welcome; no need to phone first.
Transport: Local buses.
Mail order: Yes.
Catalogue: No.

New in October 1998: huge factory outlet centre on the A38 east of M1 junction 28. Phone (0171) 591 8300 for latest details.

80 South Normanton Derbys

Filigree

Berristow Lane DE55 2EF
(01773) 811630

Curtain lace, nets and other fabrics; ready-made curtains; Austrian blinds, roller blinds; duvets, pillows, other bedding. Lampshades to match curtains. Also sell net rails, drape and valance rails. Household items, eg cushion covers.

'Special sales at various times of year: please see local press, or phone.'

See our display advertisement on p. 519

Half a mile north-east of M1 exit 28.

From Alfreton/M1 exit 28: take A38 towards Mansfield (follow signs to South Normanton Industrial Estate not South Normanton) for ½ mile. Take left slip road for B6406 for Blackwell. At mini-roundabout, continue following B6406 for Blackwell. Shop is 100 yds on left.*

From Sutton-in-Ashfield via A38 towards M1: take left slip road for Blackwell B6406; at first roundabout turn right, crossing over A38; at second roundabout go straight, still on B6406 for Blackwell. Clearly marked shopis 100 yds on left.

NB. As we go to press, there are major redevelopment works on the A38. Diversions may be in place.

Open: Mon–Thur 9–4.30; Fri 9–5; Sat 9–1.30. Bank Holidays 10–4.
Closed: Christmas, Boxing and New Year's Days.
Cards: Access, Switch, Visa.
Cars: Own large car-park.
Toilets: No.
Wheelchairs: Ramp.
Teas: Nearby hotel; in Sutton, Alfreton and on motorway (going south). Area is not well endowed with refreshment places!
Groups: Groups of shoppers welcome. Prior phone call first please.
Transport: Trent Bus nos. 243 (Mansfield–Alfreton–Derby) and 247 (Chesterfield–Alfreton–Mansfield); no. 130 (Mansfield–Normanton).
Mail order: Yes. Orders taken over telephone can be posted.

81 South Normanton Derbys

Straven

Ball Hill DE55 2ED
(01773) 811576 x 135 Fax (01773) 860122

Fully fashioned knitwear in natural fibres for men and women, made here. Also sell high quality ladies' skirts and blouses.

'Perfects and slight seconds on sale. We have a reputation for high quality. We operate a mailing list for forthcoming special events.'

One mile north of M1 exit 28.

From M1 exit 28 or Alfreton: take A38 for Mansfield. (Follow signs to 'South Normanton Industrial Estate', not 'South Normanton'.) After 100 yds turn left (Carter Lane East). Pass Swallow Hotel on left, follow lane through right hand bend; go left into Ball Hill before petrol station.*

Via A38 from Sutton-in-Ashfield towards M1: turn left for 'Blackwell', at first roundabout turn right over the A38; at second roundabout turn left into Carter Lane East; pass petrol station on right, go right into Ball Hill.*

****Go down Ball Hill; over motorway: shop is shortly on right.***

NB. As we go to press, there are major redevelopment works on the A38. Diversions may be in place.

Open: Tues–Fri 10–3; Sat 9–1.
Closed: Monday; Bank Holidays; Xmas–New Year. May close before/after Bank Holidays, phone to check.
Cards: MasterCard, Switch, Visa.
Cars: Own car-park front and rear.
Toilets: Ask if desperate.
Wheelchairs: Ramp to fairly small shop.
Changing rooms: Yes.
Teas: Nearby Castlewood Hotel – bar meals; Swallow Hotel; Sutton, Alfreton and on motorway (going south).
Groups: Shopping groups please phone. No factory tours unless pre-arranged – max. 15 due to safety regulations.
Transport: Sutton–Alfreton bus nos. 243, 247 stop Ball Hill.

82 Spalding Lincs

Sundaes

The Chase, 18 High Street, Moulton PE12 6QB
(01406) 371370

Leather sandals handmade on premises using finest materials; leather linings and insoles. All hand-lasted to give proper fit. Wide choice of styles mainly for ladies, some for men and children. Amazing choice of colours.

'Always some discontinued lines and colours and slight seconds, some at half price. All guaranteed. Phone for details of our special fittings service.'

Moulton is about 5 miles east of Spalding, south of the A151.

Go into Moulton to the village green. Look for The Chase, a gravel drive between the butcher and post office. Sundaes workshop is at the far end of The Chase (parking and turning possible).

Open: *April to end Sept:* Mon–Fri 9–3; *Oct to end Mar:* by appointment. Sat 9–12 *in summer* (phone to confirm opening times).
Closed: Bank Holidays; 22 Dec–2 Jan.
Cards: MasterCard, Switch, Visa.
Cars: Own car-park.
Toilets: Yes.
Wheelchairs: Easy access.
Changing rooms: Fitting area and small showroom.
Teas: In Spalding.
Groups: Shopping groups welcome by appointment.
Transport: Infrequent local buses from Spalding.
Mail order: Yes. Send current range only.
Catalogue: Free colour catalogue. Mention this book when requesting it.

Linger in Lincolnshire

Traditionally one of the driest counties in Britain (although such statistics must be questionable when Britain is experiencing its lowest rainfall for about 200 years), Lincolnshire is renowned for agriculture, bulbs and poaching rather than manufacturing. Even the Romans drained the fens into canals (used for transport too) so that they could cultivate the land. Many readers will have experienced Lincolnshire in the form of Skegness; many, too, will know the glorious cathedral in Lincoln.

There are many other fine churches in the county, including one in Boston. Not content with having the highest medieval lantern tower in the country, Boston also boasts the tallest working windmill (seven floors), which has been restored. Milling takes place on days when the wind blows. If you plan your Boston factory shopping (cane furniture, furnishing fabrics, bedding etc) for a Wednesday – market day in Boston – you can visit this windmill and buy stoneground flour directly from the miller (01205 352188).

This town, which gave its name to the larger version in the USA, was probably the busiest port in England at the end of the 13th century: British merchants exported wool in a very prosperous trade with northern European ports in Flanders and the Rhine area.

A young man, George Bass, was apprenticed to a surgeon from Boston. He explored Australia in a ship which was also captained by another Lincolnshire man, Matthew Flinders. Their names were, literally, 'put on the map': Bass in the straits between Tasmania and the Australian mainland, and Flinders as in the Ranges in South Australia.

83 Spondon Derbys

Heritage Upholstery

35 Anglers Lane
(01332) 281614

Custom-made upholstered furniture in wide range of colours, styles, fabrics etc. Also re-upholstery service.

'All items are new and made on the premises.'

See our display advertisement opposite

3 miles east of Derby, on old Nottingham Road (A6005), not A52.

From Derby: take A52 towards Nottingham then shortly turn off to Borrowash (A6005). After ¾ mile, you see the shop on right in detached, well marked building.

From M1 exit 25: take A52 to Derby. Go left for Elvaston Country Park. In Borrowash go right on to A6005. Go towards Derby. Continue until you pass large Anglers Arms on right; the shop is immediately on left.

From M1 exit 24: take A6 for Derby. Go right (B5010) at signs to Elvaston Country Park. In Borrowash, go left on to A6005 towards Derby. Continue until you pass large Anglers Arms Pub on right; the shop is immediately on left.

Open: Mon–Fri 9–5; Sat 9–4.
Closed: Bank Holidays; Christmas–New Year.
Cards: None.
Cars: Huge car-park at rear of shop.
Toilets: Yes.
Wheelchairs: One step.
Teas: Happy to put the kettle on for weary customers!
Tours: You are welcome to see your own suite being made.
Transport: Buses from Long Eaton, Nottingham & Derby. Spondon Station is ½ mile away.

84 Sutton-in-Ashfield Notts

Claremont Garments

Bowne Street NG17 4BJ
(01623) 442466

Ladies' wear: lingerie, swimwear, casualwear (bodies, leggings etc), dresses, blouses, skirts, trousers, and tailored suits, coats and jackets. Schoolwear: boys' trousers and shirts; girls' skirts and shirts. Boys' wear: a limited range of casual shirts and trousers.

'All garments are leading chainstore perfects, seconds or ends of lines, and are offered at greatly reduced prices.'

See our display advertisement on p. 539

In the centre of town, in a small street parallel to Outram Street.

From Mansfield: take A38 west for M1; at roundabout (King's Mill Hospital on right) go straight; pass Blue Bell pub on right and Citroen showroom on left. At traffic lights, bear left (Outram Street). Take third left (immediately after zebra), Stoney Street, then first right (Bowne Street). Shop is on left.

From M1 exit 28: take A38 for Mansfield. After several traffic lights go left (Station Road, B6022). Pass Wickes on left. Go straight at traffic lights; pass Kwik Save on right. At mini-roundabout, go right into Outram Street. Pass Asda on left, go over mini-roundabout, over bridge then right into Penn Street. Take first left, Bowne Street. Shop is on right.

Open: Mon–Fri 9–4.30; Sat 9–3.
Closed: Please phone about Bank Holidays.
Cards: Most major credit cards.
Cars: Own car-park.
Toilets: Nearest are in Asda, or in town.
Wheelchairs: No steps; easy access.
Changing rooms: Yes.
Teas: Two local cafés in Outram Street (5 minutes' walk)
Groups: Shopping groups welcome, but large groups please phone first.
Transport: Lots of buses to Sutton.
Mail order: No.

Heritage Upholstery

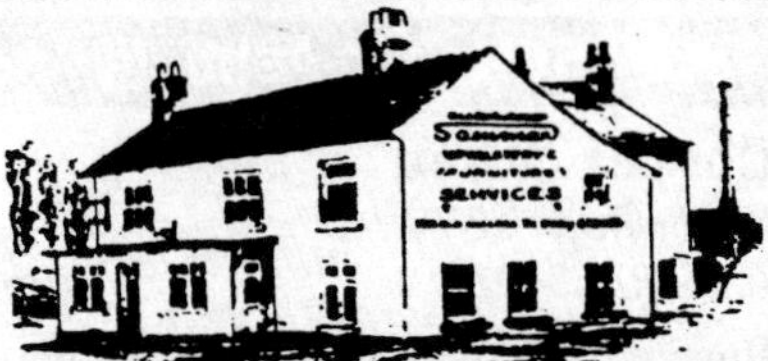
SERVICES

"Building furniture for your future"

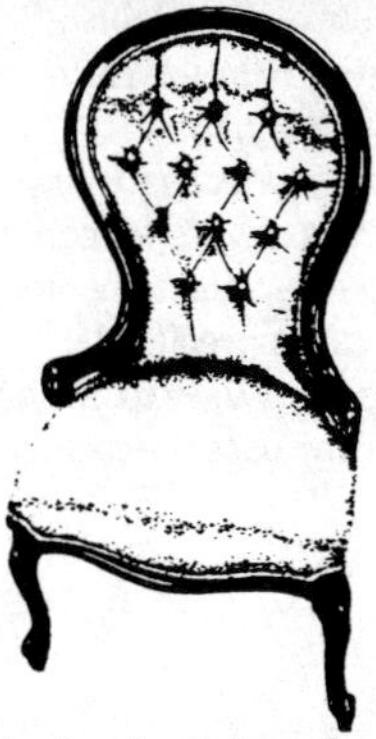

Benefit by buying directly from the manufacturer – first class workmanship (carrying a 5-year guarantee) at far less than retail prices.
You will soon find your journey very worthwhile.

We manufacture high-quality, completely different suites – custom-built to your own requirements. You choose the design, style, colour, fabric & even size to suit your home! We also offer an excellent reupholstery service. As with new suites, workmanship is guaranteed for 5 years.

35 Anglers Lane, Spondon DE2 7NP (01332) 281614 Mon–Fri 9–5, Sat 9–4 Phone or write for free brochure

See our entry opposite

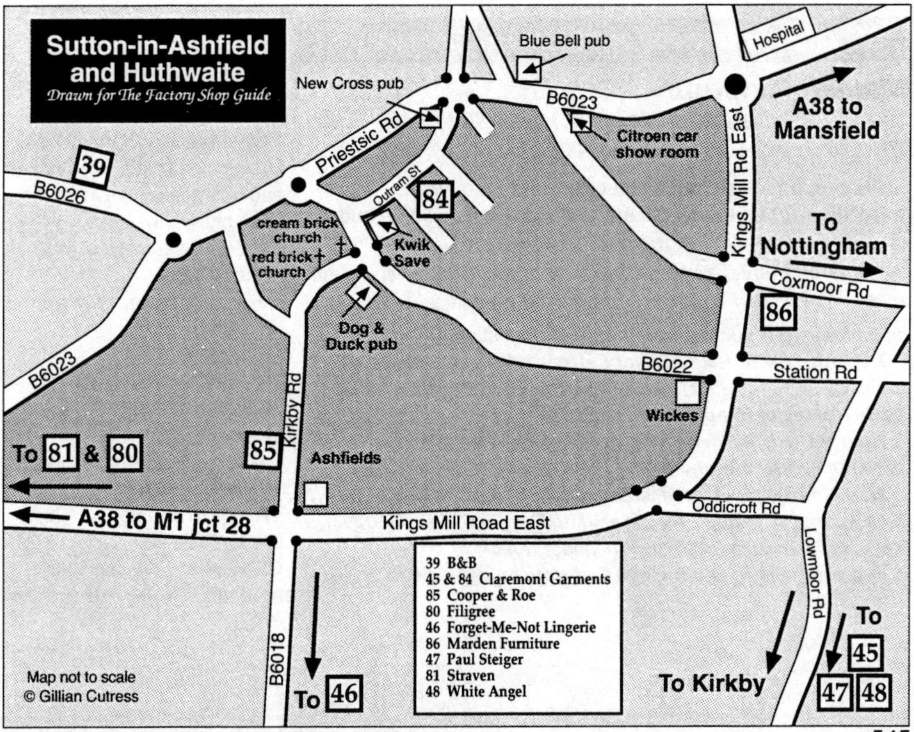
Sutton-in-Ashfield and Huthwaite
Drawn for The Factory Shop Guide
Blue Bell pub
Hospital
New Cross pub
B6023
Priestsic Rd
Citroen car show room
A38 to Mansfield
Kings Mill Rd East
39
B6026
Outram St
84
cream brick church
red brick church
Kwik Save
To Nottingham
Coxmoor Rd
86
Dog & Duck pub
B6023
B6022
Station Rd
Wickes
Kirkby Rd
To 81 & 80
85
Ashfields
Oddicroft Rd
A38 to M1 jct 28
Kings Mill Road East
Lowmoor Rd
39 B&B
45 & 84 Claremont Garments
85 Cooper & Roe
80 Filigree
46 Forget-Me-Not Lingerie
86 Marden Furniture
47 Paul Steiger
81 Straven
48 White Angel
To 45
B6018
Map not to scale
© Gillian Cutress
To 46
To Kirkby
47 48

85 Sutton-in-Ashfield Notts *see map on p. 545*

Cooper & Roe

Kirkby Road NG17 1GP
(01623) 554026

Huge range of clothing – all-wool knitwear for men and women; ladies' blouses, skirts, underwear, lingerie, hosiery; children's wear; leisurewear etc.

'Almost all items are made by this company. Seconds and export overmakes. Extended opening before Christmas. New children's play area.'

Three quarters of a mile south of Sutton centre, on the road to Kirkby (B6018) and 150 yds north of the A38.

From Sutton: factory is on right (large clear sign). Shop at back.

From Kirkby via B6018: pass Ashfield Comprehensive School (on left) and Ashfield Hotel (on right). Factory, clearly marked, is on left.

The new A38 runs 150 yds south of this company. Turn off at traffic lights on to B6018 for Sutton. Factory is 150 yds on left.

Open: Mon–Fri 9–5; Sat 9–4.
Closed: Bank Holidays; Christmas–New Year.
Cards: MasterCard, Switch, Visa.
Cars: Private car-park.
Toilets: Yes.
Wheelchairs: Ramp to huge shop now on first floor.
Changing rooms: Yes.
Teas: In Sutton.
Groups: No factory tours but groups always welcome to shop – no need to book but phone call appreciated.
Transport: Buses to Sutton and Kirkby pass the factory.

86 Sutton-in-Ashfield Notts *see map on p. 545*

Marden Furniture

Unit 12, Hamilton Road (Coxmoor Road) NG17 5LD
(01623) 512828 Fax (01623) 441195

Solid pine furniture in natural or antique finishes: wardrobes, chests, beds, bunk beds, dressers, tables and chairs etc. Also solid pine kitchens and fitted bedrooms.

'Seconds available; perfects usually to order. Prices well below retail. Will deliver anywhere in UK. Fax 01623 441195.'

Just off the new section of the A38, on Mansfield/Sutton border.

From Mansfield: take A38 for Sutton/M1. At roundabout (hospital on right) go left; after reservoir go left at first traffic lights (Coxmoor Road).*

From M1 exit 28: take A38 for Mansfield. Go through six sets of traffic lights, and turn right at seventh set (Coxmoor Road).*

From Sutton: aim for Mansfield (old A38, now B6023); turn right in front of Citroen showroom into Eastfield Side (B6021). Keep straight; cross A38 into Coxmoor Road.*

****Go over railway and through first gate on right.***

Open: Mon–Fri 9–5; Sat 10–4.
Closed: Bank Holidays; Easter Tuesday; Spring Bank Holiday week; last week July and first week August; Christmas–New Year.
Cards: Delta, MasterCard, Switch, Visa.
Cars: Large car-park at side of factory.
Toilets: No.
Wheelchairs: Easy access to ground floor shop.
Teas: In Sutton.
Groups: Groups of shoppers welcome – no need to phone.
Transport: None.
Mail order: Yes.
Catalogue: Free, but please send SAE. No seconds supplied.

Smaller towns of interest

Some smaller towns in this area, off the beaten tourist track, offer considerable interest.

East Retford has delightful Georgian and Victorian architecture, with a large and elegant market square, reflecting its former importance as a coaching centre on the Great North Road: at the height of its prosperity, 19 stage coaches (such as the Edinburgh–London Royal Mail service) clattered over its cobbles every day. (Prosperity did not prevent the Public Health Commissioner from commenting in the 1840s that the town had some of the worst slums he had ever seen.) An informative heritage trail leaflet guides you round the town centre. Retford was and still is a railway town, and you can walk along the Chesterfield canal, used to transport – amongst other things – cannon balls for the Crimean war.

Newark was – thank goodness – bypassed by the municipal and commercial vandalism of the 1960s. 'We weren't important enough to do anything with', as one long term resident explained it. How lucky. Recent developments in the heart of Newark are unobtrusive; sympathetic to the wonderful red brick building of this town.

Southwell – with its imposing Norman minster embellished with intricate stone and wooden carvings, and its Georgian houses – is a delight. Opposite the minster stands the 17th century black and white Saracen's Head where King Charles I passed his final night of freedom before surrendernig to the parliamentary forces. The Bramley Apple pub commemorates the fact that this strain of cooking apple was first cultured here. To find out more, visit Merryweather's garden centre. Five generations back, an earlier Mr Merryweather cultivated the bramley apple tree after Mr Bramley had grown the first one.

Worksop has one of the National Trust's most interesting recent acquisitions – Mr Straw's semi-detached house which had been completely unrestored for 60 years before the death of its owner in the eighties. Here too is the Pilgrim Fathers' Story – commemorating the intrepid people, many from villages in this area, who sailed to America in the Mayflower in the 1600s to escape religious demands.

Bolsover, a mining town without great tourist appeal, has an impressive castle with one of the few indoor riding schools in this country. The castle has been undergoing renovation for several years. The redecorated rooms are stunning. The castle sits high above the M1: when we last visited it, the wind was so wild that windows whistled. Very atmospheric!

Tourist Offices

(East) Retford
Arncott House, Grove Street, Retford DN22 6JU
(01777) 8660780

Newark
Gilstrap Centre, Castlegate, Newark NG24 1BG
(01636) 78962

Ollerton
Sherwood Heath, Ollerton Roundabout, Ollerton NG22 9DR (01623) 824545

Mansfield
Old Town Hall, Market Place, Mansfield NG18 1HX
(01623) 427770

H Merryweather & Sons Ltd
Halam Road, Southwell, NG25 0AH
(01636) 813204

Worksop Public Library, Memorial Avenue, Worksop S80 2BP
(01909) 501148

Mr Straw's house, Blythe Grove, Worksop. (01909 482380). Spring to autumn afternoons, by pre-booked time ticket.

Pilgrim Fathers Story, Memorial Avenue, Worksop. (01909) 501148.

Bolsover Castle
(01246) 823349

87 Swadlincote Derbys

Webb Ivory

Unit 10, The Rink Shopping Centre DE11 8JL
(01283) 226700

Fascinating variety of surplus catalogue stocks of greetings cards, wrapping papers, household goods, toys and small gifts.

'50% off catalogue prices.'

Situated in town centre pedestrian area 2 minutes' walk from shops and market hall.

Open: Mon–Sat 9.30–5 (Wed 9.30–1). Some Bank Holidays, please check.
Closed: Christmas–New Year.
Cards: Most major credit cards; Switch.
Cars: Free public car-park.
Toilets: No.
Wheelchairs: Easy access, no steps.
Teas: In Swadlincote.
Groups: No.
Transport: Two minutes' walk from central bus station.
Mail order: No.

88 Tibshelf Derbys

Harvergrange plc & Spartan Luggage

Saw Pit Industrial Estate DE5 5NH
(01773) 875393

Luggage, travel bags, suitcases, pilot boxes, leather executive cases, vanity cases etc. Stoneware and porcelain dinner and tea sets. Oven-to-tableware, knife sets, cookie jars, whole range of kitchen gadgets.

'Executive cases: leather £20–£35, PVC £6–£15; suitcases £12–£40. Tea sets (12-piece from £3.95); dinner sets (20-piece from £5.99, 45-piece from £24.99). Also oddments, discontinued lines and seconds.'

See our display advertisement opposite

From Tibshelf centre: go to north end of village, branch right on to B6014, cross the M1 and this estate is on right.

From M1 exit 28: take A38 towards Mansfield. At first traffic lights, go left. Continue to Huthwaite. At first junction, go straight; at second, turn left (sign to Tibshelf). After 1½ miles, turn left at T-junction. Estate is 500 yds on left. Company is first on right.

Open: Tues, Thur 10–5; Wed, Fri, Sat 10–4.
Closed: Monday; Bank Holidays; Christmas–New Year.
Cards: MasterCard, Visa.
Cars: Own large forecourt.
Toilets: Yes.
Wheelchairs: Easy access: one small step.
Teas: Alfreton and local pubs.
Groups: No factory tours but groups to shop welcome. Please book with Mr J Doe, mentioning this guide.
Transport: Difficult! Train to Alfreton then taxi.
Mail order: No.

HARVERGRANGE HOUSEWARES
AND
SPARTAN LUGGAGE FACTORY SHOP

VAST RANGE OF KITCHEN & HOUSEHOLD PRODUCTS

• Dinner sets • Tea sets •
• Kitchen gadgets •
• Oven-to-table ware •
• Microwave ware •
• Mugs • Knife sets •
• Cookie jars •

Oddments, discontinued lines and substandard items always available

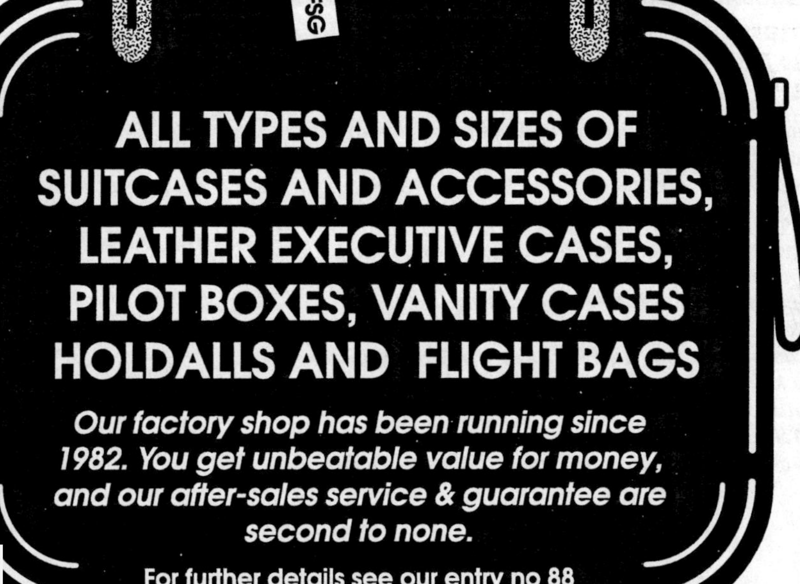

89 Trowell Derbys see map on p. 510

Swift Upholstery

Eagle Mill, Ilkeston Road NG9 3PW
(0115) 944 2596

Huge choice of upholstered suites in both leather and cloth.

'Over 2,000 sq. ft. of showroom displaying over 30 suites all made on premises. 50% off high street prices: 3-piece suites from £699–£2,500; bed settees from £300. Special sales at Easter, first two weeks of August and Christmas.'

On the south-east edge of Ilkeston, on the A6007/A609 which leads south towards the M1 (road crosses M1 but does not lead to a junction).

From Ilkeston: take A609 south. Continue downhill, along Nottingham Road. Pass Jet petrol on right then Ford on left and cross the River Erewash. As the road bends right, this shop is in the free-standing brick mill on the left.

From Nottingham on A609 or Trowell on A6007, coming north towards Ilkeston: pass the large Festival pub on right. Stay on this road, go over the railway. As the road bends left, this shop is in large detached mill on right. Entrance at far end.

Open: Seven days a week 10–4.
Closed: Christmas Day.
Cards: All major cards.
Cars: Huge car-park in mill-yard.
Toilets: Yes.
Wheelchairs: Four steps to ground floor showroom: please ring in advance for assistance. Stairs to upper floor.
Teas: Local pubs.
Transport: Buses from Ilkeston. Alight at Gallows Inn, shop 50 yds in direction of Nottingham.
Mail order: No.

90 West Bridgford Notts

P Harvey & Son

1–11 Julian Road NG2 5AJ
(0115) 982 2000

Quilted and plain fabrics, waddings, dressing gowns, housecoats; household textiles, pillows, duvets, bedspreads, sleeping bags, towels.

'Mostly firsts; some good quality seconds and ends of lines.'

On north side of West Bridgford, in the Lady Bay area.

From Nottingham: go south over Trent Bridge. Take first left into Radcliffe Road (A52); after ¾ mile go left just before pedestrian lights (opposite pillar box on right) into Rutland Road.*

Coming west into West Bridgford on A52: as you come along this fast road, look for pedestrian lights and turn right there (Rutland Road).*

***Take first right, around corner shop, then third left (Julian Road). Company is at far end, next to Cheshire Home.**

Open: Mon–Fri 10–4.
Closed: Bank Holidays; Easter week; late Spring Bank Holiday + 10 days; August Bank Holiday week; pre-Xmas–New Year. Phone to check exact dates.
Cards: No.
Cars: Own car-park.
Toilets: Yes.
Wheelchairs: Steps to first floor shop.
Changing rooms: No.
Teas: Hot drinks machine. Cold drinks on sale in shop. Café in National Watersports Centre nearby.
Groups: Tours by appointment only. Small groups welcome to shop.
Transport: Bus no. 85.
Mail order: No.

91 Wirksworth Derbys

Benco Hosiery

Cemetery Lane DE4 4FG
(01629) 824731

Men's, ladies', children's and babywear including: underwear, nightwear, casualwear, schoolwear, sportswear, outdoorwear and selected footwear; hats, gloves and scarves. A large range of hosiery including socks, tights, stockings, worksocks and legwarmers. Household linens and baby linen. Housewares and bedding.

'Very large shop on ground floor. Huge range of perfects and seconds at very low prices.'

See our display advertisement on p. 481

At the northern end of Wirksworth.

If you are going out of Wirksworth towards Matlock: pass Esso petrol on left, then turn right and immediately left (by the village school) where you see the 'Factory Shop' sign.

Coming south into town from Matlock direction: Cemetery Lane is the first turning on left (sign to Whatstandwell, Crich (B5035)). Then go immediately left again into the small lane beside the clearly marked shop.

Open: Mon–Sat 9–5; (Thur late opening to 8.30). Sun 10–5.
Closed: Christmas and Boxing Days only.
Cards: Delta, Eurocard, MasterCard, Switch, Visa.
Cars: Large car-park at rear.
Toilets: Yes.
Wheelchairs: Easy access to huge shop.
Changing rooms: Yes.
Teas: Self-service drinks and snacks; also seating and children's play area.
Tours: Working machines to view, & interesting, educational display of factory's history. Can arrange coach parties to shop after hours – visit can include pie and pea supper in nearby pub! Please arrange in advance, mentioning this guide.
Transport: Trent Bus no. R32 (Derby–Matlock–Bakewell).
Mail order: No.

92 Wirksworth Derbys

Wirksworth Factory Shoe Shop

2A The Market Place DE4 4ET
(01629) 822979

Footwear for all the family. Fashion shoes, boots, walking boots, slippers etc. Famous chainstore seconds.

'Save pounds, not pence! This is a paradise for bargain hunters.'

Easy to find in the Market Place in the centre of Wirksworth.

Open: Mon–Sat 9–5; Sun 11-4. Bank Holidays.
Closed: Christmas, Boxing & New Year's Days.
Cards: Connect, MasterCard, Switch, Visa.
Cars: Pay-&-display car-park facing.
Toilets: 150 yds.
Wheelchairs: No steps to medium-sized shop.
Teas: Several good tea rooms in Wirksworth.
Groups: Not really suitable.
Transport: Any bus to Wirksworth.

For two 'late entries', please see next page

93 Nottingham : Dunkirk *see map p. 527*

Charnwood Upholstery

The Midway NG7 2TT
(0115) 985 1444

Clearance lines of upholstered chairs, sofas, three-piece suites, footstools and recliners made here.

'All items are ends of ranges, cancelled orders, returns and seconds. A genuine factory clearance shop. Sofas £300–£600, suites £700–£1200. Delivery can be arranged.'

Dunkirk is on the south-west side of the city centre, just outside the ring road (Clifton Boulevard, A52).

Going clockwise round the dual-carriageway ring road: pass Central TV on the right then shortly turn left in front of the Showcase Cinema (Redfield Road).*

Going anti-clockwise round the ring road: go over the railway, pass Central TV on left then continue to next junction and double back along dual-carriageway.*

****Pass Makro on left. Look for Booker on left: Charnwood Upholstery is directly facing you, on corner of The Midway on left. Please go to reception.***

Late Entry

Open: Mon–Fri 9–4; Saturday four times a year (1st weeks March, June, September, December) 10–2. Please phone for exact date.
Closed: Probably closed Bank Holidays – please phone.
Cards: MasterCard, Visa.
Cars: Own car-park.
Toilets: Yes.
Wheelchairs: No steps; spacious ground-floor display area.
Teas: Pizza bar, café and restaurant five minutes' walk.
Groups: No factory tours; shop only suitable for small groups.
Transport: Buses to nearby cinema then short walk.
Mail order: No.

94 Nottingham : Central *see map p. 527*

Fabric Fabric

11 Gedling Street, Sneinton Market Square NG1 1DS
(0115) 911 0419

Large range of dress fabrics, cottons, bridal fabrics, dance fabrics, woollens, suitings etc. Also furnishing and upholstery fabrics, curtaining and linings.

'Fabrics from 99p–£10 per metre. Also offer curtain-making service.'

Close to the city centre, on the east side near ice rink. Possibly best to park near the ice rink and walk.

From city centre (Victoria Centre): go clockwise round town, into one-way Lower Parliament Street (inner ring road) towards Trent Bridge, passing ice rink on right. Go over the traffic lights (Gedling Street is on left but one-way towards you) then go left again until you reach this restored market.

From the city centre (Broadmarsh Centre): aim for Trent Bridge. At large roundabout with traffic lights, go left into one-way system, go up the hill and turn right, effectively doubling back. Look for the ice rink on right. Go over traffic lights (Gedling Street on left but one-way towards you) then go left again until you reach this restored market.

Late Entry

Open: Mon–Fri 9–5; Sat 9–4; Sun 11–4.
Closed: Bank Holidays; Christmas and New Year.
Cards: Yes.
Cars: Public car-parks nearby; some parking on-site; 20p for first hour.
Toilets: Yes.
Wheelchairs: Ramp to large shop.
Teas: Four cafés on site.
Groups: Always welcome.
Transport: Bus or train to city centre then walk.

Towns with factory shops

NUMBERS refer to the ENTRIES, NOT the PAGES

Alford	1	Straven
Alfreton	2	David Nieper
Ambergate	3	End of the Line Furniture
Ashbourne	4	Derwent Crystal
Ashbourne	5	Elite Factory Clothes Shop
Beeston	6	Floral Textiles
Beeston	7	The Mill Factory Shop
Belper	8	De Bradelei Mill Shops
Belper	9	Derwent House
Belper	10	George Brettle
Blidworth	11	The Major Oak Clothing Company
Boston	12	Ashcroft Fabrics
Burton-on-Trent	13	Webb Ivory
Calver	14	Peaklander Footwear
Calverton	15	The Wrangler Factory Outlet
Chesterfield	16	Demaglass Tableware
Chesterfield	17	Snowline Housewares
Chesterfield	18	Wynsors World of Shoes
Church Gresley	19	T G Green Pottery
Crich	20	Crich Pottery
Denby	21	Dartington Crystal
Denby	22	Denby Pottery Visitors Centre
Derby	23	Claremont Garments
Derby	24	Derwent Crystal
Derby	25	The Factory Shop
Derby	26	Filma
Derby	27	Royal Crown Derby
Derby	28	Webb Ivory
Grantham	29	Boundary Mill Stores
Grantham	30	Designer Fabric Superstore
Grantham	31	Rutland Lighting
Grantham	32	Witham Contours
Hardstoft, Chesterfield	33	Yew Tree
Heanor	34	The Fabric Factory (Nottingham)
Heanor	35	Langley Furniture
Heanor	36	The Wallpaper Factory Shop
Holbeach	37	The Factory Shop Ltd.
Hucknall	38	Jaeger
Huthwaite, Sutton-in-Ashfield	39	B & B
Ilkeston	40	Charnos
Ilkeston	41	Frank Knighton & Sons
Ilkeston	42	J B Armstrong & Co.
Ilkeston	43	Match Leisurewear Manufacturers
Ilkeston	44	R S Sports & Leisurewear
Kirkby-in-Ashfield	45	Claremont Garments
Kirkby-in-Ashfield	46	Forget-Me-Not Lingerie
Kirkby-in-Ashfield	47	Paul Steiger

Towns with factory shops

NUMBERS refer to the ENTRIES, NOT the PAGES

Town	No.	Shop
Kirkby-in-Ashfield	48	White Angel
Langley Mill	49	Coppice Side Pottery
Langley Mill	50	One Stop Factory Shop
Lincoln	51	The Curtain Factory Shop
Lincoln	52	Tanya
Long Eaton	53	Charnos
Long Eaton	54	Harrington Bridal Fabrics & Laces
Long Eaton	55	P F Collections
Matlock	56	John Smedley
Matlock	57	Matlock Shoe Sales
Matlock Bath	58	Denby
Matlock Bath	59	Fabric Design
Newark	60	Weston Mill Pottery
Nottingham : Bulwell	61	Warner's
Nottingham : Carrington	62	K & M (Leather Clothing) Mnfg. Co.
Nottingham : City Centre	63	Denby
Nottingham : City Centre	94	Fabric Fabric
Nottingham : City Centre	64	H. Jackson Fabrics
Nottingham : Dunkirk	93	Charnwood Upholstery
Nottingham : Sherwood	65	The Factory Shop,
Nottingham : Sherwood	66	Florentine Trading Co.
Nottingham : Sherwood	67	John D Maltby
Nottingham : Sherwood	68	Meridian
Nottingham : Sherwood	69	Regency Furniture Direct
Riddings	70	Charnos
Riddings	71	Standard Soap
Ripley	72	Chelsee Design
Ripley	73	Nuthall Lighting
Ruddington	74	Cooper & Roe
Sandiacre	75	Claremont Garments
Selston	76	Claremont Garments
Somercotes	77	Coats Viyella
Somercotes	78	Designer Fabric Outlet
South Normanton	79	Fabric Corner
South Normanton	80	Filigree
South Normanton	81	Straven
Spalding	82	Sundaes
Spondon	83	Heritage Upholstery
Sutton-in-Ashfield	84	Claremont Garments
Sutton-in-Ashfield	85	Cooper & Roe
Sutton-in-Ashfield	86	Marden Furniture
Swadlincote	87	Webb Ivory
Tibshelf	88	Harvergrange plc & Spartan Luggage
Trowell	89	Swift Upholstery
West Bridgford	90	P Harvey & Son.
Wirksworth	91	Benco Hosiery
Wirksworth	92	Wirksworth Factory Shoe Shop

Yorkshire & Northern Lincolnshire

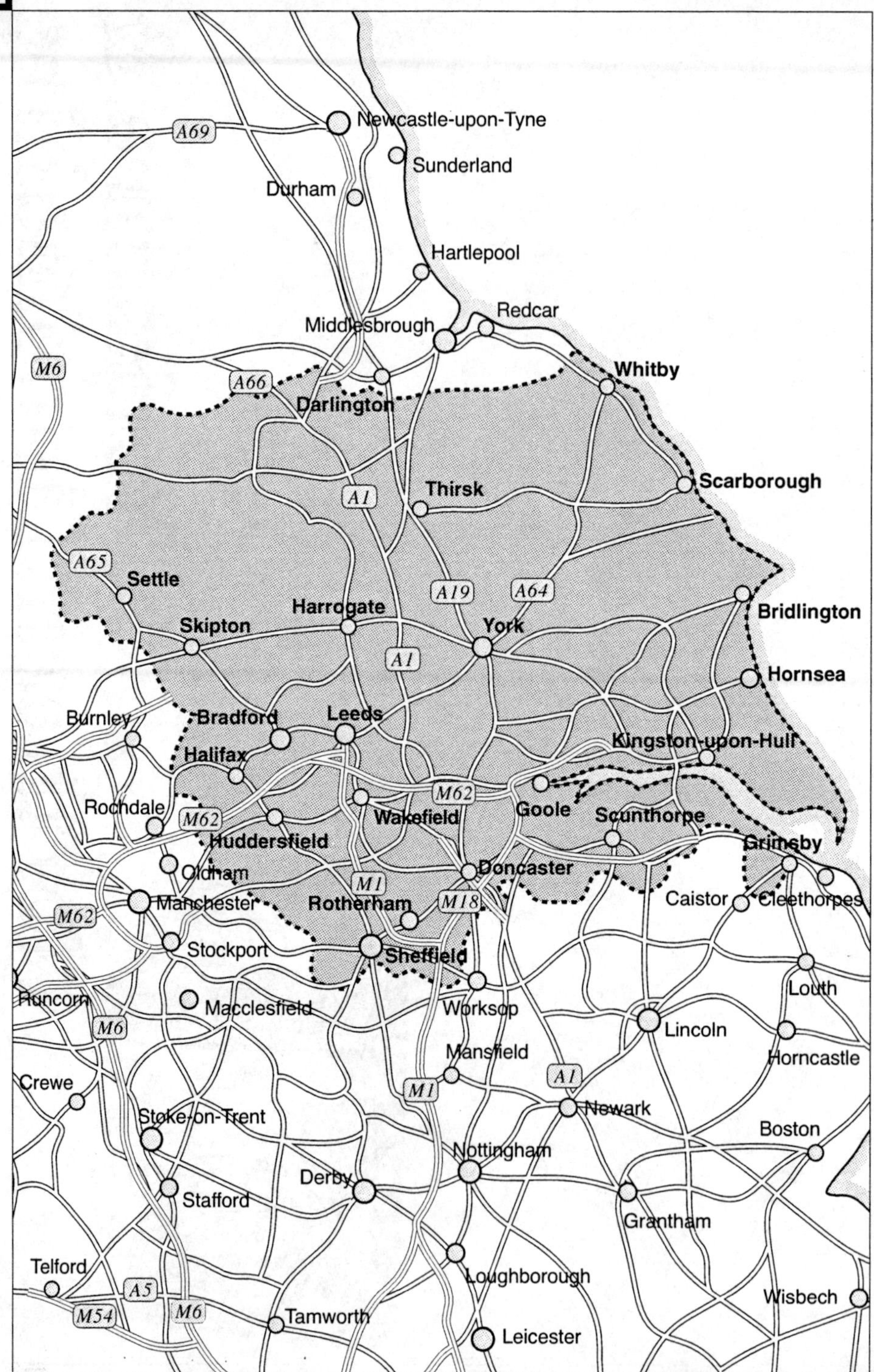

Newcastle-upon-Tyne
A69
Sunderland
Durham
Hartlepool
Redcar
Middlesbrough
M6
A66
Whitby
Darlington
Scarborough
A1
Thirsk
A65
Settle
A19
A64
Bridlington
Harrogate
Skipton
York
A1
Hornsea
Burnley
Bradford
Leeds
Halifax
Kingston-upon-Hull
M62
Rochdale
M62
Goole
Scunthorpe
Wakefield
Huddersfield
Grimsby
Oldham
Doncaster
M1
Caistor
Cleethorpes
Manchester
M18
M62
Rotherham
Stockport
Sheffield
Louth
Runcorn
Macclesfield
Worksop
Lincoln
M6
Mansfield
Horncastle
A1
Crewe
M1
Newark
Stoke-on-Trent
Boston
Nottingham
Derby
Stafford
Grantham
Loughborough
Telford
A5
Wisbech
M54
M6
Tamworth
Leicester

Yorkshire & Northern Lincolnshire

(formerly Yorkshire & Humberside)

This part of the world is a shopper's paradise. Three factory outlet centres, a large factory shop mill complex, modern shopping malls, a proliferation of retail parks – and an outstanding selection of individiual factory shops.

Our most recent researches in Yorkshire have brought to light some of our best purchases ever. Silver plated cutlery at a quarter of the price that department stores charge ... superb woollen skirt material woven in Yorkshire yet sold in Paris at eight times the price ... the finest worsted suiting in the world at prices way below those charged elsewhere ... chainstore family clothing (slight seconds) at a quarter of the price at chainstores ... stunningly good value in light fittings ... two enormous unbleached curtain tassels at £12 the pair ... and we bought a custom-made electric bed for an elderly relative at half the price quoted in a high street shop (saving £600, even allowing for delivery to London). Some of these purchases were one-offs; most weren't. We visit many shops and like to think we have developed a sixth sense for honing in on special bargains. Such examples illustrate the wonderful value for money to be found in factory shops.

The shopper is spoilt for choice and value when it comes to carpets and furnishing fabrics in this part of the world. The same goes for knitting yarns (many of which are available by mail order too) and pine furniture.

Amongst the most unusual shops to appear in our books is the world's largest supplier of circus equipment – supplying not just professional entertainers but selling items such as unicycles, absolutely everything needed by aspiring jugglers and items useful for parties.

Another first for us is the shop selling domestic surveillance and camera systems.

Once again county boundary and names have changed – but many organisations are still hazy as to where they are now, and continue to use 'Humberside' which has been divided up into East Yorkshire and a collection of Lincolnshires. Our use of 'Northern' aims to simplify the confusion.

Shaw Carpets

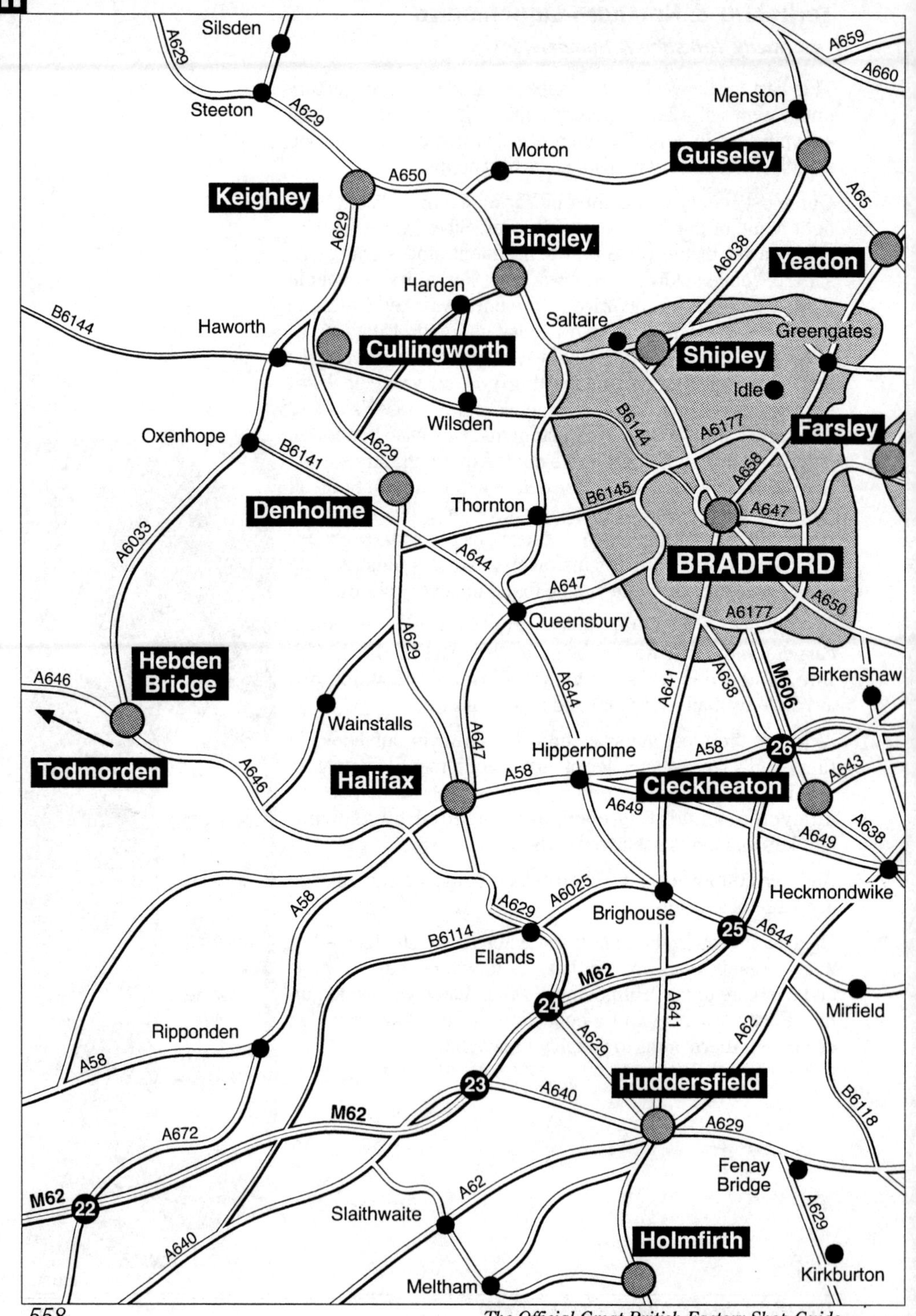
Silsden
Steeton
Keighley
Morton
Guiseley
Menston
Bingley
Yeadon
Harden
Haworth
Cullingworth
Saltaire
Shipley
Greengates
Idle
Wilsden
Oxenhope
Farsley
Denholme
Thornton
BRADFORD
Queensbury
Hebden Bridge
Todmorden
Wainstalls
Birkenshaw
Hipperholme
Halifax
Cleckheaton
Heckmondwike
Brighouse
Ellands
Mirfield
Ripponden
Huddersfield
Fenay Bridge
Slaithwaite
Holmfirth
Meltham
Kirkburton
A629
A650
A659
A660
A65
A6038
B6144
B6141
A6177
A658
A647
B6145
A644
A650
A6033
A646
A641
A638
M606
A58
A643
A649
A6025
B6114
M62
A62
A640
A672
B6118
22
23
24
25
26

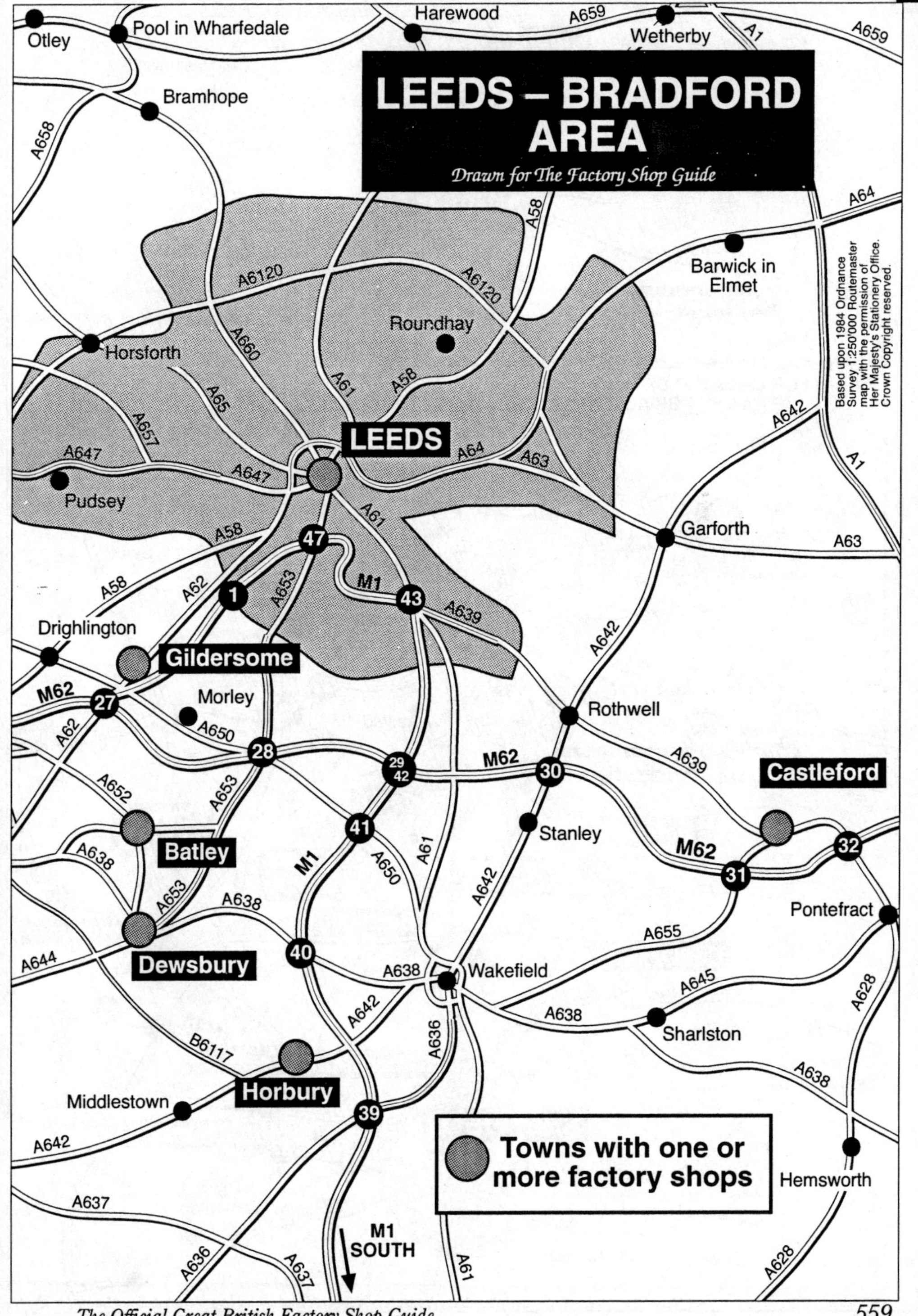
LEEDS – BRADFORD AREA
Drawn for The Factory Shop Guide
Based upon 1984 Ordnance Survey 1:250'000 Routemaster map with the permission of Her Majesty's Stationery Office. Crown Copyright reserved.
Otley
Pool in Wharfedale
Harewood
Wetherby
Bramhope
Barwick in Elmet
Roundhay
Horsforth
LEEDS
Pudsey
Garforth
Drighlington
Gildersome
Morley
Rothwell
Castleford
Stanley
Batley
Pontefract
Dewsbury
Wakefield
Sharlston
Horbury
Middlestown
Hemsworth
Towns with one or more factory shops
M1 SOUTH
M62
M1
A659
A1
A658
A58
A64
A6120
A660
A61
A65
A657
A647
A642
A63
A652
A653
A639
A650
A62
A638
A644
A655
A645
A628
A636
A637
B6117
1
27
28
29
42
30
31
32
40
41
39
43
47

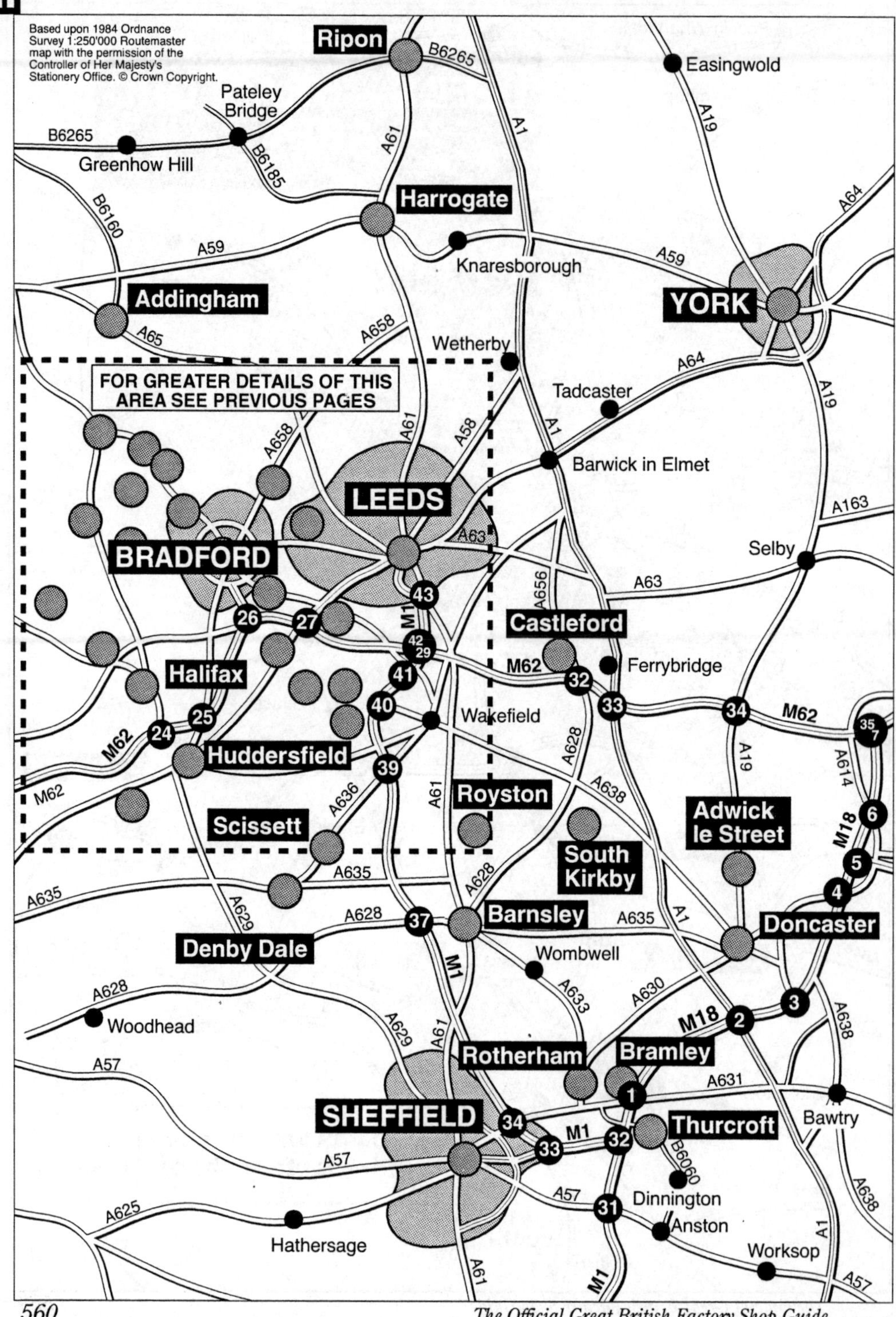
Based upon 1984 Ordnance Survey 1:250'000 Routemaster map with the permission of the Controller of Her Majesty's Stationery Office. © Crown Copyright.
Ripon
B6265
Easingwold
Pateley Bridge
B6265
Greenhow Hill
B6185
A61
A1
A19
Harrogate
B6160
A59
Knaresborough
A59
A64
Addingham
A65
A658
Wetherby
YORK
FOR GREATER DETAILS OF THIS AREA SEE PREVIOUS PAGES
Tadcaster
A64
A19
A658
A61
A58
A1
Barwick in Elmet
LEEDS
A163
BRADFORD
A63
Selby
A656
A63
43
M1
26
27
42
29
Castleford
M62
Ferrybridge
Halifax
41
32
33
34
M62
40
Wakefield
35
7
25
24
M62
Huddersfield
A628
A614
39
A638
M62
A61
Royston
Adwick le Street
A636
6
M18
Scissett
South Kirkby
5
A635
A628
4
A635
A1
A629
A628
37
Barnsley
A635
Doncaster
Denby Dale
Wombwell
M1
A633
A630
A628
3
Woodhead
M18
2
A629
A61
A638
Rotherham
Bramley
A57
A631
1
SHEFFIELD
34
Bawtry
M1
32
Thurcroft
A57
33
B6060
A57
Dinnington
A625
31
Anston
A638
Hathersage
A1
Worksop
A61
M1
A57

▲Continued on page 562 / 563▲

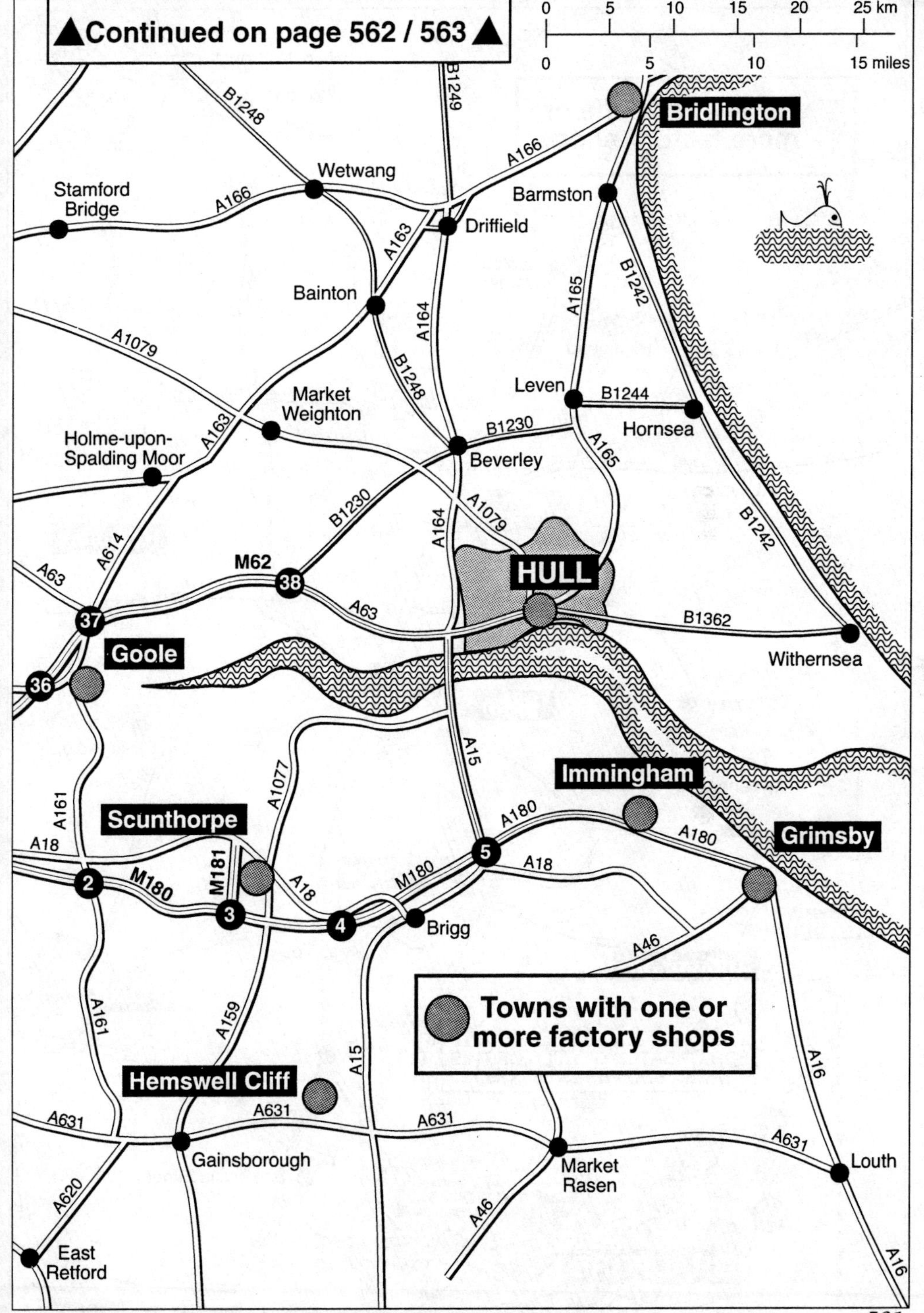

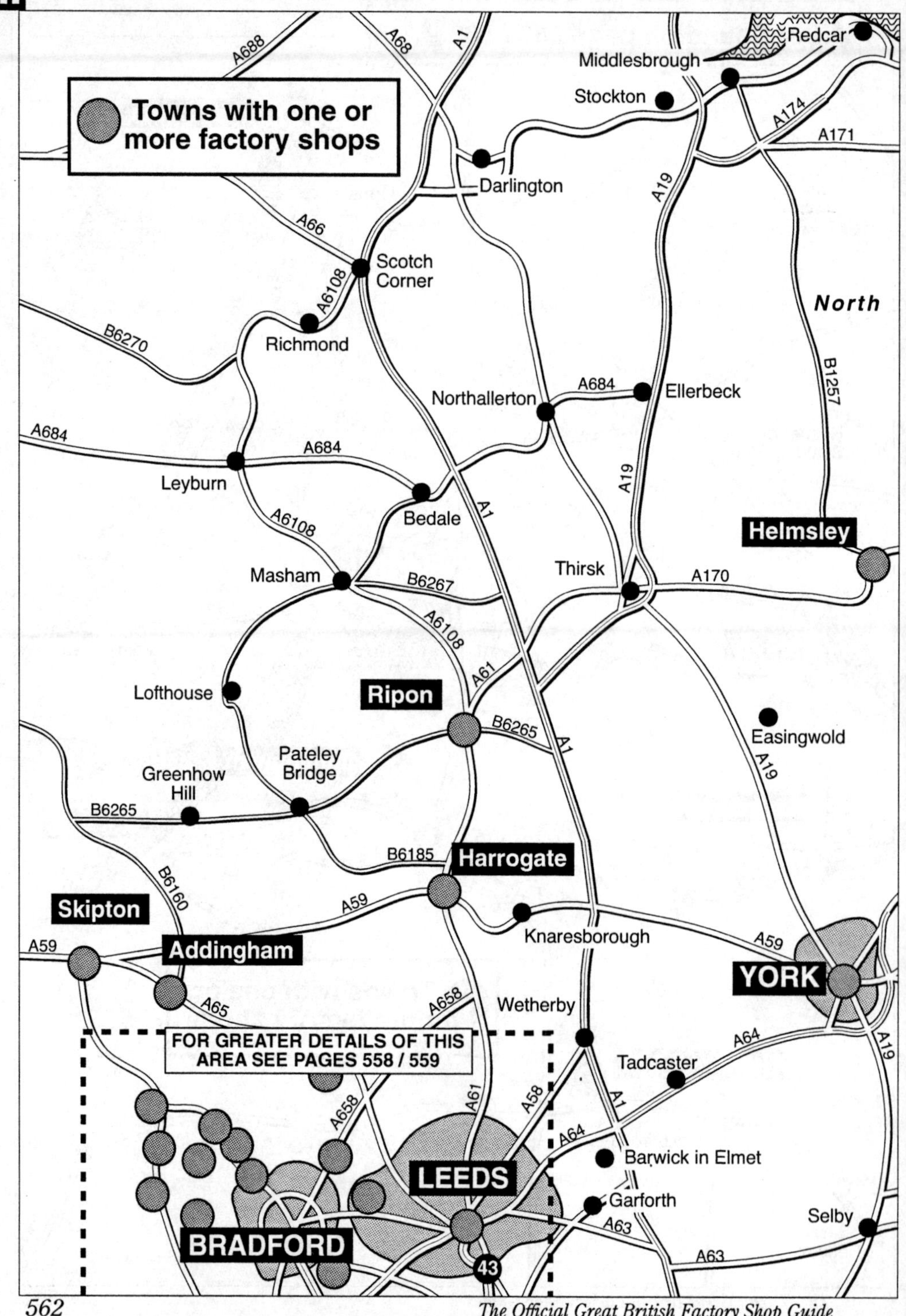

Towns with one or more factory shops
A688
A68
A1
Redcar
Middlesbrough
Stockton
A174
A171
Darlington
A19
A66
Scotch Corner
A6108
North
Richmond
B6270
B1257
Northallerton
A684
Ellerbeck
A684
A684
Leyburn
A19
Bedale
A1
A6108
Helmsley
Masham
B6267
Thirsk
A170
A6108
A61
Lofthouse
Ripon
B6265
Easingwold
A1
Pateley Bridge
Greenhow Hill
A19
B6265
B6185
Harrogate
B6160
Skipton
A59
Knaresborough
A59
A59
Addingham
YORK
A65
A658
Wetherby
FOR GREATER DETAILS OF THIS AREA SEE PAGES 558 / 559
A64
Tadcaster
A19
A61
A58
A658
A1
A64
Barwick in Elmet
LEEDS
Garforth
A63
Selby
BRADFORD
43
A63

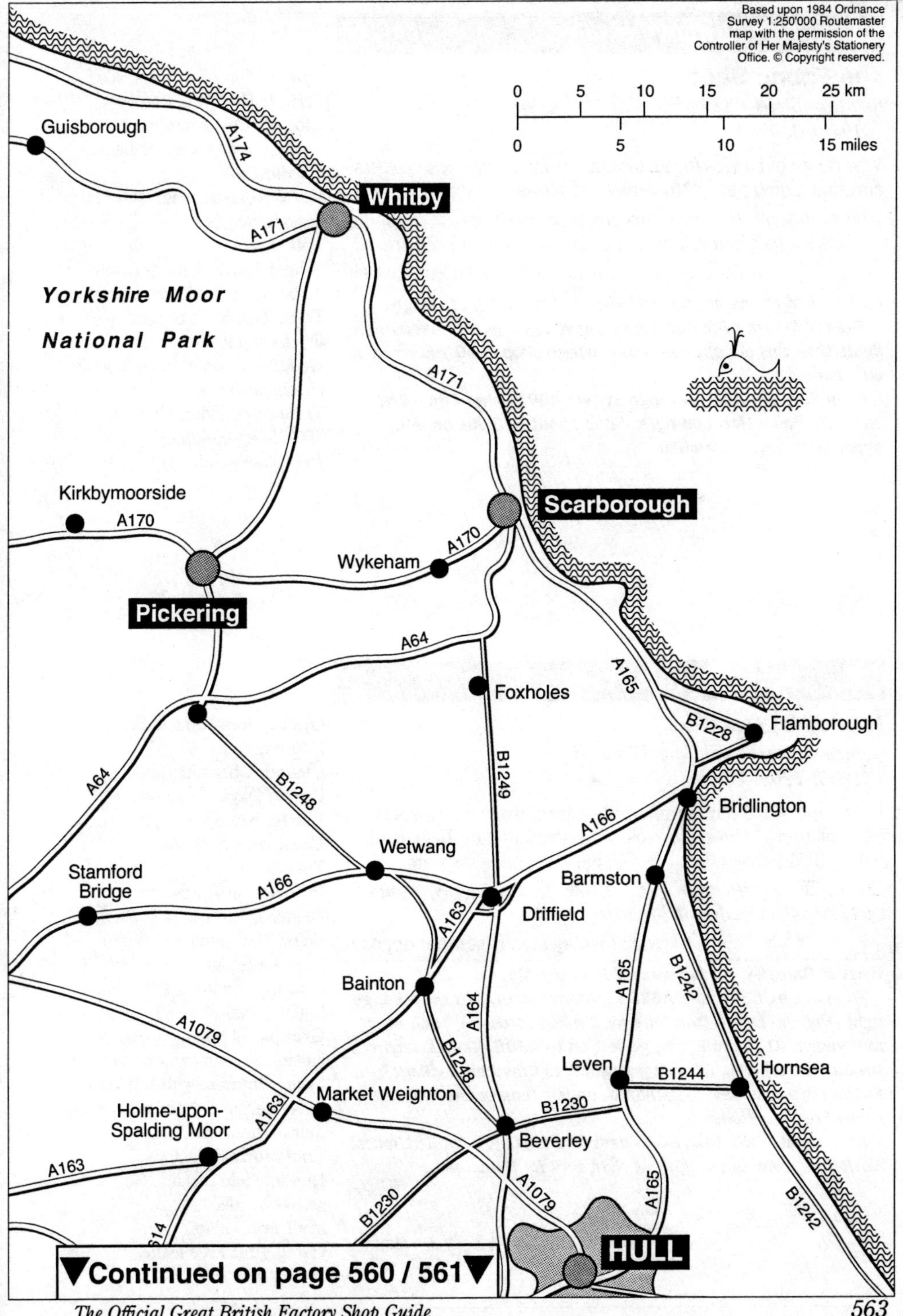

▼Continued on page 560 / 561▼

1 Addingham W Yorks

The Fabric Shop

82 Main Street LS29 0PL
(01943) 830982

Vast range of fabrics for furnishing, upholstery, loose covers, curtains, linings etc. (No velvets, dralons or nets.)

'This shop seems to stretch back for ever! Stock always changing. Perfects, seconds and remnants on sale at much reduced prices.'

See our display advertisement opposite

Easy to find on the main road (A65) in the centre of village.

From Ilkley via A65: come into the village, go over pedestrian lights then this deceptively small village shop is 50 yds on right, on a corner.

From Skipton (A65) or Keighley (via A6034): go into village, pass The Sailor Hotel on right. Shop about 150 yds on left, opposite large square chimney.

Open: Mon 10–6; Tues, Wed, Fri 9–1; Thur 12–4; Sat 10–4.
Closed: Christmas and New Year – phone for exact dates.
Cards: None.
Cars: Side street and short stay parking 50 yds.
Toilets: Yes.
Wheelchairs: Unfortunately no because of difficult stairs.
Teas: Tearooms 50 yds; five local pubs.
Groups: Cannot accommodate coach parties.
Transport: Hourly buses: 765 (Ilkley–Keighley), 784 (Ilkley–Skipton).

2 Barnsley (near) S Yorks

Naylor Clayware

Clough Green, Cawthorne S75 4AE
(01226) 790591

Large and small hand-crafted clay gardenware: strawberry pots, planters, window boxes, wall planters, sundials, bird baths, bird houses, jardinières, baskets, pedestals etc.

'"One offs" and rejects from £1–£100. This company, founded in 1890, offers traditional craftsmanship.'

See our display advertisement opposite

West of Barnsley, on the west side of the M1.

From M1 exit 37: take A628 for Manchester. After ½ mile, go right (Higham Lane). Continue for 2 miles (crossing back over motorway). At traffic lights, go left on to A635. Keep straight towards Denby Dale (do not go right into Cawthorne village). Factory is 1 mile past Cawthorne, on left (immediately by left turn-off for Penistone).

From Denby Dale: take A635 east for Barnsley; after 3 ½ miles, Naylor Clayware is on right, at right fork for Penistone.

Open: Mon–Sun and Bank Holidays 9–5.
Closed: Christmas and Boxing Days.
Cards: None.
Cars: Own car-park.
Toilets: No.
Wheelchairs: Easy access, no steps. Showroom is outside.
Teas: Tearooms and pub in Cawthorne; lunches and teas in nearby Cannon Hall country house (open all year).
Groups: Shopping groups, including coach parties, welcome by appointment with Jeff Cooke or Katherine Roberts. Regret no tour of the works.
Transport: Barnsley–Huddersfield bus no. 236 stops outside.
Mail order: No.
Catalogue: Free leaflet.

See our entry opposite

3 Barnsley (near) S Yorks

Shaw Carpets

Huddersfield Road, Darton S75 5NH
(01226) 390133 Fax (01226) 390549

Huge range of carpets including 80/20% wool; 50/50% wool twists; cut pile, cut and loop; cords; bedroom and bathroom carpets; contract carpets, rugs, underlay and accessories.

'Slight imperfects, roll ends, discontinued carpet ranges, all at bargain prices. Most stock manufactured here. Delivery service plus list of local carpet fitters. Special privilege card for purchasers for future discount offers.'

Darton is about 3 miles north-west of Barnsley.

From M1 exit 38: take A637 for Barnsley. Continue for one mile, go over motorway, pass Rose & Crown and Murco petrol station on right; then go left into entrance of Shaw Carpets; pass gatehouse, follow signs to factory shop.

From Barnsley: take A635 (A637) north-west to Huddersfield. Once out of town, at roundabout with Citroën garage on right, take A637 for Huddersfield. Shaw Carpets is on right, clearly signposted, about ½ mile after you enter Darton.

Open: Mon–Sat 9.30–4.45 (Thur to 7.30); Bank Holidays.
Closed: Christmas–New Year.
Cards: MasterCard, Switch, Visa.
Cars: Own car-park.
Toilets: Yes.
Wheelchairs: Six steps. Please ask if help needed.
Teas: In Darton, and Wooley Edge Service Station near M1 exit 38.
Tours: Please contact Kate Beresford for tours. Groups of shoppers very welcome.
Transport: Buses from Barnsley, Leeds, Wakefield etc; Darton rail station nearby.
Mail order: Yes, if customer knows requirements.
Catalogue: No.

Batley

Not officially classified as a 'factory outlet village', the Skopos Mill complex in Batley nonetheless houses an ever increasing selection of good value shops, and merits at least an hour's browsing time. (Much more time, if you are in a serious shopping mood rather than on an exploratory look-see.) One shop sells a gigantic selection of furnishing fabrics (current ranges, reduced price rolls, substandard runs and fents/remnants); also upholsterered and wooden furniture (including ex-display models), and wallpaper. With decorating in mind, walk across the car-park to a huge range of paints (including a useful colour-matching service) and wallcoverings. Wander upstairs to the shop selling antique Japanese cupboards. Lighting, carpets and pine furniture are also on sale, plus household textiles, bedding and other tempting items for the home.

Clothing is sold in abundance – from excellent value top quality countrywear down to socks. Several shops offer enormous choices of well known brands of men's and women's clothing, and footwear.

Weary shoppers can avail themselves of cakes, coffee and sandwiches on site. You'll be less exhausted if you avoid the weekend crowds.

Discover the value of Yorkshire's best kept secret

Visit Skopos Mills Batley now and find floor upon floor of inexpensive quality clothing and furnishings

Beans of Batley
Men's & Women's Fashion & Shoes

Susan Moore's
Lighting Gallery

Pine Workshop
Pine Furniture

Best for Less
Men's & Women's Fashion

First Choice Decor
Decorating Products

Skopos
Home Furnishings, Upholstery & Textiles

Sleep Shop
Beds

Double Two
Men's & Ladies' Clothing

Bacchanalia
Glass & China

Ponden Mill
Textiles

New Traditions
Furniture, Pottery, Lighting

Tansu
Antique Japanese Furniture

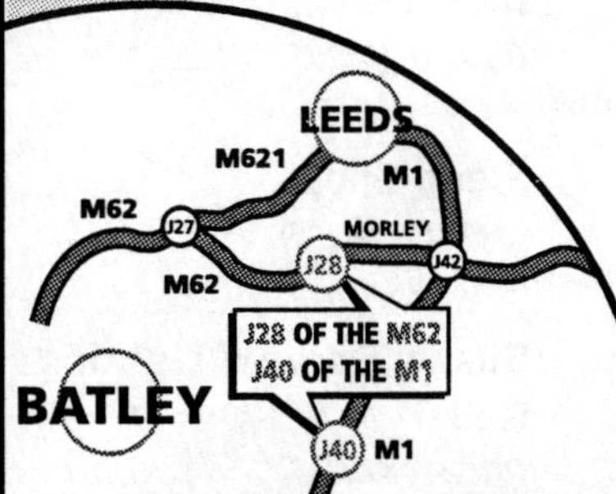

Bradford Road, Batley, West Yorkshire

OPEN 7 DAYS A WEEK

Shopping in the Yorkshire Tradition

See our entry overleaf

4 Batley W Yorks

Skopos Mills Batley

Bradford Road WF17 5LZ
(01924) 475756

Vast choice of furnishings, fashion and footwear. Seconds in exclusive designs of soft furnishing and upholstery fabrics; glassware; china; pottery; pine furniture; lighting; bedding; beds; designer fashion; antique Japanese furniture; wallpaper; paints and decorating supplies. Children's play area.

'Shopping in the Yorkshire tradition – historic mill environment, top name discounts, an exclusive range of antiques & furniture.'

See our display advertisement on previous page

Clearly visible on Bradford Road (A652), mill complex is close to traffic lights where B6124 (Soothill Lane) leads off towards M62.

From M62 exit 28: go south on A653 (for Dewsbury) then go right on to B6124 to Batley. At traffic lights, go right on to Bradford Road (A652). Large mill complex is shortly on right.

From Bradford direction: go south on A652. Large mill complex is on left, shortly before traffic lights where B6124 goes left.

From Batley market place: go downhill (Hick Lane) to traffic lights then go left.

From Dewsbury ring road: take A652 for Batley. Keep straight on this road into Batley; go over traffic lights where B6124 leads right for M62. Large mill complex is immediately on right.

Open: Mon–Sat 9.30–5.30; Sun 11–5. Bank Holidays.
Closed: Christmas Day; phone to check Boxing Day.
Cards: Shops accept credit and debit cards.
Cars: Own large car-park.
Toilets: Yes.
Wheelchairs: Easy access to shops on ground floor; please phone if special access needed.
Teas: Two cafés open 10–4 (Sun 11–4).
Groups: Coach parties welcome. Bookings preferred but not essential.
Transport: Trains to Batley. Bradford–Dewsbury buses.

5 Bacchanalia
(01924) 424000
Glass, china, cutlery, gifts.

6 Beans of Batley
(01924) 477717
Fashion, footwear and coffee shop.
See our display advertisement facing, and following page for more detail

7 Best for Less
(01924) 359090
Clothing – designer labels at affordable prices.
See following page for more detail

8 Double Two
(01924) 375951
Men's and ladies' clothing.

9 First Choice Decor
(01924) 470707
Wallpaper, paint and everything for decorating.

10 New Traditions
(01924) 477811
Furniture, pottery, lighting.

11 Pine Workshop
(01924) 422621
Quality pine furniture.

12 Ponden Mill
(01924) 444948
Linens and textiles.

13 Skopos Exclusive Interiors
(01924) 465191
Home furnishings.

14 Sleep Shop
(01924) 422196
Specialist bed centre.

15 Susan Moore's Lighting Gallery
(01924) 473335
Lamps, shades, ceiling lights and accessories.

16 Tansu
(01924) 422391
Antique Japanese furniture.

WELCOME TO

QUALITY **shopping** at **value** for money prices

Your invitation to visit us

Join us, seven days a week, at our new bigger store in Batley. We're open from 10.00 am to 5.00 pm including Sundays and Bank Holidays.

Over 20,000 square feet of shopping experience with lots of fitting rooms!

And there's a welcoming and relaxing in-store coffee shop where you and your friends can enjoy a quiet break - a cup of coffee, or lunch or afternoon tea!

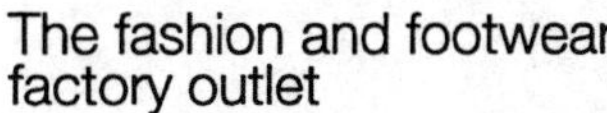

The fashion and footwear factory outlet

Discover a huge selection of beautiful ladies wear - for that special occasion, stylish fashion wear, a luggage and handbag department, jewellery, hats, a wide selection of mens suits, sports jackets, trousers, shirts, weekend wear, knitwear, ties and socks.

A place where shopping is relaxed and where the traditional values of personal and friendly service are always on hand.

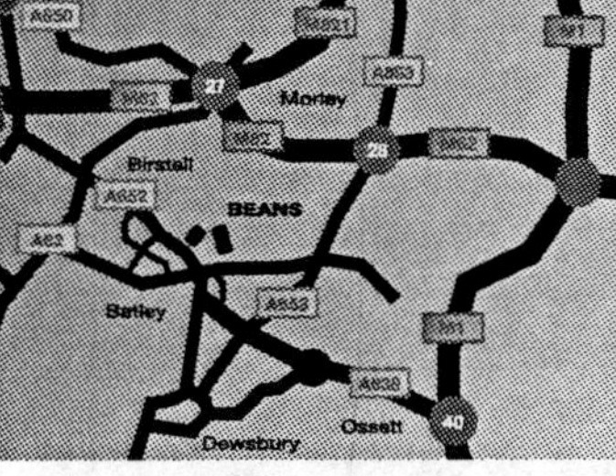

How to find us

Beans is at Skopos Mills, Batley within easy access at Junction 40 off the M1 and Junction 27 or 28 off the M62.

But best of all

You will find collections of top branded clothes at considerably less than the original price. Every garment has been specially selected by us to provide you with excellent style and great value.

Throughout the year at Beans you'll discover fantastic reduced prices on garments from winter coats to summer wear. Excellent value on day dresses, casuals and accessories. Plus superb ranges of value for money mens and ladies shoes.

With lots of space for over 600 cars so, there's no problem parking and it's free and safe.

Beans, Skopos Mills, Bradford Road, Batley West Yorkshire WF17 6LZ. Telephone 01924 477717 Facsimile 01924 477277

17 Batley W Yorks

Beans of Batley

Skopos Mills, Bradford Road WF17 6LZ
(01924) 477717 Fax (01924) 477277

Huge range of men's and ladies' quality branded fashions, including *Viyella, Mondi, Klass, Dannimac, Wolsey, Farah* and many more. Also luggage by *Antler, Revelation, Delsey.*

'Top branded fashion and footwear at up to 75% discount. 95% of our goods are perfects. Jackets reduced from £159 to £49; skirts from £79 to £29; blouses from £45 to £29. Regular sales: please ask to go on our mailing list.'

See our display advertisement on previous page

In clearly visible mill complex on Bradford Road (A652), close to traffic lights where B6124 (Soothill Lane) leads off to M62.

From M62 exit 28: go south on A653 (for Dewsbury) then right on to B6124 to Batley. At traffic lights, go right on to Bradford Road (A652). Large mill complex is shortly on right.

From Bradford: go south on A652. Large mill complex is on left, shortly before traffic lights where B6124 goes left.

From Batley market place: go downhill (Hick Lane) to traffic lights then go left.

From Dewsbury ring road: take A652 for Batley. Keep straight into Batley; go over traffic lights (where B6124 leads right for M62). Large mill complex is on right.

Open: Seven days 10–5 (including Bank Holidays).
Closed: Easter Sunday; Christmas Eve; Christmas Day.
Cards: Major credit cards; Switch.
Cars: Free parking for 600 cars.
Toilets: Yes.
Wheelchairs: Easy access to huge shop; customer lift to 1st & 2nd floors.
Changing rooms: Yes, ample.
Teas: Own Coffee Beans coffee shop.
Groups: Shopping groups welcome; please phone Janet Cook.
Transport: Trains to Batley; Bradford–Dewsbury buses.
Mail order: No.

18 Batley W Yorks

Best for Less

Skopos Mill Complex, Bradford Road WF17 5LZ
(01924) 359090

Wide range of quality clothing for men and women: silk shirts, jackets, suits, leather coats, outerwear and accessories.

'Middle and top end labelled garments for men and women who appreciate quality at a bargain price. Some seconds, but mostly perfect overmakes of current season's lines. Discounts up to 75%. Free filter coffee served in a relaxed environment.'

In clearly visible mill complex on Bradford Road (A652), close to traffic lights where B6124 (Soothill Lane) leads off to M62.

From M62 exit 28: go south on A653 (for Dewsbury) then right on to B6124 to Batley. At traffic lights, go right on to Bradford Road (A652). Large mill complex is shortly on right.

From Bradford: go south on A652. Large mill complex is on left, shortly before traffic lights where B6124 goes left.

From Batley market place: go downhill (Hick Lane) to traffic lights then go left.

From Dewsbury ring road: take A652 for Batley. Keep straight into Batley; go over traffic lights (where B6124 leads right for M62). Large mill complex is on right.

Open: Mon–Sat 10–5; Sun 10.30–5. Bank Holidays.
Closed: Easter Sunday; Christmas, Boxing and New Year's Days.
Cards: All major credit cards; Switch.
Cars: Over 600 spaces.
Toilets: Yes, and for disabled.
Wheelchairs: Easy access to large ground floor shop.
Changing rooms: Yes.
Teas: Freshly ground coffee served free.
Groups: Shopping groups most welcome, no need to book.
Transport: Trains to Batley; Bradford–Dewsbury buses.
Mail order: No mail order, but gladly post items at cost.
Catalogue: No.

19 Bingley W Yorks

Byworth Fabric Warehouse

Unit B Castlefields Industrial Estate, Crossflatts BD16 2AG
(01274) 561900

Large stock of upholstery and furnishing fabrics: cottons, linens, damasks, velvets etc. Voiles, calico, interlinings, waddings, linings. Haberdashery. Curtain rails/poles and accessories. Cushion covers and fillers. Ready-made curtains. Foam cut to shape.

'Measuring, fitting and curtain-making services. About 2000 rolls in stock. Fabrics start at £1.99 per metre.'

See our display advertisement on p. 195

About ¾ mile north-west of Bingley town centre, just off Keighley Road (A650).

From Bingley: go north along Keighley Road (A650). After ¾ mile (just before railway) go left into well marked estate.

Coming south from Keighley on A650: go over railway (station on left) then immediately go right into Castlefields Lane to well marked estate.

Open: Seven days a week: Mon–Sat 9–5; Sun 10–4. Bank Holidays 10–4.
Closed: Few days at Christmas – please phone to check.
Cards: Connect, MasterCard, Switch, Visa.
Cars: Own free car-park.
Toilets: Yes (not for disabled).
Wheelchairs: No steps.
Teas: In Bingley, Haworth, Keighley. Good local pubs.
Groups: Shopping groups welcome, no need to phone.
Transport: On main bus route, buses stop 100 yds. Crossflatts train station also 100 yds away.
Mail order: No.

Care of velvet

Velvet is an ancient and beautiful three-dimensional fabric, originally made of silk but now in cotton, nylon, viscose etc. Even with modern machinery, its manufacture is slow and labour intensive. Unfortunately for those of us who love sewing and adore velvet, working with this fabric can be tricky. The following hints come from Denholme Velvets.

- Cut the fabric with the pile 'nap' running upwards.
- Before sewing the garment, try a test piece to assess puckering and creep between the fabric layers.
- Use a long stitch (10 stitches per inch/4 per cm), decrease pressure on the presser foot, reduce thread tension and use a ball-nosed needle.
- Do not use iron-on interfacings.
- Use soft lining fabrics (harsh linings may abrade the seam edges, causing the pile to shed).
- Pressing should be minimal and done pile-down on a needleboard or a piece of scrap velvet (pile-up).
- Store garments on a padded hanger.
- If garments have to be folded, insert tissue paper.

What is velvet?

The term 'velvet' is often applied, inaccurately, to velveteen and velour.

Velvet *is woven on special looms in two layers which are cut apart to reveal two pieces of fabric with pile. Weave and fibre can both be varied according to use, eg haute couture, curtains.*

Velveteen *is woven as a single layer with numerous pile loops which are cut open and brushed. It is traditionally lighter in weight than velvet.*

Velour *is usually a knitted fabric, although sometimes woven. The pile is shorter than velvet and the fabric is lighter in weight.*

Bradford

Bradford, with its long association with the woollen trade, makes an excellent centre for mill shopping and for exploring the attractive countryside around. We usually stay west of Bradford in the area between Thornton (where the Brontë sisters were born) and Haworth where we have tracked down some delightful places to stay – from a cleverly modernised old stone farmhouse, to a spacious wing of an original mill owner's mansion. Values are excellent at about £20 pppn. Our favourite pub in England, which serves imaginative home-made food, is in this area too. Bradford itself is an ideal city for sampling Asian cuisines. Bradford Tourist Office has some restaurant guides; one devoted to Asian restaurants is in the making.

Bradford road systems remain a challenge. Each time we have visited the city over the last eleven years, we have been confronted with major changes. On our latest visit, the area north of the city centre (near British Mohair Spinnners mill shop) had sprouted a retail park. Pedestrianised Centenary Square, in the city centre, has also been redesigned – with plans for programmes of interesting local events.

For walks round the city and its varied architecture, use the Heritage Trail leaflet. Visit the industrial museum in the huge old spinning mill (01274) 631756. Enter a brilliant world at the award-winning Colour Museum (01274) 390955.
Note that the National Museum of Photography, Film and TV, and the IMAX cinema are closing for protracted redevelopment work (01274) 727488.

Bradford Tourist Office (01274) 753678
Haworth Tourist Office (01535) 642329

20 Bradford W Yorks *see map on next page*

Bateman, Ogden & Co. (The Suit Length & Fabric Centre)

918 Wakefield Road, Dudley Hill BD4 7QO
(01274) 729103 Fax (01274) 720818

Huddersfield and Scottish worsted suitings of all weights. Scottish tweeds. Large selection of fabrics specifically for ladies. Coating in cashmere/wool, all wool fabrics. Skirt lengths, satin linings, travel rugs, caps, ties and gloves.
'Annual two-week sale starts in mid-November.'

About 1½ miles south-east of the city centre.

From Bradford: follow signs to Wakefield (A650). Turn off for ring road, go right round the roundabout and down the other slip road as if going back to Bradford. Shop, clearly visible, is on left.

Coming into Bradford on A650: turn off for the ring road but go straight at the roundabout and down the slip road towards Bradford again. Shop is on left.

Open: Mon–Sat 8.30–5.
Closed: Bank Holidays; Christmas, Boxing & next day.
Cards: MasterCard, Switch, Visa.
Cars: Private car-park at rear.
Toilets: Yes.
Wheelchairs: Easy access to ground floor (stairs to upper showroom).
Teas: 'Pub grub' close by.
Groups: No factory tours. Coaches welcome to spacious shop. Please book.
Transport: Any Dudley Hill bus from Bradford Interchange.
Mail order: Yes.
Catalogue: Small free brochure. Gladly post pattern ranges at £3 per range, refundable on return of patterns. In view of extensive range of fabrics, can operate mail order on certain ranges only. No seconds sent.

21 Bradford W Yorks *see map on next page*

British Mohair Spinners

Corner of Valley Road and Cape Street BD1 4RJ
(01274) 728456

Big selection of brushed mohair knitting wools plus other yarns. Some sweaters and other clothing for all the family.

'A genuine mill shop specialising in luxury mohair at mill prices. Brushed mohair from £1.80 for 100g. Bargain lots always available.'

Just over ¼ mile north of central Bradford.

From central Bradford (Forster Square): take Canal Road for City centre north/Shipley A6037. Pass Royal Mail on left. Stay on main road. Pass Save petrol and Jaguar showroom on left and at roundabout go left into Hamm Strasse.*

Coming south from Shipley on Canal Road A6037: go right at lights (Office World on far right corner) for ring road A6081. You are in Hamm Strasse.*

***At first traffic lights go right (Valley Road): clearly marked shop is in old stone mill on far right corner of first street on right.**

Open: Mon–Fri 9–4.
Closed: Bank Holidays; Christmas–New Year.
Cards: MasterCard, Visa.
Cars: One-hour parking in Cape Street.
Toilets: Yes.
Wheelchairs: Access difficult (three steps at front door). Another door with easier access gladly opened on request.
Changing rooms: Yes.
Teas: Many places in town.
Groups: No mill tours but coach parties welcome to shop. Prior phone call appreciated.
Transport: 5–10 minutes' walk from city centre.
Mail order: Yes.
Catalogue: Shade cards £2 a set, including price list.

22 Bradford W Yorks *see map on next page*

Card and Gift Factory Outlet

Dawson Lane, Dudley Hill BD4 6HV
(01274) 689399 fax (01274) 784372

Huge range of all types of greeting cards, wrap and trim, gifts, toys, household items and mail order surplus.

'At least half off normal retail and catalogue prices. Shop recently extended and refurbished.'

About 1¾ miles south-east of Bradford.

Leave Bradford on Wakefield Road (A650). Cross ring road (Dudley Hill roundabout) and pass Asda on left. Continue straight (Tong Street). Go over traffic lights. After 200 yds go right (fourth turning) down Dawson Lane.*

Coming into Bradford from Wakefield (A650) or Dewsbury (A651): after traffic lights where these two roads merge, go over second set of lights towards Bradford. After Bramall Ford garage (about 1 mile) go left down Dawson Lane.*

***Look for security gates and factory shop on left after 100 yds.**

Open: Mon–Fri 10–5.30; Sat 10–5.
Closed: Bank Holidays; Christmas, Boxing and New Year's Days.
Cards: Mastercard, Visa.
Cars: Ample parking and turning for coaches and cars.
Toilets: No.
Wheelchairs: Four low steps down to shop.
Teas: In Asda; local pubs. Don't forget the famous fish & chip shops around Bradford.
Groups: Coaches welcome, please book first.
Transport: Regular local services.
Mail order: No.

23 Bradford W Yorks *see map facing*

Golden Shuttle

Albion Road, Greengates BD10 9TO
(01274) 623450

Gents', ladies' and children's wear of British and continental make. Ladies' sizes 10–24; men's 34–48" chest. Children's clothes 0–10 years. Worsted/wool and wool/terylene cloth by the metre. Department selling unusual gifts. Handbags and luggage.

'99% of items are perfect. Sometimes designer labels of seconds quality (usually just a minor flaw, such as the wrong shade).'

About 3½ miles north-east of Bradford. Near the junction of A658 (Bradford/Yeadon/Harrogate road) and A657 (Shipley/Calverley/Leeds road).

From Bradford: take A658 north-east for Harrogate. Otley Road becomes Harrogate Road. At traffic lights where this road is crossed by A657, go left for Shipley.*

From Harrogate coming south on A658: at traffic lights where this road is crossed by A657, go right for Shipley.*

***At large Parkland mill, turn left into Albion Road. Clearly marked shop is 100 yds uphill on left.**

Open: Mon–Sat 9.30–5. Please phone about Bank Holidays.
Closed: Christmas, Boxing and New Year's Days.
Cards: Eurocard, MasterCard, Switch, Visa.
Cars: In nearby street.
Toilets: Yes.
Wheelchairs: No – access is up nine steps.
Changing rooms: Five.
Teas: Nearby supermarket; local pubs with good bar meals.
Groups: Coach parties welcome. Please book with manager, mentioning this guide.
Transport: Bus nos. 648 from Bradford Interchange; 670 and 760 (Leeds–Keighley).
Mail order: No.

24 Bradford W Yorks *see map facing*

Lister Mill Shop

Manningham Mills, Heaton Road BD9 4SH
(01274) 480515

Velvet & dralon fabrics: sold by the metre or choose from the huge selection of ready-made curtains, pelmets, tie-backs and cushions. A selection of suiting fabrics from the roll. Rugs. Upholstered furniture which can be covered with any fabric from *Lister's* upholstery range.

'All ready-made curtains, in great range of sizes, are slightly imperfect, and sold at considerably reduced prices. We are always introducing new lines.'

NB This shop has moved (to far end of same mill).

Just over a mile north of Bradford centre, this magnificent mill with tall tower is visible above Lister Park (home of Cartwright Museum). Lots of brown signs now lead you to the museum.

From city centre:

either take Keighley Road (A650), the main Bradford/Shipley road; cross A6177 ring road traffic lights then take third left, Oak Lane. Go uphill. At traffic lights (huge stone mill on far right corner), go right (Heaton Road). Shop on left, at far end of mill.

or aim north for Bingley (B6144); cross A6177 ring road into Toller Lane; after ⅓ mile, go right (Lilycroft Road). At traffic lights, go left (Heaton Road). Shop at far left of huge mill.

Open: Mon–Fri 9.30–5; Sat 10–5.
Closed: Bank Holidays; please phone to check Christmas–New Year period.
Cards: Delta, MasterCard, Switch, Visa.
Cars: Adjacent streets.
Toilets: Yes.
Wheelchairs: Easy access to huge shop on ground floor.
Teas: Freshly brewed coffee on offer. Café in Cartwright Hall in Lister Park, 10 minutes' walk.
Groups: Coach groups welcome; booking not necessary but please mention this guide. No factory tours.
Transport: Bus nos. 620, 621 from Bradford Interchange to Lilycroft Road then walk to Heaton Road.
Mail order: No.

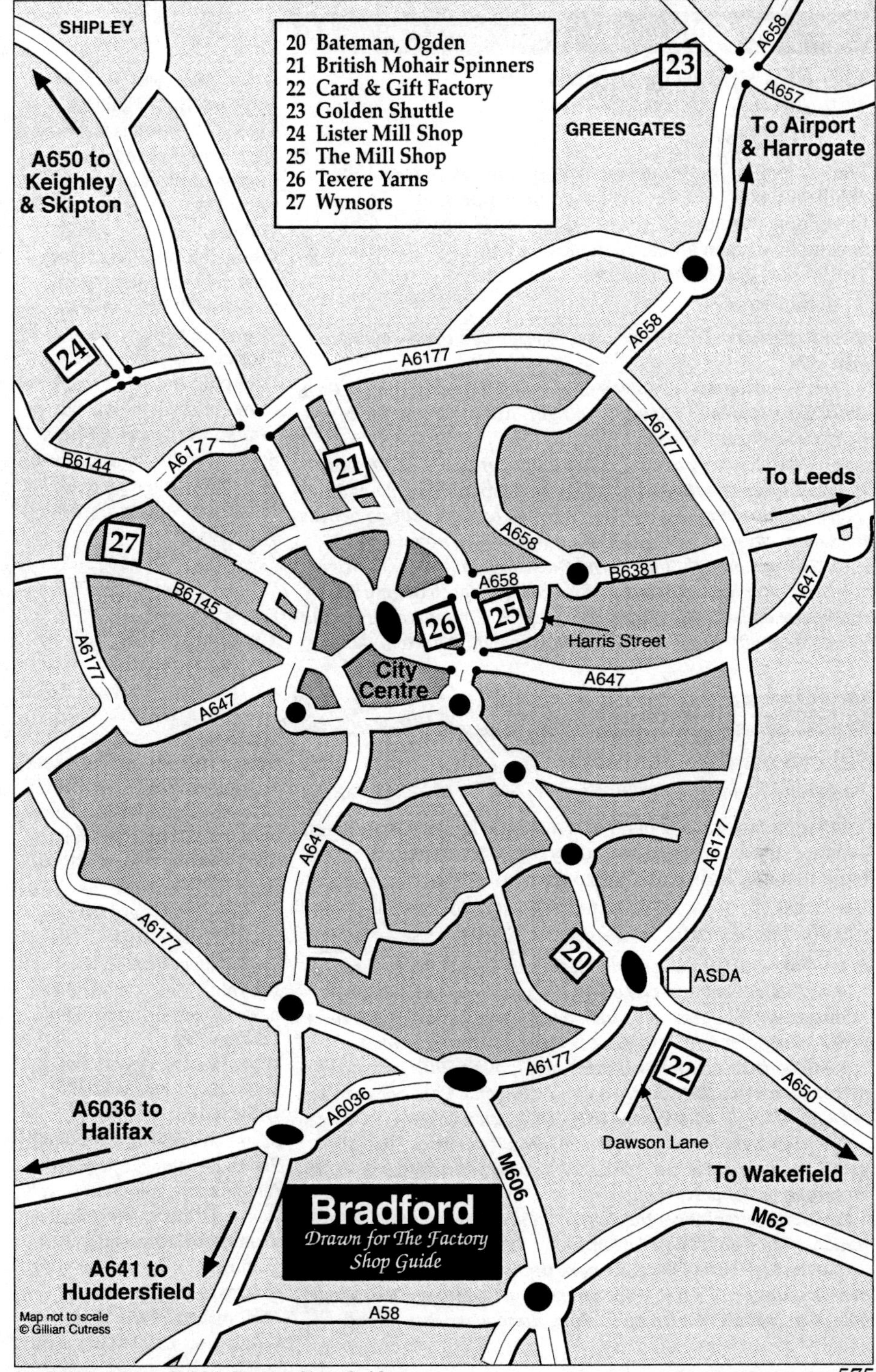
20 Bateman, Ogden
21 British Mohair Spinners
22 Card & Gift Factory
23 Golden Shuttle
24 Lister Mill Shop
25 The Mill Shop
26 Texere Yarns
27 Wynsors
SHIPLEY
GREENGATES
A650 to Keighley & Skipton
To Airport & Harrogate
To Leeds
A658
A657
A6177
B6144
A658
B6381
B6145
A647
A641
Harris Street
City Centre
ASDA
A650
Dawson Lane
To Wakefield
A6036 to Halifax
A6036
M606
M62
A641 to Huddersfield
A58
Bradford
Drawn for The Factory Shop Guide
Map not to scale
© Gillian Cutress

25 Bradford W Yorks *see map on previous page*

The Mill Shop (Bradford)

11 Harris Street BD1 5HU
(01274) 731181

Wide selection of products. Ground floor: women's clothing, children's wear, soft toys, disposable nappies.
First floor: furniture, beds, bedding, towels, rugs, lighting.
Second floor: men's wear made for famous high street stores.
Third floor: ladies and children's clearance.

'Rock bottom prices.'

Clearly visible on A650 (inner ring road), close to city centre on east side.

From Leeds on A647: go downhill almost into city centre. Pass Shell petrol and Imro car-wash on right. At next traffic lights, go right for Harrogate/airport.*

From Bradford city centre: follow signs for Leeds A647. After National Tyres on left, go left at traffic lights for Keighley A650.*

****Go up dual-carriageway (passing shop on right, but no access from here). At next traffic lights, go right for Harrogate A658. After 200 yds go right into Harris Street. Shop in mill at bottom.***

From Forster Square in city centre: go uphill for Harrogate A658 (cathedral on left). Go over traffic lights for Harrogate. After 200 yds go right into Harris Street. Shop is in mill at bottom right.

Open: Mon–Sat 9.30-5–30; Sun 10–4. Bank Holidays.
Closed: Christmas and Boxing Days; Easter Monday.
Cards: MasterCard, Visa.
Cars: Own three-tier car-park.
Toilets: Yes.
Wheelchairs: Four steps at main door; one step at front door directly on to street.
Changing rooms: Yes.
Teas: Own coffee shop.
Groups: Shopping groups welcome (prior phone call please).
Transport: Trains to Foster Square and Interchange; buses to and from Interchange.
10 minutes' walk to city centre.
Mail order: No.

26 Bradford W Yorks *see map on previous page*

Texere Yarns

Barkerend Road BD3 9AO *(01274) 722191*

Vast range of yarns for hand and machine knitting, handloom and tapestry weaving, embroidery and tassel work, rug and braid making. Knitwear and woven rugs available.

'10–15,000 kg of yarns, set out in bins, spread over two floors (10,000 square feet).'

In Bradford city centre (slightly north-east), near the cathedral.

From Forster Square in city centre: go up steep Church Bank (for Harrogate A658). Pass cathedral on left. Take 2nd right (Peckover Street) then first left (Park Gate). Company at top of road.

Going north or south round inner ring road (A650): at traffic lights, go towards 'City centre south'/cathedral. Pass company on left – go downhill, take second left, double back on one-way street.

From Leeds on A647: go downhill into city centre. Pass Shell petrol and Imro car-wash on right. At next traffic lights, go right for Harrogate/airport A650.*

From Bradford city centre: follow signs for Leeds A647. After National Tyres on left, go left at traffic lights for Keighley A650.*

****Go up dual-carriageway. At next traffic lights, go left for 'City centre south'/cathedral. Pass company on left – continue downhill, take 2nd left: double back along narrow one-way street.***

Open: Mon–Fri 9–5; weekends as arranged with Robin Smith.
Closed: Easter Friday–Tues; Spring Bank Holiday Mon and Tues; May Day; August Bank Holiday; Christmas–New Year.
Cards: MasterCard, Switch, Visa.
Cars: Upper Park Gate (downhill from company) and new car-park by traffic lights.
Toilets: Yes.
Wheelchairs: Access tricky.
Teas: Hot drinks available.
Groups: For group visits please contact Chris or Robin Smith, mentioning this guide. All knitters, embroiderers and weavers especially welcome.
Transport: 15 minutes' walk from Bradford Interchange; also taxis from there.
Mail order: Yes.
Catalogue: £2.90 shade card.

27 Bradford W Yorks *see map on previous page*

Wynsors World of Shoes

339 Thornton Road BB8 9BM
(01274) 495016

Men's, ladies' and children's fashion shoes in leather and synthetic materials.

'Massive range of branded footwear from own factory and all over the world. Stock changes daily. Prices from £1 to £100. Special lines at lowest prices in country. January and July sales.'

See our display advertisement on p. 423

NB. This shop, on the west side of Bradford, has moved down Thornton Road B6154 and is now just inside ring road (A6177).

From the city centre: take B6145 (Thornton Road) for Allerton and Thornton. After 1¼ miles, clearly marked shop is on right.

Going east on Thornton Road B6145 to Bradford: pass Morrison's on right. Cross outer ring road (A6177). Shop shortly on left.

From ring road (A6177): at traffic lights, turn on to Thornton Road B6145 for Bradford city centre. Shop is shortly on left (on corner of Weetwood Road).

Open: Mon–Wed & Sat 9–5.30; Thur, Fri 9–8; Sun 10–4; Bank Holidays 10–4.
Closed: Christmas, Boxing and New Year's Days.
Cards: MasterCard, Style, Visa.
Cars: Large car-park by door.
Toilets: No.
Wheelchairs: Ground level entrance; huge shop.
Teas: Café in shopping centre 200 yds.
Groups: No factory tours. Groups of shoppers always welcome without booking.
Transport: From Bradford Interchange: bus nos. 605, 616 (to Allerton); 607 (Thornton); 692 (Bingley); 697 (Keighley); 698 (Oxenhope).
Mail order: No.

28 Bramley S Yorks

Lighting Bug

Bawtry Road S66 0TW
(01709) 530731

Huge range of domestic lighting: soft shades and table lamps made here; full ranges of polished solid brass light fittings; crystal, wood and panel glass ceiling fittings. Wall lamps to complement ceiling fittings. Outdoor lighting, spot lights, downlighters, low voltage and fluorescent lighting. Light switches, bulbs, doorbells etc.

'Perfects and seconds at discounts of 25–50%. Always special offers on discontinued lines. Gladly pack and post (at cost) if you can't carry purchases home. We are a happy-go-lucky company and will do anything to take your money!'

Near M18 exit 1, east of Rotherham.

From M18 exit 1: go west on A631 for Rotherham. After ½ mile you come to traffic lights with The Sportsman on right corner. Company beside this pub. Go right, park & walk (no U-turns here!).

From Rotherham: aim for M18/Bawtry on A631 dual-carriageway. Go through Wickersley. Go under pedestrian overpass to traffic lights (Bramley post office on near left corner). Go over traffic lights, pass The Sportsman on left: shop is just past it.

Open: Mon–Sun 9.30–5.30. Bank Holidays.
Closed: Christmas–New Year.
Cards: Connect, Delta, Eurocard, Mastercard, Switch, Visa.
Cars: Large company car-park beside shop.
Toilets: Ask if desperate.
Wheelchairs: One step to huge shop on ground floor.
Teas: Little Chef 200 yds; local supermarket.
Transport: Rotherham–Maltby buses stop at the 'Ball'.
Mail order: Yes.
Catalogue: £4 redeemable against purchases of £50+. Please phone for catalogue (with credit card). All items sent by overnight delivery (about £10).

29 Bridlington E Yorks

Park Rose Pottery Leisure Park

Carnaby Covert Lane YO15 3QF
(01262) 602823

Large range of hand decorated ceramics made here including planters, vases, co-ordinating lamp bases and shades; tableware and kitchenware accessories; variety of collectable giftware.

'Selected seconds on sale in the seconds warehouse, often at half normal high street prices. Pottery in 12 acres of beautiful parkland, ideal location for a family day out. Owl sanctuary. Honey bee exhibition. Children's play area.'

Easy to find, 2 miles south of Bridlington between A614 (to Driffield) and A165 (to Beverley).

There are conspicuous brown signs on both these roads.

Open: Seven days a week, 10–5.
Closed: Christmas–New Year.
Cards: MasterCard, Visa.
Cars: Huge free parking area for cars and coaches.
Toilets: Yes, including for disabled.
Wheelchairs: Easy access to all facilities. Everything on ground floor.
Changing rooms: Yes.
Teas: Own licensed café for snacks, meals etc. Picnic area.
Groups: Free pottery walkabout or detailed guided tour for nominal fee. Coach parties welcome to pottery or shopping.
Transport: Buses from Bridlington.
Mail order: No.

30 Castleford W Yorks

Wynsors World of Shoes

Enterprise Way
(01977) 514774

Children's, ladies' and men' shoes: sport and leisure styles; range of comfort fit & wider shoes; leather brogues; excellent range of leather and fashion handbags; branded sports bags.

'99% perfects. Average 30% less than high street prices; special buys and promotions at least 50% off. Sales in January & July.'

See our display advertisement on p. 423

In town centre by bus & train stations, on retail park by Netto etc.

From M62 exit 32: exit for Castleford. Pass Shell on left. At roundabout, exit left for Castleford.*

From Ferrybridge: at roundabout as you reach town, go right for Castleford.*

****Pass Fina on right: at roundabout after it, go straight for Leeds A639. Keep straight. Go over level-crossing. At traffic lights (King William IV pub far right corner) go right (Akerton Road). Pass swimming pool on left. At far end, go right for Town Centre (A655).*****

From M62: take exit 31 for Castleford. At roundabout, go straight uphill on A655 for Castleford.**

*****Go over level-crossing (by Castleford Gates junction box). Pass Do It All on right. At next roundabout take third exit, into Enterprise Way (in front of Netto). Shop clearly visible on right.***

Open: Mon, Tues, Sat 9–5.30; Wed, Thur, Fri 9–8; Sun 10–4. Bank Holidays 10–4.
Closed: Christmas, Boxing and New Year's Days only.
Cards: MasterCard, Style, Visa.
Cars: Own large car-park.
Toilets: In bus station opposite.
Wheelchairs: Easy access to large shop.
Teas: Café 59 yds; pub next door.
Groups: Welcome with prior phone call to shop manager.
Transport: Near rail station. Any bus to or from town centre.
Mail order: No.

31 Cleckheaton W Yorks

Jaeger

Gomersal Mills BD19 4LV
(01274) 852303

Large range of *Jaeger* ladies' and men's wear. *Viyella* ladies' wear.

On A643 between Cleckheaton and Gomersal.

From crossroads in centre of Gomersal: take A643. Shop is 200 yds on right in conspicuous mill with 'Burnley' on tall chimney.

From Cleckheaton: take A643 for Leeds. Go uphill. Red-brick mill is on left, opposite church, just before you reach Gomersal. Go through gates; shop clearly marked on left. Follow signs.

Open: Mon–Sat 9–5.
Closed: Please phone for holiday closures.
Cards: Amex, Diners, MasterCard, Switch, Visa, Jaeger account card.
Cars: In forecourt & side road.
Toilets: At entrance to shop.
Wheelchairs: Easy access to very large shop.
Changing rooms: Yes.
Teas: Public may use the coffee bar on site (closes Sat 11.30 am).
Groups: Shopping groups welcome to shop. Please book in advance.
Transport: On bus route from Leeds/Bradford/Huddersfield.
Mail order: No.

32 Cleckheaton W Yorks

Wynsors World of Shoes

Unit B, Horncastle Street, Castle Mills BD19 3HH
(01274) 851366

Men's, ladies' and children's fashion shoes in both leather and synthetic fabrics.

'Massive range of branded footwear from own factory and all over the world. Stock changes daily. Prices from £1 to £100. Special lines at lowest prices in country. January and July sales.'

See our display advertisement on p. 423

From M62 exit 26: take A638 into Cleckheaton. After 1 mile pass big church on left; take second right, Horncastle Street.*

From town centre and Heckmondwike: take A638 for Bradford. After crossing A643, pass Yorkshire Bank on right and take first left, Horncastle Street.*

****Shop 50 yds on right.***

Open: Mon–Wed and Sat 9–5.30; Thur, Fri 9–8. Bank Holidays 10–4.
Closed: Christmas, Boxing and New Year's Days.
Cards: MasterCard, Style, Visa.
Cars: Behind building and on street.
Toilets: Opposite in market.
Wheelchairs: No steps, large shop.
Teas: Cafés and good fish & chip shop.
Groups: Groups of shoppers always welcome. No need to book.
Transport: Any bus to Cleckheaton (500 yds).
Mail order: No.

33 Cullingworth W Yorks

Coldspring Mill

Haworth Road BD13 5EE
(01535) 275646

Branded high quality knitting yarns. Mohairs, mixtures, brushed, chunky, angora-look, baby wools, double knitting, Arans. Cottons and fancy yarns. Related items: matching skirt lengths. Patterns available free with yarn purchases.

'Many yarns less than half price. Free knitting patterns with each purchase of yarn!'

North-west of Bradford, easy to find in a converted old soap mill in attractive countryside. Clearly marked on B6144 between Haworth and Cullingworth.

From mini roundabout in Cullingworth: take B6144 west. Look out for sign to mill on left. Go to end of track.

From A629 (Keighley–Halifax road): turn off opposite The Flappit for Bradford B6144. Look for well marked mill down a track on right.

Open: Seven days a week, including Bank Holidays, 10–4.
Closed: Christmas–New Year.
Cards: Major cards.
Cars: Own large car-park.
Toilets: Yes.
Wheelchairs: Three large steps so a little tricky.
Teas: Own tea room for meals, home-baked cakes, scones etc.
Groups: Coach parties welcome to shop. Please phone in advance, mentioning this book.
Transport: Bus stop at end of drive (from Bradford, Keighley, Halifax).
Mail order: Stock always changing but can sometimes send repeat items.
Catalogue: No.

34 Denby Dale near Huddersfield W Yorks

The Mill Shop

Springfield Mills, Norman Road HD8 8TH
(01484) 865082

Women's wear, men's wear and children's wear from major chainstores and selected lines.

'Firsts and some slight seconds, ends of lines and over-runs; prices reduced by 50%. Also in this mill are other shops selling furniture, cards, plaster mouldings, footwear, art supplies etc.'

Easy to find, just off the main road through village.

From M1/Barnsley: take A635 west. Keep straight. Go under huge viaduct. At next major junction, go right on to A636. Go under viaduct again into Denby Dale. After 150 yds, go right (in front of the Midland Bank) into Norman Road.*

Coming south-west into Denby Dale from M1 exit 39: take A636; go under viaduct into Denby Dale. After 150 yds, go right (in front of Midland Bank) into Norman Road.*

Coming east from Holmfirth on A635: stay on this road into Denby Dale. Go left after Midland Bank into Norman Road.*

****Go downhill. The converted old mill is shortly on left (as road bends left). Look for 'Mill Shop' signs.***

Open: Mon–Sat 9–5 (Thur, Fri till 6); Sun 10–5. Bank Holidays. (Phone to check – some shops have slightly differing times.)
Closed: Christmas and New Year's Days.
Cards: Delta, Eurocard, Mastercard, Switch, Visa.
Cars: Own car-park.
Toilets: Yes, including facilities for disabled.
Wheelchairs: Level access.
Changing rooms: Yes.
Teas: Coffee shop/café for snacks, light meals and teas.
Groups: Welcome, but no guided tours. Contact Mr or Mrs May, or any staff member.
Transport: Buses from Huddersfield, Barnsley, Sheffield, Holmfirth, Wakefield. Denby Dale rail station on main Huddersfield–Wakefield line.
Mail order: No.

35 Denholme W Yorks

Denholme Velvets

Halifax Road BD13 4EY
(01274) 832185

Cotton and rayon dress velvets, including interesting textures, unusual colours, and dévorés. Plastic-backed velvets for lining boxes etc. Curtain velvets. Low cost fents and remnants.

'This is the only British firm still making dress velvet.'

Nearly 1½ miles south of Denholme on the road to Halifax (A629).

From Denholme village going south for Halifax: clearly visible mill is on right with shop at far end.

From Bradford: take B6145 (Thornton Road). At T-junction with A629 (Keighley–Halifax road) go right: conspicuous mill 100 yds on left.

Open: Mon–Fri 1–5; Sat 9.30–5. Some Bank Holidays – please phone.
Closed: Christmas–New Year.
Cards: MasterCard, Visa.
Cars: Outside shop.
Toilets: No.
Wheelchairs: Several wooden steps.
Changing rooms: No.
Teas: Attractive local pubs.
Groups: No factory tours but groups welcome to shop; please phone first.
Transport: Bradford–Keighley buses pass the door.
Mail order: Yes.
Catalogue: Shade cards or samples given.

36 Dewsbury W Yorks

Faulty Fabrics

Unit 7 Crackenedge Lane WF13 1QD
(01924) 464727

Curtain and furnishing fabrics, and accessories. Cushion pads – non-standard sizes and shapes to order. Modern current designs in curtain and upholstery fabrics, linings, chintz, muslin, calico; tapes, tracks, accessories, toy and cushion filler, wadding, braids and fringes. Curtain-making.

'The one-stop shop for curtain-makers. New stock weekly. Mainly seconds, clearance lines and overruns. Savings of 50% plus. Examples of fabric prices (per metre): plain dyed chintz £1–£2.49; prints £1.80–£3.99; lining £1–1.80; sheeting £3.45, upholstery fabrics £3.50–£4.99.'

In the centre of Dewsbury, this shop faces the back end of the covered market and is almost under flyover. It is 100 yds to left of Mecca bingo hall, and 100 yds to right of The Station Hotel.

From all directions: aim for the market.

If you go clockwise round the ring road: take left turn-off for Market car-park. After 50 yds, go right into Crackenedge Lane. Continue downhill, under the flyover: shop is on left.

Open: Mon, Thur 10–4; Wed, Fri, Sat 9–5.30. Some Bank Holidays (for groups).
Closed: Tuesday; Christmas–New Year.
Cards: MasterCard, Visa.
Cars: Pay-&-display adjacent to shop, in Cliffe St or at station.
Toilets: In market across the road or in town.
Wheelchairs: One step with ramp.
Teas: Café in market; lots of cafés and pub lunches in town.
Groups: Shopping groups welcome (except Wed and Sat); phone Bob or Pat on Fri.
Transport: Any bus or train to Dewsbury; 5 minutes' walk from bus and rail stations.
Mail order: No.

37 Dewsbury W Yorks

S Lyles, Son & Co.

Calder Bank Mills, Calder Bank Road WF12 9QV
(01924) 436501

Large range of carpets: suitable for domestic and contract use: 80/20% wool/nylon; rugs and carpet tiles; plain in stock, patterned to order.

'First and seconds quality in plain carpets from £7.50 per sq yd. Rugs from £10. Genuine mill shop selling products made in this mill.'

Off the B6117 south-east of Dewsbury.

From Dewsbury/the east: take A644 for Brighouse and Huddersfield. Go up dual carriageway, under railway, pass tall church on right and Lookers garage then The Shepherd's Boy pub on left; take next sharp left (Fall Lane).**

From M62 exit 25: take A644 south; cross A62; take A644.*

From Huddersfield/Brighouse on A644: *enter Dewsbury; look for fire station on right then go right on to B6117 to Horbury.**

*****Go down hill, under railway; take next left (opposite The Gate pub). Shop in main building on left at end of drive.***

Open: Mon–Fri 9–5 (closed Wed); Sat 9–4. Some Bank Holidays – please phone.
Closed: pEaster Bank Holidays; Christmas–New Year.
Cards: MasterCard, Switch, Visa.
Cars: Large private car-park.
Toilets: Yes.
Wheelchairs: Ramp directly into showroom.
Teas: Several tea places and pubs in Dewsbury.
Groups: Free tours of the mill can be arranged with Timothy Lyles – please phone. Groups to shop also welcome – prior phone call also appreciated.
Transport: Five minutes' walk from bus and train stations.
Mail order: No.

38 Doncaster S Yorks

John Smedley

Rands Lane, Armthorpe DN3 3DV
(01302) 832346 Fax (01302) 300494

High quality knitwear for men and women in lambswool. Sea Island cotton sports and casualwear. Wool and Sea Island cotton underwear. Some men's shirts, ties, handkerchiefs.

'Everything at very reasonable prices. Seconds and perfect ends of ranges.'

Just over 4 miles north-east of Doncaster centre.

Leave town along Wheatley Hall Road (A630) or Leger Way (A18). Continue on A630 (towards M18); at roundabout go right at sign to Armthorpe.*

From M18 exit 4: take A630 towards Doncaster. At first roundabout, go left to Armthorpe.*

****Take first left (Mercel Avenue) and go right at end; Smedley is a few yards along on left.***

Open: Mon–Fri 11–3.30; Sat 10–3.
Closed: Easter Fri–Tues; Spring Bank Holiday week (+ previous two days); last week July + first week Aug (+ previous two days); first week Sept (+ previous two days); Xmas–New Year; Bank Holidays.
Cards: MasterCard, Visa.
Cars: Own car-park.
Toilets: Yes.
Wheelchairs: One step.
Changing rooms: No.
Teas: Locally.
Groups: No factory tours but coach parties welcome. Please book with Mr J Sutherland.
Transport: Bus no. 181 from Doncaster to Armthorpe.
Mail order: No mail order, but willing to post orders to customers.

39 Doncaster S Yorks

Nouveau Fabrics

54–58 Queens Road DN1 2NH
(01302) 329601

A wide range of printed fabrics for curtains and upholstery (cottons, linens, sateens).

'This shop sells only seconds and discontinued lines.'

Just under a mile north-east of town centre.

Leave Doncaster along Thorne Road (signed to Wheatley); after about ⅓ mile, turn left into Queens Road, a residential road. Company is a fair way down the hill on the right and is clearly marked; go through arch for shop.

Open: First Sat in each month 9–3, regardless of Bank Holidays.
Cards: None.
Cars: Own car-park.
Toilets: No.
Wheelchairs: Access now possible to showroom.
Teas: In Doncaster.
Groups: Group visits to shop gladly arranged for weekday evenings. Please phone Mr Jim Collett, mentioning this guide.
Transport: Beckett Road and Wheatley Hills buses from Frenchgate Centre. Get off at DMA or Granny's Parlour respectively.
Mail order: No.

40 Doncaster S Yorks

The Yorkshire Outlet

Doncaster Lakeside
(01302) 366444

High quality national and international branded merchandise at factory prices. Over 35 manufacturers' shops, including fashion and sports clothing, shoes, tableware and home furnishings.

'A brand new, purpose-built factory outlet centre, situated at the southern gateway to Doncaster Lakeside. The development includes the Dome leisure centre, multiplex cinema, bowls centre, range of restaurants and pubs, & many other leisure attractions.'

Situated near M18 exit 3.

From M18 exit 3: follow brown signs to Doncaster Lakeside (formerly Doncaster Business and Leisure Park). The Yorkshire Outlet is easily found at the southern entrance to Lakeside.

Open: Mon–Sat 10–6 (late night Thursday to 8); Sun 11–5. Bank Holidays 10–6.
Closed: Christmas and Boxing Days.
Cards: All major cards.
Cars: Free car-park for 1000 cars and coaches.
Toilets: Yes. Facilities for the disabled.
Wheelchairs: Easy access to all shops.
Teas: On site restaurant. Several pubs and restaurants in the Doncaster Lakeside area.
Groups: Shopping groups and coach parties welcome. Please contact the centre manager for details of special events.
Transport: Local bus services.

41 Farsley W Yorks

see map on p. 596

R L & C M Bond

93 Town Street LS28 5HX
(0113) 257 4905

An amazing range of haberdashery! Includes huge selection of buttons, zips, fringes, trimmings, thread, appliqués, shoulder pads, embroidery threads, tapestry kits, patterns – and everything else you can think of!

'Our prices are unbeatable! Allow yourself plenty of time to browse round this shop brimming with goodies.'

See our display advertisement opposite

Please see the map in the display advertisement opposite.

Town Street is main road through Farsley and shop is at the bottom left (opposite The Fleece) if you go down the hill.

Open: Wed–Sat 9–4.30.
Closed: Monday, Tuesday; Bank Holidays; Christmas, Boxing and New Year's Days.
Cards: None.
Cars: In street or to the side/rear of the shop.
Toilets: Yes.
Wheelchairs: Unfortunately no access as there are stairs.
Teas: Nearby pubs.
Groups: Coach parties very welcome. Please book, mentioning this guide. Sunday morning openings also arranged.
Transport: Buses from Bradford and Leeds pass door.
Mail order: No.

42 Farsley W Yorks

see map on p. 596

The Skep Mill Shop

Reuben Grants, Coal Hill Lane LS28 7US
(0113) 255 6769

Classic all-wool fabrics made for some of the top designer houses, including *Jean Muir, Daks Simpson, Aquascutum*. Now stock American craft fabrics, furnishing fabrics, wool coatings, wool crêpes etc. Large range of knitting yarns to complement fabrics in mohair, cotton, double knitting, aran.

'A favourite hunting ground for interesting and unusual fabrics. Most of these fabrics only seen in garments costing hundreds of pounds. Ideal chance to buy high quality designer fabrics at reasonable prices.'

See our display advertisement opposite

Please see the map in the display advertisement opposite.

Coal Hill Lane leads south off Rodley Lane/Town Street, the A657 (Leeds–Calverley–Shipley road).

From Farsley centre: turn out of Town Street at bottom of hill into Bagley Lane and go straight over into Coal Hill Lane where Bagley Lane turns sharp left. The shop, set back from road and beneath tall chimney, is clearly visible on right, half way up hill.

Open: Mon–Sat 9.30–4.30; Sunday by appointment.
Closed: Bank Holidays; Christmas–New Year.
Cards: None.
Cars: Large car-park.
Toilets: Yes.
Wheelchairs: One step.
Changing rooms: No.
Teas: Attractive local pubs with good food.
Groups: Coach parties to the shop very welcome. Contact Mr Horrocks, mentioning this guide when you book.
Transport: Buses from Bradford and Leeds.
Mail order: Yes.
Catalogue: No.

VISIT THE ONLY ALADDIN'S CAVE WHERE YOU CAN ALWAYS SEW AND SAVE

THE HOME OF SEWING SURPRISES WHERE EVEN THE GENIE CANNOT BELIEVE THE PRICES!

R.L. & C.M. BOND LTD

93 Town Street, Farsley, Pudsey, West Yorkshire LS28 5HX
Tel (0113) 257 4905 Open: Wed-Sat 9-4.30

• FOR ALL SEWING SUPPLIES • ZIPS • COTTONS • BUTTONS • • RIBBONS • ELASTICS • WAISTBANDING • CROCHET COTTON • • MOTIFS • TAPESTRY & CROSS-STICH KITS & BOOKS •

EVERYTHING AT UNBEATABLE PRICES!

• EXCLUSIVE BRODERIE ANGLAISE • FRINGES • SWISS TRIMMINGS • • BRAIDS • NUMEROUS HABERDASHERY LINES • NYLON & COTTON LACE •

COACH PARTIES WELCOME BY APPOINTMENT

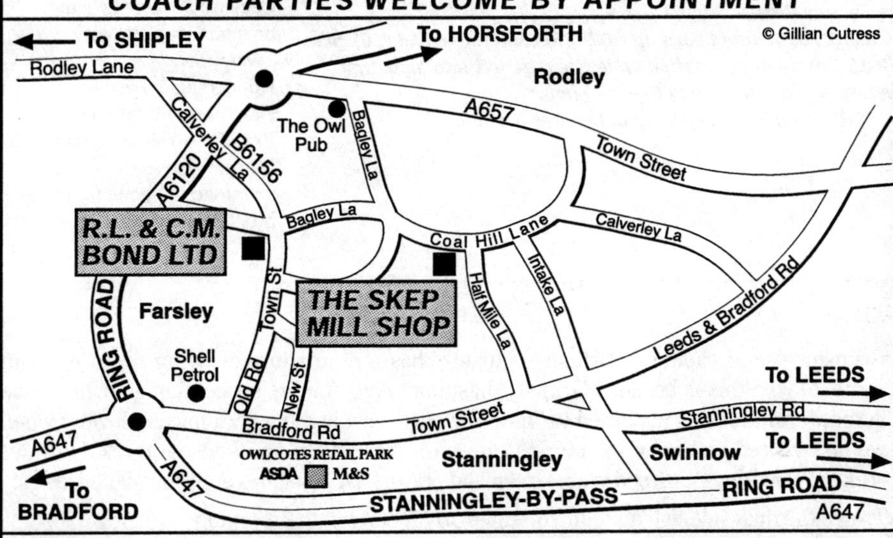

SKEP MILL SHOP

REAL YORKSHIRE VALUE FOR MONEY IN FABRICS AND KNITTING WOOLS

Browse at your leisure
Coach parties welcome

Reuben Gaunts
Broom Mills
Coal Hill Lane
Farsley
Leeds
(0113) 255 6769

Open:
Monday to Saturday
9.30 to 4.30
Sundays by appointment

43 Gildersome W Yorks see map on p. 596

BRK Crystal

Treefield Estate LS27 7LB
(0113) 253 4277

Hand-cut, hand-made, 24% lead crystal items: bud, trumpet and taper vases, posy bowls, salad bowls, sweet dishes, witch bowls, tankards, tumblers, wine glasses and decanters. Small glass animals such as cats, dogs, swans, teddy bears, frogs, snails and dinosaurs.

'All items perfect. Excellent quality at low prices.'

Off the A62, just north of M62 exit 27. Gildersome is 4½ miles south-west of Leeds.

From M62 exit 27: take A62 north for Leeds. Cross A650 at roundabout. After ⅓ mile, go right into industrial estate at sign to Factory Crystal Shop.*

Going south from Leeds on A62: cross ring road (A6110) then B6126. Pass petrol station on left and go left into industrial estate at sign to Factory Crystal Shop.*

****BRK is on left, at outside of bend at bottom.***

Open: Mon–Fri 9–5; Sat, Sun 10.30–3.30. Most Bank Holidays.
Closed: Easter & Spring Bank Holiday; Christmas–New Year.
Cards: MasterCard, Visa.
Cars: Own car-park.
Toilets: Yes.
Wheelchairs: Easy access to small shop.
Teas: In town. Can be arranged for groups if booked in advance.
Groups: Shopping groups are welcome if they phone first. Can also arrange evening presentations for parties.
Transport: On Huddersfield–Leeds, Dewsbury–Pudsey and Bradford–Wakefield bus routes.
Mail order: Yes.
Catalogue: Phone for free brochure.

Grimsby

Grimsby – food capital of Britain – unjustly has a reputation for living up to its grim name. Maybe this is because Grimsby has more cold storage space than anywhere else in the world. But this maligned town on the east coast is the mecca for fish lovers: when we last visited Grimsby we stocked up with fresh fish, smoked haddock (without artificial colouring), dressed crab, Greenland prawns, langoustines and Danish delicacies.

To see the quayside fish auction you must arrive early in the morning.

Don't be shy about driving or walking round the docks, or about visiting the companies which are based there: they are happy to serve the public even though their main trade is supplying fish retailers and the restaurant trade. Fish filleting is a skill to behold in Grimsby! Enderbys will show visitors their traditional smoke house. Another company has developed special techniques to preserve shellfish such as crabs, mussels and scallops. Kays have prime white fish – such as halibut, bream, plaice, turbot, sole etc. Remember that catches are seasonal. Prices are too – but always represent excellent value.

While in Grimsby, don't forget to stock up on great value footwear for all the family.

Enjoy lunch at the Danish Mission restaurant (near Texas, not far from the docks) which specialises in Nordic food. After lunch, visit the National Fishing Heritage Centre (01472 323345) to find out how fishermen (and their families) endured the dreadful rigours of bringing the fish home in the past.

Open seven days a week, 10–4.45 (last ticket issued then).
Entrance fee. Concessions and family tickets available.

44 Grimsby NE Lincs

Alfred Enderby

Fish Docks Road, Fish Docks DN31 3NF
(01472) 342984

7-lb boxes of freshly smoked haddock, cod and salmon direct from specialist fish smokers. Smoked Scottish salmon sliced and vacuum packed in 8-oz packs and whole 3-lb sides. Fresh haddock, cod and salmon. Irregularly sized pieces of freshly smoked fish at reduced prices usually available to callers too.

'Family business with two generations' experience. All fish processed in 80-year old traditional smoke houses ensuring a unique flavour and aroma.'

In the clearly marked fish docks.

Coming south from M18 on A180 into Grimsby: go straight at three roundabouts; at traffic lights, take left slip road for 'Fish Docks 1 & 2' (NatWest on far left corner). After 20 yds, take second left (for 'Docks'), in front of large red warehouse. Go over level crossing and follow road round (Fish Docks Road). Where the road becomes one way, look for large building on right with seven chimneys and black/yellow Enderby company sign. Park here or double back round one-way system to company.

Open: Mon–Fri 8–4; some Sats 8–11 (please phone).
Closed: Bank Holidays; Christmas–New Year fortnight.
Cards: None.
Cars: Adjacent car-park by newsagent kiosk.
Toilets: Yes.
Wheelchairs: 20 steps.
Teas: Several cafés on docks. Also the Danish Mission, Lock Hill roundabout.
Groups: Please contact Richard Enderby about tours to see smoking process (for groups, max 12 adults or 20 children, between 10 am–2 pm). Small groups welcome to shop.
Transport: Local buses stop at Riby Square Docks station.
Mail order: Yes.
Catalogue: 1.5 kilo sides of smoked salmon, sliced or unsliced. From £13 per kilo + carriage. Please mention this guide when making enquiries.

45 Grimsby NE Lincs

Kay & Son, Prime Fish Merchants

Maclure Street, Fish Docks DN31
(01472) 355974

Prime wet fish straight from the fish auction – halibut, plaice, sole, turbot, brill, salmon, cod and trout. Prices vary slightly daily and are in the range of: cod fillets £2 lb; haddock fillets £1.80 lb; plaice fillets £2.30 lb; salmon 4–7 lb size £2 lb; halibut fillet £3.50 lb; whole halibut £2.50–2.80 lb.

'Callers welcome (even better with prior phone call).'

In the clearly marked fish docks.

Coming south from M18 on A180 into Grimsby: go straight at three roundabouts; at traffic lights, take left slip road for 'Fish Docks 1 & 2' (NatWest on far left corner). After 20 yds, take second left (for 'Docks'), in front of large red warehouse. Go over level-crossing and follow road round (Fish Docks Road). Where the road becomes one-way, look for large building on the right with seven chimneys and black/yellow sign for Enderby's. Park here, or double back round the one-way system to park between Enderby's and the kiosk. Walk few yards along narrow Maclure Street to Kay's on left.

Open: Mon–Fri 9–3.30.
Closed: Bank Holidays; Christmas–New Year fortnight.
Cards: None.
Cars: Adjacent car-park by newsagent kiosk.
Toilets: Yes, upstairs.
Wheelchairs: Sales area is downstairs.
Teas: Several cafés on Docks. Also the Danish Mission, Lock Hill roundabout.
Transport: Local buses stop at Riby Square Docks station.
Mail order: No.

46 Grimsby NE Lincs

Wynsors World of Shoes

123 Cromwell Road DN31 2BC
(01472) 251627

Ladies' and girls' fashion shoes, sandals and boots in leather and synthetic materials. Many chainstore and branded items from cancelled orders. Shoes for all the family from all over world. Top brands especially in sports shoes, all at cut prices.

'99% perfects. Average 30% less than high street; special buys & promotions offering at least 50% off. Sales in January & July.'

See our display advertisement on p. 423

From M82/M180: take A180 towards town centre. Go over first roundabout, then at second roundabout go right into Pyewipe Road. Continue straight at traffic lights, down Boulevard Avenue to Market Hotel roundabout. Go left into Cromwell Road (A1136) (Presto on right). Shop is 200 yds on right.

From town hall in town centre (follow signs to town hall, then you should be in one-way road which goes behind town hall): at traffic lights go straight into Osborne Street which becomes Bethlehem Street. This is a one-way road. Pass stone church on right then bear left. At traffic lights, go right into Dudley Street (A1136). Cross over Littlefield Lane into Cromwell Road. Shop is 300 yds on left.

Open: Mon, Tues, Wed, Sat 9–5.30; Thur, Fri 9–8; Sun 10–4.
Closed: Christmas, Boxing and New Years's days.
Cards: MasterCard, Style, Visa.
Cars: Own car-park.
Toilets: No.
Wheelchairs: Easy access to large shop.
Teas: Cold drinks available; good fish & chip shop across the road.
Groups: Shopping groups welcome with prior phone call to shop manager.
Transport: Bus nos. 4, 4X, 16, 45 from town centre; X21 Cleethorpes–Hull stops outside.
Mail order: No.

47 Guiseley near Leeds W Yorks

Greenwoods Menswear

White Cross LS20 8ND
(01943) 876100 x 285

Large range of branded men's wear: suits, sports jackets, trousers, shirts and knitwear, including large sizes (38"–54"). *Jockey* underwear, *Dannimac*, *Grenadier* trousers, *Harris Tweed* etc. Formal and highland dress hire. Also Warehouse Club with special offers (phone/write re free membership).

'Mainly firsts, some seconds, at discounts up to 50% off normal high street prices. Some items on half price sale all year. Shirts from £5, jackets £40, trousers £15, cardigans £12, knitwear £12, suits £55, hats £7, caps £5.'

On A65, on north side of Guiseley, 100 yds from Harry Ramsden's original fish & chip shop.

From Leeds: take A65 north. Go through Guiseley. Greenwoods are on right, just before roundabout where A6038 comes in from Shipley/Bradford (on left). Go right before zebra.

From Bradford and Shipley: take A6038 north for Guiseley. Continue to roundabout in Guiseley where A65 comes in from Leeds (on right). Go right. Company is immediately on left.

From Otley and Ilkley: aim south for Guiseley. As you reach Guiseley, pass Harry Ramsden's. Go left at roundabout, then left after zebra in to Greenwoods.

Open: Visitor Centre (retail & hire): Mon–Sat 9–5.30; Sun & Bank Hols 11–5. Warehouse Club: 10–6, phone to check days.
Closed: Christmas, Boxing and New Year's Days.
Cards: Connect, MasterCard, Switch, Visa.
Cars: Ample car-park by shop.
Toilets: In Visitor Centre.
Wheelchairs: Easy access (ramps at entrance and exit) to medium sized shop.
Changing rooms: Yes.
Teas: Café in Visitor Centre open soon. Harry Ramsden's fish & chip shop next door. Teashops, restaurants in Guiseley and Ilkley.
Groups: No factory tours, but shopping groups of all sizes welcome; please phone manager Bryn Barclay first.
Transport: Bus nos. 650, 652, 655, 755, 733, 734 stop outside shop; Guiseley train station 10 minutes' walk.
Mail order: No.

48 Halifax W Yorks

Riding Hall Carpets

Ground floor, 6 Akroyd Place
(01422) 357120 Fax (01422) 357119

Range of colours and weights – from light to heavy domestic – in Axminster and tufted carpets made by this company. Sold by the square metre and also as roll ends of different sizes, and remnants. Small selection of vinyl floor coverings. Underlay and carpet accessories. Full fitting service.

'All items perfect unless stated. From £12.99–£18.99 per sq yd. Remnants £3–£14. Reasonably priced delivery throughout UK.'

On the north side of town, below the flyover leading to the huge Burdock Way roundabout; facing the ambulance station.

Coming south from Keighley on A629: at traffic lights, go right for Dean Clough Mill. Take first left. Drive past gigantic mill, up hill and under flyover. Go right at top, go right opposite Vauxhall into North Parade then right again. Company in mill on right.

From Huddersfield and Hebden Bridge: follow signs round town to Keighley. You come to the huge Burdock Way roundabout.*

From Leeds on A58: go over the flyover at the start of town to huge Burdock Way roundabout.*

***Exit for Huddersfield. At traffic lights go left then continue left. Opposite Vauxhall on right, go left (North Parade). Take first right. Company is in mill on right.**

Open: Mon–Sat 10–5 (Thur late night); Sun 10–2. Bank Holidays.
Closed: Christmas–New Year.
Cards: Access, Delta, Switch, Visa.
Cars: 2-hour parking outside shop. Public car-park 100 yds.
Toilets: Yes.
Wheelchairs: Easy access to ground floor shop.
Teas: Lots of places in town.
Groups: No mill tours (factory in Tyne & Wear).
Transport: Any bus or train to Halifax then walk.
Mail order: No.

49 Harrogate N Yorks

Walton's Mill Shop

41 Tower Street HG1 1HR
(01423) 520980 Fax (01423) 520920

Extensive range of household textiles. International designer furnishing fabrics and furnishing braids/trimmings at clearance prices, plus comprehensive stock of upholstery requisites. Gladly recommend local curtain and soft furnishing make-up services.

'Company set up in 1785 retains traditional emphasis on quality and service, offering exceptional, friendly design advice. Factory/clearance prices in Aladdin's cave of designer fabrics and mouthwatering braids and trimmings! A must for textile hounds. Try our famous "Knaresborough" linen dish cloth and you'll never use anything else!'

Close to town centre, on southern side.

Coming into town on A61 (from Leeds) or A658 (Otley/Bradford): cross roundabout at ring road (B6162) on to one-way system.*

From elsewhere: follow main road round town to roundabout with signs to 'Town Centre & Ripon A61'. Go to town on one-way system* (with park on left). Get into right lane. Turn right after Coach and Horses into Tower Street, at large car-park sign. Shop is 100 yds on left.

Open: Mon–Sat 10–5.
Closed: Bank Holidays; Christmas–New Year.
Cards: Delta, Eurocard, Mastercard, Switch, Visa.
Cars: Two spaces by shop; nearby multi-storey car-park – first two hours free parking.
Toilets: By car-park.
Wheelchairs: One tiny step to medium-sized shop.
Teas: Cafés and tea rooms.
Groups: Please phone Mrs Jarratt to arrange shopping group visits.
Transport: Trains and buses to Harrogate then 5–10 minutes' walk.
Mail order: Yes.
Catalogue: Send your samples, and company will supply you with cuttings of suitable fabrics and trimmings.

50 Hebden Bridge W Yorks

The Circus Factory Mill Shop

Old Town Mill, Old Town HX7 8TE
(01422) 843672 (07000 Juggle)
E-mail: beard@btinternet.com
Web page: http://www.eclipse.co.uk./pens/beard

Juggling balls, clubs, devil sticks, diabolos etc. Clubs can be custom-built. Unicycles. Books on juggling.

'The world's largest supplier of circus equipment. From elephant balls to juggling balls. Unicycles £90–£480.'

From Hebden town centre: go uphill towards Keighley on Keighley Road A6033 for 1½ miles to Old Town. Fork very sharp right (about 100 yds before Robin Hood pub on right).*

From Keighley coming downhill on A6033 towards Hebden Bridge: pass mill with red stripes around black chimney on left and then fork left about 100 yds after Robin Hood pub on left.*

****After ½ mile fork right down to mill with black chimney. Entrance through red door, or white gates.***

Open: Mon–Thur 9–5; Fri 9–3. Most Bank Holidays.
Closed: Christmas–New Year period, phone for exact dates.
Cards: Mastercard, Switch, Visa.
Cars: In front of mill or car-park to side.
Toilets: In the factory.
Wheelchairs: Ramp access at side.
Teas: Lots of local pubs; tea shops in Hebden Bridge.
Groups: Small tours of mill. Please phone first.
Transport: Hebden Bridge–Halifax bus no. 593.
Mail order: Yes.
Catalogue: Colour catalogue for £1 in stamps.

Helmsley N Yorks

Late Entry

The Knitwear Shop

11 Market Place
(01439) 770552

Cashmere and lambswool pullovers from *Pringle, Lyle & Scott, Glenmac* and own *Chas N Whillans* label. Leisurewear from *Tulchan* and *Alice Collins*; *Cross Creek* golf trousers and shirts; ladies', men's and children's outdoor wear from *Regatta.* Travels rugs, cashmere and lambswool scarves and gloves.

'Ladies' and men's cashmere pullovers in a variety of colours from £99 for perfects and around £79 for samples and slight imperfects.'

Helmsley is a small market town on A170, about 12 miles west of Pickering and 14 miles east of Thirsk.

This shop, with blue door, is in centre of town near monument and between café and delicatessen.

Open: Mon–Sat 9–5.30; Sun 12–5.
Closed: Christmas, Boxing and New Year's Days.
Cards: Major credit cards; Delta, Switch.
Cars: Short stay car-park outside shop; long stay 2 minutes away.
Toilets: Around corner from shop.
Wheelchairs: Yes, with assistance.
Changing rooms: Yes.
Teas: Plenty of cafés and restaurants on Main Street.
Groups: Shopping groups welcome.
Transport: Buses to Helmsley.
Mail order: Yes.
Catalogue: Two free catalogues each year; please phone (01450) 373128 or fax (01450) 376082.

51 Hemswell Cliff nr Gainsborough NE Lincs

Hemswell Craft Centre

Lindsey House DN21 5TH
(01427) 667066

Ever changing range of products from up to 60 craftspeople, such as jewellery, marble, semi precious stones, découpage, clothes, hats, furniture, wood turned products, decorated glass, craft kits, clocks, greeting cards, pictures, needlework, candles, wrought iron work, dried & silk flowers, pottery & china, haberdashery and lace, garden ornaments, aromatherapy oils and products, traditional children's toys, dolls, jigsaws, sailing boats, glassware etc.

'A cornucopia of affordable quality crafts, most locally made. Elegant showroom with workshops and frequent art exhibitions. Beside huge antiques centre and enormous Sunday market – allow at least a day.'

Near Hemswell, on A631 about 10 miles north of Lincoln and equidistant between Gainsborough and Market Rasen (about 10 miles each direction).

From the crossing where A631 and A15 cross: go about 1 mile west on the A631 to former RAF station. Turn right into driveway signposted Caenby Corner Estate. Go down the drive, bear right, park on old Parade Square and Craft Centre faces you.

Open: Seven days a week 10–5.
Closed: Christmas, Boxing days.
Cards: All.
Cars: Space for 400 cars (including coaches) adjacent. Free except Sundays and Bank Holidays (£1).
Toilets: Yes, and for disabled; baby changing facilities.
Wheelchairs: Easy access, ramp to 10,000 sq. ft ground floor shop.
Changing rooms: Yes.
Teas: Cafeteria on site.
Groups: Shopping groups welcome, with prior phone call if possible.
Transport: Unfortunately no.
Mail order: No.

52 Holmfirth W Yorks

Holmfirth Factory Shop

67 Huddersfield Road HD7 1AZ
(01484) 689395

Well known branded names ladies' clothing including lingerie, knitwear, skirts, blouses, nightwear etc. Also wide range of branded names men's clothing – shirts, trousers, leisurewear, knitwear.

'New goods on a weekly basis. The majority of items are perfects sold at discount prices. Special offer of 10% discount for senior citizens every Thursday.'

Easy to find, near the only traffic lights in town.

From these traffic lights, best to walk a few yards (in the Huddersfield direction). Clearly marked shop is on left, in a small parade of shops.

From Huddersfield: as you come into centre of Holmfirth, look for this shop on the right (just before traffic lights). Best to turn left at lights, go over river and park on left, then walk back short distance to shop.

Open: Mon–Sat 9–5.15; Sun 9.30–5.15. Bank Holidays.
Closed: Christmas Day; New Year's Day.
Cards: MasterCard, Switch, Visa.
Cars: Some on-street parking and nearby car-park.
Toilets: In car-park nearby.
Wheelchairs: Easy access, no steps to medium sized shop.
Changing rooms: Yes.
Teas: Lots of places in Holmfirth.
Groups: Coach groups very welcome to shop any time.
Transport: Any bus to Holmfirth.

Market days

Barnsley	Wed, Thur, Fri, indoor; Sat outdoor; Tues bric-à-brac
Batley	Fri indoor, Sat outdoor
Beverley	Sat outdoor
Bradford	Mon to Sat indoor general
Bridlington	Wed, Sat outdoor
Castleford	Mon, Thur, Fri, Sat indoor/outdoor
Cleckheaton	Mon to Sat indoor; Tues, Sat outdoor
Dewsbury	Wed, Sat outdoor; Fri second-hand
Doncaster	Tues, Fri, Sat indoor/outdoor; Wed antique outdoor
Driffield	Thur, Sat indoor
Elland	Mon flea market; Fri outdoor
Goole	Wed, Fri, Sat indoor/outdoor
Grimsby	Tues, Thur, Fri, Sat indoor
Halifax	Mon to Sat indoor; Thur second-hand in Piece Hall
Harrogate	Mon to Sat indoor/outdoor
Hebden Bridge	Thur outdoor
Heckmondwike	Tues, Sat outdoor; Thur second-hand
Holmfirth	Thur outdoor; Sat crafts
Horbury	Thur outdoor
Huddersfield	Mon, Tues, Thur, Sat indoor/outdoor; Tues, Sat second-hand
Hull	Tues, Fri, Sat outdoor
Keighley	Wed, Fri, Sat indoor
Knaresborough	Wed outdoor
Leeds	Mon to Sat indoor/outdoor; Thur flea market
Pickering	Mon outdoor
Pocklington	Tues outdoor
Pontefract	Mon, Tues, Wed, Fri, Sat indoor/outdoor
Pudsey	Tues, Wed, Fri, Sat outdoor
Richmond	Thur, Sat outdoor
Ripon	Thur pm outdoor
Rotherham	Mon, Fri, Sat outdoor; Tues second-hand; Wed bric-à-brac
Scarborough	Daily outdoor (closed Thur)
Scunthorpe	Mon to Sat indoor; Fri, Sat indoor/outdoor
Sheffield	Mon, Tues, Wed, Fri, Sat outdoor; Wed flea market and second-hand
Shipley	Mon, Tues, Thur, Fri, Sat indoor Mon bric-à-brac, second-hand
Skipton	Mon, Wed, Fri, Sat outdoor
Wakefield	Mon, Tues, Thur, Fri, Sat indoor/outdoor
Whitby	Sat outdoor (except summer)
Yeadon	Mon, Fri outdoor
York	Mon to Sat outdoor and permanent antiques

Information kindly supplied by World's Fair Publications (in their useful Markets Year Book)

See our entry below

53 Horbury W Yorks

Craft Collection/Readicut Wools Mill Shop

Terry Mills, Westfield Road WF4 6HE
(01924) 811908

Craft bargains including own screen-printed tapestry kits, hand stencilled *Readicut* rug kits, rug wool and canvas; hand-knitting yarns, cross-stitch and embroidery kits. Full range of *Paterna Persian* tapestry yarns.

'An absolute must for the craft enthusiast! Visit our Doll House and miniatures department, where we have an extensive range of 1/12th scale miniatures plus delightful selection of porcelain dolls, accessories and doll making kits.'

See our display advertisement above

Horbury is about 2½ miles south-west of Wakefield. This company is easy to find on west side of Horbury town centre, on road to Ossett (B6128).

From Wakefield: go south-west on A642; go under motorway then fork right on to B6128 through Horbury. Clearly visible company in a large detached building is just over a mile on the right in direction of Ossett. Well marked entrance at back.

From Dewsbury: you come to a T-junction in middle of Horbury. Go left. Keep straight till you see this large detached building a short distance on the right.

Open: Mon–Fri 10–4; Sat 9–3.
Closed: Bank Holidays; Christmas–New Year.
Cards: MasterCard, Visa and debit cards.
Cars: Large car-park.
Toilets: No.
Wheelchairs: Ramp into large shop.
Teas: Local cafés.
Groups: Coach parties very welcome. Please book before.
Transport: Wakefield station 3 miles. Bus nos. 126, 127 (Wakefield–Dewsbury).
Mail order: Yes. All mail order items are first class quality.
Catalogue: Free. Write, or phone (01924) 810811 (not the shop number).

54 Huddersfield : Lockwood W Yorks

Shop at the Mill

Park Valley Mills, Meltham Road HD4 7BH
(01484) 664418

Now closed

Extensive range of top quality ladies' and men's fashions for all occasions. Pure wool and poly/wool fashion fabrics, direct from the mill.

'Classic seconds – about half normal retail price. Top quality merchandise all at less than rrp.'

1½ miles south-west of Huddersfield. From M62 take exit 24.

From Huddersfield ring road: take A616 for Holmfirth; at third traffic lights go straight for Meltham (B6108). Go under railway viaduct. After 500 yds, this mill (clearly signed Parkland) is on left.

From Holmfirth: turn left off A6024 (main Huddersfield road) on to B6110 to Meltham. After ½ mile, at T-junction go right to Huddersfield. Entrance to the long private drive is on right (before the railway viaduct), where the road winds right; you must turn sharp right, almost doubling back.

Open: Mon–Sat 9.30–5. Please phone for all Bank Holidays.
Closed: Christmas Day, Easter Monday.
Cards: MasterCard, Switch, Visa.
Cars: Own car-park.
Toilets: Yes.
Wheelchairs: Two steps to medium sized shop.
Changing rooms: Yes.
Teas: In Holmfirth and Huddersfield. Nearby pubs for good bar meals.
Groups: Coach parties welcome to shop. Please make appointment with manageress.
Transport: Bus nos. 320, 321, 322 from Huddersfield centre.
Mail order: No.

55 Huddersfield : Meltham W Yorks

Fred Lawton & Son

Meltham Mills HD7 3AV
(01484) 852138

Good selection of carpets: plain dyed, tweeds, berbers, twist pile, saxony and velvet. 100% wool and 80/20% wool/nylon. Various widths – 12', 13'1", 15' broadloom in a selection of weights. Sold by the metre and as roll ends.

'Stock made from yarn spun in our own mill. Most carpets slightly imperfect at about half shop price.'

About 4 miles south-west of Huddersfield.

From Huddersfield ring road: take A616 for Sheffield; at third traffic lights, go straight to Meltham (B6108). Large mill is on left as you come downhill into Meltham.

From Holmfirth: take A6024 for Huddersfield. Shortly turn left on to B6107 for Netherthong. Keep going on this road into Meltham; go right opposite The Swan on to B6108.*

From Meltham: take road for Huddersfield (B6108).*

****After ½ mile, you see Lawton's red brick mill ahead.***

From Honley: aim for Meltham. Go downhill into Meltham, keep right, passing old mill on right. At T-junction go right. Lawtons in large mill on right.

Open: Mon–Fri 9–5.30; Sat 9–12.30. Phone for Bank Holiday openings.
Closed: Christmas–New Year.
Cards: None.
Cars: Huge car-park.
Toilets: Yes.
Wheelchairs: No access yet – 8 steps to large, spacious shop.
Teas: Cafés and pubs in Meltham and Huddersfield.
Groups: No mill tours but groups of shoppers welcome – contact Malcolm Walker.
Transport: Huddersfield–Meltham buses stop outside.
Mail order: Yes.
Catalogue: Free. Swatches available on request.

56 Hull E Riding

Cross Fabrics

Oslo Road, Sutton Fields Estate HU7 0YN
(01482) 879769

About 2000 rolls of curtaining and upholstery fabrics in stock – current modern designs alongside clearance lines and quality seconds. Linings, tapes, trims, poles and tracks and many more accessories. Quality seating foam cut to size.

'A curtain maker's dream. Prices from £2.99 per metre.'

See our display advertisement on p. 195

About 3½ miles north of city centre.

Going north or south along Beverley Road (A1079): turn east at traffic lights when you see signs to Outer Ring Road. After bridge, go right at roundabout into Stockholm Road. Take second left, Oslo Road. Shop is towards far end on left, near Do-It-All.

Open: Mon–Sat 9–5; Sun 10–4. Phone about Bank Holidays.
Closed: Christmas and Boxing Days; Easter Sunday.
Cards: Delta, MasterCard, Switch, Visa.
Cars: Large car-park nearby.
Toilets: No.
Wheelchairs: Easy access to large shop on ground floor.
Teas: Café next door.
Groups: Shopping groups welcome but please phone in advance.
Transport: Bus no. 10 from town centre to Bransholme.
Mail order: No.

57 Keighley W Yorks

The Factory Shop Ltd.

Lawkholme Lane BD21 3JR
(01535) 611703

Men's, ladies' and children's clothing, footwear, luggage, toiletries, hardware, household textiles, gifts, bedding, lighting, and new fashion concessions department with famous brand names for all. *Cape Country* pine furniture exclusively produced for The Factory Shop.

'Large stock of branded and chainstore items, all at greatly reduced prices. Deliveries of new stock every week to give an ever changing selection.'

Close to the town centre.

From the north (Skipton/Addingham): follow 'Town centre' signs, go over pedestrian lights, keep going into town centre. After Keighley News on left, go left (Alice Street), 100 yds before traffic lights.*

From Halifax: go towards town centre, through first lights, right at roundabout, left at the lights into town centre. Go over next lights, take next right (in front of Keighley News), Alice Street.*

****Shop is at far end on left.***

Open: Mon–Sat 9.30–5; Sundays and Bank Holidays 10.30–4.30.
Closed: Christmas, Boxing and New Year's Days.
Cards: MasterCard, Switch, Visa.
Cars: In street; company car–park.
Toilets: In town.
Wheelchairs: Huge shop, easy access.
Changing rooms: Yes.
Teas: In town.
Groups: Shopping groups welcome. For organiser/driver incentives please phone.
Transport: 2 minutes' walk from the centre of Keighley.
Mail order: No.
Catalogue: Home delivery service for pine furniture. Please telephone for free catalogue and price list.

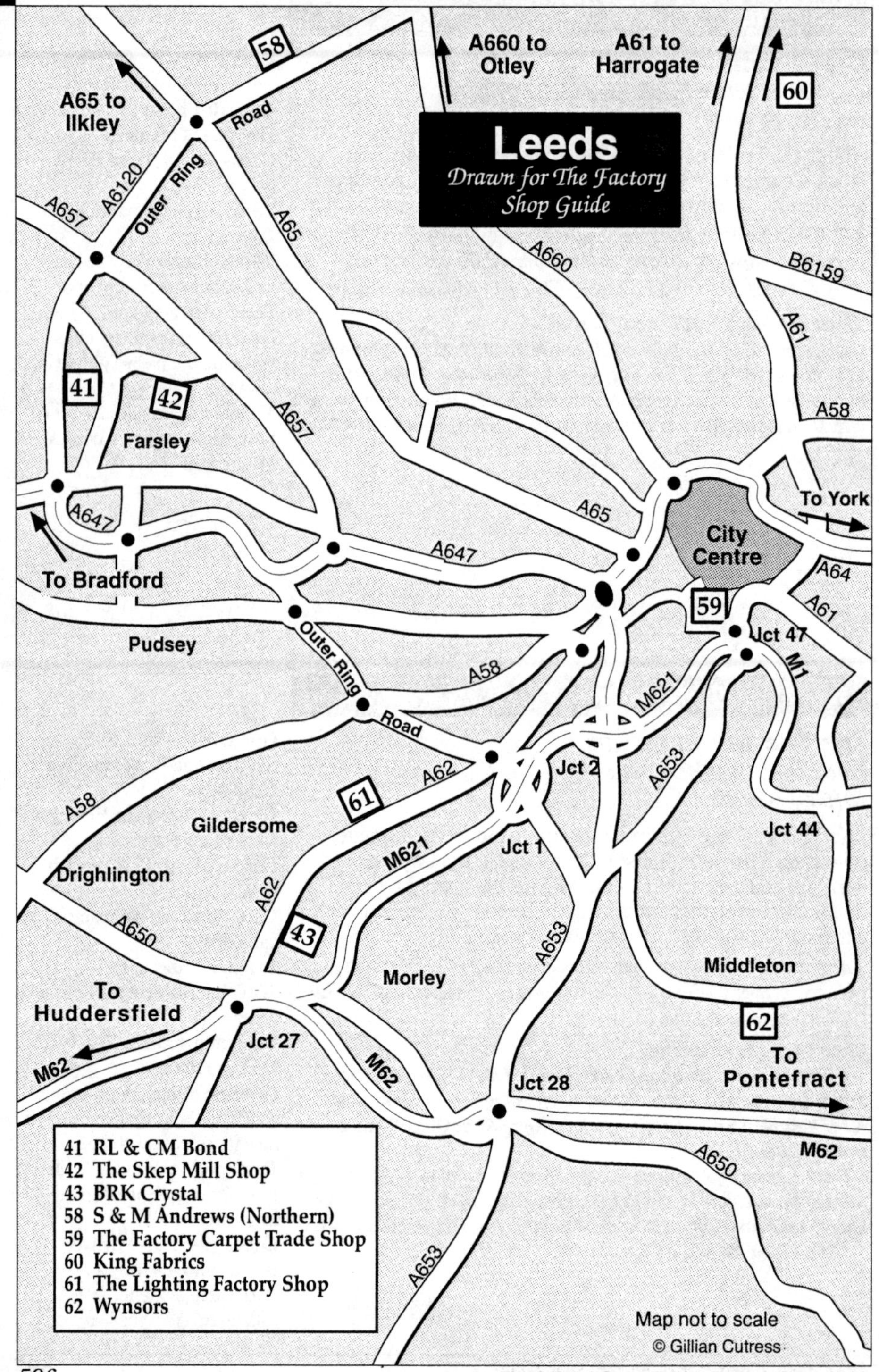

Leeds
Drawn for The Factory Shop Guide
A65 to Ilkley
A660 to Otley
A61 to Harrogate
58
60
Road
Outer Ring
A6120
A657
A65
A660
B6159
A61
A58
41
42
Farsley
A657
A647
To Bradford
A647
A65
City Centre
To York
A64
A61
59
Jct 47
M1
Pudsey
Outer Ring Road
A58
M621
Jct 2
A62
61
A58
Gildersome
A653
Jct 44
Jct 1
M621
Drighlington
A62
43
A650
A653
Middleton
Morley
To Huddersfield
Jct 27
M62
M62
62
To Pontefract
Jct 28
M62
A650
A653
41 RL & CM Bond
42 The Skep Mill Shop
43 BRK Crystal
58 S & M Andrews (Northern)
59 The Factory Carpet Trade Shop
60 King Fabrics
61 The Lighting Factory Shop
62 Wynsors
Map not to scale
© Gillian Cutress

58 Leeds W Yorks *see map opposite*

S & M Andrews (Northern)

WIRA House, Ring Road West Park
(0113) 278 1388

Wide range of luxury suit fabrics in all weights: pure new wool, wool/cashmere, cashmere/silk etc. Wool/cashmere coatings. Over 1000 different fabrics available during the year. Trouser, jacket and skirt lengths always available.

'Many top of the market fabrics not available elsewhere. Perfects, with seconds sometimes in stock. Prices well below usual retail. Advice on tailoring if required. Discount voucher given for next visit.'

On north-west section of Leeds outer ring road (A6120) near the roundabout where it crosses the A660 (Leeds–Otley road).

From Leeds: aim for A660 for Otley. At the roundabout on ring road (A6120), go left. Pass Texaco on left then Repsol petrol on right. Take second right (sign to WIRA).*

From Bradford on ring road (A6120): cross A65 (to Skipton), go straight at next roundabout and under the railway bridge: large WIRA House is on left. Go past it then left at end of this building.*

****Turn left through gate and down to lower end of car-park. S & M Andrews are on right. Go in front door.***

Open: Mon–Thur 9–4.45; Fri 9–3.45.
Closed: Bank Holidays; Christmas–New Year.
Cards: MasterCard, Visa.
Cars: Own ample car-park.
Toilets: Yes.
Wheelchairs: Easy access.
Teas: Local pubs and tearooms within 200 m.
Groups: Shopping groups welcome; please book in advance.
Transport: Buses from town centre stop nearby.
Mail order: Yes.
Catalogue: £5, refundable with order.

59 Leeds W Yorks *see map opposite*

The Factory Carpet Trade Shop

Units B & C, Aquatite House, Water Lane, Holbeck LS11 9UD
(0113) 242 5089 Fax (0113) 242 5091

Huge range of carpets including 80/20% wool; 50/50% wool twists; cut pile, cut and loop; bedroom and bathroom carpets; contract carpets, rugs, underlay and accessories.

'End of ranges, roll ends, slight imperfects all at factory prices. Delivery arranged at small extra cost.'

South of Leeds station and Leeds & Liverpool canal, about ½ mile from end of M1 and M621.

At the end of M1: get on to A653, following signs for Leeds centre. Go under M621: immediately go left for Holbeck.*

At end of M621: go left at end of slip-road (traffic lights) for Holbeck.*

****Road turns right and becomes Bridge Road. Go under railway, go right around Bristol Street Motors. Shop is immediately next to it, on right.***

Open: Mon–Sat 9–5 (Thur to 7.30); Bank Holidays.
Closed: Christmas–New Year.
Cards: MasterCard, Switch, Visa.
Cars: Own car-park.
Toilets: Yes.
Wheelchairs: Easy access to ground floor shop.
Teas: Plenty of places in Leeds.
Groups: No factory tours.
Transport: Bus nos. 52B, 54, 55 from Vicar Lane, Leeds.
Mail order: Possible if customers know their requirements.

60 Leeds W Yorks see map on previous page

King Fabrics

8 Stainburn Parade, Stainburn Drive, Harrogate Road, Moortown L17 6NB
(0113) 269 7834

Dress fabrics, particularly in natural fibres. Printed wools, wool crêpes, wool suitings, wool and wool/cashmere coatings. Some evening fabrics. Skirts lengths. In summer: printed cottons, cotton jersey, polycotton etc. Some remnants. (NB: no bridal fabrics.)

'Mostly perfect fabrics and ends of rolls supplied direct by Yorkshire wool merchant. Prices significantly reduced, eg wools from £5–£7 per m; coatings from £9.50. Twice a year (early June, end Nov) remnants from a dress manufacturer are sold by weight. Also dress-making service.'

3 miles due north of Leeds city centre, just off A61 (Scott Hall Rd).

Easiest to find from Leeds ring road: at Moortown roundabout, go south for Leeds on A61. Almost immediately, at next roundabout, take second exit (Harrogate Rd). Pass St Gemma's Hospice on right: shop in small parade of black and white shops on left.

From Leeds: take A61 north for Harrogate (Scott Hall Road). Cross traffic lights at Potternewton Lane. After ½ mile, go right into Stainbeck Road. At crossroads, bear left (Harrogate Road). Shop is in next shopping parade on right.

Open: Mon–Fri 10–4.30; Sat 10–3.30.
Closed: Bank Holidays; Christmas, Boxing (+ next day) and New Year's Days.
Cards: MasterCard, Visa.
Cars: Own parking area in front of shop.
Toilets: Yes.
Wheelchairs: Easy access, no step; shop crammed with rolls of fabrics!
Changing rooms: Yes.
Teas: Café next door.
Groups: Sewing groups and evening classes welcome with prior phone call.
Transport: Bus nos. 2 and 3.

61 Leeds W Yorks see map on previous page

The Lighting Factory Shop

Gelderd Road LS12 6NB
(0113) 276 7491

Large selection of light fittings, wall lights, downlighters, uplighters, spotlights, fluorescents, table lamps, glass shades, fabric shades, outdoor lanterns, party lights, garden lighting, security lighting, student lamps, children's lamps, nursery shades. Large range of light bulbs and fluorescent tubes.

'First and seconds. Everything we sell is reduced by comparison with high street prices: discounts between 30–50%.'

On A62, about 3 miles south-west of Leeds city centre, just outside outer ring road and near M621 exit 1.

From Leeds: take A62 south. Cross outer ring road A6110.*

From M621 exit 1: turn on to outer ring road A6110 going west. At next junction, go left on to Gelderd Road A62.*

From outer ring road A6110: turn south on to Gelderd Road A62.*

****Pass Pack Horse pub on right. Continue for ½ mile to clearly marked shop on right.***

From M62 exit 27: take A62 north for Leeds for about 2 miles. Pass cemetery on right then turn in left for clearly signed shop.

Open: Mon–Sat 9–5; Sun 10–4; Bank Holidays.
Closed: Christmas and Boxing Days.
Cards: Delta, Mastercard, Switch, Visa.
Cars: Own car-park.
Toilets: Ask if required.
Wheelchairs: No step, double doors into large shop.
Teas: Drinks machine in shop.
Groups: Shopping groups welcome; please book with Robert Sowden.
Transport: Frequent buses from Leeds city centre and Huddersfield stop outside.
Mail order: Yes.
Catalogue: No.

62 Leeds W Yorks see map on previous page

Wynsors World of Shoes

1A Middleton District Shopping Centre LS10 3NK
(0113) 271 0849

Men's, ladies' and children's fashion shoes in both leather and synthetic fabrics.

'Massive range of branded footwear from own factory and all over the world. Stock changes daily; monthly offers at probably lowest prices in the country. Shoes from £1–£100. Sales in January and July.'

See our display advertisement on p. 423

South-east of Leeds.

From Leeds: take M1 south. Take exit 44 for Middleton. At end of slip road, go right on to Belle Isle Road (dual carriageway). Go back under M1. Go straight at Belle Isle Circus; at next roundabout, take second exit. Take second exit at next roundabout: shop clearly visible.

From M62 exit 28: take A650 to Ardsley; after ½ mile go left on to A654. Go over motorway, turn left at roundabout to Middleton (Middleton Park Avenue). At large Middleton Circus, turn right on to Middleton Park Road; go right at next roundabout.

Open: Mon–Wed, Sat 9–5.30; Thur, Fri 9–8. Bank Holidays 10–4.
Closed: Christmas, Boxing and New Year's Days.
Cards: MasterCard, Style, Visa.
Cars: Large car-park outside shop.
Toilets: Yes.
Wheelchairs: No steps, easy access to very large shop.
Teas: Lots of places in Leeds.
Groups: Shopping groups welcome without booking.
Transport: Bus nos. 8, 9,10, 19, 21, 23, 77, 86, 87 from Leeds.
Mail order: No.

63 Pickering N Yorks

Thirty Six

36 Piercy End, Kirkbymoorside YO6 6DF
(01751) 433253

Extensive range of household textiles. International designer furnishing fabrics and furnishing braids/trimmings at clearance prices, plus comprehensive stock of upholstery requisites. Gladly recommend local curtain and soft furnishing make-up services.

'Company set up in 1785 retains traditional emphasis on quality and service, offering exceptional, friendly design advice. Factory/clearance prices in Aladdin's cave of designer fabrics and mouthwatering braids and trimmings! A must for textile hounds. Try our famous "Knaresborough" linen dish cloth and you'll never use anything else!'

Kirkbymoorside is 7 miles west of Pickering, and 18 miles east of Thirsk/A1. It is on A170 which links Pickering and Thirsk.

Coming east from Thirsk and Helmsley on A170: after Kirkbymoorside sign, turn left at roundabout into Piercy End.*

Coming east from Pickering on A170: continue to roundabout. Go right into Piercy End.*

***Shop is 100 yds up on left.**

Open: Tues, Wed, Fri and Sat 10–5.
Closed: Monday & Thursday; Bank Holidays.
Cards: Delta, Eurocard, Mastercard, Switch, Visa.
Cars: Outside shop.
Toilets: No.
Wheelchairs: One step; access possible.
Teas: Café next door.
Groups: Very small shop, not suitable for large groups.
Transport: Buses from Scarborough, Pickering and Helmsley.
Mail order: Yes. Send us your samples, and we will supply you with cuttings of suitable fabrics and trimmings.

64 Ripon N Yorks

Lightwater Village Factory Outlets

North Stainley HG4 3HT
(01765) 635321
E-mail: leisure@lightwatervalley.co.uk
Web page: http://www.lightwatervalley.co.uk

Large complex of retail and factory outlets with a full range of ladies' wear including blouses, skirts, suits, dresses, lingerie, outerwear, shoes and accessories. Men's wear from jeans to formal wear, shoes and boots. Home furnishings; crystal and glass; large range of pottery; garden centre with indoor and outdoor plants, large gift and toy range, book shop etc. The Yorkshire Larder for wholesome country foods; bakery, confectionery, wine, meat and huge cheese shop.

'Next door is Lightwater Valley Theme Park, home to the longest rollercoaster in the world, "The Ultimate Beast", and many, many other rides and attractions for all the family.'

See our display advertisement opposite

Three miles north of Ripon in North Yorkshire on A6108. The park is well signposted and clearly visible.

Open: 10–5 (sometimes earlier closing in winter; open up to 6 in summer, phone to check).
Closed: Christmas Day only.
Cards: Connect, MasterCard, Switch, Visa.
Cars: Ample free parking `adjacent to Village for 4000 cars and 120 coaches.
Toilets: Yes. Baby changing.
Wheelchairs: Easy access.
Changing rooms: Yes.
Teas: The Granary coffee shop, Amanda's coffee shop; snack bars. Hungry Hen Carvery restaurant (phone to book).
Groups: All welcome.
Transport: No.
Mail order: Tailor-made hampers can be made up all year and posted anywhere in UK. Phone for brochure.

65 The Arches
(01765) 635453
Leading labels in ladies' and men's clothing.

66 Claremont
(01765) 635404
Men's, women's and children's quality clothing.

67 Classics for Less
(01765) 634526
Women's fashion clothing and children's wear.

68 Delicatessen
(01765) 634513
Wine, beer, dairy products, pasta, tea/coffees, fresh meats.

69 Edinburgh Crystal
(01765) 634516
Cut crystal tumblers, decanters, wine glasses, giftware etc.

70 The Factory Shop Ltd.
(01765) 635438
Family clothing, toiletries, footwear, luggage, housewares.

71 Homes and Gardens
(01765) 634522
Plants, garden tools, dried flowers.

72 Hornsea Pottery
(01765) 634447
Earthenware tableware, oven-to-table ware, kitchen storage.

73 Ladies' Fashion Theatre
(01765) 634524
Ladies' fashions: *Telemac, Jamie Oliver, Klass, Alexa.*

74 Lilley and Skinner
(01765) 634528
Brand name footwear for all the family.

75 The Lingerie Shop
(01765) 634517
Gossard, Warners, Lejaby lingerie, and hosiery.

76 Market One
(01765) 634527
Classic ladies' fashions: *Cote à Cote, Whimsey.*

77 Not Just Books
(01765) 634517
Discounted popular and classical books.
CDs and videos.

78 Staveley Gifts
(01765) 634518
Tula and Studio handbags and luggage; gifts.

79 Thorntons Chocolates
(01765) 635471
Quality confectionery: toffees, chocolates, seasonal lines.

80 Tog 24
(01765) 635338
Weatherproof outdoor and leisurewear, and weather accessories.

81 Rotherham S Yorks

Applied Security Design

Mangham Road, Barbot Hall Industrial Estate S61 4RK
(01709) 374898

Large range of outdoor security, amenity and decorative lighting, including passive infra red, low energy and photo-cell, domestic surveillance and camera systems suitable for internal and external use.

'All items guaranteed for a minimum of 1 year (some products 3 years). Firsts, seconds and chainstore items sold at about 25% lower than high street prices.'

See our display advertisement opposite

On the north-west side of Rotherham.

From Rotherham town centre: aim for Barnsley (B6089). At College Roundabout (with B&Q), take B6089 for Barnsley. After ¾ mile, go right at roundabout into Mangham Road (B6375).*

From Barnsley: take B6089 south for Rotherham. After Greasbrough, go left at roundabout into Mangham Road (B6375).*

****Turn left into industrial estate.***

Open: Tues–Fri 10–4; Sat 10–3.
Closed: Monday; Bank Holidays; Christmas–New Year.
Cards: Delta, Mastercard, Switch, Visa.
Cars: Own car-park at side of factory.
Toilets: Yes.
Wheelchairs: Five steps to shop; access can be arranged through factory.
Teas: Snacks van across from shop; Retail World nearby.
Groups: Shopping groups very welcome, prior phone call appreciated. Factory tours can be arranged by phoning Jackie.
Transport: Bus nos. 141 and 142 from Rotherham.
Mail order: Yes. Items delivered at cost.
Catalogue: Free.

82 Rotherham S Yorks

Claremont Garments

Tenter Street S60 1L6
(01709) 830575

Ladies' wear: lingerie, swimwear, casualwear (bodies, leggings etc), dresses, blouses, skirts, trousers, and tailored suits, coats and jackets. Schoolwear: boys' trousers and shirts; girls' skirts and shirts. Boys' wear: a limited range of casual shirts and trousers.

'All garments are leading chainstore perfects, seconds or ends of lines, and are offered at greatly reduced prices.'

See our display advertisement on p. 539

Outside the inner ring road (A630), just off B6089 (Rotherham–Barnsley road). This company is near B&Q at College Road roundabout on inner ring road (A630).

From Rotherham town centre: aim for Barnsley (B6089). At College Roundabout (with B&Q), take B6089 for Barnsley.*

From Doncaster or Sheffield on A630: continue to roundabout with B&Q on outside of ring road. Turn on to B6089 (to Barnsley).*

****Take first left in front of The Stag's Head (Tenter Street). Take next right (Hope St). Shop 100 yds on left, clearly signed.***

From Barnsley: take B6089 almost into Rotherham. After The Stag's Head on right, go right into Tenter Street. Take next right (Hope Street). Shop is 100 yds on left, clearly signed.

Open: Mon–Fri 9–4.30; Sat 9–2.30.
Closed: Bank Holidays.
Cards: Most major credit cards.
Cars: In street.
Toilets: In town centre.
Wheelchairs: Two steps to medium-sized shop.
Changing rooms: Yes.
Teas: In town centre.
Groups: Shopping groups welcome, but large groups please phone first.
Transport: Rotherham bus station.
Mail order: No.

See our entry opposite

83 Royston near Barnsley S Yorks

Burberry's

Midland Road S71 4BP
(01226) 728030

Men's and women's raincoats, trenchcoats, knitwear, shirts, skirts and casual wear; umbrellas, scarves, handbags etc.

Royston is north of Barnsley. Shop is on east side of the village, about ⅓ mile east of the mini-roundabout.

From A61: follow signs into Royston centre. At mini-roundabout go straight into Midland Road. Continue for ⅓ mile, passing Kwik Save on left and Salvation Army on right. Shop is on a corner site on left, opposite post office.

Coming south on B6428: pass Monckton Working Men's Club on left. Shop on next corner on right (two corners before NatWest).

Open: Mon–Sat 9.30–3.30.
Closed: Phone to check Bank Holidays and Christmas.
Cards: Access, Visa.
Cars: In side road.
Toilets: By the roundabout in town centre.
Wheelchairs: Easy access, huge ground floor shop.
Changing rooms: Yes.
Teas: Local pubs.
Transport: Any bus to Royston.

84 Scarborough N Yorks

The Factory Fabric Centre

Valley Bridge Road, Westwood
(01723) 501646

Quality curtain and upholstery fabrics; discount bedding ranges. Curtain lining, tapes, and accessories. Curtain making-up service.

'Perfects, seconds and remnants sold at discounted prices.'

Behind the station in Westwood Road, opposite Tesco.

Open: Mon–Sat 9.30–5.30; Sun & Bank Holidays 10–4.
Closed: Easter Sunday; Christmas, Boxing and New Year's Days.
Cards: Amex, MasterCard, Switch, Visa.
Cars: Car-park to rear of shop.
Toilets: No.
Wheelchairs: No steps.
Teas: Pubs and cafés in town.
Groups: Welcome to shop, prior phone call appreciated.
Transport: Scarborough train station 150 yds from shop. Local buses.
Mail order: Yes. Fabrics can be despatched by post or carrier.

85 Scissett W Yorks

Wilson Wilcox Furnishings

Nortonthorpe Mills, Wakefield Road HD8 9LB
(01484) 864522

Top quality printed furnishing fabrics and wallpapers. Co-ordinated upholstered furniture, ready-made curtains and accessories.

'Perfects and seconds on sale. This company specialises in co-ordinated furnishing products.'

Scisset is a small village south-east of Huddersfield, north-west of Barnsley and east of Denby Dale, on the A636. Wakefield Road is the main road through the village; Wilson Wilcox, easy to see, is in the mill complex at the western end of the village .

From Denby Dale: the mill is on the right, after the crossroad.

From Wakefield: pass the pedestrian lights and the Pine Factory on the left; this shop is on left in the long mill complex.

Open: Wed, Fri 9–5.30; Thur 9–7; Sat, Sun 11–4.
Closed: Mon, Tues.
Some Bank Holidays – please phone to check.
Cards: MasterCard, Visa.
Cars: By pond outside mills complex.
Toilets: Yes.
Wheelchairs: Four steps into medium sized shop; assistance available.
Teas: In village.
Groups: Groups of shoppers (max. 12 people) welcome. Please phone beforehand.
Transport: Local buses; trains to Denby Dale.
Mail order: No.

86 Scunthorpe N Lincs

Hide Park Leather Co.

38c Hoylake Road, Southpark Industrial Estate DN17 2AY
(01724) 280375

Massive selection of leather, suede and sheepskin coats, jackets, trousers and skirts, mostly made here. Larger sizes available. Made-to-measure service. Repairs and some alterations. Large range of motorbike clothing.

'Some clearance lines and seconds available at knock-down prices, but mainly perfects.'

In industrial estate south-west of Scunthorpe.

From the M180: turn on to the M181, go right at first roundabout, and right at second roundabout (large pub on near left corner). Go over next roundabout, then go left into Southpark Road. Take the first right into Hoylake Road: factory is ¼ mile on the left, clearly signposted.

Open: Mon–Sat 10–5; most Sundays. Bank Holidays.
Closed: Christmas and Boxing Days.
Cards: MasterCard, Visa.
Cars: Own car-park.
Toilets: Yes.
Wheelchairs: One step to small shop.
Changing rooms: Yes.
Teas: In Scunthorpe.
Groups: You can see garments being made, and select your own skins. Groups welcome to shop – please telephone first.
Transport: None.
Mail order: No.

87 Scunthorpe N Lincs

Marshtrend

Queensway Enterprise Zone, Dunlop Way, Brigg Road
(01724) 852983

Wide range of swimwear and co-ordinating leisurewear including T-shirts, sarongs, shorts. Costume jewellery, hair accessories, scarves and bags.

'Firsts, seconds and overmakes. Reductions of 25–50%.'

On the east side of Scunthorpe.

From M180 exit 4: go north for Scunthorpe. At first roundabout, go left on to A18. At roundabout with Morrisons supermarket, go right. Take first left, Dunlop Way A1029. Follow road round; Marshtrend is on right.

From town centre: aim for A18(T) going south-east for Humber Bridge/Grimsby. Pass steelworks entrances on left. Take last turning on right, Dunlop Way A1029 (before roundabout with Morrisons). Follow road round; Marshtrend is on right.

Open: Mon–Thur 1–5; Fri, Sat 9–12.
Closed: Some Bank Holidays; Christmas–New Year period.
Cards: MasterCard, Visa.
Cars: Outside the shop.
Toilets: Yes, including for disabled.
Wheelchairs: No steps.
Changing rooms: Yes.
Teas: Drinks/snack machine.
Groups: Groups welcome with prior telephone call.
Transport: None.
Mail order: No.

88 Sheffield S Yorks *see map opposite*

George Butler of Sheffield

12 Orgreave Drive S13 9NP
(0114) 269 4607

Sheffield-made stainless steel and silver plated cutlery. Many low priced loose items, as well as complete sets of cutlery in attractive cabinets. A good variety of cutlery patterns are generally available including cutlery serving items.

'All items either discontinued, shop soiled or slightly imperfect.'

See our display advertisement opposite

Just off the A630, near M1 exit 33, and about 5 miles east of Sheffield town centre.

From Sheffield centre: take A57/A630 east for Rotherham/M1. Keep on A630 (Sheffield Parkway) until the left turn-off for Catcliffe B6533.*

From M1 exit 33: take A630 (Sheffield Parkway) for Sheffield. After 1⅓ miles, go left for Catcliffe B6533.*

****Pass Home World on left; at next roundabout, go right for Orgreave B6066. Continue till you see Asda on left: turn left after Asda into Orgreave Road. At T-junction, go right into Orgreave Drive. Shop is 50 yds on right.***

Open: Mon–Thur 9–4; Fri 9–3; Sat please check.
Closed: Bank Holidays.
Cards: MasterCard, Visa and other major cards.
Cars: Large private car-park.
Toilets: Adjacent.
Wheelchairs: Ground level, easy access.
Teas: Nearby.
Groups: Not suitable for shopping groups.
Transport: Buses along the A57 within ¼ mile.
Mail order: No restrictions.
Catalogue: Free brochure.

89 Sheffield S Yorks *see map opposite*

Hiram Wild

64–70 Solly Street S1 4BA
(0114) 272 3568 Fax (0114) 275 4330

Wide range of cutlery, silver plated and stainless, sold loose and in canteens. Specialise in high quality stag and buffalo horn cutlery. Scissors (left-handed versions too), kitchen knives, carvery sets. Pocket knives, silver plated gallery trays, brides' cake knives, children's cutlery, christening mugs. Cutlery repair service.

'This is a genuine factory shop – HEAR cutlery being forged! Firsts and seconds on sale, all at bargain prices.'

Also new factory shop at Hillsborough opposite Radio Hallam.

Close to city centre, on north side (and inside inner ring road). Easiest to approach this shop from west sector of inner ring road.

From all directions and city centre: aim for inner ring road. Go clockwise or anti-clockwise until you reach the roundabout where A57 goes off to Glossop. From this roundabout, go downhill for the city centre/Jessop Hospital. Pass hospital on right; at bottom of hill, go left at roundabout for Chapeltown. After 150 yds go left after Sytner used car centre into Solly Street. Clearly marked shop 150 yds on right.

Open: Mon–Thur 8–5; Fri 8–3.30; Sat 9–12 (please phone to check).
Closed: Bank Holidays; late Spring Bank Holiday week; Christmas–New Year.
Cards: MasterCard, Visa.
Cars: Limited outside; nearby roads.
Toilets: No.
Wheelchairs: Five steps, so please phone first; assistance gladly given.
Tours: Groups welcome to see cutlery forged. Tours and shopping groups ring Mr Rodgers.
Transport: Ten minutes' walk from city centre. Nearest bus at West Bar.
Mail order: Yes.
Catalogue: Free catalogue showing most of range and price list gladly sent. Items gladly posted if customers know exactly what they require. No restrictions on items sent.

See our entry opposite

Sheffield

Drawn for The Factory Shop Guide

88 George Butler of Sheffield
89 Hiram Wild
90 Hiram Wild
91 Osborne Silversmith
92 Sheffield Fabric Warehouse
93 Sheffield Scene
94 Trickett's Cutlery World
95 Wynsors

To M1 junction 36 & 90

A61
A6135
Ring Road
A6102
A6109
Meadowhall
A6178
M1 Junction 34
M1
M1 Junction 33
B6070
B6079
B6074
A6109
A630
SHEFFIELD PARKWAY
A57
Hospital
B6069
A625
A621
A61
A616
A6102
Home World
Catcliffe
B6066
Road closed
ASDA
A57

Map not to scale
© Gillian Cutress

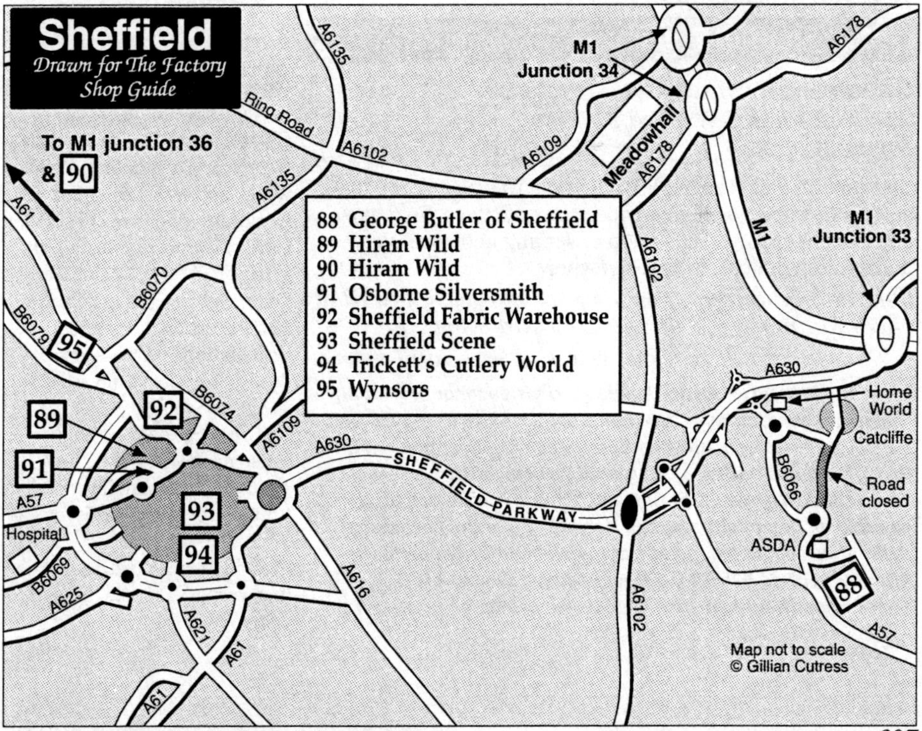

90 Sheffield S Yorks *see map on previous page*

Hiram Wild

Herries Road S6 1QU
(0114) 234 3971

Wide range of cutlery, silver plated and stainless, sold loose and in canteens. Specialise in high quality stag and buffalo horn cutlery. Scissors (left-handed versions too), kitchen knives, carvery sets. Pocket knives, brides' cake knives, children's cutlery. Cutlery repair service.

'This is a genuine factory shop. Firsts and seconds on sale, all at bargain prices.'

Nearly 3 miles north of city centre, just off A61 and within a few hundred yards of Sheffield Wednesday football stadium (Hillsborough).

From Sheffield city centre: take A61 north. Pass Hillsborough stadium on left; continue to roundabout. Go right into Herries Road (B6395). After 300 yds Hiram Wild are on right (look for sign in garden).

Coming south on A61 (Penistone Road): go under Wadsley railway bridge. At roundabout, go left into Herries Road (B6395). After 300 yds company on right (look for sign in garden).

Open: Mon–Thur 9–5; Fri 9–3.30; Sat 9–12 (please phone to check).
Closed: Bank Holidays; late Spring Bank Holiday week; Christmas–New Year.
Cards: MasterCard, Visa.
Cars: Ample street parking.
Toilets: No.
Wheelchairs: One shallow step, easy access to front area, assistance gladly given.
Teas: In town. Pubs in Wadsley Bridge; cafés in Hillsborough.
Tours: To see cutlery forged, visit the other shop in Sheffield.
Transport: Bus nos. 33, 34 from city centre; nos. 2, 20, 59 from Meadowhall.
Mail order: Yes. Free catalogue showing most of range and price list gladly sent if you phone. Items gladly posted if customers know exactly what they require. No restrictions on items sent.

91 Sheffield S Yorks *see map on previous page*

Osborne Silversmiths

West Wick Works, Solly Street S1 4BA
(0114) 272 4929

Made-in-Sheffield top quality cutlery: silver plated, sterling silver and stainless steel in wide range of styles. Sold loose and in canteens. Also selection of serving and accessory items (often difficult to find elsewhere).

'Perfects and slight imperfects at up to 50% reduction on retail prices. We are only 8 miles from Derbyshire boundary.'

See our display advertisement opposite

Close to city centre, on north side (and inside inner ring road). Easiest to approach this shop from west sector of inner ring road.

From all directions, and city centre, aim for inner ring road. Go clockwise or anti-clockwise until you reach the roundabout where the A57 goes off to Glossop. From this roundabout, go downhill for city centre/Jessop Hospital. Pass the hospital on right; at bottom of hill, go left at roundabout for Chapeltown. After 150 yds go left after Sytner used car centre into Solly Street. Clearly marked shop is 100 yds on left.

Open: Mon–Fri 8.30–4; some Sats (phone first to check).
Closed: Bank Holidays; Xmas–New Year; Spring Bank Holiday week; last week July & first week Aug (phone to check).
Cards: Eurocard, MasterCard, Visa.
Cars: Public parking adjacent.
Toilets: Ask if desperate.
Wheelchairs: Access via despatch bay on request.
Teas: In Sheffield.
Groups: Shopping groups welcome, please phone first.
Transport: Ten minutes' walk from city centre. Nearest bus at West Bar.
Mail order: No restrictions on items sent.
Catalogue: Free.

See our entry opposite

92 Sheffield S Yorks *see map on previous page*

Sheffield Fabric Warehouse

204–206 Gibraltar Street, Shalesmoor S3 8UD
(0114) 275 5657

Large range of upholstery and furnishing fabrics: cottons, linens, damasks, velvets etc. Nets, voiles, calico, interlinings, waddings, linings. Haberdashery, fringing. Curtain rails/poles and accessories. Cushion covers and fillers. Ready-made curtains. Foam cut to shape. Dress fabrics.

'Probably the largest fabric warehouse in Yorkshire. 8000 rolls in stock. Curtain-making service.'

See our display advertisement on p. 195

On north side of city centre, on A61 (part of the ring road).

Going anti-clockwise, the shop is 400 yds on right (from roundabout where Gibraltar Street West meets Bar).

Open: Mon–Sat 9–5; Sun & Bank Holidays 10–4.
Closed: Christmas Day; possibly few other days – please phone to check.
Cards: Connect, Delta, MasterCard, Switch, Visa.
Cars: Own car-park at rear (side entrance). Also coach space.
Toilets: Yes, including for the disabled.
Wheelchairs: Ramp at rear to huge ground floor shop.
Teas: Lots of places in city.
Groups: Shopping groups welcome, no need to phone.
Transport: Shalesmoor supertram stop 400 yds.
Mail order: No.

93 Sheffield S Yorks *see map on earlier page*

Sheffield Scene

49 Surrey Street S1 2LC
(0114) 273 1723

Top quality stainless steel and silver plated cutlery. Sheffield-made scissors, penknives, cooks knives, pewter goods, photo frames, pictures, postcards and books. All made in Sheffield.

'Firsts and seconds. We can manufacture any English or continental Sheffield-made pattern. Prices about 50% less than high street, with many items even less. Teaspoon seconds 50p, perfects £1.45. Gift boxed top quality stainless steel salad servers £11.50.'

In town centre, opposite town hall; three minutes' walk from Crucible Theatre.

From M1 exit 33: take A630 (Sheffield Parkway) for Sheffield. As you reach Sheffield, at huge roundabout aim for station. At roundabout just past the station, take second exit, Paternoster Row following signs to theatres. Follow these signs until you pass Lyceum Theatre on left. Take first left after Crucible Theatre into Norfolk Street; pass cathedral on right; take next right. Shop is 100 yds on right.

Open: Mon–Fri 9–5.
Closed: Christmas, Boxing and New Year's Days; Bank Holidays.
Cards: No.
Cars: Meters outside shop; NCP Crucible car-park.
Toilets: Ask if desperate.
Wheelchairs: Easy access, no steps.
Teas: Cafés in city centre.
Groups: No factory tours but shopping groups welcome.
Transport: Any bus for Sheffield city centre; 5 minutes' walk from Sheffield Interchange.
Mail order: Yes. Gladly post certain items (at extra cost).
Catalogue: No.

94 Sheffield S Yorks *see map on earlier page*

Trickett's CutleryWorld

White Rose Works, 61 Eyre Lane S1 3GF
(0114) 272 4656 Fax (0114) 249 0922

Finest quality hand-crafted cutlery in silver plate and stainless steel. Specialists in staghorn, cream (bone style) and mother-of-pearl cutlery. *CutleryMate* – unique, simple fitted cutlery drawer system. Range of tankards, trays, goblets and awards in pewter and silver plate. Small stock of local history books relevant to cutlery trade.

'Many old patterns available. Discontinued lines, slight seconds and ends of lines (some at up to 65% reduction). Silver plated salt spoon £1.70, silver plated cream ladle £5.70, letter opener £6.05. Special commisions undertaken. Repair, re-plating and knife re-sharpening services.'

5% discount on production of this book.

See our display advertisement opposite

In the city centre, on southern side.

From M1 exit 33: take A630 (Sheffield Parkway) for Sheffield. As you reach Sheffield, at huge roundabout aim for station. At roundabout just past station, take second exit, Paternoster Row. Continue along Brown Street; bear left into Sidney Street. Take first right, Matilda Street; then second left, Eyre Lane. Company is in second building on left (on corner of Newton Lane).

Open: Mon–Thur 9.30–5; Fri 9.30–3; Sat by arrangement.
Closed: Bank Holidays; last week July & first week August; Christmas–New Year period.
Cards: Mastercard, Visa.
Cars: Parking meters; 2 large car-parks within 2 mins' walk.
Toilets: Please ask if desperate.
Wheelchairs: Shop accessible but no wheelchairs on tours.
Teas: Many cafés in city centre.
Tours: Factory tours for 4–16 people (min age 16) must be booked in advance, £2 per person. Shopping groups welcome.
Transport: Sheffield train and bus stations 5 minutes' walk.
Mail order: For *CutleryMate* storage system; and repair and re-plating services. Specific items also sent.
Catalogue: Free.

See our entry opposite

95 Sheffield S Yorks *see map on earlier page*

Wynsors World of Shoes

108 Infirmary Road S6 3DC
(0114) 273 7903

Men's, ladies' and children's fashion shoes in both leather and synthetic fabrics.

'Massive range of branded footwear from own factory and all over world. Stock changes daily; monthly offers at lowest prices in the country. Shoes from £1–£100; January and July sales.'

See our display advertisement on p. 423

On the north-west side of town.

From town centre: take A61 for Penistone/Huddersfield. Fork left on to B6079 for Hillsborough. Shop is on right, opposite huge Safeway.

From north on A61: pass Sheffield Wednesday football ground on right. After 1 mile go right at traffic lights (Great Mills on far left corner). Shop is on right corner at next crossing.

Open: Mon, Tues, Wed, Sat 9–5.30; Thur, Fri 9–8; Sun 10–4. Bank Holidays 10–4.
Closed: Christmas, Boxing and New Year's Days.
Cards: MasterCard, Style, Visa.
Cars: Own car-park.
Toilets: Opposite.
Wheelchairs: No steps, large shop.
Teas: Café 100 yds; in town.
Groups: Shopping groups always welcome without prior notice.
Transport: Bus nos. 13, 14, 57, 58, 66, 67, 81–84, 86 stop outside; supertram from city centre also stops outside.
Mail order: No.

Sheffield Plate

The quest for luxury at affordable prices is by no means a modern phenomenon. The invention of Old Sheffield Plate gave the rising middle classes of the eighteenth century access to tableware and trinkets which closely resembled similar items made from silver, but at a fraction of the cost. The tables of middle class families could now be laid with Sheffield plated items which closely followed contemporary designs in solid silver. Their servants wore uniforms with silver plated buttons, imitating the sterling silver livery of the royal household and aristocracy.

Sheffield Plate was invented in 1743 by Thomas Boulsover, a Sheffield cutler. He set up in business with a loan of £70, and was so successful that by the following year he had paid off his loan with interest.

Boulsover's invention consisted of a laborious process of fusing a thin layer of silver on to the surface of an ingot of copper, with no dirt or moisture trapped between them. He not only discovered that silver and copper could be fused to form a permanent bond, but that, once fused, they behaved as one homogeneous material. The result was so versatile that it could be used to produce many articles. Boulsover himself, however, only applied it to the manufacture of buttons, snuff boxes and other small items, and it was left to others to exploit the extensive commercial possibilities.

The second major phase in the history of silver plating was discovery of Electro-Plated Nickel Silver (EPNS). This process is much faster, and the base metal need not be copper. Sheets of metal are suspended in baths of molten silver, and electrical charge is passed through causing the silver to fuse to the base metal. This method also needs clean conditions, as any grease or dirt on the base metal can make the plating uneven, or produce blow holes which subsequently cause the silver coating to wear off the metal.

Electro-silver plated asparagus dish & drainer which cost £4.10/- in 1889

The Sheffield plating process became obsolete after the introduction of electro-plating, but Old Sheffield Plate articles are now much sought after and are collectors' items.

Thanks to Abbeydale Industrial Hamlet

Electro-silver plated oval entrée dish with fluted cover and shell gadroon mounts, sold for £4.10/- in 1889

Destination Sheffield
(0114) 273 4671
for tourist information

96 Shipley W Yorks

British Mohair Spinners

Otley Road BD17 7EV
(01274) 583111 Fax (01274) 591564

Colourful selection of brushed mohair knitting wools plus other yarns such as natural yarns (Swaledale etc), arans, double knitting etc. Some sweaters & other clothing for men and women.

'Luxury mohair at mill prices.'

Nearly ½ mile north-east of Shipley on A6038.

From Shipley: go north-east on A6038 for Otley. Go over river, through first traffic lights, past the DIY centre on right, then shop is clearly visible in old mill on right.

From Otley (A6038) or Baildon (B6151): this mill is on left beside traffic lights where these two roads join. Shop is at far end of building.

Open: Mon–Fri 9–4.
Closed: Bank Holidays; third week September (please ring to check); Christmas–New Year.
Cards: MasterCard, Visa.
Cars: Own car-park outside shop.
Toilets: Yes.
Wheelchairs: Ramp to shop.
Changing rooms: Yes.
Teas: In Shipley and Saltaire.
Groups: No mill tours but group visits and coach parties welcome to shop. No need to book.
Transport: Buses from Bradford: 650 to Ilkley; 653, 654 to Harrogate; 655, 755 to Leeds.
Mail order: Yes.
Catalogue: £2 for shade card for all mohair colours, plus natural yarns, eg arans, Welsh wools, Swaledale, Herdwick etc.

97 Shipley W Yorks

Praxis Tailoring

31 Saltaire Road BD18 3HH
(01274) 539869 (or 531919)

High quality ladies' jackets, skirts, trousers. Luxury lingerie. Ladies' stretch bodies and tops. Swimwear, including large sizes, for all the family. Children's wear including school uniforms. Some men's wear. Bedding and raincoats as available.

'Perfects, seconds, ends of lines at reduced prices, all made to a high standard in our own factories. Phone enquiries welcome.'

On A657 in centre of Shipley, short distance from Saltaire Village.

From Bradford: take Keighley Road (A650). After 2½ miles go right at traffic lights in front of The Branch pub for Shipley Town Centre (A6038 Otley Road). Go left at third traffic lights into Commercial Street (becomes Saltaire Road).*

From Otley coming south: as you reach Shipley, do NOT go on to overpass. Cross river then canal and go right at next lights into Commercial Street (becomes Saltaire Road).*

****Pass Ford garage on left and The Shipley Pride on right then go sharp right down Back Saltaire Road (North); shop entrance and parking at rear of Praxis building.***

From Bingley via A650: at roundabout, go left on to A6038 for Otley (Saltaire Road). Go left before UK petrol on left; continue round into Back Saltaire Road (North); factory is on right.

Open: Mon–Sat 10–4.30.
Closed: Bank Holidays; Christmas–New Year; for local summer holiday closures please check.
Cards: Mastercard, Visa.
Cars: Ample, near shop entrance.
Toilets: On request.
Wheelchairs: Easy access; no steps, large ground floor shop.
Changing rooms: Yes.
Teas: In Saltaire village or Shipley.
Groups: Shopping groups welcome with prior phone call.
Transport: Any bus to Shipley town centre, then 5 minutes' walk.
Mail order: No.

Saltaire

While you are in Shipley stocking up on family clothing, and making the most of the wonderful selection of mohair, be sure to explore Saltaire, one of Britain model villages, purpose-built by a nineteenth century industrialist for his workers and their families.

Saltaire was opened in 1871 when Sir Titus Salt – who had introduced alpaca wool into England's textile industry – moved his alpaca and mohair mills to a 'healthier' situation by Shipley. The village comprises 850 terraced houses and at one time had a population of over 4000. As you walk round, notice the three-storeyed houses which were built for senior staff. Only backyards, no gardens, were provided but there is a fine park. In Gothic style, 45 almshouses housed those of 'good moral character and incapacity for labour by reason of age, disease or infirmity'. Also supplied were schooling, libraries, public baths, a Turkish bath & steam laundry. A Congregationalist, Sir Titus banned alcohol – so there are no pubs. But there is an impressive church.

Alongside the Leeds & Liverpool Canal (near the River Aire), Salt's Mill itself is huge; it employed 2500 people at one time. Eventually cloth production ceased. In recent years it has been restored. Two huge shops sell furnishing fabrics (including fents and reduced price rolls), wallpapers, upholstered, modern and old furniture. Another shop has a large range of stylish kitchen accessories. You can buy fashion clothes. Eat at the large restaurant and browse in the bookshop. The mill is well known for its association with David Hockney – many pictures by him are on display, and you can buy prints and postcards of his works.

Salt's Mill. Seven days a week, 10–6. (01274) 531163.

With thanks to Duncan Smith for the historical information from his book 'South & West Yorkshire Curiosities'
Other interesting books written by this author and published by The Dovecote Press are: North & East Yorkshire Curiosities; Exploring South Yorkshire *(Ian Dawson);* Yorkshire: A Portrait in Colour *(over 200 photographs of picturesque countryside* and of *mill towns, ports and great industrial cities too).*

Saltaire Mills in 1878

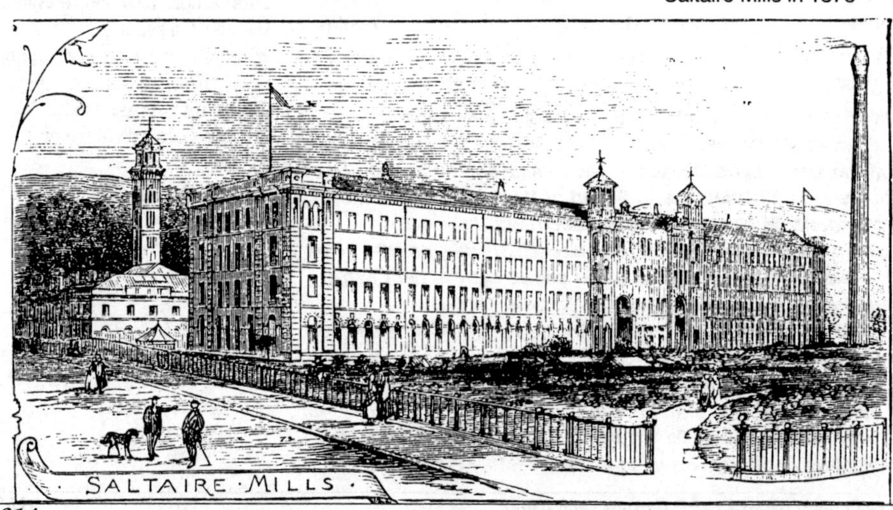

98 Skipton N Yorks

Embsay Mills Needlecraft Centre

Embsay BD23 6QE
(01756) 700946

Everything for needlecraft, cross stitch, embroidery, tapestry; patchwork and quilting fabrics, patterns and accessories; wadding, charts and books. *Coats, DMC, Tootal, Kinetic, Paterna* and many more. Tapestry kits, quilted cushion kits.

'Perfects and seconds. A good choice of specials always on sale, which can be as much as 50% off. Our staff are experienced needlecrafters and can assist and advise.'

Nearly 2 miles north-east of Skipton, in centre of Embsay village.

From Skipton town centre and Skipton castle: follow sign to A59 (Harrogate–Settle road). Go left at signs 'Embsay 1 mile' and 'The Steam Railway'. Look for the Cavendish Arms on right; the drive to shop is immediately on left.

From A65 (Harrogate–Settle road), Skipton by-pass: follow signs to 'Embsay Steam Railway'. Mill entrance is on left, directly opposite the Cavendish Arms.

Open: Seven days a week, 10–5.
Closed: Christmas Eve, Christmas, Boxing and New Year's Days.
Cards: Delta, MasterCard, Switch, Visa.
Cars: Own coach and car-park.
Toilets: Yes.
Wheelchairs: Welcome; easy access to ground floor; stairs to upper showroom. Staff assist.
Teas: Own coffee shop upstairs for sandwiches, snacks, cakes, fresh tea and coffee.
Groups: Shopping groups welcome; please book with manager.
Transport: Trains and buses to Skipton. Bus no. 214 from Skipton to Embsay.
Mail order: Yes. Gladly accept telephone orders.
Catalogue: No.

99 Skipton N Yorks

Skipton Mill Shop

Albion House, Rope Walk BD23 1EE
(01756) 791149

Clothing for men and women: including leisurewear, shoes, jackets, dresses, blouses etc. Also pottery, gifts and home furnishings.

'Perfects and seconds often with 30–50% price reductions.'

Easy to find in town centre, next to bowling green near town hall.

In the town centre, go into High Street (main shopping street) which has a church, castle and roundabout at top end.

Coming uphill, ie towards church/castle: go right into car-park just before town hall on right and 50 yds before roundabout.*

From top end, ie by church: go down High Street for 50 yds, turn left to car-park immediately after town hall.*

****Once in car-park, go down to public toilets and go right around the building to entrance.***

Open: Mon–Sat 9–5.30; Sun 11–5.30; Bank Holidays.
Closed: Christmas and Boxing days only.
Cards: MasterCard, Visa.
Cars: Pay-&-display car-park. Coach park.
Toilets: By car-park.
Wheelchairs: No steps, large shop.
Changing rooms: Yes.
Teas: Several attractive places in town.
Groups: Shopping groups welcome – please contact Richard Tankard.
Transport: Any bus or train to Skipton.
Mail order: No.

100 Thurcroft near Rotherham S Yorks

Wynsors World of Shoes

Wynsor House, Woodhouse Green S66 9AM
(01709) 540876

Men's, ladies' and children's fashion shoes in both leather and synthetic fabrics.

'Massive range of branded footwear from own factory and all over the world. Stock changes daily; monthly offers at lowest prices in country. Shoes from £1 to £100. January and July sales.'

See our display advertisement on p. 423

From Rotherham: take A6021 for Maltby then join A631 at Stag roundabout. Follow this dual carriageway to next roundabout with The Mason on left: go right on to B6060 (Morthen Road).*

From M18 exit 1: go towards Rotherham on A631. At next roundabout (The Mason on far right), turn left on to B6060 (Morthen Road).*

****The B6060 takes you over motorway to Thurcroft. Pass garage on right: shop is on right after The Double Barrel.***

Open: Mon, Tues, Wed, Sat 9–5.30; Thur, Fri 9–8; Sun 10–4. Bank Holidays 10–4.
Closed: Christmas, Boxing and New Year's Days.
Cards: MasterCard, Style, Visa.
Cars: At front of shop.
Toilets: Locally.
Wheelchairs: No steps, large shop.
Teas: Pub next door. Café and fish & chips ½ mile.
Groups: Shopping groups always welcome without prior booking.
Transport: Bus nos. 19, 19a and 208 from Rotherham.
Mail order: No.

101 Todmorden Lancs

Bottoms Mill Co.

Rochdale Road, Walsden OL14 7UB
(01706) 812691

This company makes flannelette and cotton sheets with matching pillowcases; polycotton sheets; tea towels, dusters, chamois cloths, dishcloths, dust sheets, terry towels, counterpanes; cleaning rags and large cloth remnants.

'Small family company which weaves a range of cotton cloths. Perfects and seconds available.'

Walsden is about 7 miles north-east of Rochdale.

From Burnley or Halifax: take A646 to Todmorden. Then go nearly 2 miles south on the A6033 (towards Littleborough). Shop is on the right, opposite Gordon Rigg's garden centre. Walk through the arch and follow signs.

Open: Mon–Fri 9.30–5; Sat and Sun 10.30–4.30.
Closed: Christmas–New Year; 31 Dec and 1 Jan.
Cards: Major debit and credit cards.
Cars: Ample space.
Toilets: At the garden centre.
Wheelchairs: Easy access, medium sized ground floor shop.
Teas: Drinks machine at garden centre. Pubs, and fish & chips nearby.
Tours: Groups welcome to shop. Small numbers can also visit weaving sheds. Please arrange in advance, mentioning this book.
Transport: Rochdale–Halifax bus nos. 589 and 590 pass door.
Mail order: Yes. Goods gladly forwarded by post or carrier.
Catalogue: No.

BEEVERS

ALL TYPES OF HIGH QUALITY CUSTOM MADE BEDS *at* FACTORY DIRECT PRICES DIRECT TO YOU!

NBF

NATIONAL BED FEDERATION MEMBER

Installation Service
Delivery Service

(01947) 604351

VISIT OUR SHOWROOM
Stakesby Vale,
Whitby, N. Yorks YO21 1JZ

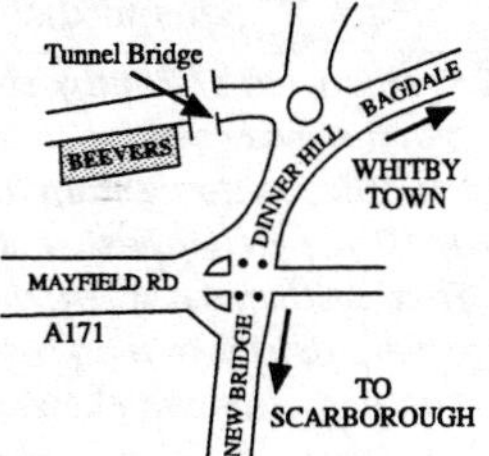

- **All beds and mattresses are made INDIVIDUALLY here, to optional height and to any size, shape or design.**
- **Giant American type single pocketed or DUO pocketed sprung beds. Up to 2900 pocketed springs in the mattress alone. Traditional curled hair, lambswool and cotton felt fillings. Latex mattresses made.**
- **Various qualities and sizes of electrical adjustable beds with optional massage units. We manufacture state of the art pocketed, conventional and electrically adjustable beds.**
- **Mattresses and bases supplied to fit inside pine or antique beds.**
- **Medical beds, electrical adjustable beds with electrically adjustable base.**
- **Reflex foam mattresses. Hypo-allergenic mattresses.**
- **Better hotel contract beds and mattresses up to F.R. Crib 7.**
- **Solid brass, cast iron bedsteads and LITS BATEAUX supplied.**
- **ALL conform to appropriate fire regulations.**
- **BED LINEN SUPPLIED TO ANY SIZE OR SHAPE.**
- **Established 14 years, with hundreds of satisfied customers throughout the UK. Testimonials available.**
- **ABSOLUTELY NO OBLIGATION, friendly advice, phone enquiries welcome.**
- **No pushy salesmen will camp on your doorstep following an enquiry, because we don't employ any!**

See our entry overleaf

102 Whitby N Yorks

Beevers of Whitby

Stakesby Vale YO21 1JY
(01947) 604351

Hand-made open coil and pocketed sprung beds to any size; electric adjustable beds; water resistant beds; contract beds all made here; bases and mattresses sold separately. All on show. Also huge showroom with carpets, and pine and upholstered furniture, vinyls, pine chairs, curtains; linens first and second quality.

'Always mix/match, seconds available. Finest hand-made beds made to any size for bad back sufferers. Up to 2900 pocketed springs in the queen luxury size. Factory prices. Delivery anywhere on UK mainland.'

See our display advertisement on previous page

A ¼ mile west of Whitby station.

From railway station: leave Whitby on A171 Guisborough road. After 400 yds go right up A174 Sandsend/Saltburn road. After only 10 yds go left beside of Arundel Hotel (signposted Beevers).*

From Saltburn on A174: go into town. Ten yards before T-junction, go sharp right into road before Arundel Hotel.*

****Go under tunnel: showrooms on left.***

Open: Mon–Sat 9–5.30 (late evening Fri to 8); Sun 11–5. Some Bank Holidays – please phone.
Closed: Christmas, Boxing and New Year's Days.
Cards: Delta, MasterCard, Switch, Visa.
Cars: Own car-park.
Toilets: Yes.
Wheelchairs: Three floors accessible with ramps; help available for access to top floor.
Teas: Tea and coffee available. Cafés and pubs in Whitby.
Tours: Groups welcome to see round factory (2 miles from shop) for talk and demonstration; phone Derek or Gordon first. No coach park at shop.
Transport: From station take Sleights & Castle Park bus, alight at Arundel Hotel.
Mail order: Yes.

Fred Lawton

Best for Less

Naylor Clayware

Riding Hall Carpets

See our entry below

103 Yeadon near Leeds W Yorks

The Old Mill Shop

Kirk Lane LS19 7ER
(0113) 250 2211

Wide range of own brand *Renaissance* curtain accessories (much of the stock assembled on premises). Also sell fabrics, ready-made curtains, beds with traditional or pocket sprung mattresses, pine furniture. Wide range of wool carpet roll ends.

'Perfects and slight seconds at discounted prices. Some carpets reduced up to 50% against pattern book. Frequent special promotions. Visit the adjacent Dog Mill Ponds, a "green jewel" nature reserve containing a wonderful variety of wild life.'

See our display advertisement above

In a large old mill in the centre of Yeadon.

Coming south on A65 from Guiseley: go over traffic lights with retail park and McDonald's on right. Pass park on left. At next lights, go left.*

Coming north into Yeadon: stay on A65 (go over huge roundabout with 'JCT 600' and Fina petrol). Pass Shell petrol on left and Jet petrol on right. Go right at traffic lights.*

****Continue 1/3 mile to conspicuous mill set back on right.***

Open: Mon–Wed 9.30–5.30; Thur, Fri 9.30–7. Bank Holidays please check.
Closed: Phone for Christmas.
Cards: No.
Cars: On site, and adjacent. Coach parking by appointment.
Toilets: Yes.
Wheelchairs: Large shop, but unfortunately too difficult (stairs). Assistance gladly given.
Teas: Tea, coffee and biscuits available for groups; local café; lots of fish & chip shops in area.
Groups: Shopping groups and coach parties phone in advance.
Transport: Buses pass door. Bus nos. 735 and 736 from Leeds bus and train stations, 648 and 747 from Bradford Interchange; 5 minutes from Leeds/Bradford airport.
Mail order: Yes. Curtain accessories and stock ranges.
Catalogue: Brochure and Old Mill Shop Newspaper free with A4 SAE or 50p stamp.

104 York N Yorks

Bridge of York

3 Main Street, Fulford YO1 4HJ
(01904) 634508 Fax (01904) 631624

Now closed

Ladies' blouses (sizes 10–24; long/short sleeves) in wide range of *Viyella* fabrics, cotton lawn prints, viscose in many designs. Men's shirts in traditional styles (sizes 14½–19½) including fuller fit and longer body with long, short and extra-long sleeves. Ties, socks.

'Excellent quality, competitive prices. Satisfied customers at home and abroad!'

A short way south of York.

From A64: take A19 towards York. Go through two sets of traffic lights, pass church on right then this factory is on the right, next to Adam's House Hotel.

From York: take road (A19) south for Selby; pass Fulford Barracks. Go over one set of lights then factory is 150 yds on left, down the drive. Look for wrought iron sign.

Open: Mon–Sat 9–4.30.
Closed: Christmas and New Year; Bank Holidays.
Cards: MasterCard, Visa.
Cars: Beside factory.
Toilets: Yes.
Changing rooms: Can be arranged.
Teas: In town.
Groups: Tours for groups by appointment. Groups welcome to shop – please phone first.
Transport: York–Fulford buses.
Mail order: Yes, but no seconds sent.
Catalogue: No.

105 York N Yorks

History Craft

Barnby Way, Stonegate Walk YO1 2QQ
(01904) 638707

History Craft giftware – clocks, men's gifts, walking sticks, scrimshaw (carved reproduction whalebone), board games etc. Also pottery, stationery, imported china and hand-crafted wooden pieces.

'Most goods slight seconds, ends of runs, discontinued lines etc at factory prices.'

In York City Centre.

From York Minster: go straight down Stonegate, turn right into Stonegate Walk.

Open: Seven days a week 10–6.
Closed: Christmas, Boxing and New Year's Days.
Cards: Amex, Eurocard, MasterCard, Switch, Visa.
Cars: Multi-storey car-parks in city.
Toilets: Near Tourist Office.
Wheelchairs: No steps to large shop.
Teas: Lots of places locally.
Groups: Welcome. Please phone in advance.
Transport: Local buses and train station. Park-and-ride services available.
Mail order: Items posted if customers know what they want.
Catalogue: No.

New in November 1998: factory outlet centre near York.
Phone (0171) 591 8300 for latest details.

106 York N Yorks

Wynsors World of Shoes

Clarence Street YO3 7EV
(01904) 637611

Ladies' and girls' fashion shoes, sandals and boots in leather and synthetic materials. Many chainstore and branded items from cancelled orders and shoes for all the family from all over world. Top brands especially sports shoes, all at cut prices.

'99% perfects. Average 30% less than in high street; special buys; promotions with at least 50% off. January and July sales.'

See our display advertisement on p. 423

Close to York Minster, outside the walls on north side of city.

From the minster: walk along High Petergate and through Bootham Bar. Turn right into Gillygate. Continue straight in Clarence Street; shop and car-park are on right on the corner (with Lord Mayor's Walk).

Open: Mon, Tues, Wed, Sat 9–5.30; Thur, Fri 9–8; Sun 10–4.
Closed: Christmas, Boxing and New Year's Days.
Cards: MasterCard, Style, Visa.
Cars: Own car-park and large public car-park opposite.
Toilets: Facilities across road.
Wheelchairs: Easy access to large shop.
Teas: Cold drinks available; four cafés and two pubs within 100 yds.
Groups: Shopping groups welcome with prior phone call to shop manager.
Transport: Any bus to town centre.
Mail order: No.

See next page for two late entries (in Adwick-le-Street and South Kirkby)

RC & CM Bond

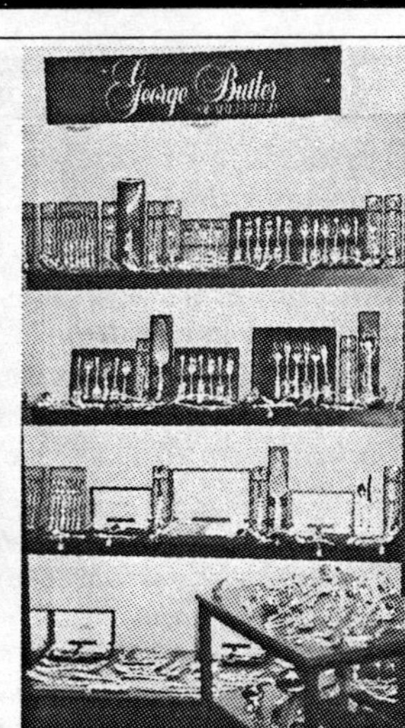

George Butler

Adwick-le-Street nr Doncaster S Yorks

S B's

49–51 Church Lane DN6 7AJ
(01302) 722902

Top quality men's wear: suits, trousers, sports jackets, dinner suits and leisurewear.

'Firsts and seconds, all originally made for major high street names, at factory prices. Discounts of 50% plus off RRP: waistcoats from £5; trousers £15; sports jackets £30–£40; suits £65–£85.'

On north-eastern side of Adwick, on B1220 near train station.

From north (A1 exit 38 or Wakefield): take A638 south into Woodlands. Continue to roundabout, go left on to B1220 and stay on B1220 (Doncaster Lane) for Carcroft. Go over railway. Shop is 300 yds on right, opposite car auction.

From south (Doncaster): take A638 north for Woodlands/ Adwick. At roundabout, go right on to B1220 and stay on B1220 (Doncaster Lane) for Carcroft. Go over railway. Shop is 300 yds on right, opposite car auction.

Late Entry

Open: Mon–Sat 10–3.
Closed: Bank Holidays; Christmas–New Year.
Cards: None.
Cars: Large car-park; also in road.
Toilets: No.
Wheelchairs: One small step to medium-sized shop.
Changing rooms: Yes.
Teas: Local cafés and pubs.
Groups: No factory tours; shopping groups welcome, please phone Alix Spedding on (01977) 608800.
Transport: Doncaster–Carcroft buses; Adwick train station 300 yds.
Mail order: No.

South Kirkby nr Pontefract

S B's

Langthwaite Grange Industrial Estate WF9 3AP
(01977) 608800

Top quality men's wear: suits, trousers, sports jackets, dinner suits and leisurewear.

'Firsts and seconds, all originally made for major high street names, at factory prices. Discounts of 50% plus off RRP: waistcoats from £5; trousers £15; sports jackets £30–£40; suits £65–£85.'

South Kirkby is south of Pontefract and north-east of Barnsley. This estate is on east side of South Kirkby, south of main road (B6422) through village.

From main road (B6422) through village: turn south for Langthwaite Grange Industrial Estate. Pass Thyssens. At top of hill, go right: shop is on left before the main factory gates.

Late Entry

Open: Mon, Wed, Fri 11.30–2.30; Sat 9–12.
Closed: Tuesday, Thursday; Bank Holidays; Christmas–New Year.
Cards: None.
Cars: Outside shop.
Toilets: Yes.
Wheelchairs: Small step, assistance gladly given.
Changing rooms: Yes.
Teas: Local cafés and pubs in town 1 mile.
Groups: No factory tours; shopping groups welcome, please phone Alix Spedding.
Transport: None.
Mail order: No.

Towns with factory shops

NUMBERS refer to the ENTRIES, NOT the PAGES

Towns with factory shops

NUMBERS refer to the ENTRIES, NOT the PAGES

Huddersfield : Lockwood	54	Shop at the Mill
Huddersfield : Meltham	55	Fred Lawton & Son
Hull	56	Cross Fabrics
Keighley	57	The Factory Shop Ltd.
Leeds	58	S & M Andrews (Northern)
Leeds	59	The Factory Carpet Trade Shop
Leeds	60	King Fabrics
Leeds	61	The Lighting Factory Shop
Leeds	62	Wynsors World of Shoes
Pickering	63	Thirty Six
Ripon	64	Lightwater Village Factory Outlets
Ripon	65	The Arches
Ripon	66	Claremont Garments
Ripon	67	Classics for Less
Ripon	68	Delicatessen
Ripon	69	Edinburgh Crystal
Ripon	70	The Factory Shop Ltd.
Ripon	71	Homes and Gardens
Ripon	72	Hornsea Pottery
Ripon	73	Ladies' Fashion Theatre
Ripon	74	Lilley and Skinner
Ripon	75	The Lingerie Shop
Ripon	76	Market One
Ripon	77	Not Just Books
Ripon	78	Staveley Gifts
Ripon	79	Thorntons Chocolates
Ripon	80	Tog 24
Rotherham	81	Applied Security Design
Rotherham	82	Claremont Garments
Royston near Barnsley	83	Burberrys
Scarborough	84	The Factory Fabric Centre
Scissett	85	Wilson Wilcox Furnishings
Scunthorpe	86	Hide Park Leather Co.
Scunthorpe	87	Marshtrend
Sheffield	88	George Butler of Sheffield
Sheffield	89	Hiram Wild
Sheffield	90	Hiram Wild
Sheffield	91	Osborne Silversmiths
Sheffield	92	Sheffield Fabric Warehouse
Sheffield	93	Sheffield Scene
Sheffield	94	Trickett's CutleryWorld
Sheffield	95	Wynsors World of Shoes
Shipley	96	British Mohair Spinners
Shipley	97	Praxis Tailoring
Skipton	98	Embsay Mills Needlecraft Centre
Skipton	99	Skipton Mill Shop
South Kirkby nr Pontefract	p622	S B's
Thurcroft near Rotherham	100	Wynsors World of Shoes
Todmorden	101	Bottoms Mill Co.
Whitby	102	Beevers of Whitby
Yeadon near Leeds	103	The Old Mill Shop
York	104	Bridge of York
York	105	History Craft
York	106	Wynsors World of Shoes

J

Northern England

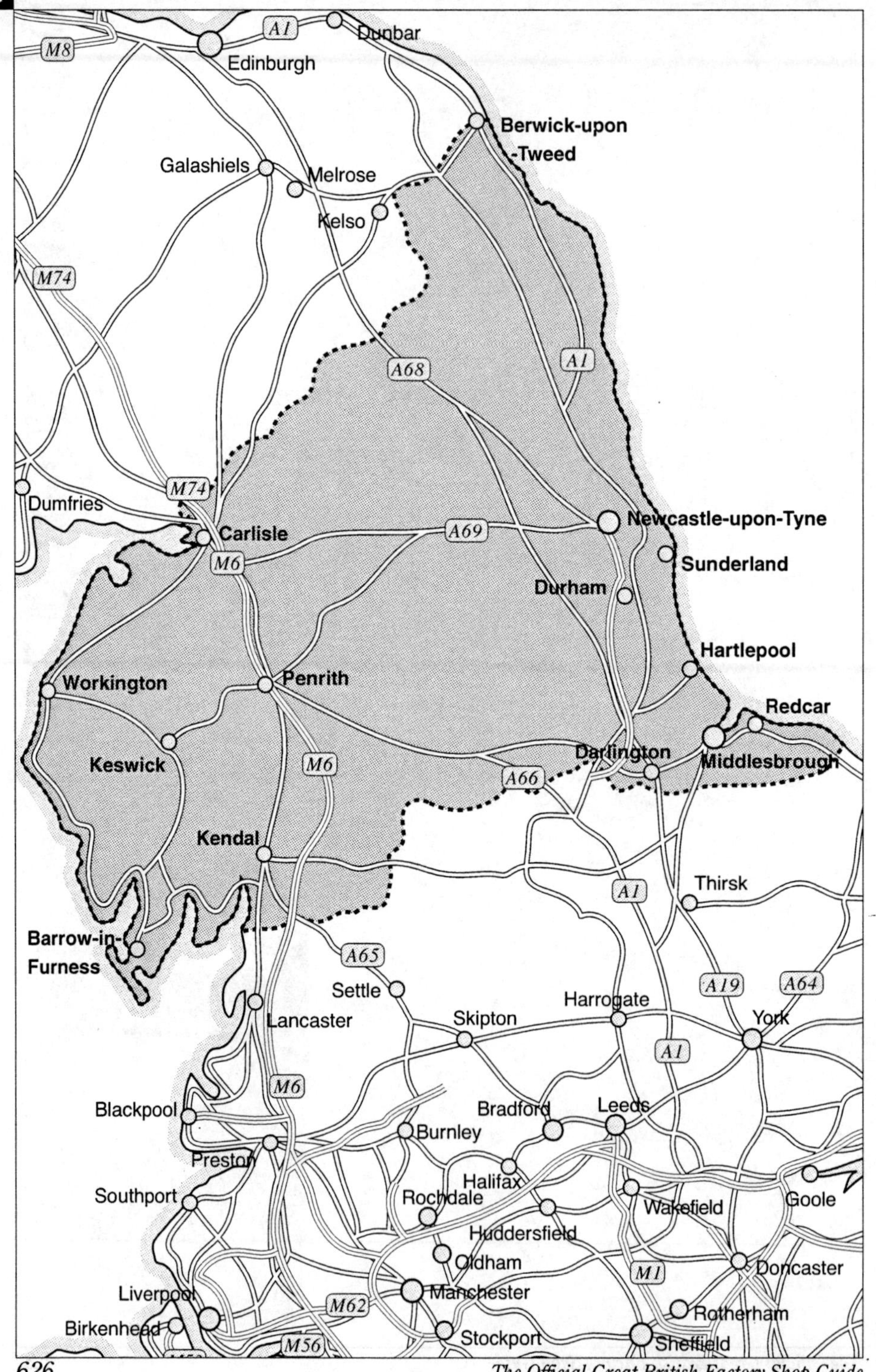

A1
M8
Dunbar
Edinburgh
Berwick-upon
-Tweed
Galashiels
Melrose
Kelso
M74
A1
A68
M74
Dumfries
Newcastle-upon-Tyne
Carlisle
A69
M6
Sunderland
Durham
Hartlepool
Workington
Penrith
Redcar
Keswick
M6
Darlington
Middlesbrough
A66
Kendal
A1
Thirsk
Barrow-in-
Furness
A65
Settle
A19
A64
Harrogate
Lancaster
Skipton
York
A1
M6
Blackpool
Bradford
Leeds
Burnley
Preston
Halifax
Southport
Rochdale
Wakefield
Goole
Huddersfield
Oldham
M1
Doncaster
Liverpool
M62
Manchester
Rotherham
Birkenhead
M56
Stockport
Sheffield

Northern England

The North of England is now home to three purpose-designed factory outlet villages, plus a factory shop centre. They offer convenient shopping for visitors to either the east or west coast and each has an excellent variety of products. The newest of these developments, in North Shields, is located beside the ferry terminal for boats plying across the North Sea – so is a magnet for Scandinavian as well as British customers. Shopping in Britain is so popular with other north Europeans that shops in the Newcastle area stay open 24 hours a day at busy periods such as Christmas.

This area is well known for a wide variety of footwear, sportswear and sports shoes. Those with a yen for the outdoor life can stock up on rucksacks, waterproof outdoor clothing, accessories for all water sports, international brand trainers and walking boots. Also famous oiled jackets and countrywear which Europeans die for. This part of the country is the only place where we have come across a factory shop selling active sportswear designed for professional canoeists, rally drivers and skiers. Here too you can buy top name hats and knitwear and stylish award-winning bags in multi-layered canvas – otherwise to be purchased in leading department stores around the world.

Away from the traditional industrial centres (most of which concentrated on heavy engineering or mining) northern England offers delightful surprises on the factory shop front. Combine your visit to Hadrian's Wall with a shopping trip to the tiny village of Bardon Mill in order to stock up with large salt-glazed garden pots. Pick up unique glass ornaments (made in the factory shop itself) at Hadrian Crystal, also near the attractive small town of Hexham. Enjoy the vistas of the Pennines at Sedbergh and buy fleece jackets for your family at the same time. The west coast railway, one of the few rural rides left in England, offers a most enjoyable journey from Barrow to Carlisle, via Sellafield, and you can stock up in factory shops at both ends of the line.

The latest attraction in the area is, of course, the magnificent Angel of the North, with its wing span of 54 metres. It is hard (if not impossible!) to miss it as you travel north on the A1 towards Gateshead.

Bardon Mill

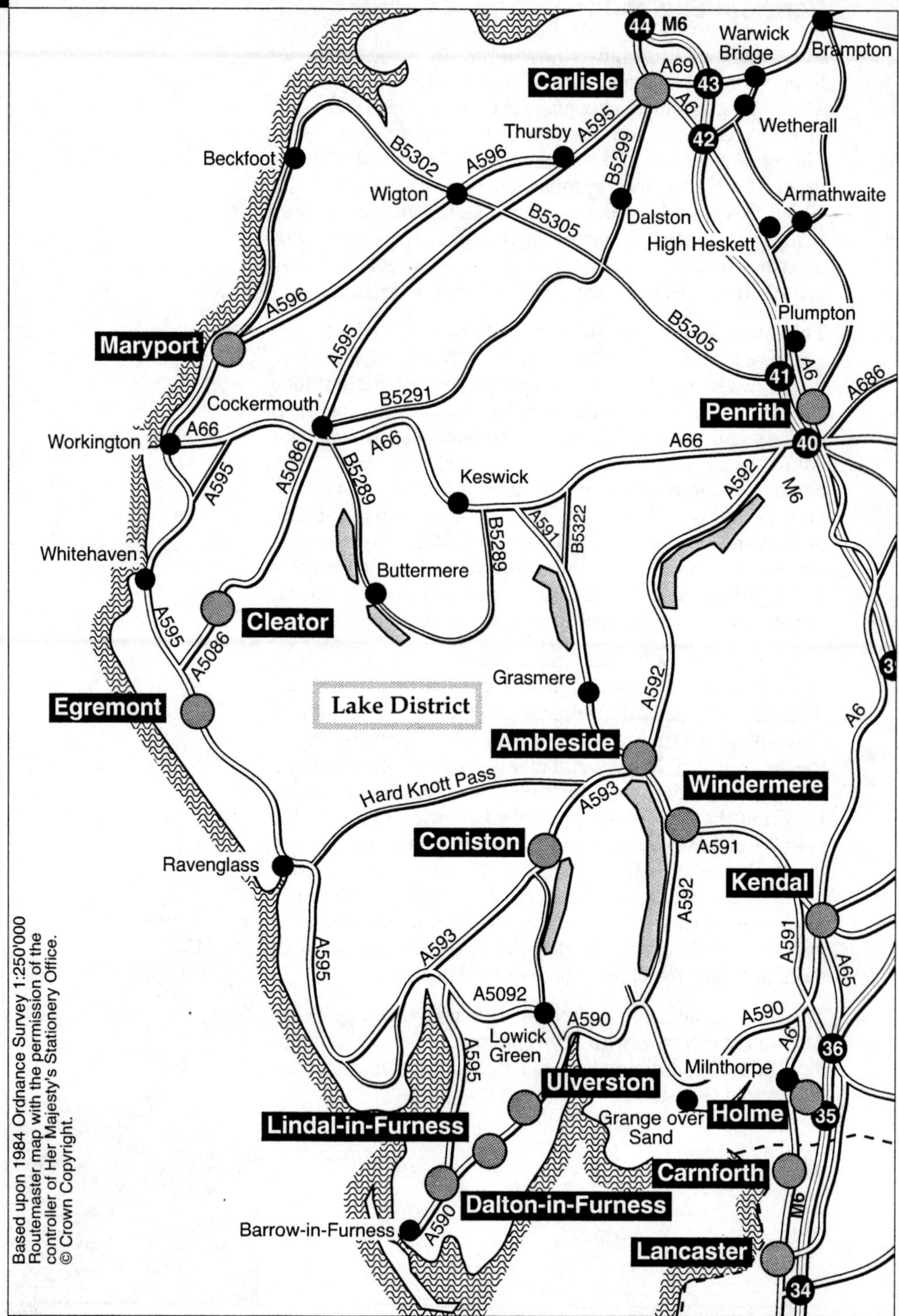

44
M6
Warwick Bridge
Brampton
Carlisle
A69
43
A6
42
Wetherall
Thursby
A595
Beckfoot
B5302
A596
B5299
Wigton
Dalston
Armathwaite
B5305
High Heskett
A596
Plumpton
Maryport
A595
B5305
41
A6
A686
Cockermouth
B5291
Penrith
Workington
A66
A66
A66
40
A595
A5086
B5289
Keswick
A592
M6
B5322
A591
B5289
Whitehaven
Buttermere
Cleator
A595
A5086
Grasmere
A592
Egremont
Lake District
A6
Ambleside
Hard Knott Pass
Windermere
A593
Coniston
A591
Ravenglass
A592
Kendal
A595
A593
A591
A65
A5092
A590
A590
Lowick Green
A6
36
A595
Milnthorpe
Ulverston
Grange over Sand
Holme
35
Lindal-in-Furness
Carnforth
Dalton-in-Furness
M6
Barrow-in-Furness
A590
Lancaster
34

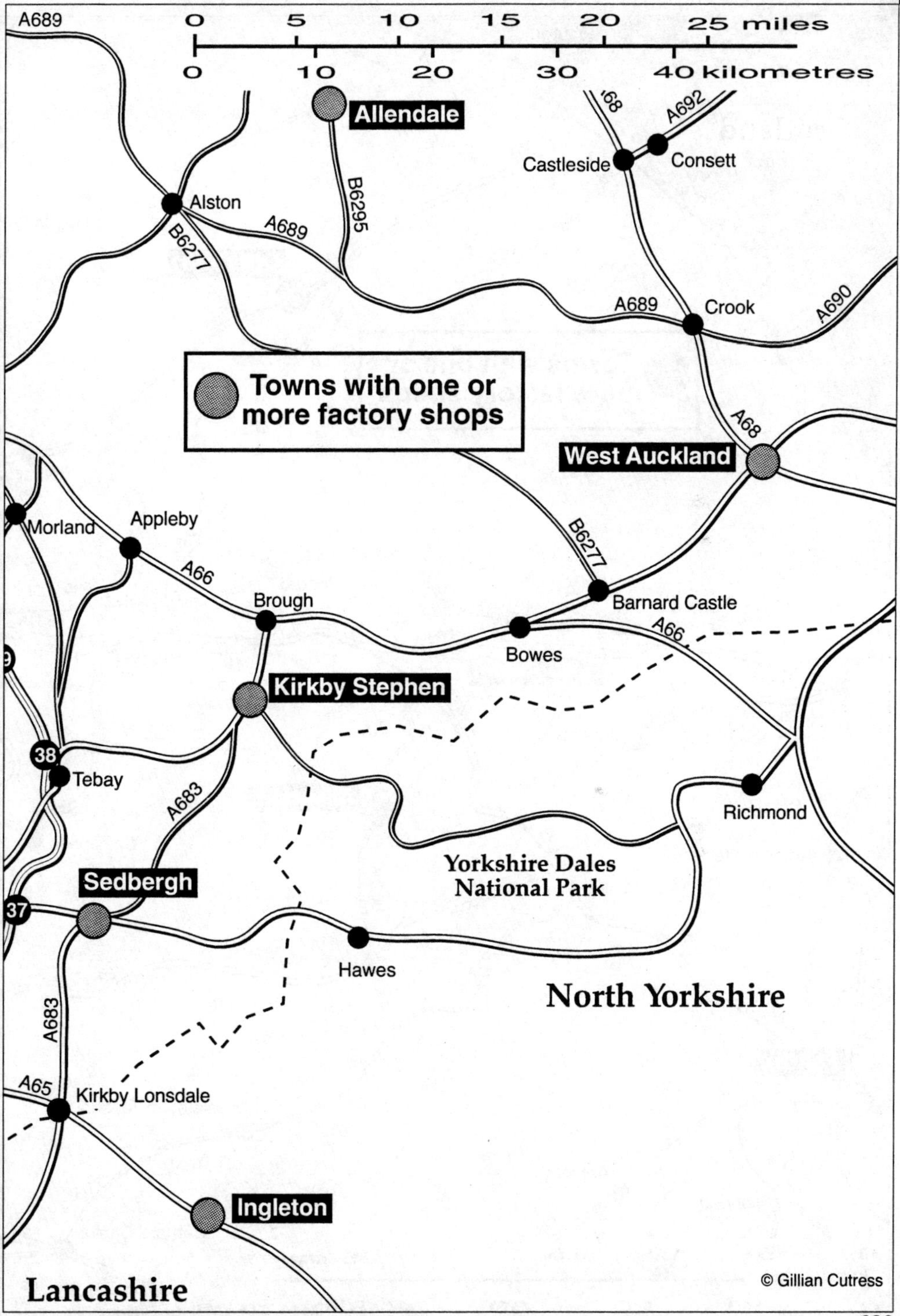

0 5 10 15 20 25 miles

0 10 20 30 40 kilometres

A689

Allendale

A68

A692

Castleside

Consett

Alston

B6295

A689

B6277

A689

Crook

A690

Towns with one or more factory shops

A68

West Auckland

Morland

Appleby

B6277

A66

Brough

Barnard Castle

Bowes

A66

Kirkby Stephen

38

Tebay

A683

Richmond

Yorkshire Dales National Park

Sedbergh

37

Hawes

North Yorkshire

A683

A65

Kirkby Lonsdale

Ingleton

© Gillian Cutress

Lancashire

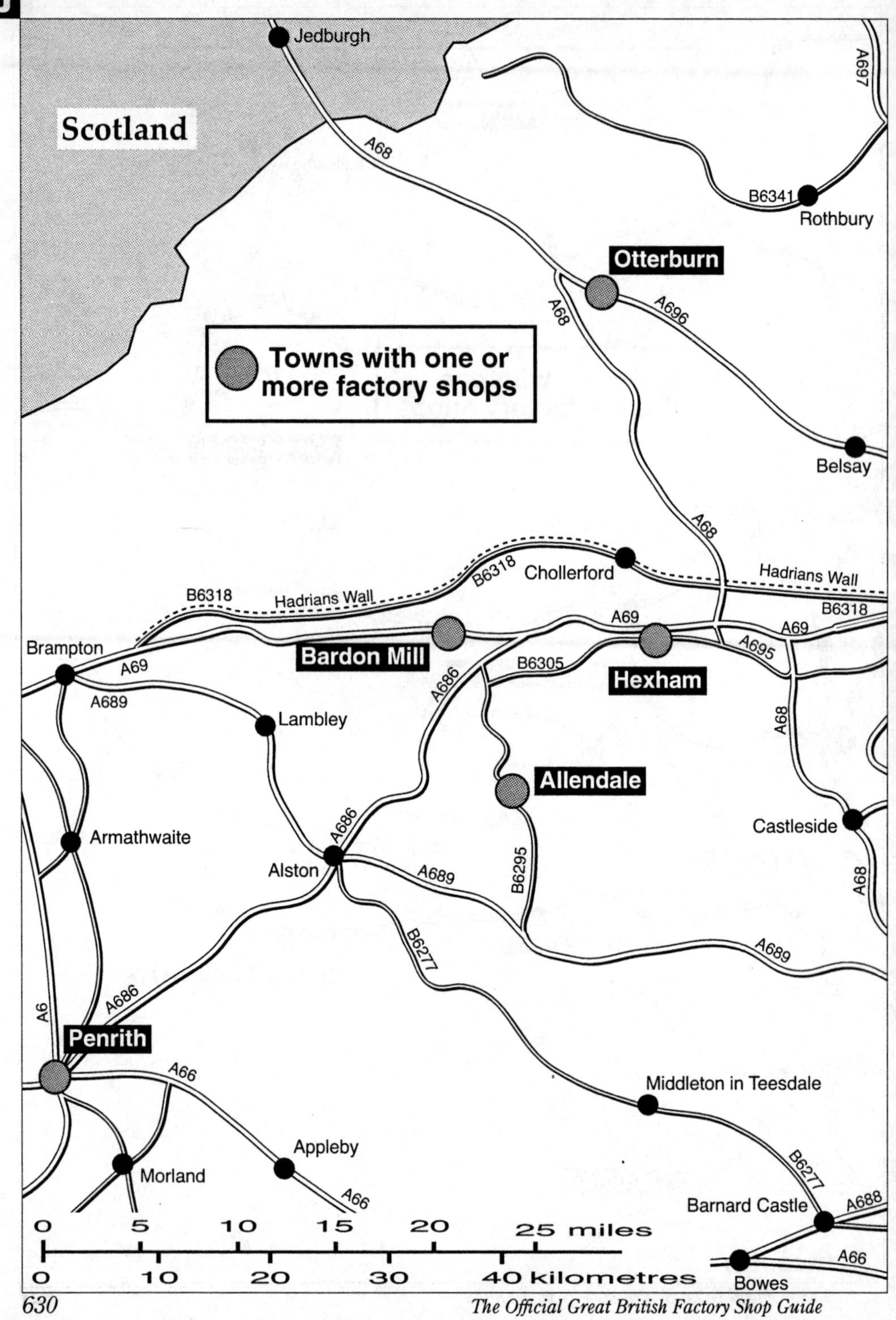
Scotland
Towns with one or more factory shops
Jedburgh
A68
A697
B6341
Rothbury
Otterburn
A68
A696
Belsay
A68
Chollerford
B6318
Hadrians Wall
B6318
Hadrians Wall
Hadrians Wall
B6318
A69
A69
A69
Brampton
Bardon Mill
Hexham
A695
B6305
A686
A689
Lambley
A68
Allendale
Castleside
Armathwaite
A686
Alston
A689
B6295
A68
B6277
A689
A686
A6
Penrith
A66
Middleton in Teesdale
Appleby
Morland
A66
B6277
Barnard Castle
A688
A66
Bowes
0 5 10 15 20 25 miles
0 10 20 30 40 kilometres

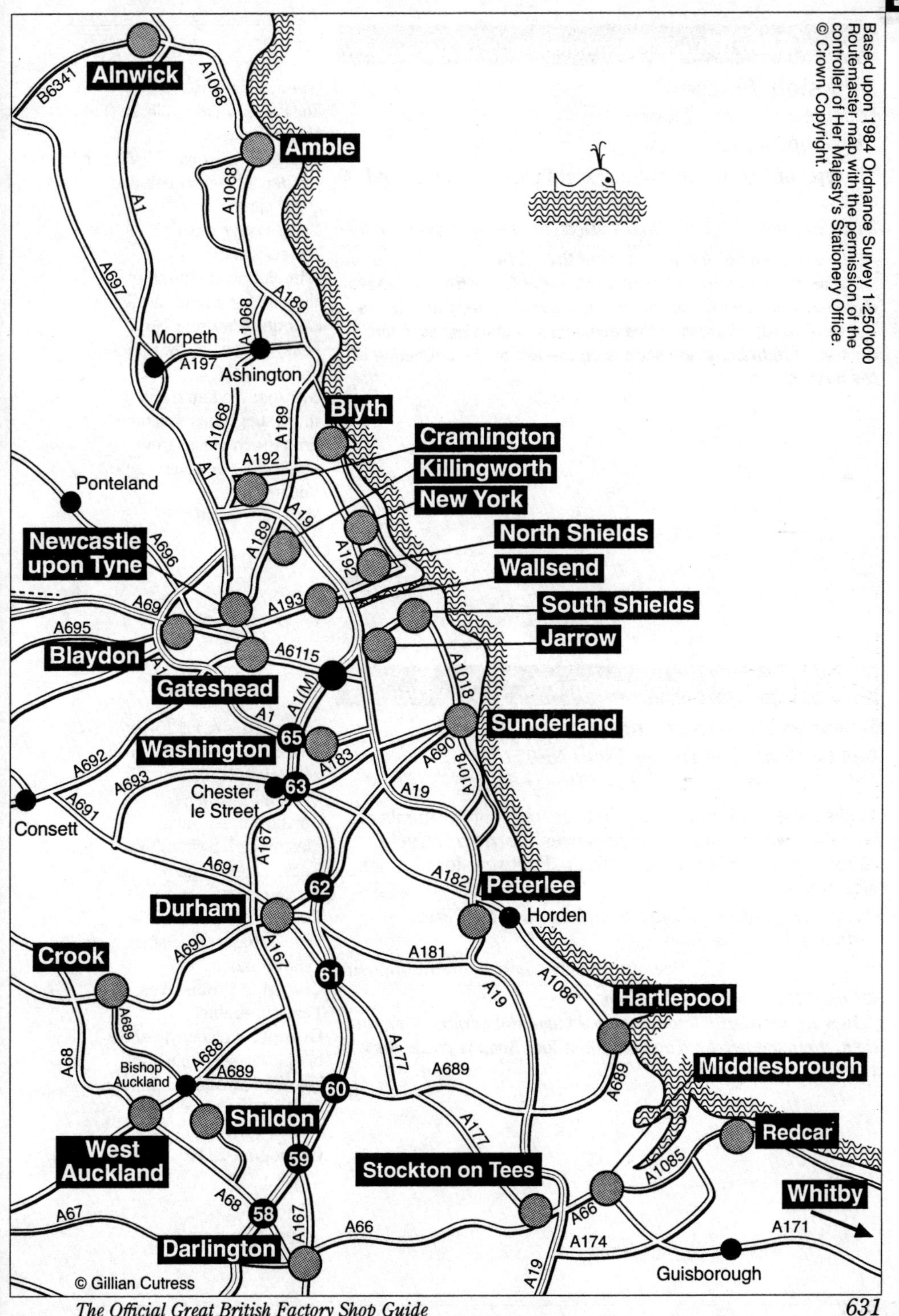
Based upon 1984 Ordnance Survey 1:250'000 Routemaster map with the permission of the controller of Her Majesty's Stationery Office. © Crown Copyright.
Alnwick
Amble
Morpeth
Ashington
Blyth
Cramlington
Killingworth
New York
North Shields
Wallsend
South Shields
Jarrow
Ponteland
Newcastle upon Tyne
Blaydon
Gateshead
Sunderland
Washington
Chester le Street
Consett
Peterlee
Horden
Durham
Crook
Hartlepool
Middlesbrough
Bishop Auckland
Shildon
West Auckland
Redcar
Stockton on Tees
Whitby
Darlington
Guisborough
© Gillian Cutress

1 Alnwick Northumberland

Diffusion Textiles

Willowburn Industrial Estate
(01665) 605556

Waterproof, breathable outdoor clothing, polar fleece and accessories.

'Firsts and seconds at discounted prices. Made-to-measure service.'

At the south end of Alnwick, just off the A1 bypass.

Follow the brown tourist signs to House of Hardy from whichever direction you enter town. Going south out of town, you will see House of Hardy. In front of this conspicuous building, turn left. Go around right bend and shop is on the left at the beginning of the next right bend.

Open: Mon–Fri 9–5; Sat 10–2. For Bank Holidays please phone to check.
Closed: Christmas–New Year.
Cards: All major debit and credit cards.
Cars: Own car-park.
Toilets: No.
Wheelchairs: One step, but alternative entrance available.
Changing rooms: No.
Teas: In town, a few minutes' walk away.
Groups: No tours, but shopping groups welcome.
Transport: Buses from town centre and Newcastle stop nearby.
Mail order: No.

2 Amble Northumberland

Karrimor International

Unit 6c, Coquetdale Trading Estate NE65 0PF
(01665) 713869/513209 Fax (01665) 513208

Rucksacks, child carriers, cycle bags, outdoor garments including waterproofs. *Trangia* stoves, *Karrimats*. Cycle clothing range. *Phoenix* ski clothing. Footwear for outdoor activities.

'Perfects, seconds, ex-display, samples and ends of lines including Gore-Tex items.'

See our display advertisement opposite

Off the A1068, south of the town.

Turn off the A1068 into the Amble Industrial Estate. Then turn right, go round left bend and take first left. Shop is in the first two units on the right.

Open: Tues & Fri 10–5; Wed & Thur 10–7; Sat 10–5.
Closed: Monday; Christmas–New Year.
Cards: Amex, Delta, MasterCard, Switch, Visa.
Cars: Large car-park outside factory.
Toilets: Yes.
Wheelchairs: One small step to large shop.
Changing rooms: Yes.
Teas: In Amble.
Groups: Welcome to shop, but please telephone first.
Transport: About 5 minutes' walk from town centre.
Mail order: Yes.
Catalogue: £2.50.

See our entry opposite

3 Amble Northumberland

Shark Group

Nordstrom House, North Broomhill NE65 9UJ
(01670) 760365

Wetsuits, drysuits, buoyancy aids, inflatable life jackets and accessories for all watersports.

'We sell slight seconds at very competitive prices.'

Three miles south of Amble, at the southern end of North Broomhill.

Follow the sign to the Radar pub (on your left if you come from Amble); go behind the pub to the factory.

Open: Mon–Fri 2–4 all year; *also early April–mid Dec:* Sat 10–12.
Closed: Three weeks in late July/early Aug; one week late Oct; three weeks at Christmas; Bank Holiday weekends.
Cards: MasterCard, Visa.
Cars: Outside factory.
Toilets: No.
Wheelchairs: One large step so not suitable.
Changing rooms: Yes.
Teas: In Amble.
Groups: No tours but groups of shoppers welcome any time if they arrange in advance.
Transport: Regular bus services to North Broomhill.
Mail order: Yes.
Catalogue: Free on request.

4 Ambleside Cumbria

Briggs & Shoe Mines

The Annex, Salutation Hotel LA22 9BY
(015394) 32757

A wide range of regular, sub-standard and clearance footwear of all types for men, women and children.

'All stock made by branded manufacturers.'

See our display advertisement on p. 651

Close to the centre of this small town.

From Kendal: get into one-way system and go around, following signs first to 'Town Centre' then continue towards Kendal again.*

From Keswick: turn left immediately after Jumpers on the left.*

****The shop is behind the large and conspicuous Salutation Hotel on the left, on the first floor.***

Open: *Nov–Easter*: daily 9.30–5.30; *Easter–Nov*: daily 9.30–7.30.
Closed: Christmas Day.
Cards: Amex, Connect, MasterCard, Switch, Visa.
Cars: Car-park adjacent.
Toilets: Behind Bertrams Restaurant, 30 yds downhill towards Kendal.
Wheelchairs: Unfortunately no access to first floor shop.
Teas: In Ambleside.
Groups: Coach parties welcome to shop. Drivers can obtain a £2 voucher for each passenger.
Transport: Bus stops opposite shop. Local transport and buses from further afield.
Mail order: Yes. Pleased to supply by mail order items in stock if customers know size, fitting and style. Ask for the manager.

5 Ambleside Cumbria

Lakeland Sweaters

The Factory, Old Lake Road,
(015394) 32445

Pure British wool sweaters. Also socks and gloves.

'It's worth a trip to the Lakes to get your knitwear direct from the factory. Our prices are lower than in high street shops.'

On the south side of town, on the main Ambleside–Windermere road (on the uphill side of the road). Located 100 yds from large garden centre, on the opposite side of the road, and next to the large Fisherbeck Hotel.

Open: Seven days 9.30–1 & 2–5.30. Bank Holidays.
Closed: Christmas, Boxing and New Year's Days.
Cards: MasterCard, Switch, Visa.
Cars: Large public car-park in front.
Toilets: In car-park.
Wheelchairs: Four steps; assistance given.
Changing rooms: No.
Teas: In town.
Groups: No guided tours, but shopping groups welcome. Large groups please phone first.
Transport: About 10 minutes' walk from town centre.

6 Bardon Mill near Hexham Northumberland

Errington Reay & Co (Bardon Mill Pottery)

Tyneside Pottery Works NE47 7HV
(01434) 344245

Good selection of large traditional salt-glazed garden pots and domestic storage jars, strawberry and herb pots etc.

'Bargain seconds normally available.'

In the middle of the village of Bardon Mill.

Turn south off the A69 (major Newcastle–Hexham–Carlisle road) to Bardon Mill. The tall square chimney of the kiln is clearly visible opposite the road to the station. Follow the signs to the car-park.

Open: Seven days 9–5.
Closed: Please phone to confirm times.
Cards: No.
Cars: Behind shop, signposted.
Toilets: Ask if desperate.
Wheelchairs: Fairly steep cobbled path.
Teas: In Bardon Mill.
Tours: No.
Transport: Trains to Bardon Mill from Carlisle and Newcastle.
Mail order: No.

7 Blaydon-on-Tyne Tyne & Wear

Factory Carpets and Factory Beds

Tundry Way, Chainbridge Industrial Estate NE21 5SJ
(0191) 414 5887 *see Gateshead map*

Large range of quality plain and patterned tufted carpets in all yarns and mixes. Axminsters and Wiltons, shadow pile, berbers, twists, underlay, gripper rods etc. In other premises opposite (0191 414 6331): beds and mattresses of all sizes; sofa beds, guest beds; headboards.

'Roll ends and samples always available. Free fitting locally on most carpets.'

Immediately south of the Tyne between A1 and Scotswood bridge.

From A1 Western Bypass of Newcastle: turn on to A695 for Blaydon (south of river). Go under approach to old river bridge; take first left for 'Chainbridge Industrial Estate'. The Factory Shop Centre is on left after you cross next bridge.

From Blaydon on A695: go under A1 Western Bypass, take first left into Chainbridge Industrial Estate. The Factory Shop Centre is on right just after left bend.

From Newcastle station: take A695 west. Pass long Vickers factory, go left over Scotswood bridge. After bridge, take first left, go under Scotswood bridge, take first left to Chainbridge Industrial Estate. The Factory Shop Centre is on left after you cross next bridge.

Open: Mon–Sat 9–5 (Thur 9–7); Sun and Bank Holidays 10–4.
Closed: Christmas, Boxing and New Year's Days.
Cards: Eurocard, MasterCard, Visa.
Cars: Own car-park.
Toilets: Yes.
Wheelchairs: Easy access.
Teas: Own café.
Transport: Many buses from Gateshead and Newcastle.
Mail order: No.

8 Blaydon-on-Tyne Tyne & Wear

Factory Fabrics

see Gateshead map

Tundry Way, Chainbridge Industrial Estate NE21 5SJ
(0191) 414 4515

Vast range of fabrics for curtains, furnishing, upholstery, loose covers etc, including leading designer names and department store clearance stock and over-runs. Curtain lining, tapes, and accessories. Curtain-making service.

'Perfects, seconds and remnants sold at discounted prices.'

Immediately south of the Tyne between A1 and Scotswood bridge.

From A1 Western Bypass of Newcastle: turn on to A695 for Blaydon (south of river). Go under approach to old river bridge; take first left for 'Chainbridge Industrial Estate'. The Factory Shop Centre is on left after you cross next bridge.

From Blaydon on A695: go under A1 Western Bypass, take first left into Chainbridge Industrial Estate. The Factory Shop Centre is on right just after left bend.

From Newcastle station: take A695 west. Pass long Vickers factory, go left over Scotswood bridge. After bridge, take first left, go under Scotswood bridge, take first left to Chainbridge Industrial Estate. The Factory Shop Centre is on left after you cross next bridge.

Open: Mon–Fri 10–5 (Thur 10–7); Sat 9–5; Sun and Bank Holidays 10–4.
Closed: Easter Sunday; Christmas, Boxing and New Year's Days.
Cards: Amex, MasterCard, Switch, Visa.
Cars: Own car-park.
Toilets: Yes.
Wheelchairs: One step; easy access.
Teas: Own café.
Groups: Groups welcome, prior phone call appreciated.
Transport: Many buses from Gateshead and Newcastle.
Mail order: Yes. Fabrics can be despatched by post or carrier.

9 Blaydon-on-Tyne Tyne & Wear

McIntosh's Factory Shop

see Gateshead map

Tundry Way, Chainbridge Industrial Estate NE21 5SJ
(0191) 414 8598

Large selection of bedding including duvet covers, quilts, bedspreads, pillows, mattress covers, baby bedding; ready-made curtains, net curtains; cushion covers, towels, tea cosies, tablecloths, dusters, dishcloths etc.

'Wide range of perfects and slight seconds.'

Immediately south of the Tyne between A1 and Scotswood bridge.

From A1 Western Bypass of Newcastle: turn on to A695 for Blaydon (south of river). Go under approach to old river bridge; take first left for 'Chainbridge Industrial Estate'. The Factory Shop Centre is on left after you cross next bridge.

From Blaydon on A695: go under A1 Western Bypass, take first left into Chainbridge Industrial Estate. The Factory Shop Centre is on right just after left bend.

From Newcastle station: take A695 west. Pass long Vickers factory, go left over Scotswood bridge. After bridge, take first left, go under Scotswood bridge, take first left to Chainbridge Industrial Estate. The Factory Shop Centre is on left after you cross next bridge.

Open: Mon–Fri 10–5 (Thur 10–7); Sat 9–5; Sun and Bank Holidays 10–4.
Closed: Good Friday, Christmas, Boxing and New Year's Days.
Cards: MasterCard, Switch, Visa.
Cars: Own large car-park.
Toilets: Yes.
Wheelchairs: One step, but assistance given.
Teas: Own café.
Groups: Groups welcome to shop.
Transport: Many buses from Gateshead and Newcastle.
Mail order: No.

10 Blyth Northumberland

Burberrys

Kitty Brewster Trading Estate NE24 4RC
(01670) 352524

Trench coats, jackets, trousers, shirts; dresses, coats, skirts, sweaters; bags, umbrellas and accessories.

On the west side of Blyth.

From A189 (Spine Road): turn on to A193 for Blyth. After two pedestrian lights go left at mini-roundabout: follow sign to estate.

From Blyth town centre: follow signs to A193, Ashington/North. As you leave town, turn right into Kitty Brewster Trading Estate at mini-roundabout; shop is in first building on right.

Open: Mon–Thur 10–3.30; Fri 10–3; Sat 9–12.30.
Closed: Phone to check for Bank Holidays and Christmas.
Cards: Yes.
Cars: Outside shop.
Toilets: No.
Wheelchairs: One sizeable step to medium-sized shop.
Changing rooms: No.
Teas: In Blyth.
Transport: Local buses from Ashington, Blyth, Morpeth, Newcastle, North Shields, Whitley Bay Metro.

11 Blyth Northumberland

Claremont Garments

Ennerdale Road, Kitty Brewster Trading Estate NE24 4RF
(01670) 351195

Ladies' wear: lingerie, swimwear, casualwear (bodies, leggings etc), dresses, blouses, skirts, trousers, and tailored suits, coats and jackets. Schoolwear: boys' trousers and shirts; girls' skirts and shirts. Boys' wear: a limited range of casual shirts and trousers.

'All garments are leading chainstore perfects, seconds or ends of lines, and are offered at greatly reduced prices.'

See our display advertisement on p. 539

On the west side of Blyth.

From the A189 (Spine Road): turn on to A193 for Blyth. After two pedestrian lights turn left at mini-roundabout, following sign to Kitty Brewster Trading Estate.*

From Blyth town centre: follow signs to A193, Ashington/North. As you leave town, turn right into the Kitty Brewster Trading Estate at mini-roundabout.*

****Take first left: shop is 200 yds on right.***

Open: Mon–Fri 9–4.30; Sat 9.30–2.30.
Closed: Bank Holidays.
Cards: Most credit cards.
Cars: Own car-park.
Toilets: In Asda.
Wheelchairs: One small step to medium-sized shop; assistance given.
Changing rooms: Yes.
Teas: In Asda.
Groups: Shopping groups welcome, but large groups please phone first.
Transport: Local buses from Ashington, Blyth, Morpeth, Newcastle, North Shields, Whitley Bay Metro.
Mail order: No.

12 Carlisle Cumbria *see map opposite*

The Factory Bedding and Fabrics Shop

Atlas House, Nelson Street, Denton Holme CA2 5NB
(01228) 514703

Large selection of ready-made bedding: duvet covers, quilts, bedspreads, pillows, mattress covers, baby bedding; ready-made curtains, net curtains; cushion covers, towels, tea cosies, tablecloths, dusters, dishcloths etc. Huge selection of sheeting, curtaining, upholstery fabrics. Make-up service.

'Wide range of perfects and slight seconds.'

On south-west side of town, off the road to Dalston.

From Dalston (going north on B5299): pass Caldew Hospital on left then turn right immediately before pedestrian lights into Nelson Street. Shop at end of four-storey mill, about 400 yds along.

From other directions: follow signs to station/Motorail terminal. Do not enter station but go into town between two arches like castle (The Citadel). From city centre, follow signs 'West'. Cross Victoria Viaduct to roundabout (baths on left). Take road to Workington; cross bridge, fork left, take fourth right (Nelson Street). Shop on corner of second turning on left.

Open: Mon–Fri 10–5.30; Sat 9–5. Bank Holidays 10–4.
Closed: Good Friday; Christmas, Boxing and New Year's Days.
Cards: Connect, MasterCard, Switch, Visa.
Cars: Outside shop.
Toilets: No.
Wheelchairs: Easy access to spacious shop, but assistance given for first floor.
Teas: Own coffee shop.
Groups: Groups welcome to shop.
Transport: Buses from Woolworths to Morton/Denton Holme – get off by Co-op.
Mail order: No.

13 Carlisle Cumbria *see map opposite*

John Chapman

Gallery House, Harraby Green Business Park CA1 2SS
(01228) 514514

Huge collection of award winning fishing bags, shooting and hunting bags, travel and shoulder bags, in multi-layered canvas, tweeds and tartans with leather trim and solid brass fittings.

'These bags are found only in the finest department stores and speciality shops worldwide. Bags of classic British design and rugged construction, built from all British raw materials to last a very long time. First quality, test models, some seconds and used bags available.'

In beautiful old mill at southern edge of Carlisle, close to British Telecom tower.

From town centre: take A6 south. By BT tower (large transmitting aerial with satellite dishes), go right (20 yds before Esso petrol on left) to Harraby Green Business Park (signposted).*

From M6 exit 42: take A6 into Carlisle. By BT tower, take first left after Esso petrol (on right).*

***Immediately go sharp left betwen two rows of terraced houses to Gallery House (signposted).**

Open: Mon–Thur 9–5; Fri 9–3.
Closed: Bank Holidays; Christmas–New Year. Please check for spring and summer holidays (usually Spring Bank Holiday week; last week July, first week August).
Cards: MasterCard, Switch, Visa.
Cars: Outside.
Toilets: Yes.
Wheelchairs: Two small steps to shop.
Teas: Local pubs; teas in town.
Groups: Suitable for small shopping groups only.
Transport: Bus nos. 61, 62 south from town. Get off at Harraby Green/BT tower.
Mail order: Yes.
Catalogue: Please phone or write for free catalogue.

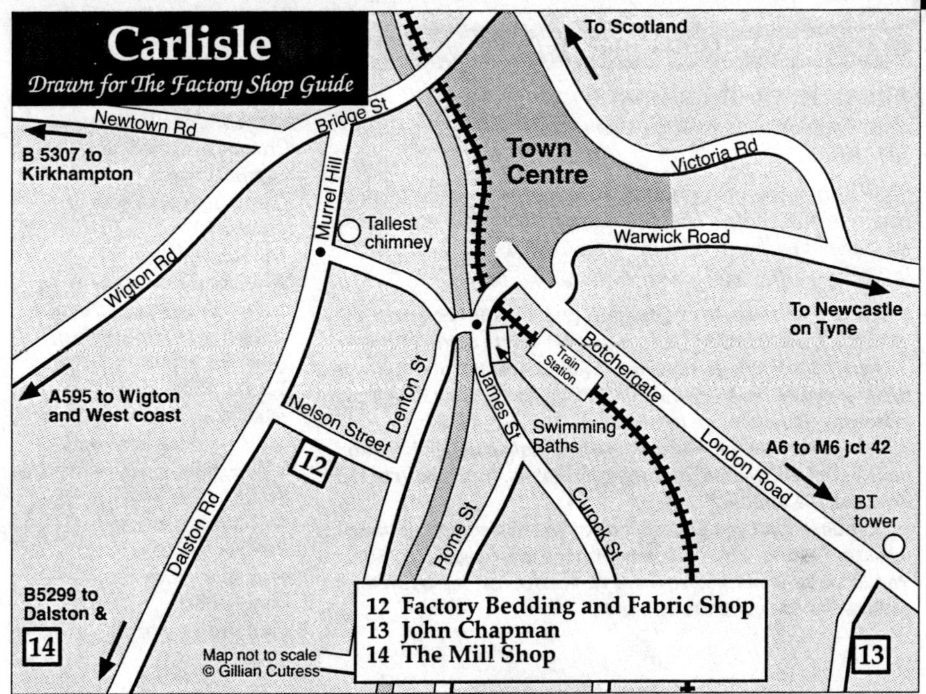

14 Carlisle Cumbria *see map above*

The Mill Shop

Cummersdale Print Works
(01228) 25224

Large selection of quality printed and plain curtain and furnishing fabrics; range of quilt covers, flat and fitted sheets, pillow cases, valances; pillows and cushions; curtain tapes, tie-back stiffeners, cords and other trimmings; complete range of sewing threads; velcro and piping cord; broad lace fabric.

'Fabrics and bedding are slight seconds or ends of ranges.'

About 2 miles south-west of Carlisle.

From B5299 (Carlisle–Dalston road): follow signs east to Cummersdale. Go through village, and go left at bottom of hill by river. Shop, clearly signed, is in low building on left.

Open: Mon–Fri 9–4; Sat 10–4.
Closed: Christmas–New Year; Bank Holidays. Please phone to check.
Cards: Delta, Switch.
Cars: Visitors' car-park.
Toilets: Yes.
Wheelchairs: Easy access to medium-sized shop on ground floor.
Teas: Pubs in Carlisle or Dalston.
Groups: Shopping groups wishing to visit should phone first, mentioning this guide.
Transport: None.

15 Carnforth (Holme) Lancs

Abbey Horn of Lakeland

Units 6a & 6b Holme Mills, Holme LA6 1RD
(01524) 782387

Shoe horns, spoons, spatulas, salad servers, soldiers' mugs, paperweights, bottle openers, corkscrews, walking sticks, all made of ox horn. Also horn ships, brushes, combs.

'All items perfect with prices reduced by a third.'

Holme is 6 miles north of Carnforth (west of M6) between M6 exits 35 & 36. Company is in industrial estate south of Holme.

From M6 exit 36: go towards Kirkby Londsale; after 150 yds go right for Holme on A6070. After 2 miles go right for Holme over motorway. In Holme, go left opposite The Smithy pub.*

From Milnthorpe on A6: turn towards Holme at traffic lights; once out of Milnthorpe, fork right for Holme. In Holme turn right opposite The Smithy.*

****Continue until you pass mill pond on left and first entrance to industrial estate. Take second entrance after about 200 yds. Park on right in marked spaces. Walk down 80 yds between the units: units 6A and B are on right.***

Open: Mon–Fri 9–4.
Closed: Bank Holidays; Christmas–New Year.
Cards: None.
Cars: Small area in front of factory.
Toilets: No.
Wheelchairs: Access to factory for self-guided tour but not to shop (16 steps).
Teas: Local pub.
Tours: Abbey Horn, established in 1749, is the oldest working horn works and the only one open to public. Factory visits free. Groups welcome – please call Heather McKellar first.
Transport: Bus no. 55 from Kendal.
Mail order: No.

16 Cleator Cumbria

Kangol

Cleator Mills CA23 3DK
(01946) 810312

Range of formal and casual hats for men and women; caps, berets, peak caps; handbags; scarves; golf clothing; streetgear; belts.

'First quality, ends of ranges and slight seconds available. Prices from about £2 to £30.'

About 11 miles south-west of Cockermouth, on A5086 south of Cleator Moor.

From Cockermouth on A5086: go through Frizington to Cleator Moor; at bottom of hill, after The Brook and opposite church, go left into Kangol's drive.*

From Egremont on A5086: go through Cleator, pass Grove Court Hotel on left and turn right before The Brook into Kangol's drive.*

****Shop is on left, clearly signed.***

Open: Mon–Sat 9–5.
Closed: Bank Holidays; Christmas & New Year.
Cards: Amex, Diners, MasterCard, Switch, Visa.
Cars: Own car-park; adequate coach parking.
Toilets: Yes, including facilities for disabled in Kangol café.
Wheelchairs: Easy access to large shop.
Teas: Kangol Shop café next door to shop.
Tours: No factory tours.
Transport: Whitehaven–Egremont buses stop in Cleator.
Mail order: No.

17 Coniston Cumbria

John Countryman & Co

The Rural Workshops, Lake Road
(015394) 41129

Hand-printed tablecloths, napkins, roller blinds, scarves, cushions, tablemats etc. Also picture gallery showing work of local artists: prints and originals.

'On the shore of Lake Coniston. All our designs are unique and exclusive to us.'

Near the lake south-east of village centre.

From the south on A593: turn right at the first crossing signposted to Gondola Steam Yacht Pier.*

From Ambleside or Hawkshead: go through the village, over the river and take the first left after petrol station, signposted Gondola Steam Yacht Pier.*

****After ⅓ mile go straight instead of turning left for the lake, then follow the signs.***

Open: Mon–Sat 10–5.
Closed: Bank Holidays; Christmas–New Year.
Cards: Not yet.
Cars: Own car-park.
Toilets: In Coniston.
Wheelchairs: Easy access, no steps to medium-sized premises.
Teas: At Bluebird Café and many other local places.
Groups: Shopping groups welcome, no need to book.
Transport: Buses from Windermere and Ambleside stop 50 yds away.

18 Cramlington Northumberland

Cramlington Textiles

Nelson Way, North Nelson Industrial Estate NE23 9JT
(01670) 713434

Vast selection of quilt covers, sheets, pillowcases, quilts, pillows and towels. Lighting accessories and ready made curtains.

'We sell perfects, seconds and rejects.'

West of Cramlington town.

From Blyth or Bedlington: take A189, then A192 to 'Cramlington Industrial Estate'.*

From A19 north of Tyne Tunnel: take A189 going north; pass Cramlington town, take A192 to 'Cramlington Industrial Estate'.*

****Once on A192 continue on to A1068 and turn left. Follow signs to Nelson Way Industrial Estate; factory is first on left.***

From Newcastle: take A6125 or new Western Bypass; go north and branch on to A1068 for Bedlington. Turn off A1068 into Nelson Industrial Estate (signposted); shop is first on left. Enter through gate and turn right to customer car-park.

Open: Mon–Fri 9.30–5; Sat 9.30–4.30.
Closed: Bank Holidays; Christmas, Boxing and New Year's Days. Please phone to check Christmas opening.
Cards: MasterCard, Visa.
Cars: In factory car-park inside security gates.
Toilets: Yes.
Wheelchairs: Ramp to large shop.
Teas: In Cramlington.
Groups: No guided tours, but groups welcome to shop.
Transport: Bus no. 442 (Ashington–North Shields) stops outside factory.
Mail order: No.

19 Crook Co. Durham

Best Dress Club

New Main Road, DL15 8EH
(01388) 764900

All women's wear: dresses, blouses, skirts, etc.

On the A689 at the south end of town.

From Bishop Auckland: this is the first factory on your left as you enter town. The shop is at the far end of the building.

From Crook town centre traffic lights: turn towards Crook Industrial Estate (signposted). this is the factory just after the estate on the right. The shop is at the beginning of the factory, set back from the road.

Open: Mon–Fri 10–5; Sat 10–4.
Closed: Bank Holidays; Christmas–New Year.
Cards: None.
Cars: Own big car-park.
Toilets: No.
Wheelchairs: One step to big shop.
Changing rooms: Yes.
Teas: In town.
Transport: Bus from Bishop Auckland to Crook every ½ hour.
Mail order: No.

20 Dalton-in-Furness Cumbria

Furness Footwear

Long Lane, off Mill Brow
(01229) 468837

Men's, ladies' & children's fashion shoes, leather and synthetic.

'Vast range of branded footwear from own factory and all over the world. Stock changes daily. Prices from £1 to £100.'

Off the old A590 south of Dalton-in-Furness.

From Ulverston and Askam-in-Furness: take new by-pass turning right at roundabout towards Barrow-in-Furness. At next roundabout follow signs for Barrow and at third roundabout (with golf driving range) go left signed to Furness General Hospital.*

From Barrow-in-Furness via A590: go straight at roundabout signed to Furness General Hospital.*

****Pass the hospital on left and after 500 yds at the top of the hill get in right hand lane and turn right towards Stainton. Shop in second building on right.***

Open: Mon–Sat 9–5.30 (Fri late night to 8). Bank Holidays.
Closed: Christmas, Boxing and New Year's Days.
Cards: Access, Switch, Visa.
Cars: Factory car-park.
Toilets: Ask if desperate.
Wheelchairs: Easy access to large shop.
Teas: Hot-drinks machine; sweets, crisps, biscuits on sale.
Groups: Welcome to shop.
Transport: Main Barrow–Ulverston buses stop at shop.
Mail order: No.

21 Darlington Co. Durham

Hall & Son – a Lotus Shoes factory shop

6 Blackwellgate DL1 6HL
(01325) 466009

Ladies' court shoes and sling backs, sandals, leather casuals, fashion shoes. Men's city styles, casuals and sandals. Also seasonal footwear such as slippers and ladies' fashion boots. Handbags.

'This is a factory shop belonging to Lotus Shoes. A visit here could be part of a day's shopping trip.'

In the centre of town near the Market Hall (with a large clocktower).

From the top end of the Market Hall: go left of Binns department store and keep going around it. Hall & Son are on the same side of the road, 50 yds beyond Binns.

Open: Mon–Sat 9–5.30. Bank Holiday Mondays.*
Closed: *Tuesdays after Bank Holiday Mondays. Christmas & New Year.
Cards: Access, Switch, Visa.
Cars: Double yellow lines. Large car-park at lower end of the Market Hall. Also Skinnergate.
Toilets: Below Market Hall.
Wheelchairs: Easy access, some steps to back of shop.
Teas: In town.
Groups: Coach parties welcome: please contact Mrs L Kell.
Transport: About 300 yds from the main bus stop in town.
Mail order: No.

22 Durham Co. Durham

Chapman Curtains and Covers

Units 2 & 3 Abbey Industrial Estate, Abbey Road, Pity Me
(0191) 386 7117

Curtains, caravan seat covers.

In north-west outskirts of Durham, off the A167 western by-pass of Durham.

From the north: take A167 (from A1(M) exit 63) and at first roundabout fork left for Pity Me.*

From other directions: go through town centre and follow signs to A691 for Consett. At roundabout where A167 crosses A691 turn north for Newcastle. At next roundabout turn right for Pity Me.*

****Take first left before Abbey service station, go straight at the roundabout and take first right. Then fork left and shop is in middle of building on right.***

Open: Mon–Fri 9–5; Sat 10–4.
Closed: Please phone to check.
Cards: MasterCard, Visa.
Cars: Own car-park.
Toilets: In town.
Wheelchairs: 1 step to shop.
Teas: In town.
Groups: No.
Transport: Trains to Durham.

23 Egremont Cumbria

The Factory Shop Ltd.

Empire Buildings, Main Street CA22 2BD
(01946) 820434

Clothing and footwear for all the family. Good range of branded bedding, towels, toiletries, pottery, lighting and fancy goods. Branded electricals. Fashion concessions department with famous brand names. *Cape Country* pine furniture exclusively produced for The Factory Shop.

'Large stock of branded and chainstore items, all at greatly reduced prices. Deliveries of new stock every week to give an ever changing selection.'

In the town centre beside Wyndham School (signposted).

Turn into the side road immediately beside the town hall (with magnificent clocktower) and almost opposite tourist information centre. Go to end of that road and shop is clearly signposted.

Open: Mon–Sat 9–5; Sun 10–4.
Closed: Bank Holidays; Christmas, Boxing and New Year's Days.
Cards: MasterCard, Switch, Visa.
Cars: In factory car-park.
Toilets: Ask if desperate.
Wheelchairs: Easy access to large shop.
Changing rooms: Yes.
Teas: In town.
Groups: Shopping groups welcome. For organiser/driver incentives please phone.
Transport: Buses from Whitehaven.
Mail order: Home delivery service for pine furniture. Please phone for free catalogue and price list.

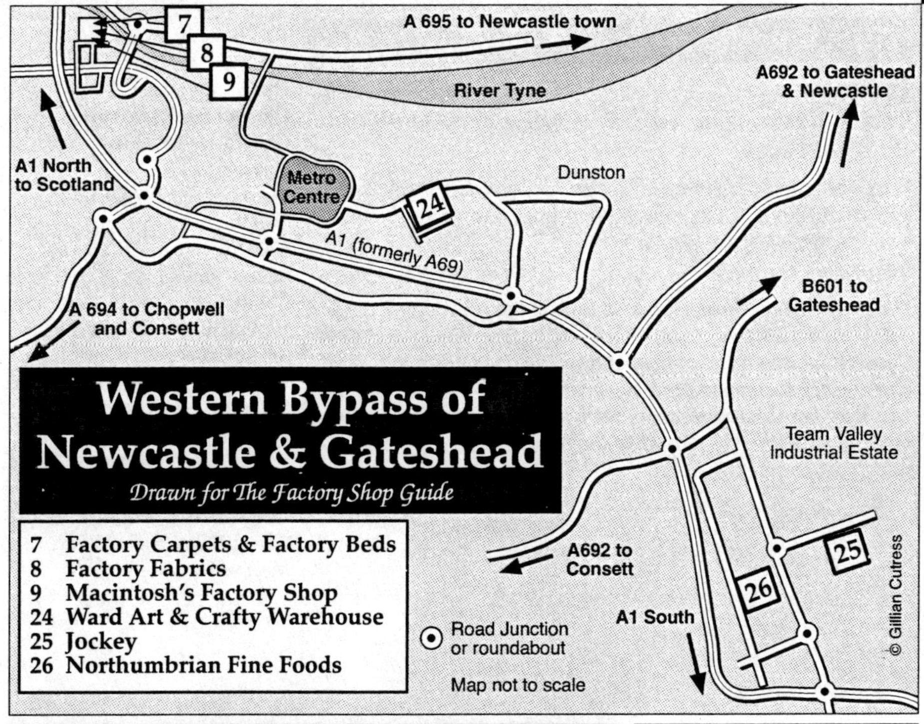

24 Gateshead Tyne & Wear see map above

Ward Art & Crafty Warehouse

Halifax Road, Dunston Industrial Estate NE11 9HV
(0191) 460 5915

Probably the biggest range of art, craft and stationery materials in the North: watercolours, silk painting, oils, glass paints, acrylics, airbrushing, gouache, stencils, textiles, sculpture, moulding, découpage, stamp art, calligraphy, drawing, sketching, pergamano, doodling, designing and much more.

'A visit is a must if you want to develop your creative instincts! Many products from around the world, and workshops to improve your techniques. Many special offers up to 50% off retail price, eg watercolour sets half-price; free videos with drawing sets; drawing pads from 65p each.'

Not far from the Metro Centre.

From the A1 (Western Bypass) going north: pass A692 turn-off into Newcastle but take next exit to Dunston.*

From A1 going south: pass Metro Centre exit; take next exit to Dunston.*

****Go downhill to Dunston. Pass Burmah petrol on left, go under railway bridge, take first left (Lancaster Road) then first left again.****

From Metro Centre: follow signs to Dunston, pass Federation Brewery on right and take next right (Lancaster Road) then take first left. *Shop is 100 yds on left, clearly signed.

Open: Mon–Sat 9–5.
Closed: Bank Holidays; Christmas and New Year's Days.
Cards: MasterCard, Switch, Visa.
Cars: In street.
Toilets: By request.
Wheelchairs: Nine steps. Access at rear on request.
Teas: In Dunston or Metro Centre and from take-away van. Sweets, ice cream and soft drinks in shop.
Groups: Shopping groups book with Karen Carpenter or Carole Creed. Free factory visits for groups of up to 15. Contact John Moreels or Miriam Wright. Sometimes art and craft demonstrations/exhibitions.
Transport: Metro Centre train station. Bus nos. 745, M3, M7, M8, M9 stop nearby.
Mail order: No.

25 Gateshead : Team Valley Tyne & Wear

Jockey

see map on previous page

Eastern Avenue, Team Valley Trading Estate NE11 0PB
(0191) 491 0088

Wide selection of men's and ladies' underwear, T-shirts, knitwear, tights, socks; towels, bedding, baby accessories, swim/sportswear (in season).

'Perfects and seconds.'

The Team Valley Trading Estate is just off the A1 Western bypass.

Exit from the A1 to 'Team Valley', NOT 'Team Valley and A692 Consett' (northern end of the estate). Continue down this dual carriageway to a roundabout signposted to Low Fell (right) and turn right into Eastern Avenue. Shop is on the right in the first building after the first turn-off to the right.

Open: Mon–Fri 9–4.
Closed: Bank Holidays; Christmas–New Year please check.
Cards: Delta, MasterCard, Switch, Visa.
Cars: Own car-park outside shop.
Toilets: No.
Wheelchairs: Easy access to large shop.
Changing rooms: Yes.
Teas: In Low Fell.
Groups: No factory tours. Groups of shoppers welcome but please phone first.
Transport: Bus from Gateshead to Team Valley.
Mail order: No.

26 Gateshead : Team Valley Tyne & Wear

Northumbrian Fine Foods

see map on previous page

Dukes Way, Team Valley Industrial Estate
(0191) 487 0070/482 2611

Selection of plain and coated biscuits in packets and in pre-packed bags by the kilo. *Dunkers.* Vegetarian ready meals, soups, jams.

The Team Valley Trading Estate is just off the A1 Western bypass.

Exit from the A1 at 'Team Valley', NOT 'Team Valley and A692 Consett' (northern end of the estate). Follow signs to 'Retail World'. At roundabout with petrol station on right, turn right into Dukes Way. Shop is in silver coloured building 400 yds on right.

Open: Mon–Fri 9.30–1.30.
Closed: Bank Holidays; last week July and first week August; Christmas–New Year.
Cards: None.
Cars: Outside shop.
Toilets: No.
Wheelchairs: Two small steps.
Teas: In Texas and Queensway in Retail World.
Tours: No.
Transport: Bus no. 915 from Newcastle; no. 83 from Gateshead.

27 Hartlepool Cleveland

Jackson's Landing

Hartlepool Marina TS24 0XM
(01429) 866989

A factory outlet mall for well known designer label fashions and household goods.

'Significant reductions on quality brand names.'

In dock area north of town centre.

From A179 southbound: follow signs for town centre/ Hartlepool Marina. Jackson's Landing on left as you pass docks.

From A689 northbound: go through town, following signs to Hartlepool Marina. Go over railway: Jackson's Landing is on right.

Open: Mon–Sat 10–6; Sun 11–5.
Closed: Christmas Day.
Cards: Major credit/debit cards.
Cars: Free parking for 250 cars and 10 coaches.
Toilets: Yes, and for disabled.
Wheelchairs: Automatic doors; lifts; wheelchairs available.
Teas: Catering facilities on site.
Groups: Shopping groups always welcome.
Transport: Hartlepool train station 10 minutes' walk.

Royal Quays

28 Hexham (Allendale) Northumberland

Hadrian Crystal

Allendale
(01434) 683541 Fax (01434) 683294

Wide range of crystal giftware (collectables, figurines, paperweights, souvenirs) plus cookware, tableware, glasses, brassware and pewter.

'Most items at ex-factory prices or less.'

See our display advertisement opposite

About 10 miles south-west of Hexham.

From Hexham (west side of town): follow signs to Allendale (B6305). Go left on to B6295 to Allendale.*

From Carlisle via A69(T): go right on to A686 for Alston. After Langley Castle take B6295 to Allendale.*

****At end of Catton village, road forks: stay on B6295. Factory is 100 yds on right.***

From Allendale town: go towards Hexham. Immediately before you enter Catton go left on to B6295; shop 100 yds down on right.

Open: Mon–Thur 9–4.30; Fri 9–3.15; Sat, Sun & Bank Holidays 10–4.
Closed: Christmas Eve–2 January.
Cards: MasterCard, Visa.
Cars: Large free car-park.
Toilets: In Allendale.
Wheelchairs: Ramp available.
Teas: In Allendale.
Groups: Groups and coaches welcome.
Transport: Very limited.
Mail order: Yes. Mail order and free newsletter through Collectors' Club. Free membership at shop.

29 Ingleton N Yorks

Daleswear Factory Shop

High Street LA6 3AD
(015242) 42373

High quality outdoor and leisurewear. Fleece jackets and pullovers, lined and unlined, jumpers, pants, salopettes and accessories. Fleece jackets, pullovers, jumpers and pants for children. Extended *Polartec* range of fleeces. Extended waterproof range including more two and three-layer *Porelle* (formerly *Aquatex*) jackets, also overtrousers and salopettes. *Kingsdale* caving oversuits and undersuits, *Gold Flash* tackle, *SRT* bags etc. *Altberg* boots at factory prices.

'Mostly firsts, competing in standard and design with market leaders, at much lower prices. Also prototypes, clearance, seconds and bargain lines.'

Ingleton Village is on A65, 28 miles north-west of Skipton and 6 miles south-east of Kirkby Lonsdale.

Follow one-way system up through village centre. The High Street is up from the square: shop is next to Wheatsheaf pub.

NB Factory Shop may move to Laundry Lane at edge of village, with own car-park.

Open: Mon–Sat 9–5 (including Bank Holidays); Sun 9.30–5.
Closed: Christmas, Boxing and New Year's Days.
Cards: MasterCard, Switch, Visa.
Cars: Limited High Street parking; main parking at Community Centre.
Toilets: Ask if desperate.
Wheelchairs: Three steps; large shop.
Changing rooms: Yes.
Teas: In Ingleton.
Groups: Shopping groups welcome; group factory tours by arrangement.
Transport: None.
Mail order: Anything sold in shop supplied by mail order.
Catalogue: Free. New designs are constantly being produced, so current catalogue does not always reflect complete range.

See our entry opposite

30 Jarrow Tyne & Wear

J Barbour & Sons

Monksway, Bede Industrial Estate NE34 2HF
(0191) 428 4707

Oiled cotton jackets, trousers, moleskin shirts and trousers, warm pile linings, corduroy trousers, sweaters, shirts, hats, bags, quilted jackets, waistcoats etc.

'All items are factory seconds and discontinued lines.'

Next to Bede Metro station and ½ mile from south entrance of Tyne Tunnel.

From roundabout at south entrance of tunnel: take A185 dual carriageway towards South Shields; after about 600 yds take first right (soon after dual carriageway ends). Turn left at T-junction, then take first right and right again before second factory. Shop is at the end of this building.

Open: Mon–Thur 10–5; Fri 10–4; Sat 9–1.
Closed: Bank Holidays; Christmas–New Year period. Please phone for exact dates.
Cards: All major credit cards.
Cars: Own car-park.
Toilets: No.
Wheelchairs: Easy access, no steps.
Changing rooms: No.
Teas: Two pubs nearby; teas in Jarrow.
Groups: Coach parties welcome to shop; please contact Mr Heads, mentioning this guide.
Transport: Next to Bede metro station.
Mail order: No.
Catalogue: Free.

31 Kendal Cumbria *see map opposite*

Briggs & Shoe Mines

Sandes Avenue LA9 4SG
(01539) 721335

Over 10,000 sq ft sales area with 100,000 pairs of boots and shoes for all the family. Wide range of sports and walking footwear. Handbags, socks, accessories etc.

'Half of shop sells reduced-price major branded, sub-standard and clearance lines, including K Shoes direct from K factories in Kendal. 60 major international brands at regular price. Measurement and fitting by qualified staff.'

See our display advertisement opposite

Within the town centre.

Sandes Avenue is the northern link in the busy one-way system round town. From the A6 (Stricklandgate), the main road which goes from south to north through Kendal: turn right for Penrith. This large conspicuous shop is on right, 25 yds from corner.

Open: *Summer*: Mon–Sat 9–7; Sun 11–5. *Winter (Nov–Easter)*: Mon–Sat 9–5.30; Sun 11–5. Bank Holidays 9.30–5.30.
Closed: Easter Sun, Xmas Day.
Cards: Amex, Connect, MasterCard, Switch, Visa.
Cars: Own car-park; multi-storey behind shop (car-park ticket gives reductions on footwear). Free coach park 120 yds away (with bus washing!).
Toilets: Yes.
Wheelchairs: Easy access to huge shop.
Teas: Café next door, many cafés in town centre.
Groups: Coaches welcome – mention this guide. Parties receive £2 voucher per person towards purchases.
Transport: 150 yds from train station; Kendal mini link buses.
Mail order: Yes. Pleased to supply items in stock if customers know size, fitting and style. Ask for manager.

32 Kendal Cumbria *see map opposite*

James Cropper

Burneside Mills LA9 6PZ
(01539) 722002

Manufacturers of wide variety of different papers and boards in a multitude of colours.

Burneside is a village about 2 miles north of Kendal.

From Kendal and south on A591: go to end of Kendal bypass, pass sign 'Lake District National Park' (engraved on a stone); take first right, signposted Burneside.*

From Staveley and north on A591: pass crossing with sign to Burneside to left and Crook to right; after end of dual-carriage section, turn left for Burneside.*

****At T-junction go left: follow signs to James Cropper Mill Shop.***

Open: Mon–Fri 10–4; Sat 9–1.
Closed: Bank Holidays; Christmas–New Year.
Cards: No.
Cars: Own car-park.
Toilets: No.
Wheelchairs: Five steps to medium shop.
Teas: In Kendal.
Groups: Groups welcome, please phone in advance.
Transport: Bus no. 45 from Kendal to Burneside.
Mail order: No.

See our entries nos. F48, F79, J4, J99, and opposite

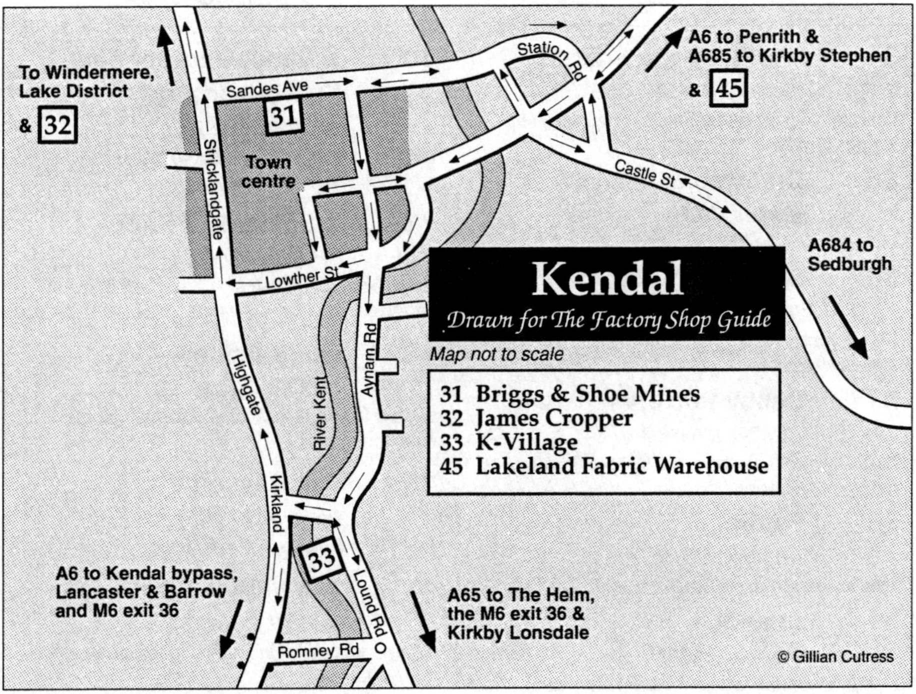

Kendal

Drawn for The Factory Shop Guide

Map not to scale

31 Briggs & Shoe Mines
32 James Cropper
33 K-Village
45 Lakeland Fabric Warehouse

To Windermere, Lake District & 32
A6 to Penrith & A685 to Kirkby Stephen & 45
A684 to Sedburgh
A6 to Kendal bypass, Lancaster & Barrow and M6 exit 36
A65 to The Helm, the M6 exit 36 & Kirkby Lonsdale
Sandes Ave
Station Rd
Castle St
Stricklandgate
Town centre
Lowther St
Highgate
Aynam Rd
River Kent
Kirkland
Lound Rd
Romney Rd
31
33

© Gillian Cutress

33 Kendal Cumbria *see map on previous page*

K Village

Netherfield LA9 7DA
(01539) 734347

Undercover mall with factory shop units operated by *Laura Ashley, Jumper, Crabtree & Evelyn, Dartington Crystal, Denby Pottery, K Shoes Full Price Shop, K Shoes Factory Shop, The Sports Factory, The Baggage Factory* and *The Village Gift Shop*.

'Shop at your leisure in undercover shopping mall and visit our unique Heritage Centre.'

See our display advertisement opposite

On the A65 on south-east side of town.

From town centre: take A6 south to M6. When you see signs to A65, follow these until you see K Village on right. Entrance at far end of complex.

From south via A65: as you come into Kendal, clearly signposted complex is on the left shortly after you reach river (on left).

From A591(T) northbound (Kendal bypass): take A6 for Kendal; go right at first traffic lights signposted K Village. Take first left after bridge then first left into car-park. (This is quickest way from M6 exit 36.)

Open: *Summer*: Mon–Fri 9.30–6 (Thur till 8); Sat 9–6; Sun 11–5; Bank Holidays 9–6.
Winter: Mon–Fri 9.30–5.30.
Closed: Christmas Day.
Cards: Access, Switch, Visa.
Cars: Large free car and coach park outside shop; spaces for disabled drivers.
Toilets: Yes, including for disabled; baby changing facilities.
Wheelchairs: Most entrances and exits have ramps for wheelchairs; shopping aisles are wide enough for easy access.
Teas: *The Food Factory* restaurant; *Upper Crust* sandwich bar.
Groups: Coaches welcome: concessions for drivers/organisers. £1 voucher per passenger to purchases in K Shoes Factory Shop. Play area for children.
Transport: Ten minutes' walk from town; bus route 41/41A.
Mail order: No.

34 The Baggage Factory
(01539) 721892
Luggage, designer handbags, briefcases and leather goods.

35 Crabtree & Evelyn
(01539) 735595
Luxury foods, toiletries, fragrances, gift baskets.

36 Dartington Crystal
(01539) 734263
Clear crystal wine glasses, bowls etc. Decorative table accessories.

37 Denby Pottery
(01539) 735418
Earthenware tableware, dishes, bowls, jugs, mugs & cookware.

38 Farah
(01539) 727129
Men's wear: trousers, knitwear, shirts & T-shirts.

39 Jumper
(01539) 732482
Knitwear and casual clothing for men and women.

40 K Shoes Factory Shop, Sports Factory
(01539) 721892
Family footwear: shoes, boots, trainers, luggage, sports clothing.

41 K Shoes Full Price
(01539) 724041
Huge selection of latest *K Shoes*. All items at full price.

42 Laura Ashley
(01539) 721392
Ladies' fashions, casual and formal. Home furnishings.

43 Van Heusen
(01539) 732337
Van Heusen shirts and silk ties.

44 The Village Gift Shop
(01539) 721892
Local crafts: porcelain dolls, glass, greenstone, mint cake etc.

See our entry opposite

45 Kendal

see map on previous page

Lakeland Fabric Warehouse

Unit 4 South Lakeland Retail Park LA9 6NZ
(01539) 721552

Large range of upholstery and furnishing fabrics: cottons, linens, damasks, velvets etc. Nets, voiles, calico, interlinings, waddings, linings. Haberdashery, fringing. Curtain rails/poles and accessories. Cushion covers and fillers. Ready-made curtains. Foam cut to shape. Dress fabrics.

'Over 4000 rolls. Curtain-making service.'

See our display advertisement on p. 195

North of Kendal, just off A6.

From north on A6: turn left immediately after Morrison's.*

From one-way system in town centre: follow signs to Penrith A6. Go under railway, pass school playing fields on right, and turn right before Morrison's.*

****Take second turn left into Morrison's car-park (by petrol station), then turn right: shop is on left.***

Open: Seven days a week: Mon–Thur, Sat 9–5.30; Fri 9–8; Sun 11–5.
Bank Holidays 9–5.30.
Closed: Easter Sunday; Christmas Day.
Cards: MasterCard, Switch, Visa (not Amex, Diners, Delta)
Cars: Ample free parking on site.
Toilets: Superstore next door.
Wheelchairs: Easy access; no steps to large shop.
Teas: In superstore next door.
Groups: Shopping groups welcome, no need to book.
Transport: Ten minutes' walk from town centre.
Mail order: No.

Newcastle-upon-Tyne as shown in The Illustrated London News, June 11, 1881

46 Killingworth Tyne & Wear

Textilion

Comet Row
(0191) 268 4637

Now closed

Ladies' fashions, skirts, blouses, dresses, knitwear; children's wear.

"Our products are mainly famous chainstore designs. Firsts and slight seconds at very reasonable prices. Occasional special sales on Saturdays. Please phone for dates.'

In the Stephenson Industrial Estate.

From Newcastle via A189 or A188: turn on to B1505 for Killingworth at roundabout where these three roads meet. Pass under railway bridge and take second left (Blucher Road).*

From Killingworth centre: go downhill, across the lake, then turn right at roundabout and take first right (Blucher Road).*

****Go to end, turn right: shop 50 yds on left, before British Gas.***

Open: Mon–Thur 10–4.15; Fri 10–12.15.
Closed: Bank Holidays; Christmas–New Year.
Cards: None.
Cars: In street.
Toilets: No.
Wheelchairs: One step.
Changing rooms: No.
Teas: Local supermarket.
Groups: Groups of shoppers welcome – prior phone call appreciated.
Transport: Three minutes' walk from town centre.
Mail order: No.

47 Kirkby Stephen Cumbria

Heredities

Hobsons Lane
(017683) 71543

Sculptured cold cast bronze and hand-painted figurines. Dog sculptures in cast stone. Collectable dolls, nautical sculptures.

On the north side of town.

Coming north on A685: go through town centre, go left into Silver Street at sign to Soulby. Take first right; go left into Hobsons Lane in front of Co-op Cumbrian.*

Coming south from Appleby: go right when you see sign 'Advance Factory'. Turn right into Hobsons Lane.*

****Go along Hobsons Lane: pass Glitsch's factory. Shop next on left.***

Open: Mon–Fri 9–5; *also summer* Sat 9.30–2.30. Bank Holidays 9.30–2.30.
Closed: Christmas–New Year.
Cards: MasterCard, Diners, Visa.
Cars: Own car-park.
Toilets: Yes.
Wheelchairs: Easy access.
Teas: In town.
Tours: No factory tours.
Transport: Short walk to town.

48 Lancaster Lancs

The Factory Shop Ltd.

Lancaster Leisure Park, Wyresdale Road LA1 3LB
(01524) 846079

Clothing and footwear for all the family. Toiletries, cosmetics, luggage and bags. Good range of branded bedding and towels. Housewares and kitchenware. Posters and toys. Fashion concessions department with famous brand names. *Cape Country* pine furniture exclusively produced for The Factory Shop.

'Deliveries of new stock every week to give an ever changing selection. Shops and restaurant areas free. Other attractions charged individually: antique centre, animals, children's attractions and train ride. Golf driving range and club house. Indoor children's play area.'

On the east side of town.

From the A6: go into town and follow signs to the Ashton Memorial; turn right when you see sign for Cattle Market. Pass the abattoir and this Leisure Park is on the right.

From the M6: go into the city centre; from here follow signs to Ashton Memorial, pass it and take next left downhill.

Open: Mon–Sat 10–5; Sun 11–5.
Closed: Christmas and Boxing Days.
Cards: Eurocard, MasterCard, Switch, Visa.
Cars: Ample free car and coach parking.
Toilets: On the leisure site.
Wheelchairs: Good access into and around the shop.
Changing rooms: Yes.
Teas: Café and restaurant on leisure site.
Groups: Shopping groups welcome. For organiser/driver incentives please phone.
Transport: Bus no. 253 bus from Lancaster bus station.
Mail order: Home delivery service for pine furniture. Please phone for free catalogue and price list.

49 Lancaster Lancs

Standfast

Caton Road LA1 3PB
No phone in shop.

Seconds in printed fabrics, including many well known designer names for curtains and upholstery (cottons, linens, chintz and sateens). Also sell small pieces suitable for cushions or patchwork.

Nearly a mile north of the town.

From Lancaster: follow signs to M6 (northbound). You go along A683 (Caton Road). Pass the clock-tower on left, then Standfast is 100 yds on left, with name clearly displayed.

From M6 exit 34: follow signs to Lancaster. Company is about a mile on right, after Shell petrol.

Please do NOT park inside main gate (hinders emergency access). Park in car-park across road.

Open: Mon–Fri 9.30–1; Sat 10–12.30
Closed: Bank Holidays; Christmas–New Year.
Cards: None.
Cars: Special car-park across the road.
Toilets: Yes.
Wheelchairs: Five steps into shop. Easier access is available via the warehouse.
Teas: In Lancaster.
Groups: No mill tours.
Transport: None.
Mail order: No.

50 Lindal-in-Furness Cumbria

Colony Country Store

LA12 0LD
(01229) 461102

All kinds of candles: tapers, pillars, decorated, scented, novelty. Many different colours and fragrances. Floral rings, candlesticks, holders, lamps. Textiles, ceramics, placemats, napkins, tablecloths, kitchen accessories (co-ordinating designs/colours). Christmas shop open all year.

'Unrivalled for colour and scent. From 10p–£60 with substantial discounts on firsts and seconds.'

On the A590, 2½ miles south-west of Ulverston on road to Barrow. Look for 'Candle Workshop' signs.

From Ulverston via A590: pass The Anchor on right then go left into London Road, just after pedestrian crossing.*

From Barrow on A590: go through Dalton-in-Furness and pass 'Lindal' sign on left. After 400 yds go right into London Road before the pedestrian crossing.*

****Go over railway bridge. Shop is on left.***

Open: Mon–Sat 9–5; Sun 12–5.
Closed: Christmas, Boxing and New Year's Days.
Cards: Delta, MasterCard, Switch, Visa.
Cars: Parking by factory; space for two coaches.
Toilets: Yes, and for disabled.
Wheelchairs: No steps.
Teas: Chandlers café on site for snacks/full lunch Mon–Sat 10–4.45, Sun 12–4.45.
Tours: See traditional candle-making through shop viewing gallery. Visit grotto where Santa tells fairy tales to animated woodland friends. Groups welcome: prior phone call appreciated.
Transport: Ulverston–Barrow buses each ½ hour.
Mail order: Yes.
Catalogue: Yes.

51 Maryport Cumbria

Grasshopper Babywear

Unit BT200/9ABCD, Solway Industrial Estate CA15 8NE
(01900) 815998

Babywear from 0–2 years. Sleepsuits, pyjamas, rompers, bodysuits, vests, underwear.

'Superior quality, value for money babywear direct to the public at factory prices. Perfects and seconds.'

Just south of the town.

Turn off the A596 (Maryport–Workington road) when you see the sign to Solway Trading Estate. Take the first left: this shop is about 100 yds on the right.

Open: Mon–Thur 10–4.
Closed: Friday. Bank Holidays. Christmas–New Year.
Cards: No.
Cars: Own car-park.
Toilets: Ask if required.
Wheelchairs: Easy access, no steps.
Changing rooms: No.
Teas: In town.
Groups: No factory tours, but shopping groups welcome.
Transport: Bus no. 300 (Carlisle–Whitehaven) a few minutes' walk.
Mail order: No.

52 Maryport Cumbria

New Balance Athletic Shoes (UK)

St Helen's Lane, Flimby CA15 8RY
(01900) 602850

Running shoes, football boots, hiking boots, basketball boots, tennis and squash shoes, cross trainers, fitness shoes, walking shoes, sports clothing, sports bags.

'First quality as well as seconds sold here.'

Off the A596, south of Flimby between Maryport and Workington.

From Maryport: go south through Flimby, turn left after Armstrong Ltd.*

From Workington: go north, pass Ectona and turn before Armstrong Ltd.*

****Take first right and enter New Balance car-park.***

Open: Mon–Fri 9.30–5.30; Sat 9–4. Bank Holidays.
Closed: Christmas, Boxing and New Year's Days.
Cards: Delta, Electron, MasterCard, Switch, Visa.
Cars: Outside shop in factory car-park.
Toilets: In Workington.
Wheelchairs: Easy access to medium-sized shop.
Changing rooms: Yes.
Teas: In Workington.
Groups: Parties welcome to shop; please contact Chris Mintoft, mentioning this book.
Transport: Maryport–Workington buses stop outside.
Mail order: No.
Catalogue: Free.

53 Middlesbrough Cleveland

Baird Outerwear Brands

Southbank Road, Cargo Fleet TS3 8BH
(01642) 247794

Ladies' and men's rainwear and casual wear. Brand names include: *Dannimac, Baracuta, Cloud Nine, Telemac* and *Thomas Marshall.*

'Seconds and discontinued lines.'

On the A175 at the eastern end of Middlesbrough centre.

From A19: take A66 for Middlesbrough and Teesport to roundabout where A171 turns right to Whitby.*

From town centre: take A175 for Redcar. This takes you on to A66 to Teesport to roundabout where A171 go right to Whitby.*

****Turn right here and left at next roundabout on to A175. Then take first right and immediately go right again on to service road. Shop is at end of this road.***

Open: Usually third Saturday of month 9–11, occasionally more often (advertised in local press). Essential to phone first.
Closed: Christmas–New Year.
Cards: MasterCard, Switch, Visa.
Cars: Own car-park.
Toilets: Yes.
Wheelchairs: Easy access to ground floor location.
Changing rooms: Yes.
Teas: In town.
Groups: For coach party visits to the shop, please contact Margaret Bennett first, mentioning this Guide.
Transport: Middlesbrough–Redcar buses go along the main road.
Mail order: No.

54 New York Tyne & Wear

Hobart Rose

Middle Engine Lane NE29 8HG
(0191) 258 2233

Soft furnishings manufacturers: made-to-measure curtains, fabrics, bean bags and cushions etc.

'Seconds, samples, ends of line etc sold here at factory prices. Also at Stakeford Lane, Stakeford, Northumberland.'

On an industrial estate south-west of New York (and north-east of North Shields).

From A19 (formerly A1) north of Tyne tunnel: exit on A1058 for Tynemouth. Take next exit and follow signs to New York Industrial Estate. Turn left after about ½ mile by the Shiremoor Farm restaurant signposted to West Chirton Industrial Estate. Take next left into Alder Road: shop is first on right, clearly signed.

From A191 (Gosforth–Whitley Bay road): turn south on to Norham Road North at roundabout with Vauxhall dealer (Reg Vardy) on near right. Take first right (Middle Engine Lane), then first left (Alder Road): shop is first on right, clearly signed.

Open: Mon–Sat 9.30–4.
Closed: Bank Holidays; Christmas–New Year.
Cards: MasterCard, Visa.
Cars: Outside shop.
Toilets: No.
Wheelchairs: Easy access to medium-sized shop.
Teas: Local pubs and cafés.
Groups: Shopping groups welcome, please phone first.
Transport: Bus nos. X10, X38, 308 from Newcastle (but much easier by car).

55 Newcastle upon Tyne

Palatine Products

Whickham View NE15 6UM
(0191) 241 0170

Wide range of beds in all price ranges: from cheaper firm-top bases to top quality sprung-edge, pocketed sprung bases. Range of mattresses. Three-piece suites. Household furnishing accessories, eg headboards, pillows.

'All items first quality. Genuine manufacturer selling at "unbeatable" trade prices.'

About 2 miles due west of Newcastle city centre.

From western bypass (A1): at large junction with A69 (Carlisle turn-off), take A69/A6115 towards Newcastle. At first roundabout, go right into Denton Road (A191).*

From central Newcastle: take A6115 for Carlisle. After about 2 miles, at roundabout where A696 crosses, go left into Denton Road (A191).*

***At next roundabout go left, Whickham View (B1311). Shop is in huge factory, ½ mile on left.**

Open: Mon, Wed, Sat 9–5; Thur–Fri 9–5.30.
Closed: Please phone about Bank Holidays; Christmas–New Year.
Cards: MasterCard, Visa. Credit facilities.
Cars: Own car-park.
Toilets: No.
Wheelchairs: Ramp to front door.
Teas: Coffee available.
Tours: Groups welcome on free factory tour if arranged in advance – please contact Mike Hughes.
Transport: Bus nos. 30, 31, 38, 38B from outside Odeon in city.

56 North Shields Tyne & Wear

Bargain Baggage Factory Shop

Bugatti House, Norham Road NE29 7HB
(0191) 258 4451

Branded luggage by *Pierre Cardin, Gino Ferrari*; business accessories and attaché cases in quality leather and man-made fibres. Wide range of small leather goods and handbags. Shopping bags, beach bags.

'Perfects, seconds & ends of lines at well below high street prices.'

On the north-east side of North Shields.

From A19 (formerly A1): turn on to A193 for North Shields. At next roundabout go left for Tynemouth (A1058). After 0.4 miles turn left immediately after Bugatti House. Shop 80 yds on left.

On A1058 from Newcastle: cross over A19 and take next exit; turn right at the top and company is ½ mile on right. Turn right immediately before Bugatti House: shop is 80 yds on left.

Open: Tues 10–2; Wed–Fri 10–3. *Also December.* Sat, Sun: phone for details.
Closed: Monday; Christmas–New Year.
Cards: MasterCard, Visa.
Cars: Outside shop.
Toilets: No.
Wheelchairs: Easy access, no steps.
Teas: In North Shields and Tynemouth.
Groups: Shopping groups please write to Christine Quinn to book.
Transport: Percy Main metro station. Buses from Newcastle and Whitley Bay. Bus nos. 42 and 55 from North Shields go past; 305 and 308 coast road buses stop outside Formica factory, then 3 minutes' walk.
Mail order: No.

57 North Shields Tyne & Wear

Midas House Furnishers

Norham Road NE29 8SD
(0191) 257 6997

Manufacturers of a large range of exclusive settees and chairs. Also made to measure. Extensive selection of fabrics and leather. Specially designed chairs created for people with spinal disabilities.

'Always bargains; showroom clearance. 12 months' interest free credit. Prices from £799 for full three-piece suite; up to £1200 for leather.'

On the north-east side of North Shields.

From the A19 (formerly A1) north of Tyne tunnel: exit on to A1058 for Tynemouth. Take next exit: follow signs to New York Industrial Estate. Shop is 500 yds on left, set back from road.

From A191 (Gosforth–Whitley Bay road): turn south into North Norham Road at the roundabout with Vauxhall dealer (Reg Vardy) on near right. Shop is ½ mile on the right, set back from road.

Open: Mon–Sat 10–4; Sun 12–4. Bank Holidays.
Closed: Christmas Day.
Cards: No.
Cars: Outside shop.
Toilets: Yes.
Wheelchairs: Two steps; easy access to large shop.
Teas: In North Shields.
Groups: No factory tours.
Transport: Percy Main metro station. Buses for Newcastle and Whitley Bay. Bus nos. 42 and 55 from North Shields go past; 305 and 308 coast road buses stop outside Formica factory, then 8 minutes' walk.
Mail order: Yes.

See our entries on next two pages

58 North Shields Tyne & Wear

Royal Quays Outlet Shopping Centre

Coble Dene, NE29 6DW
(0191) 296 3743

Over 40 individual shops selling top brand names and designer labels, many at half recommended retail price. Tourism information and bureau de change, including ATM facilities, available from Thomas Cook (0191 200 5895).

'At Royal Quays you can take advantage of retailers' end of season lines, manufacturing overruns and excess stocks at real bargain prices.'

See our display advertisement on previous page

By North Shields International ferry terminal.

From the roundabout at the north entrance of the Tyne tunnel (A19) exit for A187 to North Shields and follow signs to the ferry terminal. Keep following signs to the ferry terminal: the shopping centre is on the right as you go down towards the ferry terminal, and opposite 'Wet and Wild' water park.

Open: Mon–Thur 10–6; Fri 10–8.30; Sat 9–6; Sun 11–5.
Closed: Please phone for details on Bank Holidays and late night shopping.
Cards: All major cards.
Cars: Parking for 740 cars; 12 coaches and ranks for motorcycles and bicycles.
Toilets: Yes, including facilities for disabled.
Wheelchairs: Easy accessbility to all outlets.
Teas: Two restaurants on site.
Groups: Groups welcome.
Transport: Regular bus and metro links to North Shields and Newcastle.

59 August Silk Excess
(0191) 258 7844
Ladies' designer wear in a range of pure silks.

60 Beautiful Homes
(0191) 257 8001
Lighting, mirrors, prints, picture frames, vases and floral decorations.

Closed **Big Star Jeans**
(0191) 257 4582
Jeans and casual wear for all the family.

62 The Book Depot
(0191) 296 0178
Best sellers & children's books. Stationery, CD's.

63 Broughton's Footwear
(0191) 258 6556
Ladies' and men's footwear.

64 Card & Gift Factory Outlet
(0191) 257 4767
Greeting cards, wrapping paper, mugs, soft toys, party fillers.

65 The Chain Store
(0191) 258 5004
Men's, ladies' and children's clothing.

66 Ciro Citterio
(0191) 257 4420
Men's suits, jackets, leather jackets, trousers, shirts, shoes.

67 Charisma Leather
(0191) 257 6050
Leather jackets and caps for men and women. Handbags.

68 Diamonds Direct
(0191) 259 2229
Jewellery manufacturer and designer.

69 Direct Design
(0191) 257 4002
Casual fashions for ladies.

70 Discount Clothing Store
(0191) 296 2911
Ex-chainstore ladies' and children's clothing.

71 Easy Jeans
(0191) 296 4081
Jeans, accessories and casual wear for men, women and youths.

72 Fieldcrest Cannon
(0191) 257 3187
American towels, bedding, household linens.

73 Gleneagles Crystal
(0191) 257 4527
Hand-cut crystal: wine glasses, decanters, bowls, vases etc.

74 Honey
(0191) 257 4344
From high fashion to classics for women of all ages. Up to size 22.

75 James Barry
(0191) 296 4821
Quality men's suits, jackets, trousers, accessories.

76 Jane Shilton
(0191) 257 3672
Handbags, luggage, scarves, small leather goods, shoes and accessories.

77 Joe Bloggs
(0191) 296 1999
High fashion casual wear for men, women and children.

78 John Jenkins
(0191) 258 3581
Crystalware, porcelain tableware, ceramics and giftware.

79 Leading Labels
(0191) 296 3862
Designer and high street ladies' & men's wear.

80 Lee Jeans
(0191) 257 3606
Denim jeans, sweatshirts, T-shirts for the family.

81 Luggage and Bags – The Outlet Store
(0191) 257 4458
Luggage, executive cases, bags, leather goods, wallets, purses.

82 Mexx
(0191) 257 5001
Formal & casual wear for men, women, children.

83 Mondian
(0191) 257 2736
Ceramics and giftware including candles and basketware.

84 Mountain Outlet
(0191) 258 6141
Leisurewear, mountaineering clothes and equipment.

85 Pavers Branded Shoes
(0191) 296 4915
Branded footwear.

86 Pilot
(0191) 296 4745
Women's wear – high fashion, casuals and smart classics.

87 Ponden Mill
(0191) 257 4607
Household linens, towels, sheets, duvets, kitchen co-ordinates.

88 Remington
(0191) 258 3622
Small electricals, cutlery, scissors, kitchen knives and gadgets.

89 Sports Unlimited
(0191) 257 3568
Sports and leisurewear.

90 The Suit Company
(0191) 257 5272
Own brand and famous name men's wear.

91 Suits You
(0191) 296 2995
Famous name men's wear: suits, shirts, ties, trousers, jackets etc.

92 Thornton's
(0191) 258 0623
Quality confectionery: toffees, chocolates, seasonal lines.

93 Tog 24
(0191) 258 3754
Weatherproof outdoor wear, fleeces, walking and casual wear.

94 Tom Sayers
(0191) 257 3369
Men's designer wear, trousers, jackets, knitwear, shirts.

95 Toyworld
(0191) 257 3333
Major branded toys for all ages.

96 Warner's Lingerie
(0191) 259 6800
US manufacturer of ladies' classic and designer lingerie.

Sunderland Glass

The opening of the new National Glass Centre in Sunderland in 1998 marks a milestone in the history of British glass and has no comparison anywhere in the world. It is a unique amalgamation of an exhibition gallery, artists' studios, glass factory units, shop and restaurant. It is housed within a spectacular award winning glass building on the banks of the river Wear in Sunderland. 'Glass UK', the first exhibition, looks at the extraordinary evolution in glass-making techniques and styles over the last 30 years. It includes over 130 studio pieces made in Britain, with loans from museums, private collections and artists. Lest readers think that we have strayed from the topic of shopping, we should point out that the new centre has a large shop which is a showcase for the best in British glass and glass makers, selling a huge range of products from marbles to masterpieces. Customers can commission one-off pieces and corporate gifts, and a bridal registry and overseas sales facility are included. Promotions will include 'maker of the month' and items by artists working within the centre.

National Glass Centre,
Liberty Way, Sunderland
SR6 0GL
(0191) 515 5555
Seven days a week

Sunderland has long been associated with the glass industry. The first time that stained glass was made in Britain was over 1300 years ago: in 674, when craftsmen were brought across from France to make the windows for the St Peter's church in Monkwearmouth. However it was not until the 12th century that glass-making became firmly established in England. The Sunderland glass industry has waxed and waned over the hundreds of years since then, but the town is now British home to one of the largest glass companies in the world (who make clear glass saucepans and lids, amongst other things) and has also attracted individual craftspeople who have established studios and revitalised the industry.

Contact the tourist office about tours round glass makers working on an industrial scale and individually. You can visit Phoenix Hot Glass who make unique studio glass, the newly formed company of D Jobling Glassware (an earlier company of Joblings created glass after the style of Lalique in the 1930s) and other places of interest. Hartley Wood, a former local company with a stunning international reputation, made fine stained glass for the House of Commons, Durham Cathedral and the Hard Rock Café in Dallas etc but, sadly, has recently ceased to exist as such.

Get the leaflet about the Sunderland Glass Tourist Trail, and information on tours, from:
Sunderland Tourist Information
50 Fawcett Street
(0191) 553 2000

97 North Shields Tyne & Wear

Textilion

Norham Road North NE29 8RY
(0191) 257 0181

Ladies' fashions, skirts, blouses, dresses, knitwear; children's wear.

'Our products are mainly famous chainstore designs. Firsts and slight seconds at very reasonable prices.'

From A19 (formerly A1) north of Tyne tunnel: exit on A1058 for Tynemouth. Take next exit and follow signs to New York Industrial Estate. Shop is about 500 yds on left, set back from road.

From A191 (Gosforth–Whitley Bay road): turn south on to Norham Road North at roundabout with Vauxhall dealer (Reg Vardy) on near right. Shop is about ½ mile on right, set back from road.

Open: Mon–Sat 10–4.
Closed: Christmas–New Year.
Cards: None.
Cars: Park in front of factory.
Toilets: No.
Wheelchairs: 4 steps.
Changing rooms: No.
Teas: In North Shields.
Groups: Groups of shoppers welcome – prior phone call appreciated.
Transport: Bus nos. 42 & 55 from North Shields stop outside; 305 & 308 coast road buses stop outside Formica factory, then 8 minutes' walk.
Mail order: No.

98 Otterburn Northumberland

Otterburn Mill

(01830) 520225

Wide selection of woollen fabrics and tweeds in imaginative colours. Top quality skirts and co-ordinating knitwear. Men's jackets, trousers, hats, ties. Travel rugs.

Short distance south of Otterburn, clearly signposted on B6320.

Going north via the A696 from Newcastle: turn left on to B6320 as you enter town; follow signs to mill on right.

Going south from Jedburgh on A696: go through town; turn right after Otterburn Tower Hotel (on left); follow signs to mill.

Open: *All year:* Mon–Fri 9–5. *Also May–Christmas:* Sat 9–5. Bank Holidays.
Closed: Phone for Christmas and Bank Holidays.
Cards: MasterCard, Visa.
Cars: Large car-park.
Toilets: Yes.
Wheelchairs: Large ground-floor shop.
Changing rooms: Yes.
Teas: Own café. Also in village.
Groups: Shopping groups please phone first.
Transport: No.

99 Penrith Cumbria

Briggs & Shoe Mines

Southend Road CA11 8JH
(01768) 899001

Wide range of shoes for all the family. Self selection, with expert help and advice available. Small range of clothing and sports apparel, accessories, socks etc.

'3,000 sq ft of sales area for family footwear by famous makers, at regular, clearance or sub-standard prices.'

See our display advertisement on 651

South of the town centre.

From the town centre: take the A6 for Kendal and turn right opposite Shell petrol (signpost to 'Swimming Baths'), then follow signs to car-park. Shop is adjacent to car-park.

From M6 exit 40: take A66 east; go left at roundabout on to A6 for Penrith. Turn left opposite Shell petrol: follow signs to car-park.

Open: Mon–Sat 9.30–5.30; Bank Holidays 9.30–5.30.
Closed: Christmas Day.
Cards: Amex, Connect, MasterCard, Switch, Visa.
Cars: By shop or in adjacent car-park.
Toilets: In car-park.
Wheelchairs: Difficult access as 5 steps to main shop floor.
Changing rooms: No.
Teas: In town.
Groups: Shoppers welcome. £2 reduction per member of a coach party on purchase.
Transport: Buses pass by.
Mail order: Pleased to supply by mail order items in stock if customers know size, fitting and style. Ask for manager.

Our favourite travel writer, Mr Harper, sketched 'The entrance to Durham' in 1901. If only traffic were so light *these* days …

100 Peterlee Co. Durham

Claremont Garments

2 Doxford Drive, South West Industrial Estate SR8 2RL
(0191) 518 3026

Ladies' wear: lingerie, swimwear, casual wear (bodies, leggings etc), dresses, blouses, skirts, trousers, and tailored suits, coats and jackets. Schoolwear: boys' trousers and shirts; girls' skirts and shirts. Boys' wear: a limited range of casual shirts and trousers.

'All garments are leading chainstore perfects, seconds or ends of lines, and are offered at greatly reduced prices.'

See our display advertisement on p. 539

In large industrial estate west of the A19.

From A19 exit for 'Peterlee/Horden' B1320. Follow signs to South West Industrial Estate into Shotton Road; at next roundabout (Barclays Bank on far right corner) go left and next left again. The shop is in second building on left.

Open: Mon–Fri 10–4.30; Sat 10–4. Good Friday.
Closed: All Bank Holidays except Good Friday. Christmas to be arranged, please phone.
Cards: Most major credit cards.
Cars: Own car-park.
Toilets: No; in town centre.
Wheelchairs: Ramp; easy access.
Changing rooms: Yes.
Teas: In town centre.
Groups: Shopping groups welcome, but large groups please phone first.
Transport: Bus to Peterlee town centre.
Mail order: No.

101 Redcar (Dormanstown) Cleveland

Dewhirst

Junction of West Coatham Lane & Limerick Road TS10 5QC
(01642) 472391/2

Men's quality suits, sports jackets and blazers, trousers, shirts, coats. Ladies' blouses, skirts, trousers, dresses, suits, jackets etc. Children's clothing and schoolwear.

'Products are high quality famous chainstore slight seconds.'

West of Redcar, close to ICI Wilton works and British Steel.

From Middlesbrough or Redcar on the trunk road A1085: at roundabout, turn towards Dormanstown Industrial Estate where signed. Dewhirst is first factory on left (Limerick Road).

From Middlesbrough on A66: go towards Redcar – come on to A1085. At roundabout, go towards Dormanstown Industrial Estate as signed. Dewhirst is first factory on left (Limerick Rd).

Open: Mon–Fri 9–5.30; Sat 9–5; Sun 10.30–4.30. Bank Holidays.
Closed: Good Friday; Easter Sunday; Christmas, Boxing and New Year's Days.
Cards: Connect, MasterCard, Switch, Visa.
Cars: Own car-park.
Toilets: No.
Wheelchairs: One small step.
Changing rooms: Yes.
Teas: No.
Groups: No factory tours, but groups of shoppers always welcome (prior phone call appreciated).
Transport: Cleveland Transit and United operate Redcar–Middlesbrough buses via Dormanstown.
Mail order: No.

102 Sedbergh Cumbria

Farfield Clothing

Farfield Mill LA10 5LW
(015396) 20169 Fax (015396) 21716

Soft warm quality British polar fleece jackets and jumpers in a paintbox range of colours and styles for all ages. Children's wear from own *Tough Customer* collection and own *Original* fibre pile jackets and jerkins.

'A real factory shop selling own brands. Firsts and seconds. At least 25% reduction over the whole range. Example: seconds of polar fleece adult jackets and jumpers from £19.99.'

About 1 mile south-east of Sedbergh.

From Sedbergh: follow signs to Hawes (A684). This shop, clearly signed, is on the left. Go along the drive to the mill.

From Hawes along the A684: pass the Frostow Methodist Chapel on the left, and the mill is just over ½ mile on the right. Go slowly as you have to turn quite sharply into the drive.

Open: Mon–Fri 9–5.
Closed: Most Bank Holidays, please phone to check first.
Cards: MasterCard, Visa.
Cars: In the mill yard.
Toilets: Yes.
Wheelchairs: No steps, easy access.
Changing rooms: No, but welcome to try things on.
Teas: Posthorn café in Sedbergh, 1 mile away.
Tours: For free group visits to mill or shop please book with Mrs Jean Pearson. Maximum 10.
Transport: Bus Kendal–Sedbergh town; Settle–Carlisle train to Garsdale station 6 miles.
Mail order: Yes.
Catalogue: Free. Please phone for details on *Farfield* and *Tough Customer* clothing.

103 Shildon Co. Durham

Durham Clothing Co.

Dabble Duck Industrial Estate DL4 2QK
(01388) 777226

Men's suits, tweed jackets, trousers and blazers; dinner suits, shirts, accessories. Ladies' jackets, trousers, skirts, blouses and knitwear. Alteration service (free at time of purchase).

'First quality goods at factory prices.'

On the south side of Shildon.

From A1(M): take A68 then A6072, following signs to Shildon. As you approach Shildon, go left at first roundabout, right at second roundabout, and right again at next roundabout.*

From Bishop Auckland on A6072: cross first roundabout, go left at second roundabout and right at next roundabout.*

****Take first left on to Dabble Duck Industrial Estate: factory is second on left.***

Open: Please phone first. Mon–Sat 10–3.
Closed: Some Bank Holidays (please phone to check). Christmas Day.
Cards: Delta, MasterCard, Switch, Visa.
Cars: Own parking.
Toilets: Yes.
Wheelchairs: Stairs to medium sized shop on first floor.
Changing rooms: Yes.
Teas: In Shildon.
Groups: No.
Transport: Local buses stop 100 yds away; 5 minutes' walk from station.
Mail order: No.

Market days

Alnwick	Sat outdoor general
Ashington	Sat outdoor general
Barrow-in-Furness	Wed, Fri, Sat outdoor/indoor general
Berwick-upon-Tweed	Wed, Sat outdoor general
Bishop Auckland	Thur, Sat outdoor general
Blyth	Tues, Fri, Sat outdoor general
Carlisle	Mon–Sat indoor general
Chester-le-Street	Tues, Fri outdoor general
Cleator Moor	Fri outdoor general
Consett	Fri, Sat outdoor general
Cramlington	Thur outdoor general
Crook	Tues, Sat outdoor general
Darlington	Mon, Sat outdoor general
Egremont	Fri outdoor general
Gateshead	Mon–Sat indoor general
Guisborough	Thur, Sat outdoor general
Hartlepool	Thur outdoor general
Hexham	Tues outdoor general
Kendal	Wed, Sat outdoor general Mon–Sat indoor general
Keswick	Sat outdoor fish and fruit
Kirby Lonsdale	Thur outdoor general
Lancaster	Mon–Sat indoor general Thur, Fri, Sat bric-à-brac/antiques Wed, Sat outdoor fresh produce
Maryport	Fri outdoor general
Middlesbrough	Mon, Thur, Fri outdoor general Mon–Sat indoor general
Morpeth	Wed outdoor general
Newcastle upon Tyne	Tues, Thur, Sat outdoor general at Bigg Market Mon–Sat indoor general at Grainger Market Mon–Sat indoor general at Green Market Sun outdoor general at Quayside Market
Northallerton	Wed, Sat outdoor general
North Shields	Mon–Sat indoor general
Peterlee	Thur am outdoor flea market
Penrith	Tues outdoor general
Redcar	Wed outdoor general
Sedbergh	Wed outdoor general
Shildon	Fri outdoor general
South Shields	Mon, Sat outdoor general
Spennymoor	Sat outdoor general
Stockton	Wed, Sat outdoor general
Sunderland	Mon–Sat indoor general
Ulverston	Mon, Tues, Thur, Fri indoor general
Whitehaven	Thur, Sat outdoor general
Whitley Bay	Mon–Sun (in summer) indoor general Mon, Wed, Sat, Sun (in winter)
Wigton	Tues outdoor/indoor general
Workington	Wed, Sat outdoor general

104 South Shields Tyne & Wear

Claremont Garments

Rekendyke Industrial Estate, Eldon Street NE33 5BT
(0191) 454 8822

Ladies' wear: lingerie, swimwear, casualwear (bodies, leggings etc), dresses, blouses, skirts, trousers, tailored suits, coats & jackets. Schoolwear: boys' trousers & shirts; girls' skirts & shirts. Boys' wear: a limited range of casual shirts & trousers.

'All garments are leading chainstore perfects, seconds or ends of lines, and are offered at greatly reduced prices.'

See our display advertisement on p. 539

About ½ mile south-west of the town centre.

From South Shields town centre: take any road north towards the river (cranes at the docks); go left for Riverside B1302. At a roundabout where A194 branches left, follow signs to Riverside. Pass Halfords on left, later the Tyne Lodge pub on right: follow road round to left; go right opposite mosque into Eldon Street. Take second right, West Walpole Street.*

From Tyne Tunnel south entrance: follow signs to South Shields. Go under railway bridge immediately after roundabout, go left at second roundabout for Riverside B1302 (still dual carriage). At small roundabout by Tyne Dock pub; go right into South Eldon St. Continue over next crossing, take first left, West Walpole St.*

****Claremont shop is in the third building on the right.***

Open: Mon–Fri 9–4.30; Sat 9.30–2.30.
Closed: Most Bank Holidays, please phone to check.
Cards: Most major credit cards.
Cars: Own car-park.
Toilets: In Frederick Street in town.
Wheelchairs: No steps; easy access.
Changing rooms: Yes.
Teas: In Frederick Street in town.
Groups: Shopping groups welcome, but large groups please phone first.
Transport: Chichester Metro station.
Mail order: No.

105 Stockton-on-Tees Cleveland

Factory Fabric Centre

Unit 2, Mandale Retail Park, Ross Road, Portrack Lane
(01642) 677679

Quality curtain and upholstery fabrics. Curtain lining, tapes, and accessories. Curtain-making service.

'Perfects, seconds and remnants sold at discounted prices.'

Near steel works east of town centre, off the A1046.

From town centre: take A1046 for Hartlepool and the north (A19). At traffic lights with ARCO on far right corner turn left.*

From A66: turn on to A19 north and after bridge over river take first exit and turn left. Go straight at two roundabouts and at next lights with ARCO on near left turn right.*

From A19 southbound: turn on to A1046 Portrack Lane and Haverton Hill, and turn right for Stockton.*

****After 40 yds turn left and shop is on right, clearly signed.***

Open: Mon–Fri 10–5 (Thur 10–7); Sat 9–5; Sun and Bank Holidays 10–4.
Closed: Easter Sunday; Christmas, Boxing and New Year's Days.
Cards: Amex, MasterCard, Switch, Visa.
Cars: Own car-park.
Toilets: No.
Wheelchairs: Easy access to large shop.
Teas: In town.
Groups: Groups welcome, prior phone call appreciated.
Transport: Local buses from Stockton centre to Portrack.
Mail order: Fabrics can be despatched by post or carrier.

106 Stockton-on-Tees Cleveland

Wynsors World of Shoes

Parkfield Road, off Bridge Road TS18 3DJ
(01642) 672525

Men's, ladies' and girls' leather and synthetic fashion shoes, bags and sundries from all over the world, including many famous names.

'Special monthly offers with at least 50% reductions. Major sales in January and July.'

See our display advertisement on p. 423

On south side of town centre, in new small retail park.

From A19 going north or south: go on to A66 for Darlington.*

****From Darlington or Middlesbrough on A66: exit for A135 for Stockton west and Yarm. At end of slip road follow signs to Stockton. At T-junction with lights go right, pass the Lord's Tavern on left; at small roundabout fork right and at second roundabout turn right into Parkfield Road.*****

On foot from town: with WH Smith on left, go along Bridge Street. Cross over roundabout into Parkfield Road.**

*****Take second left into retail estate. Shop first on left.***

Open: Mon–Wed 9–5.30; Thur–Fri 9–8.00; Sat 9–5.30; Sun 10–4. Bank Holidays.
Closed: Christmas, Boxing and New Year's Days.
Cards: Access, Style, Switch, Visa.
Cars: Own large car-park.
Toilets: No.
Wheelchairs: Easy access.
Teas: Lots of places in Stockton High Street.
Groups: Shopping groups welcome. Prior phone call appreciated.
Transport: Any bus or train to Stockton.
Mail order: No.

Memories of the Past

Beamish Open Air Museum vividly illustrates life in the north of England in the 19th and early 20th centuries. 'The Town' shows a typical street of the early 1900s, with houses, a solicitor's office, dentist's surgery, newspaper office, sweet shop, garage, public house and Co-op shops. If you need a break from factory shopping, see how it used to be.

Old electric tramcars ferry visitors around. A railway passenger station has also been rebuilt, with signal box and goods shed, and a selection of locomotives and rolling stock.

Of great industrial interest (although some may find it ironic to be celebrating an industry which, so recently, has left them redundant...) is a complete North Eastern Colliery Village, recreated as in 1913. A colliery winding engine house has been rebuilt, and a complete pit head recreated with coal wagons, screens etc. The terrace of rebuilt and furnished pitmen's cottages, village school and Wesleyan Methodist chapel are open to visitors. Visitors are taken on underground guided tours of the drift mine.

In 'The Home Farm' you can see traditional breeds of livestock and poultry, a 'farmer's wife' going about her chores, and a large collection of agricultural implements.

Most recently opened is Pockerley Manor, based on a small medieval fortified manor house with stone and pantile horse yard.

Many objects await use in an appropriate setting; a reference library and photographic archive of 300,000 negatives documenting regional history are available to researchers.

(01207) 231811 Open all year but restricted in winter.

107 Sunderland Tyne & Wear

Shaw of London (Furniture)

Deptford Terrace SR4 6DD
(0191) 564 2000

High quality dining room furniture, lounge suites and occasional furniture in classical and reproduction style in various timbers. Also make up furniture to customers' requirements.

'Perfects at factory prices, ends of lines, prototypes and seconds. Individuals can see their furniture being made.'

Off the A1231 north-west of town centre.

From town centre: follow signs to Queen Alexandra Bridge and Newcastle via A1231. Pass large Cowie Ford garage on Trimdon Street. At second roundabout, in front of Queen Alexandra Bridge, go right following signs to Deptford.*

From A19: take A1231 to Sunderland following town centre route. Go south over River Wear on large Queen Alexandra Bridge; immediately after the bridge turn left signposted Deptford.*

***Factory is ½ mile on left, set back in own grounds.**

Open: Mon–Sat 10–5.
Closed: Please check for Christmas, New Year, Easter and Bank Holiday openings.
Cards: MasterCard, Visa.
Cars: Own car-park.
Toilets: Ask if required.
Wheelchairs: Unfortunately no access.
Teas: Good quality vending machine on premises for hot and cold drinks.
Groups: Tours by appointment; small shopping groups welcome anytime, larger groups please phone first.
Transport: Difficult.
Mail order: No.

108 Sunderland Tyne & Wear

Sunelm Products Sheltered Workshops

Leechmere Industrial Estate SR2 9T0
(0191) 521 1721

Beds and mattresses in all standard sizes. Occasional furniture including coffee tables and nests of tables. Pine bedroom furniture.

'Seconds and ends of lines always available.'

At the back of Asda.

From A1(M): take A183 or A690 for Sunderland, cross A19(T), turn right at signs for Grangetown. At roundabout with signs to 'Leechmere Industrial Estate EAST' fork right and take next left.*

From Teeside on A19: turn on to A1018 for Sunderland. Go through to Ryhope; go left at first roundabout, straight over next roundabout, then first right.*

From Sunderland centre: take A1018 south. When dual-carriage section ends, pass Fina petrol on left and turn right at second roundabout, then first right.*

***In industrial estate go first left then first right. Car-park is immediately on left.**

Open: Mon–Thur 9–4; Fri 9–3.
Closed: Bank Holidays; Christmas–New Year.
Cards: Yes.
Cars: Own car-park.
Toilets: No.
Wheelchairs: Easy access.
Teas: In Sunderland.
Groups: Groups please telephone sales office first.
Transport: Buses from Sunderland to Asda.

Carry out an MOT (Mattress Obsolescence Test)

Poor posture is the cause of many back problems; yet how many people consider their posture when they are lying down? We spend about a third of our lives in bed and while we are asleep we have no control over our muscles and ligaments which can relax completely, leaving the bed to support our bodies.

When you lie on your side, your spine should be straight; when on your back, it should retain its natural 'S' curve. But the bed should also have top layers which mould to the contours of your body for evenly distributed support.

Do the bed test! Lie on the bed on your back, slip your hand (palm down) between the mattress and the small of your back. If you can do this easily, and there is a gap, your mattress is harder than you need. If that is difficult, and it is an effort to turn from side to side, then the bed is probably too soft.

If you are wondering whether to buy a new bed because a back problem has developed, consider your existing bed. Is it more than 8–10 years old? Is the mattress or base sagging or lumpy? Has the mattress gone floppy? Can you feel the springs easily? All these are signs that your bed is past its best and that you need a new one.

Mattresses and bases are designed to work as a unit. Always try out a mattress with the correct base. A solid base is firmest. A sprung base prolongs the life of the mattress as it absorbs some of the wear and tear. Bases with flexible slats are quite firm but have a degree of bounce. If you buy a mattress on its own, make sure it is suitable for your own base, especially if it is slatted. Putting a mattress together with a base not designed for it could invalidate your guarantee.

The term 'orthopaedic' bed (along with a variety of derivative brand names) is used to describe beds which are firmer than normal. But there is no standard specification: manufacturers make their own permutation (usually the firmest bed in their range), through a varying combination of springs, filling materials and base construction. It is therefore vital to look at several kinds. Firmness is a very individual assessment, dependent on your weight and build, size and age, the way you sleep, the sort of aches and pains you might have, or just personal perception.

With thanks to bed manufacturer Beevers of Whitby.

109 Ulverston Cumbria

Cumbria Crystal

Lightburn Road LA12 0DB
(01229) 584400

Hand-made full lead crystal decanters, glasses, bowls, vases, jugs and many other gift items, cut and plain. Also crystal paperweights and glass novelties. Engraving to order.

'Seconds are 40% off retail price plus discount vouchers available at factory entrance. Sale in January.'

Coming south through the town on the A590: go straight over two roundabouts and then turn left at first traffic lights into Victoria Road.*

Coming north along the A590 from Barrow-in-Furness: turn right into Victoria Road at the second set of traffic lights.*

****After 100 yds along Victoria Road, turn left into Lightburn Road. Glassworks are on the right, shop entrance is in side road to the right past the factory (Brogden Street).***

Open: Mon–Fri 9–5; Sat and Bank Holidays 10–4.
Closed: Christmas–New Year.
Cards: Amex, MasterCard, Visa.
Cars: In street.
Toilets: Yes, until 4 when factory is open.
Wheelchairs: Access through factory.
Teas: Several local cafés.
Tours: *June–Sept* Mon–Thur 9–4; Fri 9–3. Groups please phone first mentioning The Factory Shop Guide.
Transport: Ulverston train station 5 minutes; bus station opposite.
Mail order: Yes. Delivery charge, please phone for details.
Catalogue: Free.

110 Wallsend Tyne & Wear

Claremont Garments

Howdon Green Industrial Estate, Willington Quay NE28 6SY
(0191) 263 1690

Ladies' wear: lingerie, swimwear, casualwear (bodies, leggings etc), dresses, blouses, skirts, trousers, and tailored suits, coats and jackets. Schoolwear: boys' trousers and shirts; girls' skirts and shirts. Boys' wear: a limited range of casual shirts and trousers.

'All garments are leading chainstore perfects, seconds or ends of lines, and are offered at greatly reduced prices.'

See our display advertisement on p. 539

In an industrial estate east of Wallsend, near Howdon Metro station.

From Wallsend: take A193 for Howdon/North Shields. In Howdon go straight at traffic lights; take fourth right, Howdon Lane (fish & chip shop on corner, large Bewick Park pub opposite).*

From the A19 just north of the Tyne tunnel: take A193 towards Howdon and Wallsend. After the A19/A193 interchange, turn left into Howdon Lane (immediately after first pedestrian crossing).*

****Continue across the level crossing at Howdon Metro Station, take the first left and next left again. Shop is 50 yds on left through the last door of that building.***

Open: Mon–Fri 9–4.30; Sat 9.30–2.30.
Closed: Some Bank Holidays; Christmas, Boxing and New Year's Days.
Cards: Most major credit cards.
Cars: Own car-park.
Toilets: No; nearest in town centre.
Wheelchairs: No steps; easy access to large shop.
Changing rooms: Yes.
Teas: In town centre.
Groups: Shopping groups welcome, but large groups please phone first.
Transport: Howdon Metro station about 300 yds; various bus routes.
Mail order: No.

111 Washington Tyne & Wear

Dainty Supplies

Unit 35, Phoenix Road, Crowther Industrial Estate, District 3
NE38 0AA
(0191) 416 7886/417 6277

Huge range of craft materials, dress fabrics, ribbons, lace, fur fabric, teddybear noses and components, plastic eyes for soft toys, toy and cushion fillings. Range of découpage frames and craft frames. Huge selection of miniature items. *Frame Craft* items. *Aida* fabric for cross stitch, embroidery silks, tapestry wool, canvas. Bridal fabrics, flowers and accessories. Bridal shoes, veils and sequinned motifs.

'We are a craft person's/sewer's paradise. Garment and toy labelling services. Gladly help with new European Toy Safety Standards.'

On north-west edge of town, near junction of A1(M) and A1.

From A194(M) south or northbound: exit on to A182 to Washington; go right on to A1231. Take next exit; at roundabout go into Crowther Industrial Estate.*

From A1 Western Bypass southbound: go left on to A1231 for Washington. Go right at first roundabout and turn off at next exit into Crowther Industrial Estate.*

****Go to end of Crowther Road, go right and follow road around to left, going uphill. Take next left – Unit 35 is shortly on right.***

Open: Mon–Sat 9–5.
Closed: Bank Holidays; Christmas and Boxing Days.
Cards: MasterCard, Switch, Visa.
Cars: Outside shop.
Toilets: Yes.
Wheelchairs: Easy access.
Teas: In town centre.
Groups: Groups of shoppers and club visits welcome – please phone first.
Transport: Very difficult!
Mail order: Yes.
Catalogue: Write or phone for free price list and samples, mentioning this guide.

112 Washington Tyne and Wear

S R Leisure

2 Phoenix Road, Crowther Industrial Estate, District 3
NE38 0AD
(0191) 415 3344

Active sportswear. Suppliers to professional skiers, walkers, golfers, fishermen, sailors, canoeists, rowers, rally drivers etc. Large selection of polar fleece, waterproofs, ski wear and accessories from gaiters to *Gore-tex* boots. Ski clothing hire. Tent/awning repairs and alterations, caravan re-upholstery.

'Corporate leisure wear from baseball caps to waterproofs made to individual requirements. Full embroidery facilities and made-to-measure service.'

On north-west edge of town, near junction of A1(M) and A1.

From A194(M) south or northbound: exit on to A182 to Washington; go right on to A1231. Take next exit; at roundabout go into Crowther Industrial Estate.*

From A1 Western Bypass southbound: go left on to A1231 for Washington. Go right at first roundabout and turn off at next exit into Crowther Industrial Estate.*

****Go to end of Crowther Road, go right and follow road around to left, going uphill. Phoenix Road is shortly on right, shop clearly visible.***

Open: Mon–Fri 9.30–4.45; Sat 9.30–2.30.
Closed: All Bank Holidays; Christmas–New Year.
Cards: Delta, Eurocard, MasterCard, Switch, Visa.
Cars: Outside shop.
Toilets: No.
Wheelchairs: One step, easy access.
Changing rooms: Yes.
Teas: In town centre.
Groups: Group of shoppers always welcome! Please phone first.
Transport: Very difficult.
Mail order: Yes.
Catalogue: Please phone for price list.

113 West Auckland Co. Durham

Claremont Garments

Greenfields Industrial Estate, Tindale Crescent DL14 9TR
(01388) 661703

Ladies' wear: lingerie, swimwear, casualwear (bodies, leggings etc), dresses, blouses, skirts, trousers, and tailored suits, coats and jackets. Schoolwear: boys' trousers and shirts; girls' skirts and shirts. Boys' wear: a limited range of casual shirts and trousers.

'All garments are leading chainstore perfects, seconds or ends of lines, and are offered at greatly reduced prices.'

See our display advertisement on p. 539

North-east of West Auckland and south-west of Bishop Auckland but these two towns are hard to differentiate! Just off A688 almost opposite Tindale Crescent Hospital.

From Bishop Auckland on A688 (towards West Auckland/ Barnard Castle): go right at traffic lights (signs to Tindale Crescent Hospital).*

From centre of West Auckland: take A688 for Bishop Auckland. At traffic lights with signs to Tindale Crescent Hospital go left.*

From A1(M)/Darlington: turn on to A68; at next roundabout take A6072. Follow signs to West Auckland. Go straight at traffic lights.*

****Industrial estate is 200 yds on left; shop is first on left.***

Open: Mon–Fri 10–4.30; Sat 10–4. Good Friday.
Closed: Bank Holidays (except Good Friday); Christmas and New Year please check.
Cards: Most major credit cards.
Cars: Own car-park.
Toilets: In Bishop Auckland, 1 mile.
Wheelchairs: One small step to large shop.
Changing rooms: Yes.
Teas: In Morrison's supermarket.
Groups: Shopping groups welcome, but large groups please phone first.
Transport: Buses to Evenwood from Bishop Auckland bus station; stop at Tindale Crescent (traffic lights).
Mail order: No.

114 West Auckland Co. Durham

Ebac

St Helen's Trading Estate DL14 9AL
(01388) 602751

Range of domestic de-humidifiers, electrical appliances which remove excess moisture from the air and help prevent condensation. New and graded stock. Humidex 4, Humidex 7, Homedry, Homedry XL, 440, 660, 670, 870, 880 & others.

'Firsts and seconds. Prices from under £100. Various discounts off graded and end-of-line goods.'

Off the A688 in St Helens Auckland which is between West Auckland and Bishop Auckland.

From West Auckland: take A688 for Bishop Auckland, pass football field on left and RMC Concrete on right, then take second right into St Helen's Industrial Estate. Shop is about 100 yds on left clearly signed.

From A1(M)/Darlington: turn onto A68. At next roundabout take A6072. Follow signs to West Auckland. Pass Hi-Q on right and at lights turn left for Barnard Castle A688.*

From Bishop Auckland: take A688 for Barnard Castle and go straight at lights with signs to Tindale Crescent Hospital.*

****Pass Elliotts Ford car garage, Focus DIY and Ebac main factory on right and take second left (about 100 yds).***

Open: Mon–Fri 10–4; Sat 10–1.
Closed: Bank Holidays. Please phone for other holiday closures.
Cards: MasterCard, Switch, Visa.
Cars: Own car-park.
Toilets: Available if required.
Wheelchairs: Two small steps, but help available anytime.
Teas: Mineral water available; also café nearby.
Groups: Individuals and small shopping groups welcome. Groups please book with R Proud or A Elliott.
Transport: From Bishop Auckland bus station, buses to Evenwood/Ramshaw. Stop at Maud Terrace, then shop is 300 yds back on same side of road.

115 Whitby N Yorks

Beevers of Whitby

Stakesby Vale YO21 1JY
(01947) 604351

Hand made open coil and pocketed sprung beds to any size; electric adjustable beds; water resistant beds; contract beds all made here; bases and mattresses sold separately. All on show. Also huge showroom with carpets, pine and upholstered furniture, vinyls, pine chairs, curtains; linens first and second quality.

'Always mix/match, seconds available. Finest hand-made beds made to any size for bad back sufferers. Up to 2900 pocketed springs in the queen luxury size. Factory prices. Delivery anywhere on UK mainland.'

See our display advertisement on p. 617

A quarter of a mile west of Whitby station.

From railway station: leave Whitby on A171 Guisborough road. After 400 yds go right up A174 Sandsend/Saltburn road. After only 10 yds go left at side of Arundel Hotel (signposted to Beevers).*

From Saltburn on A174: go into town and 10 yds before the T-junction go sharp right into road before Arundel Hotel.*

****Go under tunnel: showrooms on left.***

Open: Mon–Sat 9–5.30 (Fri till 8); Sun 11–5. Some Bank Holidays – please phone.
Closed: Christmas, Boxing and New Year's Days.
Cards: Delta, MasterCard, Switch, Visa.
Cars: Own car-park.
Toilets: Yes.
Wheelchairs: Three floors accessible with ramps; help available for access to top floor.
Teas: Tea and coffee available. Cafés and pubs in Whitby.
Groups: Groups welcome to look round factory (2 miles from shop) for talk and demonstration; phone Derek or Gordon first. No coach park at shop.
Transport: From station take Sleights & Castle Park bus, alight at Arundel Hotel.
Mail order: Yes.

116 Windermere Cumbria

The Outdoor Warehouse

2 Victoria Street
(015394) 44876

Clothing, footwear and equipment suitable for walking, climbing, mountain biking, fieldsports, sailing, skiing and general adventure and outdoor use.

'Prices 25–50% off high street prices for first quality products.'

About 50 yds from Windermere Tourist Information Centre.

From the A591: turn towards town centre at the junction with the train station and the TIC. You have to fork left into one-way system and shop is first on right.

Open: Mon–Sat 10–5; Sun 11–4. Some Bank Holidays – please phone to check.
Closed: Christmas and Boxing Days.
Cards: Delta, Electron, JCB, MasterCard, Switch, Visa.
Cars: Own car-park.
Toilets: No.
Wheelchairs: 1 small step to shop.
Changing rooms: Yes.
Teas: Local cafés and pubs.
Groups: Groups welcome.
Transport: Windermere train and bus stations.
Mail order: Yes. Any item on sale sent anywhere in the UK.

Towns with factory shops

NUMBERS refer to the ENTRIES, NOT the PAGES

Town	No.	Shop
Alnwick	1	Diffusion Textiles
Amble	2	Karrimor International
Amble	3	Shark Group
Ambleside	4	Briggs & Shoe Mines
Ambleside	5	Lakeland Sweaters
Bardon Mill near Hexham	6	Bardon Mill Pottery
Blaydon-on-Tyne	7	Factory Carpets and Factory Beds
Blaydon-on-Tyne	8	Factory Fabrics
Blaydon-on-Tyne	9	McIntosh's Factory Shop
Blyth	10	Burberrys
Blyth	11	Claremont Garments
Carlisle	12	The Factory Bedding and Fabrics Shop
Carlisle	13	John Chapman
Carlisle	14	Mill Shop, The
Carnforth (Holme)	15	Abbey Horn of Lakeland
Cleator	16	Kangol
Coniston	17	John Countryman & Co.
Cramlington	18	Cramlington Textiles
Crook	19	Best Dress Club
Dalton-in-Furness	20	Furness Footwear
Darlington	21	Hall & Son – Lotus Shoes
Durham	22	Chapman Curtains and Covers
Egremont	23	The Factory Shop Ltd.
Gateshead	24	Ward Art & Crafty Warehouse
Gateshead : Team Valley	25	Jockey
Gateshead : Team Valley	26	Northumbrian Fine Foods
Hartlepool	27	Jackson's Landing
Hexham (Allendale)	28	Hadrian Crystal
Ingleton	29	Daleswear Factory Shop
Jarrow	30	J Barbour & Sons
Kendal	31	Briggs & Shoe Mines
Kendal	32	James Cropper
Kendal	33–44	K Village
Kendal	45	Lakeland Fabric Warehouse
Killingworth	46	Textilion
Kirkby Stephen	47	Heredities
Lancaster	48	The Factory Shop Ltd.
Lancaster	49	Standfast
Lindal-in-Furness	50	Colony Country Store
Maryport	51	Grasshopper Babywear
Maryport	52	New Balance Athletic Shoes
Middlesbrough	53	Baird Outerwear Brands
New York	54	Hobart Rose
Newcastle upon Tyne	55	Palatine Products
North Shields	56	Bargain Baggage
North Shields	57	Midas House Furnishers
North Shields	58–96	Royal Quays Outlet Shopping Centre
North Shields	97	Textilion
Otterburn	98	Otterburn Mill
Penrith	99	Briggs & Shoe Mines
Peterlee	100	Claremont Garments
Redcar	101	Dewhirst
Sedbergh	102	Farfield Clothing
Shildon	103	Durham Clothing Co.
South Shields	104	Claremont Garments
Stockton-on-Tees	105	Factory Fabric Centre
Stockton-on-Tees	106	Wynsors World of Shoes
Sunderland	107	Shaw of London (Furniture)
Sunderland	108	Sunelm Products Sheltered Workshops
Ulverston	109	Cumbria Crystal
Wallsend	110	Claremont Garments
Washington	111	Dainty Supplies
Washington	112	S R Leisure
West Auckland	113	Claremont Garments
West Auckland	114	Ebac
Whitby	115	Beevers of Whitby
Windermere	116	The Outdoor Warehouse

Scotland

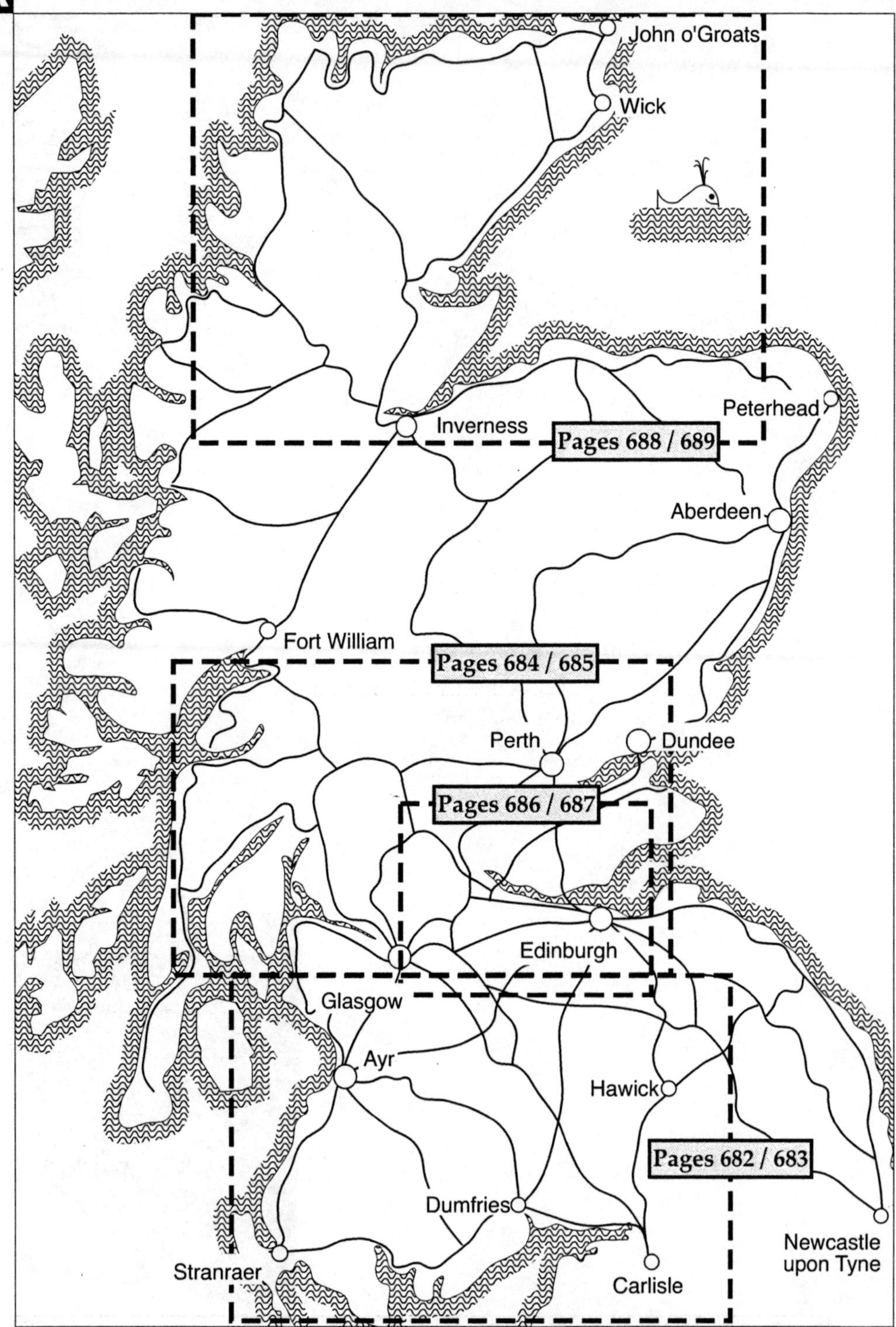
John o'Groats
Wick
Peterhead
Inverness
Pages 688 / 689
Aberdeen
Fort William
Pages 684 / 685
Perth
Dundee
Pages 686 / 687
Edinburgh
Glasgow
Ayr
Hawick
Pages 682 / 683
Dumfries
Newcastle
upon Tyne
Stranraer
Carlisle

Scotland

No wonder Scottish knitwear is coveted around the world. We even receive enquiries from Italians (not noted for admitting that other nations can produce stylish garments of better quality than their own!) about where to track down cashmere and fine lambswool. We, too, sneak off to Scotland whenever we can.

Scotland does indeed offer a wonderful selection of fine (as well as sturdier) knitwear, in original designs and colours. The factory shops here have so many other appealing products too, many with a particularly Scottish flavour. A first for us is a shop selling equipment for the sport of curling. This book also leads the canny shopper to shortbread, jams, special soups, special cheeses and whisky; to tartans, plaids, kilts, and woollen scarves and accessories; ceramics with tartan designs and unique jewellery made from Highland heather stems; even to good value golf clubs.

As a bonus for people who need fortifying while shopping, details about the whisky distilleries are included too …

Some of our own best buys ever come from Scotland. The designer cashmere sweater for £65 (normally £200); the fine wool and cashmere travel rug for £10 (normally £150); the luxurious down-filled pillows for less than half normal price, and the hand-crafted whisky tumblers. But remember that many of the shops in this book sell reduced price items vital to everyday living – such as beds, office furniture, upholstery fabrics and lampbases.

Most visitors travel to Scotland in summer, especially in July and August. We suggest that factory shoppers take a tip from the locals and avoid these months. Shopping is less stressful and more fun when there are fewer visitors. Factory shops, like other retailers, have seasonal sales; the period after Christmas might be short on daylight but it is long on factory shop bargains. And the countryside can be stunning out of season. We have travelled through Scotland at all times of year. A clear day in January, with winter sunshine lighting up the snow-brushed hills north of Perth is utterly memorable. The Outer Hebrides in late September are stunning – yet almost devoid of visitors. At these times of year it becomes much easier to find accommodation too.

A recent survey of British shopping habits showed that the Scots spend more per capita on clothes than any other groups do. We can understand why!

Regions in Scotland

Changes in names, areas and borders of regions and counties in the British Isles cause problems for us and, we suspect, for other members of the public. Scottish regions changed recently, with new names such as East Dumbartonshire, North Ayrshire and Inverclyde etc. For ease of reference to factory shops in this book, we have stayed in most cases with the former names. We hope we mitigate confusion rather than add to it!

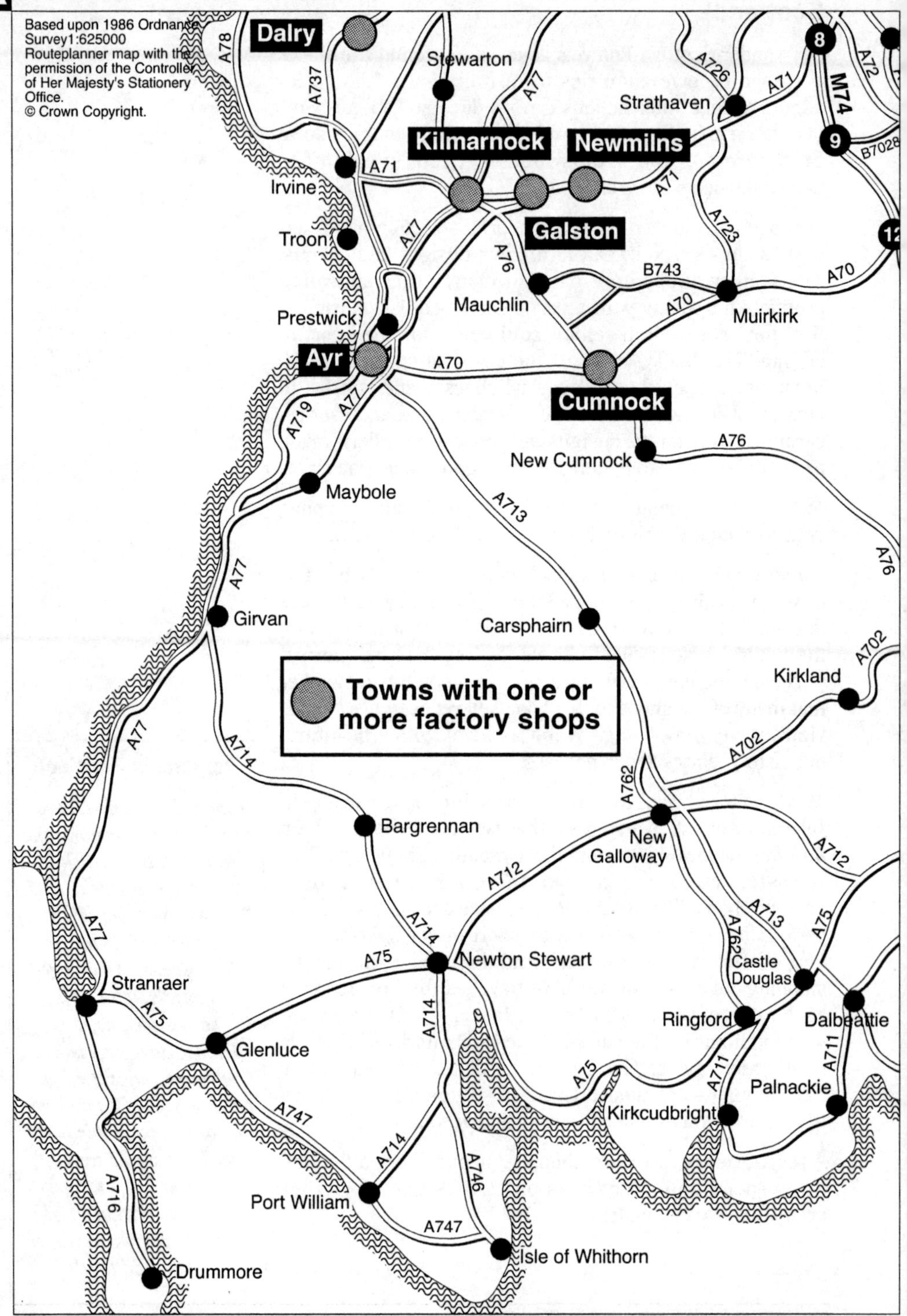
Based upon 1986 Ordnance Survey1:625000 Routeplanner map with the permission of the Controller of Her Majesty's Stationery Office.
© Crown Copyright.
Towns with one or more factory shops
Dalry
Stewarton
Kilmarnock
Newmilns
Galston
Strathaven
Irvine
Troon
Prestwick
Ayr
Mauchlin
Muirkirk
Cumnock
New Cumnock
Maybole
Girvan
Carsphairn
Kirkland
Bargrennan
New Galloway
Newton Stewart
Castle Douglas
Ringford
Dalbeattie
Stranraer
Glenluce
Palnackie
Kirkcudbright
Port William
Isle of Whithorn
Drummore
A78
A737
A77
A726
A71
M74
A72
B7028
A723
A76
B743
A70
A719
A713
A702
A714
A762
A712
A75
A711
A747
A746
A716
8
9
12

▲ Continued on page 685 ▲

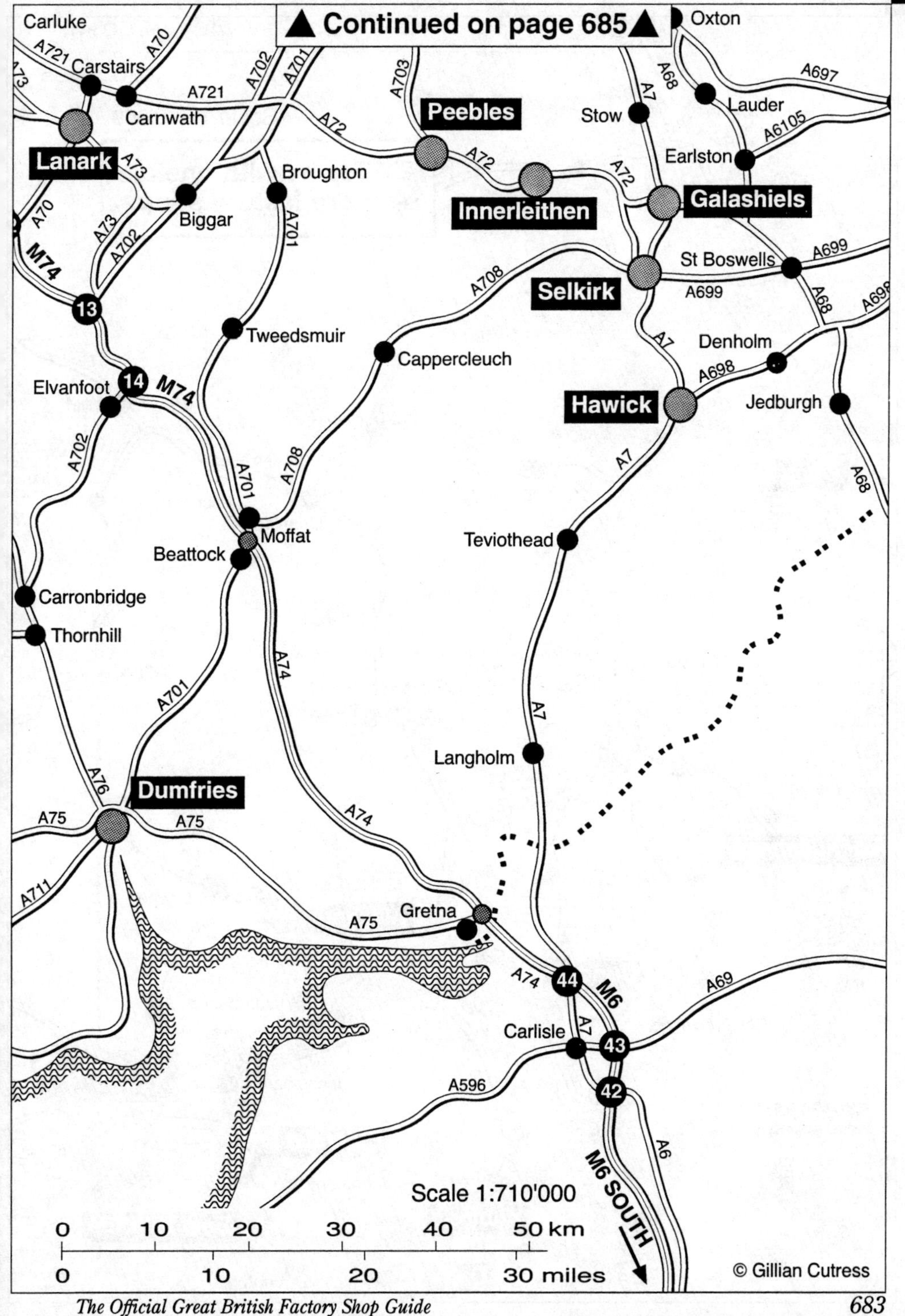

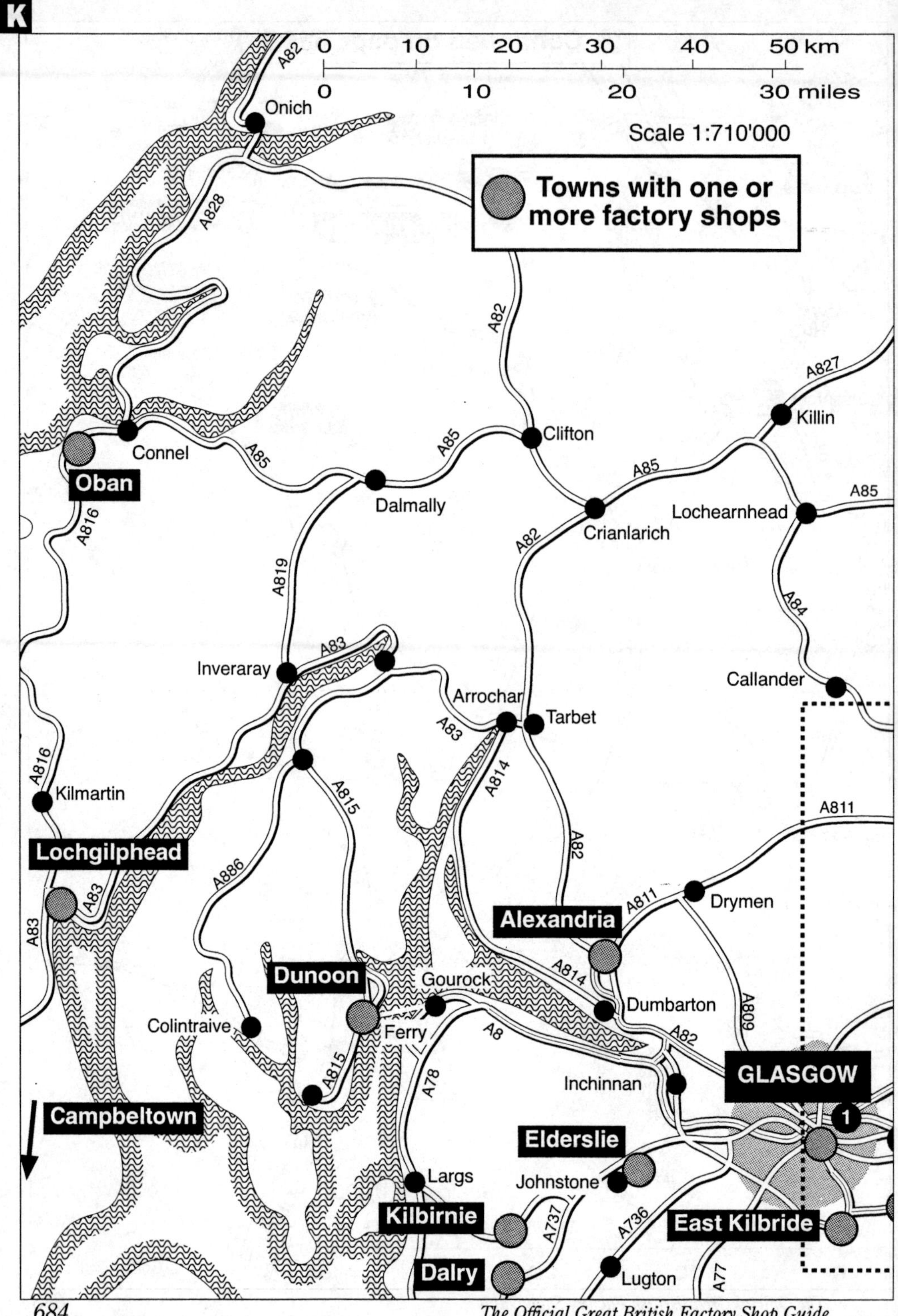
0 10 20 30 40 50 km
0 10 20 30 miles
Scale 1:710'000
Towns with one or more factory shops
Onich
A82
A828
Connel
Oban
A816
A85
Dalmally
Clifton
Crianlarich
Killin
A827
Lochearnhead
A84
Callander
A819
Inveraray
A83
Arrochar
Tarbet
A814
A815
Kilmartin
Lochgilphead
A886
A811
Drymen
Alexandria
A809
Dunoon
Gourock
Ferry
Dumbarton
Colintraive
A8
A78
Inchinnan
GLASGOW
1
Campbeltown
Elderslie
Johnstone
Largs
Kilbirnie
A737
A736
East Kilbride
Dalry
Lugton
A77

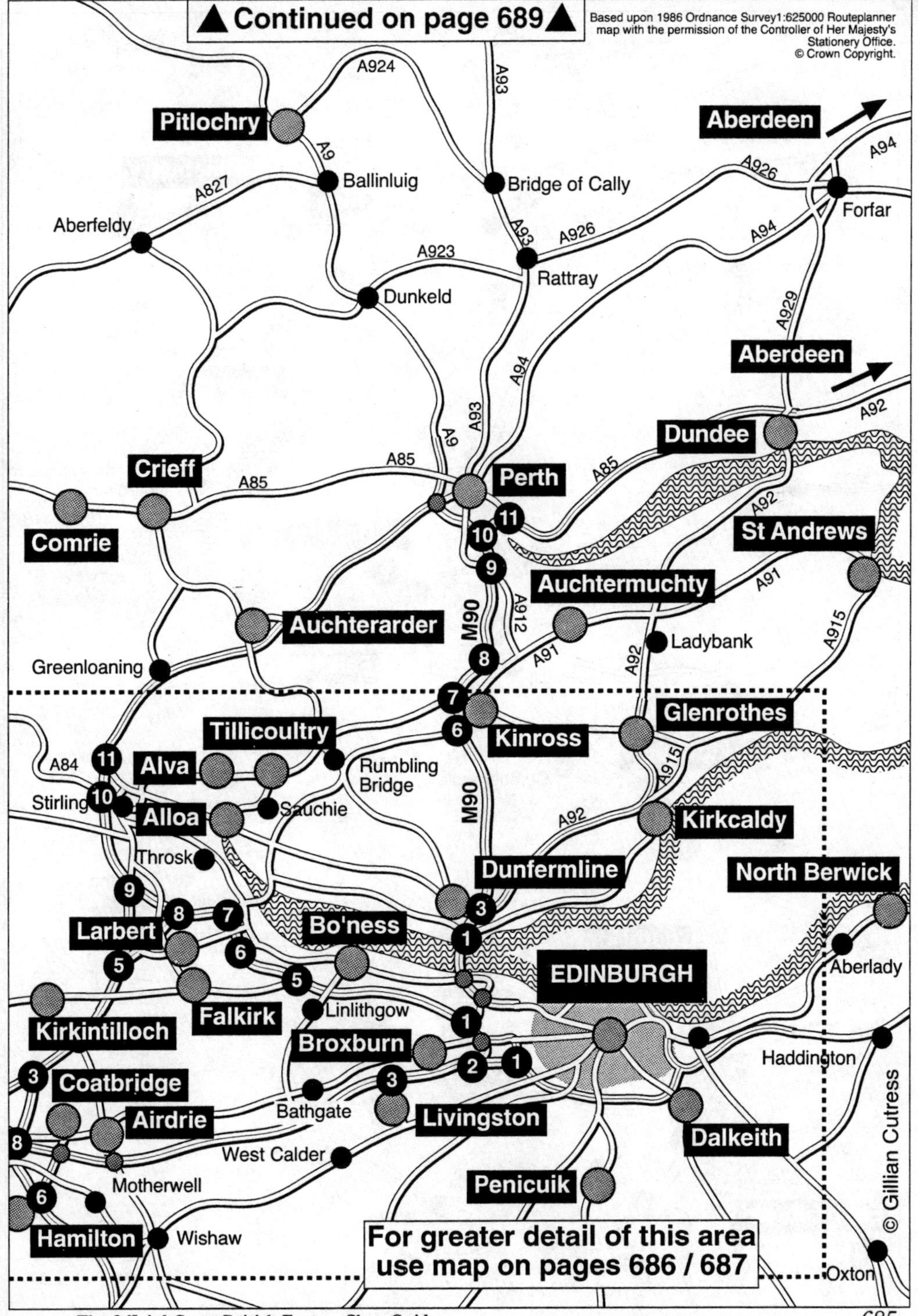

▲Continued on page 689▲
Based upon 1986 Ordnance Survey1:625000 Routeplanner map with the permission of the Controller of Her Majesty's Stationery Office.
© Crown Copyright.
Pitlochry
Ballinluig
Bridge of Cally
Aberdeen
Aberfeldy
Forfar
Rattray
Dunkeld
Aberdeen
Dundee
Crieff
Perth
Comrie
St Andrews
Auchtermuchty
Auchterarder
Ladybank
Greenloaning
Glenrothes
Tillicoultry
Kinross
Rumbling Bridge
Alva
Stirling
Alloa
Sauchie
Kirkcaldy
Throsk
Dunfermline
North Berwick
Larbert
Bo'ness
EDINBURGH
Aberlady
Falkirk
Linlithgow
Kirkintilloch
Broxburn
Haddington
Coatbridge
Bathgate
Livingston
Airdrie
Dalkeith
West Calder
Motherwell
Penicuik
Hamilton
Wishaw
For greater detail of this area use map on pages 686 / 687
Oxton
© Gillian Cutress

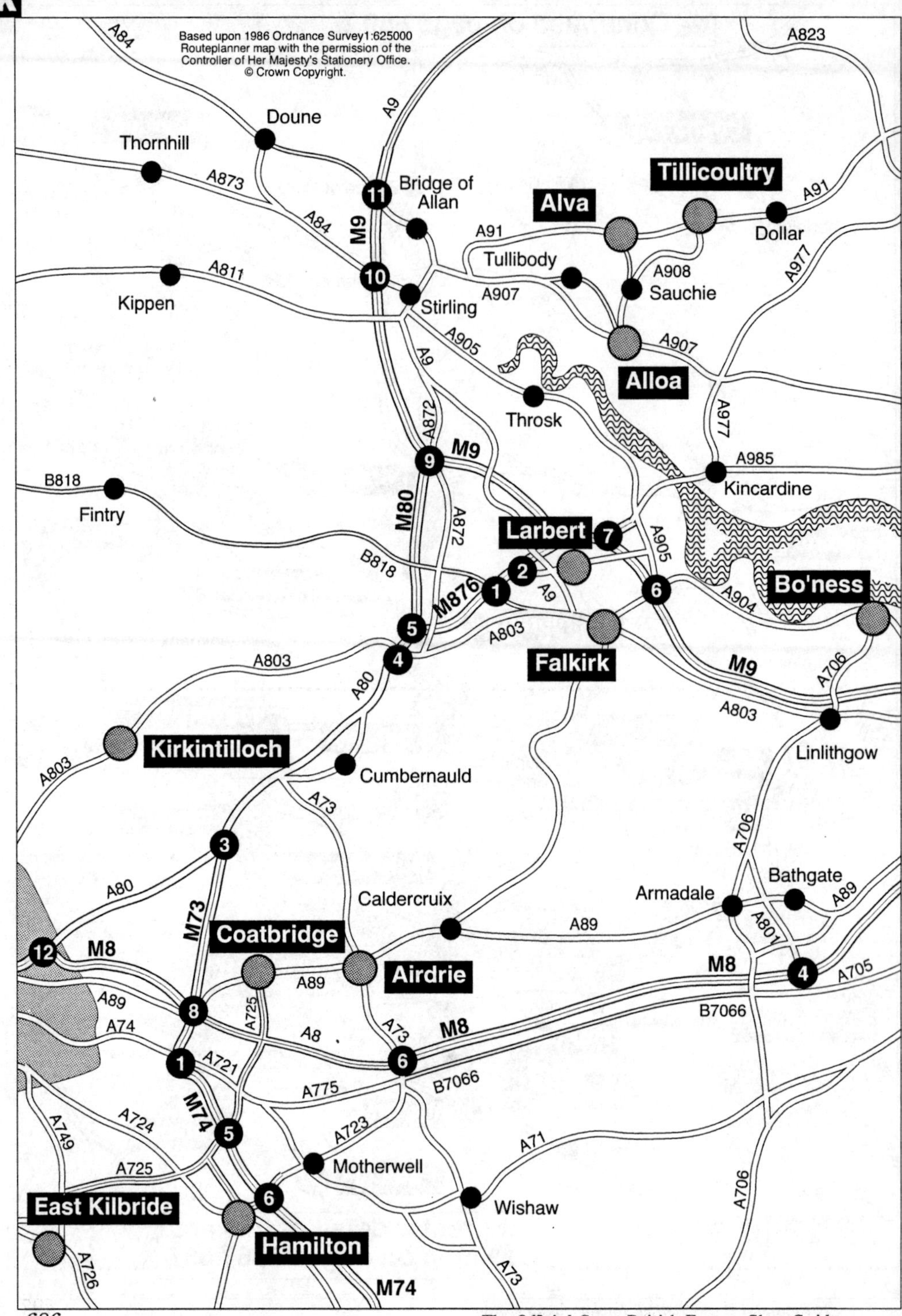

Based upon 1986 Ordnance Survey1:625000 Routeplanner map with the permission of the Controller of Her Majesty's Stationery Office. © Crown Copyright.
Doune
Thornhill
Bridge of Allan
Tillicoultry
Alva
Dollar
Tullibody
Sauchie
Kippen
Stirling
Alloa
Throsk
Kincardine
Fintry
Larbert
Bo'ness
Falkirk
Kirkintilloch
Linlithgow
Cumbernauld
Bathgate
Armadale
Caldercruix
Coatbridge
Airdrie
Motherwell
Wishaw
East Kilbride
Hamilton

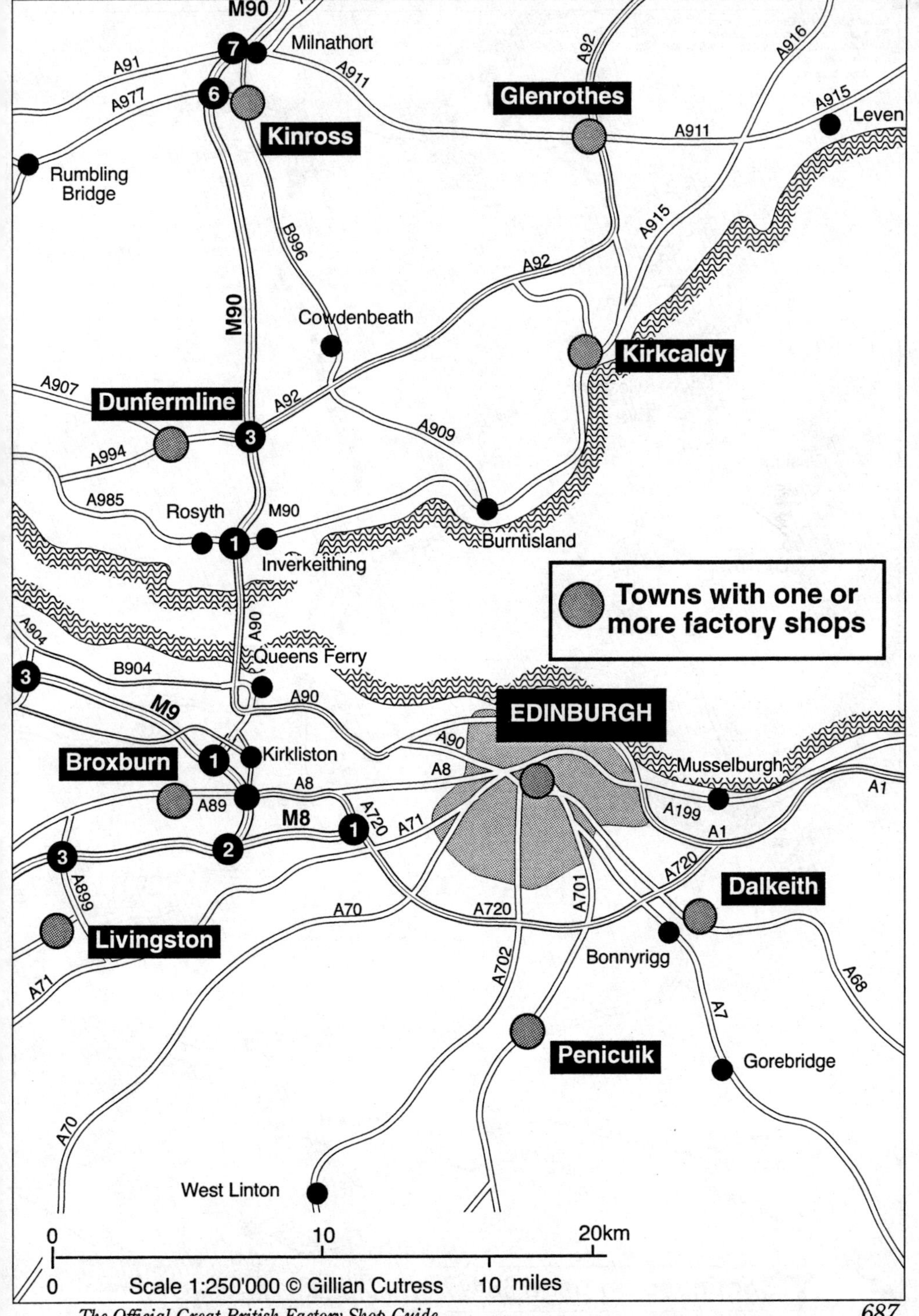
M90
Milnathort
A91
A911
A977
Glenrothes
A92
A916
A915
Leven
Kinross
A911
Rumbling
Bridge
B996
A915
A92
M90
Cowdenbeath
Kirkcaldy
A907
Dunfermline
A92
A909
A994
A985
Rosyth
M90
Burntisland
Inverkeithing
Towns with one or more factory shops
A904
A90
Queens Ferry
B904
A90
M9
EDINBURGH
A90
Broxburn
Kirkliston
Musselburgh
A8
A8
A1
A89
M8
A720
A199
A71
A1
A899
A720
Dalkeith
A70
A720
A701
Livingston
Bonnyrigg
A702
A68
A71
A7
Penicuik
Gorebridge
A70
West Linton
0
10
20km
0
10 miles
Scale 1:250'000 © Gillian Cutress

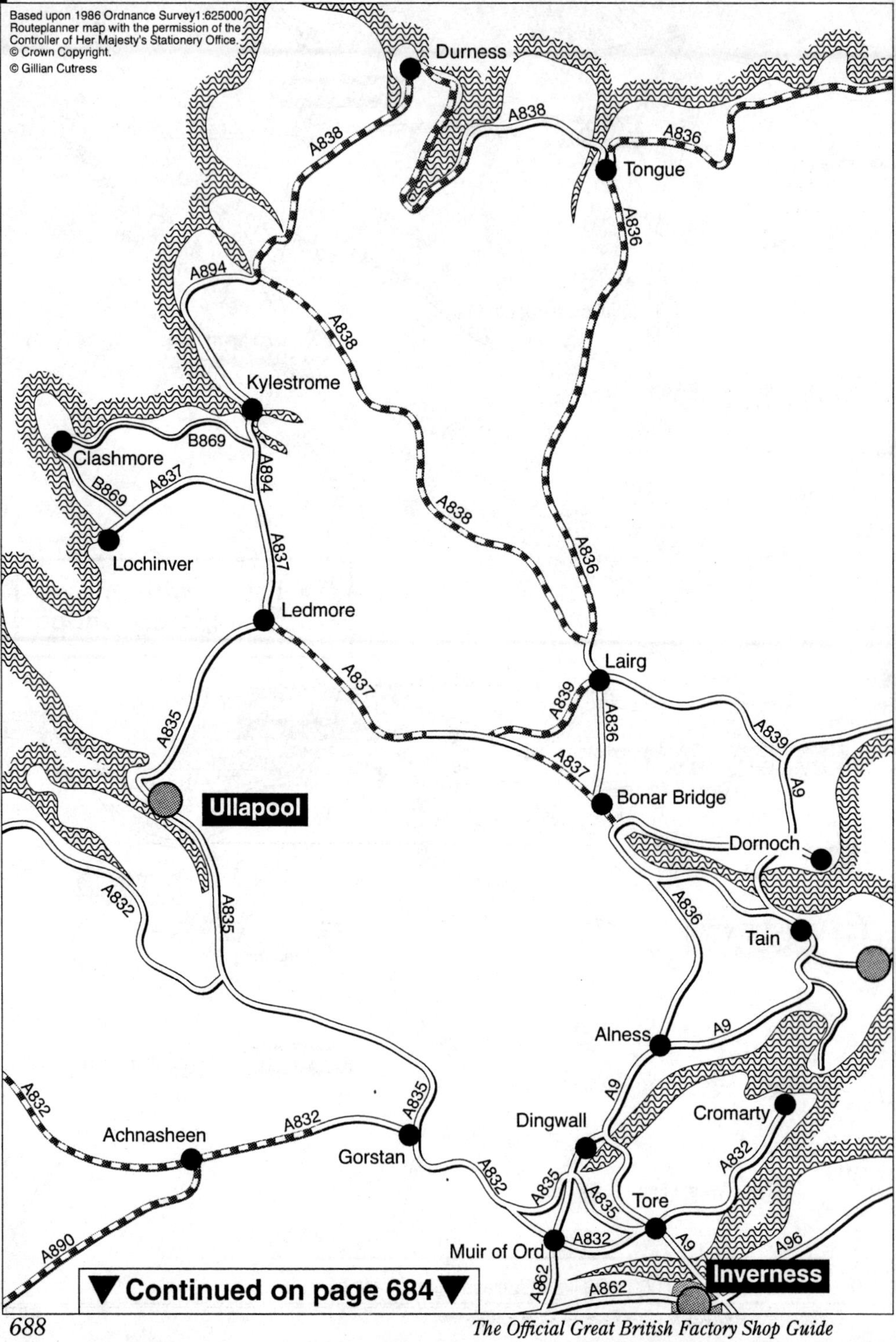

Durness
A838
A838
A836
Tongue
A836
A894
A838
Kylestrome
B869
Clashmore
A837
A894
B869
Lochinver
A837
A838
A836
Ledmore
A837
Lairg
A839
A836
A839
A835
A837
Ullapool
Bonar Bridge
A9
Dornoch
A832
A835
A836
Tain
Alness
A9
A9
A832
A835
Cromarty
Dingwall
A832
Achnasheen
Gorstan
A832
A835
A835
A832
Tore
A832
A9
A890
Muir of Ord
A96
Inverness
A862
A862

▼ Continued on page 684 ▼

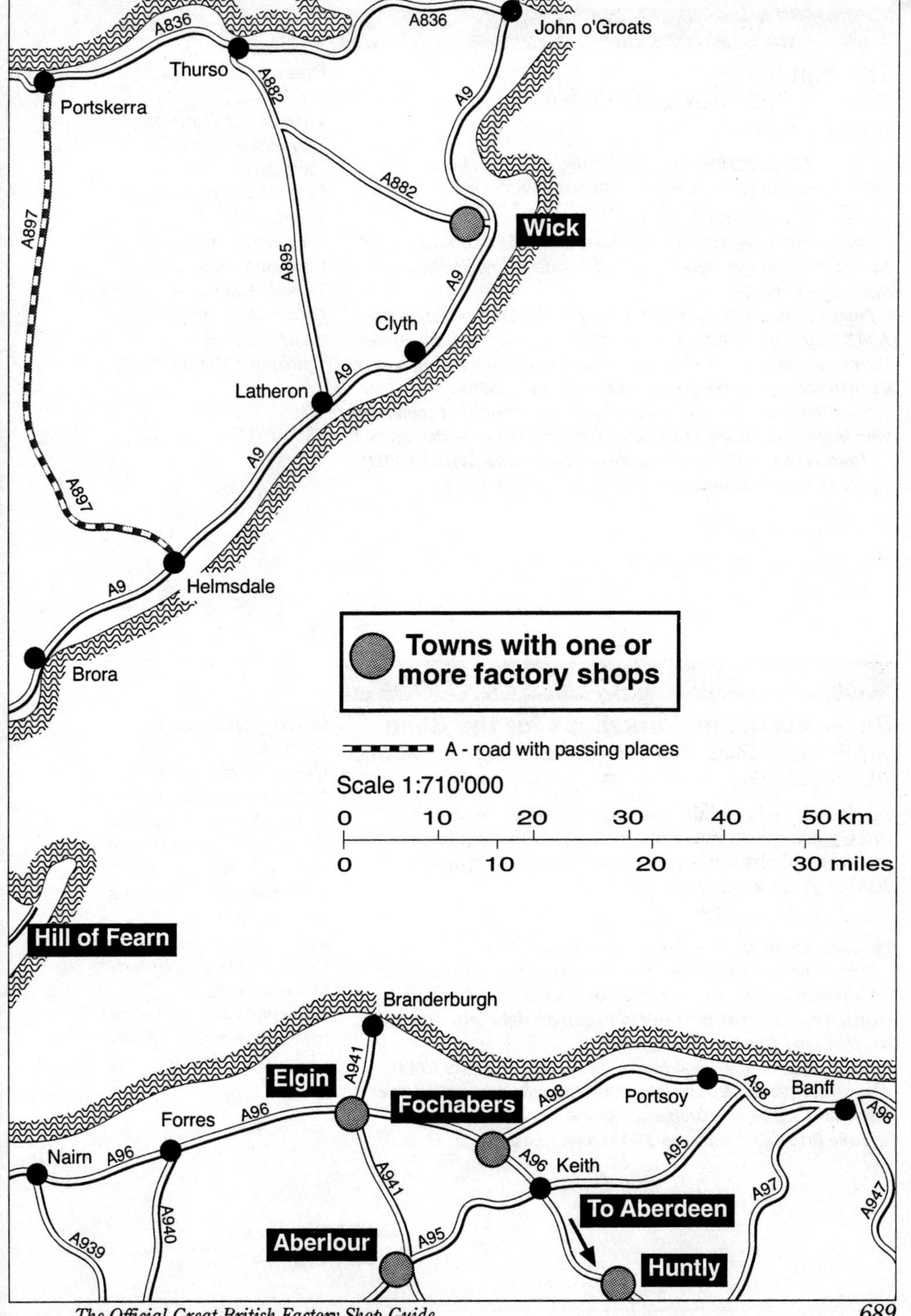
A836
A836
John o'Groats
Thurso
Portskerra
A882
A9
A897
A882
Wick
A895
A9
Clyth
Latheron
A9
A9
A897
Helmsdale
A9
Brora
Towns with one or more factory shops
A - road with passing places
Scale 1:710'000
0
10
20
30
40
50 km
0
10
20
30 miles
Hill of Fearn
Branderburgh
Elgin
A941
Fochabers
A98
Portsoy
A98
Banff
A98
Forres
A96
Nairn
A96
A96
Keith
A95
A941
A940
A939
To Aberdeen
A97
A947
Aberlour
A95
Huntly

1 Aberdeen Grampian

The Mill Shop

Grandholm Mill, Woodside AB9 2SB
(01224) 483201

Ladies' skirts, jackets, blazers, trousers, coats. Gents' blazers, sports jackets, suits, trousers, overcoats. Knitwear.

By the river Don north of town.

From town: take A96 for Inverness; at traffic lights with right turn to Fraserburgh/Peterhead/Old Aberdeen, go straight; go right at next lights.*

From south, south-west and west: go into town as far as the A947 (signposted (A96) Inverness) and turn towards Inverness. When you reach the A96 at large roundabout (Texaco on corner), go right for city centre then left at next traffic lights.*

From Inverness via A96: pass airport; go straight at roundabout with large Fiat garage at corner. Turn left at next traffic lights.*

****Take second left; at bottom go left again into Gordon's Mill Road, go over river bridge and turn right; follow signs.***

Open: Mon–Sat 9–4.30; Sun 12–4.30.
Closed: For Christmas–New Year please check.
Cards: Yes.
Cars: Own large car-park.
Toilets: Yes.
Wheelchairs: Easy access.
Changing rooms: Yes.
Teas: Restaurant & coffee shop.
Tours: Museum and audio-visual display.
Transport: Bus no. 25.

2 Aberdeen Grampian

Royal Aberdeen Workshops for the Blind

132 Wellington Road, West Tullos Industrial Estate AB9 3LO
(01224) 873366

All sizes of beds and divans, matching mattresses; three-piece suites, range of armchairs with high backs and firm upholstery; bedding, curtains, curtain-making service, re-upholstery service.

'Established since 1843. All products hand-made.'

In Tullos, south of River Dee and Aberdeen town.

From town centre: follow signs to Tullos/A956. Cross river, pass prison on left, go straight at traffic lights (Somerfield on right). Go straight at next traffic lights; go right into Craigshaw Drive at next (third) traffic lights.*

From south on A92 dual carriageway: turn on to A956 to Aberdeen Harbour. Go straight at first roundabout, then left at first traffic lights into Craigshaw Drive.*

****Take first right: entrance 100 yds on right.***

Open: Mon–Fri 8.30–5; Sat 10–4.
Closed: Bank Holidays; Christmas and Boxing Days.
Cards: Access, Amex, Visa.
Cars: Private parking by shop.
Toilets: Yes, and for disabled.
Wheelchairs: Easy access.
Teas: In Aberdeen.
Tours: Gladly show you round the works but please phone first to arrange.
Transport: Bus no. 13 from town centre to Cove. Ask for Craigshaw Drive.

3 Aberlour on Spey Grampian

Walkers Shortbread

AB38 9PD
(01340) 871555

Shortbread, cake, biscuits, meringues, oatcakes.

'Rejects at factory prices.'

About 15 miles south of Elgin. On many maps, this town is called Charlestown of Aberlour.

Company is at the eastern end of town on the main road.

Open: Mon–Fri 8.30–5; also Sat in summer. Bank Holidays.
Closed: Christmas, Boxing and New Year's Days; 2 Jan.
Cards: MasterCard, Switch, Visa.
Cars: Limited space for visitors' parking.
Toilets: No.
Wheelchairs: Ramp.
Teas: In Aberlour village.
Tours: No factory tours.
Mail order: Yes.
Catalogue: Price list on request.

4 Airdrie Strathclyde

Unique Fashions

Unit 13/14, Stirling Road Industrial Estate ML6 7UD
(01236) 762684

Huge range of ladies', gents' and children's quality suede and leather garments – jackets, coats, waistcoats, sheepskin jackets etc. Also large range of skins in different textures and colours. Accessories such as purses, wallets, gloves and bags.

'Repair and alteration service. Made-to-measure from extra small to oversize. Large choice in stock.'

On the north side of Airdrie, just off A73 (road to Cumbernauld).

Coming south on A73: as you get to edge of town, go under pylons and take next left, signposted Stirling Road Ind. Estate.*

From town: aim for Cumbernauld/Stirling (A73). Pass Jet petrol on the right, then take next right (Dykehead Road) signposted Stirling Road Industrial Estate.*

****Turn right into estate (Dalmacoulter Road) then left (Laverock Road) and continue to shop at far back right (well signed).***

Open: Mon 9–4.30; Tues–Fri 9–5.30; Sat 10–5; Sun 11–4.
Closed: Spring Bank Holidays; Christmas, Boxing and New Year's Days; 2 Jan.
Cards: Access, Amex, Switch, Visa.
Cars: Own large car-park.
Toilets: Yes.
Wheelchairs: Two steps to large shop; assistance can be given.
Changing rooms: Yes.
Teas: Many cafés and hotels nearby.
Transport: Bus no. 47 from Airdrie bus station.
Mail order: Yes. No seconds sent by post.
Catalogue: Free.

Paisley

The word 'Paisley' conjures up the famous tear drop or tadpole. Many people imagine that all 'paisley' shawls were made in Scotland, but they were manufactured elsewhere in Britain too – including Norwich – and in Lyons, Paris and Vienna. This ancient motif flourished in India and was first used for shawls made in Kashmir. It was brought to Europe by the East India Company in the 1700s. These fine shawls were expensive and rare. It took up to three years to produce one shawl, each patch of colour being woven separately. Originally rectangular, they suited the narrow empire line dresses. As fashions changed, so did the shawls. They became square, and, with the advent of the crinoline, returned to a rectangular shape but large enough to cover the vastly increased skirt!

Kashmir shawls were imitated by British manufacturers and sold for about a tenth of the price. In about 1805, weavers in Paisley – long renowned for their skills – switched from their traditional products to shawls and undercut Norwich prices by reworking the designs. Patenting of designs became legal in 1842, but by then Paisley had secured the lead in the market. The fashionable woman would go to drapers to look at 'paisleys', con-fident that that was where most of them had been made. When the bustle became de rigeur in the 1860s the shawl fell out of fashion. The bustle-clad lady would not hide her decorative rear under an all enveloping shawl!

The Paisley Museum has collected paisley shawls since the beginning of the century and has over 900. Shawls are on permanent display. If you would like to consult the reference collection of shawls, original pattern books, photos etc, you are welcome to contact the curator. Paisley Museum & Art Galleries, High St, Paisley PA1 2BA, 0141 889 3151. Mon–Sat 10–5.

Alexandria Strathclyde

Late entry

Antartex Village

Lomond Industrial Estate
(01389) 752393

Huge range of sheepskin jackets, coats, hats and gloves; also leather jackets and coats, skirts. Golf clothing and equipment. Full range of woollen clothing, knitwear, tartans and gifts for all the family.

'Stock Clever Shepherd designer co-ordinates, Leathercraft, Clan Royal.'

Lomond Industrial Estate is at the northern end of Alexandria.

From town centre: aim for Balloch and the north, pass the huge former car factory (new factory outlet centre) on right and go right immediately into Heather Avenue at traffic lights.*

From A82 going north or south: turn off at signs to Lomond Industrial Estate. Go right at next roundabout; go left at traffic lights into Heather Avenue, following signs to industrial estate.*

****After railway bridge, turn right into signposted estate. Follow signs to Antartex Village.***

Open: 7 days 10–6.
Closed: Christmas and New Year's Days.
Cards: Amex, MasterCard, Style, Switch, Visa.
Cars: Own huge car-park.
Toilets: Yes, including for the disabled.
Wheelchairs: Easy access to vast shop.
Changing rooms: Yes.
Teas: Coffee shop for light meals etc.
Groups: Free self-guided tours to see sheepskin preparation through to finished garments. No booking necessary – ask on arrival. Also see craftspeople in craft villages, and British Antartic Exhibition.
Transport: Balloch train station; local bus for hospital) at top of road.

5 Alexandria Strathclyde

BeeLine

Unit 6, Darleith Road, Lomond Industrial Estate G83 0TL
(01389) 756161

Ladies', men's and children's clothes from major high street suppliers.

'Perfects and surplus stock from high street stores. Famous names at discount prices.'

Lomond Industrial Estate is at the northern end of Alexandria.

From town centre: aim for Balloch and the north, pass the huge former car factory (now a new factory outlet centre) on right and go right immediately into Heather Avenue at traffic lights.*

From A82 going north or south: turn off at signs to Lomond Industrial Estate. Go right at next roundabout, then turn left at traffic lights into Heather Avenue, following signs to Lomond Industrial Estate.*

***After railway bridge, turn right into signposted estate. Take first left, next right, and shop is in first building on left.**

Open: Mon–Sat 10–5; Sun 12–5. Bank Holidays.
Closed: Christmas & Boxing Days; 1, 2 & 3 Jan.
Cards: Access, Switch, Visa.
Cars: Own car-park.
Toilets: Nearest in Antartex Village.
Wheelchairs: Easy access to sizeable shop.
Changing rooms: Yes.
Teas: In Antartex Village.
Groups: No tours.
Transport: Balloch railway station; local bus to hospital at top of road.
Mail order: Yes.

6 Alexandria Strathclyde

Cocoon Coats

Lomond Trade Centre, Lomond Industrial Estate G83 0TK
(01389) 755511

Top quality lightweight crease-resistant ladies' rainwear with carrying pouches, plus some coats for men. Cotton and wax look; waterproofed; optional warm lining. Made-to-order service.

'Also shops at 28 Victoria Street, Edinburgh (0131 226 2327) & 110 Kensington Church Street, London W8 (0171 221 7000).'

Lomond Industrial Estate is at the northern end of Alexandria.

From town centre: aim for Balloch and the north, pass the huge former car factory (now a new factory outlet centre) on right and go right immediately into Heather Avenue at traffic lights.*

From A82 going north or south: turn off at signs to Lomond Industrial Estate. Go right at next roundabout, then turn left at traffic lights into Heather Avenue, following signs to Lomond Industrial Estate.*

***After railway bridge, turn right into signposted estate. Shop is in third unit in first building on right after you get on to estate.**

Open: Mon–Fri 8.30–4.30; Sat, Sun 11–5.
Closed: Christmas–2 Jan.
Cards: Access, Amex, Visa.
Cars: Outside shop.
Toilets: Yes.
Wheelchairs: Easy access to medium sized shop.
Teas: In town.
Groups: No factory tours. Groups (maximum 15) welcome to shop; please phone first.
Transport: Balloch railway station; local bus to hospital at top of road.
Mail order: Yes.
Catalogue: Free.

7 Alexandria Strathclyde

Loch Lomond Factory Outlets

Argyll Works, Main Street G83 0UG
(01389) 710077

Over 20 units on three floors including: *Ponden Mill, Tom Sayers, Leading Labels, Luggage & Bags, Russell Athletic, Pavers Shoes, The Toyshop, X/S Music, The Book Depot, Hornsea Pottery, Honey, The Fashion Academy (Christian Lacroix, Louis Feraud, Mondi, Maska, Woods of Windsor), Thorntons, Gatehouse Crafts* and *Tog 24*.

'Up to 50% off high street price on leading brands in fashion, sportswear, household goods, luggage and more.'

See our display advertisement opposite

In the newly refurbished historic Argyll Motor Works on the northern end of Alexandria.

From town centre: aim for Balloch and the north; the centre is in the huge former car factory on right.

From A82 going north or south: turn off at roundabout following signs to Alexandria/Balloch. Go right at next roundabout; the centre is on the left after the first traffic lights.

Open: Seven days 10–6.
Closed: Christmas Day; 1 & 2 Jan.
Cards: All outlets take major credit and debit cards.
Cars: 630 spaces for cars and coach bays.
Toilets: Yes, and for disabled; also baby changing room.
Wheelchairs: Full access to all three floors.
Teas: Caffe Roberta Food Court and Argyll Bar; meals, snacks, tea, coffee; fully licensed.
Groups: Coach parties welcome (free coach wash; drivers' lounge; incentive schemes). Groups please book ahead. Visits to Motoring Memories (in Motor Heritage Museum) on lower ground floor: adults £1.50, OAPs and children 75p.
Transport: Balloch train station; local bus to hospital near traffic lights opposite the centre.

8 Alloa Central

Jaeger

Tullibody Road, Lornshill FK10 2EY
(01259) 218985

Large range of *Jaeger* ladies' wear: knitwear, blouses, skirts, trousers, jackets, suits. *Jaeger* men's suits, trousers, jackets, shirts and ties. *Viyella* ladies' wear.

'Quality merchandise at reduced prices.'

On the B9096 at Tullibody end of Alloa.

From Stirling on A907: go left on to B9096 into Tullibody. Go through town; factory is first building on right after large Lornshill School on left.

From A907 through Alloa: turn on to B9096 towards Tullibody at large roundabout with impressive stone town hall on one corner and modern police station on other corner. Factory is one mile from here, on left.

Open: Seven days a week, 10–4.
Closed: Please telephone for Christmas and Bank Holiday closures.
Cards: Access, Switch, Visa.
Cars: Visitors' car-park.
Toilets: In Tullibody.
Wheelchairs: Three steps to huge shop.
Changing rooms: Yes.
Teas: Cafés in Alloa.
Groups: No factory tours. Shopping groups welcome – prior phone call please.
Transport: Local buses from Alloa and Stirling.
Mail order: No.

See our entry opposite

9 Alva Central

Inverallan Hand Knitters

Alva Industrial Estate FK12 5DQ
(01259) 762292 Fax (01259) 762508

Hand-knitted pure wool and cotton traditional sweaters and cardigans. Fashion items with top designer labels. Seconds and overruns from export orders at very reasonable prices. Also yarn.

'Happy to take orders for garments in your choice of yarn and pattern at no extra charge (personal callers only). Europe's largest company of traditional and fashion hand-knitters – knitting done from home, despatched from here.'

In the industrial estate east of Alva.

From Tillicoultry on A91: take first left at beginning of Alva into the industrial estate.

From Stirling on A91: go through Alva and take last right into Alva industrial estate. Inverallan is at the end of the first drive, past Campbell's Contract Curtains.

Open: Mon–Fri 9–5. Some Bank Holidays.
Closed: Christmas, Boxing and New Year's Days, Jan 2; some local holidays – please phone to check.
Cards: All major cards.
Cars: Outside factory.
Toilets: Ask if required.
Wheelchairs: Easy access.
Changing rooms: No.
Teas: Coffee shop in Alva.
Groups: No tours. Groups, including coaches, welcome to shop. Please phone to arrange.
Transport: Buses every 20 minutes along Hill Foots Road to Alva Industrial Estate, then 100 yds walk.
Mail order: Yes.
Catalogue: Free. No seconds by mail order. (Prices lower for personal callers.)

10 Alva Central

Millshop Woollens

Ochilvale Mill Shop, East Stirling Street FK12 5HW
(01259) 760421

High quality classic knitwear in natural fibres including merino, lambswool, geelong, lamora, cashmere & cashmere blends. Hats, scarves, gloves, travel rugs, shirts, skirts and tights.

'We stock extremely well priced perfect and imperfect garments all at factory shop prices.'

At the eastern end of Alva.

From Stirling: pass Alloa B908 turn-off and shop is beside road about 400 yds on right, clearly signed.

From Alloa (B908): turn right on to A91 – shop is 400 yds on right.

From Tillicoultry: pass industrial estate on left: shop is on left, clearly signed.

Open: Mon–Fri 9–5; Sat 9.30–5; Sun 10.30–5.
Closed: Christmas and Boxing Days; 1 & 2 Jan.
Cards: Access, Switch, Visa.
Cars: Parking available.
Toilets: By the clock at B908 turn-off.
Wheelchairs: Special ramp at side entrance to medium sized shop.
Changing rooms: Yes.
Teas: Hot drinks machine; coffee shop in Alva.
Groups: No factory tours. Shopping groups welcome, no need to phone.
Transport: Buses from all local towns.

11 Alva Central

Millshop Woollens

Berryfield Mill Shop, East Stirling Street FK12 5HW
(01259) 762825

High quality classic knitwear in natural fibres including merino, lambswool, geelong, lamora, cashmere & cashmere blends.

'We stock extremely well priced perfect and imperfect garments all at factory shop prices.'

Towards the eastern end of Alva.

From Tillicoultry (A91): after you reach Alva, take second left into industrial estate.*

From Stirling (A91): continue through town, go right after Hodgson of Scotland on right (with tall silver chimney behind).

From Alloa (B908): turn right on to A91 – then right into industrial estate.

****Shop at far end of first drive on right.***

Open: Mon–Fri 9–5; Sat 9.30–5; Sun 10.30–5.
Closed: Christmas and Boxing Days; 1 & 2 Jan.
Cards: Access, Switch, Visa.
Cars: Own car-park.
Toilets: By the clock at B908 turn-off.
Wheelchairs: One step.
Changing rooms: Yes.
Teas: In town.
Groups: No factory tours. Shopping groups welcome, no need to phone.
Transport: Buses from all local towns.

12 Auchterarder Tayside

Gleneagles Knitwear

Abbey Road PH3 1DR
(01764) 662112

Knitwear for men and women, sweaters, cardigans, socks, own production 80% cashmere. *Burberry, Daks, Jaeger* outerwear.

'All items perfects, no seconds. Bargain cashmere available.'

Auchterarder is about 12 miles south-west of Perth. The shop is at the eastern end of town.

From Perth on A9(T): exit into Auchterarder via A824, main road through town. Turn left (to Great Scots Visitor Centre) opposite B8062 turn-off.*

From Stirling via A9 and from Dunfermline–Crieff road A823: go into town, then straight through shopping area; turn right opposite the B8062 turn-off.*

****Continue downhill: shop is on left in first building after river.***

Open: Mon–Sat 9–5. *Also June–Sept* Sun 11–4.
Closed: Christmas and Boxing Days, 1 & 2 January.
Cards: Amex, Delta, Diners, JCB, MasterCard, Switch, Visa. All foreign currencies.
Cars: Across road from shop entrance.
Toilets: In town car-park.
Wheelchairs: Four steps down to large shop.
Changing rooms: No.
Teas: In town.
Groups: No tours; shopping groups welcome, no need to phone first.
Transport: 10 minutes' walk from town centre.
Mail order: Yes.
Catalogue: Free.

Bee Line

Refurbishing Argyll motor works

Cotton & Chintz

Choosing lingerie

13 Auchtermuchty Fife

John Ford & Co.

30 Newburgh Rd
(01337) 828188

Good range of ladies' and men's knitwear and socks in natural fibres and wool blends. Also a range of school knitwear and socks. Country clothing including fleece jackets.

'All items perfect at reduced prices.'

Auchtermuchty is on the A91, half way between Kinross and Cupar. The shop is on the B983 north of town centre.

From the north on the B983: shop is in first factory on right.

From the A91 east or westbound: turn north on to the B983 for Newburgh and Perth. The shop is half a mile on the left in a low built factory.

Open: Mon–Fri 10–4. Most Bank Holidays, please phone to check.
Closed: For Christmas–New Year closures please check.
Cards: No.
Cars: In street.
Toilets: Ask if required.
Wheelchairs: One small step to medium sized shop, help gladly given.
Teas: Cafés and pubs in town.
Groups: No tours. Shopping groups welcome, no need to book.
Transport: Local buses from Glenrothes and St Andrews stop outside.
Mail order: No.

14 Ayr Strathclyde

Begg of Ayr

Viewfield Road KA8 8HK
(01292) 267615

High quality cashmere and lambswool: scarves, stoles, plaids, travel rugs etc, plain and tartan. Knitted garments in natural fibres from other companies.

At the northern end of Ayr, which is now pedestrianised. From Ayr you must aim for Prestwick.

From Prestwick going south on A79: go over railway bridge, turn left at roundabout into Viewfield Road.*

From Ayr town centre: aim north for Prestwick. Go north over river. Go right after Texaco on left (do not enter one-way street straight ahead); go straight at roundabout into Viewfield Road.*

From Ayr/Prestwick bypass (A77): turn into A719 for Ayr (north) [B743 leads off same roundabout]. Go straight at lights. Pass Tesco on left then racecourse. At next two roundabouts go right.*

If you go north across river: at fire station, go left (ring road north). At next roundabout go straight (for Prestwick) then right at second roundabout into Viewfield Road.*

****Shop 100 yds on left.***

Open: Mon–Fri 9.30–4.30. Please check Bank Holidays.
Closed: For Christmas–New closures please check.
Cards: Yes.
Cars: In yard.
Toilets: By roundabout.
Wheelchairs: One step to medium sized shop.
Teas: In Ayr.
Transport: Buses from Ayr–Prestwick: ask for Viewfield Road.

15 Ayr Strathclyde

Blindcraft

105 Main Street KA8 8BV
(01292) 263986

Beds, chairs, suites. Canetex furniture.

'All first quality.'

North of town centre and near Orient Bingo Club.

From Prestwick: go straight over roundabout into Main Street. After about 500 yds the shop is on corner site on right after The Newton Arms, opposite post office and next to Geordies Byre pub.

Open: Mon–Sat (except Wed) 9–5.30.
Closed: Wednesday; Glasgow holidays; Christmas, Boxing and New Year's Days.
Cards: Access, Visa.
Cars: Local car-parks.
Toilets: In local superstores.
Wheelchairs: Easy access.
Teas: Local cafés.
Groups: No.
Transport: Any bus to Ayr.
Mail order: No.

16 Bo'ness Central

Russell Corp UK

Linlithgow Road EH51 OPR
(01506) 826605

Wide range of sports clothing, sweatshirts, jogging bottoms, T-shirts, shorts, vests. Kids' sizes 22–32, adult sizes 34–50. Printed and embroidered garments. Can be personalised while you wait.

'Perfects and seconds; discontinued lines, colours and samples; printed and embroidered garments. Huge discount on retail prices. Home of Russell Athletic Sportswear.'

On industrial estate south of town, off A706.

From Bo'ness centre: take A706 for Linlithgow; cross A995 at traffic lights.*

From M9 exit 3: take A904 into Bo'ness; turn on to A706 at traffic lights.*

From main road bypassing Bo'ness centre: turn to Linlithgow at traffic lights.*

From Grangemouth & M9 exit 6: take A904; turn right on to A706 at traffic lights.*

****Go uphill, turn right immediately before modern fire station on right; shop is opposite fire station.***

From Linlithgow on A706: go left immediately after modern fire station as you enter town; shop is opposite fire station.

Open: Seven days: Mon–Fri 10–5.30; Sat 9–5; Sun 11–4. Bank Holidays.
Closed: Christmas, Boxing & New Year's Days; 2 Jan.
Cards: Access, Switch, Visa.
Cars: Own car-park and in street.
Toilets: No.
Wheelchairs: One small step.
Changing rooms: Yes.
Teas: In Bo'ness.
Groups: Shopping groups welcome.
Transport: Any bus to Bo'ness. Get off by chapel, walk uphill from lights (5 minutes).

17 Broxburn Lothian

Gleneagles Crystal

37 Simpson Road, East Mains Industrial Estate EH52 5AU
(01506) 852566

Wide range of crystal glass hand-cut here, including wine glasses, tumblers, decanters, bowls and vases, many in attractive gift boxes. Selected china, ceramic tableware and giftware from other leading manufacturers.

'Everything at factory prices. Slight seconds always available – from about £2.95 a glass.'

Nearly 6 miles west of Edinburgh.

From Edinburgh: take A8 to junction with M8; then take A89 for Broxburn. After 2 miles fork right at next roundabout on to A899.*

From Glasgow coming east on M8: take exit 3A. At Boghall roundabout go right (A89) for Broxburn. At roundabout with A899, go left.*

****Take first right into East Mains Industrial Estate. Go right at first roundabout, left at second. Clearly marked factory on left.***

Open: Mon–Sat 10–5; Sun 11–5. Bank Holidays.
Closed: Christmas, Boxing and New Year's Days; 2 Jan.
Cards: Access, Amex, Diners, Style, Switch, Visa.
Cars: In front of shop; also 100 spaces behind shop.
Toilets: Yes.
Wheelchairs: One small step into large shop.
Teas: Free coffee for visitors.
Groups: Groups welcome to shop: please book with shop manageress. Small groups (up to 6) can see glass-cutting any weekday (no charge).
Transport: Bus or train to Broxburn (East Mains Industrial Estate).
Mail order: Yes.
Catalogue: Free.

18 Campbeltown Strathclyde

Jaeger Man Tailoring

The Roading PA28 6TL
(01586) 553011

Men's wear, including suits, trousers, jackets, shirts and top quality knitwear, especially suitable for golfing. Knitwear, trousers, blouses, jackets, skirts for ladies. Bedding, towels, duvets.

'Modestly priced perfect ends of lines etc and seconds sold here.'

Easy to find on west side of Campbeltown in Kintyre.

Going south down west coast on A83: as you reach town, pass left turn-off to Carradale B842; take third right, 50 yds before Esso petrol station/Co-Op supermarket. Go right again (The Roading): well marked shop is 150 yds on right.

Going south down east coast on B842 from Arran ferry: as you reach town, do not go left for town centre but keep straight to T-junction. Turn left on to A83 then right as above before Esso/Co-Op.

From town: take west coast road (A83) north for Tarbert/Glasgow. Pass Co-Op on left then go left and first right (The Roading). Shop is 150 yds on right.

Open: Tues–Sat 10–4. Bank Holidays. Longer hours in the summer and pre-Christmas.
Closed: Monday; Christmas–New Year.
Cards: Access, Switch, Visa.
Cars: Own car-park at far end of factory.
Toilets: Ask if desperate. Public toilets 100 yds.
Wheelchairs: Three steps to small shop. Access possible with help.
Changing rooms: Yes.
Teas: In town.
Groups: Small groups welcome to shop at special times by appointment.
Transport: Any bus to Campbeltown.
Mail order: No.

19 Comrie Tayside

Mari Donald Knitwear

Craiglea, Pudding Lane PH6 2DR
(01764) 670150 (phone & fax)

Hand-framed cardigans in pure wool and natural yarns with special buttons. Patterns include dinosaurs, sheep, fish, space ships, sailing boats, music, horses etc for children and adults.

'Interesting, colourful and unique designs. Most items perfect, occasional seconds. From £9.50 for small child's sweater up to £70, according to size and design complexity.'

Located 20 yds off the main road through town (A85).

Coming east from Crieff: go over bridge, pass the Comrie Hotel on right and after 100 yds turn right into narrow Pudding Lane.

Coming from Comrie to Crieff: pass Esso petrol station on left, turn left into narrow Pudding Lane; shop is 20 yds on right.

Open: Usually Mon–Sat (small business so often closed when away for shows etc). Worth phoning first if travelling far.
Cards: Access, Visa.
Cars: In main road.
Toilets: In village.
Wheelchairs: Small showroom.
Changing rooms: Welcome to try garments on.
Teas: Local hotels.
Tours: Visitors welcome to ask to see garments made.
Transport: Infrequent buses.
Mail order: Yes.
Catalogue: Free price list and small colour swatch.

20 Crieff Tayside

Crieff Visitors' Centre

Muthill Road PH7 4HO
(01764) 654014

Pottery, plates, cups, soup tureens, tea and coffee pots; glass paperweights; whisky flagons; coloured glass bowls, vases, etc.

On the A822 south of Crieff.

From Comrie or Perth on A85: go straight through town to the T-junction at far end; turn left on to A822 for Stirling. Go straight, over river and turn right into company at end of town.

From A9: exit on to A823 for Gleneagles Hotel. Join A822 for Crieff; visitors centre is first complex on left (after Stuart Crystal on right).

Open: Seven days 9–5. Bank Holidays.
Closed: Phone for Christmas.
Cards: Yes.
Cars: Own large car-park.
Toilets: Yes, and for disabled.
Wheelchairs: Easy access to huge shop.
Teas: Own licensed restaurant.
Tours: Pottery tours, glass-works viewing gallery, video.

21 Crieff Tayside

Stuart Crystal

Muthill Road PH7 4HO
(01764) 654004

Vast range of full lead crystal: wine suites, wine glasses, tumblers, decanters, jugs, vases and extensive range of giftware. Also tantaluses (lockable display cases for decanters) and trays.

'Both best and second qualities available. Often special offers.'

See our display advertisement opposite

South of Crieff on the A822.

From Comrie or Perth on A85: go straight through town to T-junction at far end; go left on to A822 for Stirling. Go straight, over river and stay on main road until you see this well marked company on left at far end of town.

From A9: exit on to A823 as for Gleneagles Hotel. Join A822 for Crieff; Stuart Crystal, clearly visible, is first factory on right as you enter Crieff.

Open: Seven days a week, *winter:* 9–5; *summer:* 9–6.30. Bank Holidays.
Closed: Christmas, Boxing and New Year's Days.
Cards: Access, Amex, Diners, Mastercard, Switch, Visa.
Cars: Own large car-park.
Toilets: Yes.
Wheelchairs: Easy access to large shop.
Teas: Own coffee shop.
Tours: Self-guided tours to see engraving; video introduction.
Transport: About 1½ miles south of town centre.
Mail order: Yes. First and seconds sent by mail order.
Catalogue: Free stemware catalogue.

22 Cumnock Strathclyde

Cumnock Mill Shop

Caponacre Industrial Estate KA18 1SH
(01290) 421511

Extensive range of plain and tonal carpets in wool-rich and synthetic yarns, available in a wide selection of colours.

'Room size remnants and discontinued lines at heavily discounted prices to suit every pocket. UK mainland delivery arranged at minimal cost.'

In the industrial estate south of Cumnock.

From the A70, A76 southbound and town centre: head south for Dumfries for about ½ mile. Pass fire station on left, go downhill and at bottom go right into estate.*

From Dumfries coming north on A76: enter town; as you get to bottom of hill, pass Thistle Inn on left then go left into estate.*

****Follow road round to left: factory is on right.***

Open: Fri 2–6; Sat 10–4.30; Sun 12–4.30.
Closed: Mon–Thur; Friday am. Christmas–New Year.
Cards: MasterCard, Switch, Visa.
Cars: Large car-park on site.
Toilets: Yes.
Wheelchairs: Easy access; no steps.
Teas: In town.
Groups: No mill tours.
Transport: Difficult.
Mail order: No.

23 Cumnock Strathclyde

Falmer Jeans

Caponacre Industrial Estate KA18 1SH
(01290) 421577

Jeans and casualwear: dungarees, sweatshirts, cords, jumpers etc.

'All items ends of lines, previous year's ranges or slightly substandard stock at reduced prices.'

In the industrial estate south of Cumnock.

From the A70, A76 southbound and town centre: head south for Dumfries for about ½ mile. Pass fire station on left, go downhill and at bottom go right into estate.*

From Dumfries coming north on A76: enter town; as you get to bottom of hill, pass Thistle Inn on left, then go left into estate.*

****Follow road round to right: factory is on left at next T-junction.***

Open: Mon–Fri 9.30–5.30; Sat 9–4; Sun 11–4. Bank Holidays.
Closed: Christmas–New Year please check openings.
Cards: Access, Visa.
Cars: Outside factory.
Toilets: In Cumnock.
Wheelchairs: Easy access to very large shop.
Changing rooms: Yes.
Teas: In Cumnock.
Groups: Pre-booked shopping groups welcome.
Transport: Local buses.

24 Dalkeith Lothian

Dalkeith Mill Shop & Wool Centre

Thornybank Industrial Site EH22 2NE
(0131) 663 4502

Ladies' and men's knitwear in lambswool, shetland and angora. Hand knitting and machine knitting yarns. Housecoats, nightdresses, dressing gowns, pyjamas and slippers; children's clothing.

'High-quality seconds on sale. Stock changes frequently.'

Easy to find on north-east side of Dalkeith.

From the Edinburgh bypass (A720): turn off for Dalkeith (A68). At T-junction in town, go left for Musselburgh (A6094).*

From other directions: go into town and take the A6094 for Musselburgh.*

****Follow the road round; at the roundabout go straight towards Thornybank Industrial Site and Tranent. Take first left: shop is 200 yds on right.***

From Tranent, coming into Dalkeith on B6414: look for shop on left as you reach town.

Open: Mon–Thur 10–4; Fri 10–3.
Closed: Christmas–New Year; local holidays.
Cards: Access, Visa.
Cars: In road outside.
Toilets: Yes.
Wheelchairs: One step to small shop.
Changing rooms: Yes.
Teas: In Dalkeith.
Groups: Shopping groups welcome – please contact shop supervisor in advance.
Transport: Ten minutes' walk from town centre.

25 Dalry Ayrshire

The Factory Shop Ltd.

Drakemyre
(01294) 832791

Men's, ladies' and children's clothing, footwear, luggage, toiletries, hardware, household textiles, lighting and electrical goods. Fashion concessions department with famous brand names. *Cape Country* pine furniture exclusively produced for The Factory Shop.

'Large stock of branded and chainstore items, all at greatly reduced prices. Deliveries of new stock every week to give an ever changing selection.'

North of town centre on B780.

From town centre and A737: turn on to B780 for Kilbirnie. Continue following signs to Kilbirnie. The shop is on the right at the bottom of the hill as you leave town.

From the north of B780: pass the very large chemical plant on the left, and the shop is 500 yds on the left just as the road starts to climb up into town.

Open: Mon–Sat 10–5; Sun and Bank Holidays 11–5.
Closed: Christmas Day.
Cards: Switch, MasterCard, Visa.
Cars: Own car-park.
Toilets: Yes.
Wheelchairs: Easy access to shop.
Changing rooms: Yes.
Teas: Tearoom with home-made hot and cold foods.
Groups: Shopping groups welcome. For organiser/driver incentives please phone the shop manager.
Transport: Buses from Kilbirnie and Beith stop outside shop.
Mail order: Home delivery service for pine furniture. Please telephone for free catalogue and price list.

26 Dumfries Dumfries & Galloway

Factory Fabric Centre

26 Annan Road DG1 3AD
(01387) 247575

Quality curtain and upholstery fabrics. Curtain lining, tapes, and accessories. Full curtain make-up service.

'Perfects, seconds and remnants sold at discounted prices.'

On A75 east of town centre.

From the east on A75: follow signs for town centre (A75). At roundabout with John Pagan funeral directors straight ahead of you, fork right and shop is about 300 yds on left.

From all other directions: go to town centre and then follow signs for Carlisle (A75). Go over railway and go straight at roundabout with BMW garage on left. Shop is 150 yds on right.

Open: Mon–Fri 10–5; Sat 9–5; Sun and Bank Holidays 11–5.
Closed: Christmas, Boxing and New Year's Days.
Cards: Amex, MasterCard, Switch, Visa.
Cars: In street outside shop.
Toilets: No.
Wheelchairs: Easy access to large shop.
Teas: In town.
Groups: Groups welcome, prior phone call appreciated.
Transport: Bus no. 6 from Georgetown stops 200 yds from shop. Train station 600 yds.
Mail order: Fabrics can be despatched by post or carrier.

27 Dumfries Dumfries & Galloway

Robertsons of Dumfries

17 Belle Vue Street DG1 3EL
(01387) 255411 x 116

Men's and ladies' sweaters and cardigans in cashmere and geelong lambswool. Leggings, scarves etc.

'Many items ex-samples or cancelled orders. Men's cashmere V-neck sweater from £120, ladies' cashmere V-neck sweater from £110; men's and ladies' lambswool sweaters from £40.'

To the north-east side of town, on A709.

From west on A75 and north via A76/A71: get on or stay on A75 bypass (towards Carlisle) to roundabout where you meet A709. At this roundabout go towards Dumfries. Pass Peel Centre (retail centre) on left; after ½ mile turn left in front of white-painted workshop, into Balmoral Road.*

From town centre and south-west: follow signs to Lockerbie (A709). As you leave the centre go over railway, pass Shell petrol on left and after 400 yds turn right immediately after white-painted workshop into Balmoral Road.*

***After about 150 yds turn right into factory grounds and follow signs to shop.**

Open: Mon–Fri 10–4.
Bank Holidays.
Closed: Two weeks at Christmas; last week July & first week Aug.
Cards: All major credit cards except Amex.
Cars: Own large car-park.
Toilets: Yes.
Wheelchairs: One small step, wide doors, spacious shop.
Changing rooms: Yes.
Teas: In town.
Groups: No factory tours, but small groups welcome to shop, no need to book.
Transport: Dumfries rail station; Georgetown bus from Post Office in Great King Street.
Mail order: No.

28 Dundee Tayside

Dovetail Enterprises

Dunsinane Avenue, Dunsinane Industrial Estate DD2 3QN
(01382) 833890

Beds and mattresses. Standard sized beds in stock, special sizes made to order. High-backed chairs, conservatory, dining, bedroom, lounge and pine furniture.

Off Kingsway West, A90 Dundee bypass, north of town centre.

From Perth: at first roundabout (Swallow Hotel), take Kinsway West for Aberdeen. At third roundabout take sliproad for Coupar Angus; at top of sliproad go right for city centre; take first left, Dunsinane Ave. Cross Broomhill Road. Shop at next crossing.

From Aberdeen: take A90 bypass. Go straight at several roundabouts until you pass Texaco on left by one of roundabouts. At next roundabout (signposted Dryburgh Industrial Estate) go left (but take second exit) into Kings Cross Road. Take first right, Dunsinane Avenue. Take third left, Craigowl Street. Car-park is on the right.

Open: Mon–Fri 9–5; Sat 10.30–4
Closed: Bank Holidays; Christmas, Boxing and New Year's Days; local holidays.
Cards: Delta, MasterCard, Switch, Visa.
Cars: Own car-park.
Toilets: Yes, and for disabled.
Wheelchairs: Easy access, all on level ground.
Teas: In town.
Tours: No.
Transport: Bus nos. 1A and 1BB from city centre to Coupar Angus, alight at Dunsinane Ave; bus nos. 3 and 4 from city centre to Kings Cross Avenue, alight at Dunsinane Ave.
Mail order: Yes. Carriage charged at cost.
Catalogue: Free.

29 Dundee Tayside

Huskie Clothing Co.

Angus Works, North Isla Street DD1 3LS
(01382) 819990

Adults' outdoor clothing and footwear – jackets, cagoules, fleeces, jeans, cords, T-shirts, polo shirts, sweatshirts, knitwear, leisure boots, socks, hats and gloves. Workwear from top to toe – boiler suits, workshirts, coats, jackets, trousers, waterproofs, safety footwear.

'Also embroider own products for birthday presents, sports clubs, company logos etc.'

On north side of town, just off clearly marked ring road B960. Opposite Radio Tay and 100 yds from Tannadice Park and 200 yds from Dens Park football ground.

From A90 (Perth–Aberdeen Road): at large roundabout (Texaco on corner) go towards Kings Cross Hospital and Coldside (southwards on Strathmartine Road). At roundabout with 5 roads, take second exit, Moncur Crescent (runs into Dens Road). Go downhill, pass stadium (Dens Park) on left; take next left (North Isla Street) opposite car depot.

From Dundee city centre: go uphill and anti-clockwise round ring-road B960 (Victoria Road then Dens Road) for about 1 mile. Turn right into North Isla Street, opposite car depot on left.

Open: Mon–Fri 9–5; Sat 9–1. Bank Holidays.
Closed: Few days at Christmas and New Year (phone for exact dates); local holiday Mondays.
Cards: Access, Switch, Visa.
Cars: Ample street parking nearby.
Toilets: In supermarket nearby.
Wheelchairs: Level (assisted) access through loading bay to large shop.
Changing rooms: Yes.
Teas: In supermarket nearby.
Groups: No factory tours.
Transport: Buses stop in Hilltown 5 minutes away, and in Dens Road 2 minutes away.
Mail order: Yes. Phone orders accepted with credit card.
Catalogue: Free price list/ order form.

30 Dunfermline Fife

Seconds & Firsts

61 Pilmuir Street KY12 0RF
(01383) 729885

Huge range of men's wear, ladies' wear, children's wear and household goods. Occasional clearances of design room samples and fabric remnants.

'A complete offer of first and second quality famous chainstore garments at generally up to half the high street store prices.'

On A823 north of town centre.

From all directions: get on to town centre bypass. Follow signs to Carnegie Drive and A823 to Crieff. Turn off Carnegie Drive at traffic lights signed A823 to Crieff, travel 400 yds and shop is on far corner (car-park immediately after shop).

From Crieff on A823: enter town; pass first sign to Stirling, shop is on near corner (car-park before shop).

Open: Mon–Sat 9–5.30; Sun 10–5. Bank Holidays.
Closed: Christmas and New Year's Days.
Cards: Access, Style, Switch, Visa.
Cars: Own car-park beside shop.
Toilets: Yes, including for disabled.
Wheelchairs: Full access to shop with ramp to rear area.
Changing rooms: Yes, male and female.
Teas: In town.
Groups: Shopping groups welcome with prior phone call.
Transport: Four minutes' walk from main bus station in town centre.
Mail order: No.

31 Dunoon Strathclyde

Dunoon Ceramics

Hamilton Street
(01369) 704360

Wide selection of coffee mugs; stone and chinaware, milk jugs, sugar bowls etc.

At the northern end of town.

From south on A815/Dunoon Pier (ferry from Gourock): go through town centre (not along coast); go left opposite police station.

From north (Sandbank): you enter town on A815. Go right opposite police station. Pottery clearly marked.

From Hunter's Quay : go south to town. Take third right (after church) into Kirn Brae; pass school on right, fork left, Bencorrum Brae; take A815 to town. Go right opposite police station.

Open: Mon–Fri 9–12.30 & 1–4.30. Bank Holidays.
Closed: Christmas–New Year (please check).
Cards: Yes.
Cars: Car-park outside factory.
Toilets: Yes.
Wheelchairs: Ramp, sizeable shop.
Groups: Please check.

32 East Kilbride Strathclyde

Corston Sinclair

36 Glenburn Road, College Milton North G74 5BE
(013552) 38161

Workwear such as coveralls, safety & occupational footwear, high visibility clothing, waterproof clothing and chemical clothing. Also leisurewear, including outdoor, waterproof and thermal clothing, walking and rambling boots, walking and sports socks etc. Stockists of curling equipment.

'Only perfects at substantially lower than retail prices.'

In industrial area west of town.

From M74 exit 5: follow signs to East Kilbride town centre via A725. At large roundabout with steel balls in the middle follow signs to Strathaven, Paisley A725 (A726). At next roundabout go straight, and at following roundabout turn right on to A726 for Paisley. Continue straight over a few roundabouts to the one with McDonald's on far left. Turn right here for College Milton North.*

From the west on A726: go left at roundabout with McDonald's on near right corner signposted to College Milton North.*

****Take first left and immediately left again. Pass JVC on right and Hannay Recycling on right, and turn right in front of 'no entry' road. The factory is first on right after the right bend.***

Open: Mon–Thur 8.30–4.30; Fri 8.30–4.
Closed: Bank Holidays. Christmas–New Year for two weeks.
Cards: Access, Delta, Switch, Visa.
Cars: Outside shop.
Toilets: No.
Wheelchairs: No, shop is on first floor. Very large shop.
Changing rooms: Yes.
Teas: In town.
Groups: No factory tours. Small shopping groups welcome anytime, larger groups please give two days' notice by phone.
Transport: Unfortunately none.
Mail order: No.

33 East Kilbride Strathclyde

Fruit of the Loom/Big L

Unit 7B, Kingsgate Retail Park G74 4UN
(013552) 45452 & 41413

Two shops with massive range of jeans, T-shirts, leisurewear, sweatshirts, shirts and jackets.

North of East Kilbride off A749.

From M74 exit 5: take A725 to East Kilbride. At the V-junction (left to town centre) fork right for Nerston. At roundabout turn right towards Glasgow; at next roundabout exit for retail park.

From East Kilbride: take A749 for Glasgow. As you leave town, exit for retail park at roundabout with Sainsbury's petrol on left. From Glasgow and Rutherglen on A749: pass Nerston Village on left. At first roundabout, turn right for retail park.

Open: Mon–Fri 10–8; Sat 9–6; Sun 10–5.
Closed: Christmas and New Year's Days.
Cards: Yes.
Cars: Own large car-park.
Toilets: In Sainsbury's.
Wheelchairs: Easy access, no steps, large shop.
Changing rooms: Yes.
Teas: In Sainsbury's.
Groups: Shopping groups welcome.
Transport: Bus nos. 14, 14a, 14b, 66, 66a, 66b.

34 Edinburgh

Anta

32 High Street, The Royal Mile EH1 1TB
(0131) 557 8300

Tartan ceramics, furnishing fabrics, mugs, rugs, throws and flat weave carpets.

'Specialists in contemporary and reproduction tartans; makers of the original tartan tableware. All goods perfect, sold at discounted prices.'

In the centre of Edinburgh opposite John Knox House and next to the Museum of Childhood.

From the crossing of North Bridge and High Street: go down hill and the shop is about 200 yds on the right.

Open: Seven days 10–6 (during Edinburgh Festival late nights till 8).
Closed: Christmas Day.
Cards: All major credit and debit cards.
Cars: Public car-park in old bus station 5 minutes' walk.
Toilets: Nearest at Waverley Station.
Wheelchairs: Easy access; no steps to small shop.
Changing rooms: No.
Teas: Excellent café next door.
Groups: Small shopping groups welcome.
Transport: Five minutes' walk from Waverley Station.
Mail order: Yes. Only perfect goods by mail order.
Catalogue: Free.

35 Edinburgh

Belinda Robertson Cashmere

22 Palmerston Place EH12 7AM
(0131) 225 1057

Ladies' and men's knitwear in cashmere.

In the west end of Edinburgh.

From town centre, ie Princes Street: go towards Glasgow. This takes you to the one-way system by Haymarket station. Go around one-way system until you face back to Princes Street again but take first left after the Bank of Scotland (lights and signpost to Forth Road Bridge). Shop is 100 yds on left.

From the west and south-west on A70, A71 or A8: join the Haymarket one-way system. Follow sign to Forth Road Bridge at lights with Bank of Scotland on your near left and Royal Bank of Scotland on far left. The shop is 100 yds on left.

Open: Mon–Fri 9–5.30; Sat 10–4.
Closed: Phone about Christmas.
Cards: Yes.
Cars: Few pay-&-display spaces by shop. Car-parks in town.
Toilets: Yes.
Wheelchairs: Four steps.
Changing rooms: Yes.
Teas: Cafés nearby.
Groups: Shopping groups should phone in advance.
Transport: Buses to Haymarket. Edinburgh Haymarket train station.

36 Edinburgh

Blindcraft Edinburgh

Peffer Place EH16 4BA
(0131) 659 6473

Beds and bedding for hotels, contract and domestic use; special sizes to order. Pine bunks and headboards; pocket and interior sprung mattresses; pillows and quilts; ottoman and bedroom stools and chairs. Pine furniture.

'Direct from factory prices. Delivery service within the UK – ask for quotation (price usually varies with weight).'

On south-east side of Edinburgh.

From A68 (Dalkeith–Edinburgh road): take A6095 at roundabout for Craigmillar. Pass brewery on left, go left at next lights.*

From east/Musselburgh: take A6095. Go under A1; continue until you pass Shoprite on right. Go right at next traffic lights.*

***Take next right (Peffer Place): factory is first on right. Follow signs to shop.**

Open: Mon–Sat 9.30–5; Sun 11–4.
Closed: Christmas and Boxing Days; 1 & 2 Jan. Local public holidays, please check.
Cards: Access, Switch, Visa; credit terms can be arranged.
Cars: Outside shop.
Toilets: Ask if desperate.
Wheelchairs: No step.
Teas: In nearby Carmeron Toll shopping centre.
Groups: No factory tours.
Transport: Bus no. 21 from Princes Street; C3 and 14 from North Bridge.
Mail order: Yes.
Catalogue: Request brochure.

37 Edinburgh

Cotton & Chintz

Turnhouse Road EH12 8NR
(0131) 339 3292 Fax (0131) 339 5249

Furnishing fabrics, own range of linen unions, weaves, chenilles, checks and stripes. Florals and chintzes, damasks, tapestries, jaquards, silks, moirés. Some designer clearance and seconds. Large stocks, all great value.

'Designer fabric clearance shop. Fabrics from £5 to £25 per metre.'

West of Edinburgh and east of the airport, in a small industrial estate off the A8.

From the west on M8 or M9: follow signs to the airport. Once on the A8 pass the airport on left, go under the roundabout at the beginning of A720 City of Edinburgh by-pass, and turn sharp left at first roundabout signposted to Air Cargo.*

From Edinburgh on A8: as you leave town, pass The Royal Scot Hotel on left and turn right at lights,with Shell petrol on right, for A902 for Forth Bridge and Air Cargo. Immediately turn left following signs to Air Cargo.*

***After 400 yds turn right into West Craigs Industrial Estate. The shop is 150 yds on right.**

Open: Mon–Sat & Bank Holidays 9.30–5.30. Sun 12–4.
Closed: Christmas and New Year's Days. Phone to check Easter Sunday.
Cards: Access, Switch, Visa.
Cars: Huge car-park in front of shop.
Toilets: Yes.
Wheelchairs: No steps to huge warehouse.
Teas: Local pubs and cafés.
Groups: Groups welcome.
Transport: Bus no. 31 stop 250 yds away.
Mail order: Please ring for our mail order and swatch enquiry service.

See our entry below

38 Elderslie near Johnstone Strathclyde

Glenpatrick Mill Shop

see map on p. 717

Glenpatrick Road PA5 9UK
(01505) 577009

Wide range of ends of rolls in carpets, mostly 80/20% wool/nylon in a range of patterns and plain colours. Axminster, Wilton, bonded and tufted. Underfelt.

'Offcuts, remnants, discontinued lines, ends of contract orders and imperfects at prices significantly lower than elsewhere. Reasonably priced delivery arranged in UK.'

See our display advertisement above

Easy to find, between Johnstone and Paisley.

From Johnstone: turn right off B789 at traffic lights with Citroën garage facing turn-off, pub on one corner.*

From M8 exit 29: take A737 towards Irvine. At next exit turn left on to A761 for Paisley and Elderslie. Pass Asda on left, go under railway and at roundabout turn right for B789 Johnstone. In Elderslie turn left at traffic lights opposite Citroën garage.*

****Continue along Glenpatrick Road. Pass large carpet mill on left and follow signs to mill shop. Car-park at far end.***

Open: Tues, Wed, Thur, Sun 9.30–4.30.
Closed: Mon, Fri, Sat; Christmas–New Year period. Easter weekend; first full week May; last week July & first two weeks Aug; mid-Sept weekend. Phone for dates.
Cards: Mastercard, Visa.
Cars: Large car-park.
Toilets: Yes.
Wheelchairs: One small step to large shop.
Teas: Not in immediate vicinity. Pubs in area.
Groups: No mill tours.
Transport: Difficult.
Mail order: No.

39 Elgin Grampian

Johnstons Cashmere Visitor Centre

Newmill IV30 2AE
(01343) 554099 Fax (01343) 554080
e-mail: johnston@elgin.win-uk.net

Fine quality cashmere and woollen knitwear, cloth, classic tailored clothing, scarves, rugs, stoles, serapes etc.

'Perfects and occasionally seconds on sale.'

Across the river Lossie from the ruins of Elgin Cathedral.

From town centre: go east on to A96 towards Aberdeen; turn left at second roundabout.*

From Aberdeen on A96: go right at roundabout.*

From Inverness on A96: continue (towards Aberdeen) on Alexandra Road.*

From Aberlour on A941: go right at roundabout after railway bridge.*

****Follow brown signs to Johnstons Cashmere Visitor Centre.***

Open: All year Mon–Sat 9–5.30 (*July–Sept* 9–6); *also Sun June–Sept* 11–5.
Closed: Christmas, Boxing, New Year's Days & 2 Jan.
Cards: Amex, MasterCard, Switch, Visa.
Cars: Own car-park.
Toilets: Yes.
Wheelchairs: Easy access to car-park, coffee shop, toilets & large shop (lift to first floor).
Changing rooms: Yes.
Teas: Own coffee shop for light meals and snacks etc.
Tours: Free access to Visitor Centre. Audio-visual presentation in 6 languages. Free mill tours on working days by arrangement (no maximum number but large parties must book in advance).
Transport: Bus or rail.
Mail order: Yes. No seconds posted.
Catalogue: Free. Extra spring and autumn special offers.

40 Falkirk Strathclyde

Wrangler Factory Outlet

Glasgow Road, Camelon FK1 4HW
(01324) 632509

Large selection of men's, ladies' and youths' jeans, T-shirts, shirts, sweatshirts.

'Seconds and ends of lines at greatly reduced prices.'

On the A803 west of Falkirk.

From Falkirk: head west for Stirling and Glasgow. Follow signs to Mariner Centre. Pass Mariner Centre and red/yellow sign of Budget Exhausts on left; clearly marked shop is on the right.

Coming into Falkirk on A803: pass the Rover showroom on left and after 300 yds turn left into well marked company.

Open: Mon–Sat and Bank Holidays 9.30–5.30; Sun 11–5.
Closed: Christmas, Boxing & New Year's Days.
Cards: Access, Switch, Visa.
Cars: In factory car-park.
Toilets: No.
Wheelchairs: Access through side entrance at security lodge.
Changing rooms: Yes.
Teas: Local pubs.
Groups: Groups welcome but please phone first.
Transport: Bus no. 37 (Midland Bluebird) stops outside.
Mail order: No.

41 Fochabers Grampian

Baxters Visitor Centre

IV32 7LD
(01343) 820666

Full range of own world-famous speciality foods – soups, chutneys, jams. Cookshop with unusual quality gift items and cookery utensils. The *George Baxter* Cellar is stocked with the complete range of *Baxter* speciality food products and the Best of Scotland.

'Visit and share in the Baxter story.'

One mile west of Fochabers and 8 miles east of Elgin on A96 (main Aberdeen/Inverness road).

From Fochabers: go west for Elgin/Inverness. Baxters are about 1 mile out of town on right, just after you cross river.

From Inverness/Elgin direction on A96: the Visitor Centre is clearly marked on left before you enter Fochabers.

Open: Seven days 10–5.30.
Closed: Christmas and Boxing Days; 1 & 2 Jan.
Cards: Access, Switch, Visa.
Cars: Large car-park for cars and coaches.
Toilets: Yes, and for disabled.
Wheelchairs: Easy access to large Visitor Centre (but not on factory tour).
Teas: Self-service restaurant, picnic area.
Tours: Free factory tours 9.30–11.30 and 12.30–4. Last tour on Friday at 2. Parties please book in advance. No tours weekends and during factory holidays. Cooking demonstrations by appointment.
Transport: Local bus from Elgin (town) about every hour.
Mail order: Yes. Free mail order freephone 0800 186800.
Catalogue: Yes.

Fort William Highlands and Islands

Late Entry

Scottish Sweater Store

61 High Street PH33 6DH
(01397) 700799
e-mail: chasn.whillans@virgin.net

Extensive range of ladies' and men's luxury cashmere pullovers in single ply, 2-ply and 4-ply cashmere from *Pringle, Lyle & Scott* and own *Chas N Whillans* collection. *Pringle Nick Faldo* and *Cross Creek* golfwear; lambswool and cotton pullovers. Travel rugs, cashmere and lambswool gloves and scarves, *Pringle* socks.

'Ladies' and men's cashmere pullovers from £99 for perfects and about £79 for samples and slight imperfects.'

In town centre.

Aim for car-park at west end of High Street or at Cameron Square. Shop is 200 yds from Cameron Square opposite the Tourist Information Centre.

Open: Mon–Fri 9–5.30; Sat 9–5.30. Bank Holidays.
Closed: Christmas & Boxing Days; 1 & 2 Jan.
Cards: Major credit cards, Delta, Switch.
Cars: Large car-park 2 minutes' walk.
Toilets: 2 minutes' walk.
Wheelchairs: 2 steep steps to medium sized shop.
Changing rooms: Yes.
Teas: Many cafés and hotels in town.
Groups: Shopping groups welcome.
Transport: Buses to Fort William.
Mail order: Yes.
Catalogue: Two free catalogues each year; please phone (01450) 373128, or fax (01450) 376082.

42 Galashiels Borders

Rogerson Clearing Shop

38–40 High Street TD1 1SE
(01896) 753475

Wide range of ladies' and men's footwear. Brands include *Ecco, Clarks, Gabor, Van-Dal, Loake, Barker, Mephisto, H.B., Salamander, Camel, Mann* and many others.

'This is the clearance shop for Rogersons, a large chain of shoe shops in Scotland. Reductions up to 50% off high street prices. Some footwear is made especially for this company. Also buy in ends of lines, slight substandards etc.'

See our display advertisement opposite

On one-way system in the centre of town opposite Iceland.

From Peebles and Innerleithen (the west) on A72: at first traffic lights turn left into one-way system. After 30 yds turn right for town centre. At T-junction turn right – shop is 20 yds on right. Turn hard left after Iceland for car-park.

From all other directions: get into one-way system of Galashiels (you have no other choice). Continue until you get into Bank Street (long gardens on left) and follow right and left turn into High Street (over pedestrian crossing), pass Poundstretcher store on the right of the left bend – shop is 40 yds on right.

Open: Mon–Sat 9.30–5.30.
Closed: Christmas Day; 1 & 2 Jan.
Cards: Access, Diners, Switch, Visa.
Cars: Public car-park by Iceland.
Toilets: In town.
Wheelchairs: Easy access to men's department; two steps to ladies' department; medium-sized shop.
Teas: In town.
Groups: Shopping groups please phone.
Transport: Any buses to town centre. Short walk to shop.
Mail order: No.

43 Galston Strathclyde

Balmoral Mill Shop

16 Church Lane KA4 8HE
(01563) 820213 Fax (01563) 821740

Classics in cashmere, plain and patterned lambswool, kilted skirts, blouses, embroidered knitwear. Fashionable branded knitwear including *Farah, Lyle & Scott, Alice Collins, Acorn Designs.* Leisurewear including polo shirts, sweatshirts, golf shirts, pullovers and bowling wear. Ladies' and gents', children's and babies' wear.

'Many seconds (some from £4.95) including own brand plus chainstore items.'

See our display advertisement opposite

On the A719, the main road heading through Galston, by the river bridge.

From town centre: follow A719 towards A71 for Edinburgh. As road begins to rise over river you see shop on left.

From Kilmarnock or Edinburgh on A71: at roundabout take A719 for Galston. Cross the river: clearly marked shop is in first building on right.

Open: Mon–Sat and Bank Holidays 9–5; Sun 11–4.30.
Closed: Christmas, Boxing and New Year's Days.
Cards: Access, Switch, Visa.
Cars: Ample space to rear of shop.
Toilets: Yes.
Wheelchairs: Ramp from car-park entrance; front entrance five steps. Large shop.
Changing rooms: Yes.
Teas: Own coffee shop with home baking.
Groups: Coaches welcome by arrangement.
Transport: Buses from Glasgow, Kilmarnock, Ayr etc stop outside.
Mail order: Yes. Phone orders for shop stock welcome.
Catalogue: Free club brochure. Minimum order 8 garments with standard embroidery design, or 24, with club's own design.

CLEARING SHOP
BETTER SHOES FOR LESS

ENDS OF LINES, MANUFACTURERS CLEARANCE, FIRST GRADE SUBS.

GABOR, ECCO, VAN-DAL, LOAKE, CLARKS, K, MEPHISTO, SIMONSIDE, H.B., AMALFI, MANN, SIOUX, PLUS MANY MORE TOP BRANDS.

HUGE REDUCTIONS ON R.R.P....UP TO 50% OFF

38-40 HIGH STREET
GALASHIELS

01896 753475

See our entry opposite

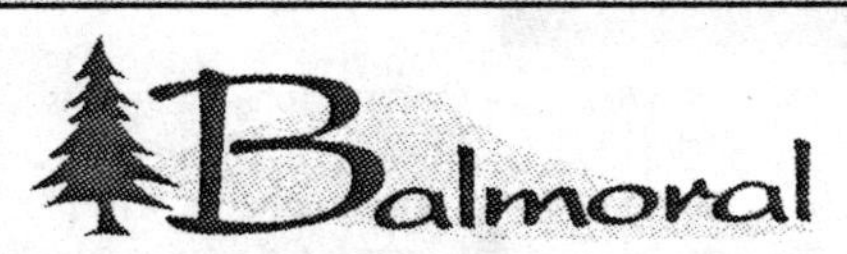

Balmoral Knitwear
15 Church Lane, Galston, Ayrshire
Tel: 01563 820213
Open Mon–Sat 9–5; Sun 11–4.30

Visit our mill shop for a wide range of classics and branded fashionable knitwear for all the family

See our entry opposite

44 Glasgow : Bridgeton *see map opposite*

Glenmore

55 Broad Street G40 2QB
(0141) 554 8444

Many styles of wax jackets including wading jackets & stockman coats; tweed shooting jackets, quilted jackets and waistcoats, blousons, anoraks, parkas. Children's T-shirts and polo-shirts. School blazers. Ladies' coats and jackets, skirts and suits. Waterproof jackets and golf suits. Materials and remnants.

'2500 sq ft filled with quality garments for all the family. Current season's overmakes, cancelled orders, designer samples, leading brands and chainstore perfects and seconds all at less than half retail price.'

In Bridgeton about 1 mile east of Glasgow city centre.

From M8 exit 15: follow signs to city centre and Glasgow Cross (large clocktower in middle of road). Continue straight across the river and take first left into A74. Cross the river again and by Bridgeton train station stay on A74, then take first left into Summer Street. The shop is straight ahead at next junction.

From Birkenshaw on A74: pass large Belvidere Hospital, and after about ½ mile pass Jet petrol on the right and take next right. The shop is straight ahead at the next junction.

Open: Mon, Wed, Fri, Sat 10–2; for Tues and Thur contact factory reception near shop.
Closed: Bank Holidays; for factory holiday closures please phone; Christmas–New Year.
Cards: Mastercard; Visa.
Cars: Own large car-park at front.
Toilets: Ask if required.
Wheelchairs: Easy access to spacious ground floor shop.
Changing rooms: Yes.
Teas: Local cafés about 200 yds.
Groups: No factory tours; shopping groups welcome (larger groups please phone).
Transport: Bridgeton rail station and Bridgeton Cross bus stop both 200 yds.
Mail order: No.

45 Glasgow : Ibrox *see map opposite*

Kingsman Antiques

247 Paisley Road West G51 1NF
(0141) 419 0002 (phone & fax)

Specialist manufacturers of traditional solid pine beds and tables; fire surrounds, cheval mirrors, wardrobes, corner units, hi-fi cupboards, CD units. All items made from old wood, waxed, polished and lacquered. From stock or made to measure.

'All items are first quality.'

On A8, south-west of town centre, near Ibrox Park football ground.

From the west on M8: take exit 21. Keep to left slip-road and at bottom go left, Seaward Street. At traffic lights turn left on to A8. Shop is about ¼ mile on left, shortly after post office.

Coming from Glasgow along Paisley Road (A8): pass Paisley Road Toll and the shop is about 300 yds on the left, shortly after the post office.

Coming from east (from Edinburgh direction) on M8: exit at 23. At end of slip road turn right, go over motorway and turn right on to A8 at the lights. Pass the Swallow hotel on the right, go through two traffic lights and the shop is shortly on right on far corner with Edwin Street.

Open: Mon–Sat 9–5.30. Most Bank Holidays, please phone to check.
Closed: Christmas and New Year's Days.
Cards: Access, Visa.
Cars: By side entrance.
Toilets: Yes.
Wheelchairs: Easy access; no steps.
Teas: Plenty of cafés nearby.
Groups: Shopping groups welcome; please phone Catherine Kingsman.
Transport: Cessnock or Kinning Park underground stations; regular bus service from Glasgow city centre.
Mail order: No.
Catalogue: Free.

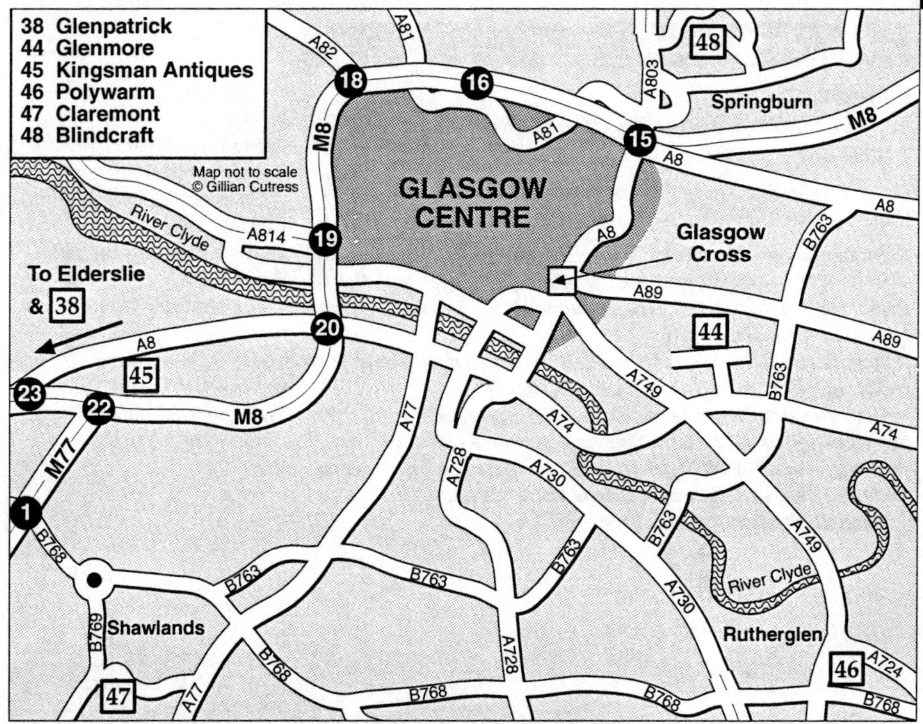

Coatbridge Strathclyde

MacKinnon of Scotland

MacKinnon Mills, Kirkshaws Road
(01236) 440702

Edinburgh Woollen Mill and specialist shops for designer knitwear, casual separates, men's and ladies' outerwear. Golf clothing and equipment. Traditional Scottish products including tartans and food.

'MacKinnon goods at bargain prices.'

South of town near junction of A8 and A725.

From Edinburgh on M8 (A8): exit for A725 Coatbridge. Cross over A8.*

From Glasgow on M8: go under M73 and leave M8 (A8) for A725 Coatbridge. At end of slip road turn right.*

****At roundabout with The Grange pub, go left. Mill is on right, clearly marked.***

Late Entry

Open: Daily 10–6 (Thur till 8).
Closed: Christmas and New Year's Days.
Cards: MasterCard, Style, Switch, Visa.
Cars: Own car-park.
Toilets: Yes.
Wheelchairs: Easy access to huge centre.
Changing rooms: Yes.
Teas: Large coffee shop/restaurant.
Groups: Shopping groups welcome. Free self-guided tour within shop.
Transport: Train to Coatbridge Central; bus nos. 17, 260, 261 from Coatbridge to Kirkshaws Road.

46 Glasgow : Rutherglen *map previous page*

Polywarm

Cambuslang Road, Farme Cross G73 1RR
(0141) 647 2392/3/4

Duvets, pillows, sleeping bags, duvet covers, cot quilts, imperfect bedding products, mattress protectors.

In Rutherglen on the A724.

From M74 exit 5: go towards Hamilton; go right on to A724 to Cambuslang and go right through Cambuslang. Go under railway bridge; shop ½ mile on left.

From East Kilbride on A749: cross Rutherglen main street at traffic lights and go right at next traffic lights.*

From Glasgow Cross: take A730 to Rutherglen. After the river, signs change to 'A730 East Kilbride'. Stay on A730 until the crossing with B768, then go left to Rutherglen and Cambuslang. Go left at next and right at following traffic lights.*

****Shop 200 yds on right.***

Open: Mon–Thur 9–4.30; Fri 9–4.
Closed: Bank Holidays; Christmas–New Year; for other closures please check.
Cards: Yes.
Cars: In company car-park.
Toilets: No.
Wheelchairs: Two steps to small shop.
Teas: In Rutherglen.
Groups: No factory tours.
Transport: 10 minutes' walk from centre. Local buses.

47 Glasgow : Shawlands *map previous page*

Claremont Garments

2 Coustonholm Road G43 1VF
(0141) 649 7080

Huge shop selling ladies' wear: jackets, separates, trousers, blouses, skirts, coats and lingerie.

'Ends of lines, slightly substandard stock etc at considerably reduced prices. Newly refurbished shop.'

See our display advertisement on p. 539

Close to Pollokshaws East train station.

Going north from Kilmarnock via A77: go under orange railway bridge marked Pollokshaws East. Take next left (Coustonholm Road). After railway bridge shop is 150 yds on left.

From Glasgow Central Station: go down Jamaica Street, cross Glasgow Bridge on to A77; pass Queens Park on left, go straight at lights at far end of park; go straight at next lights; go right after pedestrian lights in front of Bank of Scotland into Coustonholm Road. After railway bridge, shop is 150 yds on left.

From M8 westbound: at exit 22 turn on to M77. Take exit 1, go left and fork left at lights. At lights after Safeway on right, go right over railway, then right again (signs to Kilmarnock Road). In Kilmarnock Road go right after 350 yds, after pedestrian lights in front of Bank of Scotland into Coustonholm Road. After railway bridge, shop is 150 yds on left.

Open: Mon–Sat 9.45–4.45.
Closed: Easter Monday; Christmas, Boxing and New Year's Days, 2 Jan; Glasgow holidays.
Cards: Access, Visa.
Cars: In street.
Toilets: No.
Wheelchairs: No lift to upstairs shop.
Changing rooms: Yes.
Teas: Café near station.
Groups: No factory tours but groups to shop welcome. Prior phone call please.
Transport: Trains to Pollokshaws East then short walk.
Mail order: No.

48 Glasgow : Springburn *map on earlier page*

Royal Strathclyde Blindcraft Industries

Atlas Industrial Estate G21 1BR
(0141) 558 1485

Office furniture, beds, school furniture, residential furniture and computer furniture.

In Springburn, north/north-east of the city centre.

From city centre/other directions: get on M8, go to exit 15; take A803 for Kirkintilloch and Springburn (A8 also gets to this junction). At traffic lights turn right, pass Barnhill BR station; immediately go left into Edgefauld Road. Atlas Industrial Estate is next on left; Blindcraft straight ahead.

Open: Mon–Thur 9–4; Fri 9–12.30.
Closed: Bank Holidays.
Cards: Access, Visa.
Cars: Own car-park.
Toilets: In shopping centre.
Wheelchairs: Easy access to limited showroom.
Teas: In town.
Groups: No.
Transport: Bus nos. 11, 12, 37 pass nearby.
Mail order: No.
Catalogue: Free.

49 Glenrothes Fife

Keela International

Nasmyth Road, Southfield Industrial Estate KY6 2SB
(01592) 771241

High performance waterproof, breathable jackets, fleece jackets, waterproof overtrousers, golf suits, waterproof padded jackets, ventile garments, high visibility reflective clothing.

'Ends of lines, slight substandard items at reduced prices.'

South-west of Glenrothes.

From A92 northbound: at first roundabout as you come towards Glenrothes, turn left for B921 to Kinglassie.*

From A92 southbound and from town centre: stay or get on to A92 towards Kirkcaldy. At roundabout crossing the B921 turn right for Kinglassie.*

****Go straight at next two roundabouts (Stenton and Southfield roundabouts) [disregard sign to Southfield at second roundabout] and exit for Leslie and Glenrothes West at next exit. At end of slip road go right. Take second right (Cavendish Way), then first right into Ramsden Road. Shop in second unit left after left bend.***

Open: Mon–Thur 9–4.30; Fri, Sat 9–11.30.
Closed: Christmas and New Year.
Cards: Access, Visa.
Cars: Outside shop and in street.
Toilets: Yes.
Wheelchairs: One step to small shop.
Changing rooms: No.
Teas: In town.
Groups: No tours of factory but shopping groups welcome.
Transport: None.
Mail order: Yes. Only seconds by mail order.
Catalogue: No.

50 Hamilton Strathclyde

Peter MacArthur & Co.

Woodside Walk ML3 7HZ
(01698) 282544

Woollen cloths, woollen and mohair travel rugs, knee rugs and stoles; skirts and scarves in wool, mohair and cashmere. All natural fibres.

'Largest tartan manufacturers in the world. Mostly perfects, fabrics from £5 per metre, skirts from about £20. Often special offers.'

Close to town centre (south of railway line) in a one-way street.

From all directions except Strathaven: get on to town centre one-way system. Follow signs to A723 Strathaven. After leaving one-way system for Strathaven, go over railway bridge. At next roundabout go left then sharp left into one-way road.*

From Strathaven on A723: go downhill towards town centre. After Esso petrol station at roundabout go right, then take first sharp left into one-way street.*

****After next left bend, shop is 120 yds on left.***

Open: Mon–Fri 9–12.30 & 1.30–5. Bank Holidays.
Closed: Possibly week before Easter. Worth phoning if travelling far in mid-summer; Christmas–New Year.
Cards: No.
Cars: Car-park past shop on left.
Toilets: On request.
Wheelchairs: Three steps to medium sized shop.
Changing rooms: Yes.
Teas: In town.
Tours: No.
Transport: From bus/railway station go to railway bridge, go right in front of it. Take second left; shop 80 yds on right.
Mail order: Will post specific items by special request.
Catalogue: No.

Hawick Borders

see map opposite

Chas N Whillans

Teviotdale Mills, Albert Road TD9 7AQ
(01450) 373128 Fax (01450) 376082
e-mail: chasn.whillans@virgin.net

Extensive range of cashmere and lambswool pullovers from *Barrie, Pringle, N Peal, Lyle & Scott, Glenmac* and own *Chas N Whillans* label; range of *Barbour* country clothing, leisure wear from *Tulchan* and *Alice Collins; Pringle Nick Faldo* golfwear; *Cross Creek* golfwear; trousers and skirts from *Brandtex;* travel rugs etc.

'Ladies' and men's cashmere pullovers from £99 for perfects, and about £79 for samples and slight imperfects.'

In town centre, across the road from Iceland.

From Carlisle on A7: go left at first roundabout, cross the bridge, fork left and go left again into car-park.*

From Jedburgh on A698 and Newcastle on A6088: go through town centre; at roundabout take second exit, cross the bridge, fork left and go left again into car-park.*

From Galashiels on A7: turn right at first traffic lights, turn right around Thornwood Motors showroom on right, take first left and go left again into car-park.*

****Shop is opposite public car-park, next to Thornwood Motors.***

Late Entry

Open: Mon–Fri 9–5; Sat 9–5. Bank Holidays.
Closed: First Fri in June; Christmas and Boxing Days; 1 and 2 Jan.
Cards: Major credit cards, Delta, Switch.
Cars: Large free car-parks opposite and to side of building.
Toilets: In car-park opposite.
Wheelchairs: Easy access to large shop; no steps.
Changing rooms: Yes.
Teas: Coffee shop at NGT furniture store.
Groups: Shopping groups welcome.
Transport: Buses to Hawick then short walk.
Mail order: Yes.
Catalogue: Two free catalogues each year; please phone or fax.

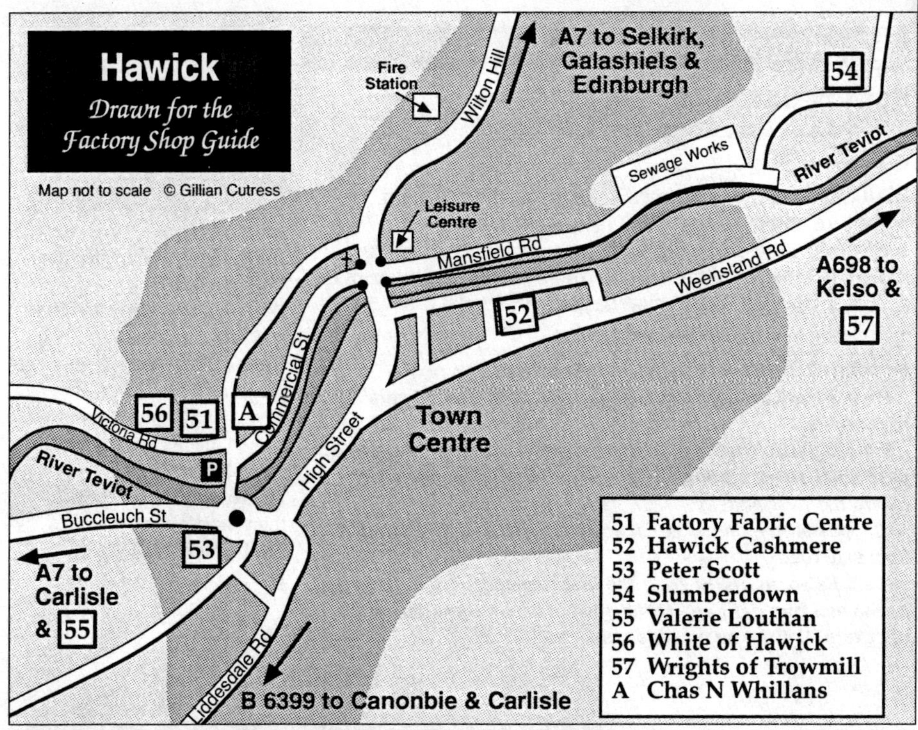

51 Hawick Borders *see map above*

Factory Fabric Centre

43 Victoria Road TD9 7NH
(01450) 373372

Quality curtain and upholstery fabrics. Discount bedding and soft furnishing items.

'Perfects, seconds and remnants at discounted prices.'

In the town centre, next door to Iceland Foods, in same building.

From Selkirk on A7: turn right at first traffic lights, just before the river. Then turn right immediately after Thornwood Motors showroom, then left and left again into the free car-park.

From Carlisle: turn left at the first roundabout, cross bridge and turn left into the car-park.

From Jedburgh and Newcastle: go through the town centre, turn right at the roundabout to go over the river, then turn left into the car park. Factory Fabric Centre is visible from the car-park, in the same building as Iceland.

Open: Mon–Fri 9.30–5.30; Sat 9–5; Sun and Bank Holidays 10–4.
Closed: Christmas, Boxing and New Year's Days.
Cards: Amex, MasterCard, Switch, Visa.
Cars: Large free car-park opposite.
Toilets: Opposite shop.
Wheelchairs: No steps.
Teas: In town.
Groups: Groups welcome, prior phone call appreciated.
Transport: Buses to Hawick.
Mail order: Fabrics can be despatched by post or carrier.

52 Hawick Borders *see map on previous page*

Hawick Cashmere Co.

Trinity Mills, Duke Street TD9 9QB
(01450) 372510

High quality ladies' and men's knitwear. Specialise in cashmere and cashmere/silk fashion styles and accessories, including skirts, trousers, capes and gloves. Range includes geelong and merino. Wholesale pieces of designer cashmere, also silk/cashmere blends.

'Good selection at competitive prices.'

By the river Teviot north-east of town centre.

From Selkirk on A7: take first left after first traffic lights and river bridge.*

From Carlisle: continue on A7 through town towards Selkirk, pass Shell petrol station on right and turn right immediately before the river bridge.*

****Shop is on the corner of second road to the right. Entrance from side road.***

From Kelso on A698: go to the first roundabout and turn right. At the end turn right again: the shop is on corner of the next right turn. Entrance from side road.

Open: Mon–Fri 10–5.
Closed: Some Bank Holidays; possibly Easter week; Christmas–New Year.
Cards: Access, Amex, Diners, Visa.
Cars: In street outside shop.
Toilets: Yes.
Wheelchairs: Easy access to spacious shop.
Changing rooms: Yes.
Teas: In Safeways nearby.
Groups: Shopping groups should telephone in advance. No mill tours.
Transport: Bus to Hawick then short walk.
Mail order: No.

53 Hawick Borders *see map on previous page*

Peter Scott

11 Buccleuch Street TD9 0HK
(01450) 372311

Top quality knitwear in cotton, lambswool and cashmere for men and women. Unusual designs.

'Founded 1878. Ladies' cashmere sweaters £99. Fine cotton sweaters £26. All perfects, probably 20% less than comparable quality in high street.'

Easy to find in town centre.

Coming into Hawick on A7 from Langholm/Carlisle: pass Hawick High School on left and look for this mill and shop on right, just before junction in town.

From other directions: follow signs to A7 Carlisle, turning into Buccleuch Street at mini-roundabout. Shop is fourth on left.

Open: Mon–Fri 10–5; Sat 10–4; Bank Holidays.
Closed: Second week April; Christmas–New Year.
Cards: Access, Amex, JCB, Visa.
Cars: 30-minute parking outside.
Toilets: Yes.
Wheelchairs: Four steps to spacious medium sized shop. Also ramp at rear.
Changing rooms: Yes.
Teas: Coffee shop next door.
Groups: Tuesday and Thursday at 2 pm prompt. Please contact Mr N Thomson or Mr N Bannerman.
Transport: Any bus to town.
Mail order: Yes.
Catalogue: No.

54 Hawick Borders *see map on earlier page*

Slumberdown Enterprises

Burnfoot Industrial Estate TD9 8RW
(01450) 374500

Duvets and pillows in natural feather and down and synthetic fibres; sleeping bags and other bedroom furnishings.

'Post Home service for bulky goods. First quality sold at factory shop prices; a few seconds.'

North-east of town centre.

From the south and town centre on A7: go over river and immediately turn right at traffic lights into Mansfield Road.*

From Selkirk and north on A7: go left at first traffic lights immediately before river bridge.*

****Continue for about ½ mile to roundabout and turn left into Hamilton Road. Slumberdown is second factory on left.***

Open: Mon–Fri 12–4; some Bank Holidays – please check.
Closed: Christmas and New Year.
Cards: Access, Visa.
Cars: Own car-park.
Toilets: Yes.
Teas: In Hawick.
Groups: Shopping groups welcome.
Transport: Local buses stop 300 yds from factory.
Mail order: Yes.

55 Hawick Borders *see map on earlier page*

Valerie Louthan at Wiltonburn Country Cashmeres

Wiltonburn Farm TD9 7LM
(01450) 372414   mobile (0374) 192551

Top of the market dresses, camisoles, trousers, jackets, capes, sweaters for men and women in cashmere and silk, by internationally famous designer. Also skirts, trousers, capes, gloves. Sometimes lambswool and cottons. Other top quality products, eg costume jewellery, local art work, books, cards and gifts.

'Subtle colours, witty designs. Mixture of cancelled orders, samples, slight seconds. Men's and women's sweaters costing £400 in London and Paris couture houses from £80. Classic styles can be made to order with special requirements, eg. shorter sleeves or longer body lengths.'

On the Carlisle side of town, about 1 ½ miles south-west of town.

Take the A7 south from Hawick: turn right on to the B711 to Roberton then go sharp right again along the riverside. Keep left, go round left corner and go into lane marked 'No through road' to far end. Wiltonburn is a white house on the right at the end of the road.

Open: Mon–Fri 10–6, or by appointment. Available most times except some Saturdays. For weekends and winter months please phone.
Closed: 2 days mid-May, 1 day mid-June, 1 day end Aug (phone to check); Christmas–New Year except by appointment.
Cards: Access, Visa.
Cars: By sales area.
Toilets: Ask if desperate.
Wheelchairs: Yes.
Changing rooms: Yes.
Teas: Lots of places in town.
Groups: No factory tours but groups welcome to shop: book with Sheila Shell. B & B and s/c accommodation available (guests receive shop discount).
Transport: None, 1 mile walk from town, or taxi.
Mail order: Yes.
Catalogue: No.

Cashmere: where it all began

White of Hawick

The first cashmere fabrics began to reach the Roman Empire 2000 years ago, brought by traders from present day Iran and Kashmir. Centuries ago, people from Kashmir had begun to spread eastwards into the area now known as Inner Mongolia, bringing with them their herds of goats. The fibre combed from these goats is the raw cashmere, one of the world's most coveted fibres.

Only some animals produce the finest natural fibres that can be used for the manufacture of luxurious fabrics and garments prized the world over. They include goats, camels, sheep, yaks, and their relatives, which live mainly in the high mountain grasslands and semi-deserts of Northern Asia, Europe and South America. Many of these have a coat consisting of an outer layer of coarse long hair, with finer shorter hair underneath. It is this fine undercoat which is used for making cashmere and other luxurious fabrics. However, the fleece of domesticated sheep and angora goats contain only one type of fibre, so all of their coat can be used. In late spring most of these animals moult their coats and grow a new one. For thousands of years man has harvested this fibre either by combing and collecting the cast hair, or, in the case of sheep and angora goats, by shearing them. Fibre harvested from angora goats is known as mohair, but what is commonly known as angora in fact comes from the angora rabbit.

Cashmere is the fine undercoat of the *cashmere* goat. It varies in colour from pure white – the most valuable – through grey, cream and fawn to dark brown. Some natural shades can be used to good effect, but most garments and fabrics require colour. In the past, natural plant and animal dyes were used but the colours were limited, unpredictable and would fade. Today, with precision mixing of chemical dyes, exact shades can be created repeatedly.

The largest producers of cashmere fibre are Iran and China. Inner Mongolia is the main cashmere producing region of China and most of it used to be exported to Britain as the centre of the international fibre trade. In recent years, however, China has reduced its exports of cashmere fibre, creating a world shortage and high prices.

Today, cashmere production is being developed in Scotland and other parts of Europe. But this development is hampered by the structure of European farm support which subsidises production of sheep and cattle in marginal areas, but not goats. Nonetheless, there are now in Scotland quite a few small herds of goats producing cashmere, and a major research and development programme is in progress.

With thanks to Johnstons of Elgin for this information.

56 Hawick Borders *see map on earlier page*

White of Hawick

2 Victoria Road
(01450) 373206

High quality cashmere, lambswool and lamora garments for men and women made here. Also other cashmere and lambswool garments, gloves, scarves and other accessories from major Hawick knitwear manufacturers.

'Designer garments at factory prices. Perfects and slight seconds. Men's cashmere pullovers from £89, lambswool from £23. Ladies' cashmere cardigans from £85, lambswool from £33. Many slightly imperfect scarves from £16; cashmere gloves from £9, cashmere socks from £7.'

In the town centre.

From Selkirk on A7: turn right at first traffic lights, just before the river. Then turn right immediately after Thornwood Motors showroom, then left and left again into the free car-park.

From Carlisle: turn left at the first roundabout, cross bridge and turn left into the car-park.

From Jedburgh and Newcastle: go through the town centre, turn right at the roundabout to go over the river, then turn left into the car park. White of Hawick is visible from the car-park, in the first building next to Iceland.

Open: Mon–Fri 9–5.15; Sat 9.30–5. Bank Holidays.
Closed: Common Riding early June (please check); Christmas & Boxing Days; 1 & 2 Jan.
Cards: All major credit cards; Switch, Delta.
Cars: Free car-park opposite.
Toilets: One; others nearby.
Wheelchairs: Six steps to shop, but access through side door if required.
Changing rooms: Yes.
Teas: Coffee shop at NGT furniture store 100 yds.
Groups: Factory tours by appointment; groups welcome to shop anytime, no need to book.
Transport: Any bus to Hawick; alight at Buccleuch Street, then walk over bridge and car-park.
Mail order: Yes.
Catalogue: Two free catalogues a year, please phone (or fax 01450 371900).

57 Hawick Borders *see map on earlier page*

Wrights of Trowmill

Trowmill TD9 8SV
(01450) 372555

Shetland and lambswool; sportscoats; ties and caps, scarves, travel rugs, skirts and tweed lengths. Locally made knitwear.

'70% of our products are exported. Perfects and seconds in this shop.'

On A698 (Hawick–Jedburgh road), 2 ½ miles north-east of Hawick.

From Hawick via A698: pass A6088 turn-off on right; mill is clearly signed about a mile further on left.

From Newcastle on A6088: go right on to A698: mill about a mile on left.

From Kelso/Jedburgh: on A698 go through Denholm; shop is 3 miles on right.

Open: Mon–Fri 9–5; Sat, Sun 10–5. Bank Holidays.
Closed: Christmas–New Year.
Cards: Access, Visa.
Cars: Outside shop.
Toilets: Yes.
Wheelchairs: Easy access to big shop.
Changing rooms: Yes.
Teas: Cold drinks and confectionery. Picnic tables on front lawn. Tea rooms in Hawick.
Tours: Self-guided tours of yarn preparation, warping and weaving in factory hours.
Transport: No local transport.
Mail order: No.

58 Hill of Fearn Rosshire, Highland

Anta

(01862) 832477

Tartan ceramics, furnishing fabrics, mugs, rugs, throws and flat weave carpets.

'Specialists in contemporary and reproduction tartans; makers of the original tartan tableware. Perfects and seconds all at greatly discounted prices. Special sale early December–end January.'

Thirty-five miles north-east of Inverness, off A9 between Hill of Fearn and Balintore, next to the old aerodrome.

From Inverness: take A9 north (signed to Wick), stay on A9, pass the turn off B817 to Alness and Invergordon; after about 11 miles (about 4 miles before Tain) turn right on to B9165, go over railway, follow road up to Hill of Fern and at T-junction turn right into B9166 signed to Ballintore. The shop is 1 ½ miles on right, next to disused aerodrome surrounded by farmland.

Open: Mon–Sat 10–5; also Sunday in summer, please phone to check. Bank Holidays.
Closed: Christmas–New Year.
Cards: Mastercard, Visa.
Cars: Own car-park.
Toilets: Ask if required.
Wheelchairs: Easy access to medium sized shop.
Teas: In picturesque Portmahomack village, 7 miles.
Groups: Tours of pottery by appointment. Shopping groups welcome anytime.
Transport: Unfortunately none.
Mail order: Yes. Only perfect goods by mail order.
Catalogue: Free.

59 Huntly Aberdeenshire

Dean's Shortbread

Depot Road AB54 5HR
(01466) 792086

A selection of home recipe and all-butter shortbread in gift boxes, tins and packets. Also a range of quality foods such as preserves, honey, pickles, toffee, soups, wines and miniatures.

'Factory shortbread seconds at half price and perfects at normal price.'

Near the fire station south-west of town centre.

From the A96 Huntly by-pass: turn towards Huntly at the roundabout where the A97 crosses the A96.

Go into Huntly. Pass the garden centre on the left then the playing field. At the first junction, turn left (Market Street); continue almost in a straight line, passing the fire station in front of you into Depot Road. Take first left: you are at the shop (in cream-coloured building with red roof).

Open: Mon–Fri 9–5; Sat 9–12. Bank Holidays.
Closed: Two weeks Christmas–New Year.
Cards: Access, Visa.
Cars: Reasonable parking at shop.
Toilets: Nearby.
Wheelchairs: Easy access; small shop but can move around easily.
Teas: Cold drinks and ice-cream for sale in shop; restaurants in town nearby.
Groups: No factory tours, but shopping groups welcome. Please phone first.
Transport: Bus nos. 7 (stops at Summerfield supermarket) and M21 (by hospital).
Mail order: No, but will wrap and post shortbread for shop customers to any destination.

60 Innerleithen Borders

Murray Allan

82 High Street EH44 6HF
(01896) 830631

Ladies' and men's knitwear in cashmere, lambswool and mixed fibres.

'First quality knitwear at genuine factory prices; occasionally seconds. All garments manufactured on site.'

On the main street in centre of Innerleithen.

From Galashiels on A72: cross river bridge, pass the bank and 20 yds further the white St Ronan's Hotel on the right; shop is 100 yds on right opposite church hall.

From Peebles on A72: pass Jet petrol station on right and shop is 100 yds further on left.

Open: Mon–Fri 9–5. Bank Holidays. Please phone about summer weekend openings.
Closed: About 2 weeks at Christmas, please phone.
Cards: Most major credit cards.
Cars: Free signposted car-park nearby.
Toilets: By car-park nearby.
Wheelchairs: Narrow access; no steps.
Changing rooms: Yes.
Teas: Café nearby.
Groups: No tours, but shopping groups welcome anytime.
Transport: Buses from Edinburgh, Peebles and Galashiels stop nearby.
Mail order: No.

61 Inverness Highlands and Islands

Highland Society for the Blind

(Northern Counties Institute for the Blind)

39 Ardconell Street IV1 3HA
(01463) 233662

Beds and accessories, mattresses and fireside chairs.

'Gladly make odd size mattresses to order.'

Close to town centre, on south side.

From A9: get on to A96 (Nairn–Inverness road). Follow signs to A82 Fort William; you come parallel to river. At traffic lights where the A82 turns right over river, go left.*

Via A862 from Beauly and A82 from Fort William: follow signs to town centre. At traffic light immediately after river, go straight.*

****Go up Bridge Street (museum & Tourist Centre on right), follow road right into Castle Street, pass castle on right, go over next traffic lights. Take next left (Old Edinburgh Road), first left (Mitchells Lane), then go left again then right. Clearly marked shop on left.***

Open: Mon–Fri 9–5; Sat 9–4.
Closed: Two weeks Christmas–New Year. Local public holidays, please phone to check.
Cards: Access, Visa.
Cars: Own small car-park.
Toilets: 250 yds half-way down the steps to town centre.
Wheelchairs: Easy access.
Teas: In town.
Groups: Factory tours by appointment please (max 12).
Transport: Bus to town. From Marks & Spencer in High Street walk up steps opposite main entrance; go right at top.
Mail order: No.

62 Kilbirnie Strathclyde

Glengarnock Garments

River Place KA25 7EM
(01505) 682759

Ladies', men's and children's trousers, bermuda shorts and waistcoats made here. Tartan and golf trouser specialists.

'95% overmakes, some seconds. Considerable discounts over high street prices.'

About 20 miles south-west of Glasgow city centre.

From Glasgow/the north on A737: pass Beith; at roundabout go right on to B777 for Kilbirnie. Go over railway by Glengarnock station; after about 1 ½ miles go straight at mini-roundabout. Fork right by Q8 petrol (Ford William Clark garage) on left.*

From Dalry on B780: turn left at first roundabout. Fork right by Q8 petrol on left.*

From Largs on A760: turn right at first roundabout, right at second roundabout for Dalry B780. Go through town centre and opposite Ford William Clark garage (Q8 petrol) turn left.*

****Cross bridge, take first left: shop in second building on right.***

Open: Wed, Thur, Fri 10.30–4; Sat 10.30–1.
Closed: Monday; Tuesday. Christmas–New Year.
Cards: Delta, MasterCard, Switch, Visa.
Cars: Own car-park.
Toilets: Ask if required.
Wheelchairs: Unfortunately too difficult.
Changing rooms: Yes.
Teas: In town.
Groups: Shopping groups up to 30 persons welcome; no need to book.
Transport: Bus stop 300 yds; Glengarnock railway station 1 mile.
Mail order: No.

63 Kilmarnock Strathclyde

Jaeger

15 Munro Place, Bonnyton Industrial Estate KA1 2NR
(01563) 265111

Large range of ladies' blouses, skirts, jackets, coats, knitwear etc. Men's suits, jackets, trousers, knitwear, shirts, ties, socks.

'Quality merchandise at reduced prices.'

West-north-west of town.

From town centre: take A735 for Kilmaurs. At roundabout with B7064, go left and left again after railway bridge.*

From the north on A77: turn on to B7038 for Kilmarnock. At first roundabout fork right on to B7064, go straight at next roundabout, then go left after railway bridge.*

From all south-east and easterly directions get on or stay on A71 for Irvine. At roundabout take B7064 for Crosshouse.**

From Irvine on A71: turn left for Crosshouse on to B7081.**

*****At next roundabout go right; go left at lights. Take first right after dual carriageway section starts.****

****Shop clearly signed at bottom of hill.***

Open: Mon, Thur 9–12 & 2–4; Tues, Wed, Fri 9–4; Sat, Sun 10–4.
Closed: First two weeks July. Please phone about Bank Holidays and Christmas.
Cards: Access, Switch, Visa.
Cars: Own car-park.
Toilets: No.
Wheelchairs: Stairs to large shop upstairs.
Changing rooms: Yes.
Teas: In town.
Groups: No factory tours. Shopping groups welcome with prior phone call.
Transport: None.
Mail order: No.

See our entry below

64 Kinross Tayside

Lochleven Mill Shop

Lochleven Mill, Bridgend KY13 7DI
(01577) 863528

Extensive range of luxury knits in cashmere and lambswool including cardigans, sweaters, jackets, coats, skirts, kilts, scarves, travelling rugs etc. Custom built *Pringle* shop-within-a-shop for wide range of ladies' and gents' sportswear and accessories. Shop also stocks an extensive range of fashionwear from prestigious names such as *Daks Simpson, barrie, Burberrys, McGeorge, Finn Karelia, Henry White* etc.

'Genuine end of lines from Pringle and other leading names at amazing bargain prices. Cashmere jumpers priced from only £50.'

See our display advertisement above

At southern end of town.

From M90 exit 6 and Kincardine Bridge via A977: enter Kinross and go right at T-junction. Continue on road to Lochleven Mills (last building on left before leaving town).

From north-east on A91: take B996 through Kinross; mill shop is located on left, after hump bridge over river.

Open: Mon–Sat 9–5.30. Bank Holidays.
Closed: Christmas–New Year.
Cards: Amex, Diners, Mastercard, Visa.
Cars: Own car-park. Coaches by arrangement.
Toilets: Yes.
Wheelchairs: Three steps down to large spacious shop.
Changing rooms: Yes.
Teas: Good selection of hotels and cafés.
Groups: No factory tours. Groups welcome to shop. Please contact Ellen Anderson (Manageress).
Transport: Regular bus service from Edinburgh, Perth and Glenrothes.
Mail order: No.

65 Kirkcaldy Fife

Babygro

Hayfield Industrial Estate KY2 5DM
(01592) 261177

Baby and children's wear, sleepwear, ladies' wear, leisurewear and underwear.

On the north side of the town centre.

From M90 exit 3: follow signs to Kirkcaldy West. At first roundabout follow sign to 'Industrial Estates'. Pass Esso and Gulf petrol. At next traffic lights go right (for Hayfield Industrial Estate), then take first left just before Shell petrol.*

From town centre: pass railway station; go left at traffic lights over railway bridge. At next two roundabouts take second exits; at third go straight. Turn right after Shell petrol on right.*

****Shell is in first building on left.***

Open: Mon 10.30–4.30; Tues–Sat 9.30–4.30; Sun 12.30–4.30. Bank Holidays.
Closed: For Christmas opening times please check.
Cards: Yes.
Cars: By factory and in street.
Toilets: No.
Wheelchairs: Three steps to sizeable shop.
Teas: In town.
Groups: Please phone to check.
Transport: Buses from town centre stop opposite factory.

66 Kirkintilloch E. Dunbartonshire

Goudies

Goudies Mill, Broadcroft G66 1HS
(0141) 776 3000

Traditional Fair Isle garments and classic ladies' and men's shetland, sports and country knitwear.

'Manufacturers of shetland knitwear for over 50 years. Quality garments at factory prices. Seconds at reduced prices.'

In centre of town near Broadcroft Hotel.

From A803: turn towards town centre and Lenzie at the traffic lights. Go straight at lights, then take next left into cul-de-sac (80 yds before the Broadcroft Hotel).

From Muirhead on B8048 and Muirhead on B757: follow signs to Bishopriggs A803. After the roundabout where these two roads join, pass the Broadcroft Hotel on the left then turn right immediately after pedestrian lights.

Open: Mon–Thur 10–5.
Closed: Bank Holidays; Christmas–New Year period; last two weeks in July.
Cards: None.
Cars: In front of shop.
Toilets: In nearby shopping centre.
Wheelchairs: Three steps down to small shop.
Changing rooms: No, but customers welcome to try on garments.
Teas: In town, or Broadcroft Hotel opposite.
Groups: No tours.
Transport: Regular buses stop outside.
Mail order: No.

Inverness Highlands and Islands

Late Entry

Scottish Sweater Store

9 Drummond Street IV1 1QD
(01463) 711325
e-mail: chasn.whillans@virgin.net

Cashmere and lambswool pullovers from *Pringle, Lyle & Scott, Glenmac,* and own *Chas N Whillans* label; leisurewear from *Tulchan* and *Alice Collins*; *Pringle Nick Faldo* golfwear; trousers and skirts from *Brandtex*. Travel rugs, scarves, gloves and socks.

'Ladies' and men's cashmere pullovers from £99 for perfects and about £79 for samples and slight imperfects.'

In pedestrianised area in town centre.

From all directions: follow signs to town centre. Best to park in Eastgate Centre, then walk down High Street, turn right by Oasis into Drummond Street. Shop is far right of next crossing.

Open: Mon–Fri 9–5.30; Sat 9–5. Bank Holidays.
Closed: Christmas & Boxing Days; 1 & 2 Jan.
Cards: Major credit cards, Delta, Switch.
Cars: Car-park 5 minutes' walk in Eastgate Centre.
Toilets: Nearby.
Wheelchairs: One step to medium sized shop, assistance gladly given.
Changing rooms: Yes.
Teas: Coffee shop nearby.
Groups: Shopping groups welcome.
Transport: Buses to Inverness; train station 5 minutes' walk.
Mail order: Yes.
Catalogue: Two free catalogues each year; please phone (01450) 373128, or fax (01450) 376082.

67 Lanark Strathclyde

Glenmuir

Delves Road ML11 9DY
(01555) 662244

Large range of knitwear and other clothing.

'Both perfects and seconds sold here.'

400 yds south of town centre (High Street) – best to walk.

Going south from Glasgow/Hamilton on A73/A72: go to lights at top of High Street, fork right. Pass Tourist Office on left, take next right. Take third left (Delves Road).

Coming north from Abington and Biggar on A73: after turn-off to New Lanark on left, take next left.

From Carstairs on A743: turn left at traffic lights (NOT sharp left). This becomes Delves Road at next crossing. Mill on left.

Open: Mon–Sat 10–1 & 1.35–4.
Closed: Phone to check.
Cards: Yes.
Cars: Own car-park.
Wheelchairs: Eleven wide steps, wide doors to large shop.
Changing rooms: Yes.
Teas: In town.
Groups: No mill tours.
Transport: Bus/train to town.

68 Lanark Strathclyde

Millshop Woollens

12 St Vincent Place ML11 7LA
(01555) 665966

High quality classic knitwear in natural fibres including merino, lambswool, geelong, lamora, cashmere and cashmere blends. Hats, scarves, gloves, travel rugs, shirts, skirts and tights.

'We stock extremely well priced perfect and imperfect garments all at factory shop prices.'

Near the rail station and opposite the Tourist Information Centre.

From Glasgow/Hamilton on A73/A72: go to lights at top of high street and fork right.*

From Carstairs on A743: turn sharp left at first traffic lights (NOT just left).*

****The shop is about 250 yds on right opposite tourist office and Somerfield supermarket.***

Coming north from Abington/Biggar on A73: turn right for town centre after cattle market on right. Shop is 100 yds past Esso petrol on left, opposite tourist office and Somerfield supermarket.

Open: Mon–Fri 9–5; Sat 9.30–5; Sun 10.30–5.
Closed: Christmas and Boxing Days; 1 & 2 Jan.
Cards: Access, Switch, Visa.
Cars: Opposite, by the Tourist Office.
Toilets: Opposite tourist office.
Wheelchairs: Easy access.
Changing rooms: Yes.
Teas: In town.
Groups: No factory tours. Shopping groups welcome, no need to phone.
Transport: Train station diagonally opposite shop.

69 Larbert near Falkirk Central

Barbara Davidson Pottery

Muirhall Farm FK5 4EV
(01324) 554430

Interesting range of vases, mugs, tableware, bowls and table lamps in hand-made stoneware.

'Firsts and seconds for sale. Good prices because products not sold elsewhere. In the gift shop all items are specially chosen to be excellent value for money, and different.'

North of town.

From Larbert/Falkirk: take A9 for Stirling. At roundabout with M876 for Glasgow, go right on to A88 (pottery signposted from here onwards). Half mile to pottery on right.

From Glasgow via M80: exit on to M876, then take exit 2 to Larbert. At roundabout go straight on to A88: signposted shop is ½ mile on right.

From either direction on M9: take exit 7 on to M876, go to end and turn right on to A905.*

From Kincardine Bridge: turn left on to A905 at first roundabout.*

****Go to next roundabout, go right on to A88. Shop is ½ mile on left (signposted).***

Open: Mon–Sat 10–5; Sun 12–5.
Closed: Two days at Christmas and three days at New Year.
Cards: Access, Delta, Switch, Visa.
Cars: Own car-park.
Toilets: No.
Wheelchairs: Easy access to both shops.
Teas: In town.
Groups: Demonstrations by prior arrangement. A small charge is made.
Transport: 12 minutes' walk from Larbert station. Bus stop at door.
Mail order: Yes.
Catalogue: Price list free. Special orders welcomed. No seconds sent by mail order.

70 Livingston Central

Russell Corp UK

Firth Road, Houstoun Industrial Estate EH54 5DJ
(01506) 442679

Sports clothing, sweatshirts, jogging bottoms, T-shirts, shorts, vests, kids' sizes 22–32, adult sizes 34–50. Can be personalised while you wait.

'Perfects and seconds, discontinued lines, colours and samples; printed and embroidered garments. Huge discount on retail prices. Home of Russell Athletic Sportswear.'

From M8 exit 3: turn off for Livingston (A899). Follow signs to Livingston/West Calder. At Houston Interchange, go left for Houston.*

From A71 on south side of Livingston: at Lizzie Brice's roundabout (Gulf garage), take A899 (M8) for Edinburgh/Glasgow. Keep straight. At junction 6, take sliproad for Houston Industrial Estate, in effect turning off to right.*

****Take first right, Grange Road; then first right, Firth Road. Follow road round to left then go right to far end.***

Open: Seven days: Mon–Fri 10–5.30; Sat 9–5; Sun 11–4. Bank Holidays.
Closed: Christmas, Boxing & New Year's Days; 2 Jan.
Cards: Access, Switch, Visa.
Cars: Own car-park and street.
Toilets: Yes.
Wheelchairs: One small step.
Changing rooms: Yes.
Teas: In Livingston.
Groups: Shopping groups welcome.
Transport: Buses to dual carriageway then longish walk to industrial estate.

71 Lochgilphead Strathclyde

Highbank Porcelain

Highbank Industrial Estate PA31 8NN
(01546) 602044

Porcelain figurines, mostly animals; vases, jugs, dishes, brooches and clowns. Pewter photo frames.

On west side of town, on A816.

From the north on A816: disregard first turn-off to 'Town Centre'; take second left into Highbank Industrial Estate; shop first on left.

From south on A83, or coming through town: go to roundabout where this road meets A816. Go towards Oban: industrial estate is 500 yds on right, clearly signed. Shop in first building on left.

Open: Mon–Fri 9–5; Sat 10–5; Sun 11–5. Bank Holidays.
Closed: For Christmas and New Year please check.
Cards: Yes.
Cars: Own car-park.
Toilets: In town.
Wheelchairs: Easy access.
Teas: In town.
Groups: Please phone about tours and shopping groups.
Transport: None.

72 Newmilns Strathclyde

Moonweave Mill Shop

Stoneygate Road KA16 9BM
(01560) 321216

Lace table covers and window furnishings; bedspreads, sheets, blankets; babywear, cots and cribs.

'Perfects and seconds for sale.'

Newmilns is about 8 miles east of Kilmarnock.

From Kilmarnock via A71: go into Newmilns; turn right at Moonweave wall sign, Brown Street.*

From Strathaven/Edinburgh via A71: pass church on left and small white chapel-like building with bell tower. After zebra crossing, go left following signs to Police Office.*

****After 450 yds take right fork and go round S-bend. Factory is signposted on second bend.***

Open: Mon–Fri 9–4.30; Sat 9–1.
Closed: Bank Holidays; Christmas–New Year.
Cards: No.
Cars: Outside shop.
Toilets: No.
Wheelchairs: Four steps to medium sized shop.
Changing rooms: No.
Teas: In town.
Groups: Factory tours not possible but bus parties gladly accommodated – please phone beforehand.
Transport: On Kilmarnock–Darvel bus route.
Mail order: No.

73 North Berwick E Lothian

Millshop Woollens

Unit 13, Fenton Barns EH39 5BW
(01620) 850284

High quality classic knitwear in natural fibres including merino, lambswool, geelong, lamora, cashmere and cashmere blends. Hats, scarves, gloves, travel rugs, shirts, skirts and tights.

'We stock extremely well priced perfect and imperfect garments all at factory shop prices.'

Fenton Barns is a small village about 2 miles south-west of North Berwick and 6 miles north of Haddington.

From the A1: turn off at Oaktree exit for Haddington and Aberlady (A6137). Follow signs to Aberlady to roundabout in front of railway bridge and turn right on to B1377 for North Berwick; go through Drem, then go up the hill and turn right to Fenton Barns. After 50 yds turn left towards Scottish Archery Centre. Millshop Woollens is straight ahead.

[Distance from roundabout in front of railway to final turn off is 3.7 miles.]

Open: Mon–Fri 9–5; Sat 9.30–5; Sun 10.30–5.
Closed: Christmas and Boxing Days; 1 & 2 Jan.
Cards: Access, Switch, Visa
Cars: Own car-park.
Toilets: No.
Wheelchairs: Easy access to medium sized shop; no steps.
Changing rooms: Yes.
Teas: In North Berwick; also coffee shop on the Fenton Barns site.
Groups: No factory tours. Shopping groups welcome, no need to phone.
Transport: Unfortunately none.

74 Oban Strathclyde

Caithness Glass Visitor Centre

Waterfront Centre, Railway Pier PA34 4LW
(01631) 563386 Internet: http://www.caithnessglass.co.uk

Glass and crystal, giftware and tableware in assorted colours and designs; vases, bowls, paperweights, jewellery, engraving and wine suites. Other gift ideas to choose from.

'First and second qualities. Vases from £4.99, tableware from £4.99, perfume bottles from £9.99, paperweights from £8.99 (prices subject to change).'

In town centre on Railway Pier at the Waterfront Centre, beside the railway station and ferry pier.

Open: All year: Mon–Sat 9–5 (*late nights June–Sept*). *Also Easter–end Oct*: Sun 11–5. Bank Holidays.
Closed: Three days at Christmas and three days at New Year.
Cards: Access, Amex, Diners, Switch, Visa.
Cars: Large public car-park nearby.
Toilets: Yes, within Waterfront Centre.
Wheelchairs: Easy access.
Teas: Tea room within Waterfront Centre.
Groups: Groups welcome. No booking required. Interpretative exhibition and audio-visual display.
Transport: Next to rail station, taxi rank and bus point.
Mail order: No.

Peebles Borders

Late Entry

Chas N Whillans

Old Corn Exchange, High Street EH45 8AG
(01721) 722053
e-mail: chasn.whillans@virgin.net

Cashmere and lambswool pullovers from *Pringle, Lyle & Scott, Glenmac* and own *Chas N Whillans* label. Leisurewear from *Tulchan* and *Alice Collins*; *Pringle Nick Faldo* golfwear; *Cross Creek* golfwear, sportswear from *Nike, Adidas, Reebok, Umbro* etc; travel rugs, cashmere and lambswool scarves and gloves.

'Ladies' and men's cashmere pullovers from £99 for perfects and about £79 for samples and slight imperfects.'

In town centre.

From Edinburgh on A703: go right at roundabout with Tweeddale Garage on right. Shop is in town centre on left near Tourist Information Centre.

From Glasgow on A72: cross Cuddy Bridge into town centre; go left into High Street. Shop is in town centre on right.

From Galashiels on A72: at roundabout with Tweeddale Garage on far right go straight into town centre. Shop is on left near Tourist Information Centre.

Open: Mon–Fri 9–5.30; Sat 9–5. Bank Holidays.
Closed: Third Sat in June; Christmas & Boxing Days; 1 & 2 January.
Cards: Major credit cards, Delta, Switch.
Cars: Large free car-park 2 minutes' walk.
Toilets: At rear of shop.
Wheelchairs: Easy access. No steps into shop, but small step inside, assistance gladly given.
Changing rooms: Yes.
Teas: Many coffee shops and hotels nearby.
Groups: Shopping groups welcome.
Transport: Buses to Peebles.
Mail order: Yes.
Catalogue: Two free catalogues each year; please phone (01450) 373128, or fax (01450) 376082.

75 Penicuik Lothian

Edinburgh Crystal

Eastfield EH26 8HA
(01968) 675128

World's largest collection of *Edinburgh Crystal:* cut crystal tumblers, decanters, wine glasses, vases, giftwear of first and second quality. Craft, gift and knitwear shop.

'Second quality crystal at least 30% off RRP. Always promotional offers. Items discounted up to 75%.'

Off the A701 near Edinburgh end of town.

From Edinburgh on A701 (Peebles Road): turn left about 50 yds into the town at the 'Crystal Visitor Centre' sign. Take next right to Visitor Centre.

From the south on A701/702 and A703: go into Penicuik, stay on A701 towards Edinburgh. Turn right immediately after BP petrol, take next right for 'Crystal Visitor Centre'.

Open: Mon–Sat 9–5; Sun 11–5. Bank Holidays.
Closed: Christmas & New Year.
Cards: Access, Amex, Visa.
Cars: Car and coach parking.
Toilets: Yes, also for disabled.
Wheelchairs: Yes, rampway to first floor. Vast shop.
Teas: Coffee shop/light meals – licensed. Picnic and children's play areas (outside).
Tours: Free crystal exhibition and audio visual theatre 7 days a week. Factory tours Mon–Fri 9–3.30. Adults £2, concessions £1, disabled free. No children under 8 (safety). Weekend tours April–Sept 11–2.30. Group rates (15+). Phone tours organiser for tours/shopping groups.
Transport: Edinburgh bus nos. 62, 64, 65, 81, 87. Free bus in summer (phone for details). Trains: Edinburgh/Waverley.
Mail order: Yes, no restrictions, catalogue free.

76 Perth Tayside

Caithness Glass Visitor Centre

Inveralmond Industrial Estate PH1 3TZ
(01738) 637373 Internet: http://www.caithnessglass.co.uk

Glass and crystal, giftware and tableware in assorted colours and designs; vases, bowls, paperweights, jewellery, engraving and wine suites. Other gift ideas to choose from.

'First and second qualities. Vases from £4.99, tableware from £4.99, perfume bottles from £9.99, paperweights from £8.99 (prices subject to change).'

At north end of Perth.

From Edinburgh via M90, Dundee via A90 or Stirling via A9: get on to or stay on A9 for Inverness. This bypasses Perth and takes you to large roundabout: exit into Inveralmond Industrial Estate, signposted 'Caithness Glass Visitor Centre'.

From the north: turn into Inveralmond Industrial Estate at first roundabout in Perth, then take first left, following signs to 'Caithness Glass Visitor Centre'.

Open: All year Mon–Sat 9–5; Sun *(April–Oct)* 10–5, *(Nov–March)* 12–5. Bank Hols.
Closed: 24–26 Dec and 31 Dec–2 Jan.
Cards: Access, Amex, Diners, Switch, Visa.
Cars: Own large free car-park near main entrance
Toilets: Yes, and for disabled; mother and baby room.
Wheelchairs: Easy access; wheelchair available.
Teas: Licensed restaurant for snacks and meals.
Tours: Viewing gallery. Free self conducted tours to see glassmaking Mon–Fri 9–4.30. Groups welcome, no need to book. Paperweight Collectors Gallery. Audio-visual theatre.
Transport: Perth rail and bus stations 3 miles; bus service to site Mon–Fri.
Mail order: No.

77 Pitlochry Perth & Kinross

Heathergems

22 Atholl Road PH16 5BX
(01796) 473863

Unique Scottish jewellery made of dried heather stems, using natural dyes and set into silver and pewter fittings, some pieces based on Celtic designs.

'Full perfect range. Limited range of seconds, discontinued lines and specials only available in the shop.'

On the south side of town centre behind Tourist Information Centre.

From the south: turn off the A9 for Pitlochry on to the A924. Go under railway bridge, pass police station then turn right for Tourist Information Centre which you then pass on the left; follow signs.

From the north: turn off the A9 for Pitlochry on to the A924. Go through town centre and turn left for the Tourist Information Centre. The shop is behind it.

Open: Mon–Sat 9–5.30; *also* Sun 9–5.30 in summer. Bank Holidays.
Closed: Christmas and Boxing Days; 1 & 2 January. Phone for other Christmas closures.
Cards: Access, Switch, Visa.
Cars: In front of shop; also public car-park next door.
Toilets: ¼ mile.
Wheelchairs: One small step to medium sized shop.
Teas: In town.
Tours: Visitors can walk through the viewing gallery and see craftworkers at work.
Transport: Bus and train to Pitlochry from north and south.
Mail order: Yes.
Catalogue: Brochure and price list sent on request.

78 Selkirk Borders *see map opposite*

Claridge Mills

Riverside Industrial Estate TD7 5DV
(01750) 20300

Cashmere, silk and fine wool accessories and couture quality fabrics.

To north of town.

From Peebles/Innerleithen on A707 and Moffat on A708: cross river and turn left immediately into Buccleuch Road. After nearly 1¼ miles go left into Level Crossing Road; shop 120 yds on right.

From Hawick on A7: go through Selkirk and turn left after Exacta and before Selkirk Glass.*

From Edinburgh and Galashiels on A7: take first right immediately after Selkirk Glass, signposted to Moffat.*

****After 300 yds take first right (Level Crossing Road).***

Open: Mon–Fri and Bank Holidays 9–4.30.
Closed: Christmas, Boxing, New Year's Days and 2 Jan.
Cards: Most major cards.
Cars: Outside shop.
Toilets: No.
Wheelchairs: Easy access to medium sized shop.
Teas: In Selkirk Glass at end of estate.
Groups: Phone to check.
Transport: Bus from Galashiels or Hawick to Selkirk Square, then 10 minutes' walk.

79 Selkirk Borders *see map opposite*

D C Dalgliesh

Dunsdale Mill, North Riverside Industrial Area TD7 5EC
(01750) 20781

Headsquares in pure new wool and pure silk. Pure silk evening sashes. Also tartan material.

'Company is tartan specialist supplier to the Queen. Feature "Reproduction Tartans", soft muted tartans resembling those made with natural vegetable dyes before 1745. Sell perfects and seconds.'

To north of town.

From Peebles/Innerleithen on A707 and Moffat on A708: cross river into Selkirk and go left immediately into Buccleuch Road. Factory clearly signed on left after ½ mile, on corner with Whinfield Road.

From Hawick on A7: go through Selkirk, turn left after Exacta on left and before Selkirk Glass.*

From Edinburgh/Galashiels on A7: take first right immediately after Selkirk Glass, signposted to Moffat.*

****Shop is clearly marked on right after nearly a mile.***

Open: Mon–Fri 9–12 & 1–4; Sat by arrangement.
Closed: Few days early April (please check); second week June (Common Riding); last two weeks July; Christmas–New Year.
Cards: No.
Cars: Outside factory.
Toilets: No.
Wheelchairs: Easy access to small shop.
Teas: In town.
Groups: Parties wanting to shop should book with Mrs Luke. Free tours round the mill – must be booked in advance. Maximum 40.
Transport: Bus from Galashiels or Hawick to Selkirk square, then 10 minutes' walk.
Mail order: Yes.

80 Selkirk Borders

see map below

Ettrick Forest Interiors

Forest Mill, Station Road TD7 5DK
(01750) 22519 Fax (01750) 22529

Own range of cotton furnishing fabrics printed on premises. Remnants. *Ettrick Valley* own brand tea towels, children's PVC aprons and cover-ups, PVC aprons and bags, oven gloves and tea cosies on Scottish and country themes.

'Plain fabrics from £4.25 per m. PVC coated fabric for tablecloths £9.95 per m. Seconds tea towels £1.95 each, seconds PVC aprons and bags £4.25 each. Curtains and soft furnishings to order.'

From Peebles/Innerleithen on A707 and Moffat on A708: cross river, go left at once into Buccleuch Road. Take first left; shop straight ahead at T-junction.

From Hawick on A7: go through Selkirk, turn left after Exacta, before Selkirk Glass.*

From Edinburgh and Galashiels on A7: take first right after Selkirk Glass.*

****After 1 mile, go right to swimming baths. Shop is straight ahead at T-junction.***

Open: Mon–Sat 10–5.
Closed: 1 day early April, 1 day early May, 3 days mid-June, 1 day mid-Oct; 20 Dec for 2 weeks. Phone for exact dates.
Cards: Access, Visa.
Cars: Outside.
Toilets: Yes.
Wheelchairs: Two steps down into shop.
Teas: In Selkirk.
Groups: Groups welcome to shop; phone call first appreciated.
Transport: Bus from Galashiels or Hawick to Selkirk square, then 10 minutes' walk.
Mail order: No mail order catalogue as stock changes, but items can be posted. Fabric & PVC fabric cuttings, and free *Ettrick Valley* tea towels colour leaflet, sent on request.

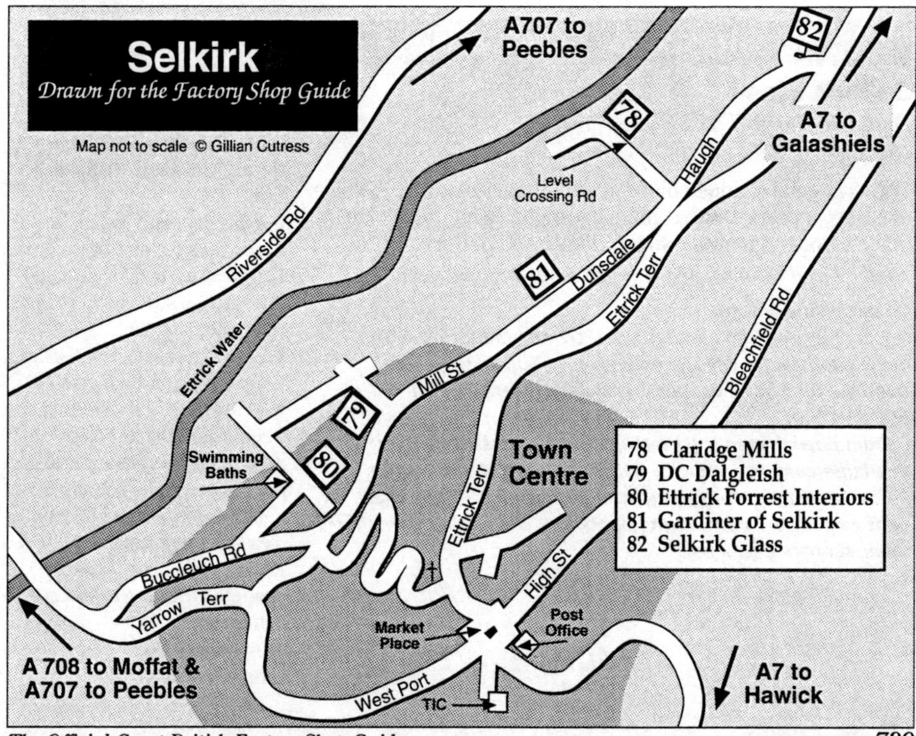

81 Selkirk Borders *see map on previous page*

Gardiner of Selkirk

Tweed Mills, Dunsdale Road TD7 5DZ
(01750) 20735 Fax (01750) 22525

Men's and ladies' tweeds in different weights and designs; co-ordinating shetland hand and machine knitting wool and knitwear. Aran knitting wool. Skirts; sometimes jackets and coats. Ties, shirts, socks. Travel rugs. Also weaving yarn and sewing accessories. Pottery.

'Genuine mill shop with most items produced in own factory next to shop. All at mill prices. Firsts and seconds. Tweeds from £5.50 per m (150 cm wide); yarn from 25p per oz; knitwear from £14.95; pottery from £6.95.'

See our display advertisement opposite

On north side of town.

From Peebles/Innerleithen on A707 and Moffat on A708: cross river into Selkirk and go left into Buccleuch Road. Shop clearly marked on left after half a mile.

From Hawick on A7: go through Selkirk, go left after Exacta and before Selkirk Glass.*

From Edinburgh and Galashiels on A7: take first right immediately after Selkirk Glass, signposted to Peebles, Moffat.*

****Shop is half a mile on right.***

Open: Mon–Sat 9–5 (possibly 10–4 in winter, please phone to check); Bank Holidays.
Closed: Christmas–New Year.
Cards: Access, Visa.
Cars: Ample parking adjacent to shop.
Toilets: Yes.
Wheelchairs: Two steps to large shop.
Changing rooms: No.
Teas: Hot & cold drinks machine, snack machine in factory (50 yds).
Groups: Groups to shop or mill please phone Mr D Weir (01750) 20283.
Transport: None.
Mail order: Will send small samples of fabric or yarn from current stock trying to match customers verbal description of requirement.

82 Selkirk Borders *see map on previous page*

Selkirk Glass

Dunsdale Haugh TD7 5EE
(01750) 20954

Wide range of unique coloured glass paperweights, animals, artglass, perfume bottles, animal sculptures etc. Some locally made wooden furniture and hand-painted pottery.

'Perfects and seconds. Many items at factory prices.'

On north side of town.

From Peebles/Innerleithen on A707 and Moffat on A708: cross river and go left immediately into Buccleuch Road. Continue for 1 ½ miles; factory is clearly signed at far end of the estate.

From Hawick on A7: go through Selkirk; pass Exacta on left; this large company is on far left corner of next left turning.

From Edinburgh & Galashiels on A7: look for Selkirk Glass on right as you come into town (just before left turning to Moffat). Clear car-park entrance.

Open: Mon–Fri 9–5; Sat 10–4.30; Sun 12–4.
Closed: One day mid-June (please check); Christmas–New Year.
Cards: Access, Visa.
Cars: Own car and coach park.
Toilets: Yes, and for disabled.
Wheelchairs: Easy access to large shop and tour.
Teas: Own café for light snacks.
Tours: Free tours of glass-works, Mon–Fri 9–4.30 (not weekends). Any numbers, no need to book in advance. Regret no unaccompanied children. Parties also welcome to shop; please book in advance with Ron Hutchinson.
Transport: Edinburgh–Carlisle bus route.
Mail order: No.
Catalogue: £1.

Scottish holidays

Dates of public holidays are in Scotland are, in our experience, unpredictable. Not only are there national bank holidays (different from those south of the border) when shops now tend to stay open, but many towns have their own traditional local days of rest – or fun. 'Common Riding' in Selkirk occurs on the first Friday after the second Tuesday in June ... on that day 500 people on horseback join in a procession which has been enacted for over 460 years ... Stirling comes to a standstill during the first week in October ... Inverness on 14 October. Some companies close the week before Easter, some the week of Easter, and some the week after Easter.

Following our usual practice, we asked all the shops to tell us which days during the year they close. But despite our prompting, some shops invariably overlook the fact that their town has special dates when they alone shut down.

If you are planning a special trip, or going far, please phone before you leave home. We know from personal experience how frustrating it is to turn up, raring to go factory shopping, only to find the town deserted and the shops shuttered.

Engraving of a splendid couple at Dunrobin Castle for the review of the Sutherland volunteers in September 1866

Heritage Golf of St Andrews

Argyll Business Park, Largo Road
(01334) 472266/477299 Fax (01334) 477099

Golf clubs. Also knitwear, waterproofs, caddy carts, 19th century reproduction clubs, golf sundries (eg videos) etc. Custom-fit specialists.

'Golf clubs at factory prices.'

Next to Safeway at south end of town.

From the south on A915: turn left immediately after Budget Tyres & Exhausts. Company is behind it.

From other directions and through centre: take A915 southbound. Shortly before you leave town, turn right by Safeway and before Budget Tyres & Exhausts. Company is clearly signed behind it.

Open: Mon–Fri 9–5; Sat 10–4; Bank Holidays.
Closed: 25 Dec–5 Jan.
Cards: Access, Amex, Switch, Visa.
Cars: Outside shop.
Toilets: No.
Wheelchairs: Easy access to large shop. No steps.
Teas: In town.
Tours: You can see some manufacturing through glass doors.
Transport: Local town service bus nos. S1, S2, S3 and S4.
Mail order: Next day delivery available. Repair & refurbishing service.
Catalogue: Brochure/price list.

Tillicoultry, the Forth valley and wool

The area around Alva and Tillicoultry (where the large mill makes a stunning picture against the hillside when seen in sunshine from the south) has long been associated with the production of woollen cloth – as far back as the mid-1500s when Mary Queen of Scots was on the throne. These villages lie in a very pleasant part of valley of the river Forth, which wends its way from Sterling to Edinburgh. Cloth production used to be done in local homes; with the development of technology, it transferred to newly built water-powered mills. Not everything was rosy. One of the first mills had no effluent: only after local women had twice destroyed the mill dam with axes and hammers in their anger at the waste water draining into the village burn was a proper sewer built. By the mid-1880s, a quarter of Scotland's woollen mills were in this area, ten in Tillicoultry alone. The weaving of coarse fabric was superseded by production of finer tartans and – as in Paisley – of woollen shawls. World War II brought prosperity with the manufacture of cloth for army uniforms. In recent times, woollen production has declined. However, quite a few companies still produce excellent knitwear.

As you drive round the area, you see signs relating to the mill trail. Leaflets are available. The visitor centre in the mill in Alva displays information about local industries. Open 7 days a week 10–5 (longer in summer). (01259) 769696.

84 Tillicoultry Central

Callant of Scotland (Knitwear)

Devonpark Mills, Devonside FK13 6HR
(01259) 752353 Fax (01259) 751876

High quality fully fashioned knitwear for men and ladies in cashmere, lambswool and shetland. Ladies' coats, jackets and skirts in 100% pure wool. Embroidery service.

'Perfects and seconds. At least 40% below shop prices on most goods.'

On A908 south of Tillicoultry.

From Alloa on A908: turn left into drive shortly after you enter town.

From Alva/Dollar on A91: turn towards Aloa on A908 by clocktower. Continue over river and after the right hand bend, go right into drive.

Open: Please phone first. Mon–Fri 9–4.30; Sat, Sun 11–4. Bank Holidays.
Closed: Christmas, Boxing and New Year's Days; 2 Jan.
Cards: Access, Visa.
Cars: Own car park.
Toilets: By clocktower.
Wheelchairs: Easy access; ramp to shop.
Changing rooms: Yes.
Teas: In town.
Groups: Shopping groups welcome – prior phone call essential.
Transport: Buses every ½ hour from Stirling and Alloa.
Mail order: Yes.
Catalogue: Yes.

85 Ullapool Highlands and Islands

Highland Stoneware Pottery

Mill Street IV26 2UM
(01854) 612980

Huge range of high-fired stoneware. Tableware, cookware with characteristic freehand painting. Unusual gifts: fish dishes, bread crocks, ashets, wall plates, vases, jugs, mugs.

On north-east of town on A835.

From south: continue on A835 through Ullapool (don't go along quayside); shop on right opposite BP petrol.

From the north: pass Morefield and keep going through town; shop on left just past Far Isles Restaurant (on right).

From the ferry: go right along quayside; at junction at end of road, go left. Look for BP petrol on left and go right opposite it. Shop clearly visible.

Open: Mon–Fri 9–6 all year; Sat 9–5. Bank Holidays. Other times by appointment.
Closed: For Christmas–New Year closures please phone.
Cards: Access, Switch, Visa.
Cars: Own large car-park.
Wheelchairs: Two small steps to shop.
Teas: In town.
Transport: Short walk from the town centre.

Western Isles & Harris Tweed

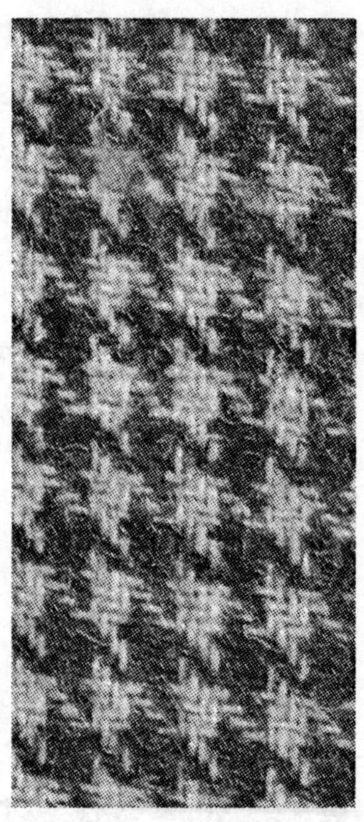

Harris tweed, the world renowned fabric traditionally associated with sporting clothes, must be made from 100% pure virgin wool, dyed, spun and finished in the Outer Hebrides, and hand-woven by islanders at their own homes. If the finished product meets the strict criteria, it is stamped with the famous orb mark, guaranteeing its authenticity.

The fine quality of this tweed has now become associated with top designers, and the fact that it is now available in different weights – including much finer weaves – means it has great versatility. New colours and designs are created for the fashion market each year.

Most of the wool comes from the Scottish mainland, with local wool added to it. In the factories of the main tweed producers in the Outer Hebrides it is washed, dyed (almost always using synthetic dyes now, in order to ensure uniformity, rather than the beautiful vegetable dyes of earlier times) and spun. The warp is delivered, with yarn for the weft, to the homes of the individual weavers around the islands who have their own treadle looms. You can see their small weaving sheds dotted about as you travel round. Each length of tweed is 85 yds long. It is returned to the factory in the 'greasy' state, then finished and checked for any imperfections. Various finishes can be applied.

You can buy Harris tweed in the islands. Hand-written signs point you down tracks where you can purchase it directly from the weaver. Remember that the traditional fabric is 28" wide (double width looms are now in use too) so take care to allow for this narrow width.

As we mentioned in previous books, Harris has an extraordinary landscape made up of millions of massive grey boulders apparently unable to support anything save the hundreds of sheep. These have a pronounced preference for sitting in the middle of the one-track roads just gazing at you as you drive ever closer. As one reader wrote to point out to us, *of course* they sit in the middle of the roads … these are the only dry spots.

Lewis, north of Harris, has wide vistas and vaster landscapes. It is possible to drive for hours without encountering people or habitation. Driving from Lewis south to Harris then via the ferries to North Uist, Benbecula, South Uist and Barra you see an amazing variation in scenery. For majestic hills, South Uist is hard to beat.

For further information: The Harris Tweed Authority, 6 Garden Road, Stornoway, Lewis HS1 2QJ (01851) 702269.

Hebrides

If you are trying to trace ancestors from the Western Isles, consult Co Leis Thu? research centre at Northon on Harris (01859) 520258.

The Clan Donald Centre in Armadale on Skye has a museum of the Isles and Hebridean cultural life (01471) 844305. The library helps people trace clan connections.

Information on island walks, coach tours, cruises, fishing trips, tweed weaving demonstrations can be obtained from tourist offices.

Caithness Glass Visitor Centre

Airport Industrial Estate KW1 5BR
(01955) 602286 Internet: http://www.caithnessglass.co.uk

Glass and crystal, giftware and tableware in assorted colours and designs; vases, bowls, paperweights, jewellery, engraving and wine suites. Other gift ideas to choose from.

'First and second qualities. Vases from £4.99, tableware from £4.99, perfume bottles from £9.99, paperweights from £8.99 (prices subject to change).'

On the north side of the town on the main A99 (previously A9), by the airport, only 5 minutes from the town centre.

Open: Mon–Sat 9–5; (*also Easter to end Dec Sun* 11–5). Bank Holidays.
Closed: Three days at Christmas and three days at New Year.
Cards: Access, Amex, Diners, Switch, Visa.
Cars: Own large free car-park by main entrance.
Toilets: Super loos and mother/baby room.
Wheelchairs: Can be provided. Full access to all areas.
Teas: Licensed restaurant for snacks and meals.
Tours: Free self-conducted tours Mon–Fri. No booking needed. Groups welcome. Viewing gallery for glassmaking and engraving Mon–Fri 9–4.30.
Transport: Wick rail & bus stations within walking distance.
Mail order: No.

Gleneagles Crystal

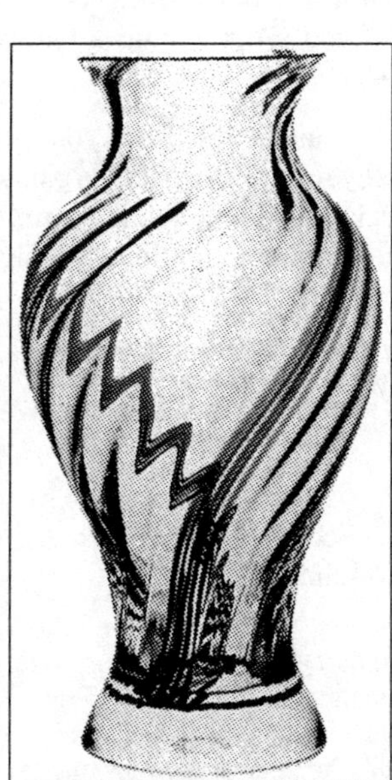

Caithness Glass

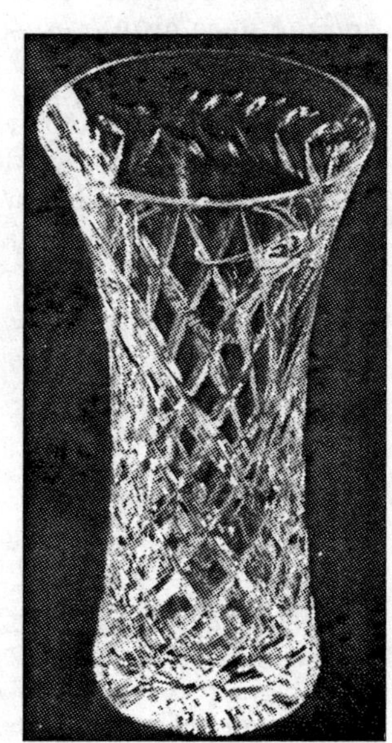

Stuart Crystal

Touring the Whisky Distilleries

We are delighted to give information about distilleries which are open to the public. As with factory shops, their hours might change without notice, and final tours of the day might begin some time before the official closing time quoted. As tours are more frequent in summer than winter, we suggest that you phone in advance to check – especially out of season. Family parties and individuals can usually join a tour just by turning up without notice, but if you *can* plan in advance, a phone call never comes amiss (especially as a large group might already be booked at your chosen time). Groups should book in advance. Companies offering tours 'by appointment' prefer two or three days' notice at least.

Some distilleries are well geared up with visitor centres, exhibitions on the history of whisky, audio-visual displays, coffee shops and picnic areas. Others, just as welcoming to visitors, are less sophisticated in their approach.

Free distillery tours are offered by some companies, but most charge £2–£5 per adult (with reduced prices for young and elderly visitors). It usually includes a free wee dram to taste. In almost all cases the entrance charge is refunded in their shop when you buy a bottle of their whisky.

We suggest that less-than-agile visitors phone first to ascertain how rigorous the tour is. Sometimes health and safety regulations prohibit small children from visiting certain areas of some distilleries, so if you are planning a family visit, ring to check.

Even if you have not got time to tour the distillery, you can usually call in to purchase whisky – do not expect bargains, but sometimes there are special products available only there. Remember that the tax on a single bottle of whisky amounts to two thirds of the retail price!

With thanks to The Scotch Whisky Association for providing much of this information.

If you are in Edinburgh, visit the Scotch Whisky Heritage Centre in the Royal Mile next to Edinburgh castle.
(0131) 220 0441

Open: Seven days a week 10–17.30 (last entry). Later in summer.
Tours: 45-minute tours every 12 minutes between 9.30–5.15 (incl.) on 300 years of Scotch whisky making. Includes video, electric barrel ride and dram. £4.50 per adult. Commentary in 8 languages. Can also book private tutored tastings for up to 10 people at £150.

When to drink whisky?

Ninety-five per cent of Scotch whisky is consumed in blended form. Served on the rocks, or with water, soda or other mixers as a cocktail, it is traditionally sipped as an aperitif (though many people drink it during a meal).

Single malts are fast gaining popularity as an alternative after-dinner drink. They are usually sipped from a snifter glass, neat or with a touch of spring water.

All whisky is retailed at a minimum of 40% by volume of alcohol for the home market. A strength of 43% might be produced for export. This is how American and British standards compare:

100° proof is equivalent to 50% alcohol by volume
86° proof is equivalent to 43% alcohol by volume
80° proof is equivalent to 40% alcohol by volume.

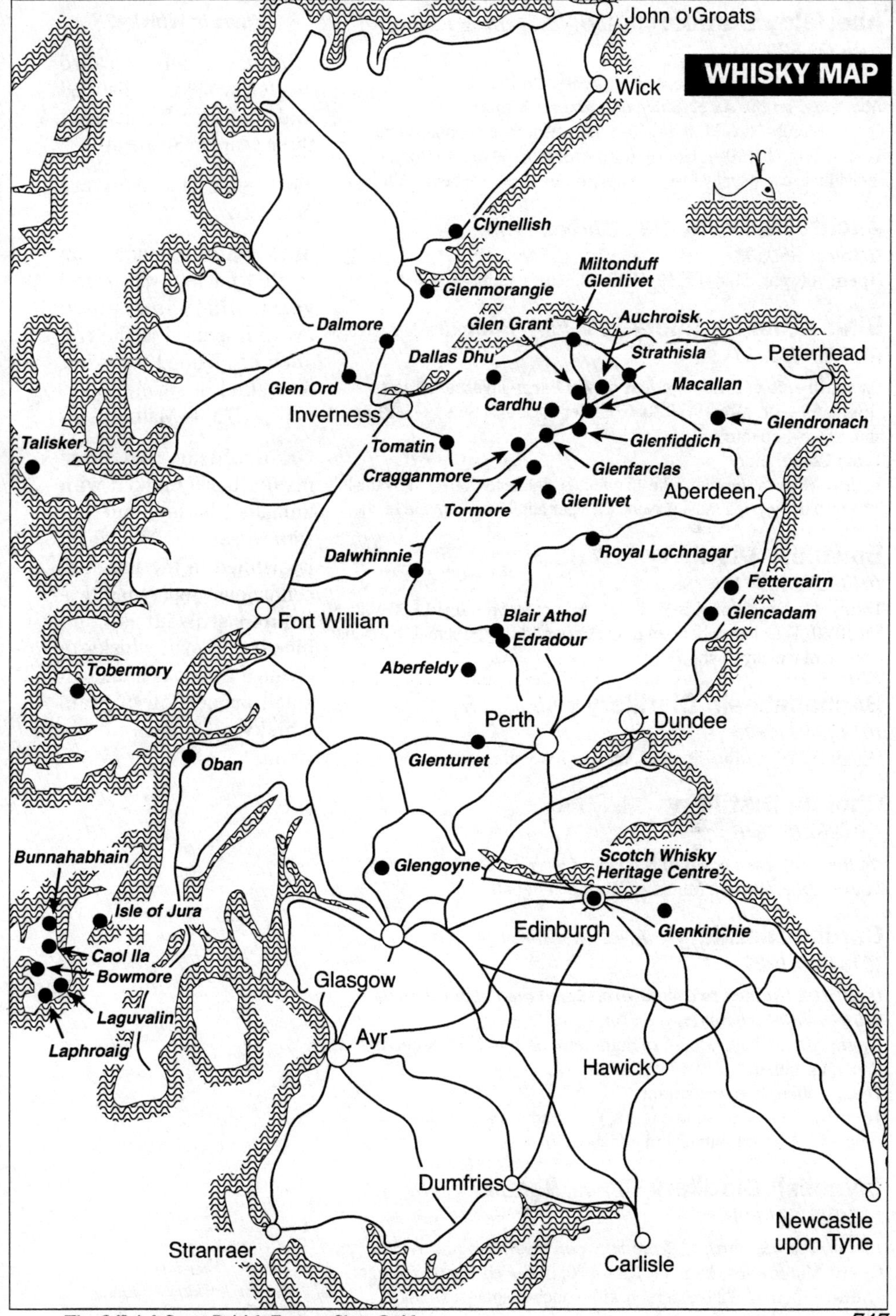

WHISKY MAP
John o'Groats
Wick
Clynellish
Glenmorangie
Miltonduff
Glenlivet
Dalmore
Glen Grant
Auchroisk
Strathisla
Peterhead
Dallas Dhu
Macallan
Glen Ord
Cardhu
Inverness
Glendronach
Talisker
Tomatin
Glenfiddich
Cragganmore
Glenfarclas
Aberdeen
Tormore
Glenlivet
Royal Lochnagar
Dalwhinnie
Fettercairn
Glencadam
Blair Athol
Fort William
Edradour
Tobermory
Aberfeldy
Perth
Dundee
Oban
Glenturret
Bunnahabhain
Glengoyne
Scotch Whisky
Heritage Centre
Isle of Jura
Edinburgh
Glenkinchie
Caol Ila
Bowmore
Glasgow
Laguvalin
Ayr
Laphroaig
Hawick
Dumfries
Newcastle
upon Tyne
Stranraer
Carlisle

Aberfeldy Distillery *Aberfeldy, Perth & Kinross*

(01887) 820330

About 10 miles south-west of Pitlochry. On the outskirts of Aberfeldy, on the A827 Ballinluig–Aberfeldy road.

Open: March–Nov, Mon–Fri 10–4. Dec–March, by appointment.
Tours: Mon–Fri 10–4. Hourly (or more) tours about 45 minutes. Individuals can usually just turn up; groups must pre-book. Adults £3.

Auchroisk Distillery *Mulben, Moray*

(01542) 860333

Open: All year, Mon–Fri 10–4. All visits by appointment.

Blair Athol Distillery *Pitlochry, Perthshire & Kinross*

(01796) 472234

On south side of Pitlochry, just off A9 Perth–Inverness road.

Open: All year, Mon–Fri 9.30–5; Easter–Oct, *also* Sun 12–5. Phone about Dec–Feb tours.
Teas: Coffee shop.
Tours: Many in summer, take 45 minutes. Phone for times. Individuals may turn up; groups must pre-book. £3 per adult, redeemable in shop.

Bowmore Distillery *Isle of Islay*

(01496) 810441

Tours: All year, Mon–Fri 10.30 & 2. Summer, Mon–Fri 11.30 & 3; Sat 10.30. Tour lasts about an hour. £2 per adult, redeemable against a bottle of whisky in shop.

Bunnahabhain Distillery *Isle of Islay*

(01496) 840646

Open: All year, Mon–Fri 10–4, by appointment.

Caol Ila Distillery *Isle of Islay*

(01496) 840646

On the north-east coast of the Isle of Islay.

Tours: Free, all year, Mon–Fri. By appointment.

Cardhu Distillery *Aberlour, Moray*

(01340) 810204

On B9102 (Rothes to Grantown-on-Spey) road about 6 miles south-west of Charlestown on Aberlour.

Open: March–Nov: Mon–Fri. Summer months: also weekends. Phone for times.
Teas: Coffee shop/restaurant.
Tours: Frequent 45-minute tours. £2 per adult (with redeemable voucher). Also exhibition and gift shop.

Clynelish Distillery *Brora, Highland*

(01408) 621444

Just off the A9, north of Brora between Inverness and Wick.

Open: March–Nov, Mon–Fri 9.30–4.30; Dec–Feb by appointment.
Tours: Frequent. £2 per person with voucher against whisky.

What is Whisky?

Whisky can only be called 'Scotch whisky' if distilled and matured for at least three years in Scotland.

Two types of whisky are produced:

Malt whisky, made from malted barley, water and yeast, which is distilled twice. It is used in the creation of blended whiskies, or bottled in small proportions as Single Malt.

Grain whisky, made from malted barley mixed with unmalted barley, together with wheat or maize, which is distilled in the massive, continuously operating two-column stills. It is combined with malt whisky to create the famous brands. A small proportion of grain whisky is sold as Single Grain.

Thanks to The Scotch Whisky Association.

Cragganmore Distillery *Ballindalloch, Moray*

(01807) 500202

Off the A95 (Elgin–Grantown-on-Spey road).
Open: June–Sept, Mon–Fri by appointment. Phone for other times.
Tours: £5 per head with discount voucher for whisky.

Dallas Dhu Distillery *Forres, Moray*

(01309) 676548

On the A96, west of Elgin.
Open: April–Sept, Mon–Sat 9.30–6.30, Sun 2–6.30; Oct–March, Mon, Tues, Wed, Sat 9.30–4.30; Thur 9.30–12.30; Sun 2–4.30.
Tours: Audio-visual theatre, exhibition and gift shop. £2.30 per adult for distillery tour and audio-visual display.

Dalmore Distillery *Alness, Highland*

(01349) 882362

Off the A9 between Dingwall and Invergordon.
Tours: Mid-Aug–mid-Dec & mid-Jan–early June, by appointment.

Dalwhinnie Distillery *Dalwhinnie, Highland*

(01528) 522208

About 25 miles north-west of Pitlochry, on the A9.
Open: Visitor centre all year, Mon–Fri 9.30–4.30. *Also* June–Oct, Sat 9.30–4. *Also* July–Aug, Sun 12.30–4.30. Phone to check Jan–March.
Tours: Frequent, £3 per person.

Edradour Distillery *Pitlochry, Perth & Kinross*

(01796) 472095

On the A9 about 10 miles north-west of Perth.
Open: April–Oct, Mon–Sat 9.30–5; Sun 12 –5. Nov–March: shop only.
Tours: Every 20 minutes in summer, admission free.

Fettercairn Distillery *Laurencekirk, Aberdeenshire*

(01561) 340205

About 15 miles north of Montrose, on the edge of Fettercairn.
Open: May–Sept, Mon–Sat 10–4.30.
Tours: Free 40-minute tours between 10 & 4pm include video, distillery and tasting.

Glen Grant Distillery *Rothes, Moray*

(01542) 783318

Rothes is about 10 miles south of Elgin on the A941.
Open: Summer months, seven days a week. 40-minute tours between 10 & 5pm. £2.50 per person (including gardens).

Glen Ord Distillery *Muir of Ord, Highland*

(01463) 870421

About 5 miles north-east of Inverness on the A96.
Open: Jan–Nov, Mon–Fri 9.30–4.30. *Also* July, Sat 9.30–4.30 & Sun 12–4.30. Dec by appointment. £2 per person.

Once the quality is approved, the spirit is placed in specially chosen oak casks. Some casks will previously have held oloroso, fino or amontillado sherries; some will have contained bourbon, and some are new. The minimum time for maturing is three years, but in practice much Scotch whisky matures for five to fifteen years, and even for 25 years or more. The age on the bottle refers to the age of the youngest ingredient (not the average age).

A blend is a careful and judicious combination of from fifteen to fifty single whiskies of varying ages, compiled to a highly secret formula by an extremely skilled blender. Some single whiskies are compatible; others fight. The skill lies in knowing which ones will combine. Once the whisky has been formulated, the blender must also be able to recreate the blend – so that satisfied customers can obtain the same drink in future.

Basically there are four categories of malt whiskies, based on the areas where they are made: from lighter flavoured gentle lowland malts, highland malts and Speyside malts to the heaviest malts from Islay.

Grain distilleries, with one exception, are located in the central belt of Scotland near Edinburgh & Glasgow.

Glencadam Distillery *Brechin, Angus*

(01356) 622217

Eight miles west of Montrose.

Open: Sept–June, Mon–Thur 2–4 by appointment.
Tours: Free.

Glendronach Distillery *Forgue by Huntly, Aberdeen*

(01466) 730202

North-east of Huntly. Leave Huntly on A96 east. Go left on to A97 north. In Bogniebrae go right on to B9001. Distillery after two miles at junction with B9024.

Open: All year, Mon–Fri 10–2. **Tours:** Free at 10 am and 2 pm.

Glenfarclas Distillery *Ballindalloch, Moray*

(01807) 500257

Off the A95 (Elgin–Grantown-on-Spey road).

Open: Winter, Mon–Fri 10–4; summer, Mon–Fri 9.30–5; *also* June–Sept, Sat 10–4, Sun 12:30–4.30.
Tours: Last 45-minute tour 1 hour before closing. £2.50. Audio-visual, whisky exhibition in 4 languages, cask filling gallery. Picnic area.

Glenfiddich Distillery *Dufftown, Moray*

(01340) 820373

Eighteen miles south of Elgin.

Open: Mid-Oct–Easter, Mon–Fri 9.30–4.30; Easter–mid-Oct, Mon–Sat 9.30–4.30, Sun 12–4.30.
Tours: Free admission to distillery, audio-visual in 6 languages, exhibition, gift shop. Picnic area.

Glengoyne Distillery *Killearn, Stirling*

(01360) 550254

Dumgoyne is on the A81, about 12 miles north of Glasgow.

Open: All year, Mon–Sat 10–4; also Easter–Nov, Sun 12–4.
Tours: Start on the hour, £3 or £4 according to what you wish to taste. Wednesday evening nosing sessions must be pre-booked: tour, selection of whiskies from all over Scotland, £10 per head.

Glenkinchie Distillery *Pencaitland, East Lothian*

(01875) 340333

From A68 south of Dalkeith: turn on to A6093 for Pencaitland/ Haddington. Follow theme signs for nearly 7 miles.

Open: All year, Mon–Fri 9–5. *Also* May–Sept, Sat 9–4, Sun 12–4.
Tours: Every half hour, £3 per head including voucher.

Glenlivet Distillery *Glenlivet, Moray*

(01542) 783220

South of Bridge of Avon (which is on the A95).

Open: Mid-March–end Oct, Mon–Sat 10–4, Sun 12.30–4. July & Aug, daily 10–6. (New visitor centre so phone to check details.)
Tours: Guided tour, interactive presentations. £2.50 per adult.

History of Whisky

The whisky industry was officially recorded over 500 years ago. In 1494, eight bolls of malt were delivered to one Friar John Cor 'wherewith to make aquavitae'. As eight bolls were equivalent to over a ton of malted barley, enough to produce 1400 bottles of spirit – production must have been well established even then. In times when the purity of drinking water was suspect, alcoholic drinks were usually safe to drink (even if extremely potent and subject to poor quality control during production). Whisky was praised for its medicinal properties and was even prescribed for improved health, longer life, and the relief of colic, palsy, smallpox and other ailments. Interestingly, the dissolution of the monasteries contributed to the spread of knowledge about distilling because the monks, driven from their inner sanctums, had no choice but to put their skills to use elsewhere.

As with most successful products, whisky (in the late 1600s) attracted the attention of parliament – looking, as always, for new sources of tax. After the Act of Union with the English, in 1707, whisky distillers were virtually driven underground. Legal restrictions here (as in Kent, where brandy was traded illicitly) were bitterly resented. In practice, they were widely

Glenmorangie Distillery *Tain, Highland*

(01862) 892477

Tain is on the south side of Dornach Firth, on the east coast.

Open: All year, Mon–Fri 10–4. Also June–Oct, Sat 10–4.

Tours: 45-minute tours cost £2, including voucher. Usually at 10.30 & 2.30 with extra tours if busy.

Glenturret Distillery *Crieff, Perth & Kinross*

(01764) 656565

On the north-west side of Crieff.

Open: All year, weekdays. Many months six or seven days a week.

Tours: Last tour about 90 minutes before closing. £2.90 per adult.

Highland Park Distillery *Kirkwall, Orkney*

(01856) 874619

Open: April–October, Mon–Fri 10–5. Also July, August, Sat, Sun 12–5. Nov–March, please phone.

Tours: Every half-hour (last tour about an hour before closing). About 30 minutes plus 15-minute audio-visual. £2.50.

Isle of Jura Distillery *Isle of Jura*

(01496) 820240

Open: Sept–May, Mon–Fri 9–4. By appointment only.

Laguvalin Distillery *Isle of Islay*

(01496) 302400

Open: All year.

Tours: At 10.30 and 2.30. £2 per head (with £3 redeemable voucher). Be sure to phone to confirm tour times.

Laphroaig Distillery *Isle of Islay*

(01496) 302418

Tours: By appointment only. Sept–June, Mon–Thur 10.30 & 2.30, Fri 10.30.

Macallan Distillery *Craigellachie, Moray*

(01340) 871471

About 20 miles south of Elgin.

Tours: Free. Best to book. Frequent tours during day.

Miltonduff-Glenlivet *Elgin, Moray*

(01343) 547433

Tours: Sept–June, 9.30–5. Not set up for large tour parties but small groups welcome. A prior phone call please.

Oban Distillery *Oban, Argyll*

(01631) 572004

Stafford Street is in the centre of Oban.

Open: All year, Mon–Fri 9.30–5 (till 8.30 in high summer). Also Easter–Oct Sat 9.30–5 (till 8.30 in high summer). Phone in winter.

Tours: Each half hour or hour. £3 per adult, redeemable in shop.

flouted and even ministers of the church were known to allow storage space under the pulpit ... and whisky was known to have been transported by coffin under certain circumstances. By 1777, eight distilleries were registered, 400 were unregistered (contributing to the gains of the freebooters who ran them). By the 1820s, 14,000 illicit stills were confiscated every year.

The Duke of Gordon finally had the sense to persuade parliament to make whisky production a profitable and legal activity. The Excise Act was passed in 1823; it sanctioned the distilling of whisky for £10 a year plus a set payment per gallon of proof spirit. Smuggling died out almost completely over the next ten years.

Malt whisky was distilled in distinctive copper pots. The invention of the continuous distilling process in 1831 allowed production of grain whisky, a less intense spirit. Both types of whisky were blended together in the 1860s to produce the popular, lighter flavoured whisky.

Another major boost to the industry was, in fact, caused by a disaster, when, in the 1880s, the wine industry of France was shattered by the *Phylloxera* plague. By the time the wine and brandy trades had recovered, whisky was well ensconced as the preferred drink of society.

Royal Lochnagar Distillery *Ballater, Aberdeenshire*

(01339) 742273

On B976 near junction with A93 Aberdeen–Braemar road.

Open: All year, Mon–Fri 10–5. Also Easter–Oct, Sat 10–5, Sun 11–4.

Toilets: Yes, including for disabled.

Wheelchairs: Yes, but not to whole site.

Tours: Hourly or half-hourly tours £2 per adult (with £3 voucher).

Scapa Distillery *Kirkwall, Orkney*

(01856) 872071

Open: All year, Mon–Thur 8–12 & 1–5; Fri 8–1.

Tours: Free (none Friday afternoons).

Strathisla Distillery *Keith, Moray*

(01542) 783044

Distillery is signposted in the centre of Keith; ¼ mile off A96.

Open: Mon–Sat 9.30–4; Sun 12.30–4 for self-guided tours including tutored nosing, tasting, coffee and shortbread. Phone about winter.

Tours: £4 per person including £2 against special purchase.

Talisker Distillery *Isle of Skye*

(01478) 640203

Open: April–Oct. Phone for winter.

Tours: 45-minutes, every 15 minutes in summer, Mon–Fri 9.30–4.30. Also Sat in high summer.

Tobermory Distillery *Isle of Mull*

(01688) 302645

Open: Easter–Oct, Mon–Fri 10–5. Phone to check Oct–Easter.

Tours: Mon–Fri through the day 10.30–4pm. £2.50 per adult. Video, tour and a wee dram, with voucher towards certain products.

Tomatin Distillery *Tomatin, Highland*

(01808) 511444

On the A9, about 15 miles south-east of Inverness.

Open: All year (not usually Saturday tours in winter).

Tours: Frequent, free, Mon–Fri 9–3.30; Sat 9–1. About 40 minutes.

Tormore Distillery *Advie, Grantown-on-Spey, Moray*

(01807) 510244

Advie is 12 miles north-east of Grantown.

Open: Sept–June, Mon–Thur 1.30–4. All visits by appointment.

Edinburgh Crystal

Towns with factory shops

NUMBERS refer to the ENTRIES, NOT the PAGES

Towns with factory shops

NUMBERS refer to the ENTRIES, NOT the PAGES

Town	No.	Shop
Glasgow : Bridgeton	44	Glenmore
Glasgow : Ibrox	45	Kingsman Antiques
Glasgow : Rutherglen	46	Polywarm
Glasgow : Shawlands	47	Claremont Garments
Glasgow : Springburn	48	Royal Strathclyde Blindcraft
Glenrothes	49	Keela International
Hamilton	50	Peter MacArthur
Hawick	p720	Chas N Whillans
Hawick	51	Factory Fabric Centre
Hawick	52	Hawick Cashmere
Hawick	53	Peter Scott
Hawick	54	Slumberdown Enterprises
Hawick	55	Valerie Louthan
Hawick	56	White of Hawick
Hawick	57	Wrights of Trowmill
Hill of Fearn	58	Anta
Huntly	59	Dean's Shortbread
Innerleithen	60	Murray Allan
Inverness	61	Highland Society for the Blind
Inverness	p731	Scottish Sweater Store
Kilbirnie	62	Glengarnock Garments
Kilmarnock	63	Jaeger
Kinross	64	Lochleven Mill Shop
Kirkcaldy	65	Babygro
Kirkintilloch	66	Goudies
Lanark	67	Glenmuir
Lanark	68	Millshop Woollens
Larbert near Falkirk	69	Barbara Davidson Pottery
Livingston	70	Russell Corp UK
Lochgilphead	71	Highbank Porcelain
Newmilns	72	Moonweave Mill Shop
North Berwick	73	Millshop Woollens
Oban	74	Caithness Glass Visitor Centre
Peebles	p735	Chas N Whillans
Penicuik	75	Edinburgh Crystal
Perth	76	Caithness Glass Visitor Centre
Pitlochry	77	Heathergems
Selkirk	78	Claridge Mills
Selkirk	79	D C Dalgliesh
Selkirk	80	Ettrick Forest Interiors
Selkirk	81	Gardiner of Selkirk
Selkirk	82	Selkirk Glass
St Andrews	83	Heritage Golf of St Andrews
Tillicoultry	84	Callant of Scotland (Knitwear)
Ullapool	85	Highland Stoneware Pottery
Wick	86	Caithness Glass Visitor Centre

Which shops do you recommend?

One of the most enjoyable yet totally unexpected aspects of producing these guides is the large number of letters we receive from readers. Some letters recount funny shopping experiences; many provide wonderful information about shops which we ourselves have not yet caught up with; others ask us for specific details.

A recurring request is that we indicate the quality of items sold in the shops. We personally feel unable to provide such information because our opinion would be too subjective. We also know, from the questionnaires which many people are kind enough to return, that views on any one shop vary according to what the customer is looking for. If you require cheap clothing for an economical family beach holiday in Spain, you will be looking for something different from that needed for a luxury cruise in the Cayman Islands. You can obtain both ranges of clothing when you buy direct from the maker and both can be excellent value for money – but how you judge the shop will depend on whether it stocked what you were looking for on the day you went and whether the service was what you expected.

However, in the best traditions of other guide books, we welcome the chance to continue building up information about those shops which you, the shopper, consider offer top value for money, good service, wide ranges of goods – or the reverse! Shopping is much more than just a question of spending money. It is a pleasure – an enjoyable aspect of a day's outing – an essential feature of a holiday. (Would you believe that 50% of money spent on holiday goes on shopping?) When you buy items from shops like the ones described in these books, there is also the 'fun of the chase'.

With your help we would like to build up a list of the best factory and mill shops. Please complete the form opposite. Unless you request otherwise, we might use your name in connection with a good report.

We need to know:

the name and address of the shop you visited;
when you shopped there;
what you bought;
the amount you spent;
and how you considered the following aspects:
How welcoming were the staff?
Was the service good/ bad/unmemorable?
What did you think of the products for sale?
Did you consider the items represented good value for money?
What was especially good or bad about your shopping trip?

To: Gill Cutress, The Factory Shop Guide, FREEPOST (SW 8510), London SW2 4BR

I should like to comment on the following shop

Name and address of the shop visited..

....

....

Date of visit...How much you spent ....

What you bought..

Comments, anecdotes etc on the shop, service, parking, goods for sale – or whatever attracted your attention!

Where did you buy your guide? ....

Your name ....

Your address ....

....

Post code ....

Phone number..Date.................................

If you would like more copies of this form, please give us a ring and we'll post them.
Phone (0181) 678 0593 Fax (0181) 674 1594

How can we make this guide even more useful?

To help us give you the information you are looking for, please fill in this questionnaire.

Why do you like Factory Shopping?

Is there anything you don't like about Factory Shops?

Which shops do you prefer? (please tick only one answer)
a. Shops which sell only those goods which they make themselves
b. Shops with a mixture of items, including related bought-in goods
c. Shops which sell anything, including imported items, if they are cheap
d. No preferences
e. Factory outlet centres
Any other comments?

How much did you spend at the last Factory Shop you visited?
a. Less than £10
b. £10 or over but under £15
c. £15 or over but under £20
d. £20 and over
e. £30 and over
f. £100 and over
g. £200 and over

Which items in Factory Shops interest you in particular?
a. Knitting wools
b. Sewing materials
c. Craft materials
d. Pottery & porcelain
e. Glassware
f. Children's clothing
g. Household linens, furnishings
h. General clothing
i. Designer clothing
j. Carpets
k. Furniture
l. What else?

Have you visited Factory Shops
a. While on holiday? Often / Sometimes / Not at all
b. While travelling on business? Often / Sometimes / Not at all
c. When visiting relatives? Often / Sometimes / Not at all
d. During day trips from home? Often / Sometimes / Not at all

Have you visited any of the 'factory outlet centres'? Yes / Not yet
If yes, which one(s)?

On the day you last went to a Factory Shop, how many individual Factory Shops did you visit in total?

Provided you have time, do you enjoy touring the factory itself when you visit a Factory Shop?
Very much / it's OK / not much / no thanks

What is the furthest you have travelled especially to go to a particular Factory Shop?

Did you buy your own copy of this Guide? Yes / No **Was the book a present?** Yes / No
Have you given a copy to anyone else? Yes / No
Have you previously bought other Factory Shop Guides? Yes / No If yes, which?

How many of the shops, mentioned in this book, were new to you? Just a few / Quite a lot / Almost all
How many people have looked through your copy of this guide? (include yourself!)
Are you male / female?
Which age bracket are you in? Under 20 20–29 30–39 40–49 50–59 60–69 70+
Which newspaper(s) do you read? Sun Mail Express Telegraph Times Independent Guardian Mirror Observer Sunday Times Others
Which weekly and monthly magazines do you see regularly?

What other information would you like this guide to give?

Any other comments?

Would you like a free book next year?

More manufacturers are opening factory shops. If you have enjoyed visiting other shops, either here, or in France or elsewhere in the world, we should be delighted to hear about them. If you are the first person to send us new details which are published next year, we shall be happy to send you a free copy of the new regional guide.

Name of company ....
Address ....
What do they sell? ....

Name of company ....
Address ....
What do they sell? ....

Name of company ....
Address ....
What do they sell? ....

Name of company ....
Address ....
What do they sell? ....

Where did you buy your copy of this guide?..
How did you hear about it?..

Your name ....
Your address..
....
Town..
Post code..
Your phone no...
Date ....

Readers in Britain only, please send to:
Factory Shop Guide, FREEPOST (SW 8510) London SW2 4BR
(0181) 678 0593 fax (0181) 674 1594

ORDER FORM

Please send the following books to me:

.....copy (ies) of the **Derbys/Notts/Lincs Guide** at £4.99 each	£	.
.....copy (ies) of the **Staffordshire & the Potteries Guide** at £3.99 each	£	.
.....copy (ies) of the **Yorkshire & Northern Lincolnshire Guide** £4.50	£	.
.....copy (ies) of the **Northern England Guide** at £4.50 each	£	.
.....copy (ies) of the **Leicestershire & Northamptonshire Guide** £4.50	£	.
.....copy (ies) of the **Western Midlands Guide** at £4.50 each	£	.
.....copy (ies) of the **North-West England & North Wales Guide** £4.99	£	.
.....copy (ies) of the **Scotland Guide** at £4.50 each	£	.
.....copy (ies) of the **SE England, London & E Anglia Guide** £4.99	£	.
.....copy (ies) of the **SW England & S Wales Guide** at £4.50 each	£	.
P&p within UK: 60p each above book, max £3.60	£	.
.....copy (ies) of **The Official Great British Factory Shop Guide** at £14.99	£	.
.....copy (ies) of **Designer Bargains in Italy** at £10.99 each	£	.
.....copy (ies) of **Road Atlas for Gardeners (SE England)** at £6.95	£	.
P&p within UK: £1.30 each above book, max £3.60	£	.

I enclose a cheque *or* please debit my MasterCard / Visa

Cheques made payable to G. Cutress **GRAND TOTAL** £ .

Credit card: MasterCard / Visa

No. .... **Expiry date** ....

Name .... **Tel. no** ....

Address ....

....

Town .... **Post code** ....

Signed .... **Date** ....

Readers in Britain only, please send to: The Factory Shop Guide, FREEPOST (SW 8510) London SW2 4BR Phone (0181) 678 0593 Fax (0181) 674 1594

Overseas readers, please send your credit card details to:
The Factory Shop Guide, 1 Rosebery Mews, Rosebery Road, London SW2 4DQ for airmail delivery (actual postage plus small packing fee).

I would like to send a gift to the following person:

Name..

Address ....

Town...**Post code** ....

.....copy(ies) of the **Derbys/Notts/Lincs Guide** at £4.99 each £ .

.....copy(ies) of the **Staffordshire & the Potteries Guide** at £3.99 each £ .

.....copy(ies) of the **Yorkshire & Northern Lincolnshire Guide** £4.50 £ .

.....copy(ies) of the **Northern England Guide** at £4.50 each £ .

.....copy(ies) of the **Leicestershire & Northamptonshire Guide** £4.50 £ .

.....copy(ies) of the **Western Midlands Guide** at £4.50 each £ .

.....copy(ies) of the **North-West England & North Wales Guide** £4.99 £ .

.....copy(ies) of the **Scotland Guide** at £4.50 each £ .

.....copy(ies) of the **SE England, London & E Anglia Guide** £4.99 £ .

.....copy(ies) of the **SW England & S Wales Guide** at £4.50 each £ .

P&p within UK: 60p each above book, max £3.60 £ .

.....copy(ies) of **The Official Great British Factory Shop Guide** at £14.99 £ .

.....copy(ies) of **Designer Bargains in Italy** at £10.99 each £ .

.....copy(ies) of **Road Atlas for Gardeners (SE England)** at £6.95 £ .

P&p within UK: £1.30 each above book, max £3.60 £ .

I enclose a cheque *or* please debit my MasterCard / Visa

Cheques made payable to G. Cutress **GRAND TOTAL** £ .

Credit card: MasterCard / Visa

No. ....**Expiry date**..........................

My name ....**Tel. no** ....

My address..

....

Town...**Post code** ....

Signed..**Date** ....

Readers in Britain only, please send to: The Factory Shop Guide,
FREEPOST (SW 8510) London SW2 4BR Phone (0181) 678 0593 Fax (0181) 674 1594
Overseas readers, please send your credit card details to:
The Factory Shop Guide, 1 Rosebery Mews, Rosebery Road, London SW2 4DQ
for airmail delivery (actual postage plus small packing fee).

Other money-saving books available from us

Ten regional Factory Shop Guides

SW England & South Wales Guide

SE England, London & East Anglia Guide

Leicestershire & Northamptonshire Guide

Western Midlands Guide

Staffordshire & The Potteries Guide

NW England & North Wales Guide

Derbyshire, Nottinghamshire, Lincolnshire Guide

Yorkshire & Northern Lincolnshire Guide

Northern England Guide

Scotland Guide

These editions correspond to area chapters in your *Great British* guide. Small enough to fit into a pocket, these inexpensive books are ideal gifts for people who prefer to do their shopping locally, or are visiting a specific area. Call us on (0181) 678 0593, or use the orders forms on pp. 759–60.

Designer Bargains in Italy

You no longer need to pay exotic prices for designer names in Italy. The secrets of how to find *Fendi, Kenzo, Missoni, Moschino, Byblos, Versace, Gaultier, Valentino, Balmain, Ungaro, Yves St. Laurent, Dior, Dolce & Gabbana* – and dozens of other famous names at greatly reduced prices are revealed in this new book. Italy produces many beautiful luxury goods ... silks, stylish shoes, cashmere, fashion jewellery, furniture, lighting, stainless steel household wares. The author, who lives in Milan, has spent many years exploring the world of seconds, showroom models, samples, ends of lines. The first of its kind in English, this unique book (available in the UK only from *The Factory Shop Guide)* leads you to 220 factory shops and other worthwhile outlets offering superb value for money. Little known to anyone except the locals, they are all close to motorways.

The Road Atlas for Gardeners – South East England

Our Road Atlas fills a huge gap in the plethora of gardening books. For the first time, a guide for gardeners and garden-lovers is combined with a large scale, easy-to-read, full colour road atlas of South East England. The area covered includes Berkshire, Hampshire, Sussex, Kent, Surrey plus London (outside the south circular road). It shows the way to over 800 places: gardens regularly open to the public, specialist and general nurseries, garden and plant centres, water garden specialists, garden artefact suppliers and pick-your-own farms. Each place is marked on its map. Many descriptions and over 150 colour photographs.

'A fabulous gift – if you can bear to part with it.'

ONLY £6.95

- GARDENS REGULARLY OPEN TO VISITORS
- SPECIALIST AND GENERAL NURSERIES
- GARDEN AND PLANT CENTRES
- WATER GARDEN SPECIALISTS
- GARDEN ARTEFACT SUPPLIERS
- PICK-YOUR-OWN FARMS

SOUTH EAST ENGLAND

Companies with factory shops

Please note that the NUMBERS refer to the ENTRIES, NOT the PAGES

> **Please note that the NUMBERS refer to the ENTRIES, NOT the PAGES**

Please note that the NUMBERS refer to the ENTRIES, NOT the PAGES

Please note that the NUMBERS refer to the ENTRIES, NOT the PAGES

Please note that the NUMBERS refer to the ENTRIES, NOT the PAGES

Please note that the *NUMBERS* refer to the *ENTRIES*, *NOT the PAGES*

Please note that the NUMBERS refer to the ENTRIES, NOT the PAGES

Please note that the NUMBERS refer to the ENTRIES, NOT the PAGES

Please note that the NUMBERS refer to the ENTRIES, NOT the PAGES

Please note that the NUMBERS refer to the ENTRIES, NOT the PAGES

Please note that the NUMBERS refer to the ENTRIES, NOT the PAGES

Please note that the NUMBERS refer to the ENTRIES, NOT the PAGES

Please note that the NUMBERS refer to the ENTRIES, NOT the PAGES

Please note that the NUMBERS refer to the ENTRIES, NOT the PAGES

Please note that the NUMBERS refer to the ENTRIES, NOT the PAGES

Please note that the NUMBERS refer to the ENTRIES, NOT the PAGES

Index to items sold

NUMBERS refer to the ENTRIES, NOT the PAGES